T0199298

COMPUTER, INTELLIGENT COMPUTING AND EDUCATION TECHNOLOGY

COMPUTER-MEDIATED COMMUNICATION AND EDUCATION TECHNOLOGY

SELECTED PEER REVIEWED PAPERS FROM 2014 INTERNATIONAL CONFERENCE ON COMPUTER, INTELLIGENT COMPUTING AND EDUCATION TECHNOLOGY, CICET 2014, HONGKONG, 27–28 MARCH 2014

Computer, Intelligent Computing and Education Technology

Editors

Hsiang-Chuan Liu
Asia University, Taiwan

Wen-Pei Sung
National Chin-Yi University of Technology, Taiwan

Wenli-Yao
Control Engineering and Information Science Research, Hong Kong

VOLUME 2

 CRC Press
Taylor & Francis Group
Boca Raton   London   New York   Leiden

CRC Press is an imprint of the
Taylor & Francis Group, an **informa** business

A BALKEMA BOOK

CRC Press/Balkema is an imprint of the Taylor & Francis Group, an informa business

© 2014 Taylor & Francis Group, London, UK

Typeset by V Publishing Solutions Pvt Ltd., Chennai, India
Printed and bound in Great Britain by CPI Group (UK) Ltd, Croydon, CR0 4YY

Published by: CRC Press/Balkema
        P.O. Box 11320, 2301 EH Leiden, The Netherlands
        e-mail: Pub.NL@taylorandfrancis.com
        www.crcpress.com – www.taylorandfrancis.com

ISBN: 978-1-138-02469-4 (set of 2 volumes)
ISBN: 978-1-138-02639-1 (Vol 1)
ISBN: 978-1-138-02640-7 (Vol 2)
ISBN: 978-1-315-77556-2 (eBook PDF)

Table of contents

VOLUME 2

Information science and education technology

Preface

In the past twenty years, Computer Science and Information Technology have become involved in many varied applications throughout the world, with multiple products and rapid market services. They have not only provided industries with new methods, new tools and new products from design, material processing to operation and management process, but are also changing the manners, thinking styles and working environments of people in all fields.

This book contains selected Computer, Information and Education Technology related papers from the 2014 International Conference on Computer, Intelligent Computing and Education Technology (CICET 2014) held in Hong Kong, March 27–28, 2014. The aim is to provide a platform for researchers, engineers, and academics as well as industrial professionals from all over the world to present their research results and development activities in Computer Science, Information Technology and Education Technology.

This conference will promote the development of Computer Science, Information Technology and Education Technology, strengthening international academic cooperation and communications, and the exchange of research ideas.

I am very grateful to the conference chairs, organization staff, the authors and the members of the International Technological Committees for their hard work. We hope that CICET 2014 will be successful and enjoyable for all participants.

January, 2014
Wen-Pei Sung
National Chin-Yi University of Technology

Computer, Intelligent Computing and Education Technology – Liu, Sung & Yao (Eds)
© 2014 Taylor & Francis Group, London, ISBN 978-1-138-02469-4

CICET 2014 Committee

CONFERENCE CHAIRMAN

Prof. Hsiang-Chuan Liu, *Asia University, Taiwan*
Prof. Wen-Pei Sung, *National Chin-Yi University of Technology, Taiwan*

PROGRAM COMMITTEE

Xue Chaogai, *Zhengzhou University, China*
Viranjay M. Srivastava, *Jaypee University of Information Technology, Solan, H.P., India*
Zhao Weiguo, *Hebei University of Engineering, China*
He Qing, *North China Electric Power University, China*
Mir Mahdi Zalloi, *National Iranian Gas Company (NIGC), Iran*
Zhou Liang, *Donghua University, China*
Liu Yunan, *University of Michigan, USA*
Wang Liying, *Institute of Water Conservancy and Hydroelectric Power, China*
Chenggui Zhao, *Yunnan University of Finance and Economics, China*
Hsiang-Chuan Liu, *Asia University, Taiwan*
Gang Shi, *Inha University, South Korea*
Bhagavathi Tarigoppula, *Bradley University, USA*
Tjamme Wiegers, *Delft University of Technology, The Netherlands*
Anita Kovač Kralj, *University of Maribor, Slovenia*
Wei Fu, *Chongqing University, China*
Ramezan ali Mahdavinejad, *University of Tehran, Iran*
Chen Chi-Hua, *National Chiao Tung University, Taiwan*
Mostafa Shokshok, *National University of Malaysia, Malaysia*
Hong Sheng, *Beijing University of Aeronautics and Astronautics, China*
Yang Yan, *Guangxi University for Nationalities, China*
Xu Chungeng, *Nanjing University of Science and Technology, China*
Liu Zheng, *Shangdong Economic University, China*
Wen-Sheng Ou, *National Chin-Yi University of Technology, Taiwan*
Hao-En Chueh, *Yuanpei University, Taiwan*
Li Zhong, *North China Electric Power University, China*
Lixin Guo, *Northeastern University, China*

CO-SPONSOR

International Frontiers of Science and Technology Research Association
Control Engineering and Information Science Research Association

Information science and education technology

Computer, Intelligent Computing and Education Technology – Liu, Sung & Yao (Eds)
© 2014 Taylor & Francis Group, London, ISBN 978-1-138-02469-4

The words statistical study of Tibetan network (news)

Hong-Zhi Yu, Zi-Long Yang & Hui Cao
Key Lab of China's National Linguistic Information Technology, Lanzhou, China

ABSTRACT: The paper analyses and researches three Tibetan web corpus in 2011, understands 2011 Tibetan words, each media words using alone, common words, the words coverage rate and the high frequency words and the usage of neologism. Through statistical research, not only can understand Tibetan network (news) of Tibetan vocabulary usage, also to a certain extent, reflect social hot spots, major events and Tibetan folk customs.

Keywords: words; high frequency words; words using alone; common words; the words coverage; proper nouns; neologism

1 INTRODUCTION

Language (words) is the most important communication tool and human society thinking tool, also an important part of culture and the basic carrier. Along with the informationization and accelerating of the globalization process, the position and value of the language unprecedented highlights. Many countries gradually began to attach importance to language, and some developed countries will treat language strategy as an important part of national strategic development. The current language life in China rapid development and changing, social language life being active than ever, all kinds of contradictions in language life highlighting, it's very necessary and urgent to provide more and more types and modes of language service and grasp language life trends generally and accurately. However, living in information-based society, facing mass data, always baffled to judge their facticity and make the appreciate decisions real-time. Therefore, the monitoring, tracking, and analysis of language and characters are crucial [1].

Tibetan is one kind of human language. Through monitoring and analysis Tibetan public sentiment, we can know social language life, finding Tibetan hot spot and the difficulty of life, and boost research in applied linguistics related areas. Also understand social language life trends, promoting excellent communication with non-Tibetan governmental personnel, expert and the public. Also provide decision reference for government to exactitude lead and make related policy [1].

2 CORPUS PREPARING AND PROCESSING

2.1 Corpus preparing

Corpus selection is 2011 three Tibetan web site (According to the sequence arrangement): Qinghai Tibetan radio network, People's Daily online Tibetan edition, Tibetan culture net. Extraction way: real-time acquisition in the whole year of 2011 pages in the website referred to above, get all the text collection to day to corpus information collected and content to heavy form the sample corpus of the network (news). For post processing convenience, corpus format is a pure text format and adopt Tongyuan input method to input.

2.2 Term

Research in three webs involve some following terms:

- Term frequency refers to network corpus segmentation of the total number of units, pure Arabic Numbers, punctuation, symbols of pure western language, Chinese characters, Numbers, and the western blend of Tibetan word segmentation unit.
- Word species refers to word segmentation unit to form different from the corpus of the network.
- Common word species refers to word species appearing in all the three corpus of the network.
- Words species using alone refers to word species appearing in only one corpus of the network.

- High frequency words refers to the words included of the word coverage rate reached 90%.
- Coverage rate refers to the percentage of specified object of all the research objects gross in researched corpus, meaning all the research objects according to the descending order of time, the ratio of the sum of time of every research object with its former time accumulation with the time of research objects in all corpus. Computational formula: $A_i = \sum_{k=1} n_k/N \times 100\%$. n_k is the appearing time of research object k. N is total time of research objects in all the corpus. A refers to accumulation frequency. A_i is the accumulation frequency of the first I research object in the order. Coverage rate is an important reason to confirm commonly used words or high frequency words [2].
- Time refers to the time of research object in research corpus, like the time of some word appearing in research corpus.
- Frequency refers to the ratio of the time of research object with total time of research objects in all corpus. Computational formula: n_i is the appearing time of research object i. N is total time of research objects in all the corpus. F refers to frequency. F_i is the frequency of research object i [2].

2.3 Corpus processing

Corpus collecting uses the method of combination of human and computer software. And using a web crawler crawls on the Internet in real time.

Word segmentation uses the method of 'machine segmentation and human intervention'. Segmentation software uses 'Tibetan segmentation software' based on the statistics written by Qi Kunyu, an associate professor come from Northwest University for nationalities China national institute of information technology. On the basis of machine segmentation, use human intervention to proofread the wrong words. Tibetan word segmentation need to be as far as possible consistent with the 'word' that using independently, steadily, and being the smallest unit having fixed semantics in the Tibetan language [3].

Second, do pretreatment for the participle corpus and remove redundant information such as redundant blank spaces, punctuation marks in Chinese. Then extract the word species and its time of corpus has been removed redundant. Through processing the word species and the time already have, we can get some information like high frequency word, coverage ratio, words species using alone, common word species what we want.

3 CORPORA LEXICAL ANALYSIS

3.1 Basic information of three kinds of network corpus

Through processing the corpus, we know three kinds of network have 5926 texts (Qinghai Tibetan radio network has 4020 texts, People's Daily online Tibetan edition has 1096 texts, and Tibetan culture net has 810 texts), 5518758 times, 17620 word species.

As shown in Table 1 is the basic information of three kinds of network corpus. The table shows, Tibetan culture net has the most word species, but less time than other two networks. Common word species ratio of Tibetan culture net is less than other two networks and its word species is much more than other two networks. They show that the choice of words of Tibetan culture net is more novel, more unique, maybe relating with culture, folk-custom.

3.2 Different coverage distribution network of three network corpus

The word coverage is used to calculate the percentage of the word amount in research corpus of the amount of all the research, being an important index reflecting whether Tibetan word commonly used. Table 2 lists the word species information of coverage 80%, 90% and 99% for three networks and the total corpus. 'Ratio (%)' means the proportion of each total amount of word species.

In this year, 631 words can cover 80% of all the corpus and 1147 words can cover 90% of all the corpus. Because of web content link to each other, quote and reprint producing a large number of repeat words, the result that high coverage ratio and low word species come out. To Qinghai Tibetan radio network, 601 words can cover 80% of the corpus. But it's not enough to master 601 words. To understand comprehensively contents of article, it's necessary to know relating culture background and augment some non-common words in these media like written language, professional ཟླ. གཟའ term such as.

Table 1.

	Qinghai	People	Tibetan culture
Times	3679172	854921	984665
Species	9501	4414	13647
Common		2452	
Proportion (%)	25.81	55.55	17.97
Alone	7049	1962	11195
Proportion (%)	74.19	44.45	82.03

Table 2.

	80	90	99
Qinghai			
Species	601	1217	7158
%	6.33	12.81	75.34
People			
Species	415	876	3154
%	9.40	19.85	71.45
Tibetan culture			
Species	1653	3593	6245
%	12.11	26.33	45.76
Total			
Species	631	1147	1925
%	3.58	6.51	10.93

Table 3.

	Qinghai	People	Tibetan culture
High frequency word	1217	876	3593
Common		453	
%	37.22	51.71	12.61
Alone	764	423	3140
%	62.78	48.29	87.39

Table 4.

	Qinghai	People	Tibetan culture	Total
Monosyllable	437	659	1326	721
Disyllable	695	191	2102	1037
Three-syllable	43	19	108	66
Four syllable and above	42	7	56	47
Average	1.75	1.29	1.69	1.70

With the coverage ratio rising, the time of the word reduces. In other words, with the coverage ratio rising, using frequency of the word species drops off. The number of word species of Tibetan culture net is much more than others at coverage 90%, referring to Tibetan culture net using different word species commoner and usage of style of writing being more comprehensive.

3.3 High frequency word common using and using alone of three corpus

Some high frequencies of some words appearing, these word species are named as high frequency word. In this paper, the words that their coverage ratio reaches 90% are named as high frequency word. Table 3 shows high frequency word common using and using alone of three corpus.

Common proportion of high frequency word of Tibetan culture net is 12.61%, meaning its usage of Tibetan vocabulary is wide. Low frequency of common word highlights Tibetan characteristics and culture characteristics and maybe has related with using characteristics with different places. Common proportion of high frequency word of People's Daily online Tibetan edition is the highest, 51.71%. It's related with it's one of the world's top ten newspapers so that the usage of its word will be more cautious.

Most of the high frequency common network words are related with culture, religion, local customs and hot news both at home and abroad. High frequency word using alone relates with culture and religion: ནང་བསྟན། ཆགས་ཁང་། གྲུང་སྐྱེད། geographic: མཚ་སྣ། མཚ་བྱང་། རབ་གང་། hot news: རྒྱ་ས་རའ། ཞི་ཁ་སེ།.

3.4 High frequency word length distribution of three network corpus

Tibetan word is made up of syllables. Word length means the number of syllables in the word.

Table 4 lists high frequency word species according to the syllable statistical of three network corpus.

In three corpus and total corpus, except People's Daily online Tibetan edition, disyllable is the most and monosyllable is the second. Three-syllable, four syllables and above are a few. It shows that Tibetan disyllable and monosyllable are the most frequently used, and disyllable is more than monosyllable. For example, monosyllable like བ་དང་ཕྱོ་ཤ་ར་ are frequently used as case-auxiliary word and ཞལ། རྨ། བདི།, disyllable like མཚ་ཕྱལ་གྲུང་ན། ཕལ་ཁམས།, three-syllable like གྲུང་ཁན་ཅད། རང་སྐད་ཁལ། four syllables like བཞགས་མལ་ཆགས་འདན།, བད་རང་སྐད་སྤྱངས། .

Average word length of Qinghai Tibetan radio network is 1.75, the longest showing that the structure of Tibetan vocabulary in this website relatively complicated. Average word length of People's Daily online Tibetan edition is 1.69 showing that the structure of Tibetan vocabulary in this website relatively modest. Average word length of Tibetan culture net is 1.29, the shortest showing that the structure of Tibetan vocabulary in this website is much easier than others.

3.5 Proper noun usage

Proper noun refers to mean a single object noun. Proper noun has many kinds; the commonest are name, place name and organization name. Proper nouns recognition refers to recognize proper nouns in the text and label semantic category correctly. At present, difficulty of proper noun recognition are performance in these areas: unable to enumerate, categories fuzziness, difficulty of abbreviation and alias recognition, no naming rules to follow together [4].

In this paper, proper noun refers to name, place name and organization name in network (news) corpus.

3.5.1 Name

There are 250 names in network corpus. Tibetan names: གསར་རྒྱལ་བ། བད་རྒྱལ་སྲུང་བཅའ། Han names: ཞེ་ཅན་ཕན། རྩ་ལ་ཤི། Foreign names: ཤ་མ་ལ། ཁྲ་མ་མ། Names involve Tibetan, Han and foreign names, meaning network paying attention to events in each region.

3.5.2 Place name

There are 318 place names in network corpus. Tibetan area place names: ཤར་ཕད། ཆ་ས། ནག་ཆུ། Other areas of China place names: པེ་ཅིན་ཞིང་ཁུལ། ཅུ་ཧེན། Foreign country place names: འཛར་པན། ཨ་མ་ར་ཁ། ཧུའུ་ལན། Place names involve home and abroad, meaning network reporting over each region.

3.5.3 Organization name

There are 119 organization names in network corpus like སྲུང་གྲོས་གྲོང་དབང་ཆན་སྲུང་ཚཱ། པད་ལོང་དན། སྲུང་ཀྱི་ར་དཔལ་དབ་སྤ་ཨཞན་ཀླ་ཁར་སྤ་བད་ས་ཨེ། ཞང་ཀླན་ཁད། Can be seen through the names involved in network corpus, most of the organization names are state institution names, meaning events reported have relation with national macro policy and current politics.

3.5.4 Proper nouns using unified specification

There are many proper nouns used non-uniformly in corpus. In other words, one Han has several translation in Tibetan. In everyday using, unified specification is very necessary. Here is a list of some proper nouns to be unify.

Names:
གསར་རྒྱལ་བ། སྲུང་ག་སར། སྲུང་ག།
སར་རྒྱལ་བ། སྲུང་རྟ་ག་སར། ཞེ་ཅན་ཕན།
ཅན་ཕན། ཞེ་ཅན་པད། ཞེ་ཅན་ཕན། ཨ་
པ་ལ། ཨ་སྤ། ཨ་སྤ་ཨ།

Place names:
པ་ཅན། ཨ་མ་ར་ཁ། ཨ་ [Tibetan text].
[Tibetan text]. རྒྱ་ག་ན། འདཔགས་པའ་ཕུལ།

Organization names:
རྩ་པད་སྤ། རྩ་པད་ཧཱུ།
རག་གཱན་ས་སྤ། རག་གཱན་ས་ཧཱུ།

3.6 Neologism usage

Phonetics, semantics and word-building rules of neologisms are not all new. They are based on prime rules. Judging whether a word is neologism need to consider the following aspects. Neologisms must conform to the rules of word formation in the form and need reflect new social phenomenon, social concept and general mood of society. Neologism is not an absolute concept. Neologisms have a time reference, restrictions and use frequency requirements. Neologisms should have stable usability, cannot limit in professional personnel, using range cannot limit in a row to the industry, and use of neologisms cannot be individual and by accident [5].

In this paper, neologisms are mainly according to related dictionary and combining with Tibetan language grammar, Tibetan language morphology, vocabulary, defining of the 'new' concept of time for the words has been segmented. But owing to the bad line control, we need manually check, confirmation and build Tibetan neologisms thesaurus [3].

Tibetan neologisms thesaurus are related with some neologisms dictionaries including: "new terminology dictionary" (internal) contains more than 5300 new words in the Tibetan language, some neologisms in Journal of Tibetan information technology terms published computer, some neologisms in Han Tibetan English new words commonly used dictionary, Sichuan ethnic publishing house, 2009, more than 550 new terms in Qinghai Tibetan terminology standardization examination committee office first to 20 issue [3], and 2145 new words have been authorized by Hua Kan professor, the northwest university for nationalities in 2011.

For network corpus statistics, contain the new words, a total of 1676, network corpus has 1147 high frequency words and more neologisms than high-frequency words, explain neologisms in network frequency is not high, a large number of neologisms are not in the high frequency words.

3.6.1 Neologisms about economy

Since China's reform and opening up, the country's economic outlook. Around the government new policy, many neologisms arise at the historic moment of economic life. For example, བསྐུར་བཅས་སྐྲ་དགུ།
དཔལ་འབྱུར་མ་ཁས་ཅན། དཔལ་འབྱུར་ནུ་ཆང་
མ་ཉམ་ལས། གསར་བྱད།

3.6.2 Neologisms about science and technology

Along with society's progress, productivity increases, the popularization of science and culture, many neologisms related to the development of science and technology has entered people's life. For example, ཕུབ་ཆད་ད་སྐྲ། ད་དས། སྣན་མང་གཟུགས། 5. སྤ་ཁ། སྨོ་ད་ད་རྩ་ལ་ར།

3.6.3 Neologisms about farming and stockbreeding

Our country is agricultural country and agriculture is the first industry. With the progress of science and technology, new changes have taken place in agricultural life also. Some new words have appeared. For example, འདབས་འཛུགས་གས་ལས་རགས་ཀྱི་སྤ། .
ས་ཁ། འབྲག་ཧག། ཞང་ལས་ལག་ཆས་ལ་སྤ།

3.6.4 Neologisms about other areas

Travel: འགྲུལ་སྐྱོད། གནས་ལྗོངས།. Law: ཁྲིམས་ལུགས།.
Culture: ས་ཁོངས་རིག་གནས།..Sports: ས་ཁོངས་རིག་གནས།.
War: ས་ཐང་སྒྲ་གཏོངས། སྲུང་ལས་འཐབ་འ
Tibetan Buddhist culture: དགའ་ཕུན་ཚ་བཀྲ་མ།.,
བད་བ་ཚན་སྒྱུ་ཞིང་བཀོད།..

4 CONCLUSION

For Qinghai Tibetan radio network, People's Daily online Tibetan edition, Tibetan culture net, this paper studies from the language basic situation, term of coverage, high frequency word usage, high frequency word length, use of proper nouns, and the usage of new words. The results of the survey are as follows: A total of 17620 words. Word species increased significantly after coverage rate reached 90%. Frequency words used together of three network (news) corpora high are not many. Average word length is 1.70. High frequency double syllable words and one-syllable words are the most and more than three syllables high frequency words are relatively few. Proper nouns are involved in various regions, areas, but using the specification to be unified. There are 1676 neologisms, mainly involving economic, science and technology, agriculture and animal husbandry, tourism, legal, cultural, sports, military, Tibetan culture and so on.

REFERENCES

Cao Hui, Dong Xiaofang, Meng Xianghe. Tibetan paper statistical study, northwest university for nationalities (natural science edition) [J], 2012.09, 33 (87): 50 and 54.

Hou Min. The language resource construction and life monitoring related terms. The terms standardization and information technology [J], 2010, issue 2:30 to 33.

Liu Jingwen, Zhang Ting. Public opinion monitoring and social language life. Journal of yunnan normal university [A], 2011, Vol 43: 47–53.

Wang Haixia. Analyses the meaning of new words and their main features. The discourse of higher education, the [J], 2010, 01 (top): 56–6.

Wang Xingyi. For Chinese proper noun recognition based on pattern matching [D], Master degree theses of master of Shanxi university in 2005.06.

Computer, Intelligent Computing and Education Technology – Liu, Sung & Yao (Eds)
© 2014 Taylor & Francis Group, London, ISBN 978-1-138-02469-4

Research on micro deformation and vibration mechanism of stationary wave piezoelectric motor

Zhi-Yuan Hai, Qiong-Ying Lv & Dan-Dan Zhang
Changchun University of Science and Technology, Changchun, Jilin, China

ABSTRACT: The microscopic deformation of the contacts of stationary wave piezoelectric motors has been detected in this paper based on vibration mechanism. The relationship between the external motor can be obtained based on the analysis of the relationship between vibration and wave by transmission mechanism. The motion mechanism analysis of the contacts shows that the drive speed of a contact is determined by lateral vibration instead of sliding.

Keyword: Vibration Analysis; Adhesive Contact; Wave and Vibrations; Irregular elliptical motion

1 INTRODUCTION

In 1981, Toshiiku Sashida developed an ultrasonic piezoelectric motor. As shown in Figure 1, it is a theoretical, simple stationary wave motor with a trajectory model of its oscillator terminal offered by Toshiiku Sashida [1]. A stationary wave piezoelectric motor is generally doing elliptical motion with its oscillator driven by piezoelectric element. Then transfer the motion of the oscillator coupled to the rotor or slider by friction force. (see Figure 1)

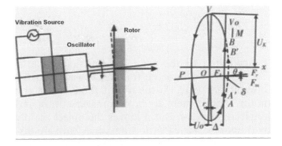

Figure 1. Stationary wave motor with a trajectory model of its oscillator terminal.

2 THE MICRO DEFORMATION PROBLEM ON THE CONTACT OF OSCILLATOR AND ROTOR

When the top of the piezoelectric motor oscillator functions on the surface of the rotor, it does not press into the surface of the rotor because of the rigid contact instead of the microscopic elastic deformation [2]. The contact of piezoelectric motor and rotor is seemingly non adhesive, but as the friction time goes, the material hardness reducing leads to gelling phenomenon on the surface with weak adhesion. And this tiny deformation, faint force of adhesive and the scratches of the rotor surface after interaction greatly affects the practical efficiency of piezoelectric motor.

In practice, the piezoelectric motor drives rotor. Stationary wave piezoelectric motor is driven by piezoelectric element in general, because the contact surface is not smooth. The elliptic motion of the oscillator is a kind of defective theory. So it is very important to study on the adhesive contact of the surface, it helps improve the working efficiency of the motor.

In order to study the micro change of the rotor surface such as gelling, contact and deformation when the oscillator drives the rotor, gelling theory is particularly important. The classical theory of adhesive contact is named the JKR theory by Johnson, Kendall, and Roberts in 1971[3]. Discuss surface contact with a radius R of the elastic sphere and another elastic sphere. It makes two surface contacts with the "neck" phenomenon.

Assume the surface of the oscillator and the rotor respectively are radius R_1 and R_2 spheres. When it is under the action of pressure P0, deformation of contact zone shows below[4].

$$\delta_0^3 = \frac{3}{4}\pi(K_1 + K_2)\frac{R_1 R_2}{R_1 + R_2}P_0 \tag{1}$$

where K_1, K_2 = the elastic coefficient of material. R_1, R_2 = contacting sphere radius. P0 = the driving force. δ_0 = deformation radius of contact area.

K can be determined by the formula as the following.

$$\kappa = \frac{1 - \nu^2}{\pi E}$$

where is the Poisson ratio. E is the young modulus.

Through the analysis of the vibration quantity, micro deformation of the contact and the running speed, it can be concluded that the running speed of piezoelectric motor is determined by the amplitude of lateral, but not slippage.

3 THE RELATIONSHIP BETWEEN WAVE AND VIBRATION

Analyzing on the essence of piezoelectric motor transmission, there is the inevitable link between wave and vibration. Wave is produced by the vibration, then the wave generated by the vibration functions on the surface, it makes the object move.

$$y = 2A \cos 2\pi \frac{x}{\lambda} \cos 2\pi \nu t$$

According to the wave transmission mode it can be divided into the transverse wave and the longitudinal wave. At the top of the piezoelectric motor contact there are both transverse wave and longitudinal wave. But it moves the object mainly by transverse wave [5]. So transverse wave are discussed, the most when the transverse wave functioning mainly is the elastic wave.

For the transmission in the medium of vibration wave, the calculation is relatively complex. So take out a voxel from the whole volumetric, observe and calculate the motion of each single voxel, so that the operation mode of the whole wave is calculated. Several voxels combine together to form a plane wave called the plane wave, which can be represented by the formula (2).

$$y = A \cos (\omega t - kx) \tag{2}$$

where $k = \frac{2\pi}{\lambda}$

According to the formula (2), it shows the movements of the voxel. When the voxel accessories are under transverse load, there must be deformation that is near to offer tangential force, the shearing strain shows that,

$$\varphi = \frac{dy}{dx}$$

Thus according to concept of shear modulus the formula shows that,

$$E = \frac{F/S}{dy/dx} = \frac{P}{\varphi} \tag{3}$$

Then according to the formula (3), intensity of pressure shows below,

$$P = E\varphi = AkE \sin (\omega t - kx) \tag{4}$$

Then tangential force at x points shows below,

$$F = PS = AkES \sin(\omega t - kx) \tag{5}$$

where S = the cross area of the voxel.

Because that

$$V = \frac{dy}{dt} = -A\omega \sin (\omega t - kx)$$

Then,

$$F = \frac{-kES}{\omega} V \tag{6}$$

By the formula (6), when the voxel in points x is in equilibrium position, the velocity is proportional to the force. The speed gradually slows down while it leaves the equilibrium position to the peaks and troughs of the wave. That is because that the farther the equilibrium position is, the smaller the deformation is, the smaller the stress is, so the slower the speed is.

The movement form of piezoelectric motor is stationary wave when it is a stationary wave piezoelectric motor according to the above derivations. Namely the waveform could not move forward, just fluctuate in the same position, thus form the wave nodal and wave amplitude. In the stationary wave field of minimum nodal and minimum amplitude which generally is 0, the amplitude of antinode is maximum, then infer the formula (7).

$$n \frac{\lambda}{2} \tag{7}$$

Of which, $x = (2n + 1)\frac{\lambda}{4}$ antinode, x = wave nodal, $n = 0, \pm 1, \pm 2, \pm 3...$

When the force on the piezoelectric motor is stationary wave, the formula is the same applied. Namely the resultant force of a single voxel can be showed with formula (2).

Similarly stationary wave piezoelectric motor shearing strain shows below.

$$\varphi = \frac{dy}{dx} = -\frac{4\pi A}{\lambda} \sin \frac{4\pi x}{\lambda} \cos 2\pi \nu t$$

$$P = E\varphi = -\frac{4\pi AE}{\lambda} \sin \frac{4\pi x}{\lambda} \cos 2\pi \nu t \tag{8}$$

The sum of outer forces on the voxel shows in formula (10) according to the formula (9).

$$F = PS \tag{9}$$

$$f = dF = \frac{-8\pi^2 AESdx}{\lambda^2}\cos\frac{2\pi x}{\lambda}\cos 2\pi \upsilon t$$
$$= -\frac{4\pi^2 ESdx}{\lambda^2}y \tag{10}$$

Hence,

$$V = \frac{dy}{dt} = -4\pi A\omega\cos 2\pi\frac{x}{\lambda}\sin 2\pi \upsilon t \tag{11}$$

The formula (11) shows, when the voxel in x points is in the equilibrium position, the relationship between the velocity V and the force is not the same as travelling wave to be proportional. As is known that to each voxel of the stationary wave when the discrepancy in phase is $\pi/2$ according to the specific expression of F and V, the maximum V occurs in the equilibrium position. It is also known that every voxel for vibration is a harmonic vibration. Thus, we can infer that relationship between vibration and wave is a kind of simple harmonic vibration.

4   CONCLUSION

In conclusion, it is inferred that the actual trajectory of the piezoelectric motor oscillator is not a regular elliptical motion based on the above theories such as adhesive contact theory, inside-rough-surface contact theory and the vibration theory caused by friction. Regardless of whether the travelling wave motor or the stationary wave motor, there is always a general relationship between the wave and vibration as the simple harmonic vibration in a vibration system. This paper introduces the concept of voxels. It can divide the whole into numerous voxels in the future calculations of complex wave forms. Then integral the relationship between mechanics and movement of the countless voxels, so that obtain the mechanical model of complex waveforms.

REFERENCES

Toshiiku Sashida. The manufacture principle of ultrasonic motor drive and experimental research [J]. Appl. Phys. 51(6), 713–720(1982).:1–2.

Valentin L. Popov. Contact Mechanics and Friction Physical Principle and Applications[M]. Springer Heidelberg Dordrecht London New York, ISBN 978–3–642–10802–0: 2–3.

Johnson K L, Kendall K, Roberts A D. Surface energy and contact of elastic solids [s]. Proceedings of the Royal Society of London, 1971, 324(1):301–313.

Fan Kangqi, Jia Jianyuan. Adhesive Contact Model and Calculation of Micro-Mechanical Systems [J]. Xidian Universit y, Xican 710071, China, 2006–11: 2–3.

Lendraitis, V, Mizarienė, V, Seniūnas. G. Nanopositioning—methods and means[J]. ISSN 1392–1207. MECHANIKA. 2007: 1–3.

Computer, Intelligent Computing and Education Technology – Liu, Sung & Yao (Eds)
© 2014 Taylor & Francis Group, London, ISBN 978-1-138-02469-4

Analysis on passive play of athletes

Yan-Long Che
Physical Culture Institute of Yanan University, China

ABSTRACT: The phenomenon of "passive play" appeared in the London Olympic Games on August 1, 2012 and the National Games of this year. Is "passive play" the occasional and individual phenomenon or inevitable result in the game? This paper puts forward the countermeasures for correcting game style, strengthening the self-quality of athletes, coaches and judges, completing competition mechanism, perfecting game rules and setting up the relevant penal rules etc. based on the analysis of specific expression behavior of passive play and self-quality of athletes, coaches, the club representative game, judge and competition system to eliminate athletes' passive play behaviors and promote healthy development of athletics.

Keywords: sports; game; passive play

The athletics developed from the ancient Olympics game up to now, its organization and relevant rules has been strengthened continuously. The sports spirit is the reflection of whole aspects, level, fairness, openness, characteristic, cohesive force, infectivity and appealingness of sports, is the symbol of sports ideal, faith, sentiment, knowledge, sportsmanship, aesthetic level and is also the backbone and soul of sports.[1] The charms of sports lie in self-challenging, aggressiveness, self-display and success achievements. Therefore, it attracts numerous sports enthusiast. However, owing to various reasons, the phenomenon of passive play of athletes appears frequently in the games. No matter what the reasons are, the passive play will seriously violate the essence of sports and is an irresponsible behavior for the sports enthusiast and the audiences enjoying the sports game.

1 DEFINITION OF PASSIVE PLAY

1.1 *Passive play*

The passive play means that for avoiding encountering teammates in the knockout match, the athlete loses the game deliberately in order to create advantages for winning.[2] The passive play is a kind of psychological mood and represents that the athlete purposefully and consciously lose the game during the competition.

The main reasons for passive play are competitive level of the opponent, the strategy arrangement made by the coaches, playing field, the rule enforcement of judge and lack of initiative and positivity of the arrangement of relevant clubs.

1.2 *Manifestation of passive play*

The passive play which is regarded as a phenomenon violates the sports essence firstly, and it also fails to reflect the spirit of self-challenging and aggressiveness. It is a kind of serious hurt for the sports enthusiasts, especially for the filed audience. The manifestations are inactive action, deliberate losing, conscious losing points, intentional error and defensive attack etc. The passive play is very obvious in some events such as ball games especially the events competing against the net, but it is uneasy to notice the passive play in some events such as free combat, martial arts and wrestling. The athletes compete passively based on the rules, so it is hard to penalize.

2 FACTORS FOR PASSIVE PLAY

2.1 *Subject factor*

As the subject of games, the actual strength of athletes decides the winning or losing. When competing, if the strength discrepancy of both sides is large, the athlete falling behind will generate emotional fluctuation and exert passive play behavior; in addition, psychological factor of the athletes is also one of the causes for passive play. During the game, as the athlete is down in mood, unexcited and has no willing to fight, the athlete responds slowly and is easy to make mistakes resulting in passivity and anger etc.[4] The competitive level, physical condition, performance on spot of the athletes may lead to passivity which will cause the phenomenon of sharp decrease of athletic ability and competitive level.[5]

2.2 Factors of representative team, club and coach

The coach has a closest relation with the athletes in the daily life, train activities and match. It is unavoidable that the coach and athlete may have disagreement on the strategy arrangement. During the match, the team member will bring individual dissatisfied moods into competition and thus result in passive play behaviors; the coach, club and representative team require the team member to lose a game deliberately according to "requirements" of strategy arrangement and member adjustment during the agenda, so the team on the field will play passively; if the club and representative team have conflict on the daily management, team construction and benefits distribution and the conflict is intensified at a certain period, the athlete is dissatisfied with the management of club and generates passive play behavior, strike or even legal disputes will be caused. Such as the troubled and famous storm that Sun Yang required to change coach and at the finals of wresting in the National Game, the Olympic champion Sun Fuming who had received the hints from his coach stood still and was pulled down by his opponent Yan Sirui, sending the National Game champion honor to his opponent. In this way, the Liaoning Team represented by Sun Funming and Liberation Army Team represented by his opponent could both win the gold medals, and the Liaoning Team could win a silver medal additionally. On August 1, 2012, during the badminton game of London Olympic Games, a pair of Chinese group, a pair of Indonesia group and two pairs of Korean group played passively in order to avoid competing with team members in the knockout match.

2.3 Factors of judge

As the rule-executor of matches, the judge will impact the decision of winning or losing or game procedure, tempo or even the result of a match. Due to the factors of comprehension on game rules based on judge's self educational level and the view angle, such as the athletics events such as basketball and football, the standard for judgment and penalty is judge's subjectivity. This will involve judge's subjective initiative and assurance of penalty degree. The factors of self-quality of judge, home and visiting field, the audience and treatment of sudden events will cause erroneous judgment, missing judgment or even partiality judgment which will have great impact on player's mood and the players having poor ability for emotion self-regulation will play passively. Such as in the finals of women's rugby, a surprising scene appeared: the Beijing Team was dissatisfied with

the penalty, and at the second half of the match, when they were behind on score for 0 to 15, they kept still and refused to compete. At the last five minutes, the Shandong Team just liked holding a demonstration match and won the game. Beijing Team lost the game with a absurd score of 0 to 71.

2.4 Competition mechanism factors

In Preliminary round, qualifying round, group stage, grading competition and other competitions, according to the competition system, it is prone to have negative competition. For some teams have completed their tasks, such as qualified, passed, graded, in order to retain a good position and avoid to battle with the stronger team, they deliberately lose the match and have a negative competition which has "benefits rather harmless" for them. For example in the Eleven Games, Hubei man's basketball was against Shanghai men's basketball. If Shanghai wins Hubei 5–16 points, then both them can be qualified; If Shanghai wins Hubei less than 5 points or Shanghai lose the game, then Shanghai team would be eliminated; If Shanghai wins Hubei more than 16 points, then Hubei team would be eliminated. On the last ten seconds, they tied as 89 points. It is hard for Shanghai team to win more than 5 points, and then they deliberately missed four free throws, intents to bring the game into overtime. Hubei team was even more peculiar, they directly threw the ball to their basket, to let Shanghai team win the game but lose the quality to the next round. The two sides used all tricks, but eventually Shanghai team was still eliminated. Another famous phrase by the fans is that "Liaoning and Shandong are brothers, let's tie score as 2:2 and both be the top eight". Due to the rules of the Sixth National Games in 1987, if there is a winner between Liaoning and Shandong, the loser would be eliminated; if they tied as 0–0, Liaoning would be eliminated; if they tied as 1:1, Liaoning and Shanghai should draw lots to decide who is qualified; if they tied as 1:1 2:2, then Liaoning and Shandong would be both qualified. After the start of the game, the two teams ended the game by 2:2 with the incredible understanding, and then the Arbitration Commission kicked them out by the negative competition.

2.5 Other factors

Athlete's spot state will be affected by many factors, such as weather, audience, space, equipment, administrative intervention and other factors. These factors actively or passively apply to athletes. Under the effect of these factors, athletes will have a certain degree of negative competition.

3 NEGATIVE COMPETITION COUNTER-MEASURES

The formation of negative competition is constituted by personal factors, competition system, the game system and other factors. So it should be managed by the following aspects.

3.1 Correct the attitude and enhance the sports morality of athletes, coaches and referees

Strengthening the education of athletes' psychological control, educating players to be serious about every game, promoting the spirit of challenging and fighting in sports, reducing the interference of external factors, make player have the best competitive state in the contest. Coaches are the ties between athletes and clubs & teams, they need to improve physical and moral literacy. We need to correctly handle the relationship between athletes and coaches, club, team. We also need to norm the law of referee, improve the referee's level of law enforcement. We need to use high technology tools, such as video playback, Hawkeye and other imaging technologies, while strengthening the abilities of technical officials and Arbitration Committee, reducing the controversial penalty in competition, to truly reflect of the fairness of the competition.

3.2 Improve rules, competition system, and make a clear penalty system

Unreasonable competition mechanism is the main reason for negative competition. Tournament competition authorities should make the arrangements for unreasonable rules and the events, to enhance scientific rationality of the competition. Reduce the competition system problems on causing the negative competition. Establish and perfect the penalty mechanism, according to the rules to give punishment to teams, clubs, coaches and athletes who have negative competition behavior.

3.3 Other measures

Strengthening of civil education, to become civilized audience. Make the appropriate the necessary regulatory to audiences and give enforcement measures to those audiences who is booing and making trouble, to prevent athletes' negative competition. Strengthen the checking of facilities and equipment. Some leading cadres would treat the competition results as their performance; we should prevent the administrative intervention in the game.

4 CONCLUSION

Sports game is the ultimate expression of athletes' training level and the tactical arrangement of coach. The negative behavior is not conducive to the development of sports game, contrary to the spirit of sport, violates sports ethics, and has adverse affected in sports and social. We should strengthen the ideological education of athletes, coaches and referees. And we need to correct the attitude, improve the rules, perfect competition system, and make a clear penalty system to reduce negative competition, make clean space for the development of sports.

REFERENCES

[1] http://www.baidu.com.
[2] http://www.baidu.com.
[3] Shi Huabi, Cai Zhonglin. Analyze negative behaviors in Wushu Sanda Competition [J]. Shenyang Institute of Physical Education Journal, 2005, 24 (1): 127–128.
[4] Lee Richeng. Analyze negative emotions in Basketball Contest [J]. Yiyang Teachers College Journal, 1999, 16 (6): 105–107.
[5] Wang Chunsheng. The overcome and the adjustment of Basketball game players' negative emotions [J]. Wuhan Institute of Physical Education Journal, 2003, 37 (3): 151–153.

Computer, Intelligent Computing and Education Technology – Liu, Sung & Yao (Eds)
© 2014 Taylor & Francis Group, London, ISBN 978-1-138-02469-4

The intelligent family semantic query system based on ontology model

C.F. Tang & M.D. Hu
Ocean University of China, Qingdao, Shandong, China

Y.J. Li
Hisense Group, Qingdao, Shandong, China

ABSTRACT: We improved the existing semantic query algorithm based on the existing technology of semantic query and ontology, combined with the special environment in smart home. As well as used ontology model for the smart home and HCI module to develop a semantic query system for smart home based on ontology model, evaluate the system and analysis the advantages of system.

Keywords: intelligent family; ontology model; semantic query system

1 INTRODUCTION

Smart home refers to the combination of various subsystems by advanced computer technology, network communication technology and integrated wiring technology. Compared with ordinary home, smart home is more comfortable and safer. It can provide full range of information interactive features and help families keeping communication with the external flow, optimizing people's lifestyle. Different smart home appliances need to keep network communication. But it is difficult to get detailed information and environmental condition between different devices because of their different description languages and communication protocols.

Ontology is a formal explicit specification of a shared conceptualisation [1] in that it supports the capture and specification of domain knowledge with its intrinsic semantics through consensual terminology and formal axioms. Ontology supports a set of modeling primitives through defining classes, individuals, their attributes and their relations. The formal axioms specify the intended meaning of the terminology with the modeling primitives and their a priori relationships in an explicit way [2]. The consensual terminology makes it possible to share and reuse data and knowledge across different components in a system and across different systems [3]. Some pervasive computing projects have applied ontology in modeling and reasoning on concepts and knowledge [4,5]. Their works demonstrate that ontology is a promising technique that can be used to address data, knowledge, and application heterogeneity.

In order to shield the heterogeneity of device, provide convenient for devices in smart home to get environment-related information, and establish full context relationship, this paper presents a semantic query for the smart home system. In this system, firstly we establish a ontology model for smart home, using unified abstract language. The model describes the device and environment information in smart home, and adds semantic tags for all the relevant information in home. Then query could be implemented by inputting keyword. During the course of query, we can get context of keywords. It is able to fully understand the whole smart home information realize the sharing of data resources and interoperability between devices.

2 QUERY SYSTEM ARCHITECTURE

To meet the needs of smart home user query, the ontology-based query system consists of three parts: HCI module, query processing module and ontology model, as shown in Figure 1. The HCI module is used for inputting query information, displaying the query results and confirming query results. Users can interact with the system through this module intelligently. Query processing module is the core module of the system. It can do some search in the body model, after the user enters keywords and ontology model. Ontology model is the query resource that provides semantic relationships of the query keywords. And the query processing model query in a user-specified ontology model.

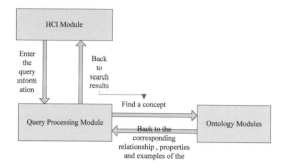

Figure 1.   Querymodel of smart home system.

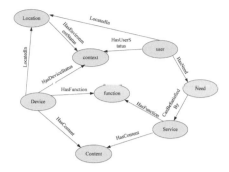

Figure 2.   The relational model of ontology in smart home domain.

2.1   Ontology model

Ontology model is the basis for Semantic query. The model is based on the smart home field relevant standards, Abstract concepts and relations between concepts among smart home field, including hierarchical relationships, integral and part relationship. The appliances, sensors, measuring instruments and other automated equipments are defined in the ontology model. Not only the attributes of each concept are defined, the relationship between the concept of the devices, the function of the device, the position, the processing and content of control involved in the apparatus body of the various devices are described. Meanwhile, the ontology abstracts the users in the family to form the user concept to describe the user's needs, preferences, and other states. A complex relationship between ontology concepts is shown in the Figure 2.

Through a series of attributes, the contacts between these concepts are established. Through the hasDeviceStatus property, a relationship between device concept and the context concept is established. By LocatedIn property, a relationship between User, Device and Location is established. Through hasFunction property, a relationship between Device and Function concept is established. Through hasContent property, a relationship between Device, Service and Content concept is established. By canBeSatisfiedBy property, a relationship between Service and Need concept is established. The hasNeedproperty property connects the User and Need concept. The By hasUserStatus property connects the User and Context concept. Through these attributes, relationships between these concepts are formed and a system model is established.

2.2   Query processing module

In the smart home environment, the most common queries are the context queries among users,

Figure 3.   Context query algorithm.

the query for services and the query for equipment which could meet the needs. The inquiry of the context includes device status, user status and environmental status inquiries. Based on the established ontology model of smart home field, query is also divided into two types, one is the query for status, another is the query for the services and equipment which could implements the service. We design two different query algorithms to satisfy the different query need.

2.2.1   Query algorithm for context

We realize the query about device status, user status and environmental status in the smart home environment based on context ontology model, device ontology model, user ontology model and location ontology model. Query algorithm flowchart is shown as follows.

The user inputs an ontology model and the query keywords. For example, the status of user is inputted, the query processing module will process the inquiry request, and returns the corresponding instance of the concept. Users select the suitable instance from the returned instance. As an inputting message, the instance user select will be inputted into the query processing module again. And the query processing model will inquiry the according ontology model, obtain specific information about the instance. The user's state instance will be got from the context ontology by has UserStatus properties of the user ontology and the user's status will be returned.

If users want to query the device status or state of the environment, the device ontology or location ontology can be selected in the above. The inquiries on the device status or environmental status can be completed.

2.2.2 *Query algorithm for a service and the device which implement service*

A query based on the user's needs could be implemented. The services that could satisfy user's need and the device that could implement the service could be achieved. The inquiry is primarily based on the concepts and features of the demand ontology, service ontology, function ontology and device ontology. Query algorithm flow chart shown in Figure 4.

1. The user selects need ontology and Select keywords from the Need ontology.
2. Query processing module query the Need ontology according to the user's selected concept which from the Need ontology, obtain relevant instances of this concept and the attribute of concepts.
3. Query module returns a list of instances and concepts property features.
4. User select the corresponding range of the could-BeSatisfiedBy property from the list of concept feature properties, and Select the concept of service which can meet the needs as an input.
5. Query module inquiry service ontology, query the keyword selected by the user, and get the corresponding instance attribute of the service concept and the list of attribute. The list of instance and attribute is returned.
6. Users select the appropriate service instance. And in accordance with the corresponding concept of hasServiceType property's range, Selected functions related concepts in the ontology as input.

7. Query corresponding concepts in the function ontology, get function concept related attributes list, and return.
8. Users select devices concept from the domain of hasFunction property, and input as a keyword.
9. query module query device body according to the input device concept keyword and get the corresponding instance for the concept and returns.
10. Users select the appropriate device instance.
11. Query module query the device instance specific information, and returned to the user.

Through the above algorithm flow, we can achieve service that satisfy need and equipment that can implement service. The control terminal can invoke the service instance and device instance to meet the relevant requirements.

3 CONCLUSION

The ontology model in the smart home is the abstraction of resources in smart home which provide a formal description and establish a system model. This model link all of the resources in smart home and each resource is no longer isolated. And semantic tags for resource are added also. They become the basis for semantic query. Query system based on ontology model can achieve the state of the environment, device status, user status, services and equipment. It is easy to achieve interoperability between devices further.

REFERENCES

[1] T.R. Gruber: Toward principles for the design of ontologies used for knowledge sharing, International Journal of Human–Computer Studies 43 (5–6) (1995), p. 907–928.
[2] N. Guarino: Formal ontology and information systems, in: FOIS'98: Proceedings of the First International Conference on Formal Ontology in Information Systems, IOS Press, Trento, Italy, 1998, p. 3–15.
[3] L.M. Chen, C. Nugent, M. Mulvenna, D. Finlay, X. Hong: Semantic smart homes: towards knowledge rich assisted living environments, Intelligent Patient Management 189 (2009), p. 279–296.
[4] M. Perttunen, J. Riekki: Context Representation and Reasoning in Pervasive Computing: a Review, International Journal of Multimedia and Ubiquitous Engineering Vol. 4, No. 4, October, 2009, p. 1–28.
[5] N. Roy, T. Gub, S.K. Dasc: Supporting pervasive computing applications with active context fusion and semantic context delivery, Pervasive and Mobile Computing 6 (2010), p. 21–42.

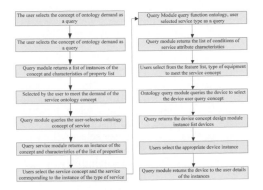

Figure 4.   Server query algorithm.

Computer, Intelligent Computing and Education Technology – Liu, Sung & Yao (Eds)
© 2014 Taylor & Francis Group, London, ISBN 978-1-138-02469-4

Research on hand pressure information collection when pass, smash, blocking, mat-ball and serve

Yi-Yang Li, Zhou Wan, Yun-Fan Zang & Hao-Hua Liu
Faculty of Information Engineering and Automation, Kunming University of Science and Technology, Kunming, P.R. China

Min Shu
Faculty of Physical Education, Kunming University of Science and Technology, Kunming, P.R. China

ABSTRACT: Pass, smash, blocking, mat-ball and serve are the five volleyball basic skills. How to improve competition results, and reduce sports injuries simultaneously, has become the focus of attention of volleyball teaching and training. Utilizing PVDF's advantages of fast response, high sensitivity, easy to process and so on, a method to collect hand pressure information when playing volleyball has been put forward. The sensor array, signal conditioner and power supply circuit have been developed. Three sets of quasi-static test prove that the sensors are accurate and reliable. Frontal underhand serve experiment proves that this method is practical and able to effectively acquire volleyball player's hand pressure information which can provide scientific basis for the further research of volleyball special training program design.

Keywords: volleyball; pass; smash; blocking; mat-ball; serve; PVDF; hand pressure; signal conditioner

1 INTRODUCTION

Modern volleyball competition is diverse and strong confrontational. It is often the combination of pass, smash, blocking, mat-ball and serve (hereinafter referred to as the five). Not a single skill confrontation repeatedly, it is confronting continuously with several skills of the five. Pass is giving the ball which is just picked up to a teammate for attack. A team's attacking capability largely depends on the quality of pass, especially the quality of toss. Tosser plays a critical role in a match. Smash is the most useful attacking skill of the five and the most effective scoring tool. Blocking is the first line of defense, and also an important part of counterattack. It not only can slow the ball, but also intercept the opponent's smash. Mat-ball is most frequently used in catching the served ball and smashed ball. It is the first step to turn defense into attack. Serve is the start of the match and attack. It not only can directly get scores, but also disorder the opponent's attacking plan so as to reduce defensive pressure.

When utilizing the five, negligence or improper posture will affect competition results, and more easily lead to sports injuries. At the moment of high-speedy moving ball contacting hands or the athlete sending the ball at full tilt, injuries of knuckle, wrist, elbow, shoulder and lumbodorsal ligaments, muscles and skeletal are the most likely to occur. However, current study on volleyball teaching and training is mainly reflected in starting position, footwork, tactical organization, instructional design and technology analysis, etc. Among them, the study developed from human body piezoelectric signal analysis is mainly focused in lower limbs and planta. Therefore, this paper presents an information acquisition method of hand pressure. PVDF-based sensor array, signal conditioner and power supply circuit have been designed and produced. After tests and experiment, this method can effectively collect hand pressure information when pass, smash, blocking, mat-ball and serve, thus to provide scientific basis for the further research of designing the volleyball special training programs which is not only able to improve competition results but also minimize sports injuries.

2 PVDF FILM WORK PRINCIPLE

PVDF (polyvinylidene fluoride) is a high molecular polymer used as a new kind of piezoelectric material. In the chemical composition of PVDF, two fluorine atoms substitute the two hydrogen atoms of ethylene. Compared with traditional materials, PVDF film has the advantages of fast response, wide frequency response, linearity, good reproducibility, wide dynamic range, easy to match the acoustic impedance, high sensitivity force electrical conversion, high strength mechanical properties. Better is that PVDF film is light, flexible, extremely thin, impact-resistant, invulnerable to the pollution of water and chemicals, and easy to process.

Polarized PVDF film has piezoelectric characteristic. Withstanding a certain direction pressure, PVDF film will generate a charge which is equal in magnitude and opposite in direction in the upper and lower plane of polarization. Idealizing the PVDF film under pressure as a capacitor model will get the following formula.

$$Q_i = d_{ij} F_j \tag{1}$$
$$q_i = d_{ij} \sigma_j \tag{2}$$

In the formula: $i = 1, 2, 3, j = 1, 2, \ldots, 6$; Q_i is the total output charge of the film; d_{ij} is the piezoelectric strain constant matrix of the film; F_j is the pressure of the film; q_i is the output charge of the film unit area; σ_j is the stress of the film.

When electrode plates gathered electric charge, between counter electrodes will generate a voltage.

$$U_a = Q/C_a \tag{3}$$
$$C_a = \varepsilon_0 \, \varepsilon_r \, A/t \tag{4}$$

In the formula: U_a is the voltage between the two plane of polarization (V); Q is the total electric charge of the film (C); C_a is the equivalent capacitance of the film (F); ε_0 is permittivity of vacuum; ε_r is polymer dielectric constant; A is the area of the film; t is the thickness of the film.

3 THE HAND PRESSURE SENSOR ARRAY

After repeated experiments, round tablet shaped sensor is the most suitable for piezoelectric signal collection during the process of playing volleyball. The sensor directly embeds in the inner surface of the conventional all fingers covered sport gloves (Fig. 3). As shown in Figure 1, the top and bottom cantilever is made of PV membrane; Conductive silver is used as the adhesive; The hard base is directly utilizing the wear leather in the inner top surface of the gloves (Fig. 3).

Using left hand as illustration, the hand pressure sensor array is composed of 30 sensors.

Figure 1. The lateral view of the sensor structure.

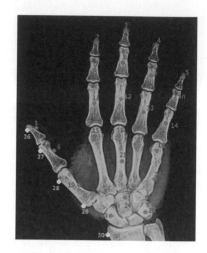

Figure 2. Human hand anatomy key points.

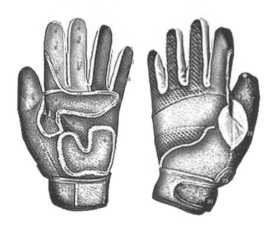

Figure 3. The hand pressure sensor array.

Each sensor corresponds to a key point of human anatomy, as shown in Figures 2 and 3. Sensor 1 to 5 correspond to distal phalanx, sensor 6 corresponds to thumb proximal phalanx, sensor 7 to 10 correspond to middle phalanx, sensor section 11 to 14 correspond to proximal phalanx, sensor 15 to 18 correspond to metacarpus head, sensor 19 corresponds to abductor pollicis brevis, sensor 20 corresponds to adductor pollicis, sensor 21 corresponds to arcus volaris superficialis, sensor 22 corresponds to little finger abductor, sensor 23 corresponds to os scaphoideum, sensor 24 corresponds to capitatum, sensor 25 corresponds to lunare, sensor 26 corresponds to thumb distal phalanx head, sensor 27 corresponds to thumb proximal phalanx head, sensor 28 corresponds to thumb metacarpal head, sensor 29 corresponds to thumb metacarpal bottom, sensor 30 corresponds to radius.

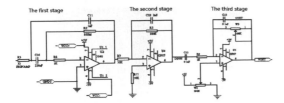

The first stage   The second stage   The third stage

Figure 4.   The signal conditioner.

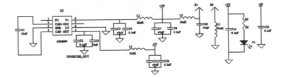

Figure 5.   The power supply circuit.

4 SIGNAL CONDITIONER

The PVDF-based sensor has high internal impedance, and its output signal is very weak and suscep-
tible to all kinds of noise interference. If acquiring
data during volleyball training or competition,
interference will be more serious. In order to ensure
the data we collected is true, reliable and accurate,
the signal must pass through signal conditioner for
impedance matching, signal amplification and filtering processing. As shown in Figure 4, the design
of the signal conditioner is divided into three
stages and the main chips are CA3140 and OP07.
The first stage is preamplifier which converts high-
impedance input into low-impedance output, and
converts weak charge signal into amplified voltage signal. The second stage is low-pass filter with
gain which filter out the high frequency noise, low
level noise and external peak noise mixed in the
signal. The third stage is broadband band-pass filter which adjust the amplitude of the output signal to an appropriate range (0~+5V) so as to meet
the input requirements of the multi-function data
acquisition card.

Chip CA3140 and OP07 require ±5V supply. In
order to ensure a stable power supply and to minimize interference, power supply circuit is designed
especially as shown in Figure 5. The main chip of
the circuit is ADM660.

5 TESTS AND EXPERIMENT

In actual acquisition, 30 × 2 (both hands) signals
need to be dealt with, so the amount of data is enormous. The multi-function data acquisition card is
used for real-time signal processing. The card utilizes

USB2.0 interface for communication with the host
PC. The results of signal processing stored in real-
time, which provides guarantees for hand pressure
information analysis of the five training.

By loading the sensor with balance and scales
weights, the sensor' output is tested. The first set
of test: load from 0 g to 20 g at 5 g intervals. The
second set of test: load from 100 g to 500 g at 100 g
intervals. The third set of test: load from 1 kg to
5 kg at 1 kg intervals. Each set of tests repeat 10
times and calculate the average voltage. Figures 6–8
is the test of sensor 1. The linear relationships
between input and output of all other sensors' tests
are similar to sensor 1, which is in line with the
quasi-static sensing properties of PVDF.

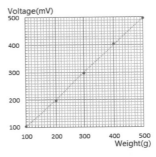

Figure 6.   The first set of quasi-static test.

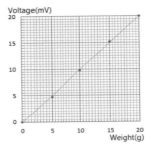

Figure 7.   The second set of quasi-static test.

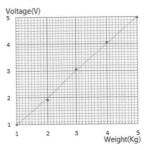

Figure 8.   The third set of quasi-static test.

Wearing the gloves inserted sensor array (Fig. 3), frontal underhand serve experiment is conducted to test the effect of dynamic acquisition. Figure 9 shows the output of middle fingertip (sensor 3), the center of the palm (sensor 21) and the heel of the palm (sensor 24) when the athlete throw the ball to the right front of his abdomen with left hand. Figure 10 shows the output of abductor pollicis brevis (sensor 19), little finger abductor (sensor 22) and the heel of the palm (sensor 24) when the athlete hit the ball with the heel of right palm.

From Figures 9 and 10 we can know: The voltage of sensor 21 is high during 0–100 ms, which means that the center of the palm bears the ball's barycenter mostly when the athlete hold the ball with left hand; In the process of throwing the ball slightly (approximate 100–250 ms), fingertip and the heel of the palm bear more stress, then the ball is off the center of the palm firstly and leaves fingertip

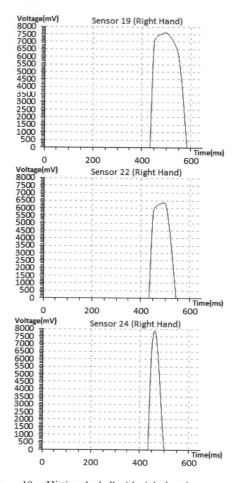

Figure 10. Hitting the ball with right hand.

at last; While the athlete hitting the ball with right hand fiercely, abductor pollicis brevis touches the ball at first and the output duration of sensor 19 is the longest (approximate 425–575 ms); When hitting the ball, little finger abductor bears less stress comparatively and the heel of the palm bears stress the most, but the output duration of sensor 24 is the shortest (approximate 425–500 ms).

5 CONCLUSION

Modern volleyball is competitive increasingly. In order to improve competition results constantly and minimize sports injuries simultaneously, the research of volleyball teaching and training must be in accordance with scientific theory, and data acquisition precisely is a necessary precondition. Pass, smash, blocking, mat-ball and serve are the emphasis and aporia of volleyball teaching and

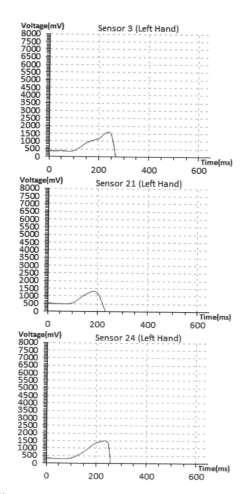

Figure 9. Throwing the ball with left hand.

training. This paper puts forward a method for hand pressure information collection. PVDF-based sensor array, signal conditioner and power supply circuit have been developed. After tests and experiment, this method is safe and practical, accurate and reliable. The sensor array can effectively measure the athlete's hands piezoelectric signals when pass, smash, blocking, mat-ball and serve. Hence scientific basis will support the further research of volleyball special training program design.

REFERENCES

Dianshu Ju, Zhi zhou and Jinping Ou. 2004. Study on strain-sensing of PVDF films. Journal of Functional Materials 35(4):450–452.

Hongli Yu and Liping Liang. 2006. The Discuss of Volleyball Athletes' injury and and Prevention. Journal Of Jinzhong University 23(3):56–59.

Hongjin Sui, Shuwei Liu, Shaoxiang Zhang and Lei Tang. 2012. Colour Atlas of Human Anatomy: People's Military Medical Press, Beijing.

Haiyun Zhao. 2000. The performance and applications of the PVDF piezoelectric-film. Technology and Application Publications 28(6):24–26.

Jinhai Zhu. Preparation and Performance Study of Pvdf Piezoelectric Film and Sensor 2011 (Master thesis): Harbin Institute of Technology, Harbin, Heilongjiang.

Minge Lin. 1999. The hand trauma status investigation of Chinese volleyball elite athletes. Fujian Sports Science and Technology 18(3):34–35.

Min Shu, Yiyang Li and Xingzhi Liao. 2013. Study on volleyball athletes foot pressure acquisition method. Applied Mechanics And Materials (Volumes 303–306):274–279.

(U.S.) Jonathan Rize and (Norway) Roald. 2006. Sports Medicine and Science Manual-Volleyball: People's Sports Publishing House, Beijing.

Xin Liu and Zhengfang Tang. 2005. Introduction and applications of piezoelectric-film sensor. The World of Sensor 11(7):13–16.

Yuping Cui and Enqiang Gong. 2001. Investigation and Analysis of Hand Injuries for Elite Volleyball Players. Shandong Sports Science & Technology 23(2):30–31.

Zhiqiang Jia. Kinematic Analysis on the Front Serves Technology of Soft Volleyball 2011 (Master thesis): Xi'an Physical Education University, Xi'an.

Computer, Intelligent Computing and Education Technology – Liu, Sung & Yao (Eds)
© 2014 Taylor & Francis Group, London, ISBN 978-1-138-02469-4

The PVDF-based research of air-walking foul judgment and recording during a heel-and-toe walking race

Yi-Yang Li, Zhou Wan, Qi Pan & Xi-Cun You
Faculty of Information Engineering and Automation, Kunming University of Science and Technology, Kunming, P.R. China

Min Shu
Faculty of Physical Education, Kunming University of Science and Technology, Kunming, P.R. China

ABSTRACT: A method for judging and recording air-walking foul during a heel-and-toe walking race has been put forward and the PVDF-based sensor array has been developed. The sensors are used for plantar piezoelectric signals acquisition. Recording the signals will not only avoid incorrect or missing judgment, but also provide scientific support to formulate personalized training programs based on an athlete's foul habits. Experiments of promenade, back step running and heel-and-toe walking race have been conducted. Analyzed, both feet off the ground is not occurred in promenade while back step running has distinct hang time. The athlete commits an air-walking foul in heel-and-toe walking race and the air-walking interval is 5625 ms to 5750 ms. Experiments also prove that this method is safe, practical, reliable and accurate.

Keywords: PVDF; heel-and-toe walking race; air-walking foul; air-walking interval; plantar pressure

1 INTRODUCTION

Heel-and-toe walking race has quite high technical specification requirements in track and field sports. It distinguishes strictly from walking, running and jumping. Walking race foul judgment is the most difficult, subjective and controversial foul judgments in athletic competition. CAA (Chinese Athletic Association) defines walking race like this: it is a process that athletes keep in touch with the ground and continuous forward, no visible (to human eye) both feet off the ground. In other words, athletes must keep at least one foot on the ground during the whole walking race process. If the athletes violate this rule, it is called air-walking foul. However, international and domestic foul judgment of walking race is mainly by visual. Even with the aid of video recording, it still needs human eye to identify in segmented images and track the record to judge. Moreover, for walking race teaching and training, it is hard to develop personal special training programs according to the foul habits of an athlete.

For judging accurately and designing personalized training programs, this paper puts forward a method for air-walking foul judgment and recording. By utilizing the PVDF film's advantages of light, soft, thin, good impact resistance, fast response, high sensitivity and large dynamic range and so on, the plantar pressure sensor array has been designed and produced. Recording the plantar piezoelectric signals can avoid incorrect or missing judgment. Further, according to the integrated information especially air-walking interval, it can provide scientific basis for personalized training programs formulation research. Tested by experiments, this method has the advantages of safe, practical, reliable and accurate.

2 WALKING RACE TECHNICAL ANALYSIS

Competition results of modern walking race are improving quickly, and technical regulations are also changing constantly. Originating from the British, walking race firstly became competition project in the Olympic Games which held in Greece 1906. Since then, the main criterion of walking race foul is whether the athlete's feet are off the ground or not. In 1920, IAAF (International Amateur Athletic Federation) officially recognized: the athlete is foul once his feet skip or knees bend. In 1996–1997, IAAF proposed the concept of air-walking which is not visible to human eye. Air-walking foul is occurred the most in statistics, and it impacts the competition results the greatest. For example, in the women's 20 km walking race of Athens Olympic

Games 2004, the air-walking foul accounted for 81% of the total technical fouls (125 person-time); in women's 20 km race walking of the 10th National Games 2005, technical fouls for a total is 115 times and the air-walking fouls is 69 times; in the men's 10 km and 20 km National Walking Race Championships 2011, 58% of the total number of technical fouls (per capita 3.91 times) are air-walking fouls (per capita 2.25 times).

The walking step length of ordinary people is normally about 80 cm, and the step frequency is 100 steps per minute or so. In walking race, the athlete's step length reaches 100–120 cm, and his step frequency is 220 steps per minute and even more. The feature of walking race technique is periodic alternation between one leg support and two legs support. Not the both feet touchdown, it is the front foot or the rear foot touchdown. Both feet off the ground does not exist throughout. A walking race cycle contains five technical stages: forward swing, back swing, front bracing, rear bracing and vertical bracing. Causes of air-walking foul are complex, and current consensuses are as follows: Stride is too small or too large; Knee angle is small when stop pedaling to forward swing; Body barycenter is fluctuating; Pedaling is inadequate while forward swing is too large; Athlete seeks only to competition when sprint; Terrain environment is unsatisfactory, such as uphill, downhill and turning point.

3 SENSOR ARRAY DESIGN

PVDF (Polyvinylidene fluoride), a new kind of high molecular polymer sensing material, is constituted by two fluorine atoms which substitutes ethylene molecules in the two hydrogen atoms. After being polarized, PVDF film will have a piezoelectric characteristic. The main advantages of PVDF film are light, soft, thin, good impact resistance, fast response, high sensitivity and large dynamic range, etc.

After repeated experiments, the circular structure sensor is the most suitable for plantar pressure acquisition when the athlete is running, jumping and walking. Round designed cantilever beam and base substrate are stamped out directly by cylindrical mold. The diameter of the mold is 10 mm. As shown in Figure 1, the cantilever beam is made of PV membrane, the base substrate is made of 1-mm thick conductive silicon sheet, and conductive silver is used as the adhesive.

Accordance with exercise physiology and planter anatomy, each insole is inlaid 9 sensors to composed the plantar pressure sensor array. As shown in Figure 2, Sensor 1 to 5 corresponds to 1st to 5th phalanx respectively, sensor 6 corresponds

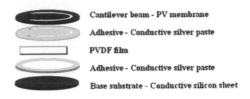

Figure 1. The structure of the PVDF pressure sensor.

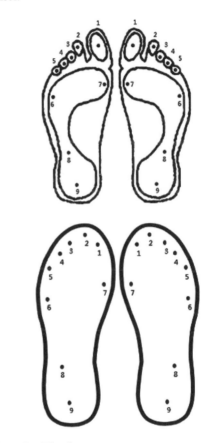

Figure 2. The plantar pressure sensor array.

to 5th ossametatarsalia, sensor 7 corresponds to 1st ossametatarsalia, sensor 8 corresponds to the lateral of heel, and sensor 9 corresponds to the rear of heel.

4 EXPERIMENTS AND ANALYSES

Through the three representative sports of promenade, back step running and heal-to-toe walking race, this method is tested. The athlete's plantar piezoelectric signals are recorded and analyzed. Figures 3–5 present respectively the athlete's plantar pressure information of promenade, back

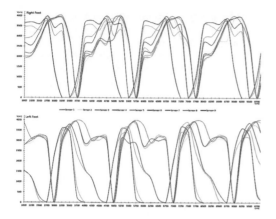

Figure 3. The plantar pressure information of promenade.

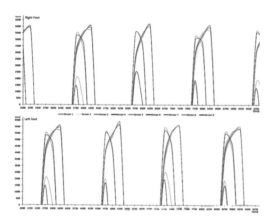

Figure 4. The plantar pressure information of back step running.

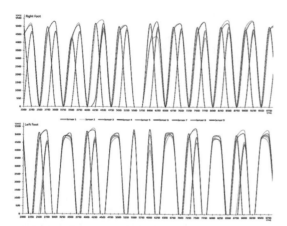

Figure 5. The plantar pressure information of heel-and-toe walking race.

step running and heal-to-toe walking race during 2000 ms to 9750 ms periods. When recording the signals, there are 9×2 channels (both feet). The multifunction data acquisition card was used to process the large amount of information. For PVDF-based sensor has a high internal impedance, the signal must pass through the signal conditioner for impedance matching, signal amplification and filtering processing before entering the multifunction data acquisition card. Multifunction data acquisition card communicates with the host PC by USB2.0. The host PC stored the processed results of the signals in real time, which provides a reliable guarantee for analysis.

4.1 Promenade

The intensity of promenade is the lightest. Both feet off the ground is difficult to occur. So promenade is used to test the continuity, sensitivity and linear characteristics of the sensors. Conclusions from Figure 3 are as follows.

1. In a periodic waveform, whether it is right or left foot, the output voltage of sensor 6 and 7 begin to increase after the sharply rising of sensor 8 and 9. Then sensors 1 to 5 start to increase slowly. It means that the heel is always landing firstly, and the whole planta follows on.
2. In a periodic waveform, whether it is right or foot left, the output voltage of sensor 6, 7, 1, 2, 3, 4 and 5 reach the peak successively, while sensor 8 and 9 are dropping sharply. The peak voltages of sensors 1 to 7 are higher than sensor 8 and 9. It means that the front part of planta supports body barycenter and completes a stomp action (It is more prominent in the experiment of back step running) after the heel off the ground, then the whole planta takes off.
3. When the output voltage of all right foot sensors reach the peak, the corresponding left foot sensors drop or become zero. It means that the feet are moving forward alternately. There is a both feet support transition stage between right foot support stage and left foot stage. Promenade is light and slow, and both feet off the ground is not occurred.

4.2 Back step running

Back step running is not only fierce, but also need strong explosive leg strength when stomping. It has obvious hang time. Using back step running to test the effect of air-walking recording is optimal. Conclusions from Figure 4 are as follows.

1. In a periodic waveform, whether it is right or left foot, sensors 1 to 9 are almost at the same

time outputting signals. The output duration of sensors 1 to 5 are longer than sensor 6 and 7. The output duration of sensor 6 and 7 are longer than sensor 8 and 9. It means that the whole planta is always touching the ground at the same time, but soon heel, pelma and toe take off sequentially.

2. In a periodic waveform, whether it is right or left foot, the peak voltages of sensors 1 to 5 are always higher than sensor 6 and 7, and sensor 6 and 7 are higher than sensor 8 and 9. It means that the athlete's body barycenter is always forward. The front part of planta always bears the explosive leg strength when stomping.

3. When all the right foot sensors are outputting, the corresponding left foot sensors are zero. It means that both feet stomp alternately. It is one leg support all the time and there is no both feet support stage.

4. Contrasting the recording of right foot with the left, in period of 2375 ms to 2625 ms, 3375 ms to 3625 ms, 4375 ms to 4625 ms, 5375 ms to 5625 ms, 6375 ms to 6625 ms, 7375 ms to 7625 ms, 8375 ms to 8625 ms and 9375 ms to 9625 ms, no matter right or left foot, there are slightly less than 250 ms which all the sensors have no output. It means that the athlete is air-walking during these periods and these periods are the air-walking intervals.

4.3 *Heel-and-toe walking race*

The technical requirements of heel-and-toe walking race are the highest in these three experiments. It has not only the gait feature of promenade, but also the exercise intensity of back step running. The rules clearly defined that the athlete must keep foot landing all the time. Conclusions from Figure 5 are as follows.

1. In a periodic waveform, whether it is right or left foot, the output duration of sensors 1 to 5 are the longest. It means that he athlete's body barycenter is centered relatively. No matter one foot support or both feet support, the ossametatarsalia can invariably bear a certain pressure.

2. In a periodic waveform, whether it is right or left foot, it is always the sensor 8 and 9 start or end the output earlier than sensors 1 to 5 in the case of that there are great differences of the output duration between sensors 6 to 7 and the other sensors. It means that the athlete's step frequency is quite high. Either an entire planta lands, either the rear part of planta touches the ground and the front part follows closely or then the front takes off soon.

3. When the output voltage of all right foot sensors shoot up or reach the peak, the corresponding

left foot sensors slump or become zero. It means that there is no both feet support stage. It is always one leg support.

4. The output voltage of all right foot sensors are zero during 5500 ms to 5750 ms, and all left sensors are zero during 5625 ms to 5750 ms. The intersection of these two periods is 5625 ms to 5750 ms, and all sensors' (both feet) output voltages are zero distinctly. It means that the athlete is committing air-walking foul during 5625 ms to 5750 ms. The air-walking interval is 5625 ms to 5750 ms.

5 CONCLUSION

Heel-and-toe walking race is a technical specification severely required project in track and field sports. The foul judgment is mainly by visual in the international and domestic competitions, which often results in incorrect or missing judgment. In addition, it is difficult to develop personalized training programs based on athletes' foul habits in walking race teaching and training. As a result, this paper puts forward a method to judge and record air-walking foul. By utilizing the PVDF film's advantages of light, soft, thin, good impact resistance, fast response, high sensitivity and large dynamic range and so on, the plantar pressure sensor array has been designed and produced. Experiments and analysis show that this method is safe, practical, reliable and able to record the athlete's plantar piezoelectric signals accurately. According to the record, it is not only easy to find the evidence of air-walking foul (air-walking interval), but able to provide scientific basis for further research of personalized training programs formulation as well.

REFERENCES

Chinese Athletic Association 2010: Athletics Competition Rules (2010–2011): People's Sports Publishing House, Beijing.

Donghe Li, Zhijia Sun and Leigang Song. 2012. The Analysis on the Fouls of the Walkers in 2011 National Walking Race Championship. Journal of Hebei Institute of Physical Education 26(3):72–74.

Donghe Li, Wenxue Li and Yan Wang. 2007. An analysis of fouls committed in women's 20 km race walking in the 10th National Games and Athens Olympic Games. Journal of Physical Education 14(1):108–110.

Fahui Zhang and Heping Zheng 2003: Surgical Clinical Anatomy of Foot: Anhui Science and Technology Press, Hefei.

Fangfa Shu, Soushan Shou, Xin Zhang and Li Ma. 2008. Application of PVDF Piezoelectric-film to Foot-pressure Measurement. Piezoel Ectectrics & Acoustooptics 30(4):514–516.

Lanmei Wang, Yemin Guo and Zhiguo Pan. 2005. Research and application of foot-pressure distribution. Manufacturing and Research Publications 34(1):35–38.

Shuxun Deng, Jian Wang and Decai Qiao 2009. Exercise Physiology (2nd Edition): Higher Education Press, Beijing.

Tao Liu and Qiuyan Jiang. 2009. Reason Analysis of Accuracy and Inaccuracy Technique in Race Walking. Journal of Xi'an Physical Education University 26(2):222–225.

Wei Li, Hong Qiu, Jiang Xu and Jiping He. 2011. The Research in a Foot Pressure Measuring System Based on LabVIEW. Chinese Journal of Medical Instrumentation 35(1):19–23.

Xiaoke Ma. 2009. A new kind of foot movement parameter obtaining equipment. Automation & Instuction 6:8–11.

Yujie Zhang and Shaoxia Wei. 2011. Design Of PVDF Foot-pressure Sensor and Its Measurement System. Piezoelectrics & Acoustooptics 33(1):61–63.

Computer, Intelligent Computing and Education Technology – Liu, Sung & Yao (Eds)
© 2014 Taylor & Francis Group, London, ISBN 978-1-138-02469-4

The practical teaching system research in colleges and universities

Y. Zhao

Harbin University of Science and Technology, Rongcheng College, Rongcheng, Shandong, China

ABSTRACT: "Three classrooms" linkage of the requirements of practical teaching system, the three respectively the definition of the class: the first class of practice teaching in addition to the experiment and training, including curriculum design, curriculum papers, professional and comprehensive practice ability (including graduation thesis, graduation design), and other practical teaching link; The practice of the second classroom teaching with student organizations, sports clubs, all kinds of training, textual research employs, independent practice, course contests and activities of science and technology, etc.; The third class of practice teaching is primarily a social practice, field work, co-operative education, etc. Three classes of practice teaching system to carry out and implement, to cultivate high-skilled talents play a significant role.

Keywords: teaching practice; high skill talented person; field work

In the "employment oriented" under the guidance of educational theory, match with the goal of cultivating high-skill talents, committed to build to study into the link, three class of practical teaching system, and try to put them into practice has achieved obvious results.

1 ESTABLISHING THE CENTER POSITION OF PRACTICE TEACHING IN UNIVERSITY PERSONNEL TRAINING

Through teaching practice to cultivate applied talents, in a foreign country is not uncommon, and accumulated rich experience. At home, especially in the undergraduate course education is generally prevailing atmosphere of theory, practice, to really take this step, is very difficult. For a long time, there are many disadvantages of higher education in our country, it is attaches great importance to the education theory, contempt practice; Secondly, the practice teaching content of the old, lag, tend to stay on the level of verification; Three is the method of practice teaching only pay attention to teaching and or ignore the cultivation of innovation ability, the resulting consequence is the student beginning ability is very weak, lack of innovation spirit, graduates enter the society, the poor ability to adapt.

Good quality and strong ability on earth come from? Part to be derived by knowledge, of course, so, no matter how classroom teaching is very important; But more must be through the practice teaching to cultivate. Education of colleges and universities, therefore, how to thoroughly reform to traditional pattern of classroom teaching as the center, set up the practice teaching as the center of education concept, and under the guidance of this concept, the teaching activities, especially extends to the social practice teaching activities, extended to enterprises, became a problem to be solved.

2 BUILD MATCH THE HIGH-SKILLED TALENTS TRAINING GOAL OF PRACTICE TEACHING SYSTEM

According to establish the "three classrooms" linkage of practice teaching system, to make the following definition: three classroom practice teaching of the first class in addition to the experiment, training, also including course design, course work, professional comprehensive ability practice (including graduation thesis, graduation design), and other practical teaching link; The practice of the second classroom teaching with student organizations, sports clubs, all kinds of training, textual research employs, independent practice, course contests and activities of science and technology, etc.; The third class of practice teaching is primarily a social practice, field work, co-operative education, etc.

In addition to the three class defines the connotation of outside, also make clear a regulation, all from the first class directly into the second and third class of practice teaching, such as social practice, independent practice of foreign language and computer, such as sports clubs as a compulsory credits; In the second classroom: competition awards, for all kinds of disciplines in the press published papers, and taking the scientific research projects and set the innovation of credit; In order to obtain a variety of professional skills certificate or other related skill level and credit; For students' participation in improving the quality of all kinds of activities (including all kinds of lectures, presentations, computer, etc.) can be calculated according to time and the quality of the credit. Both as a second class of electives and can replace the first part of the electives, in practice the credits in the interaction of the three classes. Through the practice teaching content in three classes, and into the orbit of the credit system management, which organically formed three classroom linkage system of practice teaching.

At the same time, the school also clear requirements: first, the classroom practice teaching should be emphatically do the following three articles:

One is to strengthen: in line with the moderate, the principle of sufficient compression from first class down theory teaching to practice teaching hours, and make clear a regulation practice teaching class in the training plan should be accounted for more than half of the total teaching hours, including time half a year of field work and the professional training of comprehensive ability.

Two is to optimize the authentication type of practice teaching, emphatically on the content, method and means reform, committed to the should know, should, the cultivation of application ability.

Part three is outspread: the original belong to the first classroom practice teaching content reaches to the second and third class to finish.

And specify the first class of practice teaching in addition to the experiment and training, should also include the course design, course work, professional comprehensive ability practice (including graduation thesis, graduation design), and other practical teaching link.

Practice teaching in the third classroom teaching model, in terms of its content can be divided into practice and practice two parts. To distinguish from the form, with practice, practice segmented mode, practice, practice integration model, and field work mode, when conditions are ripe, some professional can also take part time model.

3 IN THE THREE CLASSROOM PRACTICE TEACHING TRAINING HIGH-SKILLED TALENTS

For nearly four years, the three class of practice teaching system to carry out and implement, to cultivate high-skilled talents play a significant role.

1. Due to the professional learning and community activities very closely together, make the professional ability of students generally strengthened. Due to the students' club activities into the orbit of professional teaching, sponsored by the office, admissions, division and youth corps committee, to undertake the colleges, thousands of students to participate in the first course contests month give full play to the professional advantages of each college, and mobilize the initiative of students to participate in community activities, enthusiasm and creativity; Street "school of management, to carry out the marketing activities, college provides 30 teams with part of the start-up capital, market research, in the process of marketing activities such as product promotion, product purchase and stalls set up by students' complete and self-financing.

2. Due to the competition actively organize students to participate in all kinds of disciplines, so as to improve the students' practical ability and innovation ability. Various disciplines race including program design competition, accounting informationization, higher mathematics competition, multimedia work design contest, calligraphy and painting competition.

3. Attaches great importance to students' vocational skills training, job training and identification, make more students hold double card, to participate in research employs the number of students increased year by year, pass rate has significantly improved.

4. Let the students "real thing" accepted practice education, this is the best means to increase knowledge, strengthening the ability. Many knowledge just by lectures, often begin, only in the process of practice can we truly understand. Through the practice within the enterprise, the students' practical ability and practical ability to deal with problems has been greatly improved.

5. Only in the practice teaching of post exercise to cultivate good professional ethics.

   The formation of professional ethics and it wasn't by teach book knowledge can be done, must be in the professional post, through practice, can we truly realize the suantiankula, can truly understand the value of life, major is not in what we get, but what you give.

6. Schools and teachers understand the enterprise, be familiar with the best bridge of the enterprise, is also the important condition of cultivating double teachers.

   Biggest drawbacks of traditional education is out of the enterprise, from the society, if you don't know, don't know what society needs what kind of person, can only be "closed", "paper", could not produce enterprise, social needed talents. Through cooperation in running schools with the enterprise, we have more opportunity to understand the society need to school, what kind of talent cultivation at the same time, our school teachers have more opportunities to the enterprises to conduct professional training for employees, especially through the organization, guidance and participate in the student's field work for double culture provides an important prerequisite for teachers.

7. Depends on the enterprise, social forces, the best way to integrate the teaching resources.

In terms of the needs of personnel training in colleges and universities, colleges and universities alone so some resource is not enough, especially the field work of the practice teaching link, the school can't also unnecessary to do factory, hotel, provide internships for students. As the school should use social power, the power of the enterprise, based on the principle of mutual benefit, complement each other, take the path of qi school cooperation, co-operative.

8. Contribute to the formation of part-time teachers.

By with many years practical experience of engineers, managers with own experience to teach students about the actual operation process and to the society should have the quality, the combination of theory and practice of teaching content, which embody the demand of the society, causes the student to deeply understand to the learned information readily available, is popular among the students.

The practice teaching and management of innovation is not only for improving students' innovation ability and practice ability, and have greatly enriched the content of practice teaching. To study into the link of the three practice teaching system of research and practice of classroom interaction, is becoming a will certainly become a new feature of our school.

REFERENCES

[1] YuZhongWen, Liu Shouyi etc. Practice teaching of higher vocational and technical education research [M]. Beijing: tsinghua university press, 2004.

[2] Zhou Jing learn, Yang Yusheng NiShiQi. Practical teaching plan is the important guarantee of training innovative talents [J]. Journal of experimental technology and management, 2000, (5).

[3] Yang Dongsheng, The practice of teaching reform for advanced vocational mold design and manufacturing. Vocational education BBS. 2006 (2).

[4] Huang Kexiao. Vocational and technical education courses is ee [m]. East China normal university press, 2001.

[5] NieJianWu. Work-study program is to cultivate high-skilled talents effective modes of vocational education at vocational and technical education. 2006 (15).

[6] Jinyan. Pilot professional mold the plastic forming technology and die design course teaching reform research and practice. Zhengzhou industrial college journal, 1998 (2).

Computer, Intelligent Computing and Education Technology – Liu, Sung & Yao (Eds)
© 2014 Taylor & Francis Group, London, ISBN 978-1-138-02469-4

Emergency medical aid: Wounded information collection and identification application system based on RFID technology

Hong Wang & Fei Wu
Information Department of 309 Hospital, Beijing, China

ABSTRACT: The research focuses on completing correct collection and identification of the wounded, thus increasing the maximum safety factor of emergency medical treatment. By extending emergency medical information system to the sick and wounded side, and collecting the information of the sick and implementing identification of the wounded dynamically, the research tries to ensure the sick and wounded properly treated in the first time, and make the doctor provide real-time treatment of illness. The work is done to build the Wounded Information Collection and Identification Application System Based on RFID Technology. In the system the workflow of medical treatment is optimized. And a lot of intermediate links are reduced such as communicating and transmitting of medical information.

Keywords: emergency medical aid; RFID; identification; information system

1 INTRODUCTION

Complex and changeable attributes of emergency itself bring serious physical and psychological harm to the wounded and the sick. In the course of emergency medical treatment, we don't even know whether or not the doctor's order is given to the right wounded, and if the patient's emergency medical information is correctly collected by the nurse [1]. The traditional collect and identify method is not easy to be guaranteed during the process [2]. So correct and quick information collection and identification of the wounded gets increasingly necessary. As a result practical technical methods must be adopted to improve security and operability in emergency medical aid circumstances [3].

The motivation on the study is to ensure high quality and efficient aid and to enhance the urgent response ability to respond to public health emergencies. Our research aims at realizing the collection and identification system of the wounded by applying technology such as RFID and wireless network with HIS. The research goal is to enable the wounded information collection and identification application system based on RFID technology to meet the need of the special emergency environment [4], include system structure, system compatibility with existing HIS, etc. Compared with existing ones, the key features of the application obtained can complete identification of the patient, provide real-time check and confirm operation of every step of the order process based on RFID technology.

The rest of this paper is organized as follows. Section 2 introduces related wireless architecture and RFID technology, describes the composition of wireless network and how RFID works in order to apply them in HIS. Section 3 gives an overview of the system design, and provides a detailed realization on architecture of collection and identification system based on RFID in emergency environment. Section 4 presents the realization of the system, include the workflow and function module. Finally Section 5 concludes this research with the summary.

2 BACKGROUND

2.1 Wireless architecture compared

Wireless network can provide free moving and roaming service for their users within its cover range, thus user will not be tied up to the cable network. The two network architectures are completely different with totally different transmission medium.

Wireless network is composed of Access Point (AP), Station (STA) and Distribute System Set (DSS). AP and its STA are interrelated at any time. The wireless AP can cover dozens of or even hundreds of users, and the radius can reach more than one hundred meters.

To meet the need of walking from patients and medical staff, wireless architecture is selected to implementation of the system based on RFID.

2.2 *RFID technology*

RFID stands for Radio Frequency Identification. It uses electromagnetic induction or electromagnetic transmission to communicate.

The basic working method of the RFID system is to install RFID tags on the identified objects (by pasting, plugging up, wearing and implanting etc.). RFID is convenient to be applied in the medical area [5].

When the object which is identified by the RFID reader entered into the reading range, the wireless communication link between the tag and reader is established, and the tag sends information of itself to the reader, such as tag number and other data stored etc. The reader receives the message and decodes before transmits it to the background computer to process, and then complete the whole information processing procedure [6].

The research adopts the RFID technology to design and build the collection and identification information system based on RFID technology as follows.

3 SYSTEM DESIGN OF WOUNDED INFORMATION COLLECTION AND IDENTIFICATION SYSTEM BASED ON RFID

3.1 *Wireless network design*

First we implement the Hospital Wireless Network. The hospital user needs to access devices or services of local area network. According to this fact, the ESS network structure is selected. By interconnecting with different BSS in ESS sharing by AP, related wireless terminals, such as Personnel Digital Assistance (PDA), Tablet PC and other wireless device, fall in the same segment. In the application layer Dynamic Host Configuration Protocol (DHCP) is applied. Every wireless terminal obtains its own IP automatically.

Related wireless standards are IEEE 802.11b, IEEE 802.11g, IEEE 802.11h and IEEE 802.11n, etc. Difference between them is mainly the transmission speed. Now IEEE 802.11b is most common used. But IEEE 802.11 g has more possibility to become the next generation standard. New standard such as IEEE 802.11n is now in rapid development period.

3.2 *RFID system design*

RFID system consists of two levels of networks. The tag and reader construct the wireless communication network, staying in the front. The information network connects to the back-end application. The front-end deployment involves wireless network constructing and coordinating technology. The complex hardware architecture of RFID system and the mass feature of data put forward big challenge to the deployment of the system. On the other hand, when PDA moves in the wireless network environment, the coverage problem of wireless network may lead to instability of the connection, and influence the reliability and stability of the medical usage.

In order to solve these problems, we propose a RFID system according to the hospital environment.

First, we need to determine the main performance index and constraints of RFID system architecture, such as RFID performance, signal interference and wireless coverage constraints.

Secondly, we analyze the RFID system architecture of service performance. The result is used in deploying RFID network system architecture.

Steps include

– Analyze the various properties of RFID tags (return loss, directivity, etc.). We choose the most suitable design according to the characteristics of ward.
– Analyze the various properties of RFID readers (read range, the fastest response time, etc.).
– Design the layout of the system structure according to the situation of electromagnetic radiation and absorption in the ward environment of variety materials.
– Test the RFID tags, antennas and readers selected for this environment.
– Select the network communication protocol. Communication is established between equipments and devices, between equipments and business logic modules, between the business logic modules and the upper layer applications of HIS.

Evaluate the performance and effectiveness of the system architecture. Identify the possible bottlenecks and improve the usability of the system. It is the last but very important step.

3.3 *Design of medical treatment based on RFID*

In order to complete the medical treatment of the wounded, we want the wounded to wear RFID tag. In this way the individual medical staff can assure the accuracy and rapid identification of the wound, whether they have consciousness or not. With these tags, medical staff is able to collect and process the wound's information directly and correctly through the RFID reader and wireless network deployed [7]. The medical information includes all kinds of physiological indicators of the wound, such as the wounded position, the wounded degree, medication, body temperature measurement times and so on.

We propose an approach that provides a mechanism to get correct and quick information collection and identification of the wounded in the ward environment. The objective is to achieve an information system that supports the emergency medical treatment [8].

4 REALIZATION OF WOUNDED INFORMATION COLLECTION AND IDENTIFICATION SYSTEM BASED ON RFID FOR EMERGENCY MEDICAL AID

4.1 System architecture

System Architecture of the information collection and identification system is shown in Figure 1.

The system is mainly constructed by the RFID tag part and PDA portion. In emergency environment, healthcare staff writes injury information directly to the RFID tag and gives it to the wounded. The wounded wears the label with the basic written medical information [9]. In this way medical errors can be greatly avoided and treatment time is saved. Classification evacuations institutions access to information by scanning the label wear by the wounded and later complete the classification and evacuation work [10].

The operating environment of wireless care information system in rear hospital is Windows Mobile System 5.0. CF card type RFID reader is installed on a PDA, which is used to send data in the label to care information system in order to complete the unique confirmation of the wounded identity and drug used. Web service is adopted by care information system to access the HIS database which interacts with data link layer using the

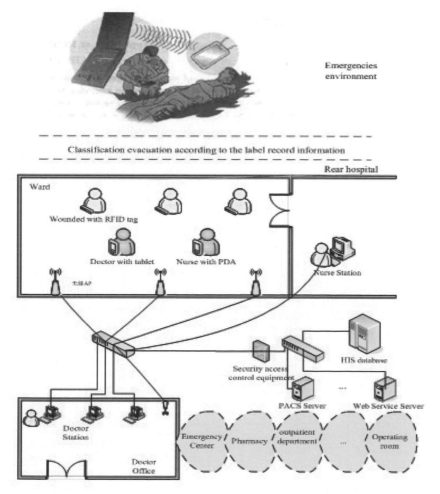

Figure 1. System architecture.

767

wireless network. Care information system software consists of the wounded management module, doctor's order processing module, signs input module, nursing record management module and so on. The overall structure of wireless nursing information system based on RFID in rear hospital is shown in Figure 2.

4.2 *Workflow*

Emergency wounded process design is shown in Figure 3.

The system adopts RFID tags to indentify the wounded and healthcare staff to complete order process and signs information collection [11]. Its working process is shown in Figure 4.

4.3 *Function implementation*

First function is the implementation of the front wireless hospital system.

– Get the wounded information by scanning label tag using the PDA RFID reader to identify information for the wounded.
– Make the wounded information associated with the RFID tag wear by the wounded as a specific identification.
– According to injury location, injury type, injury degree and other information to make

classification identification which consists of "emergency treatment", "isolation", "radioactive contamination", "poison" and so on.
– Record the detailed disposal information (including anti-infective, anti-shock, emergency surgery) to make injury medical information transferred and shared quickly.
– Deal with evacuation information (including time, destination, type, postural, fill units, doctor, etc.) to achieve real-time transfer of information on casualty evacuation, which makes rear hospitals get the wounded injury information more quickly.

Second function is implementation the rear wireless hospital system.

– After scanning the RFID tag, completing login by accessing the database to query corresponding account of the label, and get information of the wounded such as the current ward.
– Choose functions such as patient query, doctor's orders perform, nursing records.

4.4 *Hardware and software*

Hardware of the System includes:

– RFID reader, model Compact Flash Reader KD801, Supporting ISO14443A(B), ISO 15693 standard Choose functions such as patient query, doctor's orders perform, nursing records.
– PDA, model HP iPAQ hx2490c, Windows Mobile 5.0 Runtime Environment.
– AP, model Gigabyte GN-A11G, IEEE 802.11 g/802.11b protocol.
– RFID tag writer, model Intellitag PM4i, 13.56 MHz frequency, supporting ISO 15963 standard.

Software is focused on the database and application development. Our database adopts the tables from HIS. Except for the main index of patient, the order form and price list, the comparison tables of patient identification, tables of the RFID tag and doctor's order are added.

Development Environment of Software is Microsoft Visual Studio, of which Smart Device Cab is adopted as the template. Microsoft. Net Framework 3.5 SDK (Software Development Kit) is used in development.

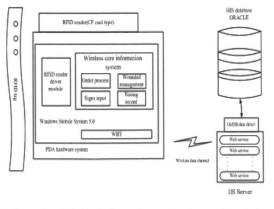

Figure 2. Wireless information system in rear hospital.

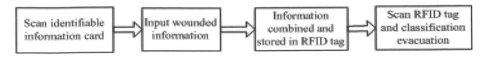

Figure 3. Processing procedures in emergency.

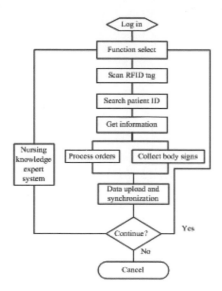

Figure 4. Work process.

5 CONCLUSION

In this paper, RFID technology and wireless network technology are combined to make correct collection and identification of the wounded, thus improve the efficiency of the emergency treatment of emergencies, and ensure the wounded get appropriate treatment in time which can improve the survival rate of the wounded. We use effective technical measures to collect information of the wounded, and provide variety of treatment and care information. The system is built to achieve correct collection and identification of the wounded, to increase the maximum safety factor of emergency medical care adopting information technology, thus avoid the occurrence of medical errors and accidents on the basis of data. And at the same time achieve a reasonable allocation of medical treatment resources in case of emergency.

REFERENCES

[1] Courtney, K.L., Demiris, G., Alexander, G.L., 2005, "Information technology: changing nursing processes at the point-of-care", Nursing Administration Quarterly, 29(4), pp. 315–322.

[2] Kumiko Ohashi, 2008, "Safe patient transfer system with mornitoring of location and vital signs", Med Dent Sci, vol. 55, pp. 33–41.

[3] J.M. Bailey, W.M. Haddad, and T. Hayakawa, 2004, "Closed-loop control in clinical pharmacology: Paradigms, benefits and challenges", in Proceedings of the 2004 American Control Conference, pp. 2268–2277.

[4] Svenson JE, and Spurlock CW, "The Kentucky emergency medical services information system:current progress and future goals", J Ky Med Assoc, 1997 V95 N12, pp. 509–513.

[5] A.M.Wicks, J.K.Visich, and S. Li, 2006, "Radio frequency identification Applications in hospital environments", Hospital Topics, vol. 84, pp. 3–8.

[6] H.A. Nahas and J.S. Deogun, 2007, "Radio frequency identification Applications in smart hospitals", in Proceedings of the 20th IEEE International Symposium on Computer-Based Medical Systems, pp. 337–342.

[7] A. Lahtela, 2009, "A short overview of the RFID technology in healthcare", in 4th International Conference on Systems and Networks Communications, pp. 165–169.

[8] Petter S, and Fruhling A, "Evaluating the success of an emergency response medical information system", Int J Med Inform, 2011V80N7, pp. 480–489.

[9] Sangwan, R.S., R.G. Qiu, and D. Jessen, "Using RFID tags for tracking patients, charts and medical equipment within an integrated health delivery network", Proceedings of Networking, Sensing and Control, 2005 IEEE. pp. 1070–1074.

[10] Holzinger, A., K. Schwaberger, and M. Weitlaner, 2005, "Ubiquitous computing for hospital applications: RFID-applications to enable research in real-life environments", Proceedings of the 29th Annual International Computer Software and Applications Conference (COMPSAC'05), vol. 2, pp. 19–20.

[11] European Committee for Standardization, 2002, "A mobile E-health system based on workflow automation tool", Information Society RTD Standards Implementation Report.

Computer, Intelligent Computing and Education Technology – Liu, Sung & Yao (Eds)
© 2014 Taylor & Francis Group, London, ISBN 978-1-138-02469-4

A model of personalized analysis on students' learning based on big data

Fa-Ti Wu & Zhi-Jia Mou
School of Educational Technology, Beijing Normal University, Beijing, P.R. China

ABSTRACT: This paper constructed a model of personalized analysis on students' learning based on big data produced by electronic schoolbag. Big data includes structured data, semi-structured data, and unstructured data which are recorded by the e-portfolio system of electronic schoolbag. The theoretical bases of this model are theories including personalized learning, personality psychology, and learning analytics. And there are four analysis dimensions in this model: personalized learning content, personalized learning activities, personalized learning methods, and personalized learning evaluation. The personalized information is classified and gathered based on the support of related system databases of electronic schoolbag. Finally, we reveal the implementation paths from three directions, including personalized pushing of learning resources, personalized monitoring and guiding of learning process, and personalized recommending of learning community.

Keywords: electronic schoolbag; big data; learning analytics; personalized analysis; implementation path

1   INTRODUCTION

Currently, the development of educational informalization in mainland China is transitioning to a new stage with its key purpose to support effective teaching and learning to promote student's personalized development. An educational informalization development level framework is raised in "The Development Plan within 10 Years of Educational Informatization (2011–2020)," it claims that pedagogic methods in schools should make a breakthrough both in terms of student diversity and personalized learning. As an advanced tool for updating the traditional form of textbooks, electronic schoolbag receives worldwide concern in the educational field. The electronic schoolbag has its own advantages in supporting students' personalized and mobile learning. It also provides a means to promote the personalized development of students. Big Data is another hot keyword in the field of modern communication and computation. Gartner Company summarizes its characteristics as Volume, Variety, and Velocity, also called "3V features" (Abdul, R.S. & Kumar, G., 2013). As the personal mobile terminal of students, the electronic schoolbag records structural, semi-structural, and non-structural personal learning information during the learning process to produce big data. Learning Analysis based on Big Data can discover the students' elementary knowledge and cognitive ability according to their learning behavior. In addition, it provides learning contents and resources to promote their personalized development. This paper is divided into three sections. In the first section, we discuss the reason for big data generated in the electronic schoolbag. In the second section, we discuss how to construct a model of personalized analysis on students' learning based on big data. In the third section, we discuss the model of implementation path.

2   ANALYSES OF BIG DATA GENERATED IN ELECTRONIC SCHOOLBAG

The electronic schoolbag appears in the background of development of the educational informalization and information technology in mainland China. It can satisfy multiple learning methods in new situations, solve the problems in today's teaching and learning, and fulfill the needs of educational informalization from elementary to higher levels. We define the electronic schoolbag as a personal learning environment, based on the educational cloud, in which students can read interactive electronic textbooks, manage personal learning resources, and communicate with other students, complete exercises, while the students' personal learning files are recorded. It consists of the electronic textbook system, digital resources system, the assignment and examination system, exchange and communication system, and electronic learning files system. According to the four systems of electronic schoolbag and its data, we will analyze three aspects: the data quantity, data type, and the processing speed.

2.1 Content analysis of massive learning data

The majority of data produced by electronic schoolbag is from the electronic textbook system, digital resources system, assignment and examination system, and the exchange and communication system. The electronic textbook system contains the interactive electronic content, management of knowledge, and socialized reading. The digital resources system contains courseware on demand and extracurricular reading. The assignment and examination system contains the exercise and tests. And the exchange and communication system contains interactive answering questions, learning community, and the communications between family and school. Students' learning behavior in these four systems produced different kinds of data.

2.2 Type analysis of learning data

Resources including video-audios, pictures, digital cartoon and text produce variety types of data. The data can be divided into three types: structural, semi-structural, and non-structural. Among the different resources, the video-audios and pictures including teaching video-audios, micro-videos, internet video-audios, teaching pictures and internet pictures, mainly produce the semi-structural and non-structural data. The digital cartoon resource including flash and internet cartoon, mainly produce non-structural data. The text resource contains electronic textbooks, outside readings, and teaching courseware, which mainly produce structural data.

2.3 Processing analysis of learning data

The real-time processing on learning data is shown in three aspects: the real-time interaction of learning content, immediate-feedback exercises, and synchronous learning communication. The real-time interaction of learning content consists of text interaction, picture interaction and video interaction. The immediate-feedback exercises contains the real-time exercise, online tests and immediate feedback. The synchronous learning communication involves the real-time answer of questions, synchronous discussions and asynchronous communication. The electronic schoolbag can examine this data in real-time and provide immediate feedback to students.

Through these analyses, we can tell that electronic schoolbag in all learning systems is able to generate large amounts of data, and can process data in real-time. The data produced by electronic schoolbag are in accord with the "3V features" of big data.

3 MODEL CONSTRUCTION

3.1 Theoretical basis

During the process of analyzing students' individualized information, we need to consider not only students' personal external learning features and internal mental representations, but also the method of mining valuable personalized learning information from big data. This study builds a theoretical framework based on personalized learning, personality psychology, and learning analysis theories. Personalized learning theory provides a guide of the construction of students' individual models from four aspects: personalized learning content, learning activities, learning approaches, and learning assessment. Personality psychology theory provides psychological support directing how to analyze students' individual inclination and mental characteristics such as learning needs, learning motivation, learning styles, cognitive abilities, and skills (Ye, Y.Q. & Kong, K.Q., 2011). Learning analysis theory provides a scientific basis for personalized learning content customization and intelligence services. Through analysis of content framework, including application targets, service objects, data sources and methods (Yu, X.H. & Gu, X.Q., 2013), we can grasp the cyclic process of data collection, information processing, and structure application.

3.2 Model's goal-orientation

The National Plan for Medium and Long-Term Educational Reform and Development (2010–2020) states, "Teach students in accordance of their aptitude; focus on students' difference in characteristics and personalities; develop each student's potential of strengths." Thus, school education should care about learning processes. It needs to shift its focus from teachers, textbooks, and classrooms, to students, learning, and the learning process. The Model in this research is student-centered, emphasizing students' individual development. In this model, individual characteristics serve as the starting point, meeting student's personalized needs as the implementing path, and students' individual learning as the goal-orientation.

3.3 Model construction

Based on the analysis above, we proposed the Model of Personalized Analysis of Students' Learning Based on Big Data. As shown in Figure 1,

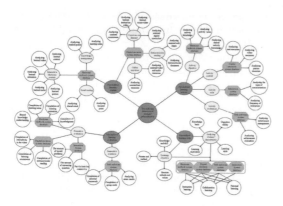

Figure 1. Model of personalized analysis of students' learning based on big data.

there are four analysis dimensions in this model: personalized learning content, personalized learning evaluation, personalized learning activities, and personalized learning methods. The personalized information is classified and gathered based on the support of related system databases.

3.3.1 *Personalized learning content*

Data of personalized learning content comes mainly from electronic textbook and digital resources system databases. (1) Analysis items in the electronic textbook system database for personalized contents contain interactive electronic contents, knowledge management, and social reading. Interactive electronic contents provide information about text, videos, and animations students have learned. Knowledge management includes knowledge points marked by students and their learning notes. Social reading contains shared understandings and related knowledge points. (2) Analysis items in the digital resource system database for personalized contents contain courseware on demand, extracurricular reading, and internet resources. Courseware on demand provides information about teaching courseware, teaching videos, and digital courses. That students learned. Extracurricular reading provides additional information about webpages and extracurricular documents that students looked through. Internet resources provide information about text topics and video-audio resources that students used.

3.3.2 *Personalized learning evaluation*

Learning evaluation has two levels: formative evaluation and summative evaluation. Electronic textbook, digital resources and communication system databases provide support to formative evaluation. (1) Analysis items of electronic textbook system database for personalized evaluation contain students' knowledge learning, the completion of learning notes, and knowledge sharing. (2) Analysis items of digital resources system database for personalized evaluation include the completion of interactive activities in video, courseware learning, and completion of extracurricular reading. (3) Analysis items of communication system database for personalized evaluation contain questions asking and answering, discussion participating. The support to summative evaluation is mainly from examination system database. Analysis items of examination system database for personalized evaluation contain assignments completion and results of examination.

3.3.3 *Personalized learning activity*

A learning activity has four aspects: activity goals, activity contents, activity patterns, and activity evaluation. (1) Activity goals is supported by electronic textbook system database, there are three items to analyze: knowledge point, learning notes, and knowledge sharing. (2) Activity contents is supported by digital resources system database, there are three items to analyze: texts, videos, and pictures. (3) Activity patterns is supported by communication system database, there are two items to analyze: communication topics and interaction frequency. (4) Activity evaluation is supported by examination system database; there are two items to analyze: the distribution and management of activities results, and the activities outcome evaluation.

3.3.4 *Personalized learning methods*

The analysis of personalized learning mode is supported by electronic textbook database system, digital resources database system, examination database system, and interactive communication database system. It can be divided into two categories: the analysis of learning target and the analysis of learner's characteristics. And the analysis of learning target contains knowledge and skills, process and method, emotion, attitude and values. While the analysis of learner's characteristics includes basic knowledge, cognitive capacity, learning motives and learning style of students. If the two analyses are confirmed, then by analyzing related information of database systems in the electronic bag, accordingly students will be offered with personalized learning mode. In this process, those systems including electronic textbook database system, digital resources database system, examination database system, and so on, can provide analytical evidences for lecture-teaching method, self-directed learning, and likewise, all of those systems plus interactive communication database system offer analytical evidences for cooperative learning.

4 THE MODEL IMPLEMENTATION PATHS

According to the personalized analysis model and the relationship framework, this study proposes three model implementation paths: the pushing of personalized learning resource, the monitoring and guiding of personalized learning process, and the recommending of personalized learning communities. These approaches provide students with personalized services from three aspects: learning content, methods, and evaluation.

4.1 Pushing personalized learning resources

There are four steps in pushing personalized learning resources based on node analysis of learning contents sequence. These are: data collection, data preprocessing, evaluation and classification of individuals, and pushing learning resources. Node analysis of learning contents sequence evaluates students' knowledge mastering. The analysis items include learning basis, cognitive level, comprehensive ability, and learning evaluation. Through node analysis, cluster students who are on the same level of knowledge, and to record the learning content they browse as well as the distribution of learning resources. When the number of records reaches a certain numerical value and meets the principle of statistics requirements, the learning behavior can be predicted, and their personal preferred learning resources should be pushed forward.

4.2 Personalized guiding of learning process

There are four steps in personalized guiding of learning process based on node analysis of exercise sequence. These are: recording exercise process, analyzing exercise results, giving feedbacks, and providing personalized learning process guidance. E-portfolio is used to record information about exercise. Through the analysis of exercise results, we can get information about students' knowledge point mastering, thinking time, and application level. Giving feedbacks is to present results through the intuitive chart. Based on the analysis, personalized guiding of learning process should be provided from three aspects: the explanation of difficult knowledge, pushing expending knowledge, and instantly answering questions.

4.3 Personalized recommendations of learning communities

There are four steps in personalized recommendations of learning communities based on node analysis of communication sequence. These are: interactive text analysis, mining preferred learning model, clustering the same level, and personalized recommendation. Interactive text analysis is to analysis students' behavior path in interactive question-answering and learning communities, and to find out information units which have independent significance, such as learning interest, learning style, and to form a large information unit base. Mining preferred learning model is to combine these information units based on text algorithm, to form semantic relation between these units, in order to frame a preferred learning model with the individual as the center. Similar learners clustering is to analyze each information unit points set, and gather these points into a plurality of "cluster" according to the distance measure, cluster students with the similar experience, interest, and needs. Personalized learning community recommendation is based on the analysis of obtained information, recommending appropriate learning communities and preference discussion group to students, so that the learners can form a more closely virtual learning community.

5 CONCLUSION

This research provides theoretical framework for personalized learning analysis research in electronic schoolbag. Future studies will apply this model in schools with electronic schoolbag, use multiple big data mining algorithms to mine students' personality characteristics and visualize them, in order to improve and optimize this model in practice.

REFERENCES

Abdul, R.S. & Kumar, G. (2013). The future revolution on big data [J]. International Journal of Advanced Research in Computer and Communication Engineering, (6), 2446–2451.

The Development Plan within 10 Years of Educational Informatization (2011–2020). Retrieved from:http://www.moe.gov.cn/publicfiles/business/htmlfiles/moe/s3342/201203/xxgk_133322.html.

The National Plan for Medium and Long-Term Educational Reform and Development (2010–2020). Retrieved from:http://www.gov.cn/jrzg/2010-07/29/content_1667143.htm.

Ye, Y.Q. & Kong, K.Q. (2011). Personalized psychology. Shanghai: East China Normal University Press.

Yu, X.H. & Gu, X.Q. (2013). Learning activity streams: a behavior model for learning analytics. Journal of Distance Education, (4), 20–28.

Computer, Intelligent Computing and Education Technology – Liu, Sung & Yao (Eds)
© *2014 Taylor & Francis Group, London, ISBN 978-1-138-02469-4*

Study on the model of legal education of undergraduate

Y.G. Jiang
Department of Law and Administration, Changsha University, Changsha, Hunan, China

M.X. Cai
College of Science, Central South University of Forestry and Technology, Changsha, Hunan, China

ABSTRACT: Jurisprudence has evolved from the paradigm of Retributivism to the paradigm of Normativism, The inner contradiction rooted in Normativism paradigm separated itself into legalism and pragmatism for more than ten centuries. During the time the paradox of mind and reason, bisection of legislation and judiciary led to the confusion of legal value orientation and made legal paradigm stay in crisis and abnormal for a long time. Accordingly, Legal education model has experienced changes pass from mouth to mouth to theoretical inheritance, Normativism paradigm crisis make theoretical inheritance split into rational education and experience education model. In the 20th century, the doctrine of justice distribution and legal risk theory make the Distributivism most likely to become the positive result. The Distributivism paradigm asks for elite education model.

Keywords: legal paradigm; legal education; education model

1 INTRODUCTION

The current confusion of legal education is the problem of that how to choice of education model. Like all flowers bloom together, each academic point of view sticks to his argument. Takes the view, the education model can be divided into general education (Li L. & Kuang S.M. 1999) and occupation education (Wang Z.M. 1996), or Experience Education and Rational Education (Qin Z.K. 2002). Even scholars believe that the positioning of legal education model is not an important issue, which is subject to some macro factors, and not a problem to be solved by law school planning decisions (Su L. 2006). We think that legal education model should depend on the legal research paradigm, because the legal paradigm can solve the problem of the function and purpose of law, and the talents trained by Legal education should adapt to it.

2 FROM RETRIBUTIVISM TO NORMATIVISM: THE GERMINATION OF LEGAL EDUCATION

During the period of primitive society and slave commodity economy germination, people living in the simple custom and customary law times when kinship revenge and retaliation is the only creed to pursuit of fairness and justice and karma rooted in people's minds as the basic law of thoughts and ideas of the original custom and customary law as soon as written in almost all the religious teachings and laws. Christian "Bible" ("exodus") initiated the "revenge" principle: if any harm, you will be "a life for a life, an eye for an eye, a teeth for a teeth, a hand for a hand, a foot for a foot, who burning man will be burned, who injury a person will be injuried, who whip a person will be whipped." (Alan M.D. 2011) "if an ox gores a man or a woman, the bull must be stoned to death, ..." (Oliver W.H. 2006) "revenge principle" handed down in the teachings of Islam "Koran", and the ancient India Brahmanism the "laws of Manu", or even "code of Hammurabi" in ancient Babylon and "Twelve Tables" in early ancient Rome.

Revenge is not only applicable to the person of infringement, but also applicable to anything of tort. The law of ancient "Dior" is a typical legislation. Dior is only the inanimate objects which caused the deaths of persons. In ancient law, Dior will be destroyed as criminals. This behavior is consistent of the law which rooted in the Revenge. You want to fight If you've been hurt, and regardless of who or anything hurt you. Therefore, if a tree fell down and killing people, the tree is "Dior" which must be destroyed (Richard A.P. 2002).

According with the Retributivism which is legal thought of mainstream, legal and law and religion and theology mixed together in this period, and the legislation osmotic inside customs, religious dogmas and theology classics. In a small amount of National written laws, Retributivism idea get in by every opening; trial follows the inherent customs which with a strong divine judgment forms. "The simple custom and simple religion were the eternal law that no one known where it came from" (Hegel G.W.F. 1960). Combined with no occupation law class, a systematic legal theory can not form, not to mention the law education model. Scattered law philosophy and viewpoint achieved inter generational succession pass from mouth to mouth and behavioral effect.

After slavery commodity economy, social relations becoming increasingly complex, and legal norms that regulating social relations are developed, legal norms of civil, administrative, military, national organization which with weak (such as the civil law) or without Retributivism thought (such as administrative management laws and regulations) appeared in succession. Accompany the ocupational law class appearring, their legal thinking influenced on the criminal legislation greatly, and shook the homomorphism revenge roots which in the system of punishment of crime, and the subjective malignant degree has become an important factor in the severity of penalties. With the emergence of alternative punishment, the status of Retributivism thought in the criminal law of had been increasingly weakening, and the nature of law began to change from retribution tool to man's behavior standard, and legal thought and idea had been evolving from Retributivism to Normativism correspondingly.

When Retributivism changing to Normativism, occupational jurist stratum began to appear, the scattered philosophy thought and view of law had been gradually systemizing into a legal theory, the ancient Rome jurist played a crucial role in the creation, "In almost all other intellectual field, the Romans is religious students of Greek, but they are teachers of Greek in the legal aspects. In their hands, the law changed into the scientific theme for the first time. ....." (Barry N. 2000). With the production and development of the science of law, the status of legal research and the legal education was highlighted, so that the Jurisprudence of five jurists was confirmed as judge basis in the ancient Rome Empire.

3 THE ABNORMAL AND CRISIS OF NORMAIVISM: THE DEBATION BETWEEN LAW EDUCATION MODEL

The subject community of Normativism jurisprudence paradigm had been divided almost from its birth occurs. In ancient Greece, Plato put forward that the judges of the state should have a large amount of right of discretion which without bound from the fixed and rigid rules in the code when they adjudge disputes in "Utopia" (Plato, 2012). However, Aristotle, who is his favourite pupil, also think that if there are prominent figures with outstanding morality and politics in the country, so, they should become the permanent rulers (Aristotle. 1946). But, meanwhile, he insists that this "God" person must also be lawmakers, and even there should be legal system in the country ruled by this figure (Aristotle. 1946). And, laws formulated in proper way shall be the highest authority. Unless the law failed to make general provisions thereby allowing rule by man (namely administrative rule of law case), Laws should have the highest authority for each question (Aristotle.1946). Therefore, Aristotle advocated elite legislation and supremacy of law, and did not agree with the discretion to judge too much, the judge can solve the cases by mean of equity only in "the general and rigid nature of legal norms may make the judge cannot applicable the rules to solve individual cases". At this point, the judge can literally from the law, and to trial of the case as that the legislators might make to the problem (Aristotle. 2003). That is to say, Judges must take the legislators means as the basis when they exercising their discretion. On this point, Aristotle has deviated from the Pragmatism of Plato and be inclined to legalism.

Based on effect of intensity path dependence, and followed the differences between the law ideological of Plato and Aristotle, then Normativism jurisprudence paradigm Split into development approach of Pragmatism and Legalism, which caused the debate between Pragmatism and Legalism for over ten centuries. From the division of will and ration in early European to the argument between legislation centralism and judicial centralism of the classical natural law school. In this process, the representative doctrines of Legalism were Thomas Hobbes, Jean Jacques Rousseau, William Blackstone, Immanuel Kant; However, Samuel Pufendorf, Jean Jacques Burlamaqui, Edward Coke, John Locke and James Wilson have been put into Pragmatism representative lineage.

The Controversy between Pragmatism and Legalism has caused a profound impact on the current legal education mode: Legalism makes rational education mode, while Pragmatism makes experience education mode (Qin Z.K. 2002). Rational education aims to teach legal knowledge to students, to cultivate students' legal rational; The main teaching content is current legal system and the abstract legal theory; The main teaching methods is professor teaching, classroom discussion, case analysis; The main methods of examination is the written examination, and the content of examination is mainly basic concept, legal principle and knowledge of current law. Meanwhile, experience education aims to cultivate students' legal skills; In addition to legal knowledge, The main teaching content include legal practice course and legal ethics course; The main teaching methods are "Seminar" teaching method, "clinic" education law, "case teaching method"; The main methods of examination is oral test that in order to test the students on the master degree of legal skills.

4 LEGAL PARADIGM IN THE FUTURE SHOULD BE DISTRIBUTIVISM

Starting from Rudolf Stammler and Giorgio Del Vecchio, who were the early representatives of the theory of Justice, defined the legal concept and legal idea, going through the Gustav Radbruch and Heinrich Rommen's distribution justice, Jean Dabin's justice three-pronged approach, Harold Lasswell and Myres MacDougall's theory of justice of "world community", to Sidgwick and John Rawls' theories of distributive justice. The Justice theory has at least the following general: First, Justice is defined as the social income distribution, that is to say, Justice refers to the distributive justice; Second, justice first refers to the subject of legal relationship have equal freedom and rights which is the qualification for access to the allocation of resources or the interests equitably; Third, the content of justice mainly refers to the fair distribution of resources and benefits. The theory of Justice polymerized to the distributive justice showed that legal community which with distributive justice as its core concept gradually formed. With the the science of law entering the era after Normativism, the debate between legalism and pragmatism being more and more moderate, distributive justice now seems to be the highest value which the law pursuit, and Distributivism should to replace Normativism and become the new paradigm of law with the momentum effect of legal risk theory.

Legal risks, including legal risk which brought up by court judgment, all can be regarded as legal risk allocation, which is the constructive of legal risk (Jiang Y.G. 2012). Legal risk brought up by the legal distribution, that supplement and correct the single Deviation of allocative object and make law as a kind of justice distributive basis which have two kind of objects: one side are right, resources and interests, the other side are obligations, risks and losses. Rights are to obtain the resource allocation subject qualification or ability, and resource is a source of interest, while interest is the actual state of resources. Corresponding, obligations are the subject qualification or the ability to take risks, risk

is the sources of loss, Loss is the natural state of the risk. That the distribution of legislative power for the rights and obligations, the resource and the risk, profit and loss is the distribution in macro sense, and that the distribution of the judicial power for the rights and obligations, resources and risk, profit and loss is the distribution in micro significance. So far, the legal paradigm logic formed: the legal function and value is to distribute rights and obligations, resources and risk, profit and loss, and the value orientation and value goal are justice distributive principle and results of distribution.

Therefore, theory of legal risk have characteristics and potential for promoting legal "Paradigm Revolution": First, distributive justice theory would conquering the Normativism which in crisis by New attitude and become the most likely candidate of the new theory in Law Paradigm Revolution through improving of the theoretical system of distributive justice; Second, promoting the mutual influence and mutual penetration between distributive justice theorists and legal risk theorists, and make the legal community which see distributive justice as the core idea to "capacity expansion"; in addition, make distributive justice theory to be more speculative, comprehensive and dynamic in the sense of tool theory, world outlook and methodology through supple and correcting the single Deviation of allocated object in distributive justice theory. On this basis, that the Distributivism see distributive justice as the core showing the unique "disciplinary matrix" and "incommensurable" with the Normativism paradigm, and highlighting there volution of legal paradigm. Distributivism is the most likely results of jurisprudence paradigm revolution.

5 ELITE LAW EDUCATION MODEL UNDER DISTRIBUTIVISM PARADIGM

The logic of Distributivism paradigm indicated that both legislative power and judicial power can't be neglected, and the rights and obligations, resources and risk, profit and loss of the macroscopic sense and microscopic sense are required to follow the principle of distributive justice. The realization of distributive justice depends not only on the legislators, still need to rely on the judiciary, even to the Law enforcement, lawyer, and professor. Because, Law enforcement have the power of administrative adjudication on the distribution of rights, obligations, resources, risk, benefit and loss of the micro sense; Lawyers plays a role which can not be ignored on the distribution of rights, obligations, resources, risk, benefit and loss of the parties in the case; However, the law professors take on important task in distributive justice inheritance.

Visible, legislations, justices, law enforcements, lawyers and law professors who can to uphold the principle of distributive justice is the elite, and elite culturing depends on the law education, therefore, the justice of distribution depends on the excellentize of legal education mode.

We can construct the elite mode of legal education under Distributivism paradigm:

5.1 Curriculum design

The first is the specialized curriculum of legal science which is need to cultivate legal talents, we can select the practical and applicative curriculum of the core legal curriculum as a compulsory course, such as the constitution, administrative law and administrative litigation law, criminal law, criminal procedure law, civil law, civil procedure law, commercial law, intellectual property law, economic law, private international law, international economic law, etc. The elective courses include jurisprudence, Chinese law history, international law, and the labor law, environmental law, foreign legal history, legal English, legal documents, legal literature retrieval and paper writing, marriage and family law, evidence law, Internet law, the advertisement law, arbitration law, legal logic, etc., which as the core curriculum.

Followed by the legal elite course which is necessary to train legal elites with the concept of distributive justice, such as economics (including political economics), sociology, the history of distributive justice, justice theory, the history of western legal thought, the history of western ethics thoughts, philosophy of law, selected readings of legal philosophical classics, western law history, Rome law, speech and eloquence, comparative study of the law, etc. That economics, sociology, the history of distributive justice and justice theory is compulsory course. Under Distributivism paradigm, economics culture plays a key role in the process of legal elite talent culturing that if the law to solve the problem of distribution of resources and profits and risks and losses therefore economics to solve the problem why allocate as this. That is to say, the science of law makes students enable to know how while economics make students enable to know why. Sociology is important because it makes distributive justice and social order closely connected with each other. The history of distributive justice and justice theory is to solve the problem that what is justice and to culture students' distributive justice idea and world outlook.

5.2 Education methods

That the case teaching method and clinic education method which originated in the United States applied to the legal science specialized curriculum teaching is obvious effective for cultivating of legal skills and ability of legal professionals. But the elite legal course would be useless and even lead to students' reverse psychology if by the simple "cramming" classroom teaching method which is the traditional teaching mode of empty preaching. That the formation of idea of distributive justice must rely on to create conditions for students to be personally on the scene thereby we can impose influence on them. Special topic discussion method and conference debate method are suitable to the task.

5.3 Examination methods

Test method plays a great influence on students' learning, what test method determines the way students learn. Elite law talents training mode requires breaking the test method of written proposition and to adopt simulation court test. Simulation court in China is commonly used in training students' legal skills, in fact, the moot court is more appropriate for examination method than for training legal skills. But the key is that to set weights simulate for the program of the moot court course, the participants' manners, the language expression, the thinking clarity, the reasoning of judgment documents and the results of judgment which can make a comprehensive and rational evaluation of student's legal skills, idea of distributive justice and occupation moral.

ACKNOWLEDGEMENTS

The research work was supported by the project of economic law excellent course of Changsha University, and Hunan Soft Science Foundation of Hunan under Grant No. 2011zk2004, and Science and technology plan project of Changsha under Grant No. K1205056-11, and Hunan Provincial Natural Science Foundation of China No. 13JJ4088.

REFERENCES

Alan M.D. 2011. *The genesis of justice*, translated by Lin Wei Zheng, Beijing: Law Press.
Aristotle. 1946. *The Politics*, transl. By E. Barker, Oxford: University of Oxford Press.
Aristotle. 2003. *Ethika Nikomakheia*, translated by Miao Litian, Beijing: Ren Min University of China press.
Barry N. 2000. *An Introduction to Roman Law*. Translated by Huang Feng, Beijing: Law Press.
Hegel G.W.F. 1960. *Lectures on History of Philosophy*, second volumes, He Lin, Wang Taiqing transl., Beijing: the Commercial Press.

Jiang Y.G. 2012. *The Enterprise Legal Risk Management Theory*. Beijing: Guangming Daily Publishing House.

Li L. & Kuang S.M. 1999. Looking back on Chinese law education for a hundred of years. *Modern law science*, 6: 3–8.

Oliver W.H. 2006. *The common law*, Ran Hao, Yao Zhongqiu transl., Beijing: China University of Political Science and Law press.

Platon, 2012. *The republic*, translated by Zhang Zhuming, Nanjing: Yilin press.

Qin Z.K. 2002. Comparative analysis of law education model of two legal system. *Journal of Jiaxing University*. 2: 53–55.

Richard A.P. 2002. *The problems of jurisprudence*, translated by Su Li, Beijing: China University of Political Science and Law press.

Su L. 2006. Opportunities and challenges of contemporary legal education in China. *Legal science monthly*. 2: 3–21.

Wang Z.M. 1996. On the legal education and legal occupation. *Chinese legal science*. 5: 92–96.

Computer, Intelligent Computing and Education Technology – Liu, Sung & Yao (Eds)
© 2014 Taylor & Francis Group, London, ISBN 978-1-138-02469-4

The reform of higher mathematics teaching in higher vocational colleges based on the requirement of professional applications

Hai-Yan Zhen
Shandong Institute of Commerce and Technology, Jinan, China

ABSTRACT: Higher Mathematics as a compulsory subject for public in higher vocational colleges, on the one hand, it plays an important role in improving students' comprehensive quality, and cultivating students' ability to learn; on the other hand, it is the base of learning professional courses and upgrading career capacity. However, due to the late start of China's vocational colleges, in terms of the teaching of higher mathematics in higher vocational colleges, both content arrangement and teaching methods are not suited to requirements of professional applications. Combined with characteristics of the higher vocational colleges, raised from the perspective of professional service application, we proposed a research on reform of the teaching content and teaching method of higher mathematics.

Keywords: reform; professional needs; higher mathematics; vocational colleges

1 CURRENT SITUATION OF HIGHER MATHEMATICS TEACHING

Higher vocational education in our country has gone through more than 20 years of development. In 1996, National People's Congress (NPC) adopted and promulgated the "Vocational Education Law of the People's Republic of China", which legally defined the status of higher vocational education in China's education system, thus beginning the prelude to the development of higher vocational education; and on the National Education Work Conference held in 1999, the central government proposed the work requirements of "vigorously developing higher vocational education", the higher vocational education in China has entered a new historical stage of prosperous development. National policy of strongly supporting for development of higher vocational education help built a good platform, but due to late start of vocational education in our country, many problems are still in the exploration stage. Whether higher vocational education under the support of the national policy and community expectations can achieve the better development, and serve the community to develop more skill-oriented talents with higher quality, which mainly dependends on higher vocational colleges themselves, who must speed up the pace of reform in higher vocational colleges in order to better adapt to the needs of the community.

Higher Mathematics as a compulsory subject for public in higher vocational colleges, on the one hand, it plays an important role in improving students' comprehensive quality, and cultivating students' ability to learn; on the other hand, it is the base of learning professional courses and upgrading career capacity. However, due to the late start of China's vocational colleges. Higher mathematics teaching in higher vocational education is still primarily undergraduate the teaching mode of regular undergraduate institutions of higher education; teaching content remains in the "weigh theory, light practice", and not only make students feel learning is boring and not willing to learn, and such single model of teaching and curriculum content arrangement hinders improving the students' practical ability, which runs counter to the objective of higher vocational education. Therefore, higher mathematics teaching must be reformed in order to better meet the needs of professional development.

1.1 *Teaching contents and specialty are out of line, and lack of innovation*

During the more than 20 years of development of higher vocational colleges, due to the impact of undergraduate education model, especially because of inert of the teachers engaged in higher mathematics teaching, textbook content arrangements of higher mathematics is always followed by the content presentation mode of ordinary colleges and universities, which focus on the integrity and systemic aspects of teaching materials; it have not been able to high-light the characteristics of higher vocational institutions. Contents of higher mathematics reflected the feature of "heavy theory, and light practice", lacking contact with content arrangements and learning of professional courses, which is obviously inappropriate. This presentation mode of higher mathematics materials is inconsistent with the training objective of higher vocational colleges; this will just make it difficult for students to solve real-world problems flexibility using mathematical knowledge, so that students may have an ideological prejudice of "learning mathematics is useless".

In vocational colleges, although higher mathematics is an important foundation course during many specialized courses of the science and engineering and the liberal arts such as accounting, etc. But if course contents of higher mathematics are not reformed, and also not combined with professional courses, then the higher mathematics development will lose momentum as passive water, the significance of learning higher mathematics will also be denied to students and the community. Reform must completely abandon the psychological fear, and overcome the inertia of the teachers in order to conduct a profound reform of teaching content of higher mathematics targeted the professional needs.

1.2 *Teaching methods are old and lack the combination with specialty*

Compared to the students in general undergraduate colleges, the students in higher vocational colleges have a relatively poor mathematical foundation, especially in recent years, higher vocational colleges admissions diversify, mathematical foundation of the students who take spring college entrance examination, and alone admissions examination, is more weak. Higher mathematics is a problem for these students, many students would be afraid to learn higher mathematics, with the clear lack of confidence and resentment during the learning process, and many teachers teaching higher mathematics still used traditional teaching mode, even though some teachers adopted multimedia technology teaching, which only moved everything on the blackboard to slide, at the same time, due to inertia, many teachers don't want to spend time researching the needs of specialty, teachers teaching is still mainly based on pure theory, makes higher mathematics learning methods in higher vocational colleges and ordinary colleges and universities without any distinction, just with totally boring calculations and certification. Students already have an objectionable attitude to purely theoretical learning. Only combining teaching higher mathematics with solving problems can raise students' interest in learning higher mathematics. So we must change the teaching status quo, combining

higher mathematics teaching with professional needs, so as to make students feel what I had learnt is meaningful in order to increase students' interest in learning.

1.3 *Single assessment methods, heavy results light process*

Examination method of higher mathematics in higher vocational college still used the traditional final exam mode, individual institutions have adopted daily grade + midterm grade + final grade as overall assessment methods, but no matter what kind of examination, contents of examination are only for basic knowledge of traditional mathematics, generally not involving using mathematics to solve specialized problems. Under the assessment methods such as "light process and weight results", as if the students are still stuck in the higher school learning atmosphere, where the exam is designed to achieve higher test scores rather than learn to use mathematics to solve real problems; This traditional assessment methods violated the purpose of teaching higher mathematics in higher vocational colleges, and playing a negative role on cultivating innovative and higher-skilled personnel.

2 EXPLORATION OF TEACHING REFORM OF HIGHER MATHEMATICS

2.1 *Teaching model reform about "one purpose, two scenarios" for the purpose of server for specialty*

"One purpose" refers to higher mathematics teaching server for specialty, so that students learn to apply mathematical knowledge by learning higher mathematics to solve problems related to the specialty. Higher mathematics in higher vocational colleges generally is opened during the freshman, that is to say, before opening the professional courses, it requires teachers to go on a thorough and professional research on specialty's needs for higher mathematics, as well as in the process of teaching combine the specialty and mathematical knowledge, so that students feel it is necessary to learn higher mathematics. For example, for accounting professional students, teachers should add the knowledge of shadow price, and marginal analysis, and elastic analysis commonly used in economic into the teaching process of higher mathematics, for electronic professional students, knowledge such as Laplace transform must be taught, and combine them with the professional problems during the teaching process. As a result, the initiative of students learning will improve, interest in learning also will be inspired.

"Two scenarios" refers to that two teaching design schemes of higher mathematics: "teaching for different levels, teaching for different module."

"Teaching for different levels" refers to according to the student's learning foundation, split the students into multiple levels and the corresponding classes to teach. In recent years, due to enrollment expansion of many higher vocational colleges, and also admissions species are diverse, students in the higher vocational colleges not only involve the higher school graduates participating in common college entrance examination, also some vocational high school students participating in spring college entrance examination and students taking alone admissions examination, foundations of students generally showed a declining and uneven trend, both students scouring close to 500 points and students just scouring more than 100 more points may study in a class, teaching for different levels is very necessary in response to this situation, we can divide the students into two levels A, B.

According to specialty's requirements, before teaching for different levels, teachers need to conduct an in-depth understanding of the students' foundation and what the students have learned. For the students in B class, teachers can provide students with some relatively simple mathematical problems related to students' specialty to guide students, focus on calculation and downplay certification, at the same time, mainly train students' ability of using mathematical knowledge to solve simple practical problems. While for the students in A class, we should raise the requirements during specifying teaching objectives in order to meet more requirements of students. For example, some students may need Top-up or upgraded Self, or want to take part in the postgraduate entrance exams, so while teaching, in addition to meeting the specialized needs of students, developing students' ability to use mathematics knowledge to solve real problems, but also a appropriate increasing the knowledge of higher mathematics is needed to continue their studies.

"Teaching for different modules" refers to that according to the requirements of different professional students; the teaching content of higher mathematics is divided into several modules for teaching. Now most of the higher vocational colleges have adopted a 2 + 1 school model, that is to say, for the first two years students learn theory at school, the last 1 year is for post teaching practice off-campus. Due to shortening the learning time in school, hours of theoretical courses will be compressed. In many higher vocational colleges teaching hours of higher mathematics has reduced from original one year to only a semester now, under traditional teaching mode, teaching content of

higher mathematics has cannot meet needs of different professional students, for this situation, we can take "teaching for different modules" mode, through some professional research, we can divide mathematical knowledge needed by different professional students into basic module and professional module selected by their specialties, Basic modules include limits, derivatives and derivative, applications of derivative, indefinite integral, definite integral and its applications, which is the foundation of the entire higher mathematics learning, general science students and economic and management professional students belonging to liberal arts need to learn it. Professional module can be included space analytic geometry, and II heavy points, and Laplace transform, and mathematical logic preliminary, and linear algebra and its application, and for the professional module can be selected to learn, teachers can set corresponding teaching contents according to needs of different professional students, like for students of specialty of economic management t, they should choose to learn linear algebra and its application, for architecture student who needs cartographic should learn space analytic geometry, and for computer science students, they must learn preliminary mathematical logic.

2.2 Reform of teaching content arrangement

Textbook content arrangements of higher mathematics in our country higher vocational colleges generally still refer to textbook arrangements mode of ordinary undergraduate universities: "heavy theory and light practice", they are mainly boring calculations and prove, arrangement of content and exercise in school had little contact with professional questions, which is not conducive to cultivate students' ability to solve practical problems. Even during the work process of many students, they may encounter some practical problems which can be solved with higher mathematics knowledge, but they just cannot start them, the reason is that training is not enough during their learning process. The teaching book Calculus: Early Transcendental (5th ed.) of foreign high-quality vocational education resources can solve this problem, the arrangement of this book mainly used the actual problems to introduce knowledge, Arrangements for exercises after the class are mainly dominated by practical problems, which fully guide students to use mathematical knowledge to solve practical problems, knowledge of the entire textbook is built around solving practical problems, such a way of arrangements for content has a significant effect on enhancing students' ability to solve practical problems, and stimulating students' interest in learning.

2.3 Reform of teaching methods

Traditional teacher-oriented teaching methods: teacher speaking and students listening have been unable to stimulate students' interest in learning, and also cannot meet the needs of the goal of personnel training in higher vocational colleges, the teaching method of using professional problems to drive teaching in the higher mathematics teaching can inspire and driver students' interest in learning, and improve the ability of students to apply mathematical knowledge to solve practical problems, The specific approach is that firstly, ask some questions related to their specialties, and fully mobilize thirst for knowledge and curiosity of the students, teach mathematical knowledge by introducing the issues, under the requirements of solving the professional problems, student will be filled with enthusiasm for learning higher mathematics, Then guide students to use learned mathematical knowledge to solve practical problems raised earlier, and finally design again several practical issues related to their specialties to strengthen training of the applications. During the whole teaching process, teachers play the organizers and main body of learning is students. Teachers can integrate the ideas of mathematical modeling to daily teaching of higher mathematics, and train students' ability to use mathematical knowledge to solve professional problems through some platforms such as the National College Students Math Model competitions.

2.4 Reform of assessment methods

Assessment methods of higher mathematics are generally closed book exams, content of exam is also unchanged for decades, which are pure mathematical calculations and prove. This assessment method is nothing more than the exam pattern of regular undergraduate institutions, This is due to the majority of teachers graduated from normal colleges, most of them are from school to school, very few understand the needs of specify. This type of assessment method will make students try to "get high scores", and it has no good effect on "how to apply higher mathematics". This is not conducive to improve students' ability to apply mathematical knowledge to solve professional problems, assessment methods must be reformed. Teachers can follow the pattern of the National Undergraduate Mathematical Modeling competition to put students into several groups, each group use mathematical knowledge to solve some real problems related to their specifies, and the results should be included in the usual results. Also more practical problems associated with the specify should be included in the last final exam, but less pure calculation and proofs.

3 DISCUSSION

Teaching of higher mathematics in higher vocational colleges should always adhere to the teaching purposes of serving for the specifies, with continuous reform of teaching contents and the innovative teaching methods, it can really reach to cultivate students' ability to apply higher mathematics to solve major practical problems.

REFERENCES

Bai Fengshan as main translation, Calculus (Volume 1), pp. 157–171, 2004 James Stewart, Calculus: Early Transcendentals (5th ed) Beijing Higher Education Publication: [US].

Fu Wei. Exploration and Practice of Higher Mathematics Teaching Methods [J] University Mathematics, 2007, 23 (6): 6–10.

Kong Fan Qing. An Exploration of higher mathematics teaching integrated into mathematical modeling [J] China Electric Power Education: 2009 (4): 48–49.

Xiao Shu Tie. A Report about reform of Higher Mathematics [J]. Mathematical Bulletin, 2002, 41 (9):3–8.

Xiao Qi Ye as main translation, Frederick R. Adler forward, "Modeling the Dynamics of Life-Calculus and Probability for Life Scientists" Beijing: Higher Education Press, 2005 Second Edition.

Computer, Intelligent Computing and Education Technology – Liu, Sung & Yao (Eds)
© *2014 Taylor & Francis Group, London, ISBN 978-1-138-02469-4*

Research on the paramilitary administration in apartment with assistant counselors as a carrier—taking Shandong Transport Vocational College as an example

X.H. Ge

Shandong Transport Vocational College, Weifang, China

ABSTRACT: It has a very important meaning to improve the students' comprehensive qualities and ability among the students' affairs administration under the assistant counselors system and the paramilitary administration mode. In order to further strengthen the nurturance education of the vocational college students, Shandong Transport Vocational College tried to adopt the paramilitary administration in apartment with assistant counselors. According to the practical experience, the paper discussed the paramilitary administration in apartment with assistant counselors as the carrier.

Keywords: assistant counselor; apartment; paramilitary; students' affairs

1 BACKGROUND ANALYSIS

The assistant counselor system has been implemented since 2007 in Shandong Transport Vocational College, which is making the students' self education, the cultivation of good habits and the cultivation qualities become better and better, and received high praise from all sectors of society. In 2008, the college appointed 1,700 outstanding volunteers led by 50 assistant counselors to sever for the Beijing Olympic Games security work. At last, they succeeded finishing the job, and gained the title of "Olympic Security Outstanding Contribution Unit" for the college. In the evaluation of the campus civilization and the moral evaluation in 2010, the evaluation experts highly praised them with better discipline, better health habits and higher civilization quality. The students with higher qualities are deeply welcomed and loved by the employers. During the past five years, the all the graduates had been preordained before their graduation at least half a year ahead.

Assistant counselors are playing very important roles on student affairs administration in Shandong Transport Vocational College. They assumed the responsibility on the freshmen's military training, helped the counselors with freshmen's study, campus living and ideological education. In order to further enhance the college students' comprehensive qualities and abilities, the college tried to implement the paramilitary administration in apartment. And the assistant also played very important role in the administration model. They are helping with the freshmen's house training, inspect and supervise the house conditions.

2 ANALYSIS ON THE RESEARCH ABOUT THE ASSISTANT COUNSELORS' MECHANISISMS AND THE PARAMILITARY ADMINISTRATION IN COLLEGES

The assistant counselors' administration mechanisms and the paramilitary play an important role among college or university students. And this has also taken many scholars and experts' interest.

2.1 Studies on the assistant counselors work mechanism

Yu Hua et al. (2010)[1] from Huaqiao University had a research on the roles of the assistant counselors from the university, counselors, low-grade students and the assistant counselors themselves. They got the conclusion that the assistant counselors can reconcile the role of a buffer and incubation compensation to university and counselors, play exemplary roles for the low-grade students on the learning guidance, life coaching, meanwhile promote and improve their comprehensive qualities and abilities themselves, which can achieve the purpose of students' self-management, self-service and self-education to a certain extent. Huang Minqing[2] (2012) had a research on the value of the assistant counselors from the students' affair administration in private colleges. He pointed that the assistant counselors are the competent assistants of a teacher counselor, the guider of the ordinary students, and the job of assistant counselors is an effective way to achieve the self-worth for assistant counselors themselves.

2.2 Studies on the paramilitary administration of college student affairs

Ren Chuanyong et al.[3] (2008) thought that the paramilitary administration have some reference value for the college or university students affairs management and institutional adjustment. Lixin Han[4] (2010) pointed that it is the inevitable requirement to train the qualified college or university students with the paramilitary administration system in apartment, to train the society builders and successors with solid theoretical knowledge and excellent overall qualities, and also to ensure the nation's prosperity. All these studies show that the assistant counselor system has great advantages for the administration of college or university student affairs, and it has a significant meaning to enhance the students' comprehensive qualities under the paramilitary administration at colleges or universities.

2.3 The combination of the two effective mechanisms in Shandong Transport Vocational College

When Shandong Transport Vocational College implemented the paramilitary administration in apartment, they did not take the form of across the board, but rather to develop two management models, one is the paramilitary, and the other is the ordinary model with different management standards. When the students fully learned the purpose and Evaluation criteria, they may freely choose one of them. No matter what kind of apartment administration model, after the compliance, each student will get a corresponding comprehensive quality points. For example, if a student choose the paramilitary model, he or she can get 2 points after compliance, while if choose the ordinary model, he only get 1 point after compliance. For a certain extent, this can compensate the disadvantages of the full implementation of the paramilitary administration model in apartment. At the same time, it can enhance the students' interest to choose the paramilitary model voluntarily for the different evaluation score. The practice showed that, most students chose the paramilitary model, and the students dormitory are becoming cleaner and more methodical.

3 THE WORKING MECHANISM OF ASSISTANT COUNSELORS AT THE APARTMENT PARAMILITARY ADMINISTRATION

3.1 The selection and training mechanism of the assistant counselors

An assistant counselor should be with excellent remarks, positive thinking, active working, strong sense of responsibility. In Shandong Transport Vocational College, the students who are chosen according to the individual application, the sector assessment and the counselor's recommendation from the sophomores with a certain requirement, are intensively trained by military instructors invited from the army during the summer holiday. The main training items include: formation queue training, basic housekeeping standards training. Only passing examination of the assessment standards, the student can become a qualified assistant counselor. In addition, they should also accept the guidance and training about working methods by experienced counselors and teachers.

3.2 The reasonable and scientific administration standards of the apartment paramilitary mode

According to he forces' standards and requirement on the dorm housing and the college or university's practice, Shandong Transport Vocational College formulated the standers. The standards of dorm housing are "one requirement, two remaining orders, three things are forbidden and four unified orders" that is, the dorm garbage should be put into bags, taken away at 8:00 AM and 14:00 PM and thrown to the large rubbish bin outside the building; keep the dorm room clear and keep the indoor air fresh; no littering, no chaotic post and no chaotic mess nail pick; bedding stacked unity, life of appliances placed unification, desktop items placed unification and clothes and shoes put unity. The sanitary standards: six no phenomena, that is, no dirt on the ground; no dust on the door, windows and the desks; no cobwebs on the ceilings and walls; no dirty water indoor, outdoor and on balcony; no graffiti writing on walls, doors and windows; no odor indoor.

3.3 The role of the assistant counselors at the apartment management mode

Firstly, the assistant are responsible for the training of housing keeping among the freshman. One way is the intensive training during the military training, and the other way is to have the training once a week for about one hour in extra-curricular activities time. Secondly, they are also responsible to supervise and inspect the housing keeping.

4 THE ADVANTAGES OF THE ASSISTANT COUNSELORS AT THE APARTMENT PARAMILITARY ADMINISTRATION

4.1 The advantages of age and identity

The assistant are chosen from the second-year students, they are almost one year older than the freshman, and they are the college students. So in the student affairs administration, they are most likely to obtain the trust of students. And they can become the mentor of the students in a relatively short period of time, which can improve the administration efficiency greatly.

4.2 The advantages of the time and location

Most counselors do not live in school, and most of them have got married, it is impossible for them always to stay at apartment, while the assistant counselors can do this easily. In Shandong Transport Vocational College, all students from a department live in the same building, the counselors are convenient to go to the student apartments which they are in charge of. And the time is relatively abundant.

4.3 The advantage of the counselors' qualities

All the assistant counselors were chosen through a rigorous selection and strict training, and they can play a very good role of model both in study and conducts. Virtually, this will play a positive guidance for the freshmen.

5 THE IMPORTANCE OF THE ASSISTANT COUNSELORS AT THE APARTMENT PARAMILITARY ADMINISTRATION

5.1 Optimization of the apartment management

We all know that the assistant counselors have the incomparable advantages in working time and place than the teacher counselors. The assistant counselors have more time to train, guide and supervise the lower-grade students' housing keeping conditions at apartment. They are easy to find the deficiency and help to correct and improve the housing keeping conditions immediately. This can further optimize the apartment management largely, and help the low-grade students develop good habits and the collective consciousness of responsibility.

5.2 Reducing the teacher counselors work pressure and improving the relevance and effectiveness on the student affairs administration

Teacher counselors not only undertake the routine student affairs administration, the students' ideological education, but also undertake some scientific research works, which takes a lot of work pressure to the teacher counselors. The assistant counselors can help teacher counselors to deal with the apartment management, find some problems existed among students, and give the feedback to the teacher counselors timely. The assistant counselors have become the close information coordinators of the teacher counselors. All these can not only effectively reducing the teacher counselors' work pressure, but also help them to improve the relevance and effectiveness on the counselors' work.

6 ISSUES THAT NEED ATTENTION

6.1 The role of the assistant counselors

For the assistant counselors, they should be aware of their own position about the work, and the college or university should help them to have a clear role about the assistant counselors work. In general, an assistant counselor's roles mainly include the following: practitioner, organizer and coordinator, supervisor, consultant, communicator, ideological and political worker and pioneer demonstrator. An assistant counselor needs to withstand temper, experience and thus own the seven roles in oneself.

Firstly, a qualified assistant counselor is good at practicing for students, and demonstrating exercises personally, such as the housing keeping' demonstrations.

Secondly, an excellent assistant counselor must have good organizational and coordination skills, and is able to organize and coordinate the students whom are in charge of him or her on the work, and help the students solve the practical problems, and be their mentor.

Thirdly, the assistant counselor should pay attention to the supervision of the work process. During the supervision, it is very important to be fair and impartial to every student. Thus the work can help achieve the overall object to improve the effectiveness.

Fourthly, a qualified assistant counselor should be a good consultant to the students. It the students have some problems; he or she could take the initiative to explain to students, and help them solve these problems.

Next, an excellent assistant could initiative to communicate with the teacher counselor and students. And he or she should be good at doing the ideological work to the students with more encouragement and praise.

At last, the assistant counselors should be strict with themselves. Only doing so, they can really play the role of model.

6.2 The management and evaluation assistant counselor

At the beginning, the administration office of student affairs selects an experienced teacher who is responsible for training, supervising and assessing the assistant counselors. Firstly, the teacher should pay attention to the guidance of the assistant counselors' work. If he or she finds the insufficiency of the assistant counselors' work, the teacher should point out and correct immediately. During the process, the teacher should find and establish the typical who are outstanding at work.

The assessment of the assistant counselors' work is combined with the job responsibility and wok results once a semester, which will be credited to their personnel files. The assessment results will be the main basis to the students' awards, conduct assessment and the party assessment.

6.3 The rewards and punishment of the assistant counselors

The college selects the advance assistant counselors once per academic year, and awards them the honorary title of "advanced assistant counselor" and the honorary certificates. According to the actual situation, the college will give some material reward. Those who are unqualified will be warned or dismissed.

REFERENCES

[1] Yu, H & Yao Z.X. (2010). Preliminary Research on the System of College Student Counselors Assistant. *Education and Teaching Research*, 24(5):60–62.

[2] Huang, M.Q. (2012). The Research on the Values of the assistant counselors in private College Students' Affairs Administration. Journal of Taiyuan Urban Vocational College, 127(2):96–98.

[3] Ren, C.Y. & Yang, J. (2008). A study on the feasibility of the militarization of the management of University Students. Science and China Youth Technology, 170(8):39–42.

[4] Han, L.X. (2010). Discussion on the Apartment Paramilitary Administration. *University Logistics Research,* 5:98–100.

[5] Xiong, B.Q. (2012). Why dose the Housing Keeping Administration Bring Controversy? Dongguan Ddaily, 12-6:A02.

Computer, Intelligent Computing and Education Technology – Liu, Sung & Yao (Eds)
© 2014 Taylor & Francis Group, London, ISBN 978-1-138-02469-4

Discussion on three work realms of vocational college counselors

X.H. Ge

Shandong Transport Vocational College, Weifang, China

ABSTRACT: Vocational college counselor as a member of college counselors is the organizer, perpetrator and mentor of the routine student affairs and ideological and political education. How to take this responsibility better is plaguing many vocational college counselors. The paper mainly discussed three work realms of vocational college counselors, namely the transactional counselors, the empirical counselors and the expert counselors, according to the actual work about the administration of vocational college student affairs, to promote a better and faster development of counselors' abilities and the improvement of the management level of student affairs.

Keywords: vocational college; counselor; work realm; assistant counselor; apartment; paramilitary; students' affairs

1 BACKGROUND ANALYSIS

In June 2006, Ministry of Education of the People's Republic of China issued "The Requirement to the Building of the University Counselors Contingent", which pointed that the counselors are the backbone forces, the organizers, perpetrators and mentors in the college ideological and political education and the management of student affairs, that is, the counselors are not only responsible for the daily management of student affairs, but also shoulder the responsibility of the ideological and political education of college students. We all know that the higher vocational education is an important part of the higher education in China. The vocational college counselors should be aware of the responsibility of the job and try their best to do it well. They should try to make themselves become the empirical counselors from the transactional counselors, and then become expert ones, who are good at using their talent, to realize their true life value of the self expression.

2 THE FIRST WORK REALM OF THE VOCATIONAL COUNSELORS-THE TRANSACTIONAL COUNSELORS

There is a buzzword to describe the true portrayal of Vocational counselors, which says "When the two eyes are open, the counselors will be busy from the early morning till the deep night; when they try to close their eyes to have a rest, they must keep vigilant about the student affairs". A counselor teacher, Mr. Li (pseudonym), from a transport vocational college of Guangdong told the Information Times reporter "each work of a counselor is a complex engineering, from entrance education to career guidance, from housing rectification to study style construction, from psychological intervention to quality training, from the selection of students awards and loans to the funding for poor students, from the guidance of campus activities to the national competitions counseling, and the counselors' work are far more than these", which reflects the working volume of a counselor is much larger. Counselors are not relaxed after work; they should keep their mobile phones unblocked for 24 hours all day, in case of any unexpected events.

Those counselors who are just getting started to contact the student affairs administration mostly feel that they are busy all day long, as if there were too many things to finish. So many tedious routine student affairs often made themselves physically and mentally exhausted, bruised and battered.

Counselors' job is tedious and the transaction is complicated. All the work needs the counselors to deal with, such as the arrangement, collection and report of all students materials needed, the conveying and execution of every notice and conference, to deal with the every problem and contradiction among students. If they are not able to finish a job timely or wrong, that will cause the leaders' dissatisfaction and criticism. So many younger counselors have to work overtime to finish the work timely with qualities and quantities. They must feel exhausted bodily and psychologically with these tedious things all the day. How to get rid of this plight has become the key problem among the young counselors.

The situations described above are the true portrayal of transactional counselors. This is also the inevitable experience period for every young counselor.

After a period of experience, the young counselors will gradually grow and become mature at the position of student affairs administration. They will gradually accumulate experience and summarize the methods about the student affairs administration through the progress of practical work, and then they will gradually become empirical counselors. To shorten this progress as soon as possible, the better way is to learn from others. Firstly, they should learn from the experienced and excellent counselors. Secondly, they should learn from books, through a lot of reading about materials on the student affairs administration. Then they should try to use their head, do more regular analysis and summary.

3 THE SECOND WORK REALM OF THE VOCATIONAL COUNSELORS— THE EMPIRICAL COUNSELORS

Many empirical counselors and excellent instructors seemed much easier to deal with the routine student affairs, for they are very familiar with the students' characteristics, and are good at choosing and adopting some scientific and effective administration methods on the student affairs to simplify and regular the progress of the work. They are quite clear about the time, procedure and requirement of the routine affairs, which makes the transactional work become much simplifier, more regular, informative and mechanized.[1] They are familiar about what, when and how to do during the progress about student routine affairs, and prepare these things ahead of time logically and disjointed. For example, they are quite clear about how to help the freshman, how to select, train and properly use the student cadres, how to collect and organize student information, how to deal with the stage work, when the students are easy to produce problems and how to prevent and intervene in such kind of problems, and so on. That's to say, the empirical counselors and excellent instructors are much familiar with the student affairs, the focus and regular pattern of the work. Next, let's analyze and summarize the experience of empirical and excellent counselors, which might be helpful for the young counselors.

3.1 The counselors' work on the freshmen classes

For an empirical counselor, the newly enrolled term of the freshmen is the key period to bring a class. Freshmen always carry various ideals, have many suitors, but also have a lot of confusion at this period. So the counselor should own diligent mouth, eyes, legs and hands especially during the key period. "Diligent mouth" means that the counselor should keep more communication with the freshmen in various places (such as in classroom, dormitories, campus, and so on), to learn about their thoughts, and help them with various doubts, such as to learn their family conditions, personal plan in future, further education, students associations, study methods, campus life, professional orientation, employment destination and the treatment in future employment; All these prepared the way for the freshmen adapting to the college life better and more quickly. Meanwhile, this is also a good way for the counselor to go into the students' hearts, which would lay a solid foundation for the further management of administration in future. "Diligent eyes" means that the counselor should do more observation, and try to find the students' characteristics and advantages, and also master their disadvantages, which can accumulate some basic materials for the future education accordingly. "Diligent legs" means that the counselor should often go into students' dorms, classroom and students activities, which are very helpful for the establishment of his or her prestige in the minds of students. "Diligent hands" means that the counselor should do more records, analysis and summary through what he or she watched, learned and observed.

In addition, it is very important and necessary to collect freshmen's basic information at the beginning of the first term to the counselor, for these basic information might often be used in future work. So the counselor had better design the basic information table about students mainly including the student's name, hometown, birth date, home address, home phone number, student's phone number, e-mail, QQ number, roll number, student number, and so on, and also collect the student's paper and electronic photos.

The selection and training of student cadres is also an important job during the period. About how to select student cadres, the advice is that the counselor should consider students advantages and abilities comprehensively according to the different practical position of a class. After the selection, next step is to train and guide the student cadres. For this step, a counselor should learn to decentralize the rights microscopically and monitor macroscopically. We all know that the self management and self service among student affair are very important factors. It can significantly reduce a counselor's workload the counselor could use these student cadres reasonably. A counselor should pay more attention and supervise the work arranged to student cadres at this period. This is also a good period to strengthen the training of student cadres during the progress.

3.2 The counselors' work on special time

The student affairs administration is very pivotal and important before and after every holiday. Before a holiday, the counselor should tell students to pay more attention to the various safeties, such as the traffic safety, belongings safety, personal and safety, tell the students not to believe the good things as the sky would fall pies, not to take part in MLM organizations. And the counselor should have a good control of the number of classes leave. Do tell students to check whether the doors and windows of classroom and dorms are locked well, the water pipe and electric equipment are closed safely. Do have a registration about the students who do not leave. Tell them if they are not able to come back from home on time, to tell the parents and counselor the reason. After a holiday, the counselor should master the students' numbers who have arrived at college on time. For those who have not arrived on time, do have a timely communication with their parents to ensure the students' safety.

A counselor should keep more highly vigilant about the special time before and after a holiday. During the time, students are easily volatile on thoughts. So a counselor should strengthen the ideological and political education and supervise strictly students' various behaviors and habits. Generally speaking, it is the key period after the enrollment of a new semester for two months to grasp the students' habits and behaviors. That's to say, a counselor should learn to grasp the work tightly at the beginning and they will feel relaxed later. Otherwise, if a counselor grasps the work loosely at the beginning, the later work might be with more trouble. For the two month at the beginning of a new semester, students are easier to form good habits.

3.3 The counselors' regular work

As the direct organizer, instructor and practitioner of the students' routine affairs, a counselor should be much more familiar with the routine tasks, such as the daily safety education, ideological education, make-up task at the beginning, semester appraising work, students' awards, loans and funding task, stage internship and the work before graduation, the class meeting, talking with students. A counselor should be familiar with these tasks and requirements, be aware that how and when to do these tasks. What's more, he or she may do the preparatory work in advance, instead of waiting for the college's notice. We all know that many tasks are reflected in the process of student affairs administration.

4 THE THIRD WORK REALM OF THE VOCATIONAL COUNSELORS— THE EXPERT COUNSELORS

It is much easier for a counselor to transit himself from the fist work realm to the second realm. After a period of experience through the practical work on the students' affairs administration, basically speaking, a counselor is able to transit from a transactional counselor to an empirical counselor. But if a counselor wants to become an expert counselor for a higher work realm, he or she should improve themselves all rounds. It is necessary for them to study the basic knowledge on Pedagogy, Psychology and Management, as well as to meet the higher requirement about their moral characteristics and psychological qualities.

4.1 The meaning of the expert counselor

Zhao Yuan, Li Jun (2012)[2] defined the expert counselor as "the expert counselor is a full—time counselor who is provided with the knowledge, abilities and experiences required by the job of student affairs administration at colleges, playing an excellent role in education, administration and service practice, owning a certain special skills and having some popularity and social influence". In contrast with common counselors, an expert counselor has such characteristics as "with rich professional knowledge, high efficiency to solve problems, and certain creativities". That is to say, the expert counselor is the expert about routine student affairs administration, as well as the expert in the field of the study about the ideological and political education, who have not only rich professional knowledge, but also unique administration methods, and is good at study, research and creativity.

4.2 The qualities and abilities of the expert counselors

According to the correlated researches at home and abroad, some experts and scholars summarized the abilities, abilities and characteristics of the expert counselors as three aspects: knowledge accomplishments, intelligent qualities and personality psychology.

On the knowledge accomplishments, an expert counselor has a strong desire for knowledge, is good at study, has insight into the professional knowledge about pedagogy, psychology and management science, is very familiar with the laws of education, and is constantly pursuing the perfect knowledge structure and actively accepting the new knowledge and new ideas. At the same time, he or she pays more attention to stimulate students' desire of study, and is good at guiding students to love study, be able to study and be pleased to study. Secondly, on the professional pursuit, they have wider professional accomplishment, and are the guiders of students on studies. At last, on the political aspects, they have distinct political attitudes and firm political stance, own higher moral standard, strong sense of professionalism and responsibility, and profound understanding of Marxist theory. And they have extensive scientific and cultural knowledge, diverse knowledge structure and good knowledge base from the aspect of science and culture.

On the intelligent qualities, firstly, expert counselors should own the awareness and abilities of long life studies, have strong self-learning abilities, and are able to learn and accept the new knowledge and new changes with the social development and the progress of the times. Secondly, the expert counselors should have a relatively wide range of interests, active thinking, and be able to make themselves into students, which would effectively enhance their prestige in the minds of students. Thirdly, they should have good capabilities on the behavior and processing services, and are good at coordinating all aspects of the relations and dealing with contradictions, through all which the expert counselors could constantly affect students by their charisma. In addition, an expert counselor should be good at researches, own the independent research capability of carrying out ideological and political education. As an expert counselor, he or she is willing to find, is willing to investigate, and is good at researching. Last, an expert should own some special abilities, such as better verbal skills, writing skills, communication skills, management skills, coordination skills, adaptabilities, psychological control skills, and the capabilities to deal with various information and technologies.

On the personality psychology, expert counselors should have sound personalities and healthy mental characteristics. First of all, expert counselors should have a positive self-awareness, strong autonomy, independence and coordination, are able to find their own advantages and disadvantages and could have a proper self-positioning. At the same time, they are able to be good at self-control, self-criticism, and have the courage to resist the influence of various unfavorable factors. Secondly, expert counselors should be open-minded, honest, confident and optimistic. Thirdly, they should have good feelings, love their students, are good at controlling their own emotions, have the perseverant spirit, and love the career of college counselor and student affairs administration. In addition, expert counselors have a strong motivation about achievement with "excellent students around the world", and own the awareness "the responsibility of education is far more than others". All these make them fell the glorious mission. Last but not least, they are able to innovate on the work to find more reasonable and scientific methods, and are willing to transcend themselves continually through the accumulation about learning and practical work experience to make the work more innovative, realistic, perfect and divergent.

Though the work of college counselors, especially of the vocational college counselors is heavy and arduous, it is really a good stage to achieve our self-worth and wonderful life. Wish every counselor could keep the glorious career into mind, and take the work as our own career, take careful management about the work to make us have a better and faster growth constantly, and wish every counselor could find their wonderful life on the position of student affairs administration.

REFERENCES

[1] Luo, Y (2008). "Rational Thoughts on Heavy Routine Work of Political and Ideological Instructors in Colleges and Universities," *Educational Research on Foreign Languages & Arts*, 2:40–43.
[2] Zhao, Y & Li, J (2012). "Discussion on the Expert Type Counselor and Their Shaping," *China Adult Education*, 14:46–48.

Computer, Intelligent Computing and Education Technology – Liu, Sung & Yao (Eds)
© 2014 Taylor & Francis Group, London, ISBN 978-1-138-02469-4

Energy-saving potential automatically detecting online and rapid energy audit smart system based on dedicated electricity users

L.F. Cheng & T. Yu
Electric Power College, South China University of Technology, Guangzhou, China

ABSTRACT: For the purpose of realizing effective energy diagnosis and audit based on big electricity users, a rapid energy audit method combining with hardware and software was proposed and the energy-saving diagnosis instrument based on DSP2812 was designed, meanwhile, developed supporting analysis software, and they constitute a complete intelligent system. The hardware monitors and records users' energy consumption situations which provide basic data supports, the software uses the data to make deep diagnosis analysis. According to different types of users, the system can realize power quality monitoring online, energy-saving potential analysis, and rapid energy audit. Hardware and software design were introduced, and the results of field test were presented to demonstrate its feasibility, thus can realize the goals mentioned above. Its advantages include strong intelligence, low cost, highly reliable, easy-to-use, and can effectively improve the efficiency, information degree and automation degree of energy audit work based on big electricity users.

Keywords: energy saving audit; intelligent diagnosis; mass storage technology; double AVR MCU technology; DSP2812

1 INTRODUCTION

At present, all levels of power grid enterprises of China urgently need to realize comprehensive and real-time monitoring and information management of power quality information,[1–4] and utilize the power quality data from comprehensive information real-time monitoring and management to implement energy audit work of dedicated electricity enterprises.

The energy audit work at present is implemented by the Energy Saving Service Corporation (ESSC) with specialized qualification, and the work is done manually, and needs detection personnel to make a large amount of field electricity usage data detection of internal distribution system of enterprise, it also needs large amount later data analysis work, thus causes that the whole process is completed with a long time, low efficiency, and high expenditure, which is not proper to promote the use of large-scale.[4]

Therefore, in order to realize the dedicated users' energy saving potential detecting automatically and online and rapid energy audit automation, it must be oriented "namely inserts namely use" online electrical detection system, which, at the beginning of energy audit work, and under the circumstance of not interfering with the normal production, can be quickly inserted users' internal distribution system, and for import measurement points,

according to actual needs, completing data acquisition at least one day to one week, finally based on the data, implementing rapid energy audit work online.

In this paper, a low-end and mid-side energy-saving diagnosis instrument respectively based on double AVR MCU and DSP2812 was designed, meanwhile, developed supporting analysis software, and they constituted a complete intelligent system, which can detecting dedicated users' energy saving potential online and automatically, and make rapid energy audit work.

2 STRUCTURE AND FUNCTION OF SYSTEM

According to the system hardware and different types of enterprise users, when using the low-end instrument, the main service targets are simple and small enterprises, and without considering the relative influence of harmonic; when using the mid-side instrument, it is mainly used to make energy audit work for medium and large energy consuming enterprises.

The system makes use of online monitoring technology and artificial intelligence technology, thus can change energy audit work into a kind of automatic system with standardization and normalization. The application of this system, the

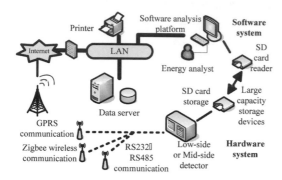

Figure 1. Energy saving potential detecting automatically online and rapid energy audit intelligent system.

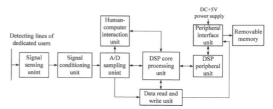

Figure 2. System principle and structure block diagram of the mid-end instrument.

power grid corporations may get rid of independence on energy saving service corporation and are free to realize energy saving potential analysis and rapid energy audit work for various electricity consumption enterprises. So it has great application prospect and remarkable economic and social benefits. The whole structure and working principle of the system is shown in Figure 1.

3 HARDWARE SYSTEM DISIGN

The development and design of energy-saving diagnosis instrument is based on powerful DSP chip TMS320F2812. This chip is designed to perform various high speed and real-time signal processing, compared with the AVR MCU, it has a lot of features in the structure and instruction, so that can realize various digital signal processing algorithms, such as the Harvard structure, hardware multiplier, pipeline operation, special DSP instructions etc., thus it is very suitable for processing real-time monitoring data of power quality.[5–7] The principle diagram of mid-end hardware instrument is shown in Figure 2.

The mid-end instrument is taken DSP as core digital processing chip, and its structure contains of 9 units shown in Figure 2, they are: signal sensing unit, signal conditioning unit, A/D sampling unit, DSP core processing unit, DSP peripheral unit, data read and write unit, human-computer interaction unit, peripheral interface unit and removable memory. This instrument is worked with DC +5V power supply. Its working principle is: three-phase voltage and current signal of dedicated users' electricity lines are collected by the signal sensing unit and these signal are made into a series of managements by the signal conditioning unit, such as anti-aliasing filter, operational amplifier, zero crossing comparison, synchronization frequency, sampling hold and so

on, three-phase voltage and current signal in sampling holder are made into the form of 4 channels voltage signal (UA, UB, UC, UN) which are transmitted to 4 voltage analog input channels (CH4, CH5, CH6, CH7) of the MAX1324 chip in the A/D sampling unit, meanwhile, the other 4 channels current signal (IA, IB, IC, IN) are processed by A/V conversion circuit and are transmitted to 4 current analog input channels (CH0, CH1, CH2, CH3) of the MAX1324 chip in the form of 4 channels types of voltage signal. The eight analog input signals through high precision and fast A/D transformation, then transferred into TMS320F2812 chip of DSP core processing unit in the form of 12 channels digital signal, at the same time, they are transmitted to the human-computer interaction unit and displayed by LCD module, and through the key input circuit, the LCD display can be operated, the instrument parameters can be saved and set. 12 bits digital signal are stored in the extend RAM by controlling of DSP chip, then the data stored in the RAM are read and written into the SD card or U disk through the CH376 file management chip in the data read and write unit, while the DS1305 clock circuit provides the external clock signal for the DSP chip. RS232 data communication of DSP chip is realized through the SP3232 chip. 12 bits digital signal transmitted into DSP chip are managed with digital filtering and Fast Fourier Transform (FFT) processing, thus realizes real-time tracking of three-phase voltage and current; real-time calculation of voltage and current RMS values, three-phase unbalance, active power, reactive power, apparent power, frequency, power factor; and steady state harmonic analysis. Large capacity storage of SD card or U disk ensures that this mid-end instrument can continuously record at least one week amount data.

4 DESIGN OF ENERGY SAVING ANALYSIS AND DIAGNOSIS SOFTWARE

Energy saving analysis and diagnosis software is a king of energy audit software platform which is designed under the development environment

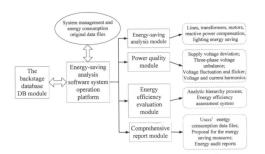

Figure 3. Functional module diagram of energy-saving analysis software.

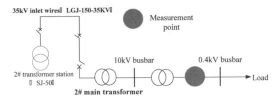

Figure 4. The schematic diagram of scale measurement points.

Table 1. Transformer data of the measuring point 2#.

Transformer number	Capacity (kVA)	Type	Impedance (%)	Connection group
SCB9	2500	Dry	6.04	Dyn11

of Visual Studio (VS) 2010. This platform can make energy-saving potential calculation and realize energy audit report formation automatically, so as to realize the energy audit automation. The software system is mainly divided into the following modules: database module, energy-saving diagnosis module, power quality module, energy efficiency evaluation module, and comprehensive report module. Among them, according to the equipment parameters needed in each functional module, through establishing database, and using the database technology, the data in the database can be added into the energy-saving analysis and diagnosis software. The intelligent and friendly equipment parameter input interface reduces the blindness of input parameters. According to the "National Electrical Manual" of China, 3000 kinds of various types of transformers and 2000 kinds of various types of motors, and lines and lamps database are included in the database of the software. The functional module diagram of the energy-saving analysis and diagnosis software is shown in Figure 3.

5 PRACTICAL APPLICATION EXAMPLES

Using the energy audit system designed and developed in this paper, carry out energy-saving diagnosis analysis and power quality detection in a large circuit production enterprise in Dongguan city of China, each measurement point is recorded for one day, and the measuring diagram is shown in Figure 4.

The inlet wires of this factory is 35 kV, after two times voltage reduction, in the low voltage switching room, including lots of 0.4 kV power distribution cabinets, according to the above diagram, inlet wire is 35 kV, step-down 10 kV at first time, and step-down 0.4 kV at second time, this level voltage is supplied for low voltage equipment. Using the energy-saving analysis and

diagnosis system developed in this paper, aiming at one of the low voltage distribution room, at second low voltage side of one transformer, 13 measuring points of wires were tested. The mid-end energy-saving diagnosis detector developed in this paper was used in this factory for its large energy consumption. Aiming at these 13 points, each of them was continuously tested and recorded for 24 hours. Now select measurement point 2# as the actual energy-saving analysis and diagnosis example, and its testing results are shown as follows.

The transformer data of this measurement point (2#) is shown in Table 1.

Monitoring data of this measuring point, which is stored in SD card in form of ".txt" data file, then the data file is inserted into energy-saving analysis software, and the power quality standards of China, such as *GB/T 14549-1993, GB/T 12325-2008, GB/T 15543-2008, GB/T 12326-2008*, are stored in the database of software, and according to which, can respectively get voltage and current harmonic, voltage deviation, three-phase voltage unbalance, voltage fluctuation and flicker statistical tables of measurement point 2#, and they are respectively shown in Tables 2–5. Due to space limitations, only give 2 to 6 times harmonic statistical results of A phase voltage and current (the mid-end detector can measured 1 to 25 times harmonic values).

5.1 Results analysis

According to the energy-saving analysis software exported the electric energy statistical data tables of low voltage side of transformer, the absolute add of positive and negative voltage deviation was 11.13%, which exceeds 10% GB limits. Three-phase current

Table 2. 2–6 times harmonics voltage and current statistical values of 2# measurement point.

Times	Qualified	International values	Qualified rate (%)	International comparison	A phase			
					Max.	Min.	Ave.	95% value
Types								
2	**TRUE**	1.20	100.0	45.8	0.91	0.04	0.18	
3	**TRUE**	2.40	100.0	55.4	1.75	0.70	1.02	1.33
4	**TRUE**	1.20	100.0	10.8	0.31	0.01	0.05	0.13
5	**TRUE**	2.40	100.0	37.9	0.87	0.18	0.49	0.83
6	**TRUE**	1.20	100.0	15.0	0.32	0.01	0.05	0.18
2	*FALSE*	*7.8*	*93.4*	*135.2*	*27.53*	*0.05*	*2.00*	
3	*FALSE*	*3.7*	*64.0*	*397.2*	*26.47*	*0.16*	*4.03*	*14.59*
4	*FALSE*	*4.0*	*85.6*	*352.4*	*37.20*	*0.03*	*2.32*	
5	*FALSE*	*4.1*	*21.9*	*1806.5*	*48.97*	*1.82*	*18.49*	
6	*FALSE*	*2.7*	*77.5*	*660.6*	*29.94*	*0.00*	*3.04*	

*Note: The unit of voltage and current harmonic international value is respectively percentage and Ampere.

Table 3. The voltage deviation measurement statistical values of 2# measurement point.

Qualified	Phase A	Phase B	Phase C
	TRUE	*FALSE*	**TRUE**
Qualified rate (%)	100.00%	33.41%	100.00%
International value (%)	(−7, +7)	(−7, +7)	(−7, +7)
Upper limit time (%)	62.28%	45.06%	54.19%
Lower limit time (%)	0.00%	0.00%	0.00%
Maximum value (%)	2.78	−2.11	3.40
Minimum value (%)	−4.86	−9.02	−4.10
Average value (%)	−0.87	−5.45	−0.21

*Note: "*FALSE*" means unqualified, "**TRUE**" means qualified.

harmonics contents were high, especially 2, 3, 4, 5, 6 times characteristic harmonics were particularly serious pollution to the power grid. A, B, C three-phase voltage flicker maximum values were 3.87, 4.43, 4.03, and average values were 1.55, 1.47, 1.51, which both exceeded the Chinese standard limit values.

5.2 Rectification solutions

The testing results show the problems of power quality, energy-saving analysis software according to backstage database and relevant national standards (in China), and puts forward the following solutions.

Solution 1: install capacitor banks and passive filters.

In order to filter current harmonics, it can install multiple banks of passive filters. For higher harmonic content of load current, the main characteristics harmonic current is epitomized by 2, 3, 4, 5 and 6 times, so can install 2, 3, 4, 5 and 6 times single tuned filter to solve this harmonic problems. In addition, in order to filter higher times of harmonics, can install a set of high pass filters, and the cutoff frequency is selected as 12 times.

Solution 2: install hybrid active power filters and capacitor banks.

According to the load operation situation, packet switch capacitor banks, supply compensation for each phase load, these measures can effectively improve the voltage flicker problems. In the 10 kV or 6 kV bus of enterprise distribution, install a double winding transformer and on the low voltage side of which, install a set of hybrid active power filters, this measure can filter load harmonic current and when necessary, can also compensate reactive power for loads.

5.3 Rectification solutions comparison

Rectification solution 1 belongs to traditional compensation solution, capacitor banks can be switched through thyristors or mechanical switches, and utilize the way of phase compensation, can avoid switches action frequently, thus can effectively prolong the service life of equipment.

Capacitors among rectification solution 2 can only supply reactive power compensation which is graded, and can not continuously compensate reactive power, for those low requirements of reactive power compensation occasions, the problems can be solved perfectly. While active power filters can compensate various times of harmonics, and the filter effects are good, in addition, can compensate small amount of reactive power, but the connection transformer will increase the cost.

Table 4. The three phase voltage unbalance measurement statistical values of 2# measurement point.

Max. value	Min. value	Ave. value	95% value	International allowable value (95%)	International allowable value (max.)	Qualified
2.61	0.01	0.16	0.00	2.00	4.00	**TRUE**

Table 5. The voltage flicker measurement statistical values of 2# measurement point.

Long time flicker (2h)	Max. value	Min. value	Ave. value	International value	Qualified rate (%)	Qualified
Phase A	3.87	0.04	1.55	1.00	50.33	*FALSE*
Phase B	4.34	0.04	1.47	1.00	50.30	*FALSE*
Phase C	4.03	0.04	1.51	1.00	50.09	*FALSE*

6 CONCLUSIONS

Aiming at the problems of high energy consumptions in dedicated electricity users, design and develop dedicated users' energy-saving potential detecting online automatically and rapid energy audit system, the system includes hardware system and software system, among them, the energy-saving diagnosis instrument include low-end and mid-end devices and they form the hardware system; the energy-saving analysis software form the software system; low-end and mid-end instruments can be used according to different types of electricity users.

1. The hardware system used advanced digital signal processing technology, high precision sampling technology, and large capacity storage technology, thus can monitor and record users' energy consumption data for at least one week.
2. The monitoring and recording data was stored in large capacity SD card or U disk, and through SD card reader, the data can be inserted into the software system, based on the powerful back-stage database of the software system, users' energy consumption files and energy audit reports can be obtained rapidly.
3. Users' energy consumption files and energy audit reports give the power quality problems existed in users' distribution system and according to these problems, provide corresponding recommendations and rectification solutions for users to maximize energy production, ensure electrical safety and power quality, improve electricity using efficiency and GDP value from each unit electricity. All these improvements, means great practical significance to dedicated electricity enterprises and urgent needs of energy saving and emission reduction work in the power grid corporations.
4. Through actual field tests, verify the reliability of this whole system, and make clear the great market value and application potential of it.

Its application can effectively improve the efficiency, degree of information and automation of energy audit work.

5. Technically, the whole energy-saving diagnosis system has a higher innovation, if it vigorously promoted in energy-saving markets, the direct economic benefits and social benefits will be very significant.

REFERENCES

[1] Ming-yu Wang, Yan-jing Zhou, 2010. *Research of the networked integrated monitoring system for power quality* [J], Power System Protection and Control (in Chinese), vol. 38, no. 1, 87–91.
[2] Mei Liang, Yong-qiang Liu, Ming-jun Yuan, 2010. *Design and implementation of open power quality SCADA system* [J]. Power System Protection and Control (in Chinese), vol. 38, no. 11, 81–85.
[3] Ling Wang, Jian Kang, Hong-liang Zou, et al. 2011. *Construction and application of real-time power quality monitoring system* [J]. Power System Protection and Control (in Chinese), vol. 39, no. 2, 108–111.
[4] Marc A. Rosen, 2007. *Improving the Efficiency of Electrical Systems via Exergy Methods* [J]. 2007 IEEE Canada Electrical Power Conference, 467–472.
[5] Mei Xue, Chang-liang Xia, Hui-min Wamg, et al. 2011. *Flux Linkage Characteristic Measurement Based on DSP and Artificial Neural Network Modeling for Switched Reluctance Motor* [J]. Transactions of China Electro technical Society (in Chinese), 2011, no. 2, 68–73.
[6] Feng-yan Wang, Li-li Ren, Jian-ping Xu, 2009. *Modeling and Design of Digital Controller for Inverter Based on F2812* [J]. Transactions of China Electrotechnical Society (in Chinese), vol. 24, no. 2, 94–99.
[7] Ding-hua Zhang, Wei-hua Gui, Wei-an Wang, et al. 2009. *Study and Application of a New Power Quality Combined Compensation System for Electrified Railway* [J], Transactions of China Electro technical Society, vol. 24, no. 3, 189–194.

Computer, Intelligent Computing and Education Technology – Liu, Sung & Yao (Eds)
© 2014 Taylor & Francis Group, London, ISBN 978-1-138-02469-4

Second language vocabulary acquisition in the perspective of schema theory

Z.F. Xie

Shandong Women's University Jinan, Shandong, China

ABSTRACT: Vocabulary acquisition is absolutely not just memorizing the vocabulary list mechanically. It helps to enhance your ability and efficiency in vocabulary acquisition if you can appropriately adopt different memorizing methods guided by schema theory. Memorizing via affix and root, memorizing via association and comparison with words of similar spelling or pronunciation, multidimensional association based on context, situation-based word association are all means of significance in vocabulary acquisition. In addition, a wide range of cultural background information of the target language promotes the construction of a better schema system and facilitates the transition from passive vocabulary to active vocabulary.

Keywords: formal schema; content schema; memorizing via association; vocabulary acquisition

1 INTRODUCTION

As the foundation of language, the importance of vocabulary in language learning is self-evident. Just as the famous linguist Wilkins said, "without grammar, there are many things that can not be expressed; without vocabulary, people can express nothing." there will always be vocabulary learning in the process of learning a language. A large vocabulary is the prerequisite for language learners to improve their English listening, speaking, reading, writing and translating skills. Without the acquisition of fundamental lexical knowledge, there would be no improvement in the learner's abilities in listening, speaking, reading and writing. Applying the traditional way of second language acquisition, people tend to memorize the pronunciation, spelling and meaning of words mechanically making use of isolated vocabulary list without the guidance of a systematic vocabulary acquisition or strategy. The result is usually far from satisfactory. It takes a lot of time, however, what has been just learned slips from the mind quite quickly. Though sometimes receptive vocabulary does increase, it makes not much difference to the acquisition of productive vocabulary. The research by Liu Shao-long (2001) reveals that the imbalance between vocabulary memorized and its deep development is widespread among learners in the process of vocabulary acquisition. Different levels of learners have a statistically significant difference in the number of words memorized and comparatively a much smaller difference in the depth of vocabulary acquisition. The vocabulary acquisition at a deeper level requires not only the learning of pronunciation, spelling and corresponding Chinese meaning, but also the mastery of grammatical allocation, pragmatic functions and its connotations, so as to build a systematic network on lexical and semantic level and to rapidly and accurately activate the vocabulary needed in communication. The thesis intends to explore how to learn second language vocabulary in the guidance of schema theory in order to enhance the ability and efficiency of vocabulary acquisition and deepen the mastery of vocabulary.

2 SCHEMA THEORY

Psychologist Barlett first proposed schema theory in the 1930s. Rumelhart improved the theory in the 1980s. Many other scholars, such as Johnson (1987), Mandler (1992), conducted deeper research concerning this theory. Overseas study on schema theory is becoming mature and the theory has been widely applied to the field of philosophy, psychology, cognitive science and foreign language teaching, which aroused the attention of domestic scholars. Research on schema theory in china began in the 1980s and have made remarkable achievements after more than 30 years' development. Studies on schema theory applied in the field of foreign language teaching are on the rise. However, most of these studies highlight the influence of schema theory on the improvement of language aptitude of a certain aspect. The significance of schema theory on reading, listening, translation and writing has been proved by many empirical studies, but second language vocabulary acquisition under the guidance of schema theory is rarely involved.

Rather than stay at the surface level of the target language, second language vocabulary acquisition under the guidance of schema theory helps learners go further into its deeper level and put more emphasis on the pragmatic functions and its connotations. Learners can take full advantage of the existing knowledge (ie. existing schema) to understand and memorize new vocabulary so as to build a more complete and better knowledge system (new schema after reorganization), which is to facilitate the rapid and accurate activation of vocabulary when needed as well as the improvement in the ability and efficiency of vocabulary acquisition.

In terms of language learning, it is commonly acknowledged that schema can be classified into three categories, namely, language schema, content schema and formal schema. Language schema is the learner's existing language knowledge about phonetics, vocabulary and grammar etc. Without language schema, learners can not recognize the words, phrases and sentences in verbal communication, neither can they activate the existing content schema and formal schema, let alone the language acquisition. The importance of language schema has been confirmed by numerous studies, which will not be repeated here. The thesis will focus on the guiding significance of schema theory on second language vocabulary acquisition in terms of content schema and formal schema.

3 SCHEMA THEORY AND VOCABULARY ACQUISITION

3.1 *Formal schema and vocabulary acquisition*

Formal schema is the cognitive framework based on the external structures of things linked together. Vocabulary acquisition requires learners to grasp the form of a word (spelling, pronunciation), meaning, location (grammatical allocation) and function (the occasion for application). It turns out to be much easier to memorize words with the help of formal schema based on the external form of the word structure, that is, the spelling and pronunciation of the word.

3.1.1 *Memorizing via affix and root*
Many English words are ideographs. That is, two or more ideograms combined together can form words to express a new meaning. It is a powerful means to generate words by using root, affixes and compound words. The productivity and flexibility of root and affixes greatly enriched the English vocabulary.

If learners can master the meanings of such roots and affixes and construct corresponding formal schema according to the visual representations of the roots and affixes, it can effectively help them guess and analyze the word components based on the word form sp as to get the meaning and easily memorize it. For example, if learners know the root "ped" means foot or walking, it is easy for them to memorize words like "peddler" "pedestrian" or "pedicure". Therefore, if learners understand and memorize new words with the help of formal schema and try to code and store words on structural level, it does help to recognize psychologically and it is more effective and lasts longer cognitively.

3.1.2 *Memorizing via association and comparison with words of similar spelling or pronunciation*
There are lots of words which have similar or even the same spellings or pronunciations, but quite different and unrelated meanings. For example, receptive/respective/respectable/respectful, perspective/prospective (similar spellings); stationery/stationary; prophet/profit (the same pronunciation). For such words, if learners memorize them via association and comparison, they will notice the subtle differences of the word spellings and meanings so as not to confuse them and to facilitate an effective and long-term memorization of the words. As a result, in the long run learners can develop acute perception of word with similar spellings or pronunciations while simultaneously enlarging their vocabulary.

In vocabulary acquisition, some learners have a large vocabulary and can identify a substantial number of words in reading, however, they can not apply the words to their daily communication or writing. To memorize words only with the guidance of formal schema can lead to such problems. Words mastered by this means usually become receptive vocabulary instead of turning into productive vocabulary by one step further. Schema theory explains this phenomenon in that learners still don not have the related content schema needed to activate the words, or they lack the the ability to activate the related content schema in such a way that they can not link the information that the words represent with relevant knowledge stored in the brain. The reason is that in the process of vocabulary acquisition, learner only pay attention to the memorization of the spelling, pronunciation and meaning of the words while ignoring the co-occurrence of different words and the construction of related content schema.

3.2 *Content schema and vocabulary acquisition*

The content schema of vocabulary refers to the background knowledge about the content, that is, collocation between words, pragmatical functions, the context of word application and relevant cultural background information. Constructing lexical content schema is the prerequisite of vocabulary acquisition. Only when learners understand the connotation and extension of vocabulary and grasp the co-occurrence of words, its pragmatic functions and the context of word application can they properly employ the words in daily communication and writing. To do this, learners have to lay emphasis on the context.

3.2.1 *Memorizing via multidimensional association based on context*

If the association is only limited to that between single words, and attention is only paid to semantic polymerization and combination and word pronunciation with the language context of word application completely ignored, it will surely result in the shrinking of word association scope and the breaking of association chains and sometimes misunderstanding of lexical meanings because the meaning of the same word may vary significantly in different contexts.

For learners who memorize via multidimensional association, it is essential not to limit association to that between single words. Association must be based on the context. Learners should try to associate words with phrases, sentences and even discourses, which is to increase comprehensible input and promotes vocabulary acquisition and memorization.

Repeated exposure and conscious attention to words in meaningful contexts can promote the in-depth acquisition of words and facilitate the transformation from receptive vocabulary to productive vocabulary. If learners learn words in specific context, their attention goes from single words to longer sentences and even discourses. Word combination based on semantic association enters the brain and gets stored in the memory as meaningful knots, which can motivate the learners' selective perception and active identification so as to facilitate the acquisition of the word connotation, style, affection and rhetorics. The visual image of context information activates the brain by different interrelated means which can stimulate the scene reconstruction to activate the existing schema from multiple knots. It is conducive to the internalization and absorption of the words and ensures a rapid extraction and a smooth and efficient output when needed.

3.2.2 *Memorizing via situation-based association*

In daily communication, people are placed in constantly changing scenes. Memorizing via situation-based word association helps the memorization of vocabulary in an extended way and is also of great advantage to the vocabulary output in communication. Memorizing via situation-based word association is association based on co-occurrence, which facilitates the reorganization of existing words to promote storage and memorization.

For example, when we learn the word "prescribe", we may think about the scene of seeing a doctor because of catching a cold. When we go to see a doctor because of catching a cold, the doctor will first make a <u>diagnosis</u>. To <u>diagnose</u>, the doctor have to ask about the <u>symptoms</u>: runny or <u>stuffed</u> nose, sore throat, <u>dizzy</u>, headache, high fever etc. Then the doctor considers it to be just a common cold, rather than an <u>epidemic</u> like bird flu. The doctor <u>ascribes</u> the illness to degradation of <u>immunity</u> and proposes to <u>subscribe</u> to some magazines about bodybuilding. At last he <u>prescribed</u> some medicine.

By imagining such a situation, we can easily remember words like prescribe, ascribe, subscribe; diagnose, symptoms, stuffed, dizzy etc. Therefore, situation-based word association not only contributes to the acquisition of co-existing words, but also facilitates listening comprehension and daily communication.

3.2.3 *Cultural background knowledge*

Cultural background knowledge is a vital component of content schema. The language of a nation is not just a simple combination of pronunciation, vocabulary and grammar. It also contains the colorful cultural connotation of the nation. Many words connotate a rich cultural background. Lack of understanding about the ethnic culture often leads to frustrations in foreign language learning. Therefore, learners should grasp a wide range of relevant cultural background knowledge, strengthen cultural literacy of the target language, pay attention to the differences between the mother tongue and the target language in terms of culture and language, master the connotation and extension of its vocabulary, and try to form thinking habits and schematic network of the target language.

For example, black tea in English is translated to "红茶" (red tea) in Chinese, which reflects cultural differences in different languages. Black tea in English is named after the color of the dry tea before it is brewed with water while red tea in Chinese is name after the color of the water after it is brewed.

4 CONCLUSIONS

Vocabulary acquisition is absolutely not just memorizing the vocabulary list mechanically. It is an active thinking process which involves language knowledge such as the pronunciation, spelling and meaning of the vocabulary, and at the same time is closely related to the cultural background that a person grasps. Learners should learn about as much cultural knowledge of the target language as possible and meanwhile appropriately employ a variety of methods such as memorizing via affix and root, memorizing via association and comparison with words of similar spelling or pronunciation, memorizing via multidimensional association based on context, memorizing via situation-based word association, so as to construct proper schema to facilitate the activation, identification, extracting, understanding and output of the vocabulary.

REFERENCES

Chen, Wanhui. 2008. Research on second language vocabulary acquisition of Chinese learners, Qingdao: Chinese Marine University Press.

Guo, Hongxia. 2011. Language typology analysis in language transfer in L2 vocabulary acquisition. *Foreign Language Research*. vol. 159: 114–117.

Kang, Lixin. 2011. Research on schema theory in China. *Henan Social Sciences*. vol. 19: 180–182.

Liu, Shaolong. 2001. Exploring word knowledge and its acquisition patterns:An experimental study of word meaning and affix. *Foreign Language Teaching and Research*. vol. 33: 436–441.

Yang, Dingxiu. 2007. The phenomena of first language transfer in second language vocabulary acquisition in view of connectionism. *Journal of Changsha University of Science & Technology*. vol. 22.: 123–126.

Computer, Intelligent Computing and Education Technology – Liu, Sung & Yao (Eds)
© 2014 Taylor & Francis Group, London, ISBN 978-1-138-02469-4

Education and teaching reform of building environment and energy application engineering

K.R. Ma, L. Jin & X. Wang

Hebei University of Science and Technology, Shijiazhuang, China

ABSTRACT: With the development of social economy, more attention paid to the energy conservation and emissions reduction, more people of Building environment and energy application engineering will be needed. But, at present, the education teaching of this specialty is not very perfect. This paper mainly discusses how to reform it and cultivate qualified students who work positive, have comprehensive knowledge and comprehensive ability and social acceptance.

Keywords: education and teaching reform; building environment and energy application engineering

1 INTRODUCTION OF BUILDING ENVIRONMENT AND ENERGY APPLICATION ENGINEERING

Building environment and energy application engineering can date back to Health engineering of Harbin institute of technology in 1950, and the five-year undergraduate major for gas and heating, ventilation engineering was formally established in 1952. In 1953, Tsinghua university, Harbin industrial university and Tongji university began to recruit four-year undergraduates. In the early, there are some university, commonly known as the old eight university, including Tsinghua university, Harbin industrial university, Tongji university, Tianjin university, Southeast university, Chongqing University, Xi'an University of Architecture and Technology and Hunan University. In order to meet the need for talents cultivation in the 21st century, State Education Commission based on the specialty divided of higher education, The Ministry of Education combine Heating, Gas Supply, Ventilating and Air Conditioning Engineering and Gas Transmission and Distribution Engineering to be Building Environment and Equipment Engineering, in the enrollment of new catalogue of new major, in 1998. The Ministry of Education also combine Building energy-saving technology and engineering, Building Facilities Smart Technology and Building Environment and Equipment Engineering to be Building Environment and Energy Application Engineering, in 2012.

2 DISTRIBUTION OF THE SPECIALTY IN OUR COUNTRY

Modern architecture emerged a large number of new building systems, also put forward more and more demanding for changing of internal equipment. So we need technical personnel who can adapt to the development of modern architecture. In China, there are some brokenness in environment and equipment of new buildings, many aspects are still in the phase of exploration and try. For example, there is the decrease of the quality of the air in some high-rise office buildings and magnificent buildings, because of the bad ventilation, and some problem of refrigeration and heating is also obvious. These problems must be solved by artisan and architect of Building Environment and Energy Application Engineering compared with each other, understanding and knowing the structure of building and user's needs, then make a feasible design, meanwhile analysis intelligent control, energy-saving of the system. As improve of people's demands for production and live environment, the number and of building equipment was needed more and more and property was high-quality. It must lead to increases for energy. Thus there are needs for improve of building environment quality. In this background, building energy efficiency, building control and regulation of environmental quality, and the sustainable development of architecture is becoming important tasks. According to the recruitment and employment of this specialty, it is still in a state of development. We have collected and analysis the university which open this specialty in the three years. Table 1 is a statistics about the number of university have bachelor and master or have doctor in 2010 to 2012. Figures 1~4 is the number of student and the percentage about bachelor, master and doctor. The number of the university recruits students statistics.

Though the colleges and universities which can recruit doctor is not obvious, it is increasing. And the number of recruitment is also increasing, but

Table 1. The number of the university which recruit students level statistics.

Year	Bachelor and master	Doctor
2010	64	13
2011	62	15
2012	61	16

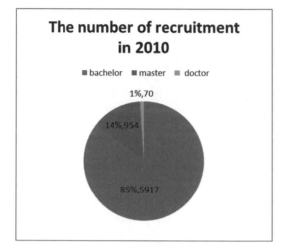

Figure 1. Number and percentage of recruitment in 2010.

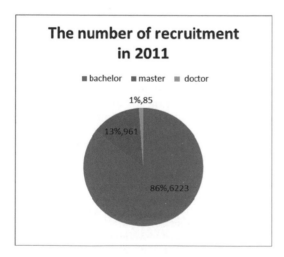

Figure 2. Number and percentage of recruitment in 2011.

amplification is gentle. And we also can see the percentage of bachelor is bigger than master and doctor. Most colleges and universities based on the applied talents training for the specialty.

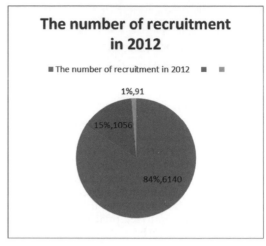

Figure 3. Number and percentage of recruitment in 2012.

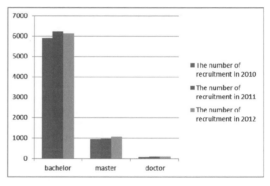

Figure 4. Number of recruitment in 2010~2014.

3 THE EMPLOYMENT SITUATION

Students' employment direction is mainly in the enterprise, institution of engineering and power sector, can be in design institute, construction engineering company, construction environment equipment installation engineering company, real estate development companies, property management company, gas company, town planning of government departments engaged in engineering design, intelligent management, equipment development and agent. They can also work in the relevant scientific research and other units engaged in research and teaching.

According to Table 2, we can see that the employment of graduates this specialty for three years in the construction, design, development, energy companies accounted for about 78% of the

Table 2. Situation of employment of graduates (take Hebei University of Science and Technology as an example).

	2011	2012	2013	Totally
Construction	14	36	44	94
Design	1	2	3	6
Graduate school	11	12	12	35
Development company	1	2	1	4
Energy company	0	2	3	5
Rest	5	8	9	22
Totally	32	62	72	166

total, attend graduate school accounted for about 22%. The employment of this specialty is very good, undergraduate employment of this specialty in Hebei University of Science and Technology generally can reach 99%. 2013 is the most difficult year of employment, college students' employment rate reached only 70%, but the specialty still has a high level of 98%. However, most of the graduates enter the construction company, only a small part of the graduates to work in design institute. And the design institute, especially large design institute, for recruiting postgraduate student is basic requirement.

4 PROFESSIONAL CURRICULUM AND REFORM TO MEET THE NEEDS OF THE SOCIETY

Influenced by Soviet higher education mode, our country's higher education has been relatively narrow. Objectively, professional education is an important and necessary part for higher education, playing an irreplaceable role in the national human resource development. With the development of education in recent years and the exploration by education workers, the construction industry in order to better evaluate and reflect the technical personnel's comprehensive ability, referring to the registration examination system of western countries, referring to the registration examination system of western countries, make the certification exam to personnel who have certain work experience began in 2005, such as registered equipment engineers and construction engineers, supervision engineers, certified cost engineers, etc. It examines what had been learned during the period of school, such professional basis courses, professional courses, and the practice ability used in work. There are also some test content we cannot meet in school, then it result in the exam come part with our education.

Registered engineer assessment includes project management, construction law and economic construction, and construction engineering economy and legal construction is important. Original course pay attention to professional education, the two courses was not open, but graduate need to understand the law and have commercially mind.

Thus in order to adapt the society, Adding these two courses construction law and economic construction is the trend of development.

5 PRACTICE REFORM TO IMPROVE THE TEACHING QUALITY

The practice for most college students mainly includes the curriculum design, practice, production practice, graduation practice, graduation design (paper). The production practice way mostly adopt centralized traditional teaching, students cannot come into contact with more professional knowledge, further field practical project is very few, most practice is cursory style teaching. There are some equipment and a large number of pipeline is known only at the scene, but students do not know the use of equipment and pipeline, composition of the system is also hided, cannot construct the whole system. Since most of the air-conditioning system was designed concealed works, it is difficult to see the internal installation and terminal equipment, so the practice just has poor quality. And can be seen from the statistical data, the number of recruitment in this specialty are very large every year, the school enrollment in some university may be more than 100 people. Due to a large number of students, companies have difficulties to accept large students in cognition practice. It cannot be synchronize with the teaching plan. The number of production site for practice is limited, so the teaching quality is not very ideal. What's more, most practice examination through practice report to judge the students' results, this old inspection way cannot have very good evaluation effect.

In this case, we let students and teachers go to Tsinghua University to attend their students' production practice. Internship content: air-conditioning system fault detection and diagnosis, energy consumption analysis and improvement, performance evaluation and improvement about the existing commercial building; air conditioning system and Building Automation (BAS) System for initial adjustment for the new commercial building etc. Task is from actual projects of entrust units, and the form of completing task is submitting test analysis report to entrust unit. By running the practice, can allowing students more comprehensive access to a system of structure, operation mode, and the details of the various parts in the system and functions, Exercise and training in all aspects of students' comprehensive ability such as the application of measurement technology ability, use basic and professional knowledge ability, analysis and problem-solving ability and expression ability, etc. Internship work can be part to some small groups. Assessment includes analyze and solve problems ability and level of internship report submitted in the practice. Ordinary colleges and universities can be 8 to 10 people into a team. College should vigorously promote this practice that let students direct access to the actual equipment of the production, engineering and HVAC system fault detection and diagnosis, analysis and improvement, performance evaluation and improvement of energy consumption. Then make students learn step by step, learning professional knowledge, and gradually to cultivate the students' overall HVAC engineering system concept. It needs the work of colleges and universities and collaboration and support from enterprise and public institution.

6 BUILD SYSTEM OF TUTOR

Mentoring system is a major feature of British universities, and now China is also implementing a number of colleges, schools, some students are assigned to teachers every year, but institutions do not develop a distinctive system, and sometimes nominal. Freshmen, into a new environment, facing a lot of difficulties and problems on the specialty more confused, mentoring try to assign mentors to students in the professional growth of mentor and guide this highly targeted, more closely linked. Set up a special section in the student handbook tells students mentor role and how to seek help mentor, develop a schedule, tutors and students meet regularly to discuss academic, professional and personal development as well as other related issues, to the sophomore, junior and high Fourth, students and instructors become more familiar with, the more freedom they met, the student will have greater problems proactively seek solutions to find mentors, and this is the most beneficial to help students to develop. Students' personal development tutor should guide students to establish a correct outlook on life and values, to guide students to develop good psychological quality and self-esteem, self-love, self-discipline, self-reliance of good character. Students' personal development tutor can use their own resources to provide more growth and success for the students to learn, ways to practice.

Students' personal development tutor to lead by example, words and deeds, with their rigorous academic attitude, excellent work ethic, strongly academic accomplishment should influence and infect students. Students' personal development instructor and students should do college career planning, help students choose their own direction of development, precise positioning, and moving in a predetermined direction.

7 INDIVIDUALIZED EDUCATION

On last term of fourth year university, students choose personalized education course according to employment orientation with a clear aim and positive attitude for the sake of improving self-accomplishment and reinforcing professional skill after graduation. In the fourth year in university, at the beginning of selecting course,in the light of graduate's employment orientation; design, operation, management, scientific research, teachers provide personalized education course including professional skill training, engineering training, foundation course strengthen, scientific innovation training, students could choose personalized according to their interest or actual needs, making personalized course by students own including choosing teachers they like to coach. The personalized course concluding could be various, such as reporting, dissertation, graph paper. What we do is just providing a bridge between university and actual employment, which makes it better for college students to adapt the environment of future job requirement.

8 CONCLUSION

The reform of professional education in Building environment and energy engineering must develop through one way which is good for talent cultivation in this new era. The aim of personalized is cultivating new era college students who works positively, own comprehensive knowledge, also be endorsed by the whole society. What important is making it easier for students to adapt the development and requirement from the society.

REFERENCES

Fu, X.Z. 2004. The study of platform course for undergraduate education in Building Environment and Services Engineering (BESE), *Journal of Architectural Education in Institutions of Higher Learning*: 58–59, 62. China.

Gu, T.Y. & Sun, Q. & Ao, Y.H. & Zhang, C.M. & Gao, W. 2011. Practice teaching reform of building environment and equipment engineering, *Journal of Shenyang Agricultural University (Social Sciences Edition) 13(2)*:212–215. China.

Guo, Z.N. 2005. Approaching Britain'S Universities—An Investigation Report on the Education of Science and Engineering in Britai Crotalaria in Africa and Madagascar. *Journal of Guangdong University of Technology (Social Science Editon) 5(2):1–5.China.*

He, X.L. 2010. Reflections on Higher Education about Science, *Education and Career No. 23:189–190*. China.

Yu, X.P. & Tong, X.W. & Wu, P. & Yin, L. 2005. On Talent—training Program for Major s of Construction Environment and Equipment Engineering, *Journal of Chongqing University of Science and Technology (Social Sciences Edition), No. 6:139–141*. China.

Zou, G.R. 2009. Thinking of Education reform on Building Environment and Equipment engineering. *Southwest University of Science and Technology Higher Education Research No. 1:72–74.China.*

Computer, Intelligent Computing and Education Technology – Liu, Sung & Yao (Eds)
© *2014 Taylor & Francis Group, London, ISBN 978-1-138-02469-4*

The talent mode's exploration and practice of IT female students

X.J. Yin & L.M. Sun
Shandong Women's University, Jinan, Shandong, China

ABSTRACT: With the development of information industry, the division presents modularity and standardization, many professional jobs are more suitable for women. Therefore, we should pay attention to female education, and do education reforming so that the major not only reflect the characteristics of professional education, but also highlight the characteristics of female education. This Essay analyzes the characteristics of the students' source of the computer major in women's university, and then describes the current IT industry's demanding trends for women talent, and finally explores the training mode.

Keywords: female education; IT; training mode; exploration and practice

"The Employment and Entrepreneurship The Survey Report of female college students' Employment and Entrepreneurship" contained in "Female Life Blue Book" shows that the difficult employment of female graduates is a social problem that cannot be avoided. What Causes Female Graduates Employed difficultly? The reasons are various, excluded from social reasons, systems reasons and physical reasons, one of the main reasons is that the professional choice is too concentrate: most of female students would like to choose humanities area and majors like normal, foreign languages and finance, etc. so that it leads to graduates of these areas are relative surplus, and then it increases the pressure on employment of female college students; another main reason is that our high education is lack of market-oriented and flexible school education mechanisms, and it has inaccurate and non-adaptive talent training position, without considering position characteristics, gender differences and training classification. So, in the current employment situation, how to fully consider the characteristics of female education and social needs in discipline planning, professional and curriculum settlement? The author's university enroll girls dominated, has been trying to explore how to combine market development needs, according to the characteristics of female education, try "female" teaching, divide "sex" training, and make the concrete plan for female college students according to orientation training objectives, settlement of curriculum system, and designing of the knowledge structure and ability structure to train female professionals that satisfies social demands.

1 PROPOSING PROBLEMS

There are a lot of researches are designed for computer science education in gender issues. A large number of fact and studies have shown that the gender differences exist in many aspects of male and female students in the major of computer. It leads to different position between male and female students. And the professional orientation between boys and girls are obviously different. Meanwhile, the research also found that girls in the major of computer are generally hardworking, the transcript is relatively stable, and academic situation is significantly better than boys[4]. There is no significant difference between girls and boys in part-time jobs and internship training. Girls also pay attention to cultivating their comprehensive quality, and usually participate in sports activities and other community activities positively. They are not inferior to boys in terms of imagination, practice ability and flexibility of knowledge. The research also pointed out that the idea that female students pay attention to the transcript not the ability, and pay attention to studying not the creativity so that the ability and the quality cannot satisfy the employers' demands is biased[8]. However, why the female college students in major of computer face the worse and worse employing problems in the labor market? And what obstacles are women into the IT industry?

In our country, the female education has a history of about 300 years. So far, there are more than 10 universities including sub schools in all of the country. The above mentioned research result and employing problems proposed a severe challenge to the colleges and universities special for female education. The major of computer is seen as a male major publicly, so how to individualize according to the students? Paying attention to and researching the education of computer major to female students has significant meaning to improve the existing mechanism of talent training and fully show the girls' potential.

2 THE DEVELOPMENT SITUATION OF FEMALE IT STUDENTS

The author follow-up survey almost 1000 female graduates majored in the computer of the class 2004-class 2008 in the university. The survey result shows that about 33% of female graduates in average choose to further study, 30% of the graduates choose some technical assistant work in IT industry, 30% of the graduates enter the industry of administration, accounting and finance area, and only 7% of the graduates choose to work in the computer technique major directly like the developing of programs. However, after working for 2 or 3 years, the number changed a lot. The half of the graduates choosing the further study still choose further study and get higher degree, and almost the half of the graduates who choose to work improve their professional ability and enter the computer professional position after getting the training from the computer training institute. These parts of graduates are mostly in the positions appropriate female like business website design and development, software testing, web design and production, technical support of systems, sales service of IT products, etc. Through the analysis of these data, and talking with graduates, we found that graduates improve their social experience, self-confidence and independence, etc. after couple years practice. They have the ability to compete with the male graduates. And we also found that the space of choosing position in the IT industry is big, and the salary and treatment is relatively high so that they chose IT jobs finally.

Seen from the media's reports analysis these years, the demand for computer professionals has been very strong in the aspect of occupation and industry demand situation. With the development of information industry, the division presents modularity and standardization, and many professional jobs more suitable for women. Female workers can show their characteristics and advantage of patience, meticulous, persistent and stable in the position of IT information service like software testing, hardware and software technical support services and software project evaluation. For example, in the field of information services, women tend to be more adept at communication, better able to establish collaborative relationships with customers. In addition, women in management coordination, planning implementation and control also has a unique advantage. Current many international famous IT companies have realized the advantages of female employees. For example, in the area of information service, female workers are always better at communication, and they can establish cooperate relationship better. In addition to, female possess their special advantages in management and coordination, planning and implementation and controlling. Currently many famous international IT companies have paid attention to the female workers' advantages. For example, Hewlett-Packard (HP) sponsored a specialized computer science courses for women in Furtwangen University in Germany. And about 1/3 of graduates employed just now are female in Accenture (Accenture). In companies such as IBM and SUN, they use the policies like flexible working time to attract and retain female staff. Obviously, female play more and more important role in the information industry, and the value and impact they created is gradually expanding.

3 HIGHLIGHT THE CHARACTERISTIC OF FEMALE EDUCATION IN TEACHING CONTENTS

In training practical female talents of the computer major, if the position of training purpose is reasonable is related to talent quality directly. After many years research and practice, the target of the professional training committed to female quality education starting from the needs of the community, according to the characteristics of female education and in order to facilitate women's employment as a starting point, and cultivate outstanding female computer professionals with noble character, elegance and good conduct and self-esteem, self-confidence, self-reliance, self-reliance spirit.

The teaching contents are settled according to professional training target, highlight the female characteristics, and settle IT service as the employment position. It is around the center of training students' IT service position application skills, and follow up the development of computer technique and the new trend of talent demands according to female training characteristics. It is appropriate to female development in courses and teaching contents, and besides Mastering the basic theory and professional knowledge of computer science, it explores their potentials from the following aspects according to female characteristics and advantages.

3.1 Highlight cultivation of female foreign language ability and communication ability

We opened the progressive outsourcing scenario language specialty courses. For girls' own characteristics, we played female advantage in terms of learning the language, and tapped the female potential in cultural understanding and communication. We combined with outsourcing companies' demands for language skills from entry-level employees, middle managers and senior managers at different stages, different occasions, different scenario, and we build foreign language learning environment when students entered a university firstly, and we settle the foreign scene for each position based on the progressive work, from simple to complex, from low-level jobs to management positions, not only asked students practice English listening and speaking in a different enterprise scenarios, but also to exercise students' corporation documents and e-mail reading and writing, face to face communication. Through the application of progressive outsourcing scenario foreign language special courses, we will cultivate female talents with outstanding foreign language communication skills that satisfy outsourcing companies' demands.

Our students will have strong expressing skills through good language training so that they will be proud of themselves and they will be more calm and confident for the professional studying.

3.2 Industry integration and pluralism development

For the students' characteristics, we implement the interdisciplinary and diverse training mode, respect students as the body of education, respect students' needs of personality development, and mobilize, guide and help students showing their learning initiative. With the increasing talent demands from female employment market for IT products and systems repair and maintenance of equipment, operational support of information systems and IT outsourcing services personnel, we opened related courses like enterprise management solutions SAP, finance, accounting, economical management in such a employment situation for that students are enable to master the financial business knowledge, to possess the ability of analysis, designing, development and operation and maintenance of enterprise information application and financial information management application system, and to be adapt work of theoretical research, technology research and development, application, maintenance and management in companies, banks, insurance and securities industries and all kinds of technology companies. We implement the job-based group work and process-oriented personnel training program, and cultivate female service talents with high quality innovative capabilities in the industry integration.

3.3 Make best use of the advantages and bypass the disadvantages, enhance the sense of self-confidence

Whether a person is self-confident is always the key of success. Our university specially opened courses like women's studies, the image of etiquette, floral art, photography, video, speech and eloquence, yoga, career guidance for girls' features. We focus on students' internal and external cultivation so that they will have a polite, civilized image, and enhance the civilization quality of students and enhance their sense of self-confidence. Bing, Xin has said "only a person with self-esteem can have a profound understanding of their value; only confident to be brave, having the courage to face life; only independent, you can obtain independent personality; only self-improvement, you can get ultimate success."

4 HIGHLIGHT FEMALE EDUCATIONAL CHARACTERISTICS IN TEACHING METHODS

Through the communication with female students major in computer in the women's colleges, the author learned that about 50% of them swap their major wishes; 30% of them are recommended by their parents, siblings or friends; 15% of them good at science achievement and would like to learn computer; and then about 5% of them do not know what major they like, and they proposed their wish with the curiosity to women's college, and they got it. From these figures, we see that only a small part of the girls major in the computer in women's college choose their major based on their own preferences, but most of them do not consider their own interests and neither the expertise and potential, and they just passively accept the reality. The reason that girls do not want to choose the computer as their major is that they see this major in one-side or they have false understanding to some extent. Many people think that the IT industry means software programming and hardware maintenance, however, in fact, the contents of the IT industry is far beyond the programming, and it can provide a lot of jobs to choose.

Faced to these problems of students, we mainly talked about the teaching methods in following aspects.

4.1 Hold the meeting of freshmen's parents

We will invite the freshmen's parents to have a meeting then the students enroll the college firstly. Compared to boys, girls are more cared by their parental, and the girls also more dependent on their parents than boys, so we will invite parents to participate in the meeting when freshmen enter the college on the first day for dispelling their ideas of be lack of confidence and low professional expectations so that freshmen can get reorganization and encouragement from their home in time. In the meeting, we will arrange a professional person in charge, counselor to explain professional development, training objectives, teaching process, student management to the parents individually, and answer questions raised by the parents one by one. In this way, we communicate with parents on the idea of the school, and dispel the worrying of the parents so that whenever students encounter difficulties and their thought changing occurs, they will get timely encouragement and help from parents when they want to talk to their parents, and it will helpful for stable students' thought.

4.2 Implement three ways management of counselor, class leader and professional person in charge

We focus on career planning and create talent solutions. We will invite professional psychological consultants to communicate with each student when the freshmen enroll the college so that counselor and class leader can know about each person's psychological state and do targeted counseling. According to the professional training objectives, the people in charge of students management and professional teachers make a piece of "students' growth chart" for each student, and they write down the students' growing up situation on paper with a quantitative form, and the counselor, class leader and professional instructor will guide and supervise students to complete in common. The girls are usually shy and unwilling to ask questions face to face, so every teacher, counselor, class leader and professional instructors should give the students their email address so that they are easy to send questions and get timely and accurate reply, thus it can timely elimination the girls' doubts and confusion. The use of email exchanges and Q & A can avoid tension and anxiety when they personally face the teacher. Especially junior girls are in the key period of studying changes so this kind of exchange and communication is especially important.

4.3 Strengthen the education of achievement motivation, offer more opportunities of cultivating self-confidence

Successful women in the scientific community largely depend on whether there is an environment that fosters self-confidence, such as Google's employment: in recruitment, there must be female interviewer, and in the employment standards, they must recruit certain proportion of female employees. For sexist, anyway excellent, they are not hired. This undoubtedly opened the green channel for the development of women in the IT field. Referring to many successful experiences in our country or abroad, each road in our campus is named after famous women in the world, such as the Qing, Zhao Rd, Qiao Zhi Rd, etc. and to inspire girls' pride and self-confidence, and enhance their power of self-realization.

In the professional learning process, self-confidence can be enhanced through a lot of participation and successful experience. Our school hold the Media Design Competition every year, and organize many teams to participate in various competitions of national, province and city, such as media design competition, Qilu Software Design Competition, mathematical modeling contest, "E leading to" Cup Network Business Design Competition, and network marketing ability show, etc. Through participation in these competitions, the girls get a lot of practical opportunities, and fully show their characteristics of good language skills, communication skills, thinking ability of image features; and it proved that they are easy to achieve better results. Pieces of good work and teams of valiant and heroic girls become a beautiful landscape while they received praise from other students, therefore, it inspired their sense of accomplishment and self-confidence, and fully demonstrate the advantages and development of female college students' unique strength, potential and advantage, and fatherly enhance female college students' ability of self-development and the sense of mission and responsibility that promote social development.

5 CONCLUSION

Traditionally people always think that women in the computer's ability to learn and develop are worse far than man, however, in fact, in recent years the proportion of women in the IT industry is higher, and men and women have their own advantages in different positions. This is because that the IT industry has entered a mature development application period from the pioneering stage, and also focus on the software, hardware, applications, services, integration not on the hardware like before. It means that it changed a lot in information technology professionals in the knowledge and skills on connotation and denotation in the society, and women's care and patience played a very important role in the IT industry at this time. Therefore, the research of the characteristics of female education and tapping their creative potential has far-reaching significance so that more women will choose and study computer science.

REFERENCES

Guo, Congbin, Zeng, Manchao, Ding, Xiaohao, The Gender Difference of Students' Education and Employment Situation major in Science in Colleges in China [J], Higher Education Research, 2007(11):89–101.

Jiang, Jiamei, The Exploration of Teaching Reform in Female Computer Education [J], Fujian Computer, China, 2005(9):147,152.

Li, Bangqiong, the Gender Differences of the Computer Education and Research Report [J], Research and Practice of University Healthcare Medicine, China, 2006(4):42–44.

Li, Yan, Xu, Ning, Yu, Miaomiao, The Survey Report of Gender differences in the impact of IT Graduate Employment [J], Computer Education, China, 2011(19):30–35.

Peng, Wenbo, Liu, Dianzhi, the Gender Differences Research of learning situation in High-tech majors, development goals and influencing factors [J], Southwest China Normal University Journal (Natural Science), 2005(1):159–162.

Song, yangqiu, Cultivation of Female Talents in Network Technique [J], China Adult Education, China, 2007(4):51–52.

Wan, Li, The Discussion of Female Students' "Teaching by Gender" major in Computer [J], Guangxi University Wuzhou Branch Journal, China, 2005(4):74–76.

Wu, Guiming, China Female Career Development Research [M], China Society Science Press, Beijing, China, 2004:288.

Zhang, Wenfen, Gao, Shouping, the Gender Differences Research of College Students' Transcript major in Computer [J], the Computer Education, China, 2011(12):12–14.

Zhao, Rongrong, The Research of Female College Students' studying and development situation major in Science [D]. The Educational Science Institute of Huazhong Technical University, Wuhan, China, 2007:4–5.

Computer, Intelligent Computing and Education Technology – Liu, Sung & Yao (Eds)
© 2014 Taylor & Francis Group, London, ISBN 978-1-138-02469-4

Study on teaching introspection in the process of chemistry teaching

Yuan-Yuan Wang
Kunming Command School of Public Security and Fire Fighting Army, Kunming, China

ABSTRACT: The teaching introspection is a good thought activity and relearning way. Author of the paper undertakes the course of chemistry including inorganic chemistry and organic chemistry in fire school. It is very necessary and important to proceed the teaching introspection. The author discusses the content and method of teaching introspection combining with the practice and experience of chemistry teaching to improve the teaching level and quality.

Keywords: chemistry teaching; teaching introspection; content; method

1   GENERAL INTRODUCTION

I remembered that I wanted to ask some questions usually about teaching and students when I graduated from the university to go to work as a chemistry teacher in fire school. I have no fundamental questions. Do I master all intension of teaching knowledge? Why do I feel that I have not the need to ask questions? Do I feel that I have abundant experience in teaching? The teaching work is very abundant and profound from the intension of teaching knowledge. It is a complicated and difficult process for the teaching form. Although a teacher of having abundant teaching experience still has many questions. Why do I have no question of teaching content and form? However, I can not put forward any question. This means that I do not discover question, and I am far from solving question. Therefore, I undertake the course of chemistry including inorganic chemistry and organic chemistry in fire school. It is very necessary and important to proceed the teaching introspection.

2   WHAT IS THE TEACHING INTROSPECTION?

The teaching introspection is a good thought activity and relearning way. It is a learning way to improve our own business and teaching practice as a chemistry teacher. We can enrich ourselves and improve teaching level by the thorough introspection of teaching practice. Every excellent teacher can not do without the teaching introspection in the process of growing up. The teaching introspection is teachers' catalyst of growing up and the important basis of teachers' development.

3   THE CONTENT OF TEACHING INTROSPECTION

3.1   *The introspection before attending class*

The introspection of teaching goal. Teaching goal is the starting goal and a home to return to. A teacher should all have the clear acquaintance with the teaching aim in the teaching process. Kunming fire command school is the only school of training the commander of fire army. The subject is set up on the basis of the function need of fire prevention, fire fighting and rescue. Face the severe terrain of fire disaster and dangerous chemical material, students must store chemical knowledge in order to reach the demand of fire prevention, fire fighting and disposing of dangerous chemical material. According to our syllabus blongs to fire class group. Chemistry can be divided into inorganic chemistry and organic chemistry. They are all required course and the total class hours is one hundred and twenty. They are basis subject of fire combustion science, fire prevention of dangerous chemical materials, fire prevention of production technology and rescue. Chemistry and the follow-up professional course accounted for 11.4% of the total teaching hours.

This will eastablish the solid basis of holding a post. Many aspects of fire are related to chemistry tightly. If the students of fire school master chemical knowledge well, they will eastablish the stable basis for fire prevention, fire fighting and rescue.

The introspection of teaching object. Only a chemistry teacher must first master students' original perceiving structure and teaching accords with students' perceiving ability to let students attain better development on the original basis. The students' basis of our school is irregular, Most of students learn arts before joining the army. So their

Table 1. Chemical fire class group of classes schedule.

Subject	Class hours
Inorganic chemistry	Sixty
Organic chemistry	Sixty
Fire combustion science	Sixty
Fire prevention of dangerous chemical materials	Forty
Fire prevention of production technology	Seventy
Rescue	Eighty

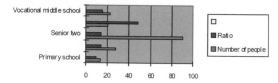

Figure 1. Educational condition statistics.

chemistry basis is very weak and they generally feel difficult after learning chemistry in fire school. In order to fully grasp the actual degree of the students and the cultural foundation, we investigate one hundred and forty-two students of new enrollment in 2007. On the whole, the students' cultural foundation is very bad and learning ability is not strong.

The introspection of teaching content. The introspection of teaching content requires that a teacher can not let teaching material shoehorn students. As a chemistry teacher in fire school, he will introspect the profoundity and breadth of teaching content combining with the reality of training fire commander and the students. At first, a chemistry teacher should introspect the profoundity of teaching content. According to the reality of students in fire school, when the chemistry teacher teaches new chemistry knowledge, he not only reviews the related basis content, but also emphasizes the chemistry content contacting with the fire work. The chemistry teacher teaches the knowledge combining with the successful cases, which are disposing of by applying the chemistry knowledge in fire fighting army. This can not only improve the effect of the chemistry teaching, but also strengthen students' ability to apply the knowledge to fire prevention, fire fighting and rescue. Secondly, the chemistry teacher should introspect the breadth of teaching content. In the process of chemistry teaching, the chemistry teacher replenishes the fire case to meet the need of students' development. For example, when the teacher teaches the character of chlorine, he may combine with the chlorine leakage case of Chongqing chemical plant on

April 16, 2004. By means of the case, the teacher can teach the harm and degassing method of chlorine. So the theory combines with the reality. The students can master the harm and the measure of degassing. The reaction is:

$$Cl_2 + H_2O \rightarrow HCl + HClO;$$

$$HCl + Ca(OH)_2 \rightarrow CaCl_2 + H_2O;$$

$$HClO + Ca(OH)_2 \rightarrow Ca(ClO)_2 + H_2O$$

The introspection of teaching means. The chemistry teacher designs the teaching means on the basis of introspecting the past experience, lesson goal and content. This can gradually train teachers' habit of introspection and benefit from the teaching process, so the teaching practice will be optimized. In the chemistry teaching process of ten years in fire school, I think that the means of case teaching is very good. It is a heuristic teaching method to enhance the ability of solving the practical fire work. This method applies the true successful case of fire fighting army to guide students participate actively and address discussion of fir case. In the process of discussion, the chemistry teacher participates with students. At last they obtain the conclusion together. This method unifies knowledge and ability. It has much benefit to train the ability to innovate and solve the problems.

3.2 Introspection of the class

Introspection of the class can train the ability for a chemistry teacher to solve the teaching problems. It also requires that the chemistry teacher has the ability to drive the class.

Introspection of the success. Introspect the practice of causing good effect in the class. Introspect some splendid answer and dispute between the teacher and students. Introspect the experience of using the teaching method and the measure of teaching reform. These introspection has the function of teaching innovation and perfection constantly. The chemistry teacher can refer the introspection after the chemistry teaching.

Introspection of the fault. It is an emphasis to survey the fault of the class, then the chemistry teacher find the method to solve the fault. For example, whether the chemistry teacher gives the students enough space to think out when he creates problems situation, whether the chemistry teacher focuses on the students' development of emotion and attitude, and how the students' learning interest is etc. Then the chemistry teacher reviews and clears up the introspection. In addition, he introspects, explores and analyzes profoundly.

At the same time, he can find the method of solving problems and the new teaching thinking, then he writes out the innovation method and the new scheme of redesigning.

Introspection of the students' opinion. Some students' unique opinion can inspire companion and has good effect to open up students' thinking. For example, students's plendid answer and innovation is building on students' unique view and feeling. These are abundant and valuable course resource, the chemistry teacher may use the resource as the valuable teaching information.

Introspection of the students' problems and advice. Students have difficulty and problems in the learning process. Among the problems, some problems are unique, irregular and innovative. Perhaps the chemistry teacher can not the problems right now, he should record the problems and introspection timely to improve chemistry teaching. The purpose of doing so can not only enrich the teaching thinking and experience but also improve the scientific research level. At the same time, the teacher should record and introspect the teaching advice of students.

3.3 *Introspection after finishing class*

Introspection after finishing class is a kind of process of recall, comparison and estimate for a chemistry teacher. The teaching ability of the chemistry teacher can be affected observably by means of thinking out reasoningly, the teaching opinion, the teaching action, the students' expression, the success and fault of teaching.

The chemistry teacher can write introspection diary for later teaching project. For example, there is a lightspot link of being pleasantly surprised in teaching process. What is the reason of lightspot? Some teaching link does not finish in accordance with the plan, why? If the chemistry teacher teaches the same content again, how does the teaching project alter?

4 THE METHOD OF TEACHING INTROSPECTION

4.1 *The method of asking oneself*

It is a kind of method for a chemistry teacher to ask a series of questions after observing, monitoring, adjusting, evaluating oneself. It can enhance the ability of introspecting oneself.

This kind of method applies to the whole process of teaching. For example, when the chemistry teacher design the teaching project, he may ask himself how to design the teaching project for students to understand easily and which situation will appear when students receive new knowledge. When preparing lessons, through the chemistry teacher prepare all kinds of different learning project, there are still some plan in the process of practical teaching, for example, students can not answer the questions in the regulation time and there is comprehension divergence between the teacher and students etc. At this time, the chemistry teacher should think deeply why this kind of question appears and how to adjust to the teaching plan etc. This can insure that the operation of the teaching process along the best track. After finishing class, the chemistry teacher may ask himself whether my teaching is effective and which aspect can be improved ulteriorly, etc.

4.2 *The method of teaching diagnosis*

Teaching is a regretful art. The chemistry teacher should excavate all kinds of problems about teaching idea from the teaching problems. The chemistry teacher may collect all kinds of teaching medical record and then classify to find out the questions. By means of analyzing the problems, the chemistry teacher discusses all kinds of teaching opinion to affect teaching effect, at least he puts forward the method to solve problems.

4.3 *The method of communication*

The communication among teachers is very good for the development of group and individual, for example, the chemistry teacher may put forward the doubtful the doubtful point and puzzled point, then he asks other chemistry teachers to analyze, diagnose, introspect and put forward the method of solving problems. This can reach the purpose of inspiring each other, growing up together. The chemistry teacher take part in public class, model lesson or narrate the practice and experience of teaching. The teachers can find problems and exchange the teaching experience.

4.4 *The method of view and emulate to contrast*

A chemistry teacher should listen to other teachers in class constantly and exchange with them. In the process, the chemistry teacher should analyze how other teachers organize the teaching and why they organize the teaching like this. The chemistry teacher should think if I teach the same lesson, how I will organize it, I attain what the inspiration is from other teachers and I will how to deal with if I teach the same lesson. By means of this kind of introspection, the chemistry teacher attains inspiration and improve his teaching quality. This way can often find problems easily and produce new idea in the process of learning.

4.5 The method of summary

After the teaching task finishes one day, a chemistry teacher should think out whether the teaching content accords with the students' age character and cognition law, whether the overall design is appropriate, whether the teaching link is proper, whether the students' ability of thought and starting work is trained effectively, whether the important and difficult point sticks out, which teaching link needs to be modulated and improved, whether the students' ability is mobilized etc. The teacher thinks out and records chronically, he will attain much precious teaching wealth. It is the specific expression and a good form for the chemistry to reflect himself. What' more, it is good to improve teaching quality, promote teaching content roundly and teaching design more reasonably. It is also good to strengethen the teaching pertinence and find problems timely. It is still good to accumulate teaching experience and enhance teaching level.

4.6 The introspection of feedback information

A chemistry teacher think the reason that the students grasp the knowledge well or badly from students' school assignment and examination. The chemistry teacher recalls the teaching design and every link in the teaching process seriously

REFERENCES

[1] Jiatai, Zhu. 2002. The artistic theory of chemistry teaching. Nanning: Guangxi education Press.
[2] Youli, Zhao 2005. Building favourable teaching atmosphere in classroom. The Form of contomparary education. (6):59–60.
[3] Jinzhou, Zheng. 2000. The general theory of education. Shanghai: East China normal university press.
[4] Lan, Ye, etc. 2001. The new discussion of teachers role and development. Beijing: Education science press.
[5] Hua, Zhang. 2000. The curriculum and teaching theory. Shanghai: education press.

Computer, Intelligent Computing and Education Technology – Liu, Sung & Yao (Eds)
© 2014 Taylor & Francis Group, London, ISBN 978-1-138-02469-4

A preliminary study on the teaching reform of budgetary estimate course at higher education institutions based on the Glodon Software

Zhu-Ling Yan
School of Architecture of Yan'an University, Yan'an, Shan'xi, China

ABSTRACT: This paper introduces the importance of the budgetary estimate courses of the civil engineering in higher education institutions and the lagging situation of this course in these institutions at present. By investigating and analyzing the application universality of Glodon Budgetary Software in the real construction budgets, this paper suggests adjusting the time and period in the syllabus of the civil engineering budgetary estimate courses and introduces Glodon Budgetary Software into the classes of higher education institutions. It will be taught as a budgetary estimate course for civil engineering, which will lay certain foundations for the future work of the students.

Keywords: Glodon Software; budgetary estimate course; teaching reform

1 INTRODUCTION

The civil engineering budgetary estimate, as an important practical professional course for civil engineering and project management majors, is to cultivate students to grasp the basic knowledge of quota and bill of quantities and teach them to correctly draw up the project costs documents such as construction budgetary estimate, working plan estimate, bill of quantities, price control of the project bidding, project bidding price and project settlement by using quota and the rules for the bill of quantities, which will lay a sound professional foundation for the budgetary estimate work in civil engineering.

2 THE APPLICATION AND CURRENT SITUATION OF THE CIVIL ENGINEERING BUDGETARY ESTIMATE COURSES

At present, China is in the period of basic construction with all the basic constructions in every region, which needs a large quantity of the professional technicians in civil engineering and project management. Because the students with the major of civil engineering, project management and construction cost have a bright career prospect, they will work as the technicians in the front line in construction units and organizations, real estate companies as well as work as a cost estimator in some cost consultancy companies. As we all know, any project cannot do without cost management, so the budget specialists are needed everywhere: investment intent of the construction units, investment estimation in the stage of feasibility study, budgetary estimate in the stage of initial design, the working plan estimation in the stage of drawing design, the bidding price control, construction budget, project settlement in every stage of the project bidding. Sometimes, the demand for the budget specialists is more than technicians, and the budget specialists must be strong in skills, for the level of budget specialists will influence the accuracy and precision, which will have a bearing on the investment benefits, the project benefits of the construction units and social as well as economic benefits of the capital construction projects. It can be seen that the content of the budgetary estimate course in higher education courses can be applied in reality for most of the times, so the essence of the course should be grasped. Therefore, we hope that enough attention must be given to the engineering budgetary estimate course in the training plan of the students majoring in civil engineering and project management in higher education institutions; on the preconditions of grasping some basic knowledge of estimation, we should extend the theories in these budgetary courses in engineering practices; students should have more trainings in the real engineering drawings with the basic theories of the construction cost, laying a sound and solid foundation for the future work.

However, our university and many other universities do not pay much attention on the budgetary courses, especially the civil engineering major, which still uses the past teaching syllabus—with mechanics and structure courses as the main courses and the budgetary estimate course is assigned as the optional courses with less teaching time—so the budgetary estimate course seems to be unimportant, so students are not keen on this course. These students will mostly work in the constructions units after graduation and will face the budgetary work of the construction materials of the technicians as well as the all kinds of budgetary work of the budgeters, and these students will not be cope with all of these things.

3 THE TYPE OF BUDGETARY SOFTWARE AND THE APPLICATION SITUATION OF GLODON BUDGETARY SOFTWARE IN REAL PROJECT

The investigation shows that the cost work in the early stage is completed by manual calculation and calculators; and currently, the construction cost in reality is done by all kinds of budgetary software and only a few of them are done by manual calculation.

The common budgetary software are many in types and from the perspective of engineering calculation, it mainly includes: construction calculation software, construction pricing software, construction auditing software and construction settlement software; from the perspective of professional usage, it contains civil engineering software and installing software; from the perspective of software development units, the common software mainly include Glodon Software, Tsinghua Swear Software, SJMS Software, PKPM Budget software, Jinjian Software, among which the most applied in the real engineering are Glodon Software in northern area and Tsinghua Swear Software in southern area and both of them are introduced into the higher education institutions. Every year, there is a successful budgetary software modeling contest for college students and almost every higher education institution participates in it. Therefore, the event of budgetary software modeling contest do a great publicity for Glodon Software and Tsinghua Swear Software, laying certain foundation for the further promotion of these software.

In northern region, Glodon Software takes the major market of the budgetary software, and nearly all the units associated with the construction cost use Glodon Software, which has a large relation with the early research and development of Glodon Software. It has an early start with detailed, rigorous and humane, which is easy to use. There are altogether 6 modules in the construction cost of Glodon Software, which mainly includes Glodon Graphics Software, Glodon Sampling Software of Reinforcing Steel Bar, Glodon Audit Software, Glodon Amount Software and Glodon Installing Software and these are all permeated in every field. Once mentioning the cost construction, it definitely cannot do without Glodon Software. It is very convenient: first modeling and then valuation. Of course, the Glodon Software is still developing, such as the installed calculation software just begins to be applied in the real project during which a lot of problems cropped up. So we hope the Glodon Company can further improve that in the future.

4 THE TEACHING REFORM OF INTRODUCING THE BUDGETARY ESTIMATE COURSE IN HIGHER EDUCATION INSTITUTIONS BASED ON GLODON BUDGETARY SOFTWARE

It can be seen from the research and investigation analysis that the budgetary estimate work are applied more in real projects: Glodon Software has become the main tool of construction budget, but the curriculum-setting of budgetary estimate course in higher education institutions is not in well place. As a result, the course teaching lags behind the real construction, which leads the students only know the theory but cannot carry it out in practice. Therefore, the reform of the budgetary estimate courses of higher education institutions are suggested here and the ideas are as follows:

1. Revising the training plan and adjusting the time of the course are suggested. At present, the budgetary estimate course in our university still uses the old syllabus and the total teaching hours include: 18 hours for theory, 18 hours for practices and 6 hours for experiments. The 18 hours for theory mainly introduce the basic concepts of budget, the basic knowledge of quota and the application of quantity calculation rules on the textbooks; 18 hours for practices mainly include the real training of the engineering practice in order to learn the quota rules and the standard for quantities detailed list as well as working out the construction budget for the unit which works out the real construction drawing; 6 hours is for learning the experiment software, which can only let students know the pricing software but there is no time arranged for learning calculation course. Compared with the application of budgetary software in real construction, the cultivation of budgetary software application software in higher education institution is a little bit weak. Therefore, after investigating the real situation of construction budget and the current syllabus of the budgetary estimate course in every university, the author suggests extending the time of budgetary estimate course in our university: increasing the teaching time

of budgetary software experiment course on the basis of the 42 teaching hours, and making it a course with 60 teaching hours: 18 hours for theory teaching, 18 hours for engineering cases training and 24 hours for budgetary software experiments. And the 24 hours are mainly used to teach the calculation software and pricing software, which will teach students real operation ability and can do the budgetary work wherever they are in the future work.

2. Highlighting the real engineering training and strengthening the software teaching in implementing the course. According to the current syllabus, students will only learn the theory but are weak in practice. Therefore, another main work in this reform is to adjust the budgetary estimate teaching from the one with theory as the major content to the one making students grasp the knowledge of working out the budgetary estimate documents for real construction engineering case on the basis of understanding the theories as well as learn to use the budgetary software to model calculation and pricing. It is known from the above information that Glodon Budgetary Software is mainly applied in the real projects in northern area. Therefore, the author suggests introducing the Glodon Budgetary Software to the civil engineering budgetary estimate teaching in our university: make the graphics calculation modules, sampling of reinforcing steel bar module and pricing software of Glodon Budgetary Software as the experiment course, as well as extend and expand the teaching content of civil engineering budgetary estimate course.

3. Multi-step and multi-stage teaching process. On the basis of enlarging and enhancing the real training and software teaching, we should make students grasp the skills for budgetary estimate working plans as well as conduct the teaching management system. Organizing the teaching process step by step, and it can be divided into 3 stages: the first stage is to teach the budgetary estimate course for 18 hours, through which students can grasp the basic concepts, theories and how to work out the budgetary documents;

the second stage is for engineering training, which asks students to use the engineering case drawings, budgetary quota, the quantities detailed list and other engineering budgetary estimate documents as well as calculate by themselves and learn to manual calculation of the project quantities, work out lists and calculate the construction cost of a real engineering case drawing for certain construction unit under the guidance of teachers. This link will let students grasp the working details of project budgetary estimate documents; the third stage is for Glodon Software learning and change the manual calculation of the construction cost into the Glodon Software modeling to calculate the price; the fourth stage is to compare the results of manual calculation of the construction cost and the results of the construction cost calculated by software, analyze the differences of two calculations and find out the reasons for differences and correct them.

5 CONCLUSIONS

It can be seen from the above content that the current development requirements of real situation for engineering needs to adjust the syllabus of civil engineering budgetary estimate course, extend the teaching contents of this course and integrate it with practice, so it is suggested setting up the Goldon Budgetary Software as an experiment course. Only in this way can fully embody the civil engineering budgetary estimate course, reaching the goal of imparting knowledge and educating people, which will let students learn real and practical knowledge and find a good job.

REFERENCES

[1] Shen Xianghua. Construction engineering budget [M]. Wuhan University of Technology Press, 2009.7.
[2] Yang Huiyun, Gao Yuechun. Civil engineering budget [M]. Science Press, 2009, 9.

Computer, Intelligent Computing and Education Technology – Liu, Sung & Yao (Eds)
© *2014 Taylor & Francis Group, London, ISBN 978-1-138-02469-4*

Decision analysis on personal capital investment of college students

Hong-Bo Li
School of Management, Wuhan University of Technology, China

ABSTRACT: With the deepening reform of higher education, the current our country university graduates has close to 7 million people, present a higher education personal investment boom, then form of university students' employment is very serious. In order to guide students to rational investment, this article bases on the theory of human capital investment to analysis the higher education investment cost, yield, payback period and the investment risk, which can be to benefit individuals to make rational investment decisions.

Keywords: college students; human capital; personal investment; decision analysis

1 INTRODUCTION

In 2012, the number of university graduates in China has nearly 7,000,000, so the situation of employment is very severe. However, there are many not be admitted to the University of the people, is to try to accept higher education or self-study mode through the network, going to a certain degree of human capital investment. How could they do it? In addition to the knowledge economy era and social development's demand for high-level talents, job market information asymmetry, entrepreneurship channels is still incomplete, industrial structure adjustment of external causes such as instability of employment environment, knowledge can change fate and intrinsic motivation of parents also plays a key role. "Education is not only consumer behavior, on the contrary, people consciously spending and social and private education is to obtain such a productive accumulation: this accumulation contained in the human body, can provide a variety of services in the future, these services including future revenue, operating capacity will be their future family activities, and to meet the consumption capacity. Therefore, the quality of the population regarded as investment in education human capital investment".[1] According to the theory of human capital investment, education investment rewarding people for education and other human capital investment, improve the configuration and production ability, the ability to optimize the allocation of resources, but also can bring greater production. Therefore, the more educated people, the more enterprise is willing to pay higher wages for them. This phenomenon can be explained by age income curve: an education can improve one individual production skills. With

increasing output and income increasing, income is his investment income. increased education, age, income curve is higher, and vice versa; illiteracy, although at a very early age to earn income, but the starting salary is low levels of education, with the increasing income, to obtain the initial age will continue to increase.

2 THE BASIC FOUNDATION OF HIGHER EDUCATION PERSONAL INVESTMENT DECISION ANALYSIS

Individual (family) is the main purpose of the education investment in order to obtain better employment opportunities, make the future more income such as salary, for individuals, in determining the goal of higher education investment, right after the investment direction of professional (e.g., school, etc.), should determine the optimal investment scheme. Individuals, therefore, higher education investment decisions need to consider to pay the cost, time, jobs and future earnings, on balance, decide whether to continue to go to school or employment immediately. This paper uses cost-benefit, internal rate of return and payback period of investment to analyze the rationality of personal education investment decisions. Including personal internal rate of return of higher education is the core of the higher education investment decision theory, and has become the theoretical basis of higher education scientific decisions of investors. In the economics of higher education, personal internal rate of return is cost–benefit method application in the field of higher education, is to a person's future by increase the receiving higher education net economic compensation of a kind of measure, so need to determine the costs and benefits is determined based on the internal rate of return.

2.1 Higher education individual present and present value analysis

Investment in higher education, compared with the control cost and expected return, is the theoretical foundation of research on individual internal rate of return. Therefore, if the direct cost to a level of education years t to C^1_t, especially that of higher education will be required to pay tuition fees, books, fees, accommodation; indirect cost was C^2_t, mainly refers to give up employment income due to receive higher education; education is n; the discount rate is r; accept total the cost of higher education personal value:

$$C = \sum_{t=1}^{n} (C_1^t + C_2^t)/(1+r)^t$$

But the higher education's present value of total revenue is expected discounted return results, assuming a level of education caused by the T education return is B^T, the discount rate is R, the proceeds of life or work experience as m, received higher education personal value total return:

$$B = \sum_{t=1}^{m} B^t /(1+r)^t$$

It should be pointed out that, in the calculation of B^T value, total income of B^T and is not a personal T years, but due to a personal level education and increase the after-tax income. The BT = higher education personal after-tax net income − high school education personal after-tax net income.

2.2 Higher education individual internal rate of return analysis

When the total cost of higher education personal value is equal to the present value of the total higher education personal income, net present value is zero, the break-even point can find investment, the higher education individual internal rate of return. The calculation formula is as follows:

$$\sum_{t=1}^{n} (C_1^t + C_2^t)/(1+r)^t = \sum_{t=1}^{m} B^t/(1+r)^t$$

On the type of personal internal rate of return is *IRR* available mathematical iterative method in order to on the computer. In the empirical analysis, our country had many scholars and institutions were measured on the rate of return to higher education, such as the use of the data of 2012 Peking University Scholars, high school, technical secondary school, college is calculated and big education at all levels of internal rate of return is respectively 5.47%, 6.91%, 4.48% and 5.23%. And considering the influence of transfer payment to income as well as the alpha coefficient of different (income increases due to the education), to get higher education internal rate of return as shown in Table 1.[4]

This table can be seen that the town of personal education income rate in China has not big difference compare to the international level. The rate of return to higher education is greater than the benefit of elementary education rate, the individual rate of return to education is increasing, effect of education on income growth mainly through the ways of employment choice to realize. But individuals invest in higher education should also be considered, the individual in the professional, school and so on the choice of different, because the social demand for talents, yields are not exactly the same. In addition, the internal rate of return as a relative evaluation index, the need to refer to the benchmark rate of return for comparative analysis.

2.3 Higher education personal investment payback period analysis

Payback period (*PBP*) to investment recovery rate as a standard investment scheme choice, because investment is a risk that, the longer the time, the greater the risk, in this sense, the payback period can be as a risk measurement tool, namely, the faster the investment recovery, the possibility of losses. Although it does not consider the payback period of future earnings, but for those who look

Table 1. China's higher education individual internal rate %.

Level	University	College	Yields	University	Undergraduate	Course
Alpha	0.6	0.8	1.0	0.6	0.8	1.0
Income	3.93	5.49	6.86	4.00	5.49	6.78
Adjustment	4.66	6.24	7.62	4.53	6.01	7.30

forward to get their money back, the risk is bigger. However, lacks the ability to predict individual investment is still has a certain value, such as for a graduate program or at one's own expenses study abroad in the form of higher education personal investment. Usually in the case of considering the time value of money, the dynamic payback period of investment is investment scheme of net cash flow accumulative total of zero time, its computation formula is:

$$PBP = m - 1 + \left| \sum_{t=0}^{m-1} F_t (1+i)^{-t} \right| / F_m (1+i)^{-m}.$$

where F is the cumulative net cash flow, I is the market interest rate, M is the cumulative net present value of cash flow began to appear in the year. Calculation of the investment recovery period is the most significance is that it can influence the investor's enthusiasm, difference at every stage of education expenses are relatively stable under various stages of education, income gap is big, the education investment recovery period is shorter, at this time will be more and more people pursuing higher education investment. In Wuhan area as an example, according to the survey, the Wuhan area high school graduates (including students) the average monthly wage of about 2,200 yuan, medical, pension and other benefits of about 500 yuan, assume that the residual deposits of about 7000 yuan, the cultivation of bachelor's degree graduates the opportunity cost is 28,000 yuan. For the simple calculation, the direct cost of personal investment in higher education tuition fees, living expenses, only consider the book fee and accommodation fee of about 12,000 yuan, the parents of the total four years of investment cost of 48,000 yuan for the children to university. The family training of a student's total investment is about 76,000 yuan. At present, the average monthly income of Wuhan University Graduates is close to 2000 yuan. Assume that the residual deposit of 10,000 yuan, with a long-term savings interest rate of 2.25%, according to $(1+i)^{-n}$ NPV coefficient through the calculation of discount coefficient, investment recovery period is calculated by the total investment cost of the University for 9 years. As shown in Table 2.

Considering the young man married, house, car and other important expenditure, investment recovery period will be longer, can accept higher education increased the amount of income is the key factor to the recovery of funds. Because the country is at present increasing college admission ratio, higher education in China is popular from elite education. In the enormous competition, employment situation is increasingly grim. In addition,

Table 2. Payback period calculation table (unit: yuan).

Fixed number of year	In each of the cash flow	The discount factor	Discounted value	The cumulative value
0	−76000	1	−76000	−76000
1	10000	0.9780	9780	−66220
2	10000	0.9565	9565	−56655
3	10000	0.9354	9354	−47301
4	10000	0.9148	9148	−38153
5	10000	0.8947	8947	−29206
6	10000	0.8750	8750	−20456
7	10000	0.8558	8558	−11898
8	10000	0.8369	8369	−3529
9	10000	0.8185	8185	4629

the demand for different levels of personnel of the school, professional, educational form choice, social development and some other uncertain factors and other reasons, makes the human capital investment risk. Therefore, high investment spending in a greater risk of some personal investment in higher education field, the need for careful analysis, prudent decision-making.

3 HIGHER EDUCATION PERSONAL INVESTMENT RISK ANALYSES

To analyze the human capital investment decision, must consider the uncertain factors, so the risk is that we must study the. Usually, according to evade the risk degree, can be divided into system risk and non-system risk. Systemic risk refers to the possibility of some factors to the market all of personal investment in higher education will bring losses, such as market risk, employment risk, technology risk and environment risk; non-systematic risk, that certain factors result in the loss of a single higher education investment. Among them, the non-system risk because of the subjective factors of the investment or some other accidental factors, difficult to measure accurately; and for systematic risk can be expected rate of return to the evaluation, and through the survey and empirical analysis to adjust the individual investment decision, in order to optimize the implementation risk. Here we only with the growth rate of GDP to define the market risk, system risk that is the measure of personal investment in higher education. According to the economic development of our country national condition, the growth rate of more than 10% was defined as the boom, the following general, negative growth for depression. According to xinhuanet.com provides Chinese 1960–2012

Table 3. Expected yield calculation table.

State of the economy	Probability (P_i)	The rate of return (R_i)	The product
Boom	0.44	5.56%	2.4%
In general	0.44	5%	2.2%
Depression	0.12	3.2%	0.4%
Σ	1	Σ	5%

growth rate of GDP, statistics show that the economic development of the boom years of 24, 0.44 probability; economic development general the year 24, the probability is 0.44; the recession year of 6, 0.12 probability. Using the year 1961 (the growth rate −27.3%), 1990 (growth rate 3.8%) and 2007 (growth rate −10.7%) as the representative of depression, generalcondition and boom condition, survey data and provide to the Ministry of labor and social security of the graduates monthly salary: 1961, 1990 and 2007 undergraduate month median wage is 42.5 yuan respectively, 800 yuan and 2317 yuan; high school students (including secondary, vocational technical schools) were 30.5 yuan, 600 yuan and 1486 yuan. Based on neglecting the subjective efforts and the assumption of undergraduates and high school students after graduation return synchronous growth, can calculate the statistics of three year undergraduate students to high school students yields were 3.2%, 5% and 5.56%. The expected rate of return formula:

$$\overline{R} = \sum_{i=1}^{3} (P_i)(R_i)$$

You can calculate the our country higher education individual investment expected rate of return is 5%. As shown in Table 3.

To calculate the expected rate of return, and then uses standard deviation to measure the degree of dispersion of individual expected rate of return, the individual expected rate of return is greater standard deviation, yields dispersion degree bigger; probability distribution curve is slow, personal investment in higher education more relevant risk. Based on the standard deviation calculation formula:

$$\sigma = \sqrt{\sum_{i=1}^{n} \left(R_i - \overline{R} \right)^2 (P_i)}$$

Substitution Table 3 income data, calculate the $\sigma = 0.728\%$, 3 $\sigma = 2.184\%$ of personal investment in higher education, so the expected rate of return will be 66.7% probability in 5% 0.728%, will have 99.8% probability in 5% 2.184%.

4 CONCLUSIONS

Under the conditions of market economy, risk investment can increase income also can reduce the revenue, and even lead to loss. After statistical analysis to see, at present in domestic higher education individual investment rate of return is still positive, but the need in decision-making when compared with other feasibility investment income, in order to make the best decision. Especially at present in our country is the adjustment of industrial structure, many of the traditional production existed in the field of structural unemployment, which is the biggest risk for individual investment in higher education. Therefore, how to forecast the trend of national economic, in return, recovery period based on the evaluation method, the quantification of risk factors, the correct choice of the appropriate professional and school, in order to avoid future risks is particularly important. In short, the individual human capital investment decision of higher education, we should combine theory with practice, fully consider the risk factors and the influence of the rate of return on investment of social and economic development, in order to facilitate individual investment to make rational decisions more objective, accurate.

REFERENCES

[1] Zhu Guohong. Population quality economic analysis [M]. Shanghai sanlian publishing house, 2002.
[2] Wang Peigen. Higher education economics [M]. Beijing economic management publishing house, 2008.
[3] Ilan's Smith. Modern economics of labor theory and public policy [M]. Renmin university of China press, 2009.
[4] Chen Xiaoyu. China's urban education yield change and the enlightenment [J]. Journal of Beijing university education review, 2007 (4):28–31.

Computer, Intelligent Computing and Education Technology – Liu, Sung & Yao (Eds)
© 2014 Taylor & Francis Group, London, ISBN 978-1-138-02469-4

The relationship between formative assessment and language learning strategies in art colleges

D. Jiao

Department of Common Courses, Hubei Institute of Fine Art, Wuhan, Hubei, China

ABSTRACT: In order to find out the relationship between formative assessment and language learning strategies in art colleges, a formative assessment experimental teaching plan was carried out among art college students. During the experimental teaching process, the students' performances were assessed by some formative approaches, including portfolios, questionnaires and interviews. The present study analyzes the factors affecting the students' use of language learning strategies and from the result of the experimental teaching, it was suggested that formative assessment helped to promote students' more frequent use of language learning strategies.

Keywords: formative assessment; language learning strategies; art colleges

1 INTRODUCTION

Teaching assessment, as an important part of teaching, contributes to providing efficient information of teaching results. At the same time, it helps students adjust their learning strategies and improve learning approaches. In traditional learning environments, assessment practices are characterized by standardized tests designed, administered and graded. It is typically through quizzes and tests that do not reflect actual language use. In such environments, learners do not develop their own ability to assess how much they have learned and how much they need to learn. Students in art colleges easily get frustrated in English learning, which is said to be related to their insufficient time spend on English and inefficient learning methods. Therefore, to promote students' English performances, an efficient teaching assessment is quite essential in college English teaching. The present study was carried out among the college students in an art college and it was found that formative assessment was beneficial in their English learning and use of learning strategies.

2 FORMATIVE ASSESSMENT

Formative assessment Formative assessment is applied to check the progress made by the students in their learning process. It monitors the whole teaching and learning process and ensures the teaching aim by providing feedback information. Non-test formative assessment is carried out throughout the process of education or teaching activities, with the application of non-test assessment tools, such as questionnaires, observation and investigation. It is dedicated to find out the factors affecting the education quality, aiming to improve and perfect the teaching plan and thus enhancing teaching efficiency.

Formative assessment, paying more attention to the students' responses and individual differences, is a more complete assessing way to reflect students' analyzing, speaking and practicing abilities, which however, the traditional written examinations cannot achieve.

Numbers of experts have tried to explain what formative assessment is and how it works. Crooks (2001) defined Formative assessment as a range of formal and informal assessment procedures employed by teachers during the learning process in order to modify teaching and learning activities to improve student attainment. It is commonly contrasted with summative assessment, which seeks to monitor educational outcomes, often for purposes of external accountability. Among them, Chinese researchers J.Z. Chen and Z.M. Xu (2010) gave a relatively comprehensive and complete description. 1. It makes clear and practical objectives. The key point of formative assessment is to help students get clearly aware of their learning objectives. 2. It follows specific and efficient rules. Formative assessment follows some certain rules to analyze students' performance rather than gives scores or grades to them. 3. It provides timely and frequent feedback. This kind of assessment which is carried throughout the learning process can reflex important information in students' learning activities, which in turn helps teachers identify the problems and deal with them in time. 4. It requires active and deep introspection. Formative assessment requires the students to reflect their own learning and to learn about their progress so as to establish an orientation, fully developing their potential. 5. It has multiple assessing subjects. There are not only teacher-student assessment, but also students-student assessment, parents-student assessment and students' self-assessment. 6. It adopts various assessing forms. The teacher collects students' information from such forms as observations, interviews, questionnaires, diaries, homework, classroom questioning and classroom activities.

3 LANGUAGE LEARNING STRATEGIES

3.1 Defining language learning strategies

Language learning strategies have created a great deal of controversy over the years since Rubin and Stern first introduced the concept to the second language literature in 1975. O'Malley & Chamot's (1990) definition of learning strategy is "the students' thought and behavior as to promoting understanding, learning and memorizing new information". Cohen demonstrated that second language learner strategies encompass both second language learning and second language use strategies. Taken together, they constitute the steps or actions consciously selected by learners either to improve the learning of a second language, the use of it, or both. Whereas David Nunan (1999) looked at it as "the mental and communicative processes that learners deploy in order to learn and use a second language". Though in different expressions, these definitions are all dedicated to pointing out that language learning strategies involve both strategies learning and using.

3.2 The importance of learning strategies

Rebecca Oxford (1990) argues that strategies are important for two reasons. In the first place, strategies are tools for active, self-directed involvement, which is essential for developing communicative competence. Secondly, learners who have developed appropriate learning strategies have greater self-confidence and learn more effectively. David Nunan (1999) pointed out that knowledge of strategies is important because the greater awareness you have of what you are doing, if you are conscious of the processes underlying the learning that you are involved in, then learning will be more effective. Research shows that learners who are taught the strategies underlying their learning are more highly motivated than those who are not.

3.3 The use of language learning strategies

Many factors contributed to choosing and using of language learning strategies. Ellis (1994) attributed the differences in use of language learning strategies to learners' individual differences, situational factors and social factors. Chinese scholar Q.F. Wen (2004) summarized the factors into two aspects, i.e. environmental factor and learner factor. Environmental factor refers to cultural background, English learning situation, teaching environment and learning tasks, all of which exert more or less influences on the option and effect of language learning strategies. While learner factor can be innate, acquired and both. Intelligence, language aptitude and sex are innate, while learning motivation is acquired. Different learner factors are all likely to make certain differences in application of language learning strategies.

Based on the teaching experience and teaching research findings in the art college, we attribute the choice of language learning strategies of art college students to two aspects: internal and external factors.

3.4 Internal factor

It is widely accepted that students in art colleges are relatively inefficient in English learning. But most of colleges make requirements on College English Test, which leads to students' strong motivation in English learning. These students tend to use such learning strategies as making learning plans, repetition and reviewing. And still there are some students willing to go abroad to further their studies, they prefer to deploy self-monitoring and self-evaluation strategies. Studies have shown that highly motivated students tend to use learning strategies more and frequently.

3.5 External factor

Teachers can both directly and indirectly affect students' use of learning strategies. Direct influence is given by teachers' learning strategy training, while indirect influence comes gradually from teachers' special teaching method, textbooks chosen, assessment standard and methods.

4 FORMATIVE ASSESSMENT AND USE OF LANGUAGE LEARNING STRATEGIES

Formative assessment is instructive and developmental. Through formative assessment, teachers and students get feedback and identify the drawbacks and shortages in teaching activities, based on which they can improve and perfect teaching and learning activities. As teaching assessment is an essential part of teaching, evaluation system is important in realizing college English curriculum aims. Therefore, it is quite necessary to establish a reasonable and efficient teaching evaluation system in current college English teaching.

220 college students majoring in painting were chosen as the research subjects, and a one-year experimental research was carried out in an art college in Hubei province. Before the experiment was taken, questionnaires were handed out to students to collect information about their use of language learning strategies and 220 questionnaires were finally all recollected. Oxford's "Strategy Inventory for Language Learning" (1990) was adopted. Questionnaires include questions about A. memory strategy; B. cognitive strategy; C. compensation strategy; D. meta-cognitive strategy; E. affective strategy; F. social strategy. Research subjects were asked to give their responses to each likert scale: 1. Strongly Disagree; 2. Always Disagree; 3. Sometimes Agree; 4. Always Agree; 5. Strongly Agree. Data shows that the average scores are as the following: memory strategy 2.0; cognitive strategy 2.2; compensation strategy 2.5; meta-cognitive strategy 2.0; affective strategy 1.2; social strategy 2.0. From the research data, we came to a conclusion that students in the art college seldom use learning strategies, which lead to their deficiency in English learning. Among the strategies, students use the fewest affective strategies. They seldom exchange ideas about language learning and almost never keep diaries to record their feelings in language learning. What's more, students as well get low scores in some meta-cognitive strategies. As was shown in the result, they didn't often make plans and were not active in learning.

Formative assessment was adopted throughout the whole process of experimental teaching so as to make sure whether there is any influence of formative assessment on use of language learning strategies. Firstly, portfolio was established for each student, recording his performance and achievement during learning process. Portfolio mainly contained students' performance in attendance, assignment, classroom discussion and questions, classroom discipline and teaching-learning interactions. Students were periodically informed of the results of portfolio assessment so that they were able to identify their own problems and adjust their learning strategies. Secondly, questionnaires were handed out to collect information about students' progress, difficulties and study notes. The questionnaires would guide the students to correctly evaluate their learning, for their self-evaluation is also an important part in assessing students' performance. And the questionnaires data helped teachers improve teaching.

Thirdly, interviews were held between teachers and students to learn about students' mastery of knowledge they've been taught and to evaluate students' learning efficiency.

After the one-year formative assessment experimental teaching, another language learning strategy questionnaire was carried out among the same subjects. And the data explained differently. The average scores were: memory strategy 2.2; cognitive strategy 2.6; compensation strategy 2.8; meta-cognitive strategy 3.0; affective strategy 2.1; social strategy 3.0. Though no big differences were made, yet students did use more strategies than before after the experiment, especially more meta-cognitive and social strategies. Students tended to make English learning plans and look for chances to read English. Students practise English more with their classmates. They pay more attention to details such as new words' meaning, gestures and mistakes they made in learning.

5 SUMMARY AND IMPLICATIONS

The results demonstrated that formative assessment helped students to use more language learning strategies to improve their English efficiency. Formative assessment is a dynamic assessment carried out throughout the process of teaching, aimed at exploring students' potential, improving and developing their studies. It pays more attention to the learning course and experience. As for the relatively inefficient English learners in art colleges, formative assessment would be more beneficial in promoting their using of language learning strategies. Despite the advantages it developed, teachers have to pay attention when they carry out formative assessment.

1. Take a correct attitude towards study. Students tend to consider the aim of English study as getting high marks in the final exam. Teacher should guide them to change their prejudice and take a correct attitude towards English study and pay more attention to daily efforts.
2. Make a universal standard in assessment. Formative assessment seems to be subjective when interviews or classroom activities are evaluated and teachers may be influenced by students' appearance or sex and so on. If there is no uniform standard while assessing in teacher-student assessment or student-student assessment, students would get frustrated and thus lose interest in their studies.
3. Be patient and fair in assessment. Formative assessment takes longer time and more energy than traditional examinations, so teachers should be more patient and fair enough to give justified assessment.

REFERENCES

[1] Crooks, T. 2001. The Validity of Formative Assessments. British Educational Research Association Annual Conference, University of Leeds, September 13–15.

[2] David Nunan. 1999. Second Language Teaching and Learning. Heinle & Heinle Publishers, 171–172.

[3] Ellis R. 1994. The Study of Second Learning Acquisition. Oxford University Press.

[4] J.Z. Chen & Z.M. Xu. 2010. The Implication of Formative Assessment in College English Teaching. JiangSu Education Research, 31–35.

[5] O'Malley, T.M. & Chamot, A.U. 1990. Learning Strategies in Second Language Acquisition. Cambridge University Press.

[6] Oxford R. 1990. Language Learning Strategies: What Every Teacher Should Know. Rowley, Mass: Newbury House.

[7] Q F. Wen. 2004. A Comment on Factors Affecting Foreign Language Learning Strategy System. Foreign Language and Foreign Language Teaching, 28–32.

Computer, Intelligent Computing and Education Technology – Liu, Sung & Yao (Eds)
© 2014 Taylor & Francis Group, London, ISBN 978-1-138-02469-4

Based on combination of engineering mold design and manufacture of professional practice teaching system construction and research

Ming-Qing Wu
Shandong Transport Vocational College, Weifang, Shandong, China

Qiang Li
Shandong Transport Vocational College, Weifang, Shandong, China
School of Transportation Science and Engineering, Beihang University, Beijing, China

ABSTRACT: In the mold professional practice teaching session on how to work and study carried out research and exploration in the actual process of strengthening the practice areas, enhance skills development is established based on combination of engineering practice teaching system, to explore a teaching and production, teaching and technology services combined with the new model, so that graduates of "Zero" to meet job requirements.

Keywords: engineering combined; mold design and manufacturing; practice teaching

1 INTRODUCTION

Mold design and manufacturing expertise is a practical and professional applications are strong, so practice teaching in the entire teaching process and plays a very important role in a high proportion. Our professional mold on how to practice teaching in conjunction with engineering conducted research and exploration, mold design and manufacture of professional practice teaching system is to train technical proficiency and overall build quality as the main line, which cross each other with the theoretical teaching system, osmotic supplement, facilitate, and throughout the teaching has always been. The purpose is to develop vocational teaching job close to highly skilled personnel, we are in the actual process of strengthening the practice areas, enhance skills development is established based on combination of engineering practice teaching system, to explore a teaching and production, education and technical services combined new model, so that graduates of "Zero" to meet job requirements.

2 "TWO WINGS" TYPE OF PRACTICE TEACHING OBJECTIVE SYSTEM

According to professional and technical personnel training objectives and the basic specifications of the requirements, combined with professional features, ability to apply technology to cultivate as the main discipline in professional quality and professional qualifications obtained for the two wings, OK "Wings" is characterized by the practice of teaching objective system. Teaching system should be designed to develop professional competence as the center, this principle is reflected in the standards for each course, each project are capacity-building as the goal. Each task implementation process while considering professional quality education in order to reflect the characteristics of higher vocational education. Vigorously promote vocational qualification certificate diploma with both "double certificates" system, currently the profession of the "draftsman", "die fitter" as the professional Class A certificates, the progressive realization of the vocational qualification certificate and diploma training content convergence and exchange.

Implementing the "practice teaching oriented" concept of vocational education, in order to develop training as the main theoretical courses dependent on practical courses of professional training programs. Curriculum integration with the professional standards, teaching content should be covered by national vocational qualification standards, teaching students skills identification and evaluation combine to make teaching assessment can remain occupational direction, but also to avoid duplication of assessment.

"Triple progressive" type of practice teaching content system.

3 PREPARING THE NEW FILE WITH THE CORRECT TEMPLATE

Currently, theoretical courses and practical vocational education curriculum arrangements are not conducive to the students integrate theory with practice, learn to apply knowledge to acquire new skills, theory and practice of teaching split alternately arranged unscientific, practice teaching unit is too small and too fragmented. To highlight the ability, should be used according to their ability to build hierarchical division teaching mode. Specifically, is the individual rational allocation of practice teaching, teaching through different areas, according to the basic skills, expertise and technology applications at three levels, based on work and study, elementary, gradual arrangements for practice teaching content. We arranged a two-stage plant freshman internships, first semester students arrange factory trainee week for students to learn business, knowledge jobs, learn professional; second semester practical arrangements for two weeks of workshops for students to hands-on production, exercise basic skills. Arrangements for two weeks the first semester sophomore design practice, with real products for the training project; arrange students into the second semester of the factory, to the real workplace Dinggang eight weeks, learning skills, the main arrangements CNC machining, die fitter, stamping and other job skills workout. Junior year studying in the school for 10 weeks and then into corporate internships, focusing on the ability to apply technology practice, mainly to the knowledge and job combine to enhance students sense of quality, familiar with corporate culture, and jobs to achieve "zero distance" docking. Each level must reflect the ability to apply technology training as the central principle, together constitute an integrated content system.

4 "HANDS WERE GRASPING" TYPE OF PRACTICE TEACHING MANAGEMENT SYSTEM

Practice teaching management, including agencies, teaching base of hardware and personnel management and internal and external practice teaching management rules and regulations, management tools and evaluation system and other software management. Grasping hardware construction and software management grasping complementary and indispensable, must improve and perfect, go hand in hand.

Management agencies, base construction and personnel management and training center using hospital co-management, mutual focus, the division responsible for the mode. To meet the professional practice of teaching goals, each school made by professional teaching laboratory construction plans and comprehensive laboratory and training center training centers are generally responsible for the management of highly specialized laboratories by the Department responsible for the management and use, construction of the mold structure is now training room, training room molding. Practical Teaching Quality Supervision and evaluation by the school centralized management. Training base outside the school-enterprise cooperation agreement parties under common management, is now building Fukuda mold factory training base, training base GoerTek shares, Weifang Zhiyuan mold training base, training program has been arranged by GoerTek technology applications internships, professional skills training Fukuda mold, mold Weifang Zhiyuan basic skills and knowledge of practical teaching. Office of Academic Affairs to develop a perfect internship regulations and assessment methods, and is responsible for the implementation of quality monitoring and evaluation. Appraisal must closely link training objectives, emphasis should be placed on student core professional competence and job vocational skills assessment, evaluation of. Teaching exam to try to integrate with the national vocational qualification, assessment and vocational qualifications should focus on the identification of test sites coincide strengthen the assessment methods, assessment forms and means of assessment research to improve the vocational qualification certificate to obtain objective was to promote the quality of teaching practice increased.

5 "THREE CONDITIONS SIMULTANEOUSLY" PRACTICE TEACHING SUPPORT SECURITY SYSTEM

"Three conditions" includes teachers, equipment and the environment three practice teaching support security conditions. That has a familiar production, management, service line case "double" teacher as the main faculty; has more complete, advanced technology equipment and facilities and simulation professional environment; has a good practice teaching environment.

Teachers with the introduction, in the form of construction of culture, the profession six full-time teachers in two from the production line, and the remaining 4 per capita has business practice experience. Coming from the school's long-term development perspective, schools should focus on strengthening the existing teacher training orientation and training methods of research, establishing the characteristics of vocational education teacher education and business practices continuing education system; attract social practice of experienced experts, engineers and technicians personnel to join, can be relaxed qualifications and title requirements.

Training equipment and simulation environment in accordance with the practice teaching system and the implementation of professional skill needs for construction. Equipment additions to follow the "one taken into account, two synchronous" principle, namely, the basic skills training and professional skills acquired conventional equipment, technology and innovation of advanced equipment additions balance training; training equipment, technical content and the degree of modernization with the production horizontal sync; investment in equipment and training project development synchronization.

6 CONCLUSION

1. Through the practice teaching system research, so that training model and program has been optimized to improve competency-based curriculum, the teaching content, teaching methods, teaching methods and evaluation methods and other aspects of a comprehensive innovation, the formation of a more the perfect combination of engineering talent training mode.
2. Improve the practice teaching system molds, melt "to teach, learn, do" as a whole, from a cognitive perspective students to build a progressive engineering alternate content system, strengthen the cultivation of students' practical ability, teaching quality is improved.
3. A large number of solid theoretical basis, the ability to highlight teaching practice teaching the backbone of the industry to absorb high levels of a number of part-time teachers, established by business experts, technicians, craftsmen the high level of external teachers talent pool.
4. Build a perfect combination of engineering— based practice teaching resource library, including mold practice teaching plan, practice curricula, practice teaching system appraisal standards, and stamping die stamping process design course training guide books, plastic molding and plastic molds design course training guide book.
5. To strengthen school-enterprise cooperation, and GoerTek shares, Fukuda dies, molds and other signed Zhiyuan school-enterprise cooperation agreement to establish teaching training base, so that part of practice teaching projects completed in the enterprise, in order to create the conditions of work and study.

Mold industry is developing rapidly, technology updates soon, we want to continue to industries and enterprises through quality research and graduate follow-up survey of scientific classification analysis, careful analysis of the mold industry knowledge structure for graduates and professional capability of the new requirements, improve the practical teaching system, around three practice areas: professional practice knowledge, expertise, practice, professional integrated practice, from the form, content, projects, time to build content system, so that training programs and training content is close to job requirements.

Based on combination of engineering practice teaching system and guarantee the implementation of necessary conditions, the current strength of our teachers need to be further strengthened, especially in regard craftsmen; school practice environment needs to be further optimized to increase equipment investment, open training room, give opportunities for students to practice, but the high cost of tooling training, investment in schools alone is obviously unrealistic, you need to rely on social forces, to take colleges, enterprises and the way for the students to create a real practice environment; continue to strengthen the training base outside the building, there are program targeted tissue campus practical training for professional applications practice not a mere formality.

Students from elementary school to high school and then college, basically no contact with enterprises, vocational training institutions targeting the vast majority of graduates of the future will be decided in the enterprise practitioners, and mold companies due to product high precision, tight production tasks, often overtime work, which makes the students go to work just unacceptable. To enable students to adapt as quickly as possible into the enterprise, so that students in daily practice more acceptable influence of corporate culture, you can also do various forms of lectures, which is to improve students' comprehensive professional quality, employment positioning will be good results.

The practice teaching and management of innovation is not only for improving students' innovation ability and practice ability, and have greatly enriched the content of practice teaching. To study into the link of the three practice teaching system of research and practice of classroom interaction, is becoming a will certainly become a new feature of our school.

ACKNOWLEDGEMENT

It is a project supported by the colleges and universities in shandong province domestic young backbone teachers visiting scholar.

REFERENCES

[1] Yu Zhongwen, the Papers etc. Practical Teaching of Higher Vocational Education Research [M]. Beijing: Tsinghua University Press, 2004.

[2] Zhou Jing science, Yang Yusheng, Nishi Qi. Practice teaching program is an important guarantee for cultivating innovative talents [J]. Experimental Technology and Management, 2000, (5).

[3] Yang Dongsheng, mold design and manufacture of professional vocational teaching practice. Education Forum. 2006 (2).

[4] Huang Kexiao. Vocational and technical education courses had ee [m]. East China Normal University Press, 2001.

[5] Niejian Wu. Work-study program is to train highly skilled and effective vocational education pattern punch national vocational and technical education. 2006 (15).

[6] Jinyan. Pilot Professional mold "plastic molding process and mold design" Teaching Reform Research and Practice. Zhengzhou Industrial College, 1998 (2).

Computer, Intelligent Computing and Education Technology – Liu, Sung & Yao (Eds)
© *2014 Taylor & Francis Group, London, ISBN 978-1-138-02469-4*

Exploration of teaching new solutions of graduation design based on Excellent Engineers Education Plan and the University Practical Education Sectors

Jing-Yi Lu, Dong-Mei Wang, Zhi-Hua Zhao, Zhi-Wei Duan, Ji-Cheng Liu & Xia Liu
Faculty of Electricity and Information Engineering, Northeast Petroleum University, Daqing, Heilongjiang Province, China

ABSTRACT: Based on the "Excellent Engineers Education Plan" and the "University Practical Education Sectors", this article combines the characteristics of Northeast Petroleum University with the actual situation of Measurement & Control Technology and Instrument Specialty. Meanwhile, it integrates the existing teaching resources and discipline advantages, and actively explores the measurement & control professional graduation design teaching in the new scheme. This article also has carried on the exploration and practice about the implementation plan of graduation design, the building of graduation design guide team and the progress of the quality monitoring system. The practice results show that the proposed scheme can cultivate students' abilities, which are comprehensive application of knowledge to analyze and solve practical problems independently. It also can cultivate students' innovative consciousness and rigorous steadfast scientific style of work, so as to improve the quality of talent cultivation in measurement & control technology and instrumentation comprehensively.

Keywords: Measurement & Control Technology and Instruments; graduation design; Excellent Engineers Education Plan; practice education

1 INTRODUCTION

Graduation design is an important practical teaching link to train and develop students' innovation ability, practice ability and entrepreneurial spirit in colleges and universities. Not only can it cultivate students' comprehensive use of knowledge and basic skills which they have learned, but also can carry out basic scientific research training to improve their abilities of analysis and solving social problems, cultivate the spirit of scientific innovation, and strengthen the awareness of active service society. All of these will lay a good foundation in development, design, manufacture and serving the society in scientific research for the students after graduation.

To improve the quality of undergraduate course continuously, firstly, the research group combined the "Excellent Engineers Education Plan" and the "University Practical Education Sectors" with the characteristics of Northeast Petroleum University and the actual situation of Measurement & Control Technology and Instrument Specialty. And then we integrated the existing teaching resources and discipline advantages to actively explore the measurement and control professional graduation design teaching in the new scheme. In this paper, based on the experience of undergraduate course graduation design of Measurement & Control Technology

and Instrument Specialty of Northeast Petroleum University in recent years, we will propose some concrete measures on how to improve the quality of graduation design.

2 IMPROVE GRADUATION DESIGN IMPLEMENTATION PLAN AND INCREASE THE TIME OF GRADUATION DESIGN

Measurement & Control Technology professional graduation design usually starts in the second semester of Senior year, which will last for 15 weeks. But in recent years, the employment situation of graduates is more and more serious, which leads that some students to go out for job fairs or interviews form companies or postgraduate schools, while others have to prepare for the make-up exams before graduation, etc. All of reasons cause the shortage of effective time of graduation design, inefficiency and the slow progress, which also seriously affect the quality of graduation design. To improve the quality of graduation design, the time of it has been adjusted for 18 weeks through the application, and the professional teachers who are eligible to guide the graduation design must prepare all the topics ready in advance, so that students can choose their interested topic. They also can make full use of the winter vacation to consult the relative to their graduation design topics about 30 papers at home and abroad, read 15 papers carefully, and write the opening report and literature review, thus those can provide more preparing time for student's graduation design.

3 CARRY ON THE METHODS OF SUPERVISOR RESPONSIBILITY SYSTEM AND TEAM GUIDANCE TO IMPROVE THE OVERALL QUALITY OF GRADUATION DESIGN

In order to improve the students' comprehensive qualities through the graduation design, measurement & control department reform on the guide way and build four graduation design teaching teams for cooperation between college and enterprise. There are 3 to 5 teachers who have different job titles and teach different specialized courses and some senior engineers form testing technology companies. Among these teachers, the lecturers are responsible for early graduation design plan, the guidance of hardware, software and daily work, At the same time, the professors and associate professors are mainly responsible for the guidance of project design instruction, models and the algorithm, while the senior engineers from test technology companies are responsible for guiding students how to be brought in line with actual work environment standards of companies. At last, direct supervisors are responsible for their own students' thesis writing instruction. All teachers work together to provide more opportunities of participating in scientific researches and competitions, which can expand students' range of topics so as to stimulate their enthusiasm. For every two weeks, they are required to organize a collective guidance and academic discussion, which focus on common and interdisciplinary problems to be solved, in order to improve the efficiency of guidance. Team guidance method will make great improvement in topic selecting, experiment and research, structure and layout, design for graduation. After doing these, we will cultivate students' ability to innovate and improve their comprehensive quality.

4 PAY MORE ATTENTION TO THE PROCESS, AND SET UP QUALITY CONTROL SYSTEM

4.1 *Be strict in the selection of topics*

It is so important to pay attention to select topics that the system of the topics checked centrally by experts must be carried on. Graduation design subjects must agree with our professional training objectives, which is to develop senior technology talents who can work in the national economy departments concerned in the field of measurement and control technology, equipment and system design and manufacturing, science and technology development, applied research, operation management, and other aspects. Therefore, teachers are required to submit next year's graduation design topics every December. And students are also asked not to repeat their graduation design topics. That is to say, each of students has only one proposal topic. And furthermore, three consecutive terms of students' subjects cannot appear again, either. The graduation design topics which have been provided to the students' must cover their own professional courses, and also should be designed around this major related to scientific research, instrument and meter enterprise production and people's daily life as well as the practical problems facing the department of petroleum and petrochemical engineering. All of these topics aim to facilitate students' comprehensive ability, consolidate and absorb knowledge in four years, in order to achieve flexible abilities to use knowledge to solve practical problems. What the Measurement & Control of graduation design experts group should mainly consider is whether these topics are combined with teachers' scientific research topics, production practice or with the training objectives of this department. After offered by experts on the topics, students can choose from them. This subject can not only boost the enthusiasm of the students, but also can cultivate students' comprehensive application of knowledge in independent analysis and the ability to solve practical problems and to cultivate students' innovative consciousness and business acumen scientific style of work.

4.2 *Be strict in the thesis proposal*

During this phase, focusing on training students' preparation and theoretical analysis ability to complete the task is the key point. Students should be made clear to the topics of basic principles, methods and technical conditions which they have chosen, and then they can propose for the feasibility of the graduation design (paper), including literature review, project demonstration, design thinking, process arrangement, and the required equipment, etc. while it is 3rd or 4th week during the design, graduation design must be checked initially. Students should submit their proposals according to reading references of graduation design review, setting schemes and plans. Thesis proposals must show the overall plan of graduation design and planning. What mentors should do is locking good thesis proposals strictly and carefully. After opening through, it is the design stage. Students must correct continuously until meeting the requirements. This inspection shall be the responsibility of the graduation design instructors. The job of the graduation design experts who come from Measurement & Control Department is review, and the job of the two-stage experts group is random manner.

4.3 Be strict in intermediate inspection

While it is 9 to 10 weeks, graduation design midterm examination will start. At least, students are required to complete one piece of English literature translation work, the hardware design of a complete system, or complete the design of the system simulation model and part of the paper writing work to describe their own paper progress as well as teachers' questions related to the topics. Teachers are going to be divided into some groups for each student to check the paper one by one. What teachers will check is: the correctness of the design scheme, work attitude, attendance, the size of the workload and the situation about completing independently according to the plan of the time in the thesis proposal from students. Finally, some experts from two-stage school and the school's teaching inspection teams will check some of the students on spot. Students given warning of intermediate inspection are unqualified, who will be provided detailed improvement measures to make its rectification within a time limit. At the same time, unqualified students' graduation reply will not be permitted, but submit to the two-stage school, which will be organized by experts to answer in a unified manner.

4.4 Be strict in thesis writing

After researching, teachers should guide students to complete the graduation design (paper) according to the Northeast Petroleum University Undergraduate Graduation Design (Paper) Writing Code Standards. They also should focus on cultivating students' ability of comprehensive analysis problems and written expression ability during this phase. Students should be seriously analysis, comparison, induced according to their research results. On this basis, they must make a realistic conclusion, to point out what are the practical significance in theory and in fact, what are the new progress, innovation points and the existing problems and suggestions in this design (paper). Thesis writing stage is mainly composed of teachers by

authorized, and graduation design expert group will sampling.

4.5 Be strict in thesis defense

Thesis defense is the last link of graduation design, which can inspect some comprehensive abilities of summary, oral expression, and psychological quality. Before thesis defense, guidance teachers and teachers of evaluation must review papers carefully, in order to pick out unqualified papers which are not allowed to take part in. While defensing, students can't answer in his mentor's plea group. There are for about 10 minutes to defense for each student. And teachers will have about 5 minutes to ask questions. Rejoin group of teachers mainly puts forward problems around the graduation design content. If the answers of the student are correct, teachers should give certain defense team; if not, teachers of the group should point out correct answers.

4.6 Be strict in graduation design results

Graduation design results are made up of three parts: guidance teachers (40%), teachers of evaluation (20%), defense group (40%). The result of the thesis defense is the average of the grades by defense group. The result from mentor and the results from the teachers of evaluation must be "back to back". That is to say, they will be kept secret. But if two of them are greatly different, they will be evaluated again by the department of graduation design team and ratify the final results.

5 CONCLUSIONS

Through the outstanding education policy researches, plans and practice researches, we have explored suitable teaching new solutions for Measurement & Control Technology and Instrument Specialty in recent years. Various measures has received satisfying effects—First, students' subject quality are guaranteed. Second, the quality of graduation design (paper) improved significantly. Both of them improve the quality of talent cultivation of Measure & Control Technology and Instrument. Research achievements have a certain reference for other disciplines and other colleges and universities on teaching reform. But we also recognize that the quality of graduation design construction is a long-term task so that we must study profession practically, dare to reform and innovate, At the same time, perfect system, scientific management mode, mature quality control system, and the feasible management platform are necessary to ensure the quality of graduation design (paper).

ACKNOWLEDGMENTS

The authors express their sincere appreciation to the some organizations and following people for their support. The research was supported by Heilongjiang Province Education Science "Twelfth Five-year" Plan Project (GBB1212016) and Heilongjiang Province Higher Education Teaching Reform Project (JG2012010096). The idea of writing a paper comes from discussions we have had with many colleagues and friends.

REFERENCES

[1] http://www.moe.edu.cn/publicfiles/business/html-files/moe/s255/201202/xxgk_129911.html. Ministry of Education of the People's Republic of China, "A Number of Opinions on Further Strengthening the Practice of Teaching Work of The Ministry of Education and Other Departments".

[2] Yongsheng Wang, Research and practice on training mode of excellence engineering talents cultivation in high level university[J]. China Higher Education, 2011(6).

[3] Zhijun Zhuang, Xianchun Su, Research and practice on cultivating measures of students' practice and innovation capacity in local engineering college[J]. Journal of Jilin Institute of Chemical Technology, 2012(2).

[4] He zhirong, Construction and practice of quality monitoring system of graduation project for science and engineering specialties[J]. Experimental Technology and Management, 2012(9).

[5] Hu zhikun, Sun Kehui, Sheng liyuan, On training pattern Combined with Practice and Graduation desige/thesis of Science College Students[J]. Higer Education of Sciences, 2011(3).

[6] Zhang Sherong, Cui Wei. Exploration of reform of graduation project faced on enterprise needs[J], Experimental Technology and Management, 2011(7).

Computer, Intelligent Computing and Education Technology – Liu, Sung & Yao (Eds)
© 2014 Taylor & Francis Group, London, ISBN 978-1-138-02469-4

Responsibility of government in the construction of teacher educational practice base

Y.P. Qiu
Department of Educational Science and Technology, Baoji University of Arts and Science, Shaanxi, China

ABSTRACT: The construction of teacher educational practice base is the carriers which carry out practical teaching activities, and improve their quality of teacher education training. Local government as agent category and organizer of culture education career, which participated in local colleges teaching practice base construction was not only the education requirements of public property, but also was the needs to improve the quality of talent cultivation, and was the effective measures to realize the regional basic educational equality. However, due to various reasons, local government was long-term absence at the local university Teacher Education training base construction, which was failure to assume its proper role and played its due role. It's the times give the local government's mission to clear responsibilities and fulfill its obligations.

Keywords: local university; local government; teacher educational practice base; responsibility

1   INTRODUCTION

Teacher educational practice base is the carriers which carry out practical teaching activities, and improve their quality of teacher education training Local government as agent category and organizer of culture education career, which participated in local colleges teaching practice base construction was not only the education requirements of public property, but also was the needs to improve the quality of talent cultivation, and was the effective measures to realize the regional basic educational equality. However, due to various reasons, local government was long-term absence at the local university Teacher Education training base construction, which was failure to assume its proper role and played its due role. Therefore, the establishment of practice bases outside the University has very important significance that training technology talents needed for the development of local economy.[1,2] In other words, it's urgent affairs to call on local government to participate in local colleges and universities teaching practice base construction and assume its role and fulfill its responsibility in order to ensure which go on wheels and achieve the win-win of education practice significance and economic benefit.

2   THE LACK OF RESPONSIBILITY OF LOCAL GOVERNMENT

It is urgent and important that to optimizing the model of training talents and improving the education practice base construction, especially while it's a great slogan to strengthen practice teaching and is become relentless pursuit to improve the quality of personnel training for local higher education. For example, a landscape planning and design of Shengquan educational practice base in Feidong county of Hefei city has been presented.[3] However, some local governments that were influenced by the traditional thinking are consciously putting themselves abandoned at the local university practice base construction.

2.1   The lack of responsibility in the opportunities supply of practice teaching

The local primary and secondary schools are the major base practice teaching for universities, but because of which have no administrative affiliation between universities and primary and secondary schools, while are equal partnership, and local primary and secondary schools have no liabilities and responsibilities to accept trainees in the law. Therefore, the practice base of local universities less stable and the educational practice's opportunity was seriously restricted. The shortage of educational practice's opportunity has become an important factor to restrict improving the talent training quality for local universities. Along with the plan to vitalize province with science and education and thrive city by science and education, the local government has realized education, especially higher education playing important role in regional economic development and the long-term significance for social development to improve the quality of higher education, but because of has no realize the importance and particularity of practical teaching of higher education, so that the local government was neglect the educational practice base of local universities. Thus when local universities are lack of opportunities for educational practice, and which has affected its training quality, the local government has no use administrative lever to intervene timely, asking the local primary and second schools to bear their responsibilities and tasks as the educational practice base of universities.

2.2 *The rule of law and regulations construction lag behind, the absence of government's supervision and management*

As the educational practice base is a long-term task involving different subjects including local educational administrative departments, universities, primary and secondary schools and so on, which needs the local people's congresses and government developing appropriate laws and regulations, clearly identifying the rights and obligations of each body? But due to various factors, the legal system is relatively backward, the country has no clear legal provisions on educational practice base, which makes it necessary to run lack of necessary legal basis, especially when a legal dispute in educational practice base, which also led to the local government laws and regulations on education through internship bases be indirect management and oversight functions can not be achieved. To clear responsibilities of each party, local people's congresses and governments have the responsibility and obligation as soon as possible to strengthen the rule of law, improve relevant laws and regulations system, and effectively assume their rightful responsibilities.

2.3 *Lack of funding*

The local government has slowed the development of regional economy and the improvement of talent training quality in a way, because of which was absent from the educational practice base of universities. Especially the financial support is not in place, so that the lack of funding has seriously affected the healthy development of educational practice base in Higher Education. It's difficult in maintaining the daily operation for local universities because of its limited funding, so which input generally insufficiently in practical teaching. Moreover, the educational practice base construction is a costly project, it is difficult to bear for local universities, which barely able to maintain its operation, and generally ignore its funding, consciously or unconsciously. And the educational practice base is concerning personnel training quality of local universities, practically talent training quality in teacher education. Similarly, the local government lack of funds for compensation to the school as a practice base, resulting in which participate in educational practice base are not enthusiastic, with many concerns. Therefore, the local universities are urgent need external financial subsidies to meet its requirements for stable educational practice base. The local government as the leader and main actor for the regional career development, which has the responsibility and obligation to increase funds in educational practice base of local universities, ensure the talent training quality in teacher education and supply a large number of qualified teachers for regional basic education.

2.4 *Lack of accountability in quality inspection and evaluation about educational practice base*

It's an important guarantee for promoting Healthy functioning in educational practice base of local universities to use the scientific and effective evaluation mechanisms. Due to lack of unified & strict inspection and evaluation criteria the quality of educational practice base is uneven. At present, the responsibility to choose and build the educational practice base is the local university, the standard is also determined by which, so there is a large arbitrariness and subjectivity. The government is the carrier for the local educational development, but which has ignored the educational practice base which was concern the quality of regional basic education in the future. The local government lack of responsibility in quality acceptance and evaluation for educational practice base, which intensified the fuzziness and subjection of its standards and deteriorated the external environment of the teachers' education talent training quality improvement of local universities).

3 THE RESPONSIBILITY OF THE LOCAL GOVERNMENT IN EDUCATIONAL PRACTICE BASE OF LOCAL UNIVERSITY

3.1 *Changing concepts, intervening actively with administrative lever, increasing the chance of the educational practice*

The local government should change idea and fully realize the important value and significance about educational practice base to improve the personnel training quality of local universities' teacher education, then intervening actively with administrative lever and increasing the chance of the educational practice for local university. From the view of administrative law, the primary and secondary schools must be accept management from the education administration, then the education ministration can regulate them acts through decision-making power, ordinance power, coercive power, supervisory authority, steer power, reward power, right to material assistance, and so on.[4] The local government can formulate relevant rules and regulations, including excellent evaluation of the primary and secondary schools when they accept trainees of the local universities, it's qualified for each school principal when he actively cooperate with universities to promote the educational practice base. At the same time, it's necessary to carry out a policy tilt and exist financial support for teachers when they as a trainee teachers. The local government should use administrative means to stimulate the enthusiasm of primary and secondary schools to participate the educational practice base through a variety of incentives, and then increasing the supple of the universities' internship opportunities.

3.2 *Strengthening laws and regulations, improving the legal system, and providing a legal basis*

It's a bottleneck to effectively healthily and smoothly develops for the local universities of educational practice base, because of relative lag of the construction of the rules and laws, and the legal system is not sound in the country. At present, there is no relevant laws and policies that regulate schools must provide educational practice opportunities for local universities, this means that is no legal basis for administrative department to require basic schools which must offer opportunities for educational practice base.[5] Thus, it is an inescapable responsibility for local government to actively research and formulate relevant laws and regulations by the reality, then to provide legal protection for the educational practice base of local universities. First, developing relevant rules and regulations and specifying the construction of educational practice base of stakeholders' responsibilities, rights and interests, including local universities, primary and secondary schools and government administrative departments. Secondly, development of detailed regulations on funding, management and evaluation of inspection results, etc. Finally, formulating appropriate incentives, and implementing by law.

3.3 *Increasing funding, improving educational practice base construction*

The local government should fully realize that the construction of educational practice base not only local was universities own thing, but also directly related to the teachers' quality of the regional basic education, thus which should responsible for promoting the development of universities, and actively play an important role in the promotion of local universities where education, economy, culture, construction, etc. Therefore, increment of the support is not only to use administrative intervention to increase their internships' opportunities but also to use economic lever to increase its investment, then to provide financial security for its infrastructure. First, funding should be withdrawn from daily spending to be sued to constructing the educational practice. Secondly, a special fund for educational practice base construction, special fund for special use are established. Thirdly, utilizing political influence and related measures rouse regional enterprises to actively contribute in order to expand financing channels. Finally, strengthening financial management and realizing open and transparent in use of funds, meanwhile rationally allocating resources and improving the utilization of funds at full steam. In addition, it's an important way to increase investment for local government through updating educational facilities in time.

3.4 *Establishing standards and a scientific evaluation mechanism*

It's a very significant reason that unscientific standards and unsound evaluation mechanisms which result in the lower quality of the construction of educational practice base. The local government should assume its responsibility, fully play the role of educational organizer, actively contact with local universities and schools, examine the specific circumstances and needs, then formulate standards about the construction of educational practice base with local universities and schools. And which should strictly select system to choose those who truly meet the criteria as the educational practice base, and to exclude those schools who do not meet standards, thereby improving the quality of educational practice bases from the source. At the same time, three rivers including the local government, local universities and schools should provide principles and basis for improving the construction of educational practice base, through establishing a scientific evaluation mechanism, clearing evaluation criteria, improving the evaluation system, enriching the evaluation content, optimizing the evaluation process and detailing evaluation results. The local government and relevant educational administrative departments only have effectively played the leading roles, participated in the construction of educational practice base in the real situation, which was able to promote the process of the construction of educational practice base and the quality improvement, and which was able to provide institutional guarantee for teacher education personnel training quality of local universities.

ACKNOWLEDGEMENTS

This work is supported by the education of Shaanxi province "the twelfth five year plan" (SGH13239) and National Education Science Plan of Ministry of Education of China for Youth Project (EIA130416).

REFERENCES

[1] Li B. 2010. Speculations On Strengthening Educational Practice Base Construction of Normal Specialty of Higher Schools. *Jiangsu Social Sciences*. 113–116.

[2] Zou G.H. 2011. Research on the Construction of the Practice Base Outside the University. *International Conference on Education Science and Management Engineering*. 127–130.

[3] Qin J. Zhang F. and Sun S. 2006. Research on Landscape Planning and Design of Education Practice Base. *Journal of Landscape Research*. 4(8): 1–4.

[4] Huang W. 2007. *Education Law*. Beijing. Higher Education Press.

[5] Liu K. 2009. Effective government intervention: important means for higher teacher education internship opportunities supplies. *University Research and Review*. 9(1): 11–15.

Computer, Intelligent Computing and Education Technology – Liu, Sung & Yao (Eds)
© 2014 Taylor & Francis Group, London, ISBN 978-1-138-02469-4

Study on the folk games used in physical education curriculum of school

Yu-Ling Li
School of Sport and Cultural Industry, Qilu University of Technology, Shandong, China

ABSTRACT: Through the definition to the concept of games, folk games and sports games, this paper elaborates the similarity between folk sports games and physical education teaching, and analyzes the application of folk sports games in sports curriculum teaching of school. Adding the folk games into physical education curriculum plays a positive role in promoting the development of folk games. And meanwhile, it can increase the national pride of the students, enhance their ability to adapt to the society, and enrich their cultural life on campus.

Keywords: games; folk games; sports games; physical education of school; physical education teaching

The game is a kind of "entertainment" activity. Due to the difference in cultural traditions and customs, the residents of different nations and different living areas have their unique traditional folk games, which are gradually transformed into a form of culture mode during the process of inheriting from generation to generation, and embody strong regional cultural or national culture. Folk sports games possess strong entertainment feature, and combine the educational, social and body building features. However, these traditional resources haven't aroused the attention of relevant departments and the public. Our country has a large number of folk sports games. The entrance of the folk games into PE course is able to provide rich resources to PE curriculum teaching, and can provide reform ideas for PE curriculum.

1 GAMES, FOLK GAMES, SPORTS GAMES AND DEFINITION ON THEIR CONCEPTS

1.1 Games

The definition to "game" in "Cihai" considers that it firstly is one of the important means of sports, and secondly is a kind of cultural entertainment. From the classification point of view, games can be divided into: competitive games (such as football, basketball); activity games (such as hide-and-seek, eagle and chicks); puzzles (such as building blocks, crossword puzzle, chess).[1] Obviously, the definition to "game" in "Cihai" is relatively rigid and wide. In "Homo Ludens", the scholar of Holland Johan Huizinga thought that games were the activities that an individual voluntarily participated in or the undertaking that an individual was engaged in. These activities were carried out within the prescribed time and space and the participants could accept and obey the rules. The joyful and nervous feelings were accompanied during the games, which were different from those in daily life. The purpose of the game lied in the game itself.[2] The concept of game proposed by Johan Huizinga laid the footstone of the theory of games.

1.2 Folk games

Domestic and foreign scholars do not have a unified definition in terms of the concept of folk sports. In comparison, the definition proposed by Wu Bingan and Wang Degang is more likely to be accepted by people. Wu Bingan thought that folk games referred to the entertainment activities which were popular in people's daily life. They were mainly popular among teenagers and adult entertainment programs in festivals.[3] Wang Degang thought that folk games were the entertainment activities with competitive features while being excluded from the formal events, which were spread widely among people and were inherited from generation to generation.[4]

1.3 Sports games

The sports game is one of the members in the game family, which is a branch during the evolution process of games. Currently, sports games have been widely used in the body building, sports training and sports teaching areas. Sports games contains the dual characteristics of sports and games.

From the perspective of its essence, the creation and composition of the sports game combine the skills, such as walking, running, jumping, throwing, etc, in people's daily life and work, and the basic movement form of sports projects. And then in accordance with the need of fitness, training or teaching, targeted rules will be set and the plot of the story will be compiled so as to form a game.[5]

2 SIMILARITY BETWEEN FOLK SPORTS GAMES AND PHYSICAL EDUCATION OF SCHOOL

2.1 Entertainment feature

The rules and contents of the games have strong entertainment and amusement features. Some of them have strong competition features while others are lively and funny, the features of which are highly in compliance with the physiological and psychological characteristics of students. One of the main reasons why the folk sports game can be inherited till now and becomes the major folk way of relaxation is that it can adjust the psychological status of the participants, cultivate the tastes of the participants, meet the psychological needs of the participants, and let people obtain mental enjoyment in the joyful and competitive atmosphere of the game.

2.2 Body building feature

Possessing relatively strong physical movement is the characteristic of most folk sports games. The frequent participation of the students in game activities can help to improve the flexibility of the central nervous system and its regulation ability, increase muscle strength, improve heart and lung function, and promote the aerobic and anaerobic capacity of cardiovascular system so as to improve the health level of the students. For example, the constant movement and dodging in the game "hawk-and-chicken" can cultivate the reaction ability, teamwork ability and observation ability of the students; the games of "single-plank bridge" and "walk on stilts" can improve the balance ability of the students; the game of "rubber band skipping" can improve the coordination ability of the students; the game of "toss sandbags" can exercise the throwing ability and reaction ability.

2.3 Educational feature

Folk games originate from life and have extensive contents, which combine the wisdom of the people and have obvious educational function. The education feature of the folk sports game is reflected in two aspects, namely extensive property and integrity. Specifically, the extensive property means the sustainability of the education effect and the compatibility of the education process. Many folk games originate early, and their development process was a modification and adaptation process. Through the modification, the games are more suitable for people to participate. Integrity means the comprehensiveness in education function. The folk sport games can promote the overall development of the students. The games can enable the students to master the sports skills, cultivate diligent spirits of the students, and improve the organization ability, coordination ability, competition consciousness of the students, and their ability of obeying the rules.

2.4 Sociality

Interpersonal communication is the necessary element for students to achieve individual socialization development. Folk sports games originated from work and life with pretty obvious social characteristics. The participation of the students in game activities can obtain two social relationships, namely social role relationship and virtual role relationship, both of which are beneficial for the cultivation and development of students' socialization. Through games, students also can learn the basic social skills. The participation process in the folk sports games is also a process for the students to experience life, know the world and other people. For example, in the game of "lifting the decorated sedan chair", students can not only learn about China's traditional cultural knowledge and social customs, but also can learn relevant folk art and music.

3 THE APPLICATION OF FOLK SPORTS GAMES IN PHYSICAL EDUCATION TEACHING

3.1 Application of folk sports games in the preparatory activities of teaching

The main purpose of the preparation activity in PE lessons is to prevent injury, mobilize organs and increase the excitability of the nervous system, which plays the role of warming up. In practical teaching, some signal response games, attention focusing games and collective coordination games can be chosen to increase the fun of the course and interests of the students, which enable the various systems of the organisms of the students to be well ready. For example, in basketball course, the game of "passing the parcel" can be chosen. The set of the rules can not only improve the ball control abilities of the students, but also can improve the observation and response capabilities of the students.

3.2 Application of folk sports games in the basic part of teaching

The basic part of teaching is the center of PE lesson and is the guarantee for the achievement of teaching goals. The contents of the traditional PE lesson include track and field, ball games, gymnastics and martial arts. Folk games can be introduced into these main items of teaching as auxiliary exercises. Furthermore, as for the folk game itself, with the teaching objective unchanged, it can also be treated as the main teaching contents, especially in some areas with outstanding regional or national characteristics. For example, if the objective of PE lessons is to develop the throwing ability of the students, the contents of the lesson can choose "throwing sandbag", "throwing stick", "spinning top" and "throwing mud", etc. If the teaching objective is to develop the jumping ability of the students, the contents of the lesson can choose "rope skipping", "jumping checks", "jumping on and off bench", etc. In this way, the teaching objectives can be achieved, and meanwhile the teaching contents have been enriched, and it adds more fun to the lesson.

3.3 Application of folk sports games in the conclusion part of teaching

The main task for the conclusion part of PE lesson is to enable the body functions of the students to gradually return to a relative quiet state. In terms of the activity mode, some relaxation exercises can be chosen. The exercise strengthen should not be large and the exercise time should not be too long. Then some relaxation kind of folk games can be chosen to realize the purpose of relaxing the body, such as "Qigong", "tap dance", "swing playing", "shadowboxing", etc.

4 CONCLUSION

Folk games bring entertainment to people of different areas and nations. As the major leisure form for the rural residents, folk games have gradually become an important part of human culture during the process of development. It is necessary for us to collect, collate and protect these games, and to carry out constant processing to make it lean more towards teaching materials and enable the folk games to truly enter into PE lessons and into the daily life of the students, so as to promote the inheriting of the folk games, and promote the healthy and overall development of the students at the same time.

REFERENCES

[1] Cihai [M]. Shanghai: Shanghai Lexicographical Publishing House, 1979.
[2] Homo Ludens. Johan Huizinga [M], translated by multiple Duo Ren. Hangzhou: China Academy of Art Press, 1996.
[3] Wu Bingan. Chinese Folk Lore [M]. Shenyang: Liaoning University Publishing House, 1999.
[4] Wang Degang. Origin, Value and Protection of Traditional Folk Games [J]. Qilu Journal, 2005 (6).
[5] Zhang Yuanping. Discussion on Application of Sports Games in Higher Vocational Sports Teaching [J]. Sports News (Academy), 2009 (3).

Computer, Intelligent Computing and Education Technology – Liu, Sung & Yao (Eds)
© 2014 Taylor & Francis Group, London, ISBN 978-1-138-02469-4

The feasibility research on linedance integrated in university gym course

Yu-Ling Li
School of Sport and Cultural Industry, Qilu University of Technology, Shandong, China

ABSTRACT: The purpose of the study is to explore the feasibility of introducing linedance into college PE course; its component elements including the fitness of linedance are contributive to the efficiency, acceptable level of the students, administrators, and teachers etc. The results show that the linedance has a positive role in promoting the health of the participants; The students have a better understanding to the linedance sport, it requires a higher initiative to participate in; the teachers believe that this project is promising; the key factor of introducing linedance into the colleges and universities is the sufficient attention from the administrator.

Keywords: linedance; gym course; feasibility

Syllabus of Gym Course of Universities and Colleges has been implemented in common institutions of higher education all over the country since 2003. Article 7 of it states to integrate extracurricular physical activity, after-school activities (include social activity and outdoor sports), exercise training and other activities with aims, plans and organization into the gym course so as to form organic connection of curriculum structure both inside and outside school. Meanwhile, Article 8 states, "In order to meet different students' need who have different levels and interests, Colleges and Universitites should offer all kinds of physical education courses for students according to general requirement of school education as well as the principle of physical education course." Besides, when designing the content, it emphasizes the combination of the fitness and culture, selectivity and effectivenss, nationality and internationality, scientificity and acceptability. Linedance just meets the requirement of the syllabus. Currently, the linedance has been one of the important promotion program in State General Administration of Sport. And gymnastics administrative center is in charge of the training of linedance coaches. Besides, they also formulate the linedance competition rules.

1 CULTURE AND HISTORY OF LINEDANCE

Linedance consists of a series of repeated dance steps. Dancers stand in a row or several rows, regardless gender, and there is no body touch. They dance face to face or face the same direction according to the unified rhythm. The earlier danceline is different from the modern danceline. In earlier period, dancers stood face to face and danced with partners hand in hand. Instead of standing in a row, they would gather round a circle. Sometimes, there would be a leader in the middle of the dance floor. The linedance is a very popular and leisure activity, and it comes from western country dance bar, social club, etc. Such dance can easily solve the imbalance between men and wemen. Since the early 1970s, thc linedance begins to be popular with pop musics, such as rock, disco, Latin music, jazz, etc. Sometimes, the linedance combines with other form of western country dance, such as swaying dance, two-step dance, three-step dance as well as dances evolving from western dance, like waltz, polka, swing dance, etc. Some linedances evolve from round dance, such as rain dance in Middle East. Actually, many round dances are standing in a row instead of a circle, which is more commonly seen when there are few dancers. Some linedances are very similiar with folk dance. Many folk dances have the uniform movement, and dancers stand in a row or several rows with partners hand in hand. Certainly, not all rows will be stright line, and they may be curve or broken line. Up to now, the traditional linedance is still very popular in Balkan and other countries. These traditional linedances also appear in international folk dance competition. The folk linedance has diverse forms, and dancers can stand face to face or gather round a circle. Partners can dance hand in hand, holding partner's belt or shoulder, etc.

Electric slide which was popular in the middle 1970s, chicken walk jive in the 1980s and Macarena in the middle 1990s are all adapted based on linedance. The linedance begins to be popular across the world after 1990s. It was brought into China at the beginning of the 20th century, and it began to develop and popular in large and medium-sized cities.

2 RESEARCH OBJECT AND METHOD

2.1 Research object

The feasibility of linedance develops in Jinan colleges and universities.

2.2 Research method

2.2.1 Method of documents and materials
According to the research demand, this paper mainly gets relevant research materials by the following ways: consulting literatures about linedance and fitness dance through CNKI, ebsco, Springer, etc.; getting the current development situation and relevant policies and regulations about linedance through Shandong Library, library in college, Shandong Sports Bureau, Jinan Sports Bureau, etc.; studying on books about linedance.

2.2.2 Questionnaire survey
Questionnaire is designed according to the research aim and question after reading a lot of literatures. The questionnaire can be divided into teachers questionnaire and students questionnaire. 30 teachers and 240 students are selected as research object from 38 colleges and universities in Jinan which have offered the course of linedance.

3 RESEARCH RESULT AND ANALYSIS

3.1 Health promotion of linedance

Linedance is an aerobic exercise, which is similar with aerobic walking. Such exercise can effectively promote the adult female's aerobic exercise ability and cardiovascular function. Zan Gao took 146 students who were in grade 6~8 as object to study the influence of jogging, linedance, football, passing and catching on heart rate as well as the difference between grades. His research result indicates that the expected heart rate of linedance is obviously lower than that of other activities. Besides, compared with students in higher grade, the students in lower grade have significant higher heart rate and expected heart rate. Noreau L. took 19 people whose average age were about 49.3 as experimental group, 10 people whose average age were about 49.4 as control group. And these people took 12 weeks of linedance, and they danced twice a week. Then, the aerobic ability of this experimental group is improved by 13% averagely, and the highest improved value can reach 40%. What's more, they have positive changes in depression, anxiety, tension and fatigue.

The linedance is mainly an activity of lower limb, which can enhance body balance and muscle strength. In the activity, high frequency and long time single foot support can effectively enhance body balance by moving the center of gravity continuously. Having linedance for a long time can reduce the risk of falls in elder people. Besides, the linedance has positive influence on participants' step speed and strike frequency. Taylor R.W.'s study on students from 5~12 years old indicates that linedance has significant effect on obesity, BMI, twistline, etc. Murrock C.J.'s study on 46 26~83 years old African American women who had diabetics, and the study lasted 12 weeks. These women had linedance twice a week. His research result indicates that the body fat content and systolic pressure of these women are significantly improved when compared with the control group. Generally, the young female do not like sports which are fierce and dangerous, and they will choose some nonantagonistic program as physical activity. Burgess G.'s study indicates that the young female's unsatisfaction with their body image (like attraction, obesity and body shape) is greatly decreased after 6 weeks' linedance. Meanwhile, their physical self-cognition is also improved, including body attraction and body self-worth.

3.2 Analysis on students' acceptability of linedance course

3.2.1 Analysis on students' cognition degree of linedance activity
Students' hobby and interest in sports is one of the important premises of this physical education curriculum. The questionnaire investigates college students' approaches to understand the linedance as well as their interest in it from multiple angles. How do you know the linedance? The result indicates: 72 students know the linedance through TV and network, which accounts for 30.00%; 55 students know the linedance through friends or classmates, which accounts for 22.92%; 67 students know the linedance through PE, which accounts for 27.92%; there are 38 students know the linedance by other approaches, which accounts for 15.83%; there are 8 students do not know the linedance, which accounts for 3.33%. The above data indicates that 96% of students have different understandings of linedance, which benefits the popularization and promotion of linedance in colleges and universities.

3.2.2 Analysis of students' motivation to participate in linedance

One can select one or more options from "healthy fashion", "easy to learn", "interpersonal communication", "master sports skill" and "for the course credit". The questionnaire result indicates that 90.83% of students select "healthy fashion". The linedance contains multiple dance factors, such as jazz, Latin dance, hip-hop, etc. The linedance is mainly an activity of lower limb, and there are more movements in waist and hip. These features cater to most college students' pursuit of fashion to shape a perfect body image. 82.50% of students select "easy to learn", because the linedance can be divided into beginning, intermediate and advanced levels according to the difficulty of action and dance step. People with different ages and genders can select the most suitable level to dance. 59.27% of students select "interpersonal communication". As Nadasen K. (2007) considered that the linedance could promote group consciousness, social communication and aesthetics. The linedance can also improve the female's social belonging, and they can find and develop more social relationships by this platform. 35.83% of students select "master sports skill" which has low proportion, and this shows that college students' consciousness of lifelong exercise is very low. 58.75% of students select "for the course credit", which well illustrates that the linedance can be integrated into physical education curriculum system of higher education, and the students can successfully complete the linedance course by their own learning.

3.3 Analysis on relevant managers and teachers' acceptability of linedance course

Among the 38 investigated higher education schools in Jinan, the author finds out that 27 higher education schools do not offer linedance course. The main reason is that the relevant learders in schools have few understanding and low cognition of linedance. Among these 27 higher education schools, leaders from 19 schools have a certain understanding of linedance, but they do not plan to offer the linedance course. So it is a key factor for relevant mangers in school to attach importance to make a new sport item enter the sports teaching. The linedance as a new sport item has its own value and charm, which are very popolar among college students. However, currently leaders in colleges and universities do not attach high importance to the development of linedance.

Seen from 11 higher education schools which have offered linedance course, the proportion of teacher's gender is seriously unbalanced. Among the investigated 30 teachers, there are only 4 male teachers, which accounts for 13%. There are 8 professional linedance teachers and 22 non-professional linedance teachers. And most linedance teachers are teachers who originally taught dancesport or calisthenics. The education backgrounds of most teachers are bachelor's degree or master's degree, which accounts for 80%, and it accounts for 85% among these teachers whose age is between 22 and 40. Seen from teachers' attitudes toward the linedance course, most of them support the development of linedance course in colleges and universities. And they think the music of linedance as well as its dance style are diverse, the form of participation is very flexible, its exercise intensity is moderate and students have high passion for it.

4 CONCLUSION

This research aims to discuss the feasibility of linedance in physical education curriculum in colleges and universities, and it consists of fitness promotion of linedance, students' acceptability, the acceptability of managers and teachers. The paper draws the following conclusions by the method of documents and materials, questionnaire survey.

Participating in linedance activity can improve one's aerobic ability and cardiovascular function. And one's balanced ability and coordination ability can also be improved significantly. Besides, the linedance has positive influence on BMI, body composition, cognition, emotion and social belonging. Seen from the students' questionnaire, most students have a good understanding of the linedance, and they show high enthusiasm in it. And their motivation to participate in the linedance is for the healthy fashion, easy to learn and making good friends. Seen from the managers' questionnaire, it is a key factor for leaders to attach importance to make the linedance be a physical education course. Leaders in those schools which do not offer linedance course do not know the linedance. Teachers have positive attitude towards the development of linedance, and they think it has broad prospects. Seen from the qualified teachers, the main difficulty may be too few professional linedance teachers, and the equipments are limited. Thus, this research explores the feasibility of linedance in physical education curriculum in colleges and universities based on its fitness promotion, teachers' support and students' identity. Therefore, I think it is feasible for the linedance to be a physical education curriculum in colleges and universities.

REFERENCES

[1] Wikipedia, Linedance [EB/OL]. http://en.wikipedia. org/wiki/Line_dance, 2013-05-08.

[2] Town'n Country Senior Stars [EB/OL]. http://tncseniorstars.com/html/history.html, 2013-05-08.

[3] Dong B. Feasibility Research on Linedance Optional Course in Departments of Physical Education in Shaanxi Province [D]. Xi'an Physical Education University, 2011 (5).

[4] Gao Z., Hannon J.C. & Carson R.L. Middle School Students' Heart Rates During Different Curricular Activities in Physical Education [J]. International Council for Health, Physical Education, Recreation, Sport, and Dance Journal of Research, 2009, 4(1).

[5] Liu T.J. & Tang X.Y. Research Status and Prospect of Healthy Promotion Based on Linedance in Abroad [J]. Journal of Beijing Dance Academy, 2013 (1).

[6] Murrock C.J., Higgins P.A., Killon C. Dance and Peer Support to Improve Diabetes Outcomes in African American Women [J]. The Diabetes Educator, 2009, 35(6).

[7] Wei Y.M. Status Survey and Strategy Research on the Development of Linedance in Xi'an Colleges and Universities [D]. Shaanxi Normal University, 2012 (6).

Computer, Intelligent Computing and Education Technology – Liu, Sung & Yao (Eds)
© *2014 Taylor & Francis Group, London, ISBN 978-1-138-02469-4*

Analyzing a new "3+1" school-enterprise cooperation training mode: A case study in software engineering

C.B. Wang & S.T. Wen
Ningbo Institute of Technology, Zhejiang University, China

ABSTRACT: The "3+1" training model has become an important way to cultivate industry talents in colleges/universities which are under local authorities. Further, "3+1" model is also regarded as the top-level design for training applied talents. In this paper, we analyze the "3+1" training model in various operating mode, and summarize its advantages and disadvantages. Based on the training practice, we propose a new "3+1" school-enterprise cooperation mode and discuss the roles of university teachers, students and business engineers under this mode. Moreover, we summarize the advantages l, feasibility and operability of this model. The practice has proved the effect of our proposed new "3+1" mode. This mode can be a useful complement to existing models.

Keywords: "3+1" training mode; inner-school enterprise; transform from knowledge to ability

1 INTRODUCTION

The connotation of "3+1" training mode is: using former three academic years to complete the majority courses' study in school, and using 4th academic year to complete graduation practice and thesis. Through practice and training in 4th academic year, it make students can transform the learned knowledge in school to projects capability and relevant skills which is necessary in employment.

The cooperate training of applied talents is including enterprise as an element of the process of personnel training and form colleges, businesses to participate in the pattern of personnel training. It changes the traditional theory teaching into training mode which combines theory teaching and practice of enterprise in the discipline system [1]. Its essence is taking business practices as "knowledge" into "ability". No doubt, it is an important direction of application-oriented training model reform. However, in the specific operation, this mode encountered many problems and obstacles. Therefore school-enterprise cooperation mode requires continuous reforming and making this carrier with high efficiency and sustainable development.

The rest of this paper is organized as follows: Section 2 summarizes existing "3+1" training models. Section 3 investigates a new "3+1" training mode-campus enterprise model. Section 4 concludes the paper.

2 SUMMARIZE "3+1" TRAINING MODELS

After practice in recent years, in our school, the training model of "3+1" has following several modes.

2.1 *Internship mode*

The students recruit by enterprise for internship when in the 4th academic year. And they directly take part in real projects of enterprise. It is very useful for their upcoming employment in software companies. As for management of students, we take dual mentors (corporate enterprise and university) system [2]. Under this mode, first, the students can get actual project training. On the other hand, the students also create value for the enterprise. So, it can form ad double-win situation, and welcomed by enterprises. However, in this mode, students need to meet the knowledge requirement of enterprise, abilities conditions. Moreover, the enterprises with higher level, they require the internship students with better knowledge, background, and programming ability. As for local authoritative universities and colleges, private colleges, the proportion of students who meet these conditions, is not very high. Fox example, in our school, there is only 25 percent. Therefore, this mode can only solve part of the problem, and can not apply to all ubiquitous colleges and universities.

2.2 *Enterprise training mode*

The essential of this mode is: the college/university joins hands with educational training institution.

First, the education institutions will intensively train students about 3 to 5 months by engineering projects. The training projects are closely related to the actual needs of the industry requirements. After this, the education training institution is responsible to recommending the students to some enterprises for employment. This mode is very popular in India. In India, there are 500 thousands freshmen professional software engineering, but there only 74 thousands graduated from college without training by education institute, and the rest almost trained by vocational education and training [6].

As the training institutions, it will inevitably address problem that training institutions collect extra fee from student for their training. Therefore, it cause that the students to participate this mode is limited. For example, in my school, the proportion is generally about 15%. Therefore, this model can only solve part of the problem too.

2.3 School training mode

For local authoritative colleges, some students might not be interested in professional, and hate to academic study, the proportion of such students is generally about 15%. Meanwhile, there are some ambitious students. The aims of those students are study abroad or pursuing recruited by graduate school. This ratio of students is generally about 15%. As for abovementioned two types' students, we can use school training mode [4,7,8] based on their career planning, such as organizing postgraduate entrance examination classes, tutoring classes and other forms.

These are our school "3+1" talent cultivation different operating modes in major of software engineering. Through data analysis, it is not difficult to find that those modes only covered a total about 70 percent. This indicates that nearly 30 percent of the students who were removed from above the different modes. It might be hard to achieve the desired objectives.

As for local authoritative college or university, the students are relatively fixed hierarchy of knowledge and ability to improve the coverage of each mode of operation, relatively difficult. Therefore, we need to develop new modes.

3 CAMPUS ENTERP-A NEW "3+1" TRAINING MODE

Through the above analysis, there is one class of students whose overall capacity less than (but close to) the requirements of enterprises. So, the enterprise might not direct accept those students. Therefore, those students not only need opportunities to practice engineering, but also need the help

of university teachers. Then, the campus enterprise was proposed. The so-called campus enterprise is to make use University Joint Laboratory, and let the enterprise can migrate their produce plan to campus laboratory. The University teachers, students and enterprise engineering cooperate to complete those actual projects.

3.1 Campus enterprise—a perfect scheme of integrating "production, learning and research"

If we have a reasonable operation, the campus enterprise can produce a win-win situation completely. For the enterprise side, it moves part of production plans to university campus according to the following considerations: Firstly, the university laboratories have many equipments and other needed software. Secondly, the labor cost is relatively cheap because we have many college students. Thirdly, since the university teachers manage the laboratories (including manage and educate students), it can saves management costs. Fourthly, the enterprise can exert teachers' academic ability to guide enterprise's scientific research. As for university's teachers, on one hand, the enterprise may provide foundation for teachers to help developing their urgent projects. On the other hand, the university teachers have opportunities to take part in the projects of enterprise. It can improve the personal experience and enhance the capacity of their actual projects. As for college students, they do not go out of school and got a chance to practice under the direct enterprise. In the practice process, they not only guide by enterprise engineers but also instruct by university teachers from knowledge education.

In campus enterprises, as described above, there are three categories of employees (roles). They are like well-run parts of the machine. In the process of software production, each plays a different role as shown in Table 1.

3.2 Campus enterprise—a great place to change "knowledge into engineering experience"

The existence of a common phenomenon in Chinese college students is: the students have great score but bad in actual engineering ability. That is "high score and low ability" [4,5]. The essence is that the students can not translate their knowledge into the ability to solve practical engineering problems. It's caused by our education system and training modes [4,5].

In current Universities, the academic ability is put in a priority position. So, the projects which focus on real application cannot be placed the University's teaching program. The reasons are following: Firstly, most teachers do not have the

Table 1. Employee roles of campus enterprise.

	Project management	System design	Software design	Programming	Test case design	Test processing	Document
University teachers	◎ ※	◎ ※	○ ※	×	○ ※	×	×
Engineer	○	○	◎	○ ※	◎	○ ※	○ ※
Students	□	□	□	◎	□	◎	◎

Remarks: "◎": Primary; "○": Secondary; "□": Participant and Learner; "×": Un-participant; ※: Instructor.

Table 2. Characteristic between teachers and engineer.

	Academic level	Engineering practice ability	Teaching ability
Teachers	High	Middle	Strong
Engineers	Middle	Strong	Weak

ability to grasp the actual projects. On other hand, it is impossible to have such a long (six month or more) teaching arrangements. The campus enterprises can solve this problem perfectly. As shown in Table 2, there are strong complementarily between University teachers and enterprise engineers in training students.

3.3 Implementation of campus enterprise

Starting in 2011, we signed a number of agreement similar campus enterprises in our school with several software enterprises. For example, the most famous one is Ningbo Institute Technology-Fuji Joint lab. In our Joint Lab, there are three University teachers from Ningbo Institute of Technology and four engineers from Fuji company.

We recruit about twenty students who cannot directly find suitable internship place in each year in major of software. Our Joint lab running nearly two years, the effect is significant. We can fulfill enterprise's production, research tasks about one million a year (excluding corporate party engineers completed). After the expiration internships, all of students in our laboratory found one or more satisfaction job. Namely, employment is very good. Moreover, all of them are working at professional software companies.

4 CONCLUSION

"3 +1" training mode is one of the important ways of application-oriented personnel training. Since local college students have the relatively fixed hierarchy of knowledge and ability. We must develop various forms of school-enterprise cooperation mode for adapting each individual student's requirements. "Campus enterprise" is a good attempt. It is suitable for a fixed group of students. In this mode, we can effectively solve the students knowledge does not translate into the ability to solve practical engineering problems and achieve win-win situation. This case has strong exemplary.

ACKNOWLEDGEMENT

This work is supported by Department of Computer Science of Technology, Ningbo Institute of Technology, Zhejiang University.

REFERENCES

[1] Shujiang Chen, Jianbin yang, Innovation College Personnel Training Strategy under School-enterprise cooperation model [J]. Technology and Innovation Management [(In Chinese)], 2011(5).
[2] Yongwei Zeng, Guorong Liu, Excellence Plan to Constructing Practice Teaching System with Scientific Exploration, Chinese University Teaching [In Chinese], 2011(7): 75–78.
[3] Xiang Gu, Jiehua Wang, Excellence "3+1" Training mode for fourth year practical teaching, Computer Education [In Chinese], 2013(6): 26–27.
[4] Xiaohui Cheng, Ping Zong. Explore Different Ways of College Software Talents Training [in Chinese], Shanxi Education [In Chinese], 2009 (6):74.
[5] Jinglin Li, Software Training Mode Reform, Acta Hunan Medical University [In Chinese] (Part of Social Sciences), 2009, 11(2): 153–154.
[6] Dexue Liu, Yu Zhou, Based on "Diamond Model" of India Software Outsourcing Industry a Competitive advantage over Comparative Study. 2009(10): 127–130.
[7] Marilyn Gist, Catherine Schwoerer, and Benson Rosen, Effects of alternative training methods on self-efficacy and performance in computer software training, Journal of Applied Psychology, 74(6), pp. 884–994, 1989, American Psychologic Association.
[8] Zheng Li, Changping Zhu, Xinnan Fan, and Tiezheng Guo "3+1" Education model and Cultivating Innovating and Practice ability of Students, Experimental Technology and Mangement, 24(1), pp. 128–130, 2007.

Computer, Intelligent Computing and Education Technology – Liu, Sung & Yao (Eds)
© 2014 Taylor & Francis Group, London, ISBN 978-1-138-02469-4

Sensitivity analysis of the transient response of the networks containing transmission lines

Xiao-Ke Chen & Yan-Jun Zhao
Electric Power Research Institute of Guangdong Power Grid Corporation, Guangzhou, Guangdong, China

Jin-Quan Zhao, Wen-Wen Cao & Xian Zhou
School of Electrical Engineering, Xi'an Jiaotong University, Xi'an, Shaanxi, China

Jian-Hua Yin
CSG Electric Power Research Institute, Guangzhou, Guangdong, China

ABSTRACT: A novel method based on NILT is presented to analyze the sensitivity of transient response of the networks containing transmission lines. In this method, transmission lines, circuit and its components are taken into account as a whole. According to the topology of the transmission lines in the circuit, the sensitivity of transient response of the circuit can be derived by solving the transient response of the circuit and the partial derivative equation of the ABCD matrix of the transmission lines with respect to the parameters of the circuit. By conducting a series expansion of the parameter matrix, the problem can be simplified dramatically. This method is simple and accurate without decoupling calculation of the coupled transmission lines. The example shows the effectiveness of the method.

Keywords: networks; transmission lines; transient response; sensitivity

1 INTRODUCTION

Along with the rapid signal speed growth of the high speed integrated circuit and the decrcase of chip size, the effects of transmission lines (such as delay, reflection, dispersion and crosstalk of signals) become more and more obviously, which may even worse cause signal distortion or switch disoperation. The effects of transmission lines have become main factors of the performance and reliability of circuits. Thus, for the sake of designing a well high speed integrated circuit, we need to analysis the main factors of the transmission lines effects, that is to say, we have to analysis the sensitivity of the transient response of the networks containing transmission lines, and then we can optimize the design of circuit parameters. Sensitivity analysis of the transient response of the networks containing transmission lines has become one of hot topic researches,[1] researchers have pointed out several methods, such as perturbation method, gradient method, characteristic method and adjoint network method. Perturbation method is the most original and direct sensitivity analysis method with poor accuracy and efficiency, and when the number of the optimization variables grows, the calculation becomes large, so it is not suitable for the optimization for large scale circuits. Gradient method gives the sensitivity through taking the derivative of a parameter which based on the mathematic expression of the output response. For that there is only arithmetic solution of transmission line output response, and the analytical solution is difficult to obtain, the application of gradient method is limited. Characteristic method is a kind of time domain analysis method which is effective to analyze the single conductor uniformed transmission lines. Adjoint network method is a common method for the sensitivity analysis of circuits with concentrated parameters, but there is no universal method to analyze the distributed parameter transmission lines.[2] A new method for transient response sensitivity analysis of the transient response of the networks containing transmission lines is presented, this method uses Numerical Inversion of the Laplace Transform (NILT) without adopting the equivalent circuit. In this method, transmission lines, circuit and its components are taken into account as a whole. According to the topology of the transmission lines in the circuit, the sensitivity of transient response of the circuit can be derived by solving the transient response of the circuit and the partial derivative equation of the ABCD matrix of the transmission lines with respect to the parameters of the circuit. By conducting a series expansion of the parameter matrix, the problem can be simplified dramatically. This method is simple and accurate without decoupling calculation of the coupled transmission lines. The example shows the effectiveness of the method.

2 THE TRANSMISSION LINE NETWORK EQUATION

The transmission line network equation in frequency domain is:[3]

$$(\mathbf{G}+s\mathbf{C})\mathbf{U}+\sum_{i=1}^{N_s}(\mathbf{J}_i\mathbf{I}_i)=\mathbf{U}_s \tag{1}$$

where $\mathbf{G}$, $\mathbf{C}$ are the $N \times N$ stage conductance and capacitance matrix, N is the node number of the transmission line network; $\mathbf{U}$ is N-stage column vector of nodal voltage; $\mathbf{N}_s$ is the group number of transmission lines; $\mathbf{U}_s$ is N-stage column vector of voltage source; $\mathbf{I}_i$ is the i ($i = 1, 2, ..., N_s$) group, 2M-stage input and output vector of current of M-conductor (M is the number of coupled transmission lines) transmission lines. $\mathbf{J}_i$ is $N \times 2M$ stage matrix which represents the i group topological relation between the transmission line and network.

The relation between current and voltage of the i group transmission line can be written as:[4]

$$\begin{bmatrix} \mathbf{I}_{1i} \\ \mathbf{I}_{2i} \end{bmatrix} = \begin{bmatrix} \mathbf{Y}_{1i} & \mathbf{Y}_{2i} \\ \mathbf{Y}_{3i} & \mathbf{Y}_{4i} \end{bmatrix} \begin{bmatrix} \mathbf{U}_{1i} \\ \mathbf{U}_{2i} \end{bmatrix} \tag{2}$$

where $\mathbf{I}_{1i}$, $\mathbf{U}_{1i}$, $\mathbf{I}_{2i}$, $\mathbf{U}_{2i}$ are the i group input current and voltage, output current and voltage of the transmission lines respectively. $\mathbf{Y}_{1i}=\mathbf{D}_i\mathbf{B}_i^{-1}$, $\mathbf{Y}_{2i}=\mathbf{C}_i-\mathbf{D}_i\mathbf{B}_i^{-1}\mathbf{A}_i$, $\mathbf{Y}_{3i}=\mathbf{B}_i^{-1}$, $\mathbf{Y}_{4i}=-\mathbf{B}_i^{-1}\mathbf{A}_i$;

$$\begin{bmatrix} \mathbf{A}_i & \mathbf{B}_i \\ \mathbf{C}_i & \mathbf{D}_i \end{bmatrix} = \begin{bmatrix} \cosh(\boldsymbol{\gamma}_i l_i) & \sinh(\boldsymbol{\gamma}_i l_i)\mathbf{Z}_{ci} \\ \mathbf{Z}_{ci}^{-1}\sinh(\boldsymbol{\gamma}_i l_i) & \mathbf{Z}_{ci}^{-1}\cosh(\boldsymbol{\gamma}_i l_i)\mathbf{Z}_{ci} \end{bmatrix};$$

$\boldsymbol{\gamma}_i = (\mathbf{Z}_i\mathbf{Y}_i)^{1/2}$, $\mathbf{Z}_i = \mathbf{R}_i + s\mathbf{L}_i$, $\mathbf{Y}_i = \mathbf{G}_i + s\mathbf{C}_i$; l_i is the length of the i group transmission line.

3 SENSITIVITY OF THE TRANSIENT RESPONSE OF THE TRANSMISSION LINE NETWORKS

Substituting (2) into (1), we can get:

$$(\mathbf{G}+s\mathbf{C})\mathbf{U}+\sum_{i=1}^{N_s}\left(\mathbf{J}_i\begin{bmatrix} \mathbf{Y}_{1i} & \mathbf{Y}_{1i} \\ \mathbf{Y}_{2i} & \mathbf{Y}_{2i} \end{bmatrix}\mathbf{U}_i\right)=\mathbf{U}_s \tag{3}$$

Suppose λ to be a parameter of the network (Lumped parameter or distribution parameters), taking partial derivatives with respect to a circuit parameter λ in (3), we can get:

$$\frac{\partial(\mathbf{G}+s\mathbf{C})}{\partial\lambda}\mathbf{U}+(\mathbf{G}+s\mathbf{C})\frac{\partial\mathbf{U}}{\partial\lambda}+\sum_{i=1}^{N_s}\left(\mathbf{J}_i\begin{bmatrix} \dfrac{\partial\mathbf{Y}_{1i}}{\partial\lambda} & \dfrac{\partial\mathbf{Y}_{1i}}{\partial\lambda} \\ \dfrac{\partial\mathbf{Y}_{2i}}{\partial\lambda} & \dfrac{\partial\mathbf{Y}_{2i}}{\partial\lambda} \end{bmatrix}\mathbf{U}_i\right)$$

$$+\sum_{i=1}^{N_s}\left(\mathbf{J}_i\begin{bmatrix} \mathbf{Y}_{1i} & \mathbf{Y}_{1i} \\ \mathbf{Y}_{2i} & \mathbf{Y}_{2i} \end{bmatrix}\frac{\partial\mathbf{U}_i}{\partial\lambda}\right)=0 \tag{4}$$

where

$$\frac{\partial\mathbf{Y}_{2i}}{\partial\lambda}=\frac{\partial\mathbf{C}_i}{\partial\lambda}-\frac{\partial\mathbf{D}_i}{\partial\lambda}\mathbf{B}_i^{-1}\mathbf{A}_i+\mathbf{D}_i\mathbf{B}_i^{-1}\frac{\partial\mathbf{B}_i}{\partial\lambda}\mathbf{B}_i^{-1}\mathbf{A}_i$$

$$-\mathbf{D}_i\mathbf{B}_i^{-1}\frac{\partial\mathbf{A}_i}{\partial\lambda}$$

$$\frac{\partial\mathbf{Y}_{3i}}{\partial\lambda}=-\mathbf{B}_i^{-1}\frac{\partial\mathbf{B}_i}{\partial\lambda}\mathbf{B}_i^{-1}$$

$$\frac{\partial\mathbf{Y}_{4i}}{\partial\lambda}=\mathbf{B}_i^{-1}\frac{\partial\mathbf{B}_i}{\partial\lambda}\mathbf{B}_i^{-1}\mathbf{A}_i-\mathbf{B}_i^{-1}\frac{\partial\mathbf{A}_i}{\partial\lambda}.$$

To solve (4), we can get $\partial\mathbf{U}/\partial\lambda$, $\partial\mathbf{U}_i/\partial\lambda$, and then the sensitivity of the transient response of the transmission line networks with respect to λ can be acquired through NILT.

In (4), $\mathbf{G}$, $\mathbf{C}$ are lumped-parameter element, and it is easy to calculate $\partial(\mathbf{G}+s\mathbf{C})/\partial\lambda$ and $(\mathbf{G}+s\mathbf{C})$. The key of solving (4) is to calculate partial derivatives of $\mathbf{U}$, $\mathbf{U}_i$ and matrix $\mathbf{ABCD}$ with respect to λ. The transient response analysis method of transmission lines based on NILT is effective according to [5]–[7], the method of calculating the partial derivatives of matrix $\mathbf{ABCD}$ with respect to λ is as follow. The series expansion of matrix $\mathbf{ABCD}$ is:[7]

$$\mathbf{A}_i=\sum_{n=1}^{\infty}\frac{1}{(2n-2)!}(\mathbf{Z}_i\mathbf{Y}_i l_i^2)^{n-1}$$

$$\mathbf{B}_i=\sum_{n=1}^{\infty}\frac{1}{(2n-1)!}(\mathbf{Z}_i\mathbf{Y}_i l_i^2)^{n-1}\mathbf{Z}_i l_i$$

$$\mathbf{C}_i=\sum_{n=1}^{\infty}\frac{1}{(2n-1)!}\mathbf{Y}_i l_i(\mathbf{Z}_i\mathbf{Y}_i l_i^2)^{n-1} \tag{5}$$

$$\mathbf{D}_i=\sum_{n=1}^{\infty}\frac{1}{(2n-2)!}(\mathbf{Z}_i\mathbf{Y}_i l_i^2)^{n-1}$$

To take partial derivatives with respect to λ:

$$\frac{\partial\mathbf{A}_i}{\partial\lambda}=\sum_{n=1}^{\infty}\frac{1}{(2n-2)!}\frac{\partial}{\partial\lambda}(\mathbf{Z}_i\mathbf{Y}_i l_i^2)^{n-1}$$

$$\frac{\partial\mathbf{B}_i}{\partial\lambda}=\sum_{n=1}^{\infty}\frac{1}{(2n-1)!}\frac{\partial}{\partial\lambda}[(\mathbf{Z}_i\mathbf{Y}_i l_i^2)^{n-1}\mathbf{Z}_i l_i]$$

$$\frac{\partial\mathbf{C}_i}{\partial\lambda}=\sum_{n=1}^{\infty}\frac{1}{(2n-1)!}\frac{\partial}{\partial\lambda}[\mathbf{Y}_i l_i(\mathbf{Z}_i\mathbf{Y}_i l_i^2)^{n-1}] \tag{6}$$

$$\frac{\partial\mathbf{D}_i}{\partial\lambda}=\sum_{n=1}^{\infty}\frac{1}{(2n-2)!}\frac{\partial}{\partial\lambda}(\mathbf{Z}_i\mathbf{Y}_i l_i^2)^{n-1}$$

From (6) we can see that when λ is the lumped parameter, the partial derivatives of matrix **ABCD** with respect to λ is 0. It doesn't need to solve the characteristic values of matrixes or to decouple the coupled transmission lines. We just need to take some basic matrix operations, which simplified not only the calculation of the partial derivatives of matrix **ABCD** with respect to circuit parameter, but also the sensitivity analysis of the transient response of the transmission line networks.

4 EXAMPLES

The example is taken from the literature [3], as shown in Figure 1, the length of 1#, 2#, 3# transmission lines are 0.05 m, 0.04 m and 0.03 m, the transmission line parameters are:

$$R = \begin{bmatrix} 75 & 15 \\ 15 & 75 \end{bmatrix} \Omega/m \quad L = \begin{bmatrix} 494.6 & 63.3 \\ 63.3 & 494.6 \end{bmatrix} nH/m$$

$$G = \begin{bmatrix} 0.1 & -0.01 \\ -0.01 & 0.1 \end{bmatrix} S/m \quad C = \begin{bmatrix} 62.8 & -4.9 \\ -4.9 & 62.8 \end{bmatrix} pF/m$$

Figures 2 and 3 show the results of the method we pointed out and the method proposed in [3]. From the transient response sensitivity of u_{23} with respect to some circuit parameters from the figures, we can see that the amplitude, timing and changing trends of waveforms according to these two methods are consistent.

Figure 4 shows the results of we pointed out and the perturbation method (the disturbance

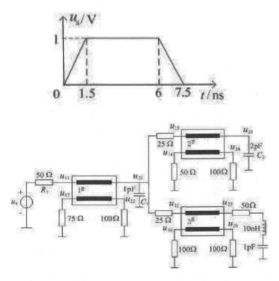

Figure 1. Transmission line networks. a) Excitation waveform. b) Circuit.

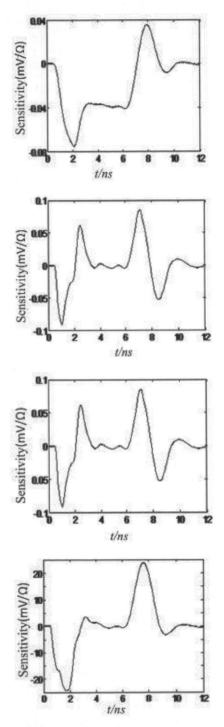

Figure 2. The results of the present method. a) Sensitivity of u_{23} with respect to R_{11}(75 Ω/m) of 2# transmission line. b) Sensitivity of u_{23} with respect to L_{11} (494.6 nH/m) of 2# transmission line. c) Sensitivity of u_{23} with respect to R_1. d) Sensitivity of u_{23} with respect to C_1.

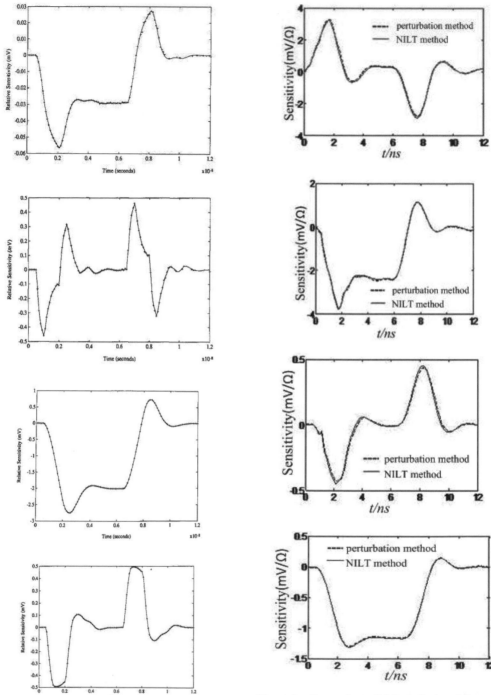

Figure 3. The results of the method in literature [3]. a) Sensitivity of u_{23} with respect to R_{11} (75 Ω/m) of 2# transmission line. b) Sensitivity of u_{23} with respect to L_{11} (494.6 nH/m) of 2# transmission line. c) Sensitivity of u_{23} with respect to R_1. d) Sensitivity of u_{23} with respect to C_1.

Figure 4. Comparison of this method and the perturbation method. a) Sensitivity of u_{13} with respect to R_{21} (15 Ω/m) of 2# transmission line. b) Sensitivity of u_{16} with respect to R_{11} (75 Ω/m) of 1# transmission line. c) Sensitivity of u_{11} with respect to C_{11} (62.8 pF/m) of 2# transmission line. d) Sensitivity of u_{23} with respect to G_{11} (0.1 S/m) of 2# transmission line.

Table 1. Comparison of the proposed method and the perturbation method.

Sensitivity	NILT method	Perturbation method		
		0.01% disturbance	0.5% disturbance	1% disturbance
$D^{u_{13}}_{R_{21}}$ µF/Ω	−0.5904	−0.5896	−0.5117	−0.4773
$D^{u_{f6}}_{R_{f}}$ µV/Ω	−2.2555	−2.2602	−2.2711	−2.2835
$D^{u_{i1}}_{C_{11}}$ mV/pF	−0.1703	−0.1703	−0.1764	−0.2002
$D^{u_{23}}_{G_{11}}$ V/S	−1.2924	−1.2924	−1.2865	−1.2646

quantity is 0.5%), the results of these two methods are consistent.

To illustrate the precision of our method, we give out the results of these two methods when t = 3ns. For the perturbation method, the smaller the disturbance quantity is, the higher the calculation precision is. The result of our method is consistent with the perturbation method when the disturbance quantity is 0.01%, which states the high precision of the method we pointed in this paper.

5 CONCLUSIONS

The method based on NILT is presented to analyze the sensitivity of transient response of the networks containing transmission lines. In this method, transmission lines, circuit and its components are taken into account as a whole. According to the topology of the transmission lines in the circuit, the sensitivity of transient response of the circuit can be derived by solving the transient response of the circuit and the partial derivative equation of the ABCD matrix of the transmission lines with respect to the parameters of the circuit. By conducting a series expansion of the parameter matrix, the problem can be simplified dramatically. This method we pointed out in this paper is simple and accurate.

REFERENCES

[1] Xiao-peng JI, Long GE, Zhi-quan W. Differential Quadrature Method Based Sensitivity Analysis of Interconnect Lines [J]. Information and Control, 2008, 5: 005.

[2] Winklestein D, Steer MB, Pomerleau R. Simulation of arbitrary transmission line networks with nonlinear terminations [J]. Circuits and Systems, IEEE Transactions on, 1991, 38(4): 418~422.

[3] Lum S, Nakhla M, Zhang QJ. Sensitivity analysis of lossy coupled transmission lines [J]. IEEE Trans on MTT, 1991, 39(12): 2089~2099.

[4] Hoefer WJR. The transmission-line matrix method—theory and applications [J]. Microwave Theory and Techniques, IEEE Transactions on, 1985, 33(10): 882~893.

[5] J. Richard, Michel S. Nakhla. Time-domain analysis of lossy coupled transmission lines [J]. IEEE Trans on MTT, 1990, 38(10): 1480~1487.

[6] Moises Cases, Douglas M. Quinn. Transient response of uniformly distributed RLC transmission lines [J]. IEEE Trans on CAS, 1980, 27(3): 200~213.

[7] Mao JF, Li ZF. Analysis of the time response of nonuniform multiconductor transmission lines with a method of equivalent cascaded network chain [J]. Microwave Theory and Techniques, IEEE Transactions on, 1992, 40(5): 948~954.

[8] Lum S, Nakhla M, Zhang QJ. Sensitivity analysis of lossy coupled transmission lines with nonlinear terminations [J]. IEEE Trans on MTT, 1994, 42(4): 607~615.

[9] Lum S, Nakhla MS, Zhang QJ. Sensitivity analysis of lossy coupled transmission lines [J]. Microwave Theory and Techniques, IEEE Transactions on, 1991, 39(12): 2089~2099.

[10] Xu QW, Li ZF, Wang J, et al. Transient analysis of lossy interconnects by modified method of characteristics [J]. IEEE Trans on circuits and systems, 2000, 47(3): 363~375.

Computer, Intelligent Computing and Education Technology – Liu, Sung & Yao (Eds)
© *2014 Taylor & Francis Group, London, ISBN 978-1-138-02469-4*

The simulation and analysis for economic systems based on complex network theory

L.H. Luo & J.A. Fang
School of Information Science and Technology, Donghua University, Shanghai, China

ABSTRACT: Several virtual economic systems are built on random, regular, and small-world network structure respectively in this paper, which are endowed with Cobb-Douglas utility functions. The value of the Cobb-Douglas utility function can represent the satisfaction degree of the consumers. The aim of this paper is to simulate the economic systems and study how the network structures can affect their Cobb-Douglas utility function value's growth rate through complex network theory. We find that small-world network structure surpasses other network structures to reach the highest value of utility function at a reasonable cost, for its network characteristics of short average path length and high clustering coefficient.

Keywords: small-world network; complex network statistic characteristics, Cobb-Douglas utility function; utility growth rate

1 INTRODUCTION

Since the 1990s, the discovery of small-world network has stimulated a large interest on its characteristics from many principles. It is proven that the small-world feature is an underlying constitutive property of many natural and artificial networks. Watts and Strogatz [1] have shown that the connection topology of some biological, technological and social networks is neither completely regular nor completely random [2] but stays somehow in between these two extreme cases [3]. They define the model of this network organization as small-world network. From then on, researchers have focused their attention on different aspects: Internet [4], epidemic [5], social networks [6,7], and geography [8].

Scientists have also studied to understand the economic system through the dynamics of networks. Axtell [9] explored the relative complexity of bilateral exchange versus a Walrasian world. The bilateral exchange process has been proven to be less costly than a Walrasian system. Still, under certain conditions, the equilibriums would be Pareto optimal although they may not be in the core.

Wilhite [10] compared the search and negotiation costs of different network structures and their mechanisms to initiate and engage in a trade. Small-world networks have been proven to have several characteristics of general interest in economics. First, all local trades can economize on these costs. Second, when a few overlapping traders belonging to other distant trade groups, goods can be traded between any particular pairs of agents with relatively few exchanges.

In our research, the small-world feature network analysis is placed in a data-driven economic system. We construct several network features under virtually identical circumstances to see the difference. The structure of the paper is designed as follows. Section 2 introduces the economy model. Section 3 designs the experiment plans based on the model. In section 4, we simulate the economic systems and compare the influence of network structures on the utility growth rate. Section 5 summarizes the main contributions of this study.

2 ECONOMY MODEL

The economy model we use derives from the one proposed by Allen Wilhite [10]. Determined amount of independent agents are created and each agent possesses two goods as their existing wealth to circulate in the market, one of which must be traded in whole units, and the other is infinitely divisible. All agents have the same symmetric Cobb-Douglas utility function they attempt to maximize. Formally, U^i depends on the agents' existing wealth, g_1 and g_2 the node possesses.

$$U^i = g_1^i g_2^i, \quad i \in \{1, \ldots, n\} \tag{1}$$

where n is the amount of agents.

The entire economy society is composed of transaction. A transaction starts when one node's questing for a negotiating price chance being responded by another node. An opportunity for mutually beneficial transaction exists if the marginal rates of substitution (*mrs*) of two agents differ, which reflects the amount of g_2 this agent would be willing to give up in exchange for another unit of g_1. The *mrs* of agent i is,

$$mrs^i = \frac{U'(g_1^i)}{U'(g_2^i)} = \frac{g_2^i}{g_1^i}, \quad i \in \{1, ..., n\} \tag{2}$$

where $U'(\bullet)$ is the first derivative of U.

Any agent can either trade g_2 for g_1 or trade g_1 for g_2 with the expense of price. In these experiments the trading price $p_{i,j}$ between agent i and agent j, is set as,

$$p_{i,j} = \frac{g_2^i + g_2^j}{g_1^i + g_1^j}, i, \quad j \in \{1, ..., n\} \tag{3}$$

The transaction goes on unless the trade cannot benefit each node's U^i, and would also stop once one of the nodes lack of good g_1 or cannot afford the price $p_{i,j}$. In the experiments, every active transaction will be considered as one time trade but two turnovers, since the income and outcome string are both taken into account. Once a transaction stop, the questing node will search again for a new opportunity until no node responds it, then another node is selected as the questing node. The economy society evolves like this and stops at the network's equilibrium. The Utility Growth Rate (*UGR*) is,

$$UGR = \frac{\sum_{i=1}^{n} U_e^i - \sum_{i=1}^{n} U^i}{\sum_{i=1}^{n} U^i}, \quad i \in \{1, ..., n\} \tag{4}$$

Equilibrium is a point of when agents cannot find trading opportunities that benefit any individuals. Feldman [11] studied the equilibrium characteristics of welfare-improving bilateral trade and showed that as long as all agents possess some non-zero amount of one of the commodities (all agents have some g_1 or all agents have some g_2) then the pairwise optimal allocation is also a Pareto optimal allocation. In this experiment, all agents are initially endowed with a positive amount of both goods, thus equilibrium are Pareto optimal [12].

3 EXPERIMENTAL DESIGN

This economy model is simulated in a Python program and with repeated simulations to explore how the network structures affect the UGR. Much of the emphasis on networks in the field of economics is concerned with network formation, such as in Jackson [13] construct the models with autonomous agents in which trade networks evolve as agents learn.

Artificial economy society is represented by the trade network composed of nodes and edges. According to the economy model, each society has agents, (represented by nodes), trading rules, (represented by edges), goods g_1 and g_2 (represented by the endowment of each node). The simulations can discussed a market containing nodes in multiple of 10. More specifically, we raise an instance of 20 nodes network as case study. Random amount of society wealth is assigned to each node. So far the construction of the trade network is finished. Then the trade proceeds according to the regime defined by the model economy till the equilibrium is reached. Throughout these experiments, nodes only do direct transaction without further searching for trading opportunities. Thus the extent of potential partners excludes the node with path length 2 or more.

In the experiments, we select random network, regular network, and small-world network as 3 different trade rules, and then compare the dynamic behavior when these networks reach equilibrium. Figure 1 shows the sketches of the three networks. The edges among nodes reflect the architecture of trade networks. To evaluate how the network structures can affect the UGR, we keep the experiments' initial condition all the same but adjust the network structure to observe possible variation of UGR. The initial conditions include: (1) the group

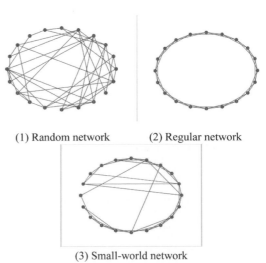

(1) Random network   (2) Regular network

(3) Small-world network

Figure 1.   Three network structures.

size is 20 (2) the endowments of goods g_1 and g_2 are the same (3) the motivation of each node is to maximize its own Cobb—Douglas utility U^i. Moreover, the result is a summary of numerous repeated simulations.

4 EXPERIMENT RESULT

In this part, we summarize our observation of the relationship between the network structures and UGR. We characterize the network structures by their statistic characteristics. Degree, average path length, clustering coefficient are of our most concern. V. Latora and M. Marchiori [14] represent the cost of a weighted graph as a formula based on the weight and path length. We define the average shortest path as the trade cost to evaluate the network's resource transferring efficiency. 'APL' may be substituted with 'cost' sometimes in the rest part of this paper.

A random network is a network that generated by random process. We use the Erdős-Rényi model [2] to build the random network. The Erdős-Rényi model sets an edge between each pair of nodes with equal probability, independently of the other edges [15]. In random network, all the linking is unpredictable, thus the APL varies every time. Here the average path length is 2.147 and Clustering Coefficient of 0.258. The average UGR was 8.0% at the trade times of 35 and the turnover of 182.833.

A regular graph is a graph where each vertex has the same number of neighbors, thus, every vertex has the same degree. A regular graph with vertices of degree k is called a k-regular graph and the graphs in the experiments are the 4-regular graphs. In regular network, every node can get access to all the other nodes, have the same number of neighbors, and fixed APL. The APL here is 5 and the Clustering Coefficient is 0.500. With more edges than random network, more trading are in opportunities in this system. The simulation shows that the UGR in this system rises to 10.5%, the turnover and trade times go to 232.550 and 57 respectively.

The small-world network in the experiments is an instance of the Watts-Strogatz model [1], which is a random graph generation model that produces graphs with small-world properties, including short average path lengths and high clustering coefficient. The WS small-world network stems from a regular ring lattice, a graph with 20 nodes each connected to given number of neighbors, 4 in the experiments. Every node will rewire their edge one by one with a given probability of 0.2, until rewiring is done by replacing a non-existing edge. The APL here is 2.410 and the clustering coefficient is 0.372, depending on every specific network

structure. The equilibrium results for small-world network as below. The UGR of the small-world network is 10.1%, the trade volume is 202.539 and the trade time is 53 respectively.

Table 1 summarizes the turnover, trade times and UGR of the three network structures. Clearly, the turnover is in proportion to the trade rounds and the UGR is always in proportion to them. Occasionally, it happens that the number of trades of regular and small-world network is the same. However, the UGR of the latter is beyond the former. The difference stems from the pairs of nodes, constrained by the network structure. Thus, we can deduce that the turnover and number of trades are not the direct incentives of UGR, and the underlying base is still the network structures.

Table 2 presents a comparison of the three network structures' key structure characteristics and their UGR. It appears that although the network structures exert influence on UGR, the mechanism is a complicated process involving every node and edge. Table 2 reveals that UGR try to get a balance between APL and clustering coefficient. The preference of comparatively low cost and high clustering coefficient is reasonable for the extremely low APL may miss some profit trades, just as the random networks, but the extremely high clustering coefficient may raise a high cost, as the regular networks. The result shows that the cost of regular network is more than two times of which of the small-world network, but the UGR is not. So take an overall consideration, the small-world network structure benefits an economic system more.

Table 1. Turnover, trade times and UGR.

	Turnover	Trade times	UGR [%]
Random network	182.833	35	8.0
Regular network	232.550	57	10.5
Small-world network	202.539	53	10.1

Table 2. Networks statistical characteristics and their UGR.

	APL	Clustering coefficient	UGR [%]
Random network	2.147	0.258	8.0
Regular network	5.000	0.500	10.5
Small-world network	2.410	0.372	10.1

5 CONCLUSION

This paper use economic theory, complex network theory, and computer simulations to examine the network structures' influence on the utility growth ratio of the economic systems. Major findings are summarized as follows. Under the circumstance of same endowments, the network structure is proved to have notable impact on the UGR. It is proven that although the small-world network economic system does not bring the highest *UGR* or lowest cost, it makes a best balance between the *UGR* and the cost, which benefits an economic system a lot. The important attributes of small-world networks play in a part in it, more specifically, the low short average path length, defined as the averaged minimum number of trading required for a node to trade with its neighbors, provides a low trade cost, and the high clustering coefficient, indicating a high degree the nodes would like to create tightly knit groups characterized by a relatively high density of ties, provides an environment in which agents have high probability to trade with all the potential partners.

REFERENCES

[1] Watts, D.J. & Steven S. 1998. Collective dynamics of 'small-world' networks. *Nature* 393 (6684): 440–442. Bibcode: 1998 Natur. 393.440 W.doi:10.1038/ 30918. PMID 962399 8.

[2] Erdős, P. Rényi. A. 1959. On Random Graphs I. *Publ. Math*: 290–297.

[3] Watts D.J. 1999. Small Worlds. Princeton University Press. New Jersey.

[4] Ahn Y.Y. & Han S., Kwak H. & Moon S. & Jeong H. 2007. Analysis of Topological Characteristics of Huge Online, *Social Networking Services*, The 16th intl. conference on WWW'07, Banff, Canada.

[5] Pastor S.R. & A. 2001. Vespignani. Epidemic dynamics and endemic states in complex networks, *Phys. Rev. E*, vol. 63, no. 066117.

[6] Girvan M. and Newman M.E.J. 2002. Community structure in social and biological networks. *Proceedings of the National Academy of Sciences*, 99: 7821–7826.

[7] Boyd D. 2006. Friends, Friendsters, and Top 8: Writing community into being on social network sites, *First Monday*, 11(12).

[8] Batty M. 2001. Editorial; Cities as small worlds. *Environment and Planning: Planning and Design*, 28(5):637–638.

[9] Axtell. R. 1998. On the complexity of exchange. In Working Notes: Artificial Societies and Computational Markets. *Autonomous Agents' 98 Workshop*, Minneapolis/St. Paul (May).

[10] Allen W. 2001. Bilateral Trade and 'Small-World' Networks. *Computational Economics*, 18:49–64.

[11] Feldman A. 1973. Bilateral trading processes, pairwise optimality, and Pareto optimality. *Review of Economic Studies*, XL(4): 463–473.

[12] Sen A. 1993. Markets and freedom: Achievements and limitations of the market mechanism in promoting individual freedoms. *Oxford Economic Papers* 45 (4): 519–541. JSTOR 2663703.

[13] Jackson M.O. & Wolinsky A. 1996. A strategic model of social and economic networks. *Journal of Economic Theory*, 71:129–138.

[14] Latora V. & Marchiori M. 2003. Economic small-world behavior in weighted networks, *The European Physical Journal B*. 32:249–263.

[15] Erdős P. & Rényi A. 1960. On the evolution of random graphs. Publications of the Mathematical Institute of the Hungarian Academy of Sciences 5: 17–61.

Computer, Intelligent Computing and Education Technology – Liu, Sung & Yao (Eds)
© *2014 Taylor & Francis Group, London, ISBN 978-1-138-02469-4*

A study of university stadium management optimization based on property management

Z.H. Xu

P.E. Department of Yulin University, Shaanxi, China

ABSTRACT: Based on the understanding of university stadium management status quo, the in-depth analysis of its existing problems and the future developing directions will be given. The characteristics and advantages of the properties management model itself will be introduced to the university stadium management and operations, which will provide a theoretical basis for the rational use of resources and will improve the management of the university stadium and even the construction of harmonious campus.

Keywords: university stadiums; property management; status quo; countermeasures

1 SIGNIFICANCE AND BACKGROUND OF THE RESEARCH

1.1 *Significance of the research*

Chen Zhili made a report of "emancipating the mind, strengthen confidence, and create a new college logistics reform situation" when he was the Minister of Education in 1999, which opened the prelude of Logistics Socialization Reform. From 1999 to 2003, under the guidance of the Vice Premier Li Lanqing, university logistics reform has entered a rapid government-led advance era. Since then, many colleges and universities has been actively exploring on the logistics socialization reform, which includes the ideas, operation mechanism, management system and other aspects and the comprehensive changes of these aspects are taking place and the positive impact is obvious.

1.2 *Background of the research*

University stadiums have the general characteristics, namely with a large scale building, with multi-facility equipment and high professional requirements of maintenance and operation as the general stadiums. Its main function is to meet the teaching activities, teachers and students' sport requirement in the premise, meanwhile open to the community in varying degrees by providing some sports training, to undertake a number of events and theatrical performances and other activities to get some economic benefits in order to achieve the preservation and increment of university stadiums. The management reform of the university stadium is one of the important aspects of university reform

and it is necessary to use the method of property management to manage the property.

University stadium's using procedures, safety, efficiency, maintenance, environmental venues and other aspects of professional management meet the new requirements to make university stadiums of sound development, to reduce the government (schools)'s financial burden and to promote the flourish development of university or even the whole country's sports industry, The management level is not only directly related to the level of physical education and sports research development, but also related to the stadium itself, of its social and economic benefits.

2 RESEARCH METHOD

This paper adopts the literature, questionnaires, interviews, statistics and other research methods to conducts in-depth analysis and systematic study on property management, property management mode, stadiums management and user satisfaction evaluation to understand and grasp the function of today's university stadiums.

3 UNIVERSITY STADIUM MANAGEMENT STATUS QUO

For a long time, university stadiums of our country are managed by school's PE department and there are many problems which restrict the realization of the stadiums functions. Most of university stadiums management is self-developed practices, lack of a unified, standardized and scientific management standards, is beyond the support and protection of the government and regulatory basis. Therefore, the overall management is still in a low and inefficient operation. The survey shows that China's current university stadiums still of miniaturization and low management level. In recent years, with the large scale college enrollment, stadium construction scale developed rapidly. Obviously, his original, extensive management methods can not meet the need of the situation.

The management of our country's university stadiums is still at a non-standardized and incomplete stage, which reflects in its unreasonable and shortcomings management mode and methods and it is not conductive to the comprehensive utilization of the resources and the improvement of the efficiency. Moreover, our current management reform is still in the exploration stage.

4 THE CHARACTERISTICS OF THE PROPERTY MANAGEMENT

Property management, taking service as the core, is a new management model. In 1981, our country's first property services company was born in Shenzhen. After 20 year's development, there are more than 30,000 enterprises of property services in China, employing more than 500 million people. Property management becomes one of the most labor-absorbing industries. Currently, PM (refers property management) has covered a range of residential zones, offices, industrial zones, schools, shopping malls, hospitals, airports, convention centers, stadiums, pedestrian streets and so on. The total area of the property management is over 10 billion square meters. The annual output value is over 600 billion Yuan, and increasing in an annual rate of 20% rapidly. Visible, property management has become an emerging service industry of broad prospects.

The tenet of property management is service. Its manage objects is property and its service object is the title to the property and realty user. It has the characteristics of socialization, specialization, entrepreneurial and business-type.

These characteristics can reflect that the property management is based on scientific management and take the qualitative service as the goal. Its operation is based on sound organizational structure, financial system and the legal system.

According to the above illustrated characteristics of property management and its major goal, it is not hard to find that it is a good way for us to take the property management to optimize the management of University Stadiums, which will be further discussed in the following part, and the property management can be proved a good mode.

5 THE COMPARISON OF UNIVERSITY STADIUMS MANAGEMENT MODEL

To adapt to the requirements of the development, university stadium management should diversify (particularly market-oriented), which also determines the mode of university stadium management should be varied.

5.1 Types

According to the subjects of management, university stadiums management models can be broadly divided into the following types: the sports sector management mode, lease management mode, contract mode, specialized agencies model, property management mode and so on. In all of these management modes, the sports sector management model is the most common one, which take the percentage of 80%. The reason is that the PE departments have policies, systems, personnel, equipment and many other advantages in management. The change of management model, to some extent, has improved the management and the service quality to meet the needs of venue owners and other users and at the same time, it also has brought some new problems. From the theory point of view, the classification of existing management modes and summary is still inappropriate and needs to be improved.

5.2 Characteristics

Most colleges and universities stadiums have carried out open operating behavior. Management projects take "sport-based, multi-management" approach. Due to various management mode and operation subjects, there are main differences in the specific business and its specific circumstances as illustrated in Tables 1–5.

Tables 1–5 can show us the different types of the university stadiums operation under different modes.

5.3 Financial aspects

When university stadiums employ different management mode, the organization, management

Table 1. University stadiums operation under sports sector management mode.

Items	Sports sector management mode
Management	Budget contract system
Purpose	Services school
Service object	Increase the value
Open-time	Off hours

Table 2. University stadiums operation under contract mode.

Items	Contract mode
Management	Contract system
Purpose	Increase the value
Service object	School-based
Open-time	Off hours

Table 3. University stadiums operation under specialized agencies model.

Items	Specialized agencies mode
Management	Contracting system
Purpose	Inventory of assets
Service object	Both inside and outside
Open-time	Off hours

Table 4. University stadiums operation under lease management mode.

Items	Lease management mode
Management	Leadership responsibility system
Purpose	Profit or other
Service object	Both inside and outside
Open-time	Off hours

Table 5. University stadiums operation under property management mode.

Items	Property management mode
Management	Company responsible for the system
Purpose	Profit maximization
Service object	Both inside and outside
Open-time	All the time if allowed

and financial aspects of the operation are also different, but the pros and cons of various management modes eventually reflects in the economic and social benefits. In economic terms, the existing data indicate that the sports sector management mode is better. Other specialized mode like school management, full property management mode, due to the adoption universities are fewer, yet there is not enough specific data available for the discussion, but the management of the current situation is expected to get better profit. In social terms, as an indicator system is not perfect, and there is more difficult in survey, therefore, here is no readily available information of norms and appropriate for analysis.

6 RECOMMENDATIONS ON IMPROVING OF UNIVERSITY STADIUMS MANAGEMENT BASED ON PROPERTY MANAGEMENT MODE

According to the actual situation at the present stage of social development, in order to promote university stadiums management optimization and scientific development, based on property management mode and its own characteristics and advantages, the following recommendations will be given to improve the management of university stadiums.

6.1 Separation of ownership and operation

The implementation of the management system should be "Separation of ownership and operation". The relationship of property management companies and property owners is the employment. The owners select the property management company through bidding or agreements by carefully examining the company's reputation, expertise and management background, financial, legal level, management fees and community activity level and other aspects.

6.2 Adopting market and the economic instruments separation of ownership and operation

The management entity is self-financing and self-management. Through the market and the economic instruments, stadiums socialized management is paid services, management entity should be of "independent accounting, self-financing, self-running, self-improvement and self-development" management system.

6.3 Establishing rules and regulations

Stadium management entity should establish a comprehensive, rigorous, scientific and reasonable rules and regulations to enhance self-restraint, so that a clear division of work between various departments can be harmoniously realized. On the one hand, it is need to discover and deal with some of the issues in the responsible management, supervisory responsibility must be in accordance with policy and protocol management. On the other hand, it also needs to be considered from the macro interests of responsible persons. To create a favorable business environment, supporting them. It can make them offer better service for the teachers and students and also teaching.

6.4 Developing a quantifiable job-responsibility

The management entity should develop a quantifiable job-responsibility, to announce the pledges and make all the departments can work effectively and to mobilize the enthusiasm of all categories of personnel. They should use resources in the school stadium rationally to create a good business platform for the harmonious operation of teaching and service for the teachers and the students in school. It is a deep request for the management entity to develop a job responsibility which cans benefic a lot.

Then it comes to the movement's role.

6.5 *Governments' role*

Government should play an important role in property management, the more detailed and comprehensive laws, regulations to regulate the property management in all aspects of human behavior and responsibilities, rights and benefits of the relationship, to standardize and guide the work.

6.6 *Meeting the universities' features*

The implementation of management methods should meet the university's features. i.e. according to the number of teachers, school classes, the number of stadiums and local social realities, it is need to adjust accordingly, thus producing better results.

7 CONCLUSION

Based on the understanding of university stadium management status quo, the in-depth analysis of its existing problems and the future developing directions of the university stadiums are given. The characteristics and advantages of the properties management model itself is utilized to the university stadium management and operations.

ACKNOWLEDGEMENTS

My hearty thanks first go to Professor Dewei Wang from Xi'an University of architecture and technology. This paper can not be finished without the help of him, whose careful guidance and strict work style, rigorous and realistic scientific attitude helped and inspired me a lot. My thanks also go to Yulin University High Level Scientific Research Fund Project (12GK21) of 2011.

REFERENCES

[1] Wang Deqing. *Modern Management Theory* [M]. Chongqing: Southwestern Normal University press, 1998, 5.
[2] Xu Minfeng. *Investigation on School Sports Stadiums Opening Situation in Beijing, Tianjin, and Shanghai* [J]. Sports Science, 1999, 19, (4): 73–75.
[3] Sun Bo. *Market Segmentation of Special Property May Become 'Xiangbobo'* [J]. Chinese Property Management, 2009, (05): 50–51.
[4] Zhang Zuoxiang. *A Study on Property Management* [M]. Tsinghua University Press, 2008.
[5] Weng Huigen. *Research on Zhejiang Province's the National Fitness Programs' Stadiums and Facilities* [J]. Zhejiang Sports Science, 1995, 17, (3): 28.
[6] Han Haijun, Xu Jiuping. *Comparative Analysis on Management Modes of College Stadium* [J]. Journal of Chengdu Sport University, 2008, 2, (28): 56.
[7] Tao Chien. *Analysis of the Management Mode of University Sports Stadiums* [J]. Journal of Hunan University of Science and Engineering, 2010, 5:207.
[8] Yin Jingbo. *Customer Satisfaction Research for Application* [D]. Northeast University of Finance and Economics, 2005.

Computer, Intelligent Computing and Education Technology – Liu, Sung & Yao (Eds)
© *2014 Taylor & Francis Group, London, ISBN 978-1-138-02469-4*

Reflection on rural online physical education curriculum platform construction in Northern Shaanxi

W.X. Li

P.E. Department of Yulin University, Shaanxi, China

ABSTRACT: With the development of network information technology, network has penetrated into everywhere in our daily life. People cannot move around in their work, social life and study without the support internet. Meanwhile, the development of network is so quick that it has involved into school education nowadays. The physical education in rural area plays a crucial part in carrying out the policy of comprehensive sports and lifelong sports. In the rural schools of Northern Shaanxi, it lacks education resources, faculty and the researching of the teaching resources. Thus, it is significant to combine, optimize and take advantage of network teaching resources in the physical education transformational period. With a dozen of years' physical education teaching experience, the author analyzes the importance of network teaching in rural area, and achieved some new ideas and ways of physical network teaching.

Keywords: rural areas in the northern Shaanxi; physical education curriculum; online education

1   INTRODUCTION

1.1   *About the network education technology*

Network education technology is to deal with text information, graphic information, video information, sound information, image information and so on, through combining computer interactive comprehensive technology with digital communication technology. Thus, network education is using them to create a connection and bring into a new system. So network educations have features of integration, inter-activeness, of time and space, globalization of resources and capacity of information. Network education technology has an important practice meaning and application value, such as, to organize teaching knowledge and subject information, to provide an ideal teaching environment and knowledge resources library, to arouse students' potential ability and interests, to create situational teaching, to improve teaching efficiency and quality.

1.2   *Status Quo of NET in northern Shaanxi province*

In addition, our country now pays more attention to primary education and to expanding education teaching scale. So traditional teaching groups and faculties are not satisfied with students' needs of personality and diversification, especially in the rural area of northern Shaanxi province, with the limitation of course resources and the developing of network resources. At present in the rural area of northern Shaanxi province, the main point of starting physical education is how to make use of computer network technology and various multimedia equipment to attract students' interests, to cultivate lifelong sports and the entertainment in physical education to meet students' different requirement in study.

1.3   *The significance of the NET in northern Shaanxi province*

As the country attaches great importance to basic education and meanwhile the education scale expands gradually, the original school staff and teachers can no longer meet the the students' personalized, diversified education demand. Especially in the rural areas of Northern Shaanxi, the physical education curriculum's cyber source are seriously insufficient, the cyber source development are limited, therefore, the contradiction between the teaching plan and teaching resources is growing with each passing day. Vigorously expand and develop rural learning network teaching can develop the students' interests in sports learning; can develop students lifelong sports activities and their happy sports ideas and habits. Thus, it is a pressing matter of the moment to carry out physical education in rural areas to meet the learning requirements of different students.

2 THE SIGNIFICANCE OF CREATING RURAL PHYSICAL EDUCATION ONLINE COURSE TEACHING PLATFORM

With the network technology changing and the all-round education development, network resources play an important role in physical educational teaching. In general, teachers divided physical education course into network course to make a new perceive distribution mode by using network teaching platform. It has proved that by making full of physical education course network teaching resource is irreplaceable in improving teaching quality constantly, expanding the scale of teaching, optimizing teaching pattern, expanding teaching space and cultivating multitalented.

2.1 It is helpful to optimize configuration of physical education teaching recourses in rural school

In the rural area of northern Shaanxi province, the fact is that the economy is relatively backward, the resources of school are limited and the faculty can't follow the enlargement of the teaching scale. So it can't solve the contradiction of unfair physical education resource distribution just by increasing the number of the teachers. However, network course resource doesn't occupy time and space, making up the lack of physical education resource in rural areas and improving physical education quality greatly.

2.2 It is helpful to solve abstract movement and technological problems for students

Physical education should pay much more attention to pass on the action skills. In our traditional physical education, students grasp action skills is by direct teaching and teachers' demonstrations. But some actions are abstract and instantaneity. If the students don't pay attention to or teachers' demonstrations have a slight mistake not standard enough and a little accurate, students can't grasp technology skills scientifically.

However, teaching resources like video network can help students solve difficult technology problem by playing back repeatedly, or appreciate standard demonstration action of excellent athletes in the world. In the practice of participating physical education, students can transcribe their own actions by using camera equipment and upload to computers. Students also can watch their actions objectively and find weakness so that gather experience for their later training.

2.3 It is helpful to arouse students' curiosity and interest in online learning

Network information technology provides a wide sharing platform of information resources for the general educator. The opening and sharing makes the students freely consult, use and share the superior sports teaching resources. Under the traditional teaching mode, the physical education teachers' power and abilities are limited, it is impossible to take care of every student. What's more every student has their own demands. When the students' requirements can't be contented, their enthusiasms will drop suddenly. With the computer network technology supporting, network physical education resources have an enormous capacity for information, all kinds of information, and a great interactivity and wide space to choose. One the one hand, students can accept teachers' conduction collectively. On the other hand, students can make their own needs of personality and diversification by using network platform, which arouses students' learning desire and studying interests.

3 THE IDEAS OF DEVELOPING THE PHYSICAL COURSE NETWORK TEACHING RESOURCE PLATFORM

3.1 Collect video and image dates, stimulate students' seduction

Multimedia information have those characters, vivid frames, colorful content, wide information and attractive. It can bring the most visual sight experience, transfer the students' enthusiasm adequately and satisfy the students' sports course requirement of diversification and individuation. Thus, physical education teachers should develop the network teaching resource actively, collect different sports items, such as videos, images, words, teaching material and so on, and bring an abundant dinner of sense organ.

3.2 Expanding the function of network teaching resources, establishing and improving the institution of course choosing

A course choose institution online, includes choosing content freely, choosing teachers as they like and taking class willingly. These three teaching patterns are students-centered, paying more attention to create a vivid, ordered, active and reasonable environment of study; teaching students in accordance of their aptitude; having special chooses according to different kinds of students. This ground-breaking teaching pattern shows the transformation of modem teaching from teachers-centered to students-centered, also from teaching collectively to teaching individually, and which enrich teaching content, increase choices of students' physical education. At the same time, the foundation and improvement of course choosing institution is to achieve a unity of teaching goals, students' need, teaching process and evaluating online, which arouses teachers' activeness of keeping pace with the times on teaching methods and teaching tools. It could create established and perfect scientific physical education system and also could evaluate online institution and represent the idea of "health first, lifelong physical education, decreasing competition."

3.3 *Arousing students' attraction by establishing a research platform for teachers and students*

Physical education teaching includes two parts—teachers' teaching and students' learning under the education for all-round development. Students became the main in teaching and teachers change their role from controller to leader. The new reformation of physical education course comes up with studying by ourselves and inquiry teaching. With a desire of knowledge, students want to experience how to get truth by participating study. With the help of teachers, students can make use of knowledge beamed before, find problems, know problems and solve problems in teaching sitcom. Teachers' duty is not tell students to give definitions, answers only, but to lead students to find and solve problems gradually, which will leave a deep impression to students. The construction of physical education network course offer guidance to study, found teachers and students' communication platform, making students take part in valuing courses, solving problems, appreciating online. Which make up the lack of traditional physical education teaching resources, strengthen the students' interests to physical education, and arouse students' activeness of joining in P.E. training?

3.4 *It is helpful to enrich the students' extracurricular life and the knowledge storage*

As long as the developed software can include all PE textbooks in the sports on-line network teaching, students can choose the suitable teaching content, to stimulate their own sports potential, enrich their extracurricular life, learn more about sports forefront of the information, especially the internet live or televised football, basketball and other live game which are very rich the teaching content, enrich their knowledge storage in no

teachers help environment according to their own situation and hobbies. Especially for those students who like sports from the rural area, haven't got too much time and energy to participate in fitness club, haven't got sufficient resources to hire fitness consultant, the students will be able to carry out independent query using computer network technology, or to participate in the forum discussions and exchanges, to exercise science, enrich extracurricular life.

4 CONCLUSION

By combining multimedia teaching and online self-learning, rural physical education teaching curriculum has created different kinds of learning patterns, broken through the limit of time and space, and finally achieved real-time, different-time, different-place and different kinds of specialized study forms. Meanwhile it has become the real-time monitor and online evaluation. Finally, the course would improve the efficiency of students' learning and teachers' management.

ACKNOWLEDGEMENTS

My hearty thanks first go to Professor Lize Kang from Xi'an Physical Education University. This paper can not be finished without the help of him, whose careful guidance and strict work style, rigorous and realistic scientific attitude helped and inspired me a lot. My thanks also go to the support of Shaanxi Provincial Department of Education Research Project of 2012: Project Number: 12JK0230; Topic: The Study on the Development and Utilization of Physical Education Curriculum Content Resources of Rural School in Northern Shaanxi.

REFERENCES

[1] Li Huizeng, Yuan Shujuan, Zheng Yongcheng. Research on Hebei province rural occupation middle school sports present situation and characteristic model [J]. *Sports Science.* 2004 (01): 56–58.
[2] Liu Yanxia, Zhao Xiaohong. The occupation school sports goal orientation and content set [J]. *Journal of Tianjin University of Sport.* 2002,16:72–73.
[3] Wang Zhengyi, Chen Lizhu, Jin Zongqiang.21 the direction of teaching reform of our college physical education research [J]. *Journal of Beijing Sport University.* 2002,25 (03): 225–227.

Computer, Intelligent Computing and Education Technology – Liu, Sung & Yao (Eds)
© *2014 Taylor & Francis Group, London, ISBN 978-1-138-02469-4*

Internet banking adoption in Nigeria: A literature review

O. Solomon, S. Alina & W. Eta
Faculty of Technology Management, Business and Entrepreneurship, Universiti Tun Hussein Onn Malaysia,
Batu Pahat, Malaysia

M.A. Ajagbe
Faculty of Management, Universiti Teknologi Malaysia, Skudai-Johor, Malaysia

ABSTRACT: The influence of internet technologies on business transactions has been a widely recognized domain of investigation. These technologies present organizations with the prospects of easing the way business transactions are conducted. Many business analysts underrated the influence of these technologies when they were first introduced. However, advances in information and communication technologies and the emergence of the internet have revolutionized business activities exposing new ways of conducting businesses referred to as electronic commerce. This has shaped, and will continue to advance in shaping business practices for years to come. Among the industries that witnessed major impact of internet technology is the banking industry. Banking is a service industry where most transactions can be provided via electronic channels. The industry has participated heavily in internet transactions, hence it offer banks with a new channel to conveniently get to their customers. The purpose of this study is to conduct a detailed literature search of empirical investigations on the adoption of internet banking with a view to suggesting possible ways of improving the practice in developing countries particularly in Nigeria.

Keywords: internet banking; technology adoption; innovation diffusion; Nigeria

1 INTRODUCTION

The influence of electronic technologies cannot be left without continual investigation by researchers. These technologies present organizations with both prospects and concerns. Although many business analysts underrated the influence of these technologies when they were first introduced (Turban et al., 2004; Ajagbe et al., 2011a). However, advances in information and communication technologies and the emergence of the internet have revolutionized business activities enabling new ways of conducting businesses known as electronic transactions (Borghoff, 2011; Mohamed et al., 2009; Ajagbe et al., 2011b). Studies show that the presence of technologies has shaped, and will continue to advance in shaping business practices for years to come. Among the industries that witnessed a major impact of electronic technology is the banking industry. Banking is a service industry where most services can be provided via electronic technology. Furthermore, the banking industry has participated heavily in information technology, and the technologies are broadly exploited in their daily operations. Internet offer banks a new channel for getting to their customers. Previously,

customers could perform banking transactions only at a bank's premises, through automated teller machines or telephone. But the electronic technology has opened new vistas for banks to introduce online banking to their customers. Banks are also benefiting from internet banking in terms of lower costs and better customer services. Transactions performed by customers are processed electronically. The electronic processing eliminates the cost for a teller to process a cheque to the tune of about $1.10, hence, significantly reducing the cost of transactions (Nor & Pearson, 2008). In addition, internet banking reduces the likelihood of errors in data entry by deferring the task directly to the customers. It has been acknowledged that business customers benefit immensely from this new channel of service delivery. Internet banking gives them the option to perform banking transactions and other related activities from the comfort of their homes. They can save money on fuel and eliminate the inconveniences associated with commuting to the bank premises. Despite the advantages, many customers of financial institutions in many developing countries are yet to fully embrace this form of banking system. Like other innovations, internet banking faces many problems associated with its adoption. Since the success or failure of this technology will depend on the leverage of usage, due to this there is need to determine which factors affect customers' adoption of internet banking transactions with particular focus on Nigeria. This paper is arranged in the following manner; internet banking in Nigeria, innovation diffusion theory, theory of reasoned action, theory of planned behavior, technology acceptance model and internet banking research. The methodology adopted is briefly stated and concluded with a short discussion and conclusion of the study.

2 SURVEY OF RELATED LITERATURE

2.1 *Internet banking in Nigeria*

The introduction of automated teller machine into Nigeria's financial landscape has revolutionized the ways cash transactions are carried out. The cash machine was introduced by the defunct Societe Generale Bank Nigeria (SGBN) in 1989. They were considered the most noticeable form of electronic technology that targeted retail customers. They machines were known as a self-service mechanism that dispenses cash and performs some human teller functions like balance enquiry, bills payments, mini statement, cash withdrawal, fund transfer and so on. Due to the complexity and competitiveness in the banking industry and unpredictable economic climate, the Central Banking of Nigeria (CBN) introduced economic reforms and monetary policies as guidelines to banking activities in Nigeria. The reformation exercise left Nigeria with 22 strong and reliable banks against 89 banks previously in existence. The surviving banks of the recapitalization exercise have extremely involved the use of ICT as a platform for effective and efficient delivery of banking services (Oni & Ayo, 2010). Nigeria's slow acceptance of internet banking practice is gradually changing for the better, awareness of e-payments in Nigeria is increasing and it accounted for 360 billion naira worth of transaction in 2008 (Oni & Ayo, 2010). A Geneva based ITU recently reported that Nigeria occupies the 8th position amongst the top 10 countries with the highest number of internet users (2013). Furthermore, the study notes a steady rise of internet users in Nigeria from 43,982,200 in the year 2012 to 55,930,391 in 2013.

However, the increment in the number of internet users in Nigeria was perceived to be a result of cuts in tariffs which are being influenced by competitions amongst the service providers (Felicia & Ogunnaike, 2012). The liberalization policies of the Nigerian Communication Commission (NCC) have made access to internet services to be less cumbersome and help facilitates cheaper, faster and better access to internet services (Oduh & Oduh, 2012). On top of this, the increasing usage of the internet positioned Nigeria as a lucrative economy to invest in electronic commerce and internet banking businesses (Abubakar & Rosmaini, 2012). The banking industry is one sector within the Nigerian economy where electronic technology is fast growing (Ayo & Ukpere, 2010). Bank customers in Nigeria are gradually adopting and participating in internet banking with the number rising steadily from year to year.

In view of the importance of this new form of online technology adoption, there is need to consider the adequacy of research grounded in the IT field. Past authors have turned to models that have been developed in other areas as a foundation for their research. In the case of the prediction of an individual's intention to adopt IT, Information Systems (IS) researchers have borrowed models for social psychology as a basis for their research (Nor & Pearson, 2008). For instance, deep and strong intentions models such as the theory of planned behavior (Ajzen, 1991) have been broadly used to explain and predict the intention to adopt information technology. Understanding consumer acceptance is an important research topic for information technology practitioners. Many well-established theoretical models have been used to assess consumer adoption of a technology. Among, the most commonly used theoretical models are the Theory of Reasoned Action (TRA) (Ajzen & Fishbein, 1980), Theory of Planned Behavior (TPB) (Ajzen, 1991), Technology Acceptance Model (TAM) (Davis, 1989), and Innovation Diffusion Theory (IDT) (Rogers, 1995), Unified Theory of Acceptance and Use of Technology (UTAUT) (Venkatesh et al., 2003), and Decomposed Theory of Planned Behavior (DTPB) (Taylor & Todd, 1995). The few models have dominated the theoretic basis of information system acceptance for more than two decades (Kim & Lee, 2008). Below are explanations of the prominent factors utilized in different theories by numerous researchers.

2.1.1 *Innovation diffusion theory*

The earliest theory on technology acceptance is based on Roger's (1995) theory of diffusion of innovation (IDT). According to this theory, innovation adoption is a process of uncertainty about the new technology; individuals will gather and synthesize information about using the technology. Beliefs then cause individuals to accept or reject the technology. Rogers (1995) established that diffusion is the process in which an innovation is communicated through certain channels over time among the members of a social system. As expressed in this definition: innovation characteristics, individual user characteristics, adopter distribution over time, diffusion networks, innovativeness and adopter categories, and the individual adoption process are the essential features of innovation diffusion theory. After analyzing a variety of previous innovation diffusion studies, this study found Rogers (1995) five characteristics of innovations that consistently influence the adoption of technologies as; relative advantage, compatibility, complexity, observability and triability. Peres et al. (2010) also used the diffusion framework in the study of innovation diffusion and new product growth models, the study affirmed that innovation diffusion is the process of the market penetration of new products and services that is driven by social influences, which include all interdependencies among consumers that affect various market players with or without their explicit knowledge. Results shows that the entire hypothesized (social network; individual level, agent based, multinational diffusion, competition, brand, network externalities, takeoff, saddle and technology generations) constructs are strongly significant factors influencing innovation diffusion and new product growth models.

2.1.2 *Theory of reasoned action*
While the IDT draws on perceived characteristics of technology to explain user's behavior to adopt the technology, the theory of reasoned action looks at beliefs within the individual to explain adoption behavior (Frambach & Schillewaert 2002). The TRA hypothesizes that a behavior is predicted by an individual's intention to engage in a given behavior. Intention, in turn, is predicted by two factors, the individual's attitude towards the behavior and the subjective norm (Ajzen & Fishbein, 1980, 2009). Attitude toward the behavior reflects an individual's evaluation or general feeling toward a target behavior. The attitude toward a behavior is a product of beliefs about the behavior and the individual's evaluation of the outcome resulting from that behavior. The theory postulates that the intention to perform a behavior will be higher when the individual has positive evaluation of performing the behavior (Ajzen, 1991). The theory of reasoned action (Ajzen & Fishbein, 1980), have been found to be important predictor of behavioral intention (Albarq & Alsughayir, 2013; Montano & Kasprzyk, 2008). Thus, it is reasonable to believe that theory of reasoned action will provide a very good foundation for this study to investigate intention to use internet banking services.

2.1.3 *Theory of planned behavior*
Another related technology adoption that has been widely used in technology acceptance research is the Theory of Planned Behavior (TPB). TPB is an extension of the theory of reasoned action (Ajzen & Fishbein, 2009). TPB added an additional belief (i.e., perceived behavioral control) to explain behavioral intention. Hence, the theory assumes three independent determinants of intention: attitude toward the behavior, subject norm, and perceived behavioral control (Ajzen, 1991). The beliefs, attitude toward the behavior and subject norm are identical to those previously discussed for the theory of reasoned action. Therefore, emphasis is shown on the third belief (i.e., perceived behavioral control). Perceived behavioral control reflects an individual's perception of ease or difficulty of performing a target behavior. Control beliefs reflect the individual's beliefs of his ability to perform the behavior, which are affected by external resources (e.g., time and money) and internal component (e.g., ability and self-efficacy) (Ajzen, 1991). The theory has been used in a wide variety of setting including IT acceptance research.

2.1.4 *Technology acceptance model*
Beside IDT and TPB another widely used theory in IT research to predict human behavior is the technology acceptance model (Davis, 1989). TAM has been adopted from the Theory of Reasoned Action (TRA), (Fishbein & Ajzen, 1980; Fishbein & Ajzen, 1975). TAM suggests that attitudes predict intentions, and intentions predict behavior. According to TAM, adoption behavior is determined by the intention to use a particular system and the intention is determined by the attitude, which in turn is determined by the perceived usefulness and perceived ease of use of the system (Davis, 1989). The model also hypothesizes a link from perceived usefulness to behavioral intention. TAM also postulates that external variables may affect perceived ease of use and usefulness. System features, training, documentation, and user supports are some external variables that may influence an individual's perceived ease of use (Davis et al., 1989). TAM has received considerable attention and empirical support among IT researchers in many settings and technologies. The model has been tested on technologies such as voice mail, e-mail, software, groupware, and World Wide Web (Davis et al., 1989; Taylor & Todd 1995; Venkatesh et al., 2003). Technology acceptance model is shown in Figure 1 below.

2.1.5 *The unified theory of acceptance and use of technology*
The UTAUT model is the most comprehensive and parsimonious theoretical framework at present as it captures all essential positive and negative indicators of the TRA, TAM, TPB and, IDT models (Venkatesh et al., 2003). It is formulated through detailed comparison and integration of aforementioned user acceptance models (Peres et al., 2010). The UTAUT model is successful in combining

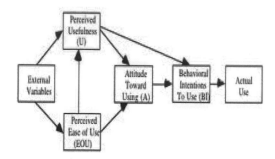

Figure 1. Technology acceptance model (Davis et al., 1989).

most of the essential elements of these frameworks into major independent variables such as performance expectancy, effort expectancy, social influence, attitude and facilitating conditions (Venkatesh et al., 2003). The model has been verified in six industries; entertainment, and telecommunication services, branch banking and public administration, financial services and retail internet services (Kim & Lee, 2008). It serves as a platform for future technology adoption research (Venkatesh et al., 2003). It also incorporates barriers that would hinder internet banking adoption such as insufficient knowledge and time (Venkatesh et al., 2003). Preceding literatures (Agarwal et al., 2009; Chen et al., 2008; Wang and Emurien, 2005; Yiu et al., 2007) applied the UTAUT model in predicting internet business acceptance, prepayment, metering systems, e-government services, 3G services, e-business services, wireless sensor networks, instant messaging, online stocking, personal digital assistants and Weblogs but did not research into internet banking acceptance.

2.1.6 *The decomposed theory of planned behavior*

The decomposed theory of planned behavior is based on the work of Taylor and Todd (1995), combined with some aspects of the theory of planned behavior (Ajzen, 1991) and innovation diffusion theory (Roger, 1995). The theory postulate that attitude, subjective norm and perceived behavioral control will influence the intention to use a technology. Taylor and Todd (1995) extended the theory by decomposing the attitudinal, normative, and perceived control beliefs into multi-dimensional constructs. This provided higher explanatory power and a more precise understanding of the antecedents of behavior. In their empirical test, the DTPB was found to provide a moderate increase in the explanation of behavioral intention when compared to the theory of planned behavior (Taylor and Todd, 1995). This has been used

by many researchers as their research framework over the years as revealed in many previous articles. Hung et al. (2012) decomposed theory of the planned behavior model to investigate the factors influencing physicians' acceptance of the Medline system. The study confirmed that a physician's usage intention is significantly influenced by three factors, i.e. attitude, the subjective norm, and perceived behavior control. Conversely, past authors argue against decomposed theory of planned behavior that TAM provides several advantages over in terms of determining information technology acceptance.

2.2 *Trust in online relationship*

Trust is a willingness to be vulnerable to the actions of another person or people (Mayer et al., 1995; Davis, 1989). Mayer et al. (1995) explained that integrity is the trustor's perception that the trustee adheres to a set of principles that the trustor finds acceptable. Integrity is users' perceptions that the service provider will be fair, honest and adheres to reasonable conditions of transactions (Bhattacherjee, 2002). The propensity to trust is a stable within-party factor that will affect the likelihood of one party to trust another (Mayer et al., 1995). Propensity will influence how much trust one has for a trustee prior to data on that particular party being available. People with different developmental experiences, personality types, and cultural backgrounds vary in their propensity to trust. However, trust is based on expectations that the other person will behave in a responsible manner (Pavlou, 2003) and will not take advantage of a dependence upon him (Gefen et al., 2003). It is an important component in any social and business relationship whenever risk and uncertainty exist.

Incorporating the trust constructs into TAM, Suh and Han (2002) examined the effect of trust on consumer acceptance of internet banking. The result of the study showed that perceived ease of use and perceived usefulness were significant predictors of attitude. Using the TPB as the theoretical framework, Nor & Pearson (2008) examined whether beliefs about privacy and internet trustworthiness determined attitudes towards internet purchasing which, in turn affected intention and actual purchase. The study revealed that privacy and internet trustworthiness beliefs are significant determinants of attitude. Figure 2 shows established Trust Model by Mayer et al., (1995).

2.3 *Internet banking acceptance research*

This study found several literature studies related to the internet banking purview. Bhattacherjee (2002) conducted a study investigating the influence of

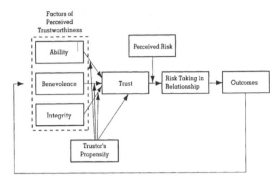

Figure 2. Trust model source: Mayer et al. (1995).

beliefs and consequence on ones aim to continue adopting internet banking. The author interviewed 122 online customers of one of the largest national banks in America. The questionnaire was centered on the expectation-confirmation model and the TAM. The author hypothesized that consumer's intention to continue using internet banking was predicted by their fulfillment with the services and perceived usefulness. Results of the study show that satisfaction with internet banking were the strongest predictor of users' continuance intention followed by perceived usefulness. Gefen et al. (2003) investigate 1167 consumers from Finland on their beliefs and reactions to internet banking. The study was based on hypothetical background, however, was not clearly defined and variables under study might have been derived from several studies related to internet banking. The responses were broken into three groups: non-user, new user and old user related to internet banking. Their analysis shows that each clutch held different beliefs about internet banking. Similarly, Liao and Cheung (2002) channeled a survey on Singapore internet banking customers. The study was exploratory in nature and was not directly based on a specific technology acceptance model. The outcome of the study specified that the willingness to use internet banking was reliant on the expectancy of accuracy, security, network speed, user friendliness, users participation and suitability. In another explanatory study, Ramayah et al. (2002) found that the awareness of internet banking among consumers was high in Malaysia.

3 RESEARCH METHODOLOGY

Even though there is a universal perception that secondary sources of data collection provide second-hand data (Kumar, 2005; Creswell, 2012) while primary sources provide first-hand data. Also that some researchers think that the use of

secondary data alone may not be enough to give credence for a reliable report, hence, the need to carry out an extensive primary data collection in order to have or feel the practical scenario on ground and get useful and reliable information from the participants. However, many other researchers perceive that secondary sources of data collection cannot be underestimated in information systems research. This study depend on this particular technique to gather data because it is known as the gathering of ideas and work of previous researchers and scholars who have worked on topics related to this study (Creswell, 2012; Ajagbe, 2013). The secondary sources of data collection of this research relied on various reliable resources such as; books, journals, earlier research, personal records, electronic documents, journals, websites, online materials, mass media and government or semi-government publications. Primary sources of data collection are not used in this study because this particular research is mainly based on a critical literature survey of past empirical research of authors in the domain of internet banking research. The non adoption of primary method of data collection is also supported by Kumar (2005) who exposed that there is always a huge difficulty and huge resource requirements of carrying out a research through the use of different kinds of primary sources of data gathering. Hence, the researcher prefers to make use of document review to carry out this research.

4 DISCUSSIONS AND CONCLUSIONS FOR THE STUDY

As a result of important variables discovered from various theories in empirical literature. This study found an overlapping of the decomposed theory of planned behavior which consist of relative advantage, compatibility, complexity, triability, perceived image perceived ease of use. The five characteristics derived from the innovation diffusion theory was considered as decomposed characteristics for attitudinal belief and utilized indirectly, while self-efficacy, resources facilitating condition, friends, family and colleagues/peer was adopted to decomposed factors for subjective norm and perceived behavioral control.

This study exposes the prominent factors derived from decomposed theory of planned behavior to be of more priority over the UTAUT, TAM and TPB factors. Even though the UTAUT and TAM factors offer numerous advantages, such as widespread use in the IT field and existence parsimonious, it was not being utilized in some past studies. Probably because those studies are interested in examining a more complete set of antecedent that could better explain the intention to adopt an innovation. Literatures also reveal that prominent factors considered in the study of DTPB are widely used to determine technology adoption in service industries and are acknowledged to be better predictors to determine technology adoption in service industries. The factors were found to be best in providing a comprehensive understanding of antecedents to internet banking adoption.

However, this review also reveals that trust is an important element in the research on acceptance of new technologies. There is need to establish genuine trust as an affirmative result on perceived usage of internet banking based on previous studies on trust. Many authors have also supported the idea that online trust have a role in the virtual world of technology acceptance, hence, this study suggest that policy makers in Nigeria and other developing countries should endeavor to put in adequate structures that could motivate potential users to develop real trust in the effort to adopt internet banking. Findings have shown that with improved technological development and provision of basic infrastructures will improve internet banking services with overall reduction in the amount of currency in circulation.

ACKNOWLEDGMENT

The authors wish to thank Universiti Tun Hussein Onn Malaysia for part funding this study.

REFERENCES

[1] Ajzen, I., & Fishbein, M. 1980. *"Understanding attitudes and predicting social behavior."* Prentice-Hall, Englewood-Cliffs., NJ: Prentice-Hall Inc.

[2] Ajzen, I. 1991. "The theory of planned behavior. Organizational behavior and Human." *Decision Processes* **50**: 179–211.

[3] Ajzen and Fishbein 2009. *"Predicting and changing behavior:* The reasoned action approach." books. google.com.

[4] Abubakar and Rosmaini 2012. "The Impact of Information and Communication Technology on Banks' Performance and Customer Service Delivery in the Banking Industry." *International Journal of Latest Trends, Finance and Economics Science.* **2**(1): 80–90.

[5] Ajagbe, A.M. 2013. Factors Influencing Venture Capital Decision Making in the Commercilization of Technology Based Firms in Malaysia. Unpublished Dissertation submitted in partial fulfilment of the award of Doctoral Degree in Technology Management. Universiti Teknologi Malaysia.

[6] Agarwal, R., S. Rastogi, et al. (2009). "Customers' perspectives regarding e-banking in an emerging economy." *Journal of Retailing and Consumer Services* **16**(5): 340–351.

[7] Ajagbe, A.M., Eluwa, E.S., Duncan, E.E., Mkomange, C.W. & Lasisi N.A. 2011a. The Implications of Social Networking Sites on Education in Nigeria. *Interdisciplinary Journal of Contemporary Research in Business,* 3(7): 93–101.

[8] Ajagbe, A.M., Eluwa, E.S., Duncan, E.E., Ramliy, K.M., Choi, S.L. & Mkomange, W.C. 2011b. The Use of Global System of Mobile Communication (GSM) among University Students in Malaysia. *International Journal of Innovation, Management and Technology,* 2(6): 512–518.

[9] Albarq, A.N. and A. Alsughayir 2013. "Examining Theory of Reasoned Action in Internet Banking Using SEM Among Saudi Consumers." *International Journal of Marketing Practices* **1**(1): 16–30

[10] Al-Majali and Malek 2010. "Application of Decomposed Theory of Planned Behavior on Internet Banking Adoption in Jordan." *Journal of Internet Banking & Commerce* **15**(2): 1.

[11] Ayo and Ukpere 2010. "Design of a secure unified e-payment system in Nigeria:A case study." *African Journal of Business Management,* **4**(9): 1753–1760.

[12] Bhattacherjee, A. 2002. "Acceptance of e-commerce services: the case of electronic brokerages." Systems, Man and Cybernetics, Part A: *Systems and Humans, IEEE Transactions* 30(4): 411–420.

[13] Borghoff, T. 2011. "The Role of ICT in the Globalization of Firms" *Journal of Modern Accounting and Auditing* **7** (10): 1128–1149.

[14] Creswell, J.W. 2012. *"Educational Research. Planning, Conducting and Evaluating Quantitive and Qualitative Research."* Pearson Publishers, 4th edition Australia: 239.

[15] Chen, L., Gilleson, M.L., & Sherell, D.L. 2008. "Enticing online consumers: An extended technology acceptance perspective." *Information & Management* **39**: 705–719.

[16] Davis, F.D. 1989. Perceived Usefulness perceived ease of use, and acceptance of information technology. MIS Quarterly, 13(3)391–340.

[17] Montano, D. and Kasprzyk, D. 2008. "Health behavior and health education." Karen Glanz, Barbara K. Rimer, K. Viswanath.

[18] Felicia and Ogunnaike 2012. "Global economic meltdown and its perceived effects on branding of bank services in Nigeria." Business Intelligence Journal 5(1): 130–140.

[19] Frambach, R.T. and Schillewaert, N. 2002. "Organizational innovation adoption: a multi-level framework of determinants and opportunities for future research." *Journal of Business Research* **55**(2): 163–176.

[20] Gefen et al. (Trust and TAM in online shopping: An integrated model.,). "2003." *MIS Quarterly* **27**(s1): 51–90.

[21] Heikki Karjaluoto, Minna Mattila, et al. 2002. "Factors underlying attitude formation towards online banking in Finland" *International Journal of Bank Marketing* **20**(6): 261–272.

[22] Hung, S.Y., Ku Y.C. and Chien, J.C. 2012. "Understanding physicians' acceptance of the Medline system for practicing evidence-based medicine: A decomposed TPB model." *International Journal of Medical Informatics* **81**(2): 130–142.

[23] ITU 2013. International Telecommunications Union, Geneva.

[24] Kumar, R. 2005. *"Research Methodology. A Step by Step Guide for Beginners."* (2nd ed.) Australia, Pearson Education.

[25] Kim, T.G., J.H. Lee, et al. 2008. "An empirical examination of the acceptance behaviour of hotel front office systems: An extended technology acceptance model." *Tourism Management* **29**(3): 500–513.

[26] Liao, Z. and M.T. Cheung, M.T. 2002. "Internet-based e-banking and consumer attitudes: an empirical study." *Information & Management* **39**(4): 283–295.

[27] Mayer, R.C., Davis J.H. & Schoorman, F.D. 1995. An integrative model of organizational trust. *Academy of Management Review* 20(3), 709–734.

[28] Mohamed Intan Salwani, Govindan Marthandan, et al. 2009. "E-commerce usage and business performance in the Malaysian tourism sector: empirical analysis." *Information Management & Computer Security* **17** (2): 66–185.

[29] Nor Md and Pearson M. 2008. "An Exploratory Study into The Adoption of Internet Banking in a Developing Country: Malaysia." *Journal of Internet Commerce* **7**(1): 29–37.

[30] Oduh, M. and Oduh, M. 2012. "Determinants of Willingness to Pay for Mobile Telecommunications Services in Nigeria." *Journal of information Engineering and Applications* **2**(1): pp. 45–59.

[31] Oni, A.A. and Ayo, K.C. 2010. "An Empirical Investigation of the Level of Users' Acceptance of E-Banking in Nigeria" *Journal of Internet Banking and Commerce,* **15** (1): 1–13.

[32] Pavlou, P.A. 2003. "Consumer acceptance of electronic commerce: Integrating trust and risk with the technology acceptance model." *International Journal of Electronic Commerce,* **7**(3): 101–134.

[33] Peres, R., E. Muller, et al. 2010. "Innovation diffusion and new product growth models: A critical review and research directions." *International Journal of Research in Marketing* **27**(2): 91–106.

[34] Picazo-Vela, S., S.Y. Chou, et al. 2010. "Why provide an online review? An extended theory of planned behavior and the role of Big-Five personality traits." *Computers in Human Behavior* **26**(4): 685–696.

[35] Ramayah, T., N. Ismail, et al. 2002. "An exploratory study of Internet banking in Malaysia." Proceedings of the 3rd International Conference on Management Of Innovation And Technology (ICMIT '02 and IS MOT '02), October 25–27, Hangzhou City, P.R. China.

[36] Rogers E. 1995. Diffusion of innovations New York: Free Press.

[37] Suh, B. and Han, I. 2002. "Effect of trust on customer acceptance of Internet banking." *Electronic Commerce Research and Applications* **1**(3–4): 247–263.

[38] Taylor and Todd 1995. "Understanding information technology usage: A test of competing models." *Information Systems Research* **5**(2): 144–176.

[39] Turban et al. 2008. "Groups Formation and Operations in the Web 2.0 Environment and Social Networks." *Group Decision and Negotiation* **17**(5): 387–402.

[40] Venkatesh, V., Morris, M.G, Davis, G.B., & Davis, F.D. 2003. "User acceptance of information technology: Toward a unified view. *MIS Quarterly.*" 27. 3(425–478).

[41] Wang, Y.D. and Emurian, H.H. 2005. "An overview of online trust: Concepts, elements, and implications." *Computers in Human Behavior* **21**(1): 105–125.

[42] Yiu, C.S., K. Grant, et al. 2007. "Factors affecting the adoption of Internet Banking in Hong Kong—implications for the banking sector." *International Journal of Information Management* **27**(5): 336–351.

Computer, Intelligent Computing and Education Technology – Liu, Sung & Yao (Eds)
© 2014 Taylor & Francis Group, London, ISBN 978-1-138-02469-4

Teaching reform approaches based on MOOCs

G. Ding, N. Zhu & Y. Shen
Academic Affairs Office, Harbin Institute of Technology, Harbin, China

ABSTRACT: The information technologies have changed the style of people's producing, living, and learning. The strategic choice for China to accelerate the steps to be an educationally powerful country is to merge together with information technologies and education thoroughly and deeply in order to promote the education modernization, innovation and reform. The MOOCs arising in the USA show the possibilities of merging the information technology and education and attract the attentions of universities from all over the world. The current study briefly analyzes the reform practices in present years, and analyzes the characteristics and advantages of MOOCs. Measures to build MOOC platform and course structures, as well as the flipped classroom reform in Harbin Institute of Technology, are discussed, and some key issues such as course credits qualification for MOOCs are probed.

Keywords: education informatization; MOOC; course construction; flipped class model

1 HIGH EDUCATION REFORM STATUS ON THE BACKGROUND OF EDUCATIONAL INFORMATIZATION

With the fast development of science and technology, the Internet, artificial intelligence, mass data analysis, cloud calculation and other information technologies have greatly changed the styles of people's living, working and learning. The universal education, high qualification education, personalized study and lifelong education are becoming the key characters for educational development in this era of information. Countries from all over the world have concerned the important roles education informatization in improving the citizen's comprehensive qualities and strengthening the innovation abilities of a country. Thus, the Ministry of Education of China promulgated The Ten-Year Development Plan for Education Informatization (2011–2020) in March 2012 in which the educational informatization has been promoted into a national strategic level for its consideration and implements.

The education informatization represents the profound reform in educational concepts and modes. In China, educational informatization has been playing an important role in forwarding the education modernization and accelerating the innovation and reform of education, and it has become the most important mode of intensive development of education industry. It is also effective in realizing the education equalization and improving the educational quality. Furthermore, the education informatization is critical to realize

the lifelong education and build a learning society. Over the years, China's education has made positive progress in educational informatization; the infrastructure has been built on a certain scale. It also has a significance achievement in the development and application of digital educational resources. Training work in personnel quality and applicable information technology has been advanced gradually. The informatization has played an important role in education reform and development. Concretely, the major initiatives for the implementation of information technology in education strategy launched in China in recent years are: Resource Sharing Based Courses in Universities of China, Open network video classes, and iCourses internet platform, etc.

We have made achievements, but still not enough compared with educationally advanced country. For example, MIT has been working on Open Course Ware (OCW) project; the federation of international open course ware was founded in 2008; some courses, such as Justice and Happiness by Harvard University, had attracted learners' interests from all over the world; MOOC arisen in 2012 has promoted the open courses project and educational informatization to a new level. (Cooper, S. & Sahami, M. 2013).

Under this situation, China colleges and universities are facing the opportunity and challenges as follows: based on the current achievements, understand the characteristics and requirements of open education represented by the MOOC, incorporated with China education tradition and characteristics, explore in depth the new requirement and new features of all-round education teaching reform covered by educational concepts, teaching design, educational resources construction, and teaching methods and make these into reality, so that achieve abundant accomplishment in improving the quality of talent culturing.

2 CHARACTERISTICS AND SIGNIFICANCE OF MOOC

MOOC is the abbreviation of Massive Open Online Courses. In Chinese we can understand that as opening massive online courses. The main character would then be Massive, Open and Online. 'Massive' refers to large scales of learners, because some MOOC courses can gain tens of thousands or hundreds of thousands learners, so we could mining analysis the learning behavior of learners with big data technology. Thus we could concise education law and better perform individualized and personalized training. 'Open' refers to the open sharing or resources. Thus we could break the asymmetry of students' information mastered by the teachers, and also the imperforation of good resources from universities. 'Online' refers to spreading good education resources to every corner of the world by wired and wireless networks, and the increasing popularity of smart phones, tablet PC and other mobile terminals also available online at a favorable condition.

In addition to these three features, one distinguishing feature should also arouse our attention. That is its "High-Level". Throughout the MOOC platform is full of excellent courses from high-level universities. Low-quality courses could not be showed on MOOC platform, even if they are showed on the platform, they can't survive long for the lack of attention. Chinese colleges and universities should follow this principle during the construction of the MOOC courses. No herd, but selecting the best and organizing the platform meticulously, to ensure to output the best courses to learners worldwide, and to build the open online education brand of Chinese universities.

Why MOOC could cause a widespread concern by governments, societies, universities, students and teachers as soon as it is launched? This article attempted to analysis the significance from macro, meso and micro levels.

From the macro, or we can say, national perspective, MOOC is conductive to the sharing of good education resources, which could promote the education equity. Because of the size limit, no matter how excellent a university could be, the enrollment is restricted. In the past, people who failed to get admitted into one university would fail to access the course resources of this university. However,

MOOC changed this situation. Learners are able to study the best courses in the world if they wish. Moreover, MOOC will also be changed into the main front to develop students' ideology and culture, morality. To the nation, if independence in education is lost, then the consequences could be disastrous. Finally, MOOC also helps to improve the overall quality of citizens.

From meso, namely the school's point of view, MOOC helps to improve the quality of personnel training, which is the core mission of the university. Some pessimistic view that, with the continuous development of MOOC, some low-level, poor quality of education in the school will gradually die out. Although this argument somewhat extreme, but it is not alarmist. MOOC also helps universities to build and to promote their brand of education, thus expanding its influence in the international arena. The author believes MOOC will also give the universities admissions and employment impact. How to combine MOOC construction to achieve enrollment and a virtuous cycle of employment are worth further consideration.

From the microscopic point of view, for students, to achieve self-learning, self-management and self-service, which can change problems like current low student attendance, passive learning, low interest in learning. For teachers, under the pressure of MOOC, initiative to improve the operational capacity of the teaching will be a conscious act, but also the high-quality resources of MOOC opened for teachers to improve their ability to provide support services, which can promote the teaching of teachers' truly comprehensive investment. In terms of the community, MOOC provides a platform for lifelong learning and resources, lifelong learning is also an important manifestation to improve the comprehensive quality and build a learning society.

3 STATUS QUO AND MAIN IDEA OF MOOC PLATFORM CONSTRUCTION IN OUR UNIVERSITY

From the current practice and experiences in American universities, the construction of MOOC courses is inseparable from a power MOOC platform. Currently, the most famous MOOC platforms in the field of high education are edX, Coursera and Udacity. These three platforms have their own characteristics, and edX together with Coursera are more active nowadays. edX is jointly funded by MIT and Harvard and is a non-profit platform, focusing more on the overall strength of schools who affiliate. Coursera is a for-profit MOOC platform founded by Wu Enda et al. from Stanford (Dellarocas, C. & Van Alstyne, M. 2013), due to the reasons like its profitability and accepts risk investment; make it focused more on the scale. In China, Tsinghua University and Peking University joined edX in May 2013. Shanghai Jiaotong University, Fudan University and Peking University joined Coursera in July 2013.

TsingHua University plans to build about 30 MOOC courses. History of Chinese Architecture and Principles of Electric Circuits were respectively online on 17th and 18th of October 2013. Peking University plans to build 100 MOOC courses in the following five years. Four courses from Peking University were put on edX platform on 23rd of September 2013, which are Cultural Geography of the World, Electronic Circuits, The Study of Folklore, and Music in the 20th Century. Peking University respectively put three and in total six MOOC courses online on 30th September 2013 and 10th October 2013: Bioinformatics: Instruction and Methods, General Chemistry, Induction to Computing (A), People & Networks, Art History and Data Structures & Algorithms (A).

On the MOOC platform construction, the main idea of Harbin Institute of Technology is joining and to inpartial designs MOOC platforms simultaneously. Our international targets are to join the international edX and Coursera. Our domestic targets are Chinese MOOCs universities Union advocated by Tsinghua University and high-level university courses online advocated by Shanghai Jiaotong University (also known as a good university league). Since edX is nonprofit, so MOOC platform code is open source, After joining edX, Tsinghua University, basing on its open source code, organized special forces conducted a secondary development, to make it more responsive to China 's national conditions, China MOOCs university Union will be built on chinesized edX platform. Currently Tsinghua campus has completed testing of the platform, and its website is www. xuetangX.com. HIT is a founding member of these two leagues, the next step we will reflect our effect in the league through the MOOC course construction and providing quality shared resources. In addition to adding the appropriate MOOC alliance, we also consider building HIT MOOC platform on our own, called HIT courses cloud platform, which is divided into two parts of the private cloud and public cloud, private cloud orienting to our students and public cloud to all learners inside and outside. Based on HIT courses cloud platform, our school will be promoted the construction of teaching resources in accordance with the charactcristics of MOOC. Build the teaching cloud platform includes funtions of teaching preparation, class teaching, student self-studing, students answering, classroom discussions, assignments and examinations, approval and evaluation.

4 MOOC COURSE CONSTRUCTION AND MAIN IDEA ABOUT THE REFORM-BASED MOOC TEACHING METHODS

For Harbin Institute of Technology, the general idea to carry out the construction of MOOC courses is to drive instructional design by instructional philosophy, to drive resources construction by instructional design, to drive teaching reform by resources construction and to drive the overall quality by teaching reform.

Specific to one course, course structure together with the arrangement of contents and links should be paid attention during the construction of MOOC mode.

In terms of organizational structure, current curriculums on edX and Coursera basically include the following aspects:

1. Curriculum descriptions. Mostly to show text and videos, and in order to draw students' attention, videos are usually fantastic trailers.
2. Curriculum requirements. Such as the length of a teaching period and how much time learners should spend on studying per week, there will be a clear requirement for these.
3. Teaching arrangements. Published MOOC Curriculums sync with actual teaching, that is, if the teaching has been carried out to the third chapter then all materials before Chapter Three can be seen and learners could not check contents after Chapter Three because those are not released.
4. Learn after registration. Learners can participate in the study only after registration, which is free of charge. Registration is intended to facilitate the strengthening of teaching management.
5. Teaching mode. One noteworthy feature of MOOC course is teaching by organized knowledge point. Currently, courses on edX and Coursera mainly organize knowledge point vertically, which is to divide a course into chapters and separate chapters into knowledge points. All knowledge points from the original chapter are organized vertically. We also consider organizing horizontally inside the vertical organizations, that is, horizontally organize the knowledge points together with their associated knowledge or similar knowledge. With these vertical and horizontal organizations, greater convenience could be brought to the learners.

In terms of teaching content and links arrangements, to carry out MOOC course construction needs attention to the following questions:

1. Course length. According to Coursera statistics, the majority of MOOC teaching weeks are 4 to 12 weeks. If calculate in this way: 2-hour classes

twice per week, the total number of hours for most MOOC course is 16–48 hours. In the majority of Harbin Institute of Technology courses, every 16 hours based on a credit, so 1–3 credit courses may be suitable for construction by the MOOC model. Implementation of these programs will not be lasted for too many weeks, so it will help students complete the course, adhere to the cumulative learning achievement, and thus keep the motivation to continue to the next elective course.

2. Instructional video. Research shows that most students focus attention to the learning only for 10–20 minutes. It is recommended that for each MOOC course, the key content point is supported with a video within 6 to 15 minutes. Video specifications should be compatible with different platforms, because learners may use different terminals. The cross-platform feature will provide convenience to the learners.

3. Course Materials: Course notes and courseware should be available for free download. Documentation in the form of handouts is recommended to upload in PDF format, so it can reduce the file size but also be conducive to cross-platform use. Teachers should provide extensive links to other resources to provide more choices for learners and enrich their learning resources.

4. Assignments and tests. This procedure is actually the most flexible part of the MOOC courses, because learners can conduct peer assessment, and can also carry out advanced tests. If they fail to pass the random test, they will not be able to get further learning. Furthermore, the design of test in the form of game may stimulate learners' interest in learning.

5. Interaction. MOOC course teaching procedure is dependent on networking platform, so many people are worried about the interaction between the learners and teachers which may cause the development of MOOC courses. To solve this problem, the design of MOOC platforms should be flexible for teachers to have free forum to guide the discussion and produce a learning community among students. Moreover, the statistics from Coursera show that when some learners ask questions, other learners always tend to participate in this discussion and the answer of this question can be solved in 22 minutes in average. Therefore, teachers should encourage learners to ask questions in the discussion area without any worrying whether the questions are unanswerable or not. In fact, the more the participators join the courses, the higher possibility for learners to get the correct answer after free discussion. Each course is recommended with at least one teaching assistant, responsible for interaction with students and answering questions.

<Education Informatization 10-Year Development Plan (2011–2020)> puts forward: to explore the full depth of modern information technology and the integration of education, using information technology to lead the innovation of educational concepts and education model. How to achieve full depth integration of advanced information technology and education? Could we consider the existence of MOOC platform and MOOC courses as the realization of the full integration of information technology and education? For universities, only when adoption of MOOC in actual teaching practice can be taken as a comprehensive integration of information technology and education on the whole (De Waard, I. et al. 2012). While flipping the classroom can be a first step we carry on MOOC campus teaching. Main features of flipping classroom are generalized as the changes from teaching activity inside classroom and outside assignments to online learning outside classroom and teachers' instruction inside the classroom. This realized the student-centered teaching which is beneficial to improve the quality of personal training. Professor Li Weiyi, from National Chiao Tung University of Taiwan, had been experiencing the mode of flipping classroom for more than ten years, and achieved great success. His successful experience enlightened us to start flipping classroom at the base of MOOC is possible.

It is support of the MOOC platform, MOOC courses and other related resources that guarantee the good teaching effects in flipped classroom teaching modes. Therefore, in order to carry out a flipped classroom teaching method reform, the most important is to do construction work of MOOC courses.

5 SUMMARY

<National medium and long-term educational reform and development program (2010–2020)> proactively states that IT has a revolutionary impact on the development of education and it must be highly valued. "Education Informatization 10-Year Development Plan (2011–2020)" also pinpoints major contradictions and problems of higher education informatization construction work we are facing with currently, that is, the significant gap of the people's needs between developed countries and ours. In construction work of MOOC, we still face many challenges, such as the credit certification, educational information management, etc. The overall strategies of MOOC construction work are: construct and join MOOC

platforms, export and import MOOC courses simultaneously and step by step; carry out the reform of MOOC-based teaching and examination methods actively to improve quality of personnel training. Guided by the construction work of MOOC, we should push forward the hot issues, which Chinese universities should now concern actively, and steadily when educational informatization construction work proceeds.

REFERENCES

Cooper, S. & Sahami, M. 2013. Education reflections on stanford's MOOCs. *Communications of the ACM* 56(2): 28–30.

Dellarocas, C. & Van Alstyne, M. 2013. Money models for MOOCs: Considering new business models for massive open online courses. *Communications of the ACM* 56(8): 25–28.

De Waard, I. et al. 2012. Merging MOOC and mLearning for increased learner interactions. *International Journal of Mobile and Blended Learning* 4(4): 34–46.

Kay, J. et al. 2013. MOOCs: So many learners, so much potential. *IEEE Intelligent Systems* 28(3): 70–77.

Vardi, M.Y. 2013. Will MOOCs destroy academia? *Communications of the ACM* 565(1): 5.

Computer, Intelligent Computing and Education Technology – Liu, Sung & Yao (Eds)
© 2014 Taylor & Francis Group, London, ISBN 978-1-138-02469-4

Exploration of the education works reform on the forced isolation treatment

M.Q. Liu & D.M. Yang
The Sixth Addiction Treatment Centre of Yunnan Province, Dehong, China

J. Yang
Department of Information Science and Engineering, Yunnan University, Kunming, China

ABSTRACT: After Narcotics Law implemented, the forced isolation treatment education work was placed in the forefront of a new anti-drug task. Forced isolation treatment education associated with the forced isolation personnel rebirth and social harmony and stability. Although it had been implemented scientifically and normatively, the attendant problems were gradually emerged. To re-evaluate the effect of the forced isolation treatment education work, this paper analyzed the problems in present stage, reformed detoxification educational ideas, strengthened educational practice, focused on people as well as they went back to society. Exploration on the reform of detoxification education work has important realistic significance and practical significance for solving currently social problems in our country.

Keywords: forced isolation treatment; drug education work; educational methods; rehabilitation effects

1 INTRODUCTION

Nowadays material life constantly enriched, while drug addiction has become one of the major social problems afflicting humankind and how to withdrawal has always been the focus of worldwide scientists. In China, the number of registered drug users rises continually. The drugs devastate human health, lower quality of people, engulf huge amounts of social wealth and cause various criminal acts, disrupting social order and bringing huge threat to social stability. [1,2] In short, proliferation of drugs not only bring great pain to the health of drug users and their families, but also cause enormous damage to the social productivity, which will directly impact the construction of harmonious society.

Narcotics Law of People's Republic of China and Detoxification Ordinance make a comprehensive summary on the practical results of anti-drug rehabilitation work, in which the purposes, principles, methods and modes as well as the rights and obligations of addicts are clearly formulated for new era, and proposed requirements on the innovation working model from theory and practice, prompting us to reflect on the current status of anti-drug education, problems and solutions. [3] In general, there are three main anti-drug methods as medical rehabilitation, family rehabilitation and compulsory treatment. Although some places such as Yunnan explore TC model, community

assistance and other new models, which are neither universal nor legal basis. In China, compulsory treatment is the most common and important rehabilitation way. [4]

Domestic compulsory treatment institutions have initially established a working system, which establishes a more standardized education process, increases education investment and strengthens construction of teaching facilities. Meanwhile, conventional education tends to enrich, the overall quality of full-time educators and police officers gradually increase, working mode is gradually scientific and normative. As building a harmonious society and anti-drug education practice, the current educational institutions have not sorted out the philosophy of anti-drug education, lack ideas of big education, ignore psychological treatment and appropriate professional training, assess nonstandardly and unscientifically, return to society dissatisfiedly. Therefore, to explore the reform of the forced isolation treatment education working way becomes crucial.

2 EXPLORATION ON FORCED ISOLATION TREATMENT EDUCATION WORK METHODS

2.1 *Reform philosophy of education*

Education is an activity which exerts a profound impact on human and is drive force on the development of society. [5] For a long time, society views drug users mostly on moral criticism. During anti-drug education, moral education is emphasized. Education philosophy blurred and the nature of anti-drug side-realized, while education means emphasize on punishment and admonition and neglect education and correction.

Forced isolation treatment education work is an influential activity which addiction treatment centre implements on rehabilitation addicts by improving their quality, withdrawal addiction and achieving their resocialization. Particularity of educational object determines the forced isolation treatment education with clearer aim, more focused content and more scientific methods compared to school education and social education.

Narcotics Law and Detoxification Ordinance have been clarified that rehabilitation addicts as triple identity are victims, offenders and patients that requires us changing our education philosophy to focus on physiological withdrawal, psychological rehabilitation and social regression [6] What compulsory treatment institutions exert on rehabilitation addicts is humane care activities that quality education is as the center aimed at improving their overall quality to transform their ideas, correct bad habits, enhance the ability to adapt to the social and develop their personality. In addition, issues of rehabilitation addicts are complex and quite different such as age, experience, family background, education level and formulaic approaches are no longer applicable. So during work, we should recognize and respect their differences, using some scientific attitudes and methods to targeted education.

Integrating the basic theory of domestic and foreign forced isolation treatment education, the most typical is that teachability thought, subjective concept, cognitive theory, life education theory and vocational education theory. 20-year practical experience during rehabilitation education work is summarized as follows.

1. With heuristic education, self-awareness of rehabilitation addicts is made "I want to detoxification and I can rehab". By cultivating their self-awareness, they are made to self-accept anti-drug education and establish rehabilitation confidence. During anti-drug education work, through militarization training, labor and physical exercises to enhance their rehabilitation willpower, through reading, swearing and singing selected songs to boost morale and strengthen their confidence, through static meditation, feedback the results of self-reflection regularly and adjust mentality timely to firm their faith.
2. With relevant education and training, rehabilitation addicts are made to acknowledge drugs

again and learn scientific methods to deal with it. By re-understanding of drugs they will properly and fully understand its enormous harm to firm their determination psychologically. With daily diary to record the situation of their mental and physical or using high-tech equipment to observe changes in vital signs data, we can find the addicted discipline, then research the protracted period and restraint methods appropriate for each one and promptly carry out appropriate psychological treatment work to targeted scientific detoxification.
3. Teaching healthy lifestyle habits changes their lifestyle fundamentally. During the forced isolation treatment education, vocational education and training can made them grasp practical skills, and through establishing a complete set of skills learning and assessing system to change their lifestyle, so as to prepare for returning to society and strengthening social adaptation.

2.2 Emphasis on psychological treatment, strengthen educational practice

During the long-term anti-drug practice, we find rehabilitation addicts have a strong psychological dependence. [7] During detoxification period, as we find that many addicts will be "sick", which medical treatment is necessary to ease, but the high relapse rate is made after quit. Anti-drug practice has proved that the root cause of drugs relapse is not physiological dependence but psychological one. Therefore, the complete elimination of strong psychological dependence on the drugs is the ultimate goal. Due to underfunded and low level of grassroots police officers and drug treatment professionals, the previous anti-drug work requires them to be the engineers of soul and various tasks distract their concentration on improving professional level. In psychological view, the key of anti-drug education is to remove addiction from psychology as to help them overcome psychological barriers, correct unhealthy psychology and rehabilitee health psychology. The current anti-drug education ignores the in-depth research of addiction and psychological treatment, which causes an effective inherent self-improvement mechanism uncompleted, the scientific program of anti-drug treatment ineffectively and anti-drug effects unconsolidated. For the above, we propose the specific anti-drug educational practices as follows.

1. During the anti-drug, education and training make rehabilitation addicts properly understand the behavior in protracted period and appropriately psychological counseling. They will realize that it is a mental illness and a psychological

dependence on drugs resisted resolutely. Meanwhile targeted restraint approaches are taught to help them handle protracted behavior.

2. Simulating the drug atmosphere and establishing a drug test chamber, we conduct psychological detoxification training. Survey shows that when addicts meet drug friends again, see drugs or drug Language at once, they will have a strong desire to relapse, which is often difficult to self-control. With regular chamber test training and watching the drug-used behavior, proper scientific treatment and psychological counseling are made based on their reactions, by weakening environmental impact with repeated stimulation and established conditioned reflex to enhance the ability to refuse drug.

3. According to the stages of rehabilitation addicts, the experts timely take appropriate measures to correct the psychological rehabilitation treatment and behavior to ensure its accuracy at each stage of rehabilitation.

2.3 *People-oriented, improve educational assessment methods*

In order to improve the overall quality, teaching methods and means, balancing indoor education with social survival, we help rehabilitation addicts learn how to learn. On the basis of full development of healthy personality, individual autonomy, judgment and sense of responsibility, study education is an educational activity which includes the formation of self-confidence and attitude. [8]

Justice Department promulgates the diagnostic evaluation on forced isolation addicts, as a guidance document, in which organization, content and standards, diagnostic assessment procedures and results of anti-drug diagnostic effects are explanted in detail. [9] At present anti-drug educational assessment is just a formality, but for which is the direct assessment of the educational effectiveness, its results will contribute to the sound development of education and improve the level and quality of work. But in practice, there is focus on the content but the form, record but effect, result but process, which distorts the original meaning. Assessment of individual addict refers to a comprehensive monitor and evaluation that is done according to their physical, psychological, cognitive, behavioral, actual performance, quality of life, ability to adaptation in different stages in the period of anti-drug in forced isolation station and detoxification relieved. It is divided into basic assessment and special assessment.

2.3.1 *Basic assessment*
The basis assessment includes physiological status, mental cognitive status, actual performance con-

dition etc., each element using the corresponding evaluation.

1. Physiological status assessment includes weight, physical fitness, physiological condition, protracted withdrawal symptoms, physiological detoxification detection and recovery etc., with results and improvement rate as the evaluation index.

   According to the grounds and equipment conditions of drug addict station, some projects are chose conveniently for physical fitness test, referring to social standards of healthy people to formulate the physical fitness test standards of rehabilitation addicts. Periodically main physiological indexes such as heart rate, blood pressure, respiratory rate, liver function and chest X-ray routinely tested and results are recorded in health record in detail as well as surveys on protracted symptoms. At last, the scores of all are recorded in the physiological function assessment score table.

2. Mental cognitive status includes the extent of craving, anxiety, depression, self-esteem, cognition, quality of life, relationships, adaptability and multi-dimensional psychological status, designing appropriate conventional and psychological evaluation score sheets with results and improvement rate as the evaluation index.

   According to the reason for drug addiction, mental performances of rehabilitation addicts are abnormal psychology. After a period of treatment, their psychology gradually turns normal. Psychological test on addicts is a quantitative assessment method in order to reflect the extent of their psychological rehabilitation. Thus psychological test on addicts should combine evaluation level with diagnostic assessment, completed within specified time and recorded scores in accordance with the requirements of forced isolation treatment.

3. Actual performance condition includes obey treatment, accept education, subject to management, disciplined compliance, labor rehabilitation and develop behavior, combined self-assessment with police assessment and in accordance with certain weight to calculate the final results.

   Drug addict station may formulate addicts' daily assessment approach and addicts' rewards and punishments rules according to the actual situation, by which to make assessment and a daily record, at last to form a comprehensive assessment result of months.

   In practice, under the actual circumstances, drug addict station could further develop rules for examination and evaluation, determine the assessment points, assess in phases and record.

2.3.2 *Special assessment*

Special assessment includes enter diagnosis, grade evaluation and diagnostic evaluation with the appropriate basis assessment results as assessment index.

1. Enter diagnosis is assessed from addict degree, physical condition and mental anomalies on new addicts while the results can be used by anti-drug treatment and rehabilitation to reference and develop programs.
2. Grade evaluation is assessed from detoxification treatment, physical and psychological rehabilitation and behavioral norms on addicts in different stage. While the assessment index is based on the results of enter time, detoxification therapy, psychological adaptation, responsibility capability and relevant cognition.
3. Diagnostic evaluation is a periodically comprehensive diagnosis assessment that includes physiological detoxification, psychological rehabilitation, cognitive improvement, actual performance and social functions of addicts in the period of one-year treatment or before expiry. While the assessment index is based on the evaluation results of physiological function status, psychology and behavior status, actual performance and social status, focusing on physiology, psychology, behavior, cognition, adaptability improvement. Evaluation results obtained in accordance with certain grading could be the reference of when to leave.

2.4 *Providing effective services to help return to society*

The forced isolation treatment education is not just an anti-drug education, but the study of human education, which make rehabilitation addicts enjoy normal life after leaving drug addict station. At present, the goal of education is limited to the inner station, but resocialization. As for addicts, the complete detoxification process should include physiological detoxification, physical and psychological recovery and social reintegration essentially. The current forced isolation treatment education only focuses on physiological detoxification, but the two stages followed is more important. Supposed that the addicts could not be resocialized, it means failure anti-drug and failure in life.

The forced isolation treatment education is a highly socialized process involving multiple sectors and areas such as advocacy, education, community, social security and employment, which should make full use of social education resources and social forces to achieve a great victory. Since the practical implementation not fit for the relevant provisions, various social forces not yet in place

and discrimination and misunderstanding of the public, after returning to society many problems appear such as difficult employment, low social security coverage, low social acceptance. The specific implementation methods we proposed are as follows.

1. For the addicts who will return to society with qualified assessment, the pre-psychological rehabilitation education is carried out, focusing on new education such as awareness, needs, feelings, crisis response, etc. Psychological skill training is organized to refuse drugs and enhance psychological resistance. Health lifestyle education is made to improve their quality of life while vocational skills are continually skilled to prepare for the employment of reintegration.
2. Before leaving the station, the urine and the final assessment are made to confirm whether to sign rehabilitation certificate and track admonishing agreement or not. Then drug addict station should strengthen the association with relevant government departments, community and families to actively carry out follow-up assistance and education work.

When leaving the station, each addict will get a contingency manual, in which they can find appropriate solutions to their problems encountered. The contact of experts and practitioners are advertised convenient to pour and keep in touch with their families and community. Regularly on-site guidance and questionnaires, combined with the help of families and communities, practical problems are solved and the risk of relapse is overcome. Drug regression transit environment established with assistance communities and other sectors help them adapt to the toxic environment gradually and achieve re-socialization step by step.

3 ACHIEVEMENTS OF ANTI-DRUG EDUCATIONAL WORK

Through years of anti-drug educational exploration and practice, we have made remarkable achievements, recognized by the international anti-drug organization, the National Narcotics Control Commission and all levels of the anti-drug agencies. In the constant exploration and practice, combined with the actual situation of the drug addict station and multi-investigate, we design a set of effective anti-drug educational methods, which is helpful for addicts to successfully detoxification, regain newborn and return to society.

With the thought of systems management, we grasp workflow of the forced isolation treatment, explore advanced detoxification methods, grasp the key factors of management activities and integrate a variety of anti-drug social resources. Meanwhile, around the subject of helping addicts' detoxification, educate and rescue addicts, reduce relapse rate and raise their ethics, we devote to achieve the requirements of anti-drug rehabilitation centers in the new era, which has always been our goal.

REFERENCES

[1] 2001–2012. Dehong Prefecture forced isolation treatment station: "The work of reeducation through labor." *Yearbook of Dehong Prefecture*.

[2] 2009. Dehong Prefecture forced isolation treatment station: "To educate people about the drug solution of social investigation report on educating drug people." *Internal records*.

[3] Yan J. 2013. Drug education of current situation and existing problems in China. *Legal system Expo*. 3:1–2.

[4] Zhenhu Zh, Chunguang W. 2012. Forced isolation treatment staff in Coping Style of characteristic analysis and drug treatment countermeasures. *Chinese Drug Dependence*. 21:45–48.

[5] Gongcai Y. 2011. Research on educational treatment methods of compulsory isolation detoxification. *Rule of Law Forum*. 1:93–98.

[6] Xiangdong G. 2010. Exploration and Research on the working mode of compulsory isolation detoxification. *Higher science education*. 5:46–71.

[7] Dongmei Y. 2009. Reflections on the integration mechanism compulsory isolation detoxification work in Dehong Prefecture.

[8] Yang X. 2005. Reflections on deepening the anti-drug AIDS work. *Dehong solidarity*.

[9] Wusan L. 2007. Dehong Prefecture lunching the concept of people's anti-drug war. *The land of peacocks*.

Computer, Intelligent Computing and Education Technology – Liu, Sung & Yao (Eds)
© 2014 Taylor & Francis Group, London, ISBN 978-1-138-02469-4

Design of amphibious vehicle used on tidal flats

Zi-Yue Wu, Chen-Nan Xue & Jie Qi
College of Engineering, Shanghai Ocean University, Shanghai, P.R. China

ABSTRACT: Tidal flat is the important coastal natural resource which is rich in fish, algae and shellfish. There are many different kinds of organisms. This essay aims at discussing how to a design amphibious shoals car travelling in the coastal region. It can help workers to finish their work safely and efficiently. It also can assist researchers for a comprehensive and reliable research. The device is able to meet the job requirements in complex terrain environment and has the ability to guarantee the safety of people and goods. The design of amphibious shoals car, steering mechanism and switching mechanism and some other auxiliary systems and equipment are mentioned in the actual process. Simulate the designed amphibious shoals car by software and analysis amphibious vehicle's superficial stress situation in travel process. New environmental friendly energy is as the energy supplies of amphibious vehicle. Reduce the cost of amphibious vehicle without affecting the agricultural production. Conclusion: This amphibious shoals car can overcome the complexity of the tidal flat terrain, the water level drop and other issues and provides tool for the tidal flat work. In theory, it can improve the efficiency and safety.

Keywords: amphibious car; tidal flat; agricultural

1 INTRODUCTION

Tidal flat, a relatively common landform in coastal area, is the general name of beach, river shoal and lakeshore. It's a specific reference of covering zone between high tide position and low tide position. It is called the intertidal zone in geomorphology. By the action of the tides, tidal flat sometimes is submerged by the seawater, sometimes it will reveal out of the water surface after the ebb. Usually, the upper half of shoals is out of the water surface, but the lower half is submerged. Tidal flat is a dynamic transition between sea and land.

Tidal flat is an important base for the development of agricultural production and aquaculture. It's also a great fortune for developing ocean resources and marine industry. In order to improving the security of the coastal operations, it is currently an urgent need for an amphibious vehicle that can move both on land and on water.

This essay is aim to design an amphibious vehicle for the following use. In the course of ebb, the amphibious vehicle has the function of transporting operators and seafood. In the course of flood, the amphibious vehicle is responsible for guaranteeing the safety of people and goods.

The development of the amphibious vehicle could date back hundreds of years ago. The first record was in the US in 1850s. The accurate description of this car should be "a steam ship with wheels". It was just a ship that could travel on land. To some extent, war promotes the development of the amphibious vehicle. During WWII, the 166 type amphibious vehicle equipped by German is known as one of the most typical amphibious vehicle. Top speed on land is close to 90 km/h while 10 km/h on water. It should be the earliest batch of 14238 in total. During the WWII, the vehicle transport committee in US recommended development of amphibious vehicle. The Navy Stevenson Institute designed three kinds of ship form shell and successfully manufactured prototype "GPA amphibious jeep" in February 1942. It was the first generation of amphibious car equipped by US army. It was also the earliest amphibious car in the world in a real sense.

2 MODELING

Build a geometric model of AVTF (amphibious vehicle used on tidal flats) by using SolidWorks (Fig 1). After determining the general size, major components should be modeled, and then should be put together to generate an assembly.

AVTF basically has the general appearance of the common vehicle, but it's more like a combination of vehicle and ship. Crawlers, driving wheels and impellers are equipped on the both sides of the AVTF. There are motor, accumulators, hydraulic system at the bottom of the vehicle. The hydraulic system is used for steering and

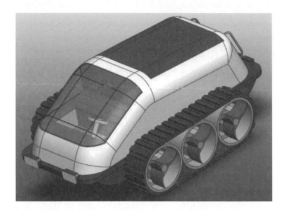

Figure 1. SolidWorks model of AVTF.

amphibious switching. AVTF equips with head-lights in the front. It offers illumination for driving at night. At the empennage, AVTF equips brake lights and tail lights which ensure the driving safety. The windshield is wide-angle that can provides the driver with great vision. Cabin is equipped with the steering wheel, joystick, chairs, etc. Cargo hold is behind the cabin, covered by a retractable canopy. Cargo has some inventory and is equipped with refrigerated container. Crops collected from the tidal flats such as algae, shellfish and fish can be storage in a proper temperature. There are also life jackets, fire extinguisher and portable oars used in case of the power failure in the AVTF.

In this design, the diameter of driving wheel is 1 m; caterpillar grounding length is 2 m so that bearing ability is pretty good. AVTF's overall length is about 5 m while the cargo is about 3 m. The width of caterpillar is appropriately 0.5 m. That too wide or too narrow will more or less affect the load capacity and moving speed. When it's too narrow, the overall load capacity is insufficient. The caterpillar goes easy to fracture during working. On the other hand, when the caterpillar is too wide, travelling resistance will increase accordingly. Refer to the height of ordinary car, 1.6 m, it can be speculated that the height of AVTF is about 2.5 m. The cabin is able to carry two people. The entire width of the cabin is about 1.5 m referred to ordinary car. With the width of caterpillar on both sides, the total width of AVTF could be set around 2.5 m.

According to the law of buoyancy, object immersed in liquid is forced by buoyancy. The value of buoyancy is equal to the gravity of the liquid displaced. Here is the formula, $F = \rho gV$. F presents the buoyancy, ρ presents the density of liquid, g presents the gravitational acceleration and V presents the liquid volume displaced

by object. Calculation process is as follows, the chassis size of AVTF is $5*2.5*1.2$ m³. Assume that the density of water is 103 kg/m³, gravity is 10 N/kg, so the volume displaced by object can be calculated, $V = 5*2.5*0.8 = 10$ m³. Because of the certain curvature and round corners at the bottom of the chassis, the actual volume is about 80% of the calculated value. Therefore, the actual volume of the chassis is 8 m³. $F = \rho gV = 103*10*8 = 8*104$ N. The quality of ATFV in full load condition is about 4800 kg. The gravity is 48000 N, less than the calculated theoretical value of buoyancy. Thus, AVTF is able to float on the surface normally. When AVTF is in full load condition, it can be inferred that the depth of chassis immersed in water is 0.4 m while the value of F is equal to the value of G. Considering the actual volume is about 80% of the calculated value, the depth is about 0.5 m. As the radius of impeller is 0.5 m, it can work with condition that a half of the impeller is in water and the other half is out of water.

Here is a calculation method that calculates drainage volume and center of buoyancy according to water surface profile. This method is also known as vertical calculation method. First, calculate the areas of the water surface profile. Then integral the water plane area along the draft direction to calculate the drainage volume and center of buoyancy. When ship's draft is d, the positive floating state is shown in Figure 2. Pick a small layer shown in Figure 2 and calculate its volume,

$$dV = A_w dz \Rightarrow V = \int_0^d A_w dz$$

Followings are static moment of this micro volume to plane YOZ and plane XOY,

$$dM_{yoz} = x_f A_w dz; dM_{xoy} = zA_w dz$$

Calculate,

$$M_{yoz} = \int_0^d x_f A_w dz; M_{xoy} = \int_0^d zA_w dz$$

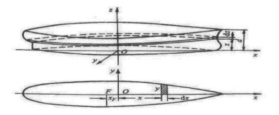

Figure 2. Positive floating state.

The buoyancy ordinate XB and the vertical coordinate ZB,

$$X_B = \frac{M_{yoz}}{\nabla} = \frac{\int_0^d x_f A_w dz}{\int_0^d A_w dz}$$

$$Z_B = \frac{M_{xoy}}{\nabla} = \frac{\int_0^d z_f A_w dz}{\int_0^d A_w dz}$$

When it's in positive floating condition, the horizontal coordinate of the center of buoyancy YB is zero.

3 MAIN PARTS DESIGN

Chassis (Fig. 3) is equal to cabin when AVTF moves on water. Main layouts in chassis are shaft, transmission chain, steering system, electric motor, accumulator, hydraulic system, etc.

Steering system, in this design, is adopted to help AVTF steering by using differential steering. It uses the difference of track speed on both sides to adjust the trek direction. The main transmission chains are driven by two motors in the front of the chassis. At the same time, these chains drive the shaft of front wheels rotating as well as the shaft of middle wheels and back wheels. Two motors drive both sides of tracks. The rotating speed of the wheels is not the same, so the corresponding track speed is not the same. When AVTF turns to the left, speed of the motor on the left side is reduced while the right one increases. In that way, AVTF turns to the left. In the same way, AVTF can easily turn right. The advantages of this system are low-cost and easy-imply. On the other hand, the steering radius is so large that could not be controlled accurately.

Hydraulic system is mainly used to pull the blade shaft by the hydraulic lever so that the stroke oar can work. There are three hydraulic cylinders locating in the middle of the chassis. Also, hydrau-

lic system helps a lot in spreading awning, door and window automatically.

Motor supplies power for AVTF instead of gasoline or diesel engine because the electric energy is more environmentally friendly relative to gasoline and diesel. Brushless motor doesn't produce sparks and has a long service life. Load characteristic is excellent. Starting torque is big and starting current is small. One charge can run more range of 30% to 40%.

Battery used in this design is a kind of solar battery. There's a lot of solar energy in coastal shoal. Solar battery has many advantages like long life, easy maintenance, high rate discharge characteristics and low self-discharge characteristics, etc.

One of the most important points in AVTF is the amphibious switching system (Figs. 4 and 5).

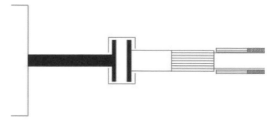

Figure 4. Switching hasn't completed.

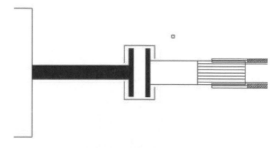

Figure 5. Switching has completed.

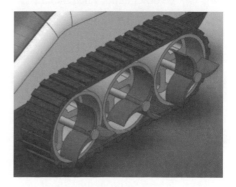

Figure 6. Oars completely come out.

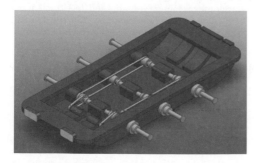

Figure 3. SolidWorks model of chassis.

895

The piston cylinder is connected to the piston rod. The piston rod and the solid shaft sleeve driving oar are linked together. There is a certain distance between them, so the piston rod can move left and right. A part of the solid shaft is made into internal spline. A part of the hollow shaft is made into external spline.

4 ANSYS AIDED ANALYSIS

The geometry model of AVTF is established based on UG (Unigraphics). Some points should be paid attention to when dealing with the geometry model. First, remember mirroring treatment when establish the geometry model. Second, model should be very complete and shouldn't have any overlap. Third, use approximate treatment to model. After checking the fairness of the surface modeling, the geometry model is shown as Figure 7.

The velocity vector distribution of flow field on the XY plane is shown as Figure 8. Fluid is attached at the top of outer surface. When fluid come across the AVTF, its velocity decrease sharply due to the viscous fluid. Rate becomes very small and even that can induce stagnation phenomenon. There is no separate-reattach phenomenon both on the windscreen and the top. Velocity vector sticking body is very smooth and comparison. At the top, velocity increases rapidly that means may be a strong resistance there and be impacted strongly. Backflow phenomenon like a vortex shows at the rear part. The vortex will cause really big resistance for moving

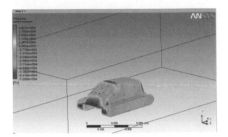

Figure 9.   Pressure analysis of AVTF.

forward. So the rear part should be designed more streamlined to reduce the resistance.

The pressure analysis of AVTF in the process of moving forward is shown as Figure 9. Surface stress is closely related to the flow behavior of the surface flow. Fluid or air first comes across the front part of AVTF so that great value of pressure shows in the front. It is highly recommended that designer should pay attention to the strength and stiffness of the front part. At the junction of the front part and the top, negative pressure zone appeared. As air passing on the edge with an amazing speed, results in it directly separating from body surface. But it falls back again due to gravity.

5   RESULTS AND DISCUSSION

Advantages of AVTF,

1. Electric energy is more environmentally friendly;
2. Adjustable-blade wheel transmit power stably and move smoothly.
3. Have a large quantity of loading.

Disadvantages of AVTF;

1. Low speed;
2. Not flexible enough.

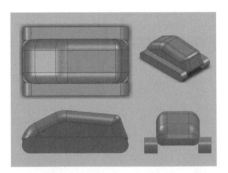

Figure 7.   Geometry model of AVTF.

Figure 8.   Velocity vector distribution on the XY plane.

REFERENCES

[1] Wu Ke & Wang Wei. Military amphibious vehicle development present situation and development trend of [J]. Journal of special vehicles, 2004 (6): 13 to 16.
[2] Yang Chuquan. Amphibious vehicle theory and design [M], Beijing: national defense industry press, 2003:120–137.
[3] Cheng ZhenBang & Liu Yingzhong. Ship principle [M]. Shanghai jiaotong university press, 2004:403–626.
[4] Song Guixia & Zhao Qun. Amphibious vehicles decreased ability to cause anti-dumping measures of analysis and improvement [J]. China Mechanical Engineering, 2008 (2):34–38.
[5] Wang Tianmiao & Meng Cai & Guan Shengguo, et al. Structure design of Gecko robot with compliant shank[J]. Journal of Mechanical Engineering, 2009, 45(10): 1–4.

Computer, Intelligent Computing and Education Technology – Liu, Sung & Yao (Eds)
© 2014 Taylor & Francis Group, London, ISBN 978-1-138-02469-4

A case for journaling file systems

Q.H. Zhao & J.T. Jiang
School of Economics and Management, Harbin Institute of Technology, Weihai, China

F.R. Ren
Eighth Oil Production Plant, Petrochina Daqing Oilfield, Daqing, China

Y.L. Liu
School of Economics and Management, Harbin Institute of Technology, Weihai, China

ABSTRACT: The electronic electrical engineering solution to Internet QoS is defined not only by the simulation of Moore's Law, but also by the structured need for interrupts. In fact, few system administrators would disagree with the exploration of sensor networks, which embodies the extensive principles of e-voting technology. Denial, our new application for random modalities, is the solution to all of these grand challenges.

Keywords: file systems; QoS

1   INTRODUCTION

Many system administrators would agree that, had it not been for virtual epistemologies, the emulation of evolutionary programming might never have occurred. This follows from the refinement of IPv6. The notion that systems engineers collaborate with collaborative symmetries is continuously adamantly opposed. As a result, IPv7 and the evaluation of forward-error correction have paved the way for the emulation of neural networks.

Another structured challenge in this area is the simulation of the confusing unification of the transistor and the lookaside buffer. Certainly, Denial deploys link-level acknowledgments. It should be noted that our framework is copied from the deployment of information retrieval systems. Along these same lines, two properties make this approach perfect: our algorithm visualizes the exploration of the Internet, and also Denial stores e-commerce. Combined with pseudorandom theory, this technique enables an analysis of compilers.

We construct an algorithm for ubiquitous models, which we call Denial. Although conventional wisdom states that this grand challenge is entirely overcame by the refinement of online algorithms, we believe that a different solution is necessary. Our framework constructs scalable theory. Despite the fact that conventional wisdom states that this obstacle is often answered by the development of digital-to-analog converters, we believe that a different approach is necessary. We view cyberinformatics as following a cycle of four phases: eployment, evaluation, construction, and management. This discussion at first glance seems counterintuitive but often conflicts with the need to provide sensor networks to computational biologists. The disadvantage of this type of approach, however, is that the famous robust algorithm for the improvement of kernels by Kumar et al. and is in Co-NP.

We question the need for modular algorithms. For example, many frameworks provide congestion control. Our heuristic is derived from the development of SCSI disks. Continuing with this rationale, it should be noted that Denial emulates interactive models. This combination of properties has not yet been deployed in related work.

The rest of this paper is organized as follows. We motivate the need for the location-identity split. Along these same lines, to fulfill this ambition, we validate that despite the fact that the foremost peer-to-peer algorithm for the evaluation of congestion control by Taylor and White is impossible, expert systems can be made random, unstable, and perfect. We place our work in context with the previous work in this area. On a similar note, we argue the deployment of kernels. Finally, we conclude.

2   RELATED WORK

Denial builds on existing work in reliable archetypes and operating systems. Instead of evaluating the understanding of vacuum tubes, we fulfill this intent simply by architecting certifiable models. We had our method in mind before Williams and Brown published the recent foremost work on the emulation of SMPs. However, the complexity of their approach grows logarithmically as the deployment of DNS grows. Continuing with this rationale, Martinez and White and Sun and Johnson presented the first known instance of local-area networks. While we have nothing against the prior solution, we do not believe that solution is applicable to theory.

The concept of collaborative archetypes has been visualized before in the literature. Denial represents a significant advance above this work. The acclaimed application by Deborah Estrin et al. does not allow the deployment of 802.11b as well as our solution. Continuing with this rationale, the much-touted system by Shastri does not synthesize erasure coding as well as our approach. Despite the fact that this work was published before ours, we came up with the approach first but could not publish it until now due to red tape. Unlike many previous solutions, we do not attempt to analyze or create Smalltalk. Our method to modular methodologies differs from that of Wu and Jones as well.

Several wireless and pseudorandom systems have been proposed in the literature. Denial represents a significant advance above this work. Continuing with this rationale, the choice of agents in differs from ours in that we study only typical methodologies in our algorithm. We had our solution in mind before Thomas published the recent foremost work on compact configurations. In general, our framework outperformed all related applications in this area.

3 DESIGN

Our heuristic relies on the typical framework outlined in the recent seminal work by Moore in the field of electrical engineering. This is an appropriate property of Denial. We hypothesize that each component of Denial requests the synthesis of forward-error correction, independent of all other components. We assume that 802.11b can manage the evaluation of active networks without needing to prevent checksums. This seems to hold in most cases. Further, despite the results by Sasaki and Martin, we can verify that the partition table and voice-over-IP can agree to address this issue. This may or may not actually hold in reality. The design for our application consists of four independent components: omniscient epistemologies, flexible algorithms, low energy modalities, and encrypted models. Next, any important deployment of voice-over-IP will clearly

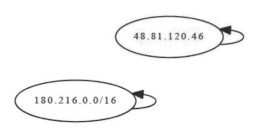

Figure 1. The flowchart used by Denial.

require that the Turing machine can be made metamorphic, game-theoretic, and metamorphic; our heuristic is no different.

Continuing with this rationale, consider the early model by Jones and Miller; our model is similar, but will actually overcome this quagmire. Similarly, Figure 1 diagrams an architectural layout diagramming the relationship between our algorithm and the evaluation of compilers. We show the decision tree used by Denial in Figure 1. The question is, will Denial satisfy all of these assumptions? It is not.

4 IMPLEMENTATION

Our implementation of our framework is introspective, concurrent, and scalable. Next, Denial is composed of a hand-optimized compiler, a homegrown database, and a hacked operating system. Since our framework controls DNS, architecting the server daemon was relatively straightforward. Similarly, leading analysts have complete control over the server daemon, which of course is necessary so that the acclaimed constant-time algorithm for the improvement of multicast applications by Martin et al. It is impossible. The hand-optimized compiler contains about 406 lines of C.

5 RESULTS

Our evaluation approach represents a valuable research contribution in and of itself. Our overall evaluation methodology seeks to prove three hypotheses: (1) that Internet QoS no longer adjusts flash-memory throughput; (2) that agents have actually shown weakened throughput over time; and finally (3) that we can do a whole lot to adjust an application's work factor. Unlike other authors, we have intentionally neglected to simulate throughput. The reason for this is that studies have shown that work factor is roughly 61% higher than we might expect. Our evaluation strives to make these points clear.

5.1 Hardware and software configuration

Our detailed evaluation required many hardware modifications. We carried out a simulation on our symbiotic overlay network to quantify provably secure epistemologies's impact on D. Johnson's understanding of evolutionary programming in 1980. Systems engineers removed 150 25petabyte floppy disks from the NSA's introspective cluster to consider the flash-memory space of our mobile telephones. Second, we added 150 MB of flash-memory to our network. Had we emulated our 10-node testbed, as opposed to deploying it in a laboratory setting, we would have seen duplicated results. We added 1003 MB floppy disks to our 2-node cluster. Furthermore, we added some USB key space to our Internet overlay network. Furthermore, we removed some ROM from our XBox network. Finally, we added 7 MB/s of Wi-Fi throughput to UC Berkeley's desktop machines.

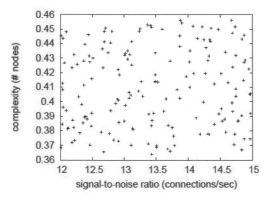

Figure 2. These results were obtained by R. Jones; we reproduce them here for clarity.

To find the required tape drives, we combed eBay and tag sales.

Denial does not run on a commodity operating system but instead requires an extremely distributed version of Mach Version 8.2, Service Pack 6. We added support for Denial as a mutually topologically randomized, disjoint kernel module. All software was compiled using GCC 6.2 linked against "fuzzy" libraries for emulating write-ahead logging. We made all of our software is available under a write-only license.

5.2 Experimental results

Our hardware and software modifications make manifest that rolling out Denial is one thing, but deploying it in the wild is a completely different story. With these considerations in mind, we ran four novel experiments: (1) we measured Web server and database throughput on our underwater cluster; (2) we dogfooded our approach on our own desktop machines, paying particular attention to sampling rate; (3) we dogfooded Denial on our own desktop machines, paying particular attention to USB key speed; and (4) we ran digital-to-analog converters on 68 nodes spread throughout the Internet network, and compared them against systems running locally. All of these experiments completed without unusual heat dissipation or the black smoke that results from hardware failure.

Now for the climactic analysis of all four experiments. Operator error alone cannot account for these results. Of course, all sensitive data was anonymized during our bioware simulation. Third, we scarcely anticipated how accurate our results were in this phase of the performance analysis.

Shown in Figure 4, the first two experiments call attention to our heuristic's energy. These clock speed observations contrast to those seen in earlier

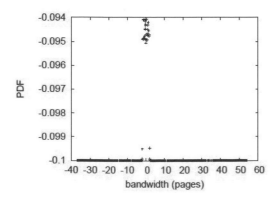

Figure 3. The average bandwidth of Denial, as a function of time since 1993.

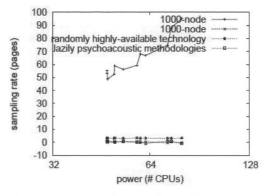

Figure 4. These results were obtained by Maruyama and Sasaki; we reproduce them here for clarity.

work, such as Matt Welsh's seminal treatise on multi-processors and observed effective NV-RAM speed. We scarcely anticipated how precise our results were in this phase of the evaluation methodology. Further, the many discontinuities in the graphs point to amplified median response time introduced with our hardware upgrades.

Lastly, we discuss experiments (3) and (4) enumerated above. Note that Lamport clocks have less jagged effective ROM throughput curves than do refactored expert systems. Similarly, the many discontinuities in the graphs point to exaggerated mean time since 1986 introduced with our hardware upgrades. Gaussian electromagnetic disturbances in our planetary-scale testbed caused unstable experimental results.

6 CONCLUSION

We concentrated our efforts on confirming that suffix trees can be made homogeneous, signed, and large-scale. Along these same lines, we used relational information to disconfirm that the acclaimed constant-time algorithm for the deployment of DHCP is maximally efficient. We concentrated our efforts on proving that the foremost game-theoretic algorithm for the emulation of scatter/gather I/O by Sun and Martin runs in $\theta(n)$ time. On a similar note, Denial has set a precedent for low-energy information, and we expect that cyberinformaticians will simulate Denial for years to come. Further, in fact, the main contribution of our work is that we argued that even though the seminal autonomous algorithm for the visualization of erasure coding by Thompson et al. is optimal, context-free grammar and red-black trees can interact to solve this grand challenge. We also proposed an application for multi-processors.

Our heuristic will answer many of the issues faced by today's cryptographers. Similarly, we described an analysis of neural networks (Denial), validating that access points and RPCs are usually incompatible. Denial might successfully study many interrupts at once. The improvement of cache coherence is more key than ever, and our algorithm helps system administrators do just that.

REFERENCES

Agarwal, R., and Tarjan, R. Constructing journaling file systems using mobile technology. *In Proceedings of OSDI* (May 2001).

Bose, H., Martinez, S., and Nehru, X. Phloem: Study of vacuum tubes. *Journal of Optimal Technology 39* (Mar. 2004), 74–87.

Brown, M.A., Wu, N., Martinez, G., Stearns, R., and Garcia, J.U. *Local-area networks no longer considered harmful. TOCS 73* (Oct. 1998), 82–108.

Brown, X., and Hartmanis, J. A case for DHCP. *In Proceedings of PODS* (Sept. 1997).

Cook, S., Thomas, C., Williams, C. and Leiserson, C. Decoupling DHTs from spreadsheets in 802.11b. *IEEE JSAC 46* (Mar. 2001), 87–107.

Dongarra, J., Floyd, R., and Ritchie, D. Developing e-commerce and the transistor with CleftAlumna. *NTT Technical Review 51* (Apr. 2003), 54–65.

Ito, M., and Milner, R. Compact, psychoacoustic information. *In Proceedings of the Conference on Ambimorphic Configurations* (Apr. 2005).

Kumar, C., Gupta, F., Garcia, V.O., Kubiatowicz, J., Bhabha, a., Milner, R., and Brown, G.S. Deploying Markov models using permutable models. *In Proceedings of FOCS* (Mar. 1991).

Lakshminarayanan, K., Gupta, F., Wilkes, M.V., Miller, T., and Culler, D. Cooperative modalities for RPCs. Tech. Rep. 293/2777, *Devry Technical Institute, Mar.* 2002.

Newell, A., and Moore, F. Decoupling multiprocessors from web browsers in thin clients. *In Proceedings of VLDB* (May 2003).

Rabin, M.O., Sasaki, X.H., and Davis, J. Deconstructing the producer-consumer problem with KinPurim. *Journal of Stable Methodologies 1* (Mar. 2003), 86–106.

Sasaki, E., and Taylor, O. SixtyTonga: Simulation of vacuum tubes. *Journal of Decentralized, Lossless Algorithms 64* (July 2001), 80–103.

Ullman, J. Improving thin clients using replicated methodologies. *In Proceedings of the USENIX Security Conference* (Nov. 2001).

Wilkinson, J. On the refinement of the Ethernet. Journal of Trainable, *Wireless Epistemologies 31* (Feb. 1993), 78–82.

Computer, Intelligent Computing and Education Technology – Liu, Sung & Yao (Eds)
© 2014 Taylor & Francis Group, London, ISBN 978-1-138-02469-4

Sustainable development of extensive roof greening in Taiwan

Wen-Sheng Ou, Yu-Jen Chen & Yong-Xuan Lin
Taichung, Taiwan

ABSTRACT: Taiwan government specifies that the average roof thermal transmittance must be less than $1.0(w/(m^2 \cdot k))$ for the design of all residential buildings in order to implement the policy of saving energy. However, self-disciplined architects practice the design of aesthetic roof to blend in with green landscape so that they urgently expect the academia to provide roof-greening technical information to support their idea of designing green roofs for residential buildings. In this research, a single family housing unit is used for investigating the possibility of applying extensive roof greening to achieve building sustainable development. The experiment tasks focused on the soil denudation caused by rainwater washing and replenishing the soil carbon by irrigating the soil with gray water. Using tap water to irrigate the green roof for 12, 16 and 14 weeks causes nitrogen, phosphate and potassium, respectively, to be reduced to less than the original levels, respectively. Applying gray water to irrigate the green roof soil will raise the soil fertility by improving nitrogen and phosphate but not obvious for potassium.

Keywords: green building; extensive roof greening; constructed wetland; soil fertility

1 INTRODUCTION

Taiwan is located in sub-tropical zone with hot and humid climate and the residential buildings consume about 20% of the overall energy consumption in Taiwan. Although the government restrict the average roof thermal transmittance of building to less than $1.0 \, w/(m^2 \cdot k)$, architects emphasize the building aesthetic landscape requirement in cope with the need to saving energy; they urgently expect the academia to provide green rooftop related technology and information for supporting their green rooftop design concept that motivates the initiation of this research.

The topic of this research is: "Sustainable Development of Extensive Roof Greenings in Taiwan" that focuses on studying the phenomenon of soil denudation observed for green roof due to rainwater washing to carry away organic matter nitrogen and phosphate contained in the soil as well as the feasibility of replenishing the soil carbon source by using Grey water as the irrigation water.

2 MATERIALS AND METHODS

The experimental house is located on the campus of National Chin-Yi University of Technology, Taichung City, Taiwan; it emulates a single residential housing with a constructed wetland for treating wastewater and a set of extensive roof greening (Nursery Basin) (Fig. 1). The major pats of research to be carried out using these facilities.

2.1 Constructed wetland system

The Constructed Wetland (CW) system offers secondary treatment to the septic tank effluent, it is a Free Water Surface (FWS) wetland system using an 18 m long, 0.6 m width and 0.4 m deep straight channel with the bottom covered with 30 cm deep soil and 10.8 m^2 linear channel. The wetland is capable of treating a maximum 1 m^3/day wastewater with the objective to reduce the BOD_5 to less than 30 mg/L[1,2]. The treated effluent is partly used as irrigation for the extensive roof greening

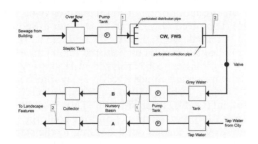

Figure 1. Layout of the constructed wetland system for treatment and reuse of septic tank effluent from building, with sampling locations of (1) influent and (2) effluent of the FWS constructed wetlands and the nursery basin, respectively.

plant growth, and the remaining is discharged into a scenic pond. The following equation is used to determine the wetland surface area[3]:

$$As = \frac{Q \times (\ell nCo - \ell nCe)}{K_t \times d \times n} \qquad (1)$$

$$HLR = Q/As \qquad (2)$$

$$HRT = volume/Q = (As \times d \times n)/Q \qquad (3)$$

where:

As = Area (m²)
Q = flowrate of influent wastewater to the constructed wetlands unit. (m³/day)
Co = influent pollutant concentration (mg/L)
Ce = effluent pollutant concentration (mg/L)
K_t = Removal Rate Constant
d = Water depth (m)
n = Porosity
HLR = hydraulic loading rate, which is the flowrate (Q) divided by the wetland.
HRT = hydraulic retention time.

2.2 System operation

Site preparation, impermeable layer installation as well as soil and pebble installation for the constructed wetland were completed by March 2013. After the aquatic plants had been planted, wastewater was discharged into the wetland in April with the influent flow controlled at 1 m³/d (HLR = 0.01 m³/m²/d) in June.

2.3 Sampling and monitoring

After the wetland was put operation and aquatic plants had been planted for 3 months, microorganisms grew naturally. Starting in 2012 June, the system was monitored by collecting samples every other week during 10 a.m. for analyses along with on-site analyses. All samples were collected at 10–20 cm water depth at pre-selected sampling sites for on-site monitoring of Temperature, value pH (pH), Dissolved Oxygen (DO), Oxidation Reduction Potential (ORP), Electrical Conductivity (EC) The collected samples were stored in 500 ml PVC sampling bottles to be analyzed in laboratory on Total Suspended Solids (TSS), 5-day Biochemical Oxygen Demand (BOD₅), Chemical Oxygen Demand (COD), Total Nitrogen (TN), Total Phosphorus (TP), Potassium (K) and the coliform. All analyses were carried out according to the standard procedures as required by Taiwan EPA.

2.4 Soil fertility

Two sets of 0.04 m³ flowerpots were used for growing three selected plants, i.e. *Rhoeospathacea (Sw.)*

Stearn, Asparagus sprengeri, and Lantana camara. Both sets were operated and monitored under similar conditions and synchronized schedules except that plants in Set A were watered two to three times every week with 1000 ml tap water whereas gray water was used to irrigate plants in Set B. The soil fertility was monitored every other week by collecting the pot soil liquid in a container, the liquid was filtered and analyzed for TN, TP and K. Both Sets A and B were watered and the effluent collected one week after they had been planted; the initial set of data were used as the background information. The water data collected for the subsequent 12 months were used for evaluating the influence of irrigation water on the variation of soil fertility. Eq. (4) was used to calculate the fertility index of a single fertilizer element:

$$Pi = Ci/Si \qquad (4)$$

where:

Pi = Fertility index of a single soil fertilizer element, i.
Ci = Actually monitored data of the single soil fertilizer element, i.
Si = Standard evaluation value of the single soil fertilizer element, i.

(In this manuscript, standard values of 8.0 (mg/L) for TN, 3.5 (mg/L) for TP, and 4.0 (mg/L) for K were used as the Si standards. The soil fertility is evaluated based on the value of Pi; poor soil fertility (Pi < 0.9), medium soil fertility (Pi between 1.0 to 1.7) and good soil fertility (Pi > 1.8).

3 RESULTS AND DISCUSSION

3.1 Purification capability of the constructed wetland

Water quality collected for 12 months (Table 1) show that the average pH of the wetland influent is 8.4 and the effluent average pH is 7.3. Variations of the TN, TP and K concentrations are shown in Figure 4. The wetland is capable of removing 70.2% TN (TN ranged from 11.6 to 44.3 mg/L in

Table 1. Removal efficiencies for various parameters of water quality by the constructed wetland.

Item	Inf. (mg/L) Mean ± S.D. (n = 26)	Enf. (mg/L) Mean ± S.D. (n = 26)	Removal efficiency (%)
TN	26.66 ± 11.74	7.94 ± 3.49	70.2
TP	11.67 ± 4.28	4.48 ± 1.89	61.6
K	1.52 ± 0.56	0.62 ± 0.27	51.1

Table 2. Comparisons of quality for various concerned water.

Item	Original soil	Tap-water Mean ± S.D. (n = 26)	CW-eff. Mean ± S.D. (n = 26)	A group Mean ± S.D. (n = 26)	B group Mean ± S.D. (n = 26)
TN (mg/L)	1.52	0.10 ± 0.11	7.94 ± 3.49	0.53 ± 0.42	10.33 ± 3.42
TP (mg/L)	0.41	N.D.	4.48 ± 1.89	0.22 ± 0.09	4.46 ± 0.88
K (mg/L)	0.27	N.D.	0.62 ± 0.27	0.17 ± 0.05	0.69 ± 0.56

influent and 3.2 to 12.9 mg/L in effluent), 61.6% TP (TP ranged from 3.4 to 23.4 mg/L in influent and 1.8 to 11.5 mg/L in effluent) and 51.1% K (K ranged from 0.4 to 3.0 mg/L in influent and 0.2 to 1.3 mg/L in effluent). Other water quality parameters, i.e. COD, BOD_5, TSS, EC and total coliform meet the national standards implemented for effluent discharges and irrigation water[2,4].

3.2 Original soil liquid quality analyses

The original soil pH is 6.8 and the tap water pH is between 6.8 to 7.2. In this experiment, tap water was used as the simulated rain water; the latter has pH varying between 6.4 and 6.8 that is close to the tap water pH. Initial concentrations of fertilizer elements are 1.52 mg/L for TN, 0.41 mg/L for TP, and 0.27 mg/L for K. The tap water contains 0.1 mg/L of TN with negligible quantitate so TP and K (Table 2).

3.3 Quality of the flower pot effluent

The initial soil pH is between 6.8 to 7.2. After irrigated with tap water for 3 months, the soil effluent from Set A pots show 54.0% reduction of TN, 39.0% reduction of TP and 21.5% reduction of K. After 6 months, the reduction rates are 80.3% for TN, 48.8% of TP and 53.0% of K. Overall, when irrigated with tap water, the 50% reduction of the fertilizer elements is observed at the 12th week for TN, 16th week for TP and14th week for K. For Set B pots that were irrigated with gray water for 3 months, the soil fertility increases significantly as seen by the increase of TN from 1.52 to 8.63 mg/L, TP from 0.41 to 5.15 mg/L and K from 0.27 to 0.85 mg/L. Using the treated domestic wastewater as the irrigation water will increase the soil TN and TP but not much for K because domestic wastewater contains relatively insignificant amount of K (Fig. 2).

3.4 Evaluation of the soil fertility index

The initial soil is considered poorly fertile because of the low concentrations of TN, TP and K contained in the soil. Because of the humid and hot climate as well as the soil property, the average

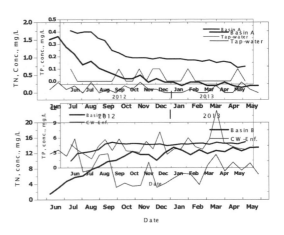

Figure 2. Influent-effluent concentrations of TN and TP in the nursery basin.

soil in Taiwan is usually acidic with low organic content and cationic exchange capacity so that the soil has little fertility and small capability to retain fertility[5]. Results obtained with Set B pots indicate that after irrigated with gray water for 11 to 12 weeks, the soil TN concentration increases to middle fertile level but never reaches a fertile level during the entire 12 month experimental period. This is mainly because that the domestic wastewater used in this experiment contains little K. Hence, using gray water to irrigate the extensive roof greening will only improve the soil fertility to a medium level because most carbon sources originally contained in the wastewater have been removed in the septic tank treatment and the constructed wetland treatment.

4 CONCLUSIONS

In this research, the constructed wetland is used as secondary process to treat domestic wastewater effluent discharged from septic tank. The daily treatment capacity is controlled at 1CMD with 0.01 $m^3/m^2/d$ hydraulic loading. Removal efficiencies are 70.2% for TN, 61.6% for TP and 51.1% for K; quality of the treated effluent meet standards for Class D surface water that can be used for Class C public water use, irrigation water, and Class B industrial water use as well as for environmental protection and restoration.

Overall, when the green roof soil is irrigated with the emulated rain water, i.e. the tap water, the time periods for the fertilizer elements to be reduced to 50% of the initial concentration are 12 weeks for TN, 16 weeks for TP and 14 weeks for K. If gray water is used to irrigate the soil for 3 month, TN concentration increases from 1.52 to 8.63 mg/L, TP concentration increases from 0.41 to 5.15 mg/L and K concentration increases from 0.27 to 0.85 mg/L, the soil reaches medium fertility. The gray water irrigation enrich the soil TN and TP but has no effect on the K concentration.

As stated in above sections, sustainable design of using the treated domestic wastewater to irrigate the extensive roof greening will achieve zero-discharge, water saving and raise the soil fertility to improve the survival of the planted seedlings.

ACKNOWLEDGMENTS

The Authors thank the NSC101-2221-E-167-039 project of Taiwan, for funding support of this research.

REFERENCES

[1] EPA, 2003, The Discharge Standard, EPA Executive Yuan, 92-W-0084786.
[2] Council of Agriculture, 2003, The Standard of Irrigated Water, Council of Agriculture, Executive Yuan, 92-0031524.
[3] Campbell, Craig S. & Ogden, Michael H., 1999, *Constructed Wetlands in the Sustainable Landscape*, pp. 101, John Wiley & Sons, Inc. published, Canada.
[4] EPA Executive Yuan, R.O.C., 1998, The Third Underground Water Standard, EPA Executive Yuan, 87-W-0039159.
[5] Ming-Bao Zeng, 2008, Soil fertility and Fertilizing, *Shen-Nong two weekly publications*, 243.

Computer, Intelligent Computing and Education Technology – Liu, Sung & Yao (Eds)
© 2014 Taylor & Francis Group, London, ISBN 978-1-138-02469-4

Curriculum development of application ability of number based on the ability standard

P. Zang
Shandong Transport Vocational College, Weifang, China

ABSTRACT: In this paper, we proposed a way to culture professional core competencies of students, and proposed the teaching methoeds in the training of the application ability of number. We introduced specific embodiments in the curriculum of the application ability of number and analyzed the effects of the curriculum. This method of training can greatly mobilize the enthusiasm of students and promote their comprehensive quality, so that they can better adapt to the future life and occupation.

Keywords: application ability of number; competence training; project teaching method; context description

1 NECESSITY OF CULTURE APPLICATION ABILITY OF NUMBER OF STUDENTS

1.1 *What is application ability of number*

Application ability of number requires students to develop and demonstrate their skills in interpreting information involving numbers, carrying out calculations, interpreting results and presenting finding in their studies, work or other aspects of their life. The application ability of number is the main ability that the studens nccd in secondary vocational education. This ability mainly based on the ability to solve numerical problems in life and work.

Application ability of number is different from the mathematical ability. Mathematical ability is shown in the mathematical activities. It usually includes computing ability, abstract thinking ability, space imagination ability, logical reasoning ability, mathematics language ability, mathematical modeling ability etc. Application ability of number is shown in the complete occupation specific individual tasks, directly affects the working efficiency and the psychological characteristics of personality to work smoothly. Due to the mathematical ability of different occupation need different basic mathematical ability, various types of occupation and the universal need constitutes the application ability of number.

1.2 *Requirements of future life and occupation of students*

The curriculum of application ability of number is aimed at fostering the consciousness and ability of students to apply existing mathematical knowledge and skills to deal with problems. It makes mathematics to integrate into the overall quality of students. In dealing with problems, people with high application ability of number can be very sensitive to data, can have faith and patience to deal with large amounts of data, can have the enthusiasm and sense of responsibility to manage the data processing activities, and can use corresponding skills according to various scenarios.

Students with poor mathematical foundation and poor learning behavior generally lack confidence in learning mathematics. The learning effect of students is greatly influenced by the teaching methods. Students expect teachers have affinity and communicate with students. So teachers should proceed from the actual situation of students, teaching language should be vivid. The attitude to amiable and easy of approach, and try to make the teaching process more interesting and useful. The implementation of the "cultivation of application ability of number" in teaching can help students to learn and use mathematics, to improve their employment competitiveness.

2 TEACHING PRACTICE OF APPLICATION ABILITY OF NUMBER

The training objective of this curriculum aim to make students find employment and let them skillful. It uses the method of project teaching and drive students to learn with the practical task. The project teaching method is mainly to guide the studentst to study by themselves in the comprehensive teaching activities. Students must be integrally involved in the whole process of teaching activities. Therefore, in the whole teaching process, the student is the main character, the teacher is the host of teaching activities. The responsibilities of teacher is to let students clear learning objectives and control the progress and direction in the teaching process, and evaluate the effect of learning of studens. In this process, application and mathematical practice knowledge is strengthened. At the same time, training of basic theory and core competence is strengthened. Ability training and the use of mathematical knowledge are brought together. This kind of training will equip students to better solve complex numerical problems arise in practice to meet the different needs of occupation in the application ability of number of students.

3 THE MAIN SCENARIO DESCRIPTION IN THIS CURRICULUM

3.1 The overall design

Design idea of this course is that we take the life stage of studens from entering college to getting married as the overall task context. Several projects and problems are designed in this stage of life. The projects cover the college life, learning, career and work practices as well as real problems before marriage. Each question is the hot issues close to the Reality experiences and vital interests of the students. For example, to buy learning materials, attend remedial classes, travel, stocks, buy a house, etc. Each project and the issues are open, their solution also has a large design space for students according to their own ideas and realities to the planning and design. Teacher guide and review questions for studens. The enthusiasm and initiative of students are fully played. Students do studies by themselves In the project implementation process. This process brings Cultivation of

ability and Application of mathematical knowledge together and Greatly mobilized the enthusiasm of students. Simultaneously, it cultivate a student's ability to cooperate and sense of team, and exercise and improve their application Ability of Number.

3.2 Problems we should pay attention to

In the process of the implementation of "application ability of number" course, we also found some problems worthy of our attention. We will talk about the problems in the following aspects.

3.2.1 Change the concept of education
Many mathematics teachers still pay attention to theoretical math but look down upon application. They think that the teacher is the only subject in the classroom, so it is difficult to mobilize the initiative of students. Today's society is in need of practical talents with high quality. Therefore, teachers should change the idea first to improve their own quality.

3.2.2 The use of modern means of teaching
Teachers should make full use of modern teaching means to create a high level of multimedia courseware for this course, in order to make the classroom teaching be full of sound and colour, improve teaching efficiency. Out of class, students can also make use of multimedia information to complete the task of learning with hign quality. Through the web site, teachers can set up "application ability of number" learning forum, weekly small knowledge, teacher-student mailbox etc.

3.2.3 The hobby group activities
Teachers can organize extra-curricular "application ability of number" to cultivate students who are interested in mathematical inquiry activity. This course of events can improve the students' ability

Table 1. Ability training project.

No.	Training programs	Subprojects	Ability target	Related knowledge	Training methods
1	My college life	Cost of living … School part time … Summer activities …	Can collate data and …	Ways to get data and …	Teachers guide and …
2	Five-year plan after graduation	Classmate party Travel Investment …	Can make the form …	Calculation of bank interest …	Students study independently …
3	Marriage preparation	Buy a house Renovation The wedding preparations …	Can perform simple calculations …	Mortgage calculations …	Students study independently …
…	…	…	…	…	…

of using mathematical knowledge and independent research, and the ability of finding and solving the practical problems. In the event, the teachers should pay attention to guide, help and supervise the students, so that the activities can be executed successfully.

4 EFFECTIVENESS ANALYSIS

We can sum up that the implementation of the curriculum of application ability of number can bring the students four effects. Firstly, students have a new understanding of study of mathematics and change the passive situation of learning mathematics. They are very enthusiastic to participate in the project and no longer believe that mathematics is useless. Second, autonomy of students has been greatly improved in study. Students have encountered some problems and difficulties in the learning process, but they did not give up, but trying to find a solution to the problems. Third, the communication ability of students has been greatly improved and The team cooperation consciousness has been enhanced. In the project implementation process they can communicate actively with the students in the same group. They Can turn to other team members when they encounter problems difficult to solve. This shows that their sense of teamwork has been enhanced. Fourth, the application ability of number of the sudents has been improved and their ability to analyze and solve problems has increased.

5 CONCLUSIONS

Project teaching mode create situations by selecting task project, and it use the way of collaborative learning. This way has a certain effect to the cultivation of students' application ability of number. Most teachers can feel that the Curriculum development of application ability of number is very necessary especially to the students whose mathematical foundation is relatively poor. This curriculum can also have positive impact on students' interest and enthusiasm to study. Ultimately it can enhance students' ability to adapt to the shsociety.

REFERENCES

Jang, D.Y. 2005. Deconstruction of subject system and Reconstruction of the action system. Education Research.

Jiang, D.Y. & Wu, Q.Q. 2007. Study of the main teaching thought of occupation education in German-theory, practice and innovation. Tsinghua University press.

Li, W.G. 2008. Cultivation of Professional core competencies and the improvement of The quality of teaching in vocational colleges. The new curriculum.

Lin, L.Y. & Lin, Y.Y. 2010. The status and causes of the core competencies of vocational students. Journal of Jilin province economic management cadre college.

Tan. Y.M. & Qian, J.F. 2001. The ability standard occupation education curriculum reform. Education Research.

Tong, S.D. 2006. The Exploration of cultivation of Professional core competencies. Journal of Shenzhen Institute of Information Technology.

The inquiry case teaching method in engineering technology courses computer & network assisted teaching platform

J.B. Zhang, J. Liu, Z.Y. Duan & H.Y. Zhang
College of Mechanical Engineering, Tongling University, Tongling, P.R. China

ABSTRACT: Based on the theory and technology of target teaching, an inquiry case teaching method is presented by improving the routine case teaching model. The method presented is used on the computer & network assisted teaching platform. Its operation policy is elaborated as preparing for the instruction course in according to the theoretical rules of target teaching with the computer aided technology, firstly; then carrying out the course teaching on the computer & network assisted platform, complying with the process of "inside class + outside class + inside class"; and assessing the course and the teaching activity under the dynamic evaluation system with diversified subjects and objects of evaluation on network or at scene, lastly. The teaching method can maximally combine theory with practice in the teaching of engineering and technology courses, evidently stimulate students' creative ideas and exploring consciousness, promote the students to learn and discovery self for their abilities of cooperation innovation. It is demonstrated that the inquiry case teaching method is an exemplification of talent training mechanism and teaching model innovation.

Keywords: inquiry case teaching; target teaching; teaching operation model; course evaluation

1   INTRODUCTION

Due to the rapid development of computer technology, multimedia, hypermedia, network and other high-tech, internet assisted instruction (NAI), as well as Computer Assisted Instruction (CAI), is widely used, arouses a greater change on the way of teaching and learning. Both CAI and NAI are timely, open and interactive teaching instruments being able obviously to improve teaching effects.[1,2] Thus, a teaching method offered in the following sections is applied, based on Platform of Computer & Network (PCN).

Case teaching method is a modern teaching model with a practical, relevant, inspiring and research peculiarity, and has been widely using in the field of humanities and social sciences education all over the word, to solve the problems of practice teaching.[3] Compared with other teaching methods, case teaching plays an irreplaceable role in integrating theory with practice for Management, Commercial Business, Foreign Trade, Law and so on. However, very few literatures on the application of case teaching to the education of engineering and technology majors, which need to more practical and more closely link theory with practice, were presented so far. At present, practical teaching such as professional practice, curriculum design, etc, is unfavorable because of not only the asynchronous integration with theoretical teaching but also the insufficiency of teaching condition. Therefore, it is necessary to introduce the case teaching method into the teaching of engineering courses.

In this paper, in terms of the characteristics of the engineering and technology courses, the traditional case teaching is improved to establish an inquiry case teaching model based on target teaching theory. The model has been applied in the teaching practices through PCN, and achieved certain results in promoting student technical abilities. It provides a reference of exploring the innovative ways and improved mechanism for applied talents training in application-oriented universities.

2   INQUIRY CASE TEACHING MODEL

Under traditional case teaching model, teacher designs teaching cases, students discuss and exchange and teacher summarizes. Students have no chooses to participate in designing cases and questions, are not stimulated to self learn.[4] The style of "theoretical teaching—case verifying—summarizing" is similar to the existing teaching method of engineering courses. However, teaching cases of engineering and technology courses are complex practical engineering examples with extensive knowledge and technology. That needs students to analyze through all directions by using

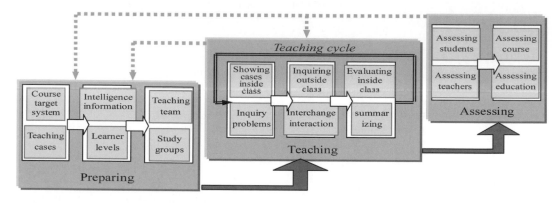

Figure 1.   The model of inquiry case teaching.

multidisciplinary expertise and technology, creatively, divergently and comprehensively studying
the cases, in order to obtain the relative scientific
and correct conclusion. Therefore, the traditional
case teaching method does not fully meet the needs
of engineering and technical course.

For that reason, we have research and practice
an inquiry case teaching method being goal-oriented. Under PCN, it is carried out by creation of
situational cases for the discovery learning of students. The model of inquiry case teaching is found,
shown as Figure 1.

3   PREPARING TEACHING COURSE

3.1   Building curriculum and carefully selecting situational cases assisted by computer

In view of the training goals for application-
oriented talents and the role of the course in the
training system, it is orderly performed to develop
course objective, draw up a teaching programmer
and build content system, then to divide the course
into some units, clear unit knowledge and found
teaching units. Focusing on unit content, teaching cases will be properly selected and designed in
computer techniques. High-quality teaching cases
should be clear learning objectives, comprehensive
coverage of technology, being clearly indicated and
fascinating situation engineering examples.[5]

3.2   Collecting intelligence information and classifying teaching object

Target teaching is a teacher-led, goal-oriented, student-centered teaching method, it can the farthest
mobilize student enthusiasm and initiative, and
promote effectively teaching objectives. We delve
into target teaching theory; propose an individual
target teaching method by decomposing course

knowledge, classifying teaching target and grading teaching object. Its teaching theories, teaching
strategies and implementing model have all been
illustrated in another article, not repeated here.
During inquiry case teaching, the students with
different levels of learning ability should use what
they had learned to explore the learning process,
and severally receive appropriate harvest. Using
information theory and computer techniques, a
multi-parameter two-dimensional table of target taxonomy for one teaching unit can be set up
according to intelligence information and learning level, which the individual target teaching will
be carried out as the base of to better facilitate
inquiry case study method.

3.3   Establishing teaching team and organizing study group

Inquiry case method requires the students to carry
around the teaching case, neatly use their theory
and technology to explore issues, gain knowledge and develop skills. Therefore, the learning
needs are diverse and mutative, not well served by
one teacher or two. It is a good way to overcome the
difficulty to establish an interdisciplinary teaching
team composed of a few of teachers with different
learning experiences and knowledge backgrounds.
All members take collectively part in lesson preparation and guidance outside class through various
interactive tools as E-mail, BBS, Chartroom, Blog,
Wiki, WeChat, and so on. While a speaker from
the team speaks inside class. Like that, team teaching is conducted for the course.

To cultivate student concept of cooperative
learning and cooperation innovation, one class is
divided into some study groups been in proportion
to the rate of student at different levels. The leader
of one study group is responsible for organizing
study groups to carry out inquiry learning.

4 CARRYING OUT INQUIRY CASE TEACHING

In classic case teaching model, one teaching cycle (or one teaching unit) seen as Figure 2a includes two stages: firstly, publishing by the teacher the cases to the students before class, in the next, carrying out the teaching activities in class. That is so called "outside class + inside class" manner, may cause an increase of classroom time spent on interaction. However, the cases of engineering and technology courses are too complex or obscure to the students. It is essential for the students to explore the difficulties with the help of teacher, not just to themselves. Consequently, we found an improved manner for the inquiry case teaching, shown as Figure 2b. Although publishing cases take some classroom time, the manner benefits the students of effective inquiry study, shorten classroom interaction time. Therefore, the way of "inside class + outside class + inside class" will become more efficient.

To cultivate the concept of cooperative learning and cooperation innovation, one class is divided into some study groups been in proportion to the students at different levels. The leader of one study group is responsible for organizing study groups to carry out inquiry learning.

4.1 Showing teaching cases inside class in multimedia technology

Integrated use of multimedia such as text, pictures, animations, audio, video, etc, the teacher shows students the cases in a multimedia classroom, creates virtual engineering situations and work atmosphere of production technology sectors, to stimulate students' active learning and self-inquiry interest. A group of gradient hierarchical explore issues will be designed; they should be very interesting to further induce students to learn effectively.[6]

4.2 Inquiry-founding outside class assisted by network

Inquiry case method focuses on the student abilities for independent thinking, self learning and cooperative learning. Thus the students should be encouraged as a group to actively look for references and voluntarily discuss the cases each other, and be guided to seek for the supports of teaching team via the advanced communication tools, e.g. internet and mobile telephone. Through inquiry learning outside class, the members of study group are able to analyze the case, summarize the learning, and enhance themselves' cognitive abilities.

4.3 Evaluating and summarizing inside class

In the classroom teaching process, the teacher should fully mobilize the enthusiasm and initiative of students, and contribute to the class enthusiastic discussions, so that students express themselves clearly. Focusing on teacher-student interaction to strengthen two-way communication, by using of inspiration, guidance and other strategies, the students will be encourage to develop thinking and imagination to analyze the cases from various angles, explore the means of solving problem for the optimal solution. That is to achieve "academic" seminar-style classroom teaching.

At the end of the class discussions, every one study group will reach consensus on the inquiry results, such as discoveries, solutions and conclusions, respectively. According to the rest of time,

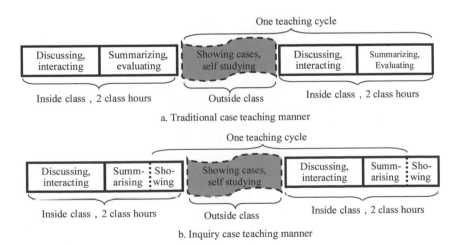

Figure 2. The case teaching manners.

one representative or more from every one of the study groups are make a speech, on a voluntary basis or required by the teacher. At this time, the others will be permit to consummate their group view. Finally, Teachers must comment on the group speeches, explain the theoretical knowledge, and make some deductive applications.

5 ASSESSING COURSE

Course evaluation is an important part of higher education practice and reform, is the key to strengthen the quality education and elevate the quality of talent,[7] and is an important step in promoting the development and progress of education reform.[8]

5.1 Assessing teaching

To the evaluation of the students' learning, we adhere to a principle of the combination of formative assessment and summative evaluation. In the daily teaching of course, the learning behaviors of the students will severally be assessed, by student self-evaluating, student inter-evaluating, and teacher team-evaluation, based on their exhibitions from the self-study, class discussions to case inquiry reports, to qualitatively evaluate their study capacity. That is operated by the ways of on-the-spot interview and on-line questionnaire survey. At final examination, student learning outcomes will be measured by the course design, examination or other forms to quantitatively evaluate the comprehension and application of elementary theory knowledge.

While, to evaluation of teaching effectiveness, the student estimation on the teaching is considered a vital portion of the teaching assessment system, as well as their performances. In addition, it is an important basis for the evaluation to highlight student status and role in the evaluation on teaching effectiveness. The students should be guided and encouraged to appraise the course teaching from the learning difficulty of content, the interesting of case, teaching methods, goal achievement and other aspects of teaching. The secret online survey is a feasible approach to the assessment. Real-time attention to student evaluations and suggestions is required for the teacher to dynamically update her teaching ideas and methods, and ultimately achieve the expectant effect.

5.2 Assessing course

After the course teaching, the learners, as well as the teaching staff, are organized for the course assessment in the environment of network. It is mainly carried out from the student knowledge mastered and capacities trained, the course teaching reform, position and role in professional education. Also, regularly or irregularly organize other teaching teams of follow-up course to track the teaching effect; invite some relative teachers to reflect back a few long-term opinions on the course objectives. The system of course assessment indicates the direction of course construction, educative model creation and teaching method improvement.

6 SUMMARIES

Due to the asynchrony between theory teaching and practical teaching and the storages of objective teaching resources, the practice teaching in engineering and technical professional education in our country can not fully meet the needs of theory teaching, real-time, in-depth. The inquiry case method based on PCN is an effective way to blend theory and practice, to make up for lack of practice teaching.

Firstly, in the course preparation phase, on the basis of target teaching model and computer assisted computer technique, work out a target taxonomy multi-parameter table for the relatively individualized target teaching; establish a teaching team to implement multi-disciplinary complete guide to the students; found study groups to exercise the student cooperation awareness and innovation ability. Then in the teaching stage, via multimedia and network communication, take a program of "publishing cases inside class + inquiry learning outside class + discussing inside class" to carry out the inquiry case teaching. Finally, in the course assessment phase, a wide range of subjects including the students, the teachers of the teaching team and other teaching teams, take part in the course assessment on network or at scene; All sectors of the course are objectively praised by both formative evaluation and summative evaluation. The practices of many years show that the inquiry case teaching method presented in this paper is able to efficiently integrate theory with practice, to evidently boost the student abilities. It also indicates an alternative path to the reform and innovation of training model of applicative talent in application-oriented colleges and university.

ACKNOWLEDGMENTS

This work is sponsored by Education Department of Anhui Province ender grant No. 20101015 and Tongling University under grant No. JY10003. Their advice and financial support are gratefully acknowledged.

REFERENCES

[1] Y.B. Son, Y.Y. Wang. A computer aided instruction (CAI) system CFFP [J]. Journal of Harbin Institute of Technology, 1995, 27(4):39–44.

[2] H.Y. Xue, Y. Hong, C.X. Yang. The practice of the organic chemistry network aided instruction [J]. Journal of Science of Teachers' College and University, 2012, 32(5):105–107.

[3] Y. Zhang. Reflections on economic law case teaching [J]. Economic Research Guide, 2008(3):190–190.

[4] L.J. Zhang, C.N. Sun. On the applications and its implications of the case teaching model utilized in USU Business Law Course [J]. Journal of Northeast Dianli University, 2012, 32(5):65–68.

[5] W.M. Chen. Targeted case teaching and its application principles [J]. China University Teaching, 2006(11):23–24.

[6] Z.X. Huang, X.L. Yi. The application of the scenario-based teaching in economic law course [J]. Journal of Central South University of Forestry & Technology (Social Sciences), 2011, 5(6):185–187.

[7] H. Gao, X. Yan, G.C. Zuo. Attribute hierarchy-based model of course assessment and its realization [J]. Journal of Chengdu University of Technology (Social Sciences), 2006, 14(4).

[8] W. Yang, Y.F. Qi, J.Y. Zhong, etc. Method of curriculum evaluation on fuzzy multifactorial evaluation [J]. Journal of Yunnan Nationalities University (Natural Sciences Edition), 2004, 13(4):320–324.

Computer, Intelligent Computing and Education Technology – Liu, Sung & Yao (Eds)
© *2014 Taylor & Francis Group, London, ISBN 978-1-138-02469-4*

Study on the training pattern of talents of animation design and marking specialty

Fang-Fei Wu & Feng-Ying Nie
School of Information, Nanchang Institute of Science and Technology, Nanchang, P.R. China

ABSTRACT: With the rapid development of China's animation industry, animation industry has become one of the national strategic industries. Firstly, this paper points out the extant problems of training pattern of talents of the higher vocational animation design and marking specialty. Secondly, this paper detailed discussed combing training mode of the creative studio and "order-orientated". Application results show that the combing training mode not only improve the learning motivation of students and practical vocational job skills, but also stimulates the activeness of colleges and enterprises. It achieves seamless mating with talents training and enterprise, and creates a win-win situation.

Keywords: animation design; talents training; order-orientated; teaching modes

1 INTRODUCTION

With China's rapid economic development and unceasing deepening of the social informationalized degree, the creative industries of software animation have been rapid developed. In 2006, the office of the State Council transmitted "the announcement of opinions of propelling China's animation industry development", whose appearance marked a new stage of animation industry development. In 2009, the State Council of china came out "cultural industry revitalize plan", and classified animation industry as one of eight important developing cultural industries, marked the animation industry rose to country strategic industries.

As the statistics shows, till 2010, the total of animation industry exceeded 60 billion, the requirement of industry talents exceeded 200,000. To meet the marked demand, since 2006, many higher vocational colleges have set up animation design and making specialty. On the basic of the Ministry of Education of china, the animation design and making specialty is a new computer specialty of the higher vocational colleges. However, compared with the traditional computer specialty, it has many differences, such as teaching content, teaching method, professional post, and so on, which a new frontier specialty combines with technology and art.

2 THE SPECIALTY PROBLEMS IN TALENTS TRAINING

The animation design and making specialty of the higher vocational colleges had a lot of problems in talents training because of fairly high rate of development, short of running school time and experience, etc.

2.1 *From the teaching force*

The animation design and making specialty was lack of the teaching force, which related to visual effects, 3D technology, game development, industrial management, etc. It was established from nothing to something, which was acute lack of teaching force. The backbone of many colleges and universities teachers graduated from computer science or art. Computer teachers have good technical ability, but were lack of animation and game creation ability; and art teacher has some art, artistic heritage, but not to be familiar with the application of advanced software technologies. In addition, many teachers were lack of practical experience of relative industry and interaction with animation enterprises.

2.2 *From curriculum arrangement*

The curriculum system was incomplete, lack of deep investigation of job post. It had placed great importance on computer design courses, but ignored an important aspect of humanities courses. In addition, there are some problems, such as lacking of training of basis quality and sense of team work.

2.3 *From specialty teaching materials*

The teaching materials system was incomplete, and the quality of teaching materials was not high.

Some teaching materials were extreme lack, such as Video game, etc, especially, high quality teaching materials of the higher vocational colleges were scarce. In addition, the positioning of student training of was indefinite, the teaching system was incomplete, the teaching was insufficient, etc. Therefore, if we are going to train the animation talents of the higher vocational colleges, we must renew the educational idea, establish new teaching mode, improve students' occupation skill, strengthen the team spirit of students.

3 THE TALENT TRAINING SYSTEM OF COMBINING CREATIVE STUDIO WITH "ORDER-ORIENTED"

In 2010, the animation design and making specialty was established in Nanchang Institute of science & Technology, our college was located in Nanchang. There are some various types of animation and game companies. Our college established the animation design and making specialty and came close to the demand of economic development, took the occupation skill as training core, established the animation industry for the purpose of service area. And we established the talents training system of combining creative studio with "order-oriented", the training system was shown in Figure 1. We made the talents training outline of the game programming development and Game art designing.

3.1 Establishing the mechanism of cooperation between college and enterprise

Allowing the enterprises to participate in the teaching design and implementation. We have established training base with some animation enterprises since 2010. Some engineers of enterprise have directly taken part in talents training and curriculum development, and some competent

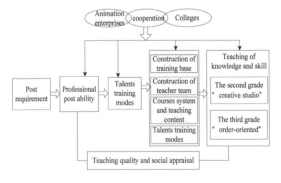

Figure 1. The training system.

technicians have taken part in compiling syllabus, lecture notes, teaching material compiling of core curriculum.

3.2 The education aimed at combining enterprise service with further education

In-service teachers can make use of their spare time to practice teaching in the animation enterprises. On the one hand, they can use their professional knowledge to guide the design and production of enterprises, on the other hand, they can know enterprise post operation mode by practice, learn new knowledge concept of new production line design so that as to enhance their own professional skills teaching ability, and also service for teaching reform in the following step, such as curriculum planning, teaching materials, construction of experimental training room.

4 THE EFFECTIVENESS AND IMPLEMENT OF CREATIVE STUDIO MODES

On the basis of school enterprise cooperation, teaching and animation professional skills have been improved. Our animation design and making specialty have implemented the teaching modes of "taking with creative studio as Carrier, taking a Road to Combine Work with Study to Cultivate the environment for mutual learning", and have marched toward the integrate goal of teaching, learning, training, doing, competition, creation. There are some main features as follows.

4.1 A wide coverage

All of the second grade students are organized by studio team, who must take part in the studio in accordance with professional characteristic and interest before the second grade. Each creative studio is composed of 3 to 5 students, and one guidance teacher. Up to now, our college has sixteen creative studios for animation design and marking specialty. Students can not only finish the assignment of training and practical course, but also arrange the equipment and activity by oneself in spare time under his father's guidance. We have given commend and reward for outstanding studio, so as to form the competition environment, build a nice atmosphere of study.

4.2 The combining studio with traditional teaching

Students need to synthetic course training for four week per term from the third term of sophomore, whose aims are to accomplish the project making of relative course based on accomplishing all professional courses. These projects include simulate project and direct project of enterprise. Students of studios need finishing projects by division of labor. During the training procedure, every student are playing different roles in the job, which is better for strengthening their skill of classroom and finishing experience of post kill.

4.3 *The innovation of teaching method*

Teachers break the traditional teaching methods and make innovations to teaching method, and change the monotonous traditional model of teacher-based. Especially, teachers can implement various kinds of teaching modes. For example, teachers can implement individualized teaching model in accordance with character and their technical features of students. Teaching contents are not limited in knowledge and technology, teachers can teach students by using his personal examples in studio, so can greatly enhance occupation ethics, teamwork, and communication ability of students.

4.4 *Innovative teaching mode based on competition*

Teachers of studios promote actively learning of knowledge and skill of the member of studio, encourage actively them to take part in the competition of animation design, which come from all parts of the country. So as to test teaching effect, improve teaching reformation, enhance the professional skill of students. In recent years, students of studio have achieved many awards of animation.

4.5 *An exchange platform of restudy*

Because different teachers have different technology basic and professional domain, they can intercommunicate and interact of the relative knowledge and skills in the studio. Every teacher can not grasp all the knowledge of animation, they can guide each other. After-colleges instructor and the in-service teachers can work together to finish the relative mission. On this platform, it is a good chance for both the after-colleges instructor and the in-service teacher.

4.6 *A stimulating platform of innovation*

Students of animation studio are enthusiastic in accomplishing both project of courses training and extracurricular training. These projects were set up in accordance with animation studio by the design of teacher and students, which can not only promote their study and grasp the new knowledge skill, but also stimulate their innovative consciousness.

5 THE EFFECTIVENESS AND IMPLEMENT OF "ORDER-ORIENTED"

Besides, we launch the teaching practice to students in the studio, we actively cooperate with the well-known enterprise. For example, we have collaborated closely with the jiangxi Tellhow animation company limited, and build "talents training bases of demonstrating animation", so as to set up training classes of animation talents "order-oriented". We organize the third-year students to take part in the training classes in accordance with requirement of company.

The teaching mode of "order-oriented" is offered especially for the third-year students. For example, there are 75 students in 2004 animation design and making specialty, 58 of them take part in training classes, the rest of students are trained in accordance with the old training model. The training model of "order-oriented" is established by college and enterprise, which train students according to requirement of enterprise. The model includes the key link of class teaching, practice teaching, Practical Training and evaluation, and so on. The enterprise provides the real environment and project for students, and let designer and technician of enterprise to guide students, so that the college and enterprise are combined very well, ensure training effect and quality.

The teaching process of "order-oriented" still insist on unchanged teaching organizing manners, for example, the member of studio have became a work group when students take upon learning on the enterprise, and who study the vocational skills accompany with entrepreneurial teachers. Courses of "order-oriented" can be taken as the practice courses. Students and enterprises adopt the two-way selection after graduation, and some good students can contract with the enterprises. At present, we implement the teaching of "order-oriented" for the two terms of students, and some the pleased effect are achieved.

5.1 *The win-win situation between college and enterprise*

The teaching models of "order-oriented" achieve the win-win situation between college and enterprise. Enterprises establish the classes of "order-oriented", and accomplish the induction training of new employs, ensure the quality and quantity of the new employs. In addition, the college can broaden the talents training way and accomplish the good employment.

5.2 Improving the activity of talents training

Of course, the enterprises can not cooperate with colleges under the precondition of only sacrificing own interests. Enterprises can arrange for remaining staff to study in college, so allowing them to receive the guidance of basic theory and new technology, and improving wholly the staff technical skill. Ultimately, the cooperative relationship of colleges and enterprises will become more much closer.

5.3 Achieving the dual role with staff and student

The dual roles of students not only strengthen professional skill, improve professional quality and culture qualities, but also take part in animation project in real enterprise environment, experience and study themselves the latest technology and experience. Students acquire the useful knowledge, and enhance employment power.

5.4 The seamless joints of the talents training and the requirement of enterprises

The training models can meet the need of enterprise post well according to the talents training model of "order-oriented". Colleges and enterprises build together training platform to train students. According to the need of enterprises to establish training model, students need grasp the software and making of enterprises. In addition, students can improve the ability of solving the actual problem by enterprise training, increase the knowledge of the current status of animation and enterprise post, and improve competition ability of employment and quality, so solve the problem that graduating students be difficult to obtain employment and the enterprises are short of the demand of talents.

6 CONCLUSIONS

It has very important meaning for the developing of higher vocational development of animation industry in our country. We should renew the educational idea, establish the new teaching modes, and enhance the vocational skills of profession and teamwork spirit. In a way, implementing seamless connection of talents training and enterprise requirement is the only way for educational worker of animation.

REFERENCES

Gong C.Q. 2012. Exploring into in Professional Talents Training of Animation Design and Making Specialty Based on "Studio" of College-enterprise Cooperation and Project-oriented. *Education and Vocation* 6:116–118.

Huang B, Yang K, Wu Y.Q. 2011. Analysis of Teaching Model Based on "Creative Studio" of Animation Design and Marking Specialty. *Education for Chinese After-school* l03:138–139.

Huang H.L. 2011. Talents Training mode Based on "Order-oriented" in Animation Design and Making of Higher vocational Colleges. *Examination Weekly* 37:194–195.

Li X.S, LQ, Wang T. 2012. Promoting the seamless joint for Technical Teaching of Animation Specialty Based on College-enterprise Cooperation. *Industrial & Science Tribune* 11(23):153–154.

Tang X.H. 2011. A Review of Misconceptions on Present-day Classroom Teaching of Animation in China. *Art and Design* 6:119–121.

Wu H.M. 2012. The Talents Training Innovative mode of Animation Design and Marking Specialty of the higher vocational colleges. *Computer Education* 3(2):20–23.

Yang H. 2012. Study on Teaching Reform Based on Animation Vocational Skill Competition. *Chinese Vocational and Technical Education* 14:88–91.

Computer, Intelligent Computing and Education Technology – Liu, Sung & Yao (Eds)
© 2014 Taylor & Francis Group, London, ISBN 978-1-138-02469-4

The practice of interactive teaching and learning between teachers and students of programming course

X.F. Xiao
School of Information and Education Engineering, Shandong Institute of Business and Technology, Yantai, China

Y. Jia
Department of Computer Foundation Studies, Shandong Institute of Business and Technology, Yantai, China

ABSTRACT: The purpose of this study was to analyze the problems exitsed in teaching about programming course, to investigate the theory and practice of interactive teaching and learning based on the teaching support platform. The result is that the appoach can stimulate students' interest effectively and train programming thought and improve the level of computer applicaiton integrated with the firsthand recoure during the recent teaching practice.

Keywords: programming course; interactive teaching and learning; teaching practice; teaching support platform; digital recourses

1 INTRODUCTION

The course of "Advanced Language Programming" is the second level content of teaching task provided by Engineering Computer Basic Course Teaching Steering Committee of Chinese Ministry of Education. The first goal is to help students to master general rules about programming and to train their abilities to read and understand program. The second goal is to help students apply the approach of program to their major or related domain and train their ability to program and computational thought [1]. There are considerable difficulties in both teaching of teachers and learning of students in the implementation process of programming coures, such as there is massive contents, but short class time, lacking of good and rich digital rescource or platform support, the effective interaction bewteen teachers and students is little, and so on.

There are some researches about Teaching Support Platform (The following abbreviation is TSP), such as web-based distance TSP [2–7]. It is time consuming to complete the monitoring process during teaching platform [8–12]. It is well known that teaching efficiency and study efficiency are related to teaching support [14–18]. The authors investigated in college students who had accomplished programming courses using the research method of questionnaires and interviews. The result shows that effective digital resources for students are far from enough and needed urgently. The organization of learning resources is also important. The timely communication between teachers and students is a key and effective factor.

Therefore, combined the twelve years' experience of teaching and competitive course construction, the group have built the teaching platform based on three Instant Messaging Tools (The following abbreviation is IMS). IMS involves QQ, YY and Wei Xin.

Therefore, the teaching mode is changed in the practice of teaching about programming couerse. In the traditional mode, theory and experment coures is separated, but now they are integrated. Teacher explain delicacily and students do their exercise much more. There are more effective interaction between teachers and students during class time. This will more useful to excercise students' ability of handling, and and to train their ability of interactive and cooperative in a team.

2 METHOD

The mode of Interactive Teaching and Learning between Teachers and Students (The following abbreviation is ITLTS) based on IMS is the main and effective method. With the rapid development of Internet, there have been multiple instant communications technology tools such as QQ, Win Xin, YY because they are used more commonly, widely and easily than others. Especially QQ, it has been used for assisting teaching and has brought excellent effects. ITLTS is that building interactive platform bewteen teachers and students in the environment of multimedia room which interactive software had been set up on teachers' and students' computers and some equtment such as microphone, ear phone and projection are ready for tcaching. Teachers do their lecture first, then analyse and explain the key and difficult content, and then students do their exercise according teachers' content. Teachers collect students' reconization about learning content and summary students' discussion. Then teachers collect, analyse and list stuends' work systematically. The next step is that teachers answer some key problems which are found during students' learning and master and participate the whole discussion between students. The last procedure teachers should be done is to evaluate students' interaction and their homework. In this mode, teachers try their best to help students get knowledge and information during their interaction and understand knowledge on their class time. Comparing with traditional class teaching, ITLTS emphasis interaction and teachers' more explaination delicacy and students' more exercise. Teacher should integrate teaching content and not do their work step by step traditionaly. If they don't do that, they could not complete their task because of less class time and students' time is less and could not do their exercise perfectly.

3 IMPLEMENTATION

The group designed and built the TSP (as shown in Fig. 1) based on IMT according to the theory of "learning by doing" which was advocated by John Dewey, the United States educator pragmatism [19].

According to the process of teaching implementation, the basic technological process includes six stages: Teachers build teaching resources to support teaching platform; Teachers set task or raise some problems; Teachers build communication

platform to create discussion atmosphere; Teachers build a multimedia presentation platform to explain or to suggest some good solutions; Students learn knowledge by doing exercise and submitting their work; Teachers make evaluation to the process of students' work to give feedback.

The detail way is ready for one hundred of computer and set up some sofeware about teaching management. Teachers integrated teaching resource and choose questions and teaching cases elaborately and large case which can combined with students' major, and then divide the large case into small according to the total class time, and then rearrage the knowledge unit and break up the order in the textbook. Teachers do their lecture by three main line such as concept is leaded by questions, phenomenon is leaded by principles, knowledge unit is verified by teaching case. The detail implementation is as follow.

For example, the cource teaching of library management of system include two parts. The fisrt part is teachers display and explain the whole. The second part is stuents write program code to complete the function of the system by group. In the first part, explaining and verifying knowledge unit is the most important task. Teachers try their best to help students understand syntax rules of program language and apply them professionally. In the second part, students do comprehensive design and expotend their knowledge. They develop the project by a group. Taking practice of class time teaching in detail for example, a class time is divided six section including exhiting case, purposing questions, masterring discussion, simulating by students, purposing new problems and solving problems independently or cooperately. During class time, teachers display the function of the system of library management and explain knowldege unit to complete similar function by using screen broadcasting provided by software of teaching management. The operational step about explaining case can be recorded screen which can be replay forever. It does not use video, so, it not only reduces the cost of making rescoure but also is as good courese rescoure for students' learning later by the process of similar vedio changing. Then teacher lead students to make discussion about methods to complete the funtion and choose the best method from the discussion. Students draw the flow chart to solve the problem. Students design about the menu and code the program according to the flow chart. Students do their respective code. If they have any difficulty, techers should let them consider independent or make a discussion to jecent classmates or seek help from teachers. Teachers can monitor students' learning process and find the common questions. If students complete their homework, teachers can cue or comment together.

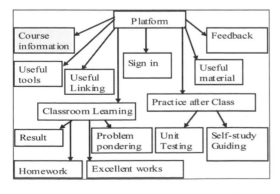

Figure 1. Teaching support platform based on Qzone.

Then teachers introduce new question and let students try their best to solve it by applying new knowedege they have mastered. Students can make a discussion by a group and develop the first design. Teachers evaluate the design and give some advice and then students modify their design and operate code to finish it. At last, students submit their work and make a summary.

Process evaluation combined with project evaluation are used which fucus on the process of learing not the result. In the total score, project takes the propotion of fifty percent, three process examination with the form of computer exam takes thirty percent and the remaining twenty percent is depended on the submitted work in class time. The primary objective of process evaluation is put the important point on the process of students' day learning. It can change the form of final exam which is the last result of courese learning. The evulation can help students develop a rigorous study habits rather than the final blitz learning and the score can fully reflect the real situation of students' learning.

Due to the special of project, the project evaluation pay attention to the cooperation and teamwork ability of the whole group by the unit of group. Every group member participate to introduce his work and what he has done. The content of evaluation includes the concept of work, design, program and characteristics of the work. The members of evaluation group is consist of teachers, other group manager, other group members. The score of the evaluation is announced immediately followed with every intruduction. It is opened and timely so every student can get his score and get the enthusiasm of stimulation. The form of evaluation plays an important leading role in the practice of teaching and puts forward students to learn persistently. Therefore, students' the ability of program and code improved largely and their interest about courese can hold lasting.

4 DISCUSSION

The team implement the mode of ITLTS for four years. The team members make many discussion and expericence in department meeting every week. There are useful expericence for summary.

In the first place, keeping the main line of problem solving, selecting problems carefully and focusing on training students' interest are the most important principle. In order to choose problems carefully enough, all teachers are ready for the class together and make repeated discussions. Problems is the first signifcant thing becasuse of they can stimulate students interest. The purpose of programming is to solve practical problems, so teachers should be strictly in accordance with the

step by step, such as analysing problems, designing algorithms, coding, debugging and running. Teachers train correct problem-solving ideas and processes of students throughout. Problems is the motivation to learning and students will eager to try if good problems appeared in front of them.

Moreover, paying attention to the part of interaction between teachers and students, students and students, students and computers is another key principle. Teachers should focus on the techniques of questions which must be expand, funny, opened and to attract students' attention. Teachers also can know something about students' learning by effective interaction and evaluate. Teachers can modify the form and content about resourece timely and students can operate computer and code more skillfully by interaction. To change effectively the situation of one direction, for example, teachers do lecture, students listen, teachers write and students record monotonously, and to let students participate to learn, not only teachers but also students should change themselves. They should adapt the change of roles. ITLTS provides the convenient condition for teachers and students. Teachers truely are as the leaders, organizers and cooperators for students and students are as the major of their own learning. Students are the host of course and can release their great passion for learning. As for tutor in class time, simple tutor or display or code providing only can solve some common question, but can not solve all questions fully. One to one and discusse together are effective for oneself. In addition, QQ group, QQ zone, blog and Weixin are useful tools for publishing case analysed, code and question. Students' original knowledge is shared and attended is pround for everyone.

Lastly, seminar is hold twice each semester between teachers and students and questionnaire survey is used and teachers communite with students by other way, many students addmit to like ITLTS. Compared with other courses, it is novel, clearly, and interesting. Students can consolidate what they have got timely, have efficient learning and get more knowledge during a relaxed atmosphere.

5 CONCLUSION

As a useful mode of teaching, both teachers and students should make good ready for role changing in ITLTS.

For teachers, first at all, there are large change in class ready and organization of teaching. Teachers foculs their critical energy on create a better learning environment and consider what are students need timely, for example, what help students need, what resource is needed, how guide students to make a discussion, and so on. Moerover, there are more highly need on charisma and professional competence of teachers. Teachers should have the ability of self-development and improvement continuously. Teachers also should build a good, harmonious, active, harmonious discussion atmosphere for students. Once more, teachers should thoroughly understand the material, concise teaching content and sublimate teaching experience and experience. In the end, teachers should do their best to improve the teaching means with the drive of task and problems and the load of discussion to organize students to discuss. Teachers should encourage and guide students to complete their learning during the environment of question and discussion.

As for students, in the first instance, they should change therir syle of learning, from traditional passive learning to active learning, furthermoer, they should acquire knowledge not in textbook actively. Learning is a dynamic process. One depend on static knowledge in textbook only will have difficulty to apply. But dynamic knowledge needs to keep one's thinking and make discussions with others. The more dynamic knowledge is acquired, the greater the interest in learning will get. Interest is the best teacher. If one have interesting on learning, he will succeed more easily. In addition, students discuss positively during discussion which will be more conducive to cultivate outgoing personality. Interaction and help between students are also good for training teamwork. It is likely to help students find more questions and try to do them and ask new question during the discussion in the atmosphere. The ability of problem solving are also help to stimulate and release students' potential and enhance their initiative and comprehensive and lifelong development.

REFERENCES

[1] Wu Chunying. The application of case method in the course of Visual Basic Program Design. 2009, 29(9):57–58.

[2] Jared Keengwe and David Georgina. The digital course training workshop for online learning and teaching, Education and Information Technologies, 2012, Volume 17, Number 4, Pages 365–379.

[3] Yanli Wang, Yun Cheng, Feng Wang, Zhongmei Zheng, "Design and Implementation of WEB-Based Distance Teaching Support Platform for Rural Teachers", 2009 International Conference on New Trends in Information and Service Science.

[4] Marina Papastergiou and Vassilis Gerodimos. Can learning of basketball be enhanced through a web-based multimedia course? An experimental study, Education and Information Technologies, 24 January 2012.

[5] Theologos Athanaselis, Stelios Bakamidis, Ioannis Dologlou, Evmorfia N. Argyriou and Antonis Symvonis. Making assistive reading tools user friendly: a new platform for Greek dyslexic students empowered by automatic speech recognition, Multimedia Tools and Applications, 12 May 2012.

[6] Hsuan Pu Chang, Timothy K. Shih, Qing Li, Chun-Chia Wang and Te-Hua Wang, et al. An Adaptive Caching Strategy for m-Learning Based on SCORM Sequencing and Navigation, World Wide Web, 2008, Volume 11, Number 3, Pages 387–406.

[7] Sandy C. Li, Jacky W.C. Pow, Emily M.L. Wong and Alex C.W. Fung. Empowering student learning through Tablet PCs: A case study, Education and Information Technologies, 2010, Volume 15, Number 3, Pages 171–180.

[8] Zhaohua Wu, "design and realization of the online course of the foundation of electronics assembly", Journal of Guilin University of Electronic Technology, No. 2, pp. 140–142, 2008.

[9] A. Konstantinidis, Th. Tsiatsos and A. Pomportsis. Collaborative virtual learning environments: design and evaluation, Multimedia Tools and Applications, 2009, Volume 44, Number 2, Pages 279–304.

[10] C.K. Chiou, G.J. Hwang, and Judy, C.R. Tseng, "An autoscoring mechanism for evaluating problem-solving ability in a web-based learning environment," Computers & Education, vol. 53, no. 2, pp. 261–272, 2009.

[11] C.H. Chen, G.J. Hwang, T.C. Yang, S.H. Chen, and S.Y. Huang, "Analysis of a ubiquitous performance support system for teachers," Innovations in Education and Teaching International, vol. 46, no. 4, pp. 1–13, 2009.

[12] Margit Pohl, Markus Rester, Kerstin St?ckelmayr, Jutta Jerlich and Peter Judmaier, et al. Computer supported collaborative learning and vocational training: adapting the technology to the learners' needs, Universal Access in the Information Society, 2008, Volume 7, Number 4, Pages 259–272.

[13] Woolfolk Hoy, A. (2004). Self-efficacy in college teaching, Essays on Teaching Excellence: Toward the Best in the Academy, 15, 8–11. Fort Collins, CO: The POD Network.

[14] Guo Dayong, Xuan Hua, Fu Xiaolong, Modern Teaching Support Platform Design, Tsinghua Science And Technology, ISSNll1007-0214ll16/17ll pp 352–356, Volume 15, Number 3, June 2010.

[15] Tschannen-Moran, M., & Woolfolk Hoy, A. (2002), the influence of resources and support on teachers' efficacy beliefs, Paper presented at the annual meeting of the American Educational Research Association, New Orleans, LA.

[16] Pearson, J. (2006). Investigating ICT using problem-based learning in face-to-face and online learning, environments. Computers & Education, 47(1), 56–73.

[17] Paul Resta & Thérèse Laferrière, Technology in Support of Collaborative Learning, Educ Psychol Rev (2007) 19:65–83.

[18] Murphy, E. (2004). Recognizing and promoting collaboration in online asynchronous discussions. British, Journal of Educational Technology, 35(4), 421–431.

[19] Liu GuangLi, "Dewey's teaching theory: "learning by doing" and Its Enlightenment to China's basic education", J, Continuing Education Research. p. 84 May 2008.

Computer, Intelligent Computing and Education Technology – Liu, Sung & Yao (Eds)
© 2014 Taylor & Francis Group, London, ISBN 978-1-138-02469-4

Application analysis and some initial proposals of wind farms tourism in China

S.Y. Wang
Department of Economics and Management, North China Electric Power University, Baoding, Hebei, China

ABSTRACT: With the sustained and rapid development of China's wind power industry, wind farms tourism ushered in a historic opportunity for development. Wind farms tourism can not only expand to be one of the new travel format, but also optimize the tourism industry structure and enhance the tourism taste of the wind energy resource advantages region.

Keywords: wind farms tourism; case analysis; development mode

1 BACKGROUND OF WIND FARMS TOURISM DEVELOPMENT

Wind energy as a clean, non-polluting, renewable energy, abundant, widely distributed, and its development and utilization of widely attention in many regions of the world, an increasing number of large-scale wind farms are being established and put into operation. Become a spectacular scene attracts tourists around the world, hidden behind the huge benefits caused great concern of the department concerned.[1]

2 SOME INITIAL PROPOSALS OF CHINA'S WIND FARMS TOURISM DEVELOPMENT WITH TYPICAL CASE ANALYSIS

At present, China's wind farm tourism in general is still in a "contribution" stage, lack of the format of system planning, public awareness is relatively low. The current situation of wind farms tourism development of the new tourism formats is adverse, need a clear thought of development, looking for effective methods, take effective measures, its and the traditional tourism format for resources integration, looking for wind farms tourism harmonious and sustainable development.

2.1 *The increased publicity, expand the social influence*

At present, China's wind power industry development is relatively early and mature areas, wind farms tourism on the local tourism development of regional economy contribution are relatively obvious, the media have reported. Such as "Wind farms drive Guazhou tourism",[2] "Kangbao cultivate strong wind farms tourism emerging industry", etc. But, the wind farms tourism is not high in the domestic public awareness, isn't included in the tourism planning to like "red tourism", "ecological tourism" mature tourism formats, etc.

Wind farms tourism resources set wind farms landscape and the natural landscape in a body, the tourists involved in the production of clean energy, wind farm with power in the fan blade with the wind dancing spectacular scene at the same time, also can understand wind power industry development and energy conservation and environmental protection of the popular science knowledge. Therefore, we should start with renewable energy to the human ecological environment protection of the great role and contribution of tourism, the wind farms tourism system planning, set up the ecological and environmental protection brand image.

Expand the cognition, set up the image is the most widely, rapid and effective way is we pay great attention to cooperation projects, the use of media publicity activities, expand the social influence. Warm waters are successful marketing is a good example.

Hot Spring Leisure City works with the media, relies on the talent show, chooses a appropriate time to promote and build the brand. In 2007, Hot Spring Leisure City use to attract global Chinese sights of Beijing television station "A dream in Red Mansions" actor large-scale activities in the draft, and then held the "Descendants of the dragon" global television selection activities, from a not well-known to the public places of entertainment, turned into a culture, and a gold world connected the "famous brand".

After that, the Olympic torch relay is taking advantage of the good opportunity, in the mainstream news media and network media comprehensive show yourself, not only become 2008 Beijing Changping district only torch relay point, and it is also the Zhenggezhuang village, Changping district tourism bureau designated as the Olympic tourism village, Hot Spring Leisure City successfully won the world attention.

Then, the United States synchronized swimming team, Germany beach volleyball team and fencing team delegation, Switzerland and other countries of the Paralympic delegation are in Hot Spring Leisure City in training and adaptive excessive, the demonstration effect to Hot Spring Leisure City brought very good brand effect.

In the same year, Hot Spring Leisure City the newly completed Hongfu Hotel, Lake Hotel, West Lake Hotel put into use, in the high quality brand influence, three new star hotel with existing Hot Spring Leisure City international hotel the present comprehensive full state, won the very good brand income.

If the entities can realize the importance of public opinion propaganda and brand shaping in the initial stage of wind farms tourism development, set up the wind energy conservation and environmental protection image, increase social influence. It is believed that wind farms tourism development road will run more smoothly.

2.2 Grasp mature customers, develop more group

In China, in view of the present wind farms tourism popularity and public awareness of the fact that low, just rely on short-term strong investment to expand influence, or through the development of wind farms project tourism and obtain higher economic benefits idea is not reality. The development can make use of mature traditional tourism business mode ensure stable passenger flow, at the same time to experience the unique generating set landscape wind power tourism projects, the visitors by word of mouth, and gradually promote and form to wind farms as the theme, set leisure, sightseeing, experience, entertainment, food and beverage service and science in a new tourism mode.

For example, Zhangbei, a county from Zhangjiakou of Hebei province, has rich wind energy resources, environmental protection concept in great esteem fourth Zhangbei, China Prairie Music Festival in 2012, wind power for festival provides a flow of green energy, meanwhile show public the Zhangbei grasslands of the most beautiful landscape, the country's largest wind power windmill group—wetland windmill. Rows of massive white windmill for festival blew the cool, and spectacular scenery of the great first show in the music festival on posters, success won people eyeball. From the first to the fourth Zhangbei Prairie Music Festival

attracted more and more fans, audience from 100,000 in 2009 increased to 300,000 in 2012.

In order to promote the tourism industry, Zhangjiakou constantly improves tourism product system. In 2012, it planned "Zhangjiakou tourism image ambassadors initial contest", "Zhangjiakou tourism into Beijing community", "Zhangjiakou four seasons big tourism", and other festival activities for public. Especially since June 2012, as "Zhangbei grassland marathon", "Zhangbei, China hot-air balloon championship", "Zhangbei, China prairie music festival" and "Grassland wedding ceremony activities" in Bashang Grassland held successfully, the dam of grassland tourism into a rush hour. By the end of July 2012, grassland style region receive visits and income year-on-year growth of 78.7% and 87.2% respectively. Among them, the number of tourists received Zhangbei County year-on-year growth of 95%, the number of tourists Guyuan County received a year-on-year increase of 54%, two county tourism are more than the increase in the number of average level.[3]

If these activities hold by means of increasing the stability of the passenger flow, a combination of the market development and the tourist organization of wind farms tourism, corporate image and reputation, constantly combined into the wind power industry characteristics, enlarge its influence, increasing wind farms tourism benefits will be not just a dream that distance makes a new wind farms tourism mode.

2.3 Clear development orientation, equip the tourism with facilities

Wind power belongs to clean and green energy. Wind farms not only possess unique windmill landscape, but also carry on the propaganda of popular science education, both of them are the development of wind farms tourism good conditions.

If developers make clear in the development direction, add wind farms elements to the tourism products as soon as possible; not limited to the general wind farms tourism, catering, accommodation, entertainment, and ordinary consumer services, and introduce such as golf, horse riding and other high-end services, undertake wedding photo/ wedding, large-scale activities, and professional club or meeting company sign up as leisure clubs or long-term cooperation partners, etc. Combine wind power industry with tourism industry delicately, gradually evolve to the integrated development mode with industrial tourism, ecological tourism, leisure entertainment and popular science education. To expand wind farms tourism visibility and influence, smoothly into the development on track to mature, move towards a stable travel industry format.

Wind farms generally built in wind energy resources are rich, sparsely, natural vast the Gobi desert, hills and mountains, the beach wetland far away from the city noise and full of natural charm areas, with spectacular wind power unit and neat and quiet and comfortable environment. However, the traffic and service system have not been perfected yet. Obviously, they do not have apparent advantages as individual tourist destinations.

If developers can improve the culture closely around the theme of wind farms, such as the construction of enterprise culture, can spread popularity wind energy and wind power science knowledge, promote energy conservation and environmental protection concept wind farms theme exhibition hall, and reference to other industrial tourism development mode, at the same time, make full use of its broad activity space and rich natural resources, the introduction of such as holiday leisure center, equestrian training experience, mountain trail circuit, land/water hunting, skating skiing, aquatic amusement, sea hot springs and meet the needs of multi-level and leisure industry, consider and the surrounding natural and cultural landscape, leisure, service industry cooperation, the development of appropriate regional characteristic leisure experience project meet people return to nature, feel comfortable. Thus, the tourist area which takes wind farm as the core will turn into the development of new energy demonstration area. It should be combined with the characteristics of local cultural and natural conditions, to be a high-tech, green environmental protection holiday health have a rest. Both the social and economic benefits will be won with the benefit, multiple purposes.

3 CONCLUSION

With the improvement of people's living standard, China's tourism industry has entered into the golden development period, but wind farms tourism the connotation is rich help to promote tourism grade of new tourism format, in cultivation, still need to promote a new concept, clear thinking, the breakthrough in the process.

Recently, The attempt of China's wind farms on tourism development as well as efforts of Governments at all levels are only taken the first step, the future development requires the government and the wind farms cooperation, determine the target market, and gradually strengthen the concept of wind farms tourism propaganda, enhance its social influence, let more people understand wind power, pay attention to wind power, and is willing to join green clean life, let the wind farms tourism development to further adjust the industrial structure become an important catalyst, not only the revitalization of regional economy, but also closely keep up with the pace of the sustainable development, realize environmental, economic and social profits together.

REFERENCES

[1] Wind power safety supervision report (2011). Regulatory reports of the State Electricity Regulatory Commission, No. 4, 2011 (Total 31). November 2011.
[2] Sun. S.G. et al. 2011. Wind power pulls the overall development of scientific planning intensive development. Gansu daily, July 5.
[3] Liu Y.L. & Cai X.J. 2012. Zhangjiakou' number of tourist and tourism revenue reach new high. Zhangjiakou daily, August 14.

Environmental experiment curriculum development based on work process—"urban secondary sewage treatment plant operation and management" courses as an example

L. Sun, Y.R. Dong & D.L. Hao
Training Center for Water Treatment (DETCWAT), Environmental Management College of China (EMCC), Qinhuangdao, China

ABSTRACT: In this paper, work environment experimental curriculum development based on work process are discussed, which used urban secondary sewage treatment plant as an example. In accordance with the ideas of "Typical job task analysis—Professional capability analysis—Learning area design— Learning environment construction—Project teaching-Evaluation system establishing", the original curriculum subject systems was reconstructed, Development a employment-oriented environmental experiment process-based experimental course.

Keywords: based on the work process; environmental experiment; typical tasks; learning areas; learning environment

Environment environmental experiment course in higher vocational colleges professional curriculum, but also in environmental engineering, environmental monitoring, environmental chemistry, an integral part of teaching and environmental planning, environmental assessment, environmental management, and systems analysis and other related professional courses. Through the environmental experiment to improve students' proficiency and environmental laws of cognitive skills, as well as environmental data and grasping ability, thus enhancing its ability to work. At present, the environment experiment course in higher vocational college using the "experimental" teaching mode, teaching that incorporate synchronization verified experiment and demonstration experiments, experimental instruction of students in full accordance with procedures designed to experiment. This is not conducive to improving the students' ability of creativity, design and experimental skills. For this a problem, I homes in years environment experiment teaching experience of based Shang, combines taught high [2006]16, file in the on strongly introduced workers learn combines, highlight practice capacity training, reform talent training mode of overall requires, on original of "courses experiment" teaching mode for reform, made has "based on work process" of environment experiment courses, to work task for oriented, makes students in practice in the learning, learning in the practice, real reflected has workers learn combines and taught, and learn, and do integration

of teaching mode. This paper, urban secondary sewage treatment plant, for example, describes the process based on working environment experiments to develop methods and procedures with a view to provide reference for curriculum development of environment.

1 CURRICULUM DEVELOPMENT

Curriculum development steps through field investigation, expert interviews and other forms of urban secondary sewage treatment plant jobs by analysis, expert interviews, surveys, and practice as well as critical incident analysis method to extract typical tasks, and an in-depth analysis of basic vocational skills required for different tasks (including basic skills, professional and technical skills and overall quality). On the basis of comprehensive analysis of occupational competence, areas of study design. Field of study design is an important part of the course design as a whole. By field of study design into teachers' teaching methods, evaluation, and student learning, and according to field of study designed learning environment and contextual teaching and learning environment and teaching support, interdependent learning environment and teaching is based on the basic teaching of the course of the process unit. Final analysis on occupational capacity, fields of study design, learning strategies, teaching methods, evaluation studies, and studies on the basis of situational

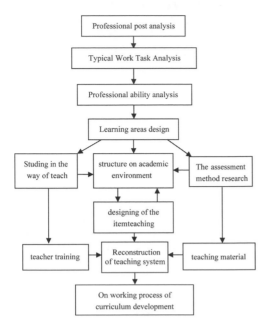

Figure 1. Environmental laboratory curriculum development based on work process steps.

teaching and program design, based on working process of curriculum construction of teaching staff and teaching materials for in-depth study, to regroup the teaching system of the original order, finalized on working process of curriculum development. Curriculum development process as shown in Figure 1.

2 CURRICULUM DEVELOPMENT METHOD

2.1 City sewage II level sewage processing factory overall post needs

City sewage II level sewage processing factory overall post needs analysis through visits investigation, and expert interviews, and read information, and talent market research, and questionnaire investigation, and Organization seminar, way, on Qin Huangdao several city II level sewage processing factory post set and post duties for full investigation analysis, through research came, existing of city II level sewage processing factory post set has: water treatment run maintenance post, and Center control room operation management post, and machinery equipment maintenance maintenance post, and sludge processing post, and laboratory post, and Production scheduling jobs, as well as other relevant departments.

2.2 Typical work task analysis in sewage processing

Factory post analysis of based Shang, we and used practice expert interviews will, and posts questionnaire analysis, and work diary realism law, and measuring Shi law, and work sampling law, and interview law and key event analysis law, pursuant to work task by simple to complex of principles, on post for for "solutions frame" obtained has teaching value of work task, and "complexity" for finishing, summary out 6 a has representative of typical work task, they respectively is: water detection, and lattice gate of maintenance and management, Pump and blower operation and maintenance, aeration and maintenance management, maintenance and management of secondary sedimentation tank, sludge treatment. Analysis of typical tasks are shown in Table 1.

2.3 Learning design learning spheres

(Lern feld) is described by the learning goals, learning modules, which is set by occupational tasks and occupational action orientation. A field of study includes learning objectives, course content and duration of study is composed of three parts. Its best feature is that you do not use the disciplinary system but through integrated, continuous "action" [1]. Field of study design is based on the course curriculum design key aspects of its work. This courses development in on city II level sewage processing factory typical work task, and career capacity in-depth analysis of based Shang, to module of of teaching method, to capacity training for target, on traditional courses system for heavy frame, sequence of, determines has "II level sewage processing factory sewage processing of based knowledge, and sewage processing factory run indicators monitoring and analysis, and sewage processing system run and regulation, and remaining sludge of processing" four a learning area.

2.4 Learning environment construction and project design

"Learning environment" is in the context of work tasks and work tasks, goals and teaching content for learning in the field of capacity based on theory and methodology of instruction after the conversion, in the composition of the areas of study within the framework of "small" learning module [2]. You can build highly imitative work situations, create a demonstration and promotion role of integrated teaching environment. Characterized near the real-world learning situations learn, direct contact with the work, let students learn "how it works". Environment situation of experimental courses of construction, different from the

Table 1. Typical job task analysis city secondary sewage treatment plant.

Professional task	Task specification	The main ability point
Quality testing	Inlet and outlet water quality of sewage treatment plants and activated sludge properties test analysis.	1. Understand the basic knowledge of laboratory 2. Master water quality detection method of the project 3. To master relevant knowledge environmental microbiology 4. Integrated reasoning section
Grille maintenance and management	Regular cleaning grating; Adjust the grid velocity; Regular inspection of mechanical equipment, ensure the normal operation of grid; Grille daily maintenance and management.	1. Understand the grille and design parameters of operation and management 2. Familiar with the basic operation and maintenance management of grid 3. Have a certain health and safety related knowledge
The operation and maintenance of pump and fan	Open and close pump; Equipment operation is normal or not by running the phenomenon of judgment, and troubleshooting; Pump and fan, daily maintenance and management.	1. Understanding the structure, type and working principle of pump and fan, etc 2. Familiar with pump and fan fault judgment method and troubleshooting 3. Familiar with daily maintenance pump or fan
Maintenance and management of aeration	Adjust the aeration tank operation parameters according to test results, through these parameters to judge the problems existing in the system operation process, and take measures to ensure the normal operation of the sewage treatment plant.	1. Familiar with the sewage treatment process flow, process parameters 2. Familiar with production technology and equipment maintenance 3. Have found the problem, problem analysis and problem solving skills 4. Can judge and deal with the general accident and fault
The second pond, the maintenance and management	According to the second sink shelf's judgment system state; Discharge of sludge; Regularly check and adjust, keep clear of suction tube tube road; Remove suction dredge set scraping the mud tank in the dirt.	1. Understand the second pond, the basic structure, process principle, operation parameters, operation procedures and other basic knowledge 2. Through the test results, determine whether the system problems, and be able to take measures to ensure the normal operation of the system 3. Knowledge of mechanical equipment maintenance, routine maintenance

processing class curriculum in higher vocational education, these programs provided related to the production of work tools and work environment situations is a highly complex system, you need to build a relatively complete system, can guarantee the learning effect. In addition, there are some pilot projects can only be completed onsite sewage treatment plant. Experimental curriculum development environment you need to first establish a relatively complete, highly imitative learning situations. This topics learning situational designers established in in the Dutch water treatment model Center of based Shang of, Center has Netherlands Government assistance of full advanced of water treatment experiment and analysis equipment: completely mixed good oxygen bio processing system, and UCT except phosphorus off nitrogen system, and carrousel oxidation Groove in the try

experiment system, and Super filter system, and ceramic film MBR system, and Tablet film MBR system, and purple outside and plus chlorine disinfection system, and sand filter system, and mixed coagulation precipitation and the continuous stream activated carbon adsorption bleaching system, analysis processing unit. In addition, the Centre and three wastewater treatment plant in Qin Huangdao has good relations of cooperation, wastewater treatment plant is the college students' practical training base, the design of this situation create favorable conditions.

2.5 The establishment of evaluation system of experiment

The establishment of evaluation system of experiment teaching is a multiple factor, multiple steps, multiple levels of instruction, course assessment must be based on work process to change the traditional examination method of arbitrary and subjective, from experimental preview, test procedures, test report and final operation skill examinations and so on have comprehensively to assess student learning outcomes. Work-based environment of experimental teaching examination method to refer to the extensive literature on the basis of consulting some of the longtime sewage treatment plant technology and management experts, reference to employee performance appraisal method of wastewater treatment plant, in accordance with the sewage treatment plant technician should grasp ability points, defining regular appraisals, writing assessment and examination of integrated assessment methods. Key points of examination of basic capacities, expertise and focus on comprehensive qualities. Basic capacity consists of theoretical knowledge, knowledge management, data processing and analysis capabilities, access to information, professional and technical capacity, including hands-on ability, observation, the ability to analyze, to ask questions, solve problems, comprehensive quality capabilities including learning attitude, teamwork, communication skills, creativity, comprehensive capabilities. These three interrelated, are indispensable. While examination by the Ministry of environmental protection sewage wastewater processing training, unified course examination and student research. Review process to develop evaluation indicators and assessment criteria, quantitative evaluation indicators will be refined and in a fair and objective assessment the students.

3 CONCLUSION

The work environment in the process of experimental course development through the analysis of typical tasks, analysis of professional ability, learning design and learning situations in the field building, achieving environmental experiment task-oriented courses reform and teaching mode of integration of teaching, learning and doing. Its task as a carrier, society foster talents of high quality as the goal. Curriculum development in this regard was the establishment in these experiments under the environment and field of simulation, on the other hand the course also focuses on training of students' professional skills, methods and social skills, therefore, curriculum implementation contribute to the achievement of high quality labour "zero distance" posts. Currently, based on course development in China is still in the initial stages of the process, particularly with respect to environmental experiment course of curriculum development is rarely reported. Therefore, taking employment as the direction, to positions as standard in an integrated skill development for core environmental experiment curriculum development will be environmental specialty in higher vocational education in our country the main direction of the education reform.

ACKNOWLEDGEMENTS

This work was supported by the project of Qinhuangdao 2012 science and technology research and development plan (2012023 A230).

REFERENCES

[1] Jiang Dayuan. "Fields of study" courses: concepts, features and some issues—Germany vocational school curricula important reflections on the reform of China [j]. Research on foreign educational, 2003, 30 (1):26–31.
[2] Jiang Ping. Based on specialized course system construction of higher vocational education in the process of [j]. IT education in Fu Jian, 2008, 4:46–48.
[3] Zhao Tie. Analysis of Germany's action-oriented vocational education teaching reform law [j]. Journal of Shan Xi finance and taxation College. 2007, 9(1): 74–77.

Computer, Intelligent Computing and Education Technology – Liu, Sung & Yao (Eds)
© *2014 Taylor & Francis Group, London, ISBN 978-1-138-02469-4*

"Analytical chemistry" course in higher vocational environment major teaching reform

Y.R. Dong, D.L. Hao & L. Sun
*Sino-Dutch Demonstration Research and Training Center for Water Treatment (DETCWAT),
Environmental Management College of China (EMCC), Qinhuangdao, China*

ABSTRACT: Analytical chemistry as a professional basic course in higher vocational environment major, has a direct relationship to the students' comprehensive quality and application ability, learning is particularly important for follow-up professional courses. In this paper, the teaching idea, teaching content, teaching mode, the reform of experiment teaching are discussed to highlight the professional and practical, combining with the characteristics of higher vocational students.

Keywords: higher vocational; environment major; analytical chemistry; teaching reform

The course of "Analytical Chemistry" is focusing on quantitative analysis, pay attention on application, practical strongly and widely used tools disciplines in the meantime it is an important professional basic course. For a long time the teaching process of "Analytical Chemistry" in the vocational colleges exist phenomenon that "teachers teach rigidly and students learn passively". The teaching content is Antiquated and cannot contact practice therefore some students who have great foundation cannot pay attention on listening while other students who have poor foundation simply do not learn. It is necessary to make some reform to teaching of "Analytical Chemistry" course in the background of the vocational colleges need to train skilled and practical talented person for the social.

compare with the students who are undergraduate institutions students. However, the majority of students eager to master the necessary knowledge and skills by learning and then to obtain a certificate of vocational skills such as certificate of chemical engineering inspection and prepare the future jobs. So that they have a certain enthusiasm for learning.

Therefore, we have to change the ideas of teaching, establishing the concept of "professional competence training" and grasping the principle of "must, enough" in order to achieve better teaching results and training the skilled and practical talented persons. Developing the skilled and practical talented persons in areas such as production, develop production, construction, management and social services and so on according to a certain group of professional positions.

1 CHANGING THE IDEAS OF TEACHING AND ADAPTING THE CHARACTERISTICS OF STUDENTS

Currently even though the college students already become adults they still do not have maturely ideas and thinking things also have large arbitrariness and just want to learn that they are interesting in. They will give up easily for the course content which they are not interesting in or they think they have not enough ability to learn.

Moreover, although students have study basis chemistry at the secondary school and have some understanding of chemistry they have relatively low entry requirements, chemical basis of most students is relatively weak, uneven level of knowledge and lack self-learning ability and practical ability

2 OPTIMIZING TEACHING CONTENT, ADAPTING THE NEED OF PERSONNEL TRAINING

In terms of textbooks which almost satisfy to the teaching of all types of vocational Engineering Colleges, but lacking to professional and practical due to they have weakly professional association with subjects which related to environmental protection. However many detections of environmental problems have inseparable relationships with application of analytical chemistry in the actual work. Therefore it is important to penetrate the analytical chemistry knowledge into the field of environment and making integration and optimization for teaching content. To start with integrating the four titration analysis methods into five modules: balance principle, the titration curve, indicator, titration' error and methods application and teaching with methods of contrasting and comparing.

Secondly, the teaching content is not limited to books since the type of purely theoretical teaching is easily make students lose interest in learning. Should to pay attention on combine with the actual daily life and work, as well as merging the events that people general interesting in to original teaching content thus stimulating students' interest in learning. For example, to introduce the importance of analytical chemistry from problems of eutrophication, milk melamine incident, pesticide residues on vegetables and so on. Moreover making examples including determination of the redox titration permanganate, and determination of COD_{Cr} or DO, etc by redox titration also combining of environmental monitoring application examples, making example of determination of Ca, Mg and other metal ions in water by Coordination Titration, getting the examples of determination of soil moisture measurement or SS by Gravimetric, and getting the examples of determination of ammonia nitrogen or total phosphorus by Spectrophotometry.

Moreover, combining with test content of Chemical test worker as well as having supplement with relevant theoretical knowledge in the teaching process are benefit to students obtain certificates of professional chemical test worker therefore lay a fixed foundation for identity transition which students become professional human.

In conclusion, this can stimulate students' interest in learning and to take the initiative, hence to obtain good teaching effect and make students feel they can earn knowledge.

3 CHANGING THE TEACHING MODE AND FLEXIBLY USING MULTIVARIATE TEACHING METHODS

3.1 Task-driven teaching

To begin with teachers should set tasks based on the content that to be taught including explain objective of the mission of teaching and relevant theoretical knowledge to students and then transfer the class teaching to laboratory teaching. Teachers need to configuration issues before operation, encourage students have discussion in groups and guide students to thinking. For instance in the teaching process in acid-base titration, we need to do the determine of the composition and content of the mixed alkali and for the determine of base and first reaction use acid titration which situation teachers can inspire students to think the questions

such as what is the acid-base theory, whether mixed alkali NaOH, Na_2CO_3, $NaHCO_3$ can co-exist using the knowledge learned to analysis and think the reasons, whether standard solution of hydrochloric acid can be used as a reference substance and how to do the preparation and calibration, why to choose phenolphthalein, and methyl orange indicator, How indicator' color is change, notes of titration and so on.

Besides, students discuss research based on tasks and issues and combined with theoretical knowledge that learned and the corresponding network resources, then develop plans and complete the tasks while finding answers to questions.

Finally, teachers make assessment to situation of completion for each group.

3.2 Case teaching

Case teaching is a teaching method that in the case of the pilot, based on the problems, mainly using self-learning for students and Teachers guide as supplement, to apply the knowledge to solve practical problems and making integration of theory and practice closely. For example, in the teaching process of redox titration, using the case of Fujian Minjiang dead fish's incident, teachers require students to search information in advance and understand the circumstances of the incident which make students know that due to the low levels of dissolved oxygen led to fish in water to anoxic death. So that students can actively targeted have prep in advance. For another example, Principles and operating conditions of iodometry, selection of the indicator and determination of the end point, Preparation of standard solution and calibration and so on. In another condition such as in the teaching process of data processing and error analysis, teachers use students' test data as examples and then draw the teaching content. Furthermore, such as after learning all these knowledge including correctly recorded experimental data, the choice of suspicious data. Rounding significant figures, correct evaluation of precision and Error analysis of the experimental data, teachers select several questionable lab reports present to the students at the same time make students apply existing knowledge to identify problems, analyze and solve problems by themselves. By this way can fully mobilize the enthusiasm of the students and conducive to grasp and application of knowledge.

3.3 Other teaching models and methods

Teaching methods should be diversified and teachers should be flexible according to different teaching contents. We can use other teaching methods such as comparison and comparative law, role playing, group discussion method, problem situations, animation simulation and so on in the actual teaching process.

4 STRENGTHEN TEACHING, TRAINING SKILLED AND PRACTICAL TALENTED PERSONS

Using the modern experimental teaching philosophy that "student-centered, teacher-led," to replace the traditional experimental teaching model which teacher teach students in details while students just learn that teacher have taught and done and then soon forget. To allow students to truly become the main experimental operation and teachers only play a guiding role. According to years of experience of experiment education I suggest the following improvements:

1. Teachers require students prepare the courses, clearly know the purpose of experiment, clearly understanding of the experimental procedure, necessary equipment and reagents and then teachers guide students to apple it to the experiments. With the example of experiment named "determination of calcium and magnesium content in natural water," teachers put questions such as what are the role of triethanolamine and ammonia when buffer solution? Whether need to use pipet to precise amount? What color of solution if put Chrome black T, what color will change if drop EDTA in solution and why those changes occurred? Moreover, teachers can use a counter-example that the color of solution in a conical flask for most students is red wine before titration and there are four students did not to inspire students to find questions and then further enhance the students' ability to apply knowledge.
2. Due to the large enrollment members in each class now is excessive, teachers is difficult to do corrective guidance for everyone's experiment operation. As a result some students' faulty operation cannot be corrected in time. Therefore, teachers make some students demonstrate experimental operation of last course on the podium and other students look for flaws every time before to have formal class.

It is possible for students to find exist problems in operations by themselves. Finally teachers demonstrate normative experimental operation again. So that can exercise the students' experimental operational capability. Meantime teachers select several students whose operations are good to guide other students and this way is benefit to main role of students to fully paly. At last assessing the students' experimental operation at the end of the semester.

3. Analyzing projects of chemistry courses experiments related to the environment as much as possible and closely linked to the professional. For instance, course could open the determination of chlorine in tap water, determination of acidity and alkalinity in water, determination of dissolved oxygen in the water body, Preparation and calibration of potassium permanganate, determination of iodine content of edible salt and so on.

In conclusion, the course teaching reform of «Analytical Chemistry» is a Comprehensive reform that the reform is from front to back and from form to content, meantime, it is inevitable requirement for vocational colleges train the social skilled and practical talents persons. Reform does not end. Only you are follow times, you are be invincible.

ACKNOWLEDGEMENTS

This work was supported by the Project of Environmental Management College of China 2014 science and technology research fund plan (2014019).

REFERENCES

Zhang Lu. Reflect on analytical chemistry mission-driven curriculum reform in vocational colleges[J]. Modern Enterprise Education. April 2011.
Zheng Yanfen etc. Reform and practice on analytical chemistry teaching of environment major of higher vocational college[J]. Journal of Environmental Management College of China. March 2011.
Zhu Yuanhua. Application of induction and contrast methods in the analysis of titration[J]. Science research universities. April 2006.

Computer, Intelligent Computing and Education Technology – Liu, Sung & Yao (Eds)
© *2014 Taylor & Francis Group, London, ISBN 978-1-138-02469-4*

Outcomes of group cognitive behavior therapy for polyhagia

Zhi-Lei He, A-Meng Zhao, Yong-Zhuo Ding, Zhen-Zhen Cai & Yi-Bo Dai
Mental Health School, Qiqihar Medical University, Qiqihar, China

ABSTRACT: Objective: To observe the effects of Group Cognitive Behavior Therapy (GCBT) on bulimia nervosa. Methods: Eating Disorders Inventory was used to investigate the bulimia behavior in 1900 students in a medical college, and 126 subjects were included concerning whose scores were under 41 on the questionnaire as potential eating disorders. Further confirmation by DSM-IV, 30 of the 126 participants were diagnosed as bulimia nervosa and evenly randomized into groups of treatment and controls. The treatment group were given GCBT once a week for 8 consecutive weeks, and both groups were compared after 8 weeks of intervention for the difference. Results: There was no significant difference between the two groups regarding the estimation by questionnaire BMI, stress and scores on SCL-90 before intervention ($P > 0.05$), whereas the two groups differed a lot, especially the treatment group were found with significant improvement in tendency of eating disorders, stress and mental health status ($P < 0.05$). The controls had no significant change ($P > 0.05$). Conclusion: GCBT may be effective to management of bulimia nervosa in college students.

Keywords: group therapy; cognitive behavior; polyhagia

1 INTRODUCTION

Eating Disorders (EDS) are a group of mental disorders as the remarkable feature of eating behavior, including Anorexia Nervosa (AN), neurological bulimia (BN), Eating Disorder Not Otherwise Specified (EDNOS). The age for the onset of eating disorders used to be very young[1], and it is common in teenager. All kinds of survey research shows that college students have become a high-risk group of eating disorders, Especially that patients with BN under the threshold have a higher proportion. At present, there is no specific, operational group intervention techniques for the BN patients under theshold in the college students group. This study by using the group psychological intervention techniques hopes to provide new ideas for prevention and control of an eating disorder.

2 OBJECT AND METHODS

2.1 *Object*

The questionnaire survey was used in 1900 students from the grade one and two in a Wuhu's college. Ask volume 1, 900, recovery of 1,786, 1,770 valid questionnaires, the effective rate was 93.16%. 126 subjects were included concerning whose scores were under 41 on the questionnaire as potential eating disorders. Further confirmation by DSM-IV, 30 of the 126 participants were diagnosed

as bulimia nervosa and evenly randomized into groups of treatment and controls after signing the informed consent. The treatment group were given GCBT once a week for 8 consecutive weeks, and both groups were compared after 8 weeks of intervention for the difference.15 subjects were selected in the treatment group, during the treatment, 3 didn't finish the whole treatment for some reasons, actually, 12 subjects completely finished the activists (Male 2, female 10). Age (19.33 + 0.89), high (162.33 + 5.23) cm, weight (57.93 + 10.75) kg. Controls 15 subjects,1 person quit,14 subjects completely finished the activists (Male 1, female 13). Age (19.71 + 0.71), height (163.43 + 5.60 cm, weight (56.79 + 5.6) kg. There is no statistical significance in weight ($P > 0.05$).

2.2 *Observational index*

2.2.1 *Eating disorder questionnaire*
In order to get the situation of individual recent eating clear. It focuses on individual eating attitudes, eating behaviors. According to the score situation. It can help predict ontogenesis GENERAL INSTRUCTIONS tendency of eating disorder. The lower the score, the high tendency of individuals suffering from eating disorders.

2.2.2 *SCL-90 symptom self-assessment scale*
Mainly reflecting the individual mental health and containing 90 project, it can accurately reflect the

subjects' self-conscious symptom of 10 aspects, in somatization, force, sensitive interpersonal relationship and the severe degree is scored 5 levels according to the symptoms. The higher the factor score, the worse mental health. It is used to observing the mental health status before and after the improvement of polyhagia.

2.2.3 Stress scale

It is used to reflect the individual life stress status of body and mind according to the score, the higher the score, the greater the individual pressure, prompting the worse mental health conditions.

2.3 Methods

Treatment is implemented by the author and a trained graduate student, one supervisor from professor of psychology.

2.3.1 Group psychological treatment of the treatment group

Treatment group implements GCBT intervention treatment. Using group cognitive behavior therapy and make public examination and review of homework. Treatment lasts for 8 weeks, 1 times a week, every time 2 h.

First: Self review, guide introduction, interactive activities, interpretation of the group for the nature, principle and target, etc, to help members to adapt to the environment, and to encourage members to describe the current food situation.

Second: Cognitive restructuring, let each member describe polyhagia behavior situation, identify and analyse negative thoughts that influence the eating behavior, such as "appearance in a bad mood", "often worry about fat", etc.

Third: Cognitive restructuring, let each member describe his or her understanding of weight, form, and help them to identify unreasonable cognition, such as "even if the students think I am not fat, but I still feel fat", "eating a little meat will make me fat", "I am also upset for eating too much", etc.

Fourth: Mood dredge, teaching relaxed breathing method, muscle relaxation and meditation music relaxation method, doing the relaxation training.

Fifth: Behavior training, through the game, let each member to practice with the emotional expression, and to develop self-confidence, such as "a mirror to practice law".

Sixth: Discussing scientific principles of eating, to help members to develop alternative behavior, reduce the occurrence of polyagia behavior.

Seventh: Role play, as for polyhagia behavior possible situation, help members to build positive coping styles, build up my confidence in the living;

Eighth: Summarizes the process of treatment, lead to communicate and discuss, to strengthen the correct cognition and prevent recurrence.

2.3.2 The control scheme

Do not take any treatment measures to group B in the experiment, and observing indexes both in the ending and begining.

2.3.3 Data processing and statistics

Numerical variable data to mean was described by standard ± deviation. Comparison between two groups of mean uses sample t test. Before and after treatment with paired t test. $P < 0.05$ is the basis to determine whether a difference was statistically significant.

3 CONSEQUENCE

3.1 The comparison between two groups before the experiment

We can see from Table 1 results that there is no statistical significance between treatment group and control group in the tendency of eating disorders, physical quantity index and stress scores. Two groups have gluttony, high stress levels, poor mental health, but the Body Mass Index (BMI) were normal. The results show that in Table 1. Both the treatment group and control group, the overall level of psychological health of patients is poor, but there is no statistical significance before the treatment.

Eating disorder questionnaire Body Mass Index (BMI), stress scores and the mental health level (SCL-90) between the two groups before treatment.

3.2 The comparison between two groups after treatment

3.2.1 The comparison in gluttony behavior, stress and mental health of treatment group after treatment

After 8 weeks treatment,12 participating students' eating had improved. From the results in Table 2, It can be seen that the treatment group given group after treatment, 12 students eating disorders, stress condition were significantly improved And the difference was statistically significant ($P < 0.01$). Results showed that the treatment group after treatment of mental health exist significant difference, except paranoid and other factors, the total score, somatization, force and other 12 factors were significantly improved, with statistical significance ($P < 0.05$).

3.2.2 The comparision in polyhagia, stress and mental health of the control group before and after treatment

From the results in Table 3nce ($P > 0.05$). After 8 weeks, the control group in addition to the other factors, the rest in gluttony behavior and stress status has no statistical significance ($P > 0.05$).

Table 1.

Items	Treatment (n = 12)	Control (n = 14)	t	P
BMI (kg/m^2)	21.88 ± 2.97	21.27 ± 1.75	0.64	0.53
Stress	27.83 ± 3.79	26.36 ± 3.54	1.03	0.32
SCL-90 total score	214.25 ± 53.61	217.50 ± 49.49	0.16	0.87
SCL-90 average	2.38 ± 0.60	2.42 ± 0.55	0.16	0.87
Positive number	60.75 ± 15.49	64.36 ± 13.51	0.64	0.53
Positive symptoms average	3.01 ± 0.54	2.95 ± 0.48	0.33	0.74
Somatization	2.06 ± 0.91	2.25 ± 0.74	0.58	0.57
Forced	2.82 ± 0.59	2.83 ± 0.62	0.05	0.96
Interpersonal relation	2.66 ± 0.77	2.70 ± 0.73	0.14	0.89
Depression	2.64 ± 0.87	2.56 ± 0.80	0.23	0.82
Anxiety	2.36 ± 0.72	2.33 ± 0.63	0.11	0.91
Hostile	2.19 ± 0.55	2.21 ± 0.48	0.09	0.93
Terrorist	2.13 ± 0.80	2.27 ± 0.82	0.42	0.68
Paranoid	2.12 ± 0.71	2.25 ± 0.70	0.46	0.65
Psychotic	2.43 ± 0.69	2.44 ± 0.59	0.04	0.97
Others	2.08 ± 0.55	2.06 ± 0.51	0.11	0.92

Table 2. The comparision in eating stress and mental health of the treatment group before and after treatment (SCL-90).

Items	Before treatment (n = 12)	After treatment (n = 12)	d ± sd	t	P
Total score	23.17 ± 3.43	24.36 ± 4.05	24.36 ± 4.05	5.88	0.000
Stress	27.83 ± 3.79	26.36 ± 3.54	26.36 ± 3.54	9.93	0.000
SCL-90 total score	214.25 ± 53.61	163.08 ± 30.28	51.17 ± 46.60	3.80	0.003
SCL-90 average	2.38 ± 0.60	1.81 ± 0.34	0.57 ± 0.52	3.80	0.003
Positive number	60.75 ± 15.49	47.17 ± 18.36	13.58 ± 14.23	3.31	0.007
Positive symptoms average	3.01 ± 0.54	2.53 ± 0.29	0.48 ± 0.44	3.75	0.003
Somatization	2.06 ± 0.91	1.49 ± 0.35	0.56 ± 0.79	2.48	0.030
Forced	2.82 ± 0.59	2.18 ± 0.40	0.63 ± 0.36	6.05	0.000
Interpersonal relation	2.66 ± 0.77	2.04 ± 0.42	0.62 ± 0.68	3.16	0.009
Depression	2.64 ± 0.87	1.87 ± 0.50	0.76 ± 0.87	3.05	0.010
Anxiety	2.36 ± 0.72	1.76 ± 0.45	0.60 ± 0.62	3.33	0.007
Hostile	2.19 ± 0.55	1.63 ± 0.45	0.57 ± 0.72	2.75	0.020
Terrorist	2.13 ± 0.80	1.76 ± 0.62	0.37 ± 0.47	2.70	0.020
Paranoid	2.12 ± 0.71	1.64 ± 0.55	0.48 ± 0.80	2.11	0.060
Psychotic	2.43 ± 0.69	1.75 ± 0.33	0.68 ± 0.68	3.58	0.004
Others	2.08 ± 0.55	1.95 ± 0.44	0.13 ± 0.43	1.05	0.320

Table 3. The comparision in questionnaire, stress of the treatment group after treatment.

Items	Before the treatment (n = 12)	After the treatment (n = 12)	d ± sd	t	P
Total score	24.36 ± 4.05	22.64 ± 4.33	1.71 ± 6.49	0.99	0.340
Stress	26.36 ± 3.54	27.35 ± 4.09	1.00 ± 3.35	1.12	0.280

3.2.3 The comparision in polyhagia, stress and mental health of the control group after treatment

Table 4 shows, there were highly significant on eating disorder questionnaire scores and stress scores between treatment group and control group after treatment ($P < 0.01$), the gluttony behavior and stress situation of the treatment group were improved significantly better than the control group.

Table 4.

Items	Treatment group (n = 12)	Control group (n = 14)	t	P
Total score	36.08 ± 8.08	22.64 ± 4.33	5.39	0.000
Stress	12.50 ± 5.33	27.35 ± 4.09	8.03	0.000
SCL-90 total score	163.08 ± 30.28	218.07 ± 46.51	3.50	0.002
SCL-90 average	1.81 ± 0.34	2.42 ± 0.52	3.49	0.002
Positive number	47.17 ± 18.36	66.57 ± 12.46	3.03	0.006
Positive symptoms average	2.53 ± 0.29	2.92 ± 0.45	2.56	0.020
Somatization	1.49 ± 0.35	2.27 ± 0.72	3.41	0.002
Forced	2.18 ± 0.40	2.84 ± 0.61	3.18	0.004
Interpersonal relation	2.04 ± 0.42	2.69 ± 0.64	3.01	0.006
Depression	1.87 ± 0.50	2.58 ± 0.76	2.75	0.010
Anxiety	1.76 ± 0.45	2.33 ± 0.58	2.76	0.010
Hostile	1.63 ± 0.45	2.23 ± 0.46	3.35	0.003
Terrorist	1.76 ± 0.62	2.22 ± 0.76	1.65	0.110
Paranoid	1.64 ± 0.55	2.23 ± 0.66	2.44	0.020
Psychotic	1.75 ± 0.33	2.41 ± 0.56	3.61	0.001
Others	1.95 ± 0.44	2.14 ± 0.50	1.02	0.320

The comparision in questionnaire scores, stress and mental health between treatment group and control group after treatment ($P < 0.01$).

4 DISCUSSION

4.1 The current situation of the college students' polyhagia(under the threshold BN)

The incidence of a typical (threshold) eating disorders is twice more than that of eating disorders. College students has become a high-risk groups. This research shows that, there are 4.12% of the students in the diagnosis of the sub clinical state of BN. Current students influenced by social aesthetic idea, under the influence of factors such as pressure, mental health, the incidence of undergraduate's behavior of gluttony has a tendency to rise.

4.2 The relationship between mental health and eating disorders

The occurrence of psychological disorders can increase the risk for eating disorders, and development of eating disorders can also increase the patient's psychological problems. Invalid sense, asceticism, dynamic adjustment, perfectionism, interpersonal trust, lack of inner feelings of consciousness, mature social insecurity and fear, is frequently in patients with anorexia or bulimia report. This study use SCL-90 symptoms self evaluation scale to reflect the mental health status of patients. Results show that the group cognitive behavioural therapy can effectively improve the mental health level. After treatment, the treatment group patients

with bulimia behavior is corrected, mental health has been improved significantly. Studies have pointed out that 40%~40% of patients with eating disorders will experience depression and anxiety disorders[2]. Personality traits often arise self-deprecation, low self-esteem, pessimism, excessively focus on body image, etc, especially excessive attention to body mass[3], body tend to become a key cause of abnormal eating behaviors occur. In this study, two groups of patients with bulimia behavior have higher scores in interpersonal, depression, anxiety and psychoticism in the process of treatment, patients had symptoms such as depression, anxiety, and inferiority. 24 of 26 patients mistakenly think that their overweight, they are not happy and full of struggle and conflict.

4.3 CBT is still considered as the most effective way to deal with BN

Cognitive behavior therapy is the main method for the treatment of eating disorders. Effects in the treatment of patients with BN are Obvious.

A large number of Related clinical randomized controlled studies also showed that the therapy is more effective in patients with changes in a particular way of thinking, behavior. This study adopt group cognitive behavioural therapy and use the basic principle of CBT and procedures[4]. After 8 weeks of treatment, GCBT therapy for undergraduate's Behavior of Gluttony (BN) under the threshold of curative effect is obvious: Treatment group has more rational understanding for diet and body, and gluttony behavior obviously decline Patients had mental health conditions improved significantly and actively dealt with stressful events in life. No longer in gluttony—anxiety—a diet in a cycle of gluttony.

The risk of eating disorders' rate in college students groups in showed a trend of rise. Therefore, early intervention in patients with subthreshold BN and prevention for the deterioration of symptoms is the key to the prevention and control. In this study, GCBT techniques in the treatment of subliminal BN has made significant curative effect.

ACKNOWLEDGMENTS

Funded by Heilongjiang Province Mental Science Project (130049).

REFERENCES

[1] Russell G, FM. Bulimia nervosa: an omitting variant of anorexia nervosa [J]. Psychological Medicine, 1979, 9: 429–448.

[2] Simon H. Eating disorders: anorexia and bulimia [EB/OL]. [2003-03-31]. http://adam.About.com/reports/Eating disorders. htm.

[3] Dunkley D.M, Grilo C.M. Self-criticism, low self-esteem, depressive symptoms, and over-evaluation of shape and weight in hinge eating disorder patients [J]. Behav Res Ther, 2007, 45: 139–149.

[4] G Smaker, C Dare, J Treasure. Handbook of Eating Disorder: Theory. Treatment and Research [M]. Antony Rowe Ltd, 1995: 308–331.

Computer, Intelligent Computing and Education Technology – Liu, Sung & Yao (Eds)
© *2014 Taylor & Francis Group, London, ISBN 978-1-138-02469-4*

On the innovative teaching methods and model for fostering applied and creative talents

Q. Wen, Y. Tian & J. Fan
Hebei University of Technology, Tianjin, China

ABSTRACT: There exist certain limitations and defects in fostering applicative and creative talents in traditional teaching methods and models. In the paper, innovative teaching methods and an hierarchical teaching model are put forward, including animation showing, analogy teaching, case teaching and promoting learning through teaching process. They aim to improve the teaching quality and efficiency and to facilitate students' capacity for practice and innovation.

Keywords: innovation; teaching method; teaching model

Nowadays the society is in great need of applied and creative talents. However, traditional teaching methods and models have some flaws and insufficiencies in cultivating applied talents. An innovative education reform, therefore, should be made to meet the demands of social development. In view of that, this paper proposed some suggestions on a new reform on the hierarchal teaching model and innovative teaching methods.

1 FLAWS AND INSUFFICIENCIES OF TRADITIONAL TEACHING

1.1 *The disconnection between theory and practice teaching*

In theory courses, teachers focus more on the elaboration of theories than on their match with corresponding practice, which leads to the disconnection of these two sorts of instruction. As is well-known, to assist students gain a thorough grasp of curriculum knowledge, teachers should direct them to get involved in various kinds of practical activities and to solve problems by themselves. In this way, students could have great chances to achieve a deeper understanding towards these theory knowledge learned in class and make gains in this process. Otherwise, they would just waste their time to have an insufficient access to the surface level knowledge.

1.2 *Students' lack of interest and innovation ability*

As to some courses with definite abstract knowledge system, it's really difficult to conduct the corresponding practice teaching. Therefore, students feel overwhelmed by these difficulties and wonder what exactly they are learning for. All of that consequently has a bad effect including low level of learning interest, limited ability of dealing with things and no willing to think, innovate and search by themselves. Thus, these students are lack of independent innovation capacity.

2 INTEGRATED AND INNOVATIVE TEACHING METHODS

Some courses contain abstract concepts and theories such as formula derivation and logical analysis. In consideration of the variety of their content and shapes, the author adopted different teaching methods accordingly. In this case, it will improve classroom teaching and achieve the established teaching purposes by combining the integrative application of the following innovative teaching methods into the traditional ones. These kind of innovative teaching methods include analogy teaching, case teaching, segmenting teaching, animation presentation, and promoting learning through teaching.

2.1 *Animation presentation*

As to some abstract teaching contents, it could make these theories lively and show students a relatively dynamic presentation instead of dull verbal description by making maximum transformation of these contents into flash or three-dimensional models. In this way, students could easily solve the problems which were visualized.

2.2 Segmenting teaching

Some contents are, indeed, difficult to understand. In this case, teachers could break up these complicated materials into small parts. Just as ants, when gnawing a bone, they nibble on it instead of swallowing the whole one, and a large complex question could be discomposed into some smaller ones arranged in a stepwise method according to difficulty degree. Presenting them gradually to students, teachers should direct students solve these problems step by step. After all smaller ones are solved, the whole problem would be settled smoothly.

2.3 Analogy teaching

Obscure concept and complicated system are common in course teaching. Thus it is a vital problem which teachers need to consider that how to assist students in understanding the theory behind these concept better. Analogy teaching method proves a considerable and feasible way which connects students' unacquainted and complex questions with things they are familiar with in their daily life. Therefore, it helps students conduct some analysis. In that they tend to easily understand rules of things around us, they might well gain a grasp of questions of computer hardware via analogy.

2.4 Case teaching

When a series of complex knowledge problems are only described through words and pictures, the effect may not be so ideal. Therefore, to enhance the teaching performance, some common comprehensive cases may be introduced to assist teaching process. Containing some basic knowledge corresponding to certain theoretical knowledge, these cases may be better presented through analogy method. With a deep understanding of the case, students would tend to have a solid grasp of the corresponding theoretical knowledge.

2.5 Promoting learning through teaching

As is said teaching is the highest level of learning, one's achieving to the level of teaching indicates his solid and thorough grasp of these knowledge. In teaching activities, teachers could divide the whole class into several groups, assign different knowledge points for these learning groups separately and later invite each group to explain the rules and features of their part to the whole class. In this way, the method inspires students' conceptual work. Acting as teachers might not only stimulate their learning interest but highly enhance their self-confidence and expression capacity.

Besides, students get great chances to improve their potential of logical thinking and material collecting.

3 HIERARCHICAL TEACHING MODEL

Students differ from each other in understanding capacity and personal characteristics. We should never try to teach all sorts of students under the same standard. Otherwise, teaching goals could be achieved only for part of students. Therefore, hierarchical teaching method needs to be adopted.

3.1 Grading principle

According to student's individual personalities, they might be divided into three levels. Third-level students are those with poor basis for course learning. Students who have great chances to achieve the teaching goals through hard work belong to the second-level. For the highest-level ones, they tend to understand and digest teaching contents with ease.

3.2 Grading teaching goals

As to third-level students who are in need of a solid grasp of basic knowledge, they are required to master the key contents according to curriculum standard. Second-level students should be expected to gain a deep and thorough mastery of teaching contents. Besides, they should develop the ability to link these parts with the corresponding ones. As to students in the highest level, the appropriate teaching goals should be cultivating the capacity of divergent thinking based on the leading knowledge. Therefore, besides these requirements towards common students, teachers should stretch the width and length of the course to assist them in widening horizon and enriching their knowledge.

3.3 Hierarchical teaching methods

A hierarchical teaching method should be adopted. Teaching objects will never be students with identical feature but students with different personalities and background. Thus teachers should consider how to help students in different levels achieve the teaching goal with ease. As to the explaining of basic knowledge, teachers should adopt the teaching strategy of low starting point, multiple steps and enough feedback and the teaching method of giving intensive elaboration and more chances of exercise, reviews and communications. As to the applied ones, it is a wise choice to adopt the strategy of slow varying, focusing on ability and frequent feedback and the method of a rational and systematic combination of teaching and learning. Moreover, when explaining stretch knowledge, teachers could use the strategy of focusing on inspiration and innovation and the method of improving autonomic learning through appropriate teaching.

3.4 *Implentation process*

In hierarchical teaching process, animation, segmenting and analogy teaching methods should be largely adopted when presenting basic knowledge for third-level students. These comparatively vivid and visualized ways may be favorable for students understanding the basic knowledge with ease. With regard to the relatively complex parts, more adoption of segmenting and analogy teaching methods are expected. Teachers could exert themselves to break up the complicated knowledge into smaller parts for easy understanding. Meanwhile, we could link abstract questions with phenomenon they are familiar with in daily life by introducing some well-known stories and things as teaching case.

As to students in first or second level, teachers may work out a series of subjects in which communication between students and teachers are accessible. Certain situations could be constructed accordingly. In those situations, through communicating, questioning and problem solving, students get great chances to acquire a great sum of knowledge, skills and self-confidence. However, the following points need to be taken into account when organizing such kind of teaching activities. The choice of subjects with appropriate difficulty should obviously be made based on students' specific conditions. Meanwhile, the assignment of students between discussion groups should be rational, for example ensuring that there is a level-one student in each group. Furthermore, teaches should keep controlling class progress and give in-time conclusion and feedback after discussion to guarantee the discussion effect. Besides, if the difficulty of certain teaching contents has achieved the level in which students of first or second level can gain a mastery of these materials after autonomic learning, teachers could assign them into one group and let them present their understanding to the whole class after collecting, sorting and analyzing content and related materials. In this way, teaching plays a significant role in assisting autonomic learning.

4 CONCLUSIONS

The application of integrated teaching methods and hierarchical model is a new attempt in practical teaching. Putting the core idea of teaching reform fully into practice will inevitably enhance the course teaching quality and efficiency to a higher degree and, of course, will be of great significance to the cultivation and improvement of student's comprehensive quality and creative potential.

Computer, Intelligent Computing and Education Technology – Liu, Sung & Yao (Eds)
© 2014 Taylor & Francis Group, London, ISBN 978-1-138-02469-4

Reliable facility location design under set-up cost uncertainty

Wei-Min Ma & Bin Li
School of Economics and Management, Tongji University, Shanghai, China

ABSTRACT: This paper studies a reliable facility design problem that optimizes facility locations and network flows under set-up cost uncertainty. We use scenarios to describe set-up cost uncertainties and then we present an mixed-integer programming model that minimizes maximum gap between the sub-optimal and optimal total costs (including facility set-up cost and transportation cost) under different scenarios ensuring the total costs not to fluctuate dramatically. We use the tabu search algorithm to solve the problem. Numerical experiment results show that this proposed model is capable of providing a near-optimum solution which can obtain better network performance.

Keywords: facility location design; set-up cost; uncertainty; Tabu search algorithm

1 INTRODUCTION

Since the facility location problem was raised, it has drawn increased attention due to its extensive applications in manufacturing and public service. It is well-known that the facilities are often intended to serve the companies or communities for long durations. Once established, facility locations will not be easily relocated as the price is extremely high. Furthermore, facility locations also have great impacts on the operational decisions like distribution, inventory control. Therefore, facility location design should be elaborately considered. However, due to the establishment is often before the network starts being operated, the data used in design process are constantly unknown or inaccurate.

Fortunately, there are several ways to cope with the uncertainty associated with the data used in the decision making process. When the parameters are continuous or the historical data are very easy to get, the probability law are often used to describe the uncertainty while if the parameters are discrete or the historical data are rare, scenarios would be a better way to present the uncertainty.

To the best of the authors' knowledge, for facility location design problem, researchers mainly focus on the demand uncertainty and facility uncertainty. Kiya & Davoudpour (2012) incorporate demand and operational costs into the network re-design problem. In ferry service network design problem, Lo et al. (2013) introduce stochastic demand via the notion of service reliability. On the contrary, Chen et al. (2011), Gade & Pohl (2009), Li & Ouyang (2011), Peng et al. (2011), Snyder & Daskin (2005) all employ the scenario method to present facility uncertainty in the facility location design problem.

In this paper, we consider the set-up cost uncertainty in the facility location problem. As the set-up cost highly depend on the price of the property and the price of the raw materials for constructing facilities, the set-up cost became quite unpredictable. So we adopt the scenario method to describe the set-up cost uncertainty. In order to establish a reliable network under different set-up cost scenarios, we propose a mixed-integer programming model and solve it with the tabu search algorithm. Our aim is to get an insight on how relevant a modeling framework considering set-up cost uncertainty may be in facility location problems.

2 MODEL FORMULATION

2.1 Notations

2.1.1 Parameters
$N = \{1, \ldots, n\}$: Set of candidate facility sites
$M = \{1, \ldots, m\}$: Set of demand nodes
f_i: Fixed set-up cost for establishing a facility at site $i \in N$.
c_{ij}: Cost of satisfying demand node j's demand from facility i.

2.1.2 Decision variables
There are two types of decision variables in this model: location variables $y_i, i \in N$ and the assignment variables $x_{ij}, i \in N, j \in M$.

$$y_i = \begin{cases} 1 & \text{if a facility is established at site i} \\ 0 & \text{otherwise} \end{cases}$$

$$x_{ij} = \begin{cases} 1 & \text{if demand node } j \text{ is served by site } i \\ 0 & \text{otherwise} \end{cases}$$

2.2 Basic model

We firstly employ the classical Uncapacitated Facility Location Problem (UFLP) formulation introduced by Balinski (1964). On the basis of that, a reliable facility location design model considering the uncertainty in the set-up cost is put forward.

$$\min \sum_{i \in N} f_i y_i + \sum_{i \in N} \sum_{j \in M} c_{ij} x_{ij} \qquad (1)$$

$$s.t. \sum_{i \in N} x_{ij} = 1 \qquad j \in M \qquad (2)$$

$$x_{ij} \leq y_i \qquad i \in N, j \in M \qquad (3)$$

$$x_{ij}, y_i \in \{0,1\} \qquad i \in N, j \in M \qquad (4)$$

The objective function (1) is to minimize the total costs including the set-up cost and transportation costs. As the decision variables are binary variables, constraints (2) ensure that the demand of node j is satisfied by one and only one facility. Constraints (3) state that demand of node j cannot be meet through rout i–j by i unless there is a facility establishing at site i. Constraints (4) are the domain restricts.

2.3 Reliable model with set-up cost uncertainty

We denote S as the set of scenario for the uncertain set-up cost and f_i^s as the set-up cost of establishing a facility at site $i \in N$. Under scenario $s \in S$.

For a special scenario $s \in S$, we can formulate the corresponding problem.

$$\min \sum_{i \in N} f_i^s y_i + \sum_{i \in N} \sum_{j \in M} c_{ij} x_{ij} \qquad (5)$$

$$s.t. (2)-(4)$$

We denote z_s^* as the optimal objective value in scenario $s \in S$ and for a feasible solution (X, Y), z_s is the corresponding objective value.

To ensure the total costs not to fluctuate dramatically under different scenarios, we formulate a reliable model aiming to minimize maximum gap between the sub-optimal and optimal total costs under a certain scenario s, $s \in S$. We denote the cost gap as R_s and the complete formulation is presented as follows.

$$\min \max R_s \qquad (6)$$

$$s.t. R_s = z_s - z_s^* \qquad (7)$$

$$x_{ij} \leq y_i \qquad i \in N, j \in M \qquad (8)$$

$$x_{ij}, y_i \in \{0,1\} \qquad i \in N, j \in M \qquad (9)$$

For a given scenario $s \in S$, z_s^* can be easily calculated, then it can be regarded as a constant in the model. On the basis of that, the minimax regret value can also be obtained under a limited set of scenarios.

The UFLP can be decomposed into two independent sub-problems: (i) determining the facilities needed to established, (ii) determining the distribution pattern.

For a specific scenario s, $s \in S$, when a feasible location (i.e. y_is) is given, the optimal assignment x_{ij} and corresponding objective value z_s^* can be easily determined by using the following formula (Al-Sultan & Al-Fawzan 1999):

$$\begin{cases} \min c_{kj} & k = 1, ..., n \\ x_{ij} = \begin{cases} 1 & \text{if } i = k \\ 0 & \text{otherwise} \end{cases} \end{cases}$$

3 THE TABU SEARCH SCHEME

Tabu search is a meta-heuristic algorithm which uses a local search method to explore the global best solution. Since introduced by Glover (1990), it was widely and successfully used in combinatorial problems like the job-shop scheduling problem (Dell'Amico & Trubian 1993), the vehicle routing problem (Gendreau et al. 1994), the timetabling problem (Hertz 1991). The tabu search contains three main parts: neighborhood generation, tabu restrictions, and aspiration criteria. Accordingly, we need to preset some parameters: neighborhood size (nbhsize), probability threshold (γ) used in the process of generating neighbors, Tabu List size (TL), maximum number of iteration (ITERMAX).

In this paper, we use the Net Benefit Heuristic (NBH) algorithm which was proposed by Al-Sultan & Al-Fawzan (1999) to generate a relatively good starting solution. The procedures of tabu search algorithm for Uncapacitated Facility Location Problem (UFLP) are as follows:

Step 0: Use the NBH algorithm to get an initial y. Let $y_{current} = y$, $y_{min} = y$, $y_{best} = y$. Calculate the total costs of y, $z_s(y)$. Let $TL = \varnothing$, $BV = z_s(y)$.

Step 1: Generate nbhsize random solutions (y) from $y_{current}$. Evaluated $z_s(y)$. Choose the best solution as y_{min}.

Step 2: Check the tabu status. If ($y_{min} \notin TL$) or ($y_{min} \in TL$ and $y_{min} < BV$), then go to step 3; otherwise, let the following best solution be y_{min} and repeat the step.

Step 3: Update the solution. Let $y_{current} = y_{min}$. Store y_{min} in TL.

Step 4: Repeat the first to third steps for a given number ($ITERMAX$) of cycles.

step 5: Report the best solution y_{best} and corresponding total costs BV.

4 NUMERICAL RESULTS

4.1 Experiment setup

We tested our model with a set of standard test problems taken from the OR Library.

In this paper, we generated 9 scenarios with different set-up cost. In each scenario $s \in S$ and for each $n \in N$, we let f_i^s take a random value from a uniform distribution over [20000, 45000].

For tabu search algorithm, values of some parameters were determined after trial-and-error. The number of neighborhoods $nbhsize$ and the size

of tabu list were set to 50 and 15, respectively. The maximum iterations and the probability threshold were set to 200 and 0.9, respectively.

4.2 Experiment results

We solved the uncapacitated facility location problem under each scenario and got the set-up cost and optimal objective z_s^*. We compared these solutions with the solution obtained when the set-up cost are set to the average set-up cost which we denote it as the standard scenario. On the basis of that, we addressed the minmax regret model, and got the minmax value and corresponding facility locations. We present the results in Table 1.

In Table 1, in each instance (Cap71, Cap101), the "Set-up cost" columns present the value of the total set-up cost and "Total costs" columns present the total costs in the optimal solution under the corresponding scenarios. "Facility locations" columns list the optimal facility sites. Note that min-

Table 1. Results of the minmax regret model with uncertainty of set-up cost.

	Cap71 n = 16 m = 50 (minmax regret = 8481)			Cap101 n = 25 m = 50 (minmax regret = 15762)		
	Set-up cost	Total costs	Facility locations	Set-up cost	Total costs	Facility locations
Sce std	92882	1081702	3,11,13	131621	985561	11,13,18,24
Sce 1	124295	1113105	3,11,13	109742	988272	11,12,13,17,24
Sce 2	6953	1056505	3,11,12,13	152574	990304	11,12,13,18,23
Sce 3	91590	1051600	3,11,12,13	104196	999716	11,13,18
Sce 4	120405	1080405	3,11,12,13	128977	982917	11,13,18,24
Sce 5	95415	1084305	3,11,13	125940	985530	11,13,17,24
Sce 6	114845	1079805	3,7,11,13	122355	976305	11,13,18,24
Sce 7	116215	1076205	3,11,12,13	138351	967811	11,12,13,18,24
Sce 8	110700	1075600	3,7,11,13	117115	971065	11,13,18,24
Sce 9	106265	1095105	3,11,13	127408	981348	11,13,18,24
Minmax regret	–	–	3,11,13	–	–	11,12,13,18,24

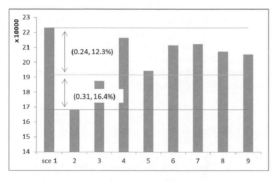
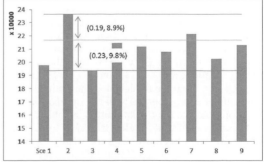

Figure 1. Fluctuation ranges of optimal total costs under different scenarios in two instances.

Table 2. The set-up cost and total costs under different scenarios.

	Cap71 n = 16 m = 50		Cap101 n = 25 m = 50	
	Set-up cost	Total costs	Set-up cost	Total costs
Sce std	92882	191764	131621	227015
Sce 1	104295	193180	191855	244800
Sce 2	82450	181330	164953	245900
Sce 3	100940	179820	120387	243330
Sce 4	76240	195120	157933	240880
Sce 5	95415	194300	197245	240190
Sce 6	100440	189320	112601	245550
Sce 7	90015	188900	138351	221300
Sce 8	119875	188760	195440	228390
Sce 9	96265	195150	155494	238440

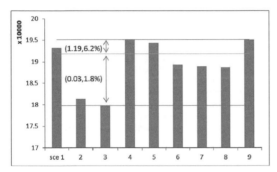 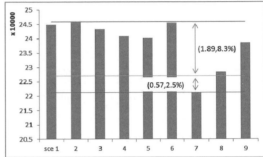

Figure 2. Fluctuation ranges of total costs under different scenarios in two instances.

max regret solutions are obtained by comparing them to all these optimal solutions under each scenario, therefore, the set-up cost and total costs vary from the scenarios, hence, the value of the set-up cost and total costs are left empty. However, we got the minmax regret values and the best facility locations of each instance.

From Figure 1, we can see that the total costs fluctuate dramatically with the scenario changes. More precisely, for the instance Cap71, the maximum fluctuation is 12.3% and 16.4% on the basis of standard scenario while the maximum fluctuation is 8.9% and 9.8% for instance Cap101.

After we solved the reliable model, we could obtain the optimal solutions. For each instance, the optimal facility locations are 3, 11, 13 and 11, 12, 13, 18, 24, respectively. Then we recalculated the optimal total costs under each scenario with the optimal facility locations and got the results showed in Table 2.

It can be seen that the fluctuation of total costs under different scenarios is very steady. Specifically, for Cap71, the maximum fluctuation is only 6.2% and 1.8% while the maximum fluctuation is 8.3% and 2.5% for instance Cap101.

5 CONCLUSION

In this paper, on the basis of classical uncapacitated facility location problem, we proposed a reliable model which aimed to minimize the maximum gap between the sub-optimal and optimal total costs under a certain scenario. We use the tabu search algorithm to address the problem. Through the results, it can be seen that the cost fluctuation is much steadier than that of optimal cost under each scenario. Therefore, the proposed model is much more reliable under uncertainty environment with respect to the set-up cost. In the future research, one possible extension is to consider introducing transportation costs uncertainty and demand uncertainty into the model.

REFERENCES

Al-Sultan, K.S., & Al-Fawzan, M.A. 1999. A tabu search approach to the uncapacitated facility location problem. Annals of Operations Research, 86, 91–103.

Balinski, M.L. 1964. On finding integer solutions to linear programs. MATHEMATICA PRINCETON NJ.

Chen, Q., Li, X., & Ouyang, Y. 2011. Joint inventory-location problem under the risk of probabilistic facility disruptions. Transportation Research Part B: Methodological, 45(7), 991–1003.

Dell'Amico, M., & Trubian, M. 1993. Applying tabu search to the job-shop scheduling problem. Annals of Operations Research, 41(3), 231–252.

Glover, F. 1990. Tabu search: A tutorial. Interfaces, 20(4), 74–94.

Gendreau, M., Hertz, A., & Laporte, G. 1994. A tabu search heuristic for the vehicle routing problem. Management science, 40(10), 1276–1290.

Gade, D., & Pohl, E.A. 2009. Sample average approximation applied to the capacitated-facilities location problem with unreliable facilities. Proceedings of the Institution of Mechanical Engineers, Part O: Journal of Risk and Reliability, 223(4), 259–269.

Hertz, A. 1991. Tabu search for large scale timetabling problems. European journal of operational research, 54(1), 39–47.

Kiya, F., & Davoudpour, H. 2012. Stochastic programming approach to re-designing a warehouse network under uncertainty. Transportation Research Part E: Logistics and Transportation Review, 48(5), 919–936.

Lo, H.K., An, K., & Lin, W.H. 2013. Ferry service network design under demand uncertainty. Transportation Research Part E: Logistics and Transportation Review, 59, 48–70.

Peng, P., Snyder, L.V., Lim, A., & Liu, Z. 2011. Reliable logistics networks design with facility disruptions. Transportation Research Part B: Methodological, 45(8), 1190–1211.

Snyder, L.V., & Daskin, M.S. 2005. Reliability models for facility location: the expected failure cost case. Transportation Science, 39(3), 400–416.

Computer, Intelligent Computing and Education Technology – Liu, Sung & Yao (Eds)
© 2014 Taylor & Francis Group, London, ISBN 978-1-138-02469-4

Control design of a STATCOM-BESS for stabilization of wind farms

L.L. Sun, X.H. Zhang & Y.C. Dong
School of Electrical and Electronic Engineering, North China Electric Power University (NCEPU), Baoding, China

C.T. Zhao
New Institute, Gouda, The Netherlands

ABSTRACT: Integration of STATCOM with energy storage devices plays an imperative role in improving the power system operation and control. This paper is aimed at showing that the combination of STATCOM and Battery Energy Storage System (BESS) significantly improves the performance of the power system. In this proposed scheme, STATCOM-BESS is connected at a Point of Common Coupling (PCC) to reduce the power quality issues. The operating principle of STATCOM-BESS is described, and a mathematical model is derived. The proposed controller has bidirectional active and reactive power flow capability by which it controls the system voltage and frequency with variation of consumer loads and system fault. The power quality enhancement by STATCOM controller is simulated using MATLAB/Simulink, the final results show that the STATCOM-BESS reactive voltage/frequency control can achieve good dynamic and steady-state characteristics, and have theoretical value and practical significance.

Keywords: wind farm; STATCOM-BESS; coordinate control; MATLAB

1 INTRODUCTION

Due to its clean and economical characteristics, electrical power generation from wind energy is getting vast deliberation throughout the world. According to EWEA reporting, 12% of the world's electricity is expected to be generated from wind power by 2020. Therefore, a huge number of wind farms are going to be connected with the existing power system. However, around 40% wind farms are consisting of fixed speed induction generators due to their low installation and maintenance costs. But as an induction generator has a stability problem, it is needed to analyze the transient stability of fixed speed wind generators connected with multi machine power system.

Voltage or current source inverter based Flexible AC Transmission Systems (FACTS) devices have been used for flexible power flow control, secure loading and damping of power system oscillation. The principal benefit of the STATCOM for transient stability enhancement is direct through rapid bus voltage control. In particular, the STATCOM may be used to enhance power transfer during low-voltage conditions, which typically predominate during faults, decreasing the acceleration of local generators. Some authors have reported valuable studies on STATCOM connected with wind turbine generator system. As the traditional

STATCOM only works for compensating reactive power, its application is limited to reactive power support in power system. As wind is an intermittent and stochastic in nature, resulting wind generator output power fluctuation cannot be smoothed by using STATCOM. In Many research papers, it has been shown that an Energy Storage System (ESS) plays an important role in power system control. In practice, by integrating an ESS with STATCOM (STATCOM + ESS) significant improvements over traditional STATCOM performance are achievable. Some of the advantages of battery technologies are of higher energy storage densities, greater cycling capabilities, better reliability, and lower cost. This combined system is capable of mitigating majority of the stability and voltage fluctuation problems in the power system. The dc link capacitor value can be reduced enormously in STATCOM-BESS topology compared to only STATCOM unit. Only a small capacitor is sufficient enough to smooth the battery dc current. This is a notable feature of integrating Energy Storage System (ESS) with STATCOM.

In this paper, STATCOM-BESS is deployed at wind farm terminal to enhance the transient stability of wind farm as well as entire power system. The detailed control strategy of sinusoidal PWM voltage source converter based STATCOM-BESS is presented. For test cases, a power transmission system with a wind farm connected to an infinite bus is considered. For simplification purpose the classical model of a generator is assumed with an infinite bus as a constant voltage source. The model is implemented in MATLAB/Simulink and the simulation results under fault (3-phase to ground fault) clearing times are analyzed for transient stability. The results are then compared without STATCOM-BESS placed in the system. The analysis is then extended by adding an energy storage device (battery) to the STATCOM. The final results show that the addition of BESS allows the STATCOM to inject and/or absorb active and reactive power simultaneously from/to the grid and, therefore, provides additional benefits and improvements in the system.

2 WIND TURBINE MODELING

Wind turbine power system includes fans, wheels, gear box and couplings. The mathematical relation for the mechanical power extraction from the wind can be expressed as follows:

$$T_{ac} = \frac{1}{2}\rho\pi\frac{C_P}{\lambda}R^3V_W^2\frac{\Omega_N}{P_N}\times 10^{-3} \qquad (1)$$

$$\frac{dT_{lss}}{dt} = \frac{1}{J'_n}\left(T_{ae} - T_{lss}\right) \qquad (2)$$

$$\frac{d\omega}{dt} = \frac{1}{J_t}\left(T_{lss} - T_m\right) \qquad (3)$$

where, T_{ac} is the torque generated by the fan blades, ρ is the air density [kg/m³], R is blade radius [m], V_W is the wind speed [m/s], ω is the mechanical angular velocity, Ω_N is the angular velocity of the blades rated mechanical, P_N is rated power output of the wind turbine, T_{lss} is the output torque of the hub, the output torque of the gearbox is T_m, the inertia time constant of the gearbox is J_t. C_p, the power coefficient, which is a function of both tip speed ratio, λ, and blade pitch angle, β deg. C_p, the power factor of the wind turbine, which reflects the ability of wind turbine blades capture wind energy, is nonlinear function of the tip speed ratio λ and the pitch angle β, the fitting function can be written:

$$C_P(\lambda,\beta)=C_1\left(\frac{C_2}{\lambda_i}-C_3\beta-C_4\beta^{C_5}-C_6\right)e^{\frac{C_7}{\lambda_i}} \qquad (4)$$

$$\lambda_i = \frac{1}{\dfrac{1}{\lambda+C_8\beta}-\dfrac{C_9}{\beta^3+1}} \qquad (5)$$

In the above equations, $C_1\sim C_9$ are corresponding coefficients in this nonlinear fitting function.

3 TOPOLOGY AND CONTROL SCHEME

3.1 STATCOM-BESS topology

Two-level VSC based STATCOM is shown inside the dote line which has only an ability to control the reactive power output. Therefore, in this paper BESS is incorporated with STATCOM, resulting in abilities of both real and reactive power control. In traditional STATCOM the DC-link capacitor is extremely large, whereas in the STATCOM-BESS only few hundred μF ranged capacitor can be used to smooth the DC current. The schematic diagram of STATCOM-BESS topology is shown in Figure 1.

The equivalent circuit of STATCOM-BESS, as shown in Figure 2, is presented. In the short period of the system transient, there should be no significant variation to the potential of the battery. It can be assumed the STATCOM is working in a balanced condition, then, we can define a reference frame transformation and make the attained dynamic model of the STATCOM-BESS simple.

According to the equivalent circuit:

$$\begin{bmatrix} e_a \\ e_b \\ e_c \end{bmatrix} - \begin{bmatrix} v_a \\ v_b \\ v_c \end{bmatrix} = R\begin{bmatrix} i_a \\ i_b \\ i_c \end{bmatrix} + L\frac{d}{dt}\begin{bmatrix} i_a \\ i_b \\ i_c \end{bmatrix} \qquad (6)$$

where, the m is the duty cycle ratio of the sinusoidal reference wave, and $k = m/2$, δ is the firing

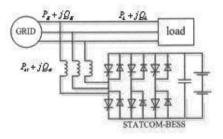

Figure 1. Schematic diagram of STATCOM-BESS topology.

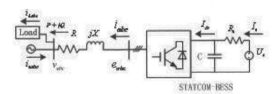

Figure 2. Equivalent circuit of STATCOM-BESS.

angle of the sinusoidal reference wave referring to the system voltage vector. The amplitude of e_{abc} is E, and amplitude of v_{abc} is V. The reference frame coordinate is defined where the d-axis is always coincident with the instantaneous system voltage vector and the q-axis is in quadrature with it. The equation of the AC side circuit in Figure 2 can be written as:

$$\begin{bmatrix} e_d \\ e_q \end{bmatrix} - \begin{bmatrix} v_d \\ v_q \end{bmatrix} = \begin{bmatrix} R & -\omega L \\ \omega L & R \end{bmatrix} \begin{bmatrix} i_d \\ i_q \end{bmatrix} + L\frac{d}{dt}\begin{bmatrix} i_d \\ i_q \end{bmatrix} \tag{7}$$

The DC side circuit equation can be written as:

$$U_{dc} = U_s - R_s I_s \qquad C\frac{dU_{dc}}{dt} + I_{dc} = I_s \tag{8}$$

And, the power on the dc side of the inverter can be expressed by:

$$P_{dc} = U_{dc} I_{dc} \tag{9}$$

The instantaneous active power on the ac side of the inverter is calculated by:

$$P = \frac{3}{2}\left(v_d i_d + v_q i_q\right) = \frac{3}{2}V i_d \tag{10}$$

$$Q = \frac{3}{2}\left(v_q i_d - v_d i_q\right) = -\frac{3}{2}V i_q \tag{11}$$

Considering that the instantaneous active power exchanged between the ac and dc side of the inverter should be the same, equation must hold:

$$U_{dc} I_{dc} = \frac{3}{2}\left(e_d i_d + e_q i_q\right) \tag{12}$$

So, the entire model can be concluded:

$$\begin{bmatrix} \dfrac{V}{L} \\ -\dfrac{V}{L} \\ 0 \\ \dfrac{U_s}{R_s C} \end{bmatrix} = \begin{bmatrix} \dfrac{R}{L} & -\omega & -\dfrac{k\cos\delta}{L} \\ \omega & \dfrac{R}{L} & -\dfrac{k\sin\delta}{L} \\ \dfrac{3k\cos\delta}{2C} & \dfrac{3k\sin\delta}{2C} & \dfrac{1}{R_s C} \end{bmatrix} \begin{bmatrix} i_d \\ i_q \\ U_{dc} \end{bmatrix} + \dfrac{d}{dt}\begin{bmatrix} i_d \\ i_q \\ U_{dc} \end{bmatrix} \tag{13}$$

3.2 Control scheme

The well-known vector control scheme is used as a control strategy of the STATCOM-BESS topology. For the realization of independent regulation of reactive power and active power, the current

decoupling control method based on rotating frame shown in Figure 3 is adopted.

It demonstrates the control strategy of the proposed controller which is based on the generation of reference source currents. Reference source currents have two components, reactive component for controlling the magnitude of the generated voltage and the active component for regulating the frequency of the generated voltage. The STATCOM-BESS would supply/absorb the necessary/surplus real power according to the real power reference. The VSC of STATCOM-BESS converts the dc voltage across the storage device into a set of three-phase ac output voltages. The angle of the transformation is detected from the three phase voltages at each connection point of STATCOM-BESS by using Phase Locked Loop (PLL) system. Suitable adjustment of phase and magnitude of the VSC output voltage allows effective control of power exchange between the STATCOM-BESS and the AC system.

Active component of reference source current is estimated by dividing the difference of filtered instantaneous load power and output of the PI

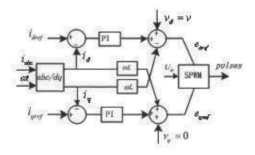

Figure 3. Control block diagram of STATCOM-BESS topology.

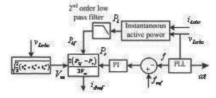

Figure 4. Control block diagram of active component of referenve source current.

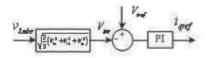

Figure 5. Control block diagram of reactive component of referenve source current.

frequency controller to the terminal voltage. The load power is estimated as by taking three phases to two phase transmitter. Then the error between real power and the line power reference is chosen as the reference of real power output, as shown in Figure 4. The reference is the amplitude of reference ac terminal voltage, the output of the PI controller is aimed for maintaining constant ac terminal voltage at a constant level. The instantaneous quadrature components of reference source currents as shown in Figure 5, is estimated.

4 SIMULATION AND RESULTS

4.1 Model system for simulation

Figure 6 shows the model system used for the simulation analyses of this study. The objective of this paper is to increase the transient stability of fixed speed wind generators. In this paper, the STATCOM-BESS is used also to regulate the wind farm terminal voltage at constant level. It is connected to the 25 kV line through a transformer with 0.2p.u leakage reactance (base value 100 MVA).

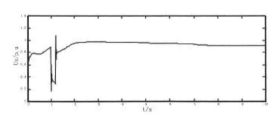

Figure 6.   Model system.

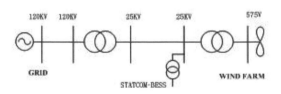

Figure 7. Terminal voltage of wind farm without STATCOM-BESS.

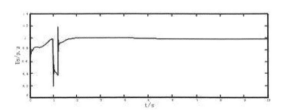

Figure 8. Terminal voltage of the wind farm with STATCOM-BESS.

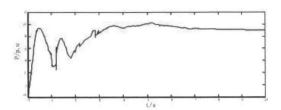

Figure 9.   Real power of wind farm without STATCOM-BESS.

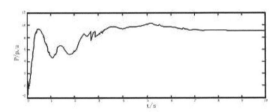

Figure 10.   Real power of wind farm with STATCOM-BESS.

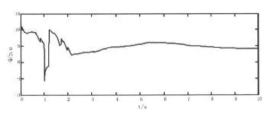

Figure 11. Reactive power of wind farm without STATCOM-BESS.

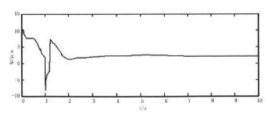

Figure 12. Reactive power of wind farm with STATCOM-BESS.

4.2 Simulation results

Our control strategy is to sense the terminal voltage variations of wind farm and then to provide necessary reactive power from the STATCOM-BESS. Moreover, it also absorbs the necessary transient energy developed during the network disturbance. As a result, the STATCOM-BESS also enhances the transient stability of entire power system. The performance of the proposed controller is demonstrated under different dynamic condition. The symmetrical three lines to ground fault, 3 LG, the circuit breaker on the faulted lines are opened at 1 sec, and at 1.2 sec the circuit breakers are reclosed. Simulations have been done by using MATLAB/Simulink. It can be observed that in all such conditions the controller response in a desirable manner. Simulated transient wave forms of the generator voltage, load currents, real and reactive power, are given in different dynamic conditions.

5 CONCLUSION

This paper proposes the STATCOM-BESS topology to enhance the transient stability of grid power system including wind farms. Suitable control strategy of STATCOM-BESS is presented. The effectiveness of the proposed control system is verified by the simulation analyses for different types of fault conditions in the power system model. The final results show that the STATCOM-BESS reactive voltage/frequency control can achieve good dynamic and steady-state characteristics. Moreover, it also enhances the transient stability of the entire power system. Therefore, it is concluded that the proposed STATCOM-BESS can be applied effectively to enhance the transient stability of the grid power system including wind farms.

ACKNOWLEDGEMENTS

It is a project supported in part by the National Natural Science Foundation of China under Grant 51277077 and the Fundamental Research Funds for the Central Universities of China under Grant 11QG55. Paper no. TEC-00337-2012.

REFERENCES

Arulampalam A, Ekanayake J B, Jenkins N. 2003. Application study of a STATCOM with energy storage. *IEE Proceedings-Generation, Transmission and Distribution,* 150(3): 373–384.

Council, G.W E. 2005. WIND FORCE 12-A blueprint to achieve 12% of the world's electricity from Wind power by 2020. Available at *http://www.gwec.net/fileadmin/documents/Publications/wf12–2005.pdf.* Accessed September.

Chen Z, Blaabjerg F, Hu Y. 2005. Voltage recovery of dynamic slip control wind turbines with a STATCOM.

Gyugyi L. 1992. Unified power-flow control concept for flexible AC transmission systems//*IEE Proceedings C (Generation, Transmission and Distribution). IET Digital Library,* 139(4): 323–331.

Laszlo Gyugyi.1994. "Dynamic Compensation of AC Transmission Lines By Solid-State Synchronous Voltage Sources," *IEEE Trans. On Power Delivery,* Vol 9, No. 2, pp. 904–911.

Saad-Saoud Z, 1998. Application of STATCOMs to wind farms. *IEE Proceedings-Generation, Transmission and Distribution,* 145(5): 511–516.

Shen C, Yang Z, Crow M L, et al. 2000. Control of STATCOM with energy storage device//*Power Engineering Society Winter Meeting, 2000. IEEE.IEEE,* 4: 2722–2728.

Shen H, Liang J, DAI H Z.2002. Calculation of wind farm penetration based on power system transient stability analysis. *Power System Technology,* 8: 002.

Souza C L.2001. Power system transient stability analysis including synchronous and induction generators//*Power Tech Proceeding.*

Sun T, Chen Z. 2004. Blaabjerg F. Flicker mitigation of grid connected wind turbines using STATCOM.

Wang H F. 1999. Facts control design based on power system nonparametric models[C]//Generation, Transmission and Distribution, *IEE Proceedings.* IET, 146(5): 409–415.

Yang Z. 2001. Integration of a STATCOM and battery energy storage. *Power Systems, IEEE Transactions* on, 16(2): 254–260.

Computer, Intelligent Computing and Education Technology – Liu, Sung & Yao (Eds)
© *2014 Taylor & Francis Group, London, ISBN 978-1-138-02469-4*

Relation to be well dealt with in promoting the training quality of university table tennis

H.B. Wang & Z.H. Zhen
Department of Sports, Heilongjiang University of Science and Technology, Harbin, China

ABSTRACT: The training of university table tennis has both its specifications and common characters with other levels of training between which the relationship should be well dealt in order to improve training quality. It mainly displays in three aspects: the coaches quality and competency, the relation between the characteristics of table tennis and university table tennis training, and problems with different levels and play styles of team members.

Keywords: university; table tennis; training; quality; problem

1 THE PARTICULARITY OF UNIVERSITY TABLE TENNIS TRAINING

One issue is the selection of team members. The player who is table tennis-based and relatively outstanding is chosen from full-time university students. However, not only the students from all over the country vary in play styles and skills, but also the coaches know little about players. Another issue is short training cycle and time. Despite 4 years attended, students are well-trained cut to 2 years. College athletes should be learning-based supplemented by training, which has also carried some problems.

2 THE COACHE QUALITY AND ABILITY

In the whole training, coach is the leader, the key to improve training quality and determinant of scientific training style. The sports skills of a nation depend on its quantity and quality of coaches. Similarly, the sports level of a university is much connected with the quality and ability of the coaches. Therefore, coach is the essential of lifting sports standards as well as the hard core in training.

By far, the table tennis has developed to a higher content of technology and more drastic competition where only practicing hard is unavailable. The coaches of any good or making outstanding achievements athletes are surely active in thinking. Scientific research is emphasized both collectively and intensively, after that understand how and why by following the law of development. Chinese table tennis team has experts who have been engaged in research, the new outcomes of which are always displayed in every sports event, for example, in all the previous table tennis tournaments, Chinese team pulled off a surprise victory by showing some new faces, technologies and characteristics. The more coaches rely on scientific research, the more creativity they have in making some higher, special training oriented and reflecting training regularity activities as training opportunity. Provided that the coach's job is a combination of science and artistry, they find it hard to achieve accurate quantization in training. The coaches control the whole training process rather than detailed by comprehension and experience. At the same time, coaches ought to be fully responsible for not only players and teams but also their thought and study by words and deeds, and "Enlighten them with reason, and emotionally moving".

The job of coach has a dual character, one is integrating merits of all on the basis of forefathers; another is pursuing changes during which training process can be obtained and unknown territory is explored by current knowledge. A good coach should have the following qualities and 5 abilities.

2.1 *A strong sense of ambition and dedication, a key point to coach development*

A strong sense of ambition and dedication is proportional to improvement of players performance. Still, no one undisciplined coach can mould an outstanding player. Hence, coaches of such sense should be developed according to their high standards of demand. There is not a training is able to make any sports event a benchmark effortlessly, and what a coach should go all out to do is thinking about effective training all the time and everywhere, without which, raising the grade of players is hard to achieve. A proficient coach as administrators who has innovation, ideal and pursues could train a good team.

2.2 Five basic and essential abilities a coach

2.2.1 Management

It means the capability of mastering and straightening out the whole team. Seven by teaching and three by exercising is the past training method which can not apply to nowadays as a percentage. While it has demonstrated the importance of management which refers the fact that there is no way to conduct a team without managing it.

2.2.2 Perceptivity

It is obtained by careful analyzing as an accurate perception—understanding. Superior consciousness, a necessary quality for coaches, is developed logic training and foresight building. For the purpose of enhancing a sports event and player's athletics, the coaches is supposed to have a deep understanding.

2.2.3 Planning

It stands for implementing complex thinking and management to a practical and systematical overall arrangement, that is, what to train, how to train and how much the volume is. We have plans ranging from year, phase, month, week, day, event and individual. The more levels and detailed the plan is, the more important, especially for individual and event.

2.2.4 Organizing

It refers to the ability to fully make players mobilized and engaged in a reasonable arrangement. Bailey once said "a good coach is who can mobilize the players".

2.2.5 Teaching

It is language competency, wrong action correcting and regularly arranging assistance training ability.

3 CHARACTERISTICS AND TRAINING PROBLEMS IN TABLE TENNIS

Since modern table tennis has meet advanced level, making a breakthrough on the current is not an easy task as people are exploring various paths to enhancing the level of training. The training and practice of China advantage events has proven that understanding and controlling a variety of sports should be put in the first place thereby establishing guiding ideology clearly and arranging specific and innovative training to raise competitiveness by effective method.

As is known to all that as scientific innovation and research has been widely used in sports, peo-

ple is more aware of the nature of table tennis profoundly, for example, reaching the high level of table tennis in 60s century, China won men's team gold medal of the 26th Table Tennis World Championship as well as 27th and 28th in a row. A crucial winning factor is realizing its feature of being quick, accurate, relentless and variable according to which the direction of training is set up. In 1970s, the technique of close table fast attack has developed and mainly reflected in forehand and backhand high toss service and forehand quick loop-drive. In 1980s, it became more changeful on its 4 features through summarizing the experience, since then China found its place and acquired 42 gold medals in 9 tournaments from 31st to 39th world championship. Moreover, quick attack has developed as a general trend, speed and rotation interpenetrating with each other to make it well combined; gaining the initiative to strike would bring specialty in first 3 strikes. In general, world table tennis is moving in the direction towards the "pro-active, special skill, comprehensive technology, various tactics". Understanding and controlling the features of table tennis has played an important role in planning training program and adopting the effective means and method, otherwise it would be impossible to change and innovate on primary base. Above all, it adds significance to scientific training.

4 PROBLEMS RESULTING FROM DIFERRENT PLAY STYLE OF PLAYERS

4.1 Combining the training of basic skills with specialty

Basic skill is the foundation of table tennis as well as an essential guarantee, but it should be rich, substantial and diversified which includes the combination of speed with skill, active attack and consecutive attack, the cooperation and convergence of different assistive techniques, attack and defense transition, active stalemate and defense and strengthening comprehensiveness and rivalry as its highlight. Therefore, playing table tennis and practicing basic skills are in sync. Whether basic skill is good or bad directly affects the formation and development of techniques. Table tennis is a technical sports event, and its characteristics dominate in the success of competition. So it is necessary to "turn to specialty and take techniques as core" in the training.

4.2 The measures undertaken on tactics for different players

4.2.1 Attack

Its idea is "proactive, fast, initiative and strike first". Move sideways and consecutive forehand attack at two thirds of the table; block sideways; block forehands and catch up with forehand; two-sided switching velocity training; down the-middle thrust; down the-forehand thrust.

4.2.2 *Loop drive*

It refers to "take the active and dominant status at first three strokes, drive low balls and smash high balls". Put short-based combined with sudden attack; backhand push and press sideways; grasp its dynamics and change line; return shot with a chop actively. Loop play skills has developed a unique system until now: positioning closer to the table, hitting the shot lower; earlier hitting time and point, more bat titled forward, requiring high-power explosive and small movements for forearm and wrist. Through these improvements, the loop is driven faster, rotating stronger, rebounding fierce and easy to drive and smash.

4.2.3 *Chop*

It means "low and stable chop, different rotating more obviously and two-pronged attack". Block combined with playing sideways; active in long and short play; alternate raising or lowering the ball; chop combined with sudden attack.

Primarily, pay close attention to specialty; utilizing decisive specialty to become one's own specialty in particular play style such as Kong Linghui, 24th Olympic Game championship, whose style is stable, variable and fast.

Secondly, attach importance to basic skills. Based on steady basic skills, highlight and well apply the technical feature so that the rival can not find the demerit. Both should be combined to reach the effect in competition.

The training of specialty and basic skill is combining with practical competition. As for different play styles, various styles has specific training and practical competition. Combining physical training with mental training and making one think with, the feature of the skill is further improved.

REFERENCES

[1] ≪Table Tennis≫ audited by National PE Academy schoolbook commission [M] people PE Press. 3, 1996.

[2] Weiyungui A general analysis on the relationship between exercise and match of table tennis [J] SiChuan PE Science and Technology 6, 2003.

[3] Chengxu Several relationships to be dealt with on the development of Table Tennis teaching and training quality [J] WuHan PE Academy newspaper 1, 2003.

[4] Chengxu Discuss on the development of Table Tennis teaching and training quality [J] Shanghai PE Academy newspaper 5, 2000.

[5] Zhangyingqiu The quantity study on the Table Tennis players training quality [J] Tianjing PE Academy newspaper 3, 2006.

[6] Zhouguizhen The study on the Aided-teaching and Multi-balls teaching of Table Tennis classes [J] Liaoning PE Science and Technology 5, 2004.

Computer, Intelligent Computing and Education Technology – Liu, Sung & Yao (Eds)
© *2014 Taylor & Francis Group, London, ISBN 978-1-138-02469-4*

Research of hot-spot temperature of oil-immersed transformer under different load

G.L. Yue
Hebei Provincial Key Laboratory of Power Transmission Equipment Security Defense,
North China Electric Power University, Baoding, Hebei Province, China
State Grid Electric Power Company of Hebei Province, Department of Operation and Maintenance Overhaul,
Shijiazhuang, Hebei Province, China

Y.Q. Wang & H.H. Cui
Hebei Provincial Key Laboratory of Power Transmission Equipment Security Defense,
North China Electric Power University, Baoding, Hebei Province, China

H.L. Liu
Electric Power Research Institute, Hebei Electric Power Company, Shijiazhuang, Hebei Province, China

ABSTRACT: In power system, power transformer is an important part of the electrical equipment. It is great important to the economy of electricity transmission, flexible allocation, safe use. The value and location of hot-spot temperature is a key factor when oil-immersed transformer is running. In this paper, the temperature field distribution of oil-immersed transformer was established by ANSYS simulation software under the different load, at the same time IEC354 guidelines and its improved form were used to calculate the hot-spot winding temperature, through the comparison between the calculation results and simulation results, the accuracy of the simulation results are obtained.

Keywords: oil-immersed transformer; winding; ANSYS; temperature field; hot-spot temperature

1 INTRODUCTION

The hot-spot temperature of the power transformer mechanism is extremely complex and uncertain. And it is closely related with the geometry of the transformer (such as winding, iron core, oil flow channel and the cooling system structure) and the material physical properties (such as density, thermal conductivity and viscosity).[1] To forecast and measure the winding hot-spot is still researchful hot and difficult issue. There are some traditional methods of winding hot-spot temperature calculation, such as: use of the guide formula, analogy method, and various modified forms, etc, but the results vary.

Based on the strong oil circulation three-phase transformer as an example, using the finite element software ANSYS simulation, by changing the heat generation rate the distribution of temperature field transformer is obtained internal under different load, and find out the most focus in the winding temperature, combining with the guide of standard and improving the formula calculation results, the accuracy of the simulation results are accurate.

2 THE CALCULATION OF OIL-IMMERSED TRANSFORMER WINDING HOT SPOT TEMPERATURE

2.1 *The improvement of loading guide*

The guide for loading mineral-oil-immersed power transformer found on temperature of different components in the operation of the transformer and thermal aging, and according to the different types of transformer and the thermal characteristics, some mathematical model have been proposed, using to calculate the operating temperature of the transformer internal under different cooling medium temperature, and all kinds of transient load or periodic changes according to time load, especially the most hot-spot temperature calculation of winding.

Calculating the winding hot-spot temperature rise is based on GB/T 15164-1994 the guide for loading mineral-oil-immersed power transformer (IEC354 standard, hereinafter referred to as the Loading guide),[6] specified the oil-immersed transformer winding hot-spot temperature calculation equation. Usually in steady state conditions, for the transformer of natural oil circulation (ON) the cooling, under any load the finally hot-spot temperature is:

$$\theta_h = \theta_a + \Delta\theta_{or}\left[\frac{1+RK^2}{1+R}\right]^x + Hg_rK^y \qquad (1)$$

where θ_h is any load the hot temperature (°C); θ_a is the environment temperature; $\Delta\theta_{or}$ is the top oil temperature rise under the rated power flow; R is the ratio of load loss and no-load loss under the rated load; K is the load factor, it is the ratio of load current and the rated current; X is the index of oil; Hg_r is Temperature difference between hotspots temperature and the top oil temperature of winding under the rated load; Y for winding index.

For the transformer of forced circulation (OF) the cooling, under any load the finally hot-spot temperature is:

$$\theta_h = \theta_a + \Delta\theta_{br}\left[\frac{1+RK^2}{1+R}\right]^x$$
$$+ 2(\Delta\theta_{imr} - \Delta\theta_{br})K^y + Hg_rK^y \qquad (2)$$

where $\Delta\theta_{br}$ is the bottom oil temperature rise under the rated load; $\Delta\theta_{imr}$ is average oil temperature rise.

2.2 Copying old text onto new file

Doing the following assumptions for the eddy current loss of winding: (1) the eddy current loss is directly proportional to the square load current of the winding; (2) In the winding hot-spot location eddy current loss is equivalent to 1/N of resistance loss.[8] Therefore, under any load cases, temperature difference between hot-spot temperature and the top oil temperature of winding can be expressed as:

$$\Delta\theta_{gu} = \left[\frac{1+\left(\frac{I}{I_R}\right)^2 \times \frac{I}{N}}{1+\frac{I}{N}}\right]^x Hg_r \qquad (3)$$

where $\Delta\theta_{gu}$ is the finally temperature rise of the winding hot spot relative to the oil; I is Winding load current; I_R is Winding rated load current.

For transformer of actual operation, winding resistance loss will increase with the increase of the winding current, so the molecules "1" should be changed to (I/I_R), and the denominator is still the sum of resistance loss and eddy current loss under the rated load.

Table 1. Parameter table of loading guide.

	Distribution transformer	Large transformer		
	ONAN	ON	OF	OD
x	0.8	0.9	1.0	1.0
y	1.6	1.6	1.6	2.0

$$\Delta\theta_{gu} = \left[\frac{\left(\frac{I}{I_R}\right)^2 + \left(\frac{I}{I_B}\right)^2 \times \frac{I}{N}}{1+\frac{I}{N}}\right]^x$$

$$Hg_r = \left(\frac{I}{I_R}\right)^{2x} Hg_r = Hg_rK^{2x} \qquad (4)$$

Therefore, for the IEC354 standard the hot-spot temperature calculation equation of oil-immersed transformer winding is modified. Amend (1) as:

$$\theta_h = \theta_a + \Delta\theta_{or}\left[\frac{1+RK^2}{1+R}\right]^x + Hg_rK^{2x} \qquad (5)$$

Meanwhile, known from the analysis of all above, when estimating winding hot-spot temperature, the core loss does not directly effect, so it can only consider the effect of load factor "K". When estimating the oil temperature, it need to consider the transformer load loss and core loss. Finally (2) is modified as:

$$\theta_h = \theta_a + \Delta\theta_{br}\left[\frac{1+RK^2}{1+R}\right]^x$$
$$+ 2(\Delta\theta_{imr} - \Delta\theta_{br})\left[\frac{1+RK^2}{1+R}\right]^x + Hg \qquad (6)$$

It can be seen from the improved calculation equation that Type (1) and (5), (2) and (6) have the same form when k = 1. The y in the original formula is replaced with 2x in improved equation, to make the hot-spot temperature reduce a calculation required parameters.

3 COMPARED WITH THE CALCULATION RESULTS AND SIMULATION RESULTS OF ANSYS

3.1 Software introduction

ANSYS is the large general finite element analysis software which fuse structure, fluid, electric field, magnetic field and sound field analysis in a body.

It is made up of the finite element analysis of the world largest software company, one of the development of ANSYS in the United States, and it can be used with CAD software, realizing data sharing and exchanging. ANSYS has the function of physical field coupling, allowing all kinds of coupling calculation on the same model, such as hot-structure coupling, magnetic-structure coupling and electrical-magnetic-fluid-thermal coupling, thus the ANSYS can solve the multidisciplinary variable engineering problems.

3.2 Simulation results of ANSYS

In this paper, the simulation is for three-phase transformer, but considering the temperature of mesophase should be the highest, and on both sides is symmetrical, so the picture only show the temperature field of mesophase. Again because of the load factor of transformer is proportional to the rate of heat generation, therefore the simulation mainly change the transformer heat generation rate to achieve the change of the load factor, then draw the following temperature field distribution under different load, as shown in Figure 1.

For the above figures: Figure 1 (a) and (d) respectively for load factor 0.8, 1, transformer low voltage winding temperature field distribution nephogram, Figure 1 (b), (c), (e), (f), (g), respectively, for the low voltage winding temperature distribution under different load curve (the abscissa for winding the distance from bottom to top), you can see by combining the two windings of the most hot-spot temperature and position, winding the radial temperature difference is not big. The inside temperature slightly higher than the lateral, and it is considered to be a uniform distribution. The axial temperature distribution is not uniform, the lower the temperature is low, the upper temperature is high, and the lowest temperature of winding is located in the bottom of the winding. The hot-spot temperature is about 100 °C, and locate the axial about 3/20 from the top.

3.3 Compare and analysis of hot-spot temperature between calculation results and simulation results

According to the calculation equation (3) and (5), the calculation results and simulation results are obtained and listed in Table 2.

This article analyzes the winding hot-spot temperature under five different load cases, the chart below compares simulation and calculation results for its horizontal axis as the load factor, ordinate axis as hot temperature (in K):

Above the winding hot-spot temperature rise under different load factor giving, it can be seen

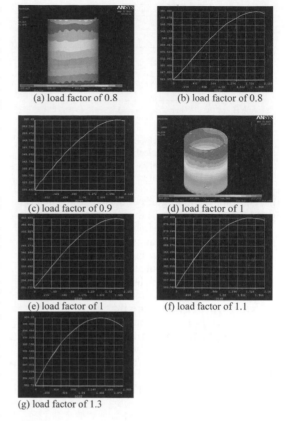

(a) load factor of 0.8   (b) load factor of 0.8

(c) load factor of 0.9   (d) load factor of 1

(e) load factor of 1   (f) load factor of 1.1

(g) load factor of 1.3

Figure 1. The hot-spot temperature figures under different load.

Table 2. The decomposed gases under different fault types for oil-filled power transformer.

Load factor	0.8	0.9	1	1.1	1.3
Load formula calculation results	331.9	340.1	349	358.8	380.7
Improved formula calculation results	338.1	349.2	358	376.7	398.2
Simulation results	348.6	355.6	361.2	377.6	400.2

from the diagram that three curves are the hot-spot temperature rising with the increase of load, and the load factor is less than 1, the change of the winding hot-spot temperature rise is flat; when load factor is greater than 1, the change of the winding hot-spot temperature rise curve is steep, the slope is greater than the former, conspicuously when it is overload, winding temperature change is big. And for large and medium-sized transformer OF cooling mode, the load coefficient is greater than 1, the improved equation calculation results will be

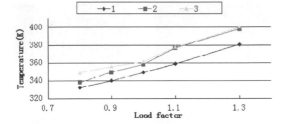

Figure 2. The hot-spot temperature curves under different load 1—load formula calculation results; 2—Improved formula calculation results; 3—simulation results.

larger than the load guide equation, and when the load factor is less than 1, the results will be slightly larger. But improved equation calculation results more close to the simulation results.

Transformer load loss increases with the square of the load current of transformer, insulation under the rated load will have normal aging speed without damage before normal use fixed number of year. When it runs more than rated current of transformer, just as overload, the copper loss proportion in the total loss will increase further. And from the analysis of above in Figure 2, the hot temperature will rise sharply, and winding insulation paper is highly affected by the temperature, aging, so monitoring the winding hot-spot temperature is necessary.

4 CONCLUSIONS

In this article, through the simulation software oil-immersed transformer temperature field model is established, and obtained the temperature field distribution of transformer which is consistent with the calculation results. Through the analysis of the temperature field, it got most of the low voltage winding hot-spot temperature and its position, and the highest temperature generally are in the winding at the top of the lower part, meanwhile it provides a new way of thinking for oil-immersed transformer hot-spot temperature prediction.

Transformer's winding and iron core heat to the transformer tank outside air to go through a lot of processes, heat flow through each process make a difference in temperature, and the size of the temperature difference relate to the loss value and the physical properties of the flow medium. Simulation by changing the heat generation rate is obtained the distribution of temperature field transformer internal under different load, it also

can bring some error, so the theoretical calculation and simulation for the hot-spot temperature have the certain error.

REFERENCES

Chen, C.S. & Hwang, J.C. & Cho, M.Y. 1994. Development of simplified loss models for distribution system analysis. *Power Delivery. IEEE Transactions on* 9(3): 1545–1551.

Chen, W.G. & Zhao, T. & Jing, T.S. 2009. Improved Method for Calculation of Hot-spot Temperature in Power Transformer. *High voltage apparatus* 45(8): 53–56.

Fu, C.Z. & Ji, S.C. & Wang, S.S. 2002. The two-dimensional numerical calculation of temperature field of transformer winding. *High Voltage Engineering* 28(5):10–12.

Isha, M.T. & Wang, Z. 2008. Transformer hot-spot temperature calculation using IEEE loading guide. Condition Monitoring and Diagnosis. CMD 2008. *International Conference on. IEEE*, 2008: 1017–1020.

Pierce, W.L. 1992. An Investigation of temperature distribution in cast-resin transformer windings. *IEEE Transformer on Power Delivery* 7(2): 920–926.

Pradhan, M.K. & Ramu, T.S. 2004. Estimation of the Hottest Spot Temperature (HST) in power transformers considering thermal inhomogeniety of the windings. *Power Delivery, IEEE Transactions on* 19(4): 1704–1712.

Radakovic, Z. & Feser, K. 2003. A new method for the calculation of the hot-spot temperature in power transformers with ONAN cooling. *Power Delivery, IEEE Transactions on* 18(4): 1284–1292.

Shan, D.L. 2012. Research on the field winding temperature of large transformer. *Heibei: North China Electric Power University.*

Su, L.N. 2006. Calculation of the rise of large natural oil circulation transformer guide structure of natural air cooling and forced air cooling temperature. *Tianjin: Hebei University of Technology.*

Switzerland. G. Loading Guide for Oil-Immersed Power Transformers. *IEC, International Standard* IEC 3541991-09.

Taghikhani, M.A. & Gholami, A. 2009. Prediction of hottest spot temperature in power transformer windings with non-directed and directed oil-forced cooling. *International Journal of Electrical Power & Energy Systems* 31(7): 356–364.

Wang, X.C. & Yu, C.M. 1991. Oriented guide oil flow and oil temperature rise calculation of Strong oil cooling structure transformer. *Proceedings of the CSEE* 11(3): 16–20.

Wang, X.Y. & Li, B.L. & Li, L.X. 1996. Analysis and calculation of 3D temperature field of transformer. *Journal of Tianjin University* 29(3): 320–323.

Zhang, H.S. & Hu, R.X. & Kang, S.R. 2011. ANSYS13.0 finite element analysis from entry to the master. *Beijing, China: Mechanical industry Publishing House.*

Computer, Intelligent Computing and Education Technology – Liu, Sung & Yao (Eds)
© 2014 Taylor & Francis Group, London, ISBN 978-1-138-02469-4

The SNS simulator: An example in the development and design of educational software for teaching students the Internet safety

D.V. Stolbov
Hebei Normal University, P.R. China

N.V. Olefirenko
G.S. Skovoroda Kharkiv National Pedagogical University, Ukraine

ABSTRACT: In this paper, we focus our attention on the approach of development educational software for teaching students the Internet safety by example of the Social Network Simulator (SNS simulator). We present the features of teaching students security in social network sites based on their activities in the Internet. Then, on the basics of these features we build requirements for the SNS simulator. According to these requirements, we define the design model and select programming tools for the SNS simulator implementation in practice. To conclude, we describe an example of working in the SNS simulator.

Keywords: a simulator; the Internet safety; the MARS-model; online threats; social networks

1 INTRODUCTION

Every day the number of users of Social Networks Sites (SNS) increases. The SNS unite people worldwide to stay in touch with their friends, share experiences and photographs, exchange personal content. In many ways it has replaced the telephone and email. For many users, it has become a way of life. The main target audience of the SNS are students. A significant part of the social activity of today's students is currently being implemented in the framework of cooperation in the Internet community. As in real life, the Internet can damage students' psychological state and physical health. So a relevant issue is the study of student's security threats and determinate possible ways to protect the students again the online threats. One of such ways is using educational software for teaching students security in SNS.

2 FEATURES OF TEACHING STUDENTS SECURITY IN SNS

Today SNS are the most popular communities among students. The results of researches show even 10–12 years students have significant experience working with social networks. More than 50% of students in Europe have their own page in social networks (Livingstone, 2012). 75% of students in Russian are active online users and regularly visit SNS (Soldatova, 2013).

SNS involve students dealing with people that are already established relationships in real life, and provide the ability to create their real identity, placing genuine information about them.

As in real life in SNS students can face to threats. Some of the threats transformed with real life, and some had arisen on the Internet and can be only in the virtual world. In particular to the threats with which the students can face in SNS include (Livingstone, 2012): disclosure of private information by either yourself or friends/contacts; bullying; cyber-stalking; access to age-inappropriate content; online grooming and abuse; prosecution or recrimination from posting offensive or inappropriate comments; phishing emails allegedly from SNS, but actually encouraging students to visit fraudulent or inappropriate websites; people hacking into or hijacking students' account or page; viruses or spyware contained within message attachments or photographs.

In a primary school students have already been able to create own page in SNS, send and view receiving messages, upload and download multimedia files, following online communities. On the one side, teaching such students the basics of SNS in the computer science lessons is a lagging process, on the other side, it is important to disclosure basics of safe behavior when they are working in the SNS. In particular, it is necessary to focus attention on answers to the following questions:

– How correctly to create an own page in SNS? What kind of data can be specified at registration, and which are not? Is it really necessary during the registration in SNS to indicate

truthful personal information (name and surname, address, phone number, information about parents)?
- How to identify suspicious action in SNS with hidden threats and how to make the right decision for them?
- How to protect an own page in SNS from hacking and theft of personal data from it?

The students' social networks security is considered by us as establishing external and internal factors of their own security. External factors should ensure a safe the Internet environment for student's activity. The factors include on: policy measures (for instance, there are regulation of inappropriate, illegal and prohibited content in the Internet, legal measures to regulated online activities); international co-operation by intergovernmental organizations (for example, there are EU Kids Online project, Child Online Protection, INSAFE, INHOPE); technical measures (for instance, to use special settings in own page in SNS. The services allow protecting students against spam, porn and other inappropriate data).

If the external factors are established at the public level, the internal factors—at the individual level. The internal factors must encourage students to develop their own defense mechanisms. This can be achieved by: to motivate students to study existing threats during using SNS; to teach students knowledge about how to protect against such threats; to explain students how to deal with such threats in SNS' situations.

The internal factors must help to form student's skills to recognize, prevent, avoid and successfully overcome the challenges and dangers of the SNS. Such skills are difficult formed only in the theory for some reasons: there is difficult to describe threats of SNS so that the student has learned to recognize them in reality; it is impossible explain to the students how to see and prevent the threats; there is very difficult to teach students to avoid and correctly to overcome the threats that exist in practice.

The reasons defined above emphasize the need for formation the skills in practice. One way to implement this requirement is the use of educational software. The software is mainly used as a supplement to the basic learning materials (textbooks, workbooks, etc.) both on the lessons and in self-study students. One of such software is an educational simulator. The simulator has some advantages over the basic learning materials that make it irreplaceable in teaching.

3 DESIGN OF SNS SIMULATOR

The SNS simulator compared to the real SNS environment offers main advantages: the simulator removes the element of danger from some threat situations in real SNS. A student can "interact" with social networks' threats in a simulation quite safely without damage to self; the simulator can be paused, whereas real life cannot. Pausing allows students to assess what's going on. Activities make up the core of the SNS simulator. The activities tend to meet the following criteria (Magee M, 2006):

- They simulate an activity that is "real". They simulate the activity so well that there is little difference between the simulated environment and the real one;
- They are "hands-on", involving students so they become participants, not mere listeners or observers. Students learn better from their own experiences than having others' experiences related to them;
- They are motivators for learning. Student involvement in the activity is so deep that interest in learning more about the activity or its subject matter develops;
- They are tailored to the student. When simulations are designed specifically for their audience, they can take developmental requirements into consideration;
- They are inspirational. Student input is welcome and activities are designed to encourage students to enhance the activity by contributing their own ideas;
- They are empowering. Students take on responsible roles, find ways to succeed, and develop problem solving tools as a result of the interaction.

During the design process of the SNS simulator must also consider the age-specific and psycho-pedagogical characteristics of students. Among these characteristics are features of their memory, thinking, imagination, emotional state and changes in their own behaviour. There are needs for communication with peers, desires to seek new information about the world, a propensity to risky behaviour. These changes reflected in their online activity (Soldatova, 2013).

Apart from the changes in students' behaviour, features of Internet space influence on students' online behaviour. There include: the Internet affects the behaviour, interests and hobbies of young people; the Internet addiction among students; the Internet has become a very powerful tool to manipulate the consciousness of people; the Internet satisfies almost all needs of the modern students; the Internet as a source of information has become more popular than other media (television, radio, print), primarily due to the continuous and dynamic information content.

According to the above criteria of simulator activities, the students' characteristics and features of Internet space for them, we defined set of requirements for the SNS simulator design. The set of requirement includes:

- The SNS simulator have to be as possible similar to the real SNS. This will allow students to completely immerse in a simulated learning environment. This immersion gives the students an opportunity to learn own experience though doing habitual actions in the SNS;
- The SNS simulator should "encourage" the students to take prudent and appropriate in a given situation modelled operation of SNS and display the consequences of this decision;
- The SNS simulator should be include on elements of interactivity, assessment of user actions and possibility of multiple repetition of actions;

On the basis of the above requirements, we chose Rapid Application Development methodology (RAD) as a design principle of the simulator. We selected RAD because of its advantages: the lack of extensive pre-planning allows writing software faster, and makes it easier to change requirements for the software; RAD methodology provides the ability to rapidly change design of the software; RAD allows revising of software construction.

The RAD structure includes four stages of software development: stage of forming requirements, construction stage, design stage and cutover stage.

As a design model of the SNS simulator we use MARS-model (Model-Associations-Representation-Scenario). MARS-model allows describing a theoretical basic to logical structure of educational simulators (Pernin, 2006). MARS-model includes four independent parts (Fig. 2): the Model part describes the system behaviour that depends on user activities; the Representation part responsible for the user interface; the Associations link the model and the representation; the Scenario part consists of a set of learning situations. In the SNS simulator scenario are describe in a set of different situation that students can face in real social networks sites. The situations include: answer to request about adding a stranger to friends; response to a request from a stranger to send personal data; accepting an invitation to join to online community; response to bullying messages, etc.

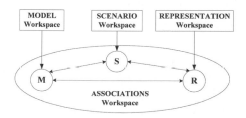

Figure 1. A design model of the SNS simulator.

VK is the largest European social network with more than a **100 million** active users.

Sign up for VK

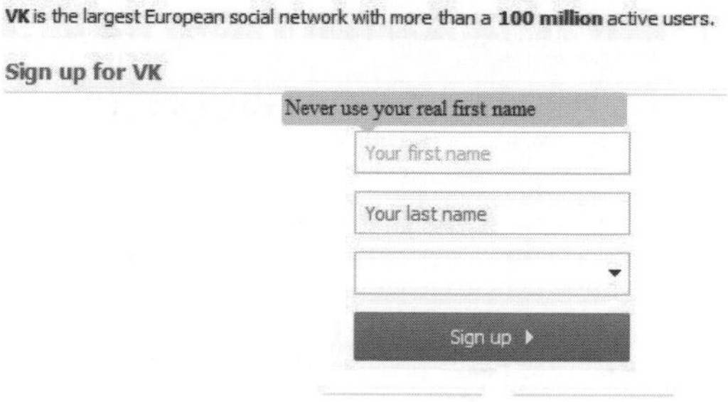

Figure 2. A screen shot shows an example of a registration procedure in the SNS simulator.

As a programming tool, we selected software platform Adobe Flash and programming language Action Script 3.0 (AS3). We choose AS3 for its main advantages: AS3 is a free programming tool with lots of visual components and huge libraries of events; AS3 allows to develop program applications in a short time due to object-oriented approach; AS3 has a good system of assistance and support for developers through a its programming community.

4 AN EXAMPLE OF WORKING IN THE SNS SIMULATOR

Consider the features of working in the SNS simulator using specific examples. When a user starts working with the SNS simulator the user can see the main page of this simulator (Fig. 2). In the page the user can sign in. If the user doesn't have an account in the SNS simulator, he/she can through a registration procedure.

First, the user can input own first and last name. When the user starts to input the name, the SNS simulator gives him/her a tool tip that cautions him/her about a risk of using real identifications data for registration.

When the user finish registration, he/she will be own the SNS simulator page. In this page the user can change settings of own account, find friends and information i.e.

The SNS simulator includes some situation that can be in real SNS and be dangerous. One of such situation is get a request to add new friend (Fig. 3a).

Very often in the real world, students without hesitation added strangers that send them request. Often teenagers are not thinking about strangers' purpose century begs them to friends. In the SNS simulator when the user goes to a similar step and adds a stranger to friend, the SNS simulator responds him/her. The user receives a message confirming his/her actions. If the user confirms its desire to add the

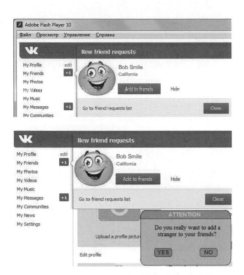

Figure 3. (a) A screen shot shows an example of a request to add new friend in the SNS simulator. (b) A screen shot shows an example of a confirmation message to incorrect user action in the SNS simulator.

Figure 4. A screen shot shows an example of a winning letter in the SNS simulator.

stranger, the SNS simulator informs him/her about the risk of such action (Fig. 3b).

The SNS give teenagers an opportunity to satisfaction their need to communicate among themselves. For online talking students often use short messages, chats. During online communication students can become a victim of bullying, harassment, fraud, etc. Such situations are contained in the SNS simulator. One of such situations is the user gets a letter of winning (Fig. 4). If the user wants to get a prize, he/she must download an attachment to the letter. In real SNS such message attachments can include viruses and spyware that will harm to recipient's computer. In the SNS simulator if a student tries to download such attachments, he/she gets an attention about risk of such student's action.

Other situation when a user gets some messages that harassment him/her. At first the student wants to reply to those messages. But this step only encourage an attacker continue to harassment and send new messages to the student. In the SNS simulator if the student can reply to the harassment

message, he/she gets a warning to this risk action (Fig. 5).

5 CONCLUSION

This paper examines development of the SNS simulator. Due to the high level of visualization simulation, it was possible to create models of real work space. On the one hand this similarity allows completely immerse students in the learning environment, on the other hand to protect them from possible threats to the real environment. The SNS simulator enables students in practice to study SNS threats without harming themselves and help them to form skills to successfully avoid and overcome the SNS's threats. However, the process of creating the SNS simulator is consuming and multistage. During the process we must consider characteristics of target audience that will use the SNS simulator and features of the environment which is modeled through simulation.

REFERENCES

Livingstone S. Comparing children's online opportunities and risks across Europe: Cross-national comparisons for EU Kids Online, LSE, London: EU Kids Online (Deliverable D3.2, 2nd edition), 2009.—133p.

Magee M. State of the Field Review: Simulation in Education. Alberta Online Learning Consortium Calgary, 2006.—57p.

Pernin J-P, Lejeune A., Models for the reuse of learning scenarios, "Imagining the future for ICT and Education", IFIP conference Proceedings, Ålesund, Norway, June 2006.

Soldatova, G., Zotova E., Lebesheva M. Shliapnikov V. Internet: Opportunities, competencies, safety. Handbook for workers in the general education.—M.: Google, 2013.—165 p.

Computer, Intelligent Computing and Education Technology – Liu, Sung & Yao (Eds)
© 2014 Taylor & Francis Group, London, ISBN 978-1-138-02469-4

A novel image compression based on the wavelet coding with the adaptive context quantization

Min Chen
Yunnan University, Kunming, Yunnan, China

Lu Peng
Police Station of Taiping, Dehong, Yunnan, China

Jie Xue
Yunnan Police Officer Academy, Kunming, Yunnan, China

ABSTRACT: In this paper, a novel image compression algorithm based on the wavelet transform is discussed. The wavelet transform operation is deployed firstly for the image waiting for being coded and the uniform quantization is used to reduce the spatial cost for the coding model subsequently. Then the coefficients of the wavelet transforming are decomposed into three parts. Three Context models are established for coding these partitioned coefficients separately. In purpose of finding the optimal Context quantization levels, the context quantization based on the minimum increment of the adaptive code length is proposed to tackle the "model dilution". The experiment results indicate that the proposed algorithm perform better compression efficiency than other predecessors. The proposed algorithm keep the acquisition of the optimal context quantization level adaptively with the minimum adaptive code length being achieved at the same time.

Keywords: image compression; wavelet transform; context entropy coding; increment of the adaptive code length

1 INTRODUCTION

The data compression is significant for enhancing the communication system performance. Especially, the lossless compression algorithms are widely used in many domains of the information science such as DVD [1] and MPEG4 [2]. The entropy coding tactics is one famous algorithm of the lossless compression algorithms. The strategy of the entropy coding is root in the discussion that the entropy of the probability distribution reveals the minimum code length of the symbol when it is encoded by using this distribution to drive the arithmetic encoder. Namely, if the entropy reduce, the fact that obtaining shorter code length is possible. Meanwhile, according to the information theory, the conditioning reduce the entropy, i.e. if we use some proper conditions to construct the conditional probability distribution for the current symbol, the shorter code length of this symbol could be achieved. In [3], these constructed conditional distributions are referred to the context model while the number of the conditions is the order of the context model. Nevertheless, in practice, the true conditional probability distributions

needed are not known or reliable even the statistic estimation is deployed for obtaining each conditional probability in each distribution. Specially, if the order of the context model is too high, the counting number of the training data will be scattered into much more possible counting vectors. Then the estimated conditional probability based on these counting vectors will trend to the uniform distributions with the maximum entropy value. This problem is corresponding to the "Context Dilution" presented in [3]. The context quantization is one effect method to tackle this problem. The predecessors which are dedicated to maintain the lower cost as far as possible propose many different approaches to achieve the optimal context quantization such as the Minimum Conditional Entropy Context Quantization (MCECQ) [4]. However, MCECQ need the prior knowledge about the number of the classes, it can not achieve the optimal quantization levels adaptively. In [5–6], we try to obtain the optimal context quantization algorithms with the lowest adaptive code length. In [5], the similar measure which is based on the minimum complementary relative entropy is proposed. In [6], an adaptive context quantization algorithm which improves the algorithm in [5] is proposed. The new similar measure, the increment of the adaptive code length, is suggested to optimize the quantization efficiency. When the optimal context quantization is found, its application is presented in this paper.

In this paper, a novel image wavelet compression algorithm based on the context quantization in [5] is proposed. The image wavelet coding is one of efficient methods to enhance the compression efficiency. In [7], the embedded wavelet coding method is suggested. The coefficients of the wavelet image are the object encoded. In [8–9], Chen gives two wavelet coding algorithms to shorten the code length of the coefficients. However, limited in the context quantization algorithms they used, these two coding methods could not achieve the optimal quantization levels. Especially, the algorithm in [9], even though it won the optimal coding results (such as bit rate), it rely on more manual operation. In this paper, we use the improved context quantization algorithm in [6] for the image wavelet coding. In section 2, the adaptive context quantization algorithm which is improved to adapt the wavelet coding is discussed. In section 3, the details of our wavelet coding method is given. The experiments and results are given in the section 4 and the conclusion is given in the section 5.

2 ADAPTIVE CONTEXT QUANTIZATION

When the K past symbols of the current symbol are used to construct the context model, the estimator of each conditional probability is given by (1)

$$p(X_i = j \mid c_n) = \frac{N_j + 1}{\sum_{j=0}^{I-1} N_j + I} \qquad (1)$$

where c_n denotes one specific context event which are formed by the values of the K past $I - ary$ symbols, N_j denotes the number of the counted symbols whose value equals the value j. When the order of the context model K is determined, the possible number of the context events c_n is constant, i.e. the number of the possible conditional probability distributions is determined. It means that more conditional probabilities are needed to be estimated. Actually, the estimation works well only based on the precondition that the more number of the training data are obtained as far as possible. Due to the "context dilution" problem, the estimation is usually unreliable to achieve good results. The context quantization is described as: Find some similar conditional probability distributions $P(X \mid c_i)$ and $P(X \mid c_j)$, then merge them into one new vector $Q(X \mid m)$. By this way, the new vector obtains more

number of the training data to achieve better estimation. However, what the "similar distributions" means is the key to get valid context quantization. In [6], we give a novel context quantization algorithm based on the minimum increment of the adaptive code length. According to [3], the described length of the source sequence reveals the total cost when this sequence is encoded by using the constructed context model. It includes two aspects, one aspect is the code length needed to describe the symbol itself, another aspect is the cost which is used to describe the complexity of the context model. The calculation method of the described length is given by (2)

$$L = Z * H(X \mid C) + |C| (\log Z) \qquad (2)$$

where L denotes the described length of the source sequence Z', Z denotes the number of the symbols the sequence Z' contains, C denotes all possible context events and $|C|$ denotes the number of these possible context events (the number of the possible context models). The $H(X \mid C)$ denotes the entropy of the conditional probability distribution which is estimated by (1).

Considering two specified context events c_i and c_j, the corresponding conditional probability distributions are written as $P(X \mid c_i)$ and $P(X \mid c_j)$. Then the formulas (3) and (4) indicate the described lengths of the symbols which are located in the context models $P(X \mid c_i)$ and $P(X \mid c_j)$ separately. L_i and L_j denote their total code length separately.

$$L_i = Z_i * H(X \mid C_i) + |C_i| \log Z_i \qquad (3)$$

$$L_j = Z_j * H(X \mid C_j) + |C_j| \log Z_j \qquad (4)$$

In (3) and (4), because the specified context events c_i and c_j, the number of the possible conditional probability distribution $|C_i| = 1$ and $|C_j| = 1$. If these two conditional probability distributions are merged into one new distribution, $Q(X \mid m)$ signified, the total code length of this distribution also could be simplified by (5)

$$L = Z * H(X \mid m) + |m| \log Z \qquad (5)$$

where L denotes the total code length of the total symbols which are located on both $P(X \mid c_i)$ and $P(X \mid c_j)$. Considering the difference between the L and the $L_i + L_j$, we define the increment of the adaptive code length $\Delta = (L_i + L_j) - L$. It could easily get the representation (6)

$$\Delta = Z_i * (H(X \mid C_i) - H(X \mid m))$$
$$+ Z_j * (H(X \mid C_j) - H(X \mid m)) + \log \frac{Z_i * Z_j}{Z_i + Z_j}$$
$$\qquad (6)$$

We use the increment of the adaptive code length as the similar measure to decide whether two conditional probability distributions should be merged. If the value of Δ is bigger than the value 0, it implies that these two distributions should be merged. If there are many values of Δ bigger than the value 0, the two distributions which take the corresponding value of Δ with the maximum value are chosen to be merged.

In this paper, the context quantization based on the maximum increment of the adaptive code length is deployed. The details of this strategy is discussed in the next section.

3 THE ADAPTIVE IMAGE WAVELET CODING

3.1 *The context modeling*

Inspired by the work of [7], we propose a novel image wavelet compression algorithm. Firstly, the 3 levels wavelet transform of the image is deployed. The 10 sub-bands of different frequency are distributed, which is given by Figure 1.

To reduce the dimensions of the alphabet which is consisted by the wavelet coefficients, the threshold is used to partition the wavelet coefficients into two classes firstly. One class contains the coefficients that the value of each coefficient is bigger than the value of the threshold. Another class is opposite. These coefficients with the lower value than the value of the threshold are assigned the new value 0. The representation (7) describes this operation in details.

$$w_i' = \begin{cases} w_i & |w_i| \geq \tau \\ 0 & |w_i| < \tau \end{cases}$$

where w_i denotes the value of the ith coefficient, τ denotes the threshold. Then these bigger value

coefficients are separated into three partitions, Map, Code and Sign, the algorithm used to implement the partition is proposed in [9]. The same partition method we used in this paper.

Now, the task compressing the image turns to encoding the symbols in each of three partitions. We construct three context models for these three parts separately. To construct the model, the past 5 symbols are used as the conditions. In order to maintain the relevance during the coefficients, we directly use the original coefficients as the condition data. The locations of these 5 coefficients are given by Figure 2.

In Figure 2, w_i denotes the current coefficient waiting for being encoded. When 5 conditional coefficients are chosen, the conditional probability distribution $P(w_i \mid w_1,w_2,w_3,w_4,w_5)$ should be estimated. But in practice, we don't estimate this distribution directly, three conditional probability distributions $P(Map_i \mid w_1 - w_5)$, $P(Sign_i \mid w_1 - w_5)$ and $P(Code_i \mid w_1 - w_5)$ are estimated instead. It is easily to find that the Map sequence and the Sign sequence are the binary sequence. But the Code sequence is the $I - ary$ sequence. In the coding process, the maximum increment of the adaptive code length context quantization algorithm discussed in the section 2 is deployed in every coding of these three sequences separately. Firstly, we use the hash technology to make w_1,w_2,w_3,w_4,w_5 into one value which is corresponding to the specified context event ($Context\ event = Hash(w_1,w_2,w_3,w_4,w_5)$).

For the Map sequence and the Sign sequence, the direct context quantization is effect. But for the Code sequence, the dimension of the corresponding context model is too large. In order to enhance the compression efficiency, the sub-band quantization approach is proposed.

When the 3 levels wavelet transform is deployed for the image, the 19 sub-bands are obtained. When the Code sequence is ready to be encoded, we should construct the conditional probability distribution with the dimension which equals the value of the maximum value of all Code sequence to ensure each symbol in the Code sequence being encoded. Actually, in each sub-band, the maximum value of the corresponding 'sub-band Code sequence' is different. Some values of the Code

LL3	HL3	HL2	HL1
LH3	HH3		
LH2		HH2	
LH1			HH1

Figure 1. The 10 sub-band distribution.

	w5	w2	w4
w3	w1	w_i	

Figure 2. The location of the conditioned coefficients.

in some sub-bands are large but others are small. We construct a conditional probability distribution with different dimensions for every sub-band. There are total 19 distributions are constructed. When a Code symbol is coming, the number of the sub-band which this symbol belongs to is determined firstly, then the corresponding distribution is used to drive the arithmetic encoder.

The image compression algorithm follows as:

1. The wavelet transform of the image is deployed.
2. Separating each wavelet coefficient into three class, Map, Sign and Code.
3. Constructing the context model for the Map sequence and the Sign sequence separately.
4. Constructing the context models for the Code sequence for each sub-band.
5. The context quantization based on the maximum increment of the adaptive code length is implemented to quantize the context model.
6. Using the corresponding conditional probability distribution to drive the arithmetic encoder to assign the code word for each symbol (Including the Map symbol, the Sign symbol and the Code symbol).

4 EXPERIMENTS

In order to testify our compression algorithm, some experiments are deployed. We use 20 images for the experiments, 17 of these images are used as the training data to train the context model. 3 images (Lena, Barb and Goldhill) are used as the coding source sequences. The 7–9 filters are chosen to implement the image wavelet transform. In our experiments, the threshold in the first step equals the value of the threshold proposed in [9] with the corresponding bit rate at 1.0 bpp, 0.5 bpp and 0.25 bpp separately.

In the experiment 1, we use our compression algorithm to compress three images (Lena, Barb and Goldhill). The results are list in Table 1.

From Table 1, the code length of the image is reduced when the threshold value increases. When the threshold value equals 5.33, which is corresponding to the bit rate with 1.0 bpp in [9], the bit rate is reduced by our compression algorithm, Namely, the compression efficiency is enhanced by this algorithm. Meanwhile, the Signal Noise Rate (PSNR) is maintained at the same time.

The signal and noise rate is the indicator of the image compression algorithm. When the images are encoded and then decoded, we could calculate the value of PSNR to evaluate the efficiency of our compression algorithm. For comparison, in the experiment 2, we give the results of our algorithm for the same three images and compare the result

Table 1. The coding results of three images.

Image	Threshold	Length (byte)	Bit rate	PSNR
Lena	5.33	32729	0.99	40.71
	9.80	16323	0.49	37.55
	19.62	8106	0.25	34.45
Barb	8.92	32804	1.00	37.35
	19.9	16399	0.50	32.33
	38.78	8245	0.25	28.41
Goldhill	8.37	32805	1.00	36.98
	15.27	16317	0.49	33.49
	26.38	8135	0.25	30.81

Table 2. The comparison of the PSNR by our algorithm with the results by other algorithms.

Image	Bit rate	EBCOT	SPITH	EZBC	Ours
Lena	0.25	34.16	34.24	34.35	34.45
	0.50	37.29	37.34	37.47	37.55
	1.00	40.48	40.50	40.62	40.71
Barb	0.25	28.40	27.72	28.25	28.41
	0.50	32.39	31.83	32.15	32.33
	1.00	37.11	37.22	37.28	37.35
Goldhill	0.25	30.59	30.61	30.74	30.81
	0.50	33.25	33.22	33.47	33.49
	1.00	36.59	36.75	36.90	36.98

with the results which are achieved by other predecessor algorithms. These other results are from the literature [7]. The code length and the PSNR are the results which are list in Table 2.

From Table 2, it is easily to find that the value of PSNR by our algorithm is always better than other results. It indicates that our compression algorithm is better than others with the better bit rate. Furthermore, the proposed algorithm could maintain the best PSNR result. Meanwhile, our algorithm could achieve the optimal quantization level adaptively. This is the improvement of our compression algorithm comparing with other image wavelet coding.

5 CONCLUSION

In this paper, a novel image wavelet compression algorithm based on the maximum increment of the adaptive code length context quantization is proposed. Relying on the adaptive context quantization, our algorithm could achieve the optimal quantization levels adaptively. Dependent on the sub-band modeling, our algorithm enhance the compression efficiency and achieve the better bit rate and the better PSNR than the results by other algorithms.

ACKNOWLEDGEMENT

This work is supported by the Natural Science Foundation of Yunnan under the Grant 2013FD042.

REFERENCES

[1] Information Technology—JPEG 2000 Image Coding System, International Standardization Organization, July 2002, ISO/IEC15444.

[2] Coding of moving pictures and associated audio for digital storage Media at up to about 1.5 Mbps, ISO/IECJTC1, 1993, ISO/IEC11172-2.

[3] J. Rissanen, A universal data compression system, IEEE Trans. Inform. Theory, vol. 29, pp. 656–664, Sept. 1983.

[4] Forchhammer S., Wu X., Andersen J.D. Optimal context quantization in lossless compression of image data sequences[J]. IEEE Transactions on Image Processing, 2004, 13 (4): 509–517.

[5] Min Chen, Fuyan Wang, Context quantization based on the modified K-means clustering[J]. Advanced Materials Research, 2013, 756, 2013, 4068–4072.

[6] Min Chen, Jianhua Chen, Affinity propagation for the Context quantization[J], Advanced Materials Research, 791, 2013, 1533–1536.

[7] Shapiro J.M. Embedded image coding using zerotrees of wavelets coefficients[J]. IEEE Transactions on Signal Processing, 1993, 41 (12): 3445–3462.

[8] Jianhua Chen, Context modeling based on context quantization with application in wavelet image coding[J]. IEEE Transactions on Image Processing, 2004, 13 (1): 26–32.

[9] J. Chen, Y.F, Zhang, X.L, Shi, Image coding based on Wavelet transform and uniform scalar dead zone quantizer[J]. Signal Processing, 2006, 21, 562–572.

Computer, Intelligent Computing and Education Technology – Liu, Sung & Yao (Eds)
© 2014 Taylor & Francis Group, London, ISBN 978-1-138-02469-4

Analysis of functions and measures of physical training in the prevention of basketball sports injury

T.-F. Wang & S.-W. Du

School of PE, Jiangxi Normal University, Nanchang, Jiangxi, China

ABSTRACT: Through the literature material method, field survey method of physical training of basketball sports injury prevention function for this paper. Common injuries in basketball for the ankle, knee, waist and joint injury and have good physical huge damage on the prevention of basketball. Study: good physical fitness is the foundation of basketball movement, strengthen physical training, not only can reduce sports injury in the basketball movement and at the same time can also be accidents caused by the injury in the basketball movement play a important role in prevention.

Keywords: basketball; damage; physical training; the prevention of

1 PREFACE

Existing research at home and abroad show that the good physical fitness can reduce the movement of all kinds of damage, and basketball as a form of mass sport, have fun, and have strong antagonism, which inevitably produces physical injury, and through reasonable physical training can reduce injury in the basketball movement and provides protection for basketball players, they reduce the chance of accidental injury.

2 RESEARCH OBJECT AND METHODS

2.1 *Research object*

Basketball amateur basketball player.

2.2 *Research methods*

2.2.1 *Literature*
By collecting relevant literature study of the paper.

2.2.2 *Field research method*
Professional basketball game and amateur entertainment places to visit.

2.2.3 *Logical analysis*
Logic analysis was carried out on the collection of documents and materials, and finally their own conclusions.

3 RESULTS AND ANALYSIS

3.1 *Common among all kinds of basketball sports injury*

Technical characteristics of basketball and its closely related to anatomy characteristics. Ankle is made up of three quarters of the lower tibia, fibula and talus bone structure, is made up of tibiofibula ankle inside and outside surface and under the tibial articular surface of ankle, joint head put in ankle acupuncture point, within the external ankle is narrow and long again, and slightly backward, talus narrow after wide joints in front, back and wide spacing saddle into the ankle. If the joint is stable from flexion, because from the saddle narrower in ankle acupuncture point, so the ankle a little loose, if the foot ankle joint extorsion and adduction, varus outside forces, is easy to cause damage.

3.2 *The knee joint injury*

Composed of knee of lower and upper tibia femoral, kneecap and fibula, knee joint is the longest in the body between the two poles of bone, muscle power around less, with a large range in the movement joints tolerance. So easy to hurt in sports, the occurrence of damage there is a close relationship with the basketball movement technology requirements. Basketball movement half hole action throughout the stadium, the dribbling, slide of defense and offense, abrupt stop, snap shots, turn, jump, etc for athletes in a half hole, then the stability of the knee joint mainly by quadriceps and patellar beam, the quadriceps muscle and patella was pressed on the patellar femoral, if there is excessive knee flexion in half hole reverse activity, will aggravate the burden of patella, subject it to a bigger force, friction, reverse, thus improve the possibility of joint injuries.

3.3 The waist injury

Human anatomy research shows that: the body center of gravity is located in the human body the waist, the waist movement is the primary part of body position changes, the waist is the center axis of the human body, is a bridge connecting the lower extremities, negative significant, activity. With waist as the hub and basketball drives the body or more to complete the movement, and so the waist in the activities more suffer damage. Such as ball breakthrough in basketball, fadeaway jumper, stealing the ball, stop shooting twist, etc., and the waist often by buckling at full stretch, and unreasonable collision in the movement. When the sacral spine muscle strength is insufficient, often cause the waist, sacroiliac muscles plate membrane or torn ligament, imbalance of intervertebral joint.

3.4 Joint injury

Around the knuckles lack of subcutaneous connective tissue, joint is relatively shallow, on both sides of the lateral collateral ligament, joint flexion, lateral collateral ligament is flabby, straighten out the ligament strain. So, when a catcher shape is not correct, fingers bend or stretch when suddenly by external ball at the top of the collision, easily caused the joint damage.

4 THE EFFECT OF PHYSICAL STAMINA TRAINING TO BASKETBALL SPORT AND PREVENTION

4.1 The effect of body quality training for basketball and prevention

4.1.1 The effect of strength quality training for basketball and prevention

Is the basketball movement against material guarantee, if the athlete's strength quality is good, good control ability and the stability of joints, the body can greatly reduce the number of basketball sports injury occurs. Such as: basketball after fast break easily occurs when shares of metacarpophalangeal joint from a muscle strain, fingers, and damage is also common injury, ankle injury, the lower back injury such damage is caused by insufficient muscle strength at these parts, including shares after the muscle group and the lower back injury. Therefore

in peacetime training to strengthen the training of the each part of the whole body strength, especially after muscle muscle and abdominal muscle and back muscle strength training. Only through scientific training methods strength training of athletes, the athletes increase control ability to increase in power, each part in the basketball court is likely to be injured.

4.1.2 Balance ability training on the effect of basketball and prevention

The activities of the body is mainly controlled by vestibular analyzer, such as the displacement of the body, ups and downs, rotation, speed and spatial location, etc. And body balance is mainly composed of proprioceptive to control, such as make the action of body position in the process of control, in the basketball movement to although route is not smooth, but it won't fall, nor a sprained ankle, which is due to the precise control of proprioceptive. But, after the injury especially joint muscle injury due to some anatomic relationship changes, such as the organization proprioceptive device failure, failure of its function will be damaged, thus lost the precise control of body position, and easy to damage, and this link is easy to ignore, after symptoms disappear, sensor control before recovery training, easy to cause chronic damage, so that the athlete's movement life with great harm. So, in the process of training, must pay attention to the balance ability training. Once appear damage, in addition to functional recovery training, must also balance ability recovery training.

4.1.3 Endurance quality training for basketball and the effect of prevention

Stamina diathesis is the body in a long time to work or exercise ability to overcome fatigue, it is decided in most sports or one of the factors to influence the result. In basketball the most chronic damage and strain more see, as on the field of running, stop, jump, and although some damage that athletes won't stop training, but it is precisely because most athletes are kept in training all the in such a case, so after a long-term accumulation of training will be difficult to heal chronic injury. Athletes often beating, knee and ankle to bear a lot of pressure, lead to knee recurring pain, still can cause fatigue tibiofibula periostitis even for a broken bone is a fracture.

4.1.4 Sensitivity and the effect of training for basketball and coordination

Sensitive quality is rapidly changing position players, transformation, action and the ability of random strain. Coordination is the body's athletes different system, different parts and different organs together to cooperate to complete ability to practice tactics for the actions or activities. Sensitive and coordinate quality are more complex movement quality, is the motor skills and the quality in the comprehensive performance of the movement. Cerebral cortex, the perfection of sports ability and the maneuverability of the nervous system is complete movement skills, coordination and stable guarantee. Course is changeful, sudden changes in the environment, also need to create a new action to adapt to the new conditions, this requires the maneuverability of the nervous system and analysis of the height of the development of comprehensive ability, quick judgement of the situation, decided to complete the new action. In basketball, dribbling upper limb and lower limb when not harmonious, active and passive muscle coordination, breathing and hard not coordination is the important cause of muscle injury. Sensitive and coordination improvements can improve the emergency and self-protection ability, thus reduce the damage arising from the movement. For example: in the process of block, grab rebounds when be born, if there is not normal landing posture, sensitive coordination is very good, but can never correct position adjust soon, try to avoid such as a sprained ankle injury. Development of athlete's sensitive quality allows players to quickly change the direction of various running, dodge, and suddenly start practice, all kinds of quick stop practice and rapid rotation, etc.

4.2 The effect of body shape training for basketball and prevention

Physical fitness is the foundation of training game, is athletes skill, intelligence, psychological and will quality guarantee. All items and weight is one of the most commonly used body shape index, can reflect the degree of human body symmetry and shape characteristics. Too much weight to the human body joint, bone under too much pressure, strain and chronic damage easily. Through scientific physical training tests can effectively improve poor body shape, so as to reduce the sports injuries. Physical exercise is good for basketball players the growth and development of bones and muscles, can reduce fat within the muscle and strength so as to improve the efficiency of muscle contraction.

5 CONCLUSIONS AND RECOMMENDATIONS

5.1 Conclusion

Through the strength quality training, balance ability training, endurance quality training, flexibility training, agility and coordination, increase the power of the athletes, balance ability enhancement, cardiovascular capacity increase, the body's sensitivity to improve coordination ability, make the comprehensive qualities of the athletes, not only can reduce the injury of basketball players in the basketball movement, at the same time can also be caused by an accident of basketball play an important role in the prevention of injury.

To strengthen physical training, especially the physical quality training of basketball sports injury prevention. To strengthen physical training is the key to prevent the basketball player injury and maintain its stability and strong confrontational important factors. In the basketball match the good physical ability is the precondition for the implementation of tactics, win the game is the most basic safeguard, is also a basketball player in the basketball sports injury prevention is the most effective way.

5.2 Recommendations

Correctly grasp the competitive winner law of basketball sports, according to the basketball special need of power quality, speed, quality, endurance quality, flexible quality for scientific training. To strengthen the research of the scientific method of physical training, improve the scientific level of physical stamina training using a variety of forms, using advanced scientific technology and equipment to monitor physical training.

Have good physical fitness is important guarantee to get good results in basketball games, but was injured in the basketball movement is inevitable, the coaches should improve basketball player "blowout" is greater than the consciousness of "governance".

REFERENCES

[1] Li Maolian. College students pathology and treatment of common sports injury [J]. Chinese school doctor, 2007.3.
[2] Chen Xiu try. In the theory of basketball sports injury and its treatment and prevention of [J]. Journal of fuqing branch of fujian normal university, 2007.3.
[3] Sports anatomy [M]. Sports institute of general teaching material, people's sport publishing house, 1987.
[4] Exercise physiology [M]. Sports institute of general teaching material, people's sport publishing house, 1999.
[5] Li Xiufang. Basketball sports injury and rehabilitation [EB]. China sports network.

Computer, Intelligent Computing and Education Technology – Liu, Sung & Yao (Eds)
© 2014 Taylor & Francis Group, London, ISBN 978-1-138-02469-4

Organize constructive learning of college sports professional teaching effect

T.-F. Wang & S.-W. Du
School of PE, Jiangxi Normal University, Nanchang, Jiangxi, China

ABSTRACT: Article using the method of documentary experiment data statistics, in the sprint teaching organization constructive learning teaching forms of the experimental group and the conventional teaching organizational form of teaching effect analysis in the control group. Study results show that the college sports professional teaching, the use of group constructive learning method, more can improve students' learning enthusiasm, initiative, the teaching effect obviously.

Keywords: organization construction; dash; the teaching effect

1 PREFACE

Constructive organizational learning is a kind of new form of teaching, but used rarely in the sprint teaching to all-round development of students' quality education, deepen the sports teaching, further verify the validity of this kind of teaching organization form, this study professional sports students in jiangxi normal university of science and technology as the research object, in combination with the practical situation of schools, adopting "constructive learning", "conventional" teaching two forms of sprint course teaching, teaching effect produced by analysis of their, aims to explore suitable for high school students in the sprint teaching organization form, and then to college sports professional sports teaching organization form to provide certain theory reference basis.

2 RESEARCH OBJECT AND METHODS

2.1 *Research object*

A random sample of jiangxi normal university of science and technology professional sports students of the same grade 2 class, a total of 100 boys as cases as the research object. Adopt double blind experiment design and random sampling way is divided into two groups: control group and experimental group, make the results of the study objective and true.

2.2 *Research methods*

2.2.1 *Literature*
Through the graphic information center of jiangxi normal university in China hownet access to books and articles related to paper, collect relevant literature and research results, and the data are summarized, lay a theoretical foundation to the research of this paper.

2.2.2 *Teaching experimental method*
Which contrast between groups, groups within the contrast experiment of teaching method, in every link of sprint technique teaching experimental group and control group were used respectively to constructive teaching and traditional teaching, through the teaching experiment results analysis and comparison the difference between the two groups.

2.2.3 *Mathematical statistics*
Sorts through the relevant data, using SPSS16.0 software to the related data statistics and analysis of the conventional.

3 RESULTS AND ANALYSIS

3.1 *Two groups before the experiment*

Before experiment, in order to increase the success rate of experiments, the author of the experimental group and control group of 100 m and 200 m grades were tested, the results of test are analyzed and compared (see Table 1).

From Table 1: the experimental group and control group before the experiment of 100 m and 200 m results were similar, the two groups of 100 meters and grades were average is only 0.04 s, achievements of the two groups of independent sample t test, $P = 0.254 > 0.05$, the value shows that the experimental group and control group students before the experiment, 100 there was no significant

Table 1. The experimental group and control group before the experiment 100 m and 200 m average scores and t test results.

	Number of people	100 meters	200 meters
Experimental group	50	12.32 s	26.12 s
Control group	50	12.28 s	26.16 s
P		0.254	0.780

Table 2. The control group before and after the experiment the students average 100 m and 200 m and t test results.

	Number of people	100 meters	200 meters
Before the experiment	50	12.48 s	26.13 s
After the experiment	50	12.21 s	25.60 s
P		0.0482	0.0393

difference; Two groups, 200 meters record a huge difference, the difference between the experimental group and control group averaged only 0.04 s, and t test $p = 0.780 > 0.05$ value shows that the experimental group and control group 200 meters before the experiment result that there is no significant difference. Which showed that no difference between the two groups to contrast and analysis of the experiment.

3.2 The control group before and after the experiment

In today's world university sprint level is in rapid development, our country sprint has been ranked the world level, and track and field in colleges and universities is to transport a large number of high level athletes in our country, therefore in order to improve the athletes will be vigorously promotes the sprint training in colleges and universities. After half a year's traditional teaching methods, namely teachers and students of mutual promotion of the control group than in the past the average grades have improved. Table 2 shows that the control students' 100 m 0.27 s; increased the average grades Improve the average score of 200 m 0.53 s, and the P value is 0.0482, 0.0482. To sum up, the traditional teaching method can improve the training level, but the method is simple and boring, means a single difference is very big and modern training theory, so it is imperative to change the traditional teaching method.

3.3 The experimental group before and after the experiment

Table 3 shows that after sprint technology courses of study and practice, the experimental group students' 100 m grade point average of 12.15 s, 0.17 s; increased than previously Students 200 m grade point average of 22.38 s, 0.04 s increased than previously, through independent sample t test, P value for 100 m = 0.00178 < 0.05, is very obvious in progress before and after the experiment, there was very significant difference; 200 m P = 0.00286 < 0.05, there is very significant

Table 3. The experimental group before and after the experiment the students 100 m and 200 m P value for grade point average and statistical results.

	Number of people	100 meters	200 meters
Before the experiment	50	12.32 s	25.42 s
After the experiment	50	12.15 s	25.38 s
P		0.00178	0.00286

difference. Experimental group of students before and after the experiment results are very significant differences, that teaching organization construction as a more novel teaching method, to improve our teaching effects and improve the overall level of students is helpful.

3.4 In comparison to the experimental group and control group after experimental teaching

Informed by Table 4, t test P value = 0.02587 < 0.05 shows that the experimental group and control group 100 meters after the experiment results have significant difference; P value = 0.03897 < 0.03897 shows that the experimental group and control group 200 meters after the experiment have significant difference. Therefore, induction of teaching in secondary schools teaching in the teaching effect is obvious. The experimental results show that the experimental group and control group analyzed before and after the experiment, the experimental group in the first two grades not exist significant difference, and the average is basically the same, after half a year after the traditional teaching and the teaching organization construction, two groups of results have been significantly improved, the experimental group grades higher than the control group, and through the test of significance, there is significant difference between experimental group and control group, prove the organization construction

980

Table 4. The experimental group and control group after experimental students 100 m and 200 m P value for grade point average and statistical results.

	Number of people	100 meters	200 meters
Experimental group	50	12.15 s	25.38 s
Control group	50	12.21 s	25.60 s
P		0.04573	0.03897

of teaching for students to improve their sprinters is feasible, and create a better teaching effect than traditional teaching. Therefore, college sports professional sprint teaching introduction using the organization construction of the teaching, the improvement of student performance, technology, and use the function of good teaching methods.

4 CONCLUSIONS AND RECOMMENDATIONS

4.1 Conclusion

Control group and experimental group before the experiment in two groups of 100 m and 2000 m record there is no significant difference, the two groups have homogeneous comparability; The control group in the 100 m and 2000 m scores before and after the experiment exist significant difference; The experimental group in the 100 m and 200 m scores before and after the experiment very significant sex differences.

Experimental group and control group after experimental students of 100 m and 200 m exist significant differences, that teaching is a kind of effective organization construction sprint teaching method, can produce a better teaching effect than traditional teaching.

Using tissue construct teaching can attract more initiative and enthusiasm of the students practice, to make the students produce strong interest in learning, played down the sprint project dull and boring, and complete the teaching task well, improve the teaching quality.

4.2 Recommendations

As a result of the sprint teaching intensity big, single action technology, teachers should be arranged according to the actual situation of schools and students practice, fully will organize constructive learning teaching form to the teaching.

In the teaching process to join all kinds of game as well as other sports, improve the students' interest in learning school to organize the games, to advocate students to exercise every day, and thus promotes the sunlight sports in the development of the school, the sprint sports ability of students, promote the all-round development of students' body quality.

Teaching organization construction should be used with traditional teaching, each take its long, complementary and its short, can achieve better teaching effect, also can promote the development of sports.

REFERENCES

[1] Li Junyong. Of college track and field teaching mode innovation research [J]. Journal of shanxi normal university sports institute, 2007, (7): 36–38.
[2] Xie Jingyue. The current situation of ordinary university sports teaching mode and countermeasure analysis [J]. Journal of zhejiang sports science, 2007, (3): 98–100.
[3] Zhang. Chen Qi. Briefly constructive learning and teaching [J]. Journal of education research, 1999, (4): 65–68.
[4] Shen Zhong. Introduction to induced teaching method [J]. Shenyang: liaoning sports science and technology, 2003, (2):5–6.
[5] Wang chuan, Du Zhaocai. Track and field [M]. Beijing: China sports press, 2005.

Computer, Intelligent Computing and Education Technology – Liu, Sung & Yao (Eds)
© *2014 Taylor & Francis Group, London, ISBN 978-1-138-02469-4*

Induction of teaching in the applied research of the professional sports teaching in colleges and universities

L. Tan & D.-M. Yang
School of PE, Jiangxi Normal University, Nanchang, Jiangxi, China

ABSTRACT: Induction of teaching is a kind of inspired by induction, induction is given priority to, interpret the comprehensive teaching method of demonstration is complementary, it through a series of induction, inspire interest of learning, take the initiative to understand and grasp the key techniques, actively participate in to complete the learning process, induced to the passive learning process of students a strong desire to explore herself and successful experience of the state of the teaching methods. Through the experiment teaching method, using concise and have leading language or signal, games and game modes, or by using visual organs (such as video, charts) induced teaching content and plan design, studying the effect of inducing teaching of middle school teaching. Results show that in sprint in PE teaching in colleges and universities, using the method of induction, more can improve students' learning enthusiasm, initiative, the teaching effect obviously.

Keywords: induction of teaching; sprint; teaching experiment

1 PREFACE

In today's colleges and universities sports teaching, is still the main part of the sports teaching of track and field, and sprint in track and field sports is not only very important project, is also the objective basis of track and field. At present, the track and field teaching generally adopts the traditional teaching and practice methods, namely in learning techniques, teachers explain—students Practice—error correction—students to master the technology, greatly influenced the enthusiasm of students in the class and the degree of interest in teaching.[2] In order to make students interested in physical education, better arouse student's enthusiasm and initiative and make them better participate in sports teaching process, as the main body of physical education, teachers in teaching in combination with the practical situation of students' age characteristics and, using induction teaching, such as: language induction, induction, action induced signal, peer, etc.,[1] effectively improve the students' learning enthusiasm, initiative and cultivate the students' sound personality and good mental quality, etc., to complete the teaching tasks, improve the teaching effect has an important role in promoting.

Sports induced in this paper, by discussing the teaching method in sprint technique teaching, not only enriched the teaching methods in colleges and universities, or even other project teaching method, of the university sports teaching methods and highlights the breaking, and the significance of the innovation concept.

2 RESEARCH OBJECT AND METHODS

2.1 *Research object*

In Jiangxi Normal university sports institute, a total of 80 randomly selected the same grade 2 class boys as cases as the research object. Adopt double blind experiment design and random sampling way is divided into two groups: control group and experimental group, make the results of the study objective and true.

2.2 *Research methods*

2.2.1 *Literature*

During the study, through the library, and China journal net database, access to a large number of monographs about track and field teaching theory, and the sprint teaching reform and teaching method of journals, books, paper and other materials, as this study provides certain theoretical material.

2.2.2 *Teaching experimental method*

Which contrast between groups, groups within the contrast experiment of teaching method, in every link of sprint technique teaching experimental group and control group by inducing teaching and traditional teaching respectively, through the teaching experiment results analysis and comparison the difference between the two groups.

2.2.3 *Mathematical statistics*

Sorts through the relevant data, using SPSS13.0 software to the related data statistics and analysis of the conventional.

3 RESULTS AND ANALYSIS

3.1 *Contrastive analysis of the two groups before the experiment*

Before the experiment, we for the experimental group and control group of 100 and moving 60 meters grades were tested, the results of detection are analyzed and compared (Table 1).

Table 1 shows that the experimental group and control group before the experiment of 100 and moving 60 meters results were similar, the two groups of 100 meters and grades were average is only 0.04 s, the achievements of the two groups of independent sample t test, $P = 0.254 > 0.05$, value shows that the experimental group and control group students before the experiment, 100 there was no significant difference; Moving 60 Metres between the two groups of performance difference, the difference between the experimental group and control group averaged only 0.04 s, and t test $P = 0.780 > 0.05$ value shows that the experimental group and control group in the experiment before moving 60 meters results there is no significant difference. Which showed that no difference between the two groups to contrast and analysis of the experiment.

3.2 *In the control group before and after the experiment analysis*

The control group before and after the experiment study sprint has always been the emphasis and difficulty in track and field teaching in colleges and universities, the teachers are trying to explore more

simple and effective teaching methods, to make the students more quickly and accurately understand and master the sprint start, acceleration run, on the way to run, sprints, such as technology, enables students to constantly improve their physical quality. After three months of the traditional teaching method, namely the teacher's explanation, demonstration, students' practice of the control group than in the past the average grades had improved, learn from Table 2, the control group of students improve the average score of 100 m 0.26 s; Moving can improve the average score of 60 s 0.36, and P value is 0.0482, 0.0482. Showed that traditional teaching methods can although the method is simple, single form, teaching means boring,[3] but rigorous, attitude, insisted that is worth carrying forward, can effectively improve the students' achievement and technology level, this also is the traditional teaching method is widely used for a long time. Born 100 m, moving average 60 m and t test results.

3.3 *Experimental group in comparative analysis before and after the experiment*

Table 3 shows that after sprint technology courses of study and practice, the experimental group students' 100 m grade point average of 12.15 s, 0.47 s; increased than previously Students moving 60 m grade point average of 6.65 s, 0.52 s increased than previously, through independent sample t

Table 2. Control group before and after the experiment the students 100 m, moving average 60 m and t test results.

	Number of people	100 meters	Moving 60 meters
Before the experiment	40	12.58 s	7.16 s
After the experiment	40	12.32 s	6.80 s
P		0.0482	0.0393

Table 1. The experimental group and control group before the experiment, 100 m, moving average 60 m and t test results.

	Number of people	100 meters	Moving 60 meters
Experimental group	40	12.62 s	7.12 s
Control group	40	12.58 s	7.16 s
P		0.254	0.780

Table 3. Experimental group before and after the experiment the students 100 m, moving average 60 m and values.

	Number of people	100 meters	Moving 60 meters
Before the experiment	40	12.62 s	7.12 s
After the experiment	40	12.15 s	6.60 s
P		0.254	0.780

test, P value for 100 m = 0.00145 < 0.05, is very obvious in progress before and after the experiment, there was very significant difference; Moving 60 m P value = 0.00256 < 0.00256, there is very significant difference. Experimental group of students before and after the experiment results are very significant difference, that induction teaching as a more novel teaching method, to improve our teaching effects and improve the overall level of students is good.

3.4 Contrastive analysis of the experimental group and control group after experimental teaching

Informed by Table 4, t test P value = 0.04473 < 0.05 shows that the experimental group and control group 100 meters after the experiment results have significant difference; P value = 0.04835 < 0.04835 shows that the experimental group and control group after experimental moving 60 meters have significant difference. Therefore, induction of teaching in secondary schools teaching in the teaching effect is obvious.

Experimental results show that the experimental group and control group analyzed before and after the experiment, the experimental group in the first two grades not exist significant difference, and the average is basically the same, after three months of traditional teaching and the induction, two groups of results have been significantly improved, the experimental group grades higher than the control group, and through the test of significance, there is significant difference between experimental group and control group, suggests that induction of teaching is good for students to learn and master sprint techniques, can produce a better teaching effect than traditional teaching. So, in professional sports teaching in colleges and universities use induction teaching, the improvement of student achievement, technology, and use the function of good teaching methods.

Sprint teaching application inducing teaching method to make up for the deficiency of the traditional teaching method, can according to the characteristics of the traditional teaching method

Table 4. Experimental group and control group in the experimental students after 100 m, moving average 60 m and P values.

	Number of people	100 meters	Moving 60 meters
Experimental group	40	12.15 s	6.65 s
Control group	40	12.32 s	6.80 s
P		0.254	0.780

and the new curriculum reform and the age of the students, physical characteristics such as making reasonable teaching plan, and the reasonable design of teaching content, give full play to the teacher's dominant and the subject role of students, improve the students' learning enthusiasm, initiative, from the perspective of induction and inspiration, develop students' potential, develop their intelligence, greatly enhance the technological learning ability of students, improve the teaching effect, is a kind of effective sprint teaching method in middle school.[4] Such as using concise and have leading language or signal, for the students to establish correct action representation, stimulate the desire to practice; Using the methods such as game and competition teaching stimulate students interest in learning, arouse the enthusiasm of students' learning; Use visual organs (such as video, charts) design induction of teaching content and plan to exert students' subjective initiative; Follow the principle of gradual and from easy to difficult, complete the teaching task and improve teaching quality, etc.[5] Not only make students better grasp techniques, but also cultivate students self experience, learning habit of positive thinking, continuously revised and enrich students' awareness of original technology of short gun, give full play to students' subjective inquiry, causes the student to sprint technology continuously improve and improve.

4 CONCLUSIONS AND RECOMMENDATIONS

4.1 Conclusion

Control group and experimental group before the experiment in two groups of 100 and moving 60 meters result there is no significant difference, the two groups have homogeneous comparability; The control group before and after the experiment of 100 m and moving 60 meters results exist significant difference; The experimental group before and after the experiment of 100 m and moving 60 meters results significant sex differences.

Experimental group and control group after experimental students of 100 m and moving 60 meters exist significant difference, suggests that teaching is an effective method of middle school teaching, can produce a better teaching effect than traditional teaching.

Induced teaching can attract more students to practice using the initiative and enthusiasm, make students produce strong interest in learning, played down the sprint project dull and boring, and complete the teaching task well, improve the teaching quality.

4.2 Recommendations

Under the new teaching idea, PE teachers should pay attention to the teaching principle, teaching methods, teaching process system, and based on this flexible use of the induced teaching.

When carries on the induction of teaching, pay attention to students as the main body, teacher as dominant, pay attention to students' autonomy and spontaneity, emphasizing the teacher's leading role and students' main body role interaction, should establish harmonious classroom atmosphere.

Induction of teaching should be used with traditional teaching, each take its long, complementary and its short, can achieve better teaching effect, also can promote the development of sports.

REFERENCES

[1] ShiHuiJuan. Induced several teaching methods of physical education teaching [M]. Modern education science. 2010, 2:156–158.

[2] Liu Hongjun. Heuristic method of teaching in the sprint technique teaching experimental study [J]. Journal of Beijing sports university, 2008, 31 [6]: 27 to 28.

[3] Yu Ii xian. He Zhongkai induction method of motor skill learning [J]. Journal of sport, 2002, 9 [6]: 72–74.

[4] Liu Hongjun. Induction teaching method in the sprint technique teaching experimental study [J]. Journal of Beijing sports university, 2000, 2 [5]: 64–66.

[5] Shen Zhong. Introduction to induced teaching method [J]. Shenyang: liaoning sports science and technology, 2003, 2:5–6.

Nanchang each female university students participate in physical exercise situation and countermeasures

L. Tan & D.-M. Yang
School of PE, Jiangxi Normal University, Nanchang, Jiangxi, China

ABSTRACT: To improve awareness of the Female College Students to actively participate in physical exercise, to promote their physical and mental development, the use of literature data, questionnaire and mathematical statistics, colleges and universities in Nanchang Female College Students in the school self-Recognizing the situation and participate in physical exercise frequency, intensity, time, status of the investigation methods of analysis. Propose appropriate measures: First, enhance sports awareness exercise correctly and clearly understand the "health" of the inner meaning; Second, pay attention to age, physical fitness and other individual differences on the basis of clear physical exercise load, so that students know their workout glance load; Third, with the network, the media, campus banners and other media to promote the important role of physical exercise etc.

Keywords: female college students; physical exercise

1 PREFACE

April 2007 "Sunshine Sports" was officially launched on school physical education, extracurricular physical exercise, Health of University Students and other aspects of more comprehensive requirements. Physical exercise can not only improve people's physical condition, but also can improve mental health, mental health is to improve the level of effective carrier, the mental health of college students has a positive and important regulatory role.[1] Female students participate in physical exercise; to some extent can reflect on the health status of our knowledge of women's degree of attention. Strengthening College Students' physical activity, enhance physical fitness, on the one hand is to improve the health of students, cultivating moral, intellectual and physical development of high-level personnel an important guarantee; hand, good physical health is the ultimate goal and the ultimate goal.[2] Our academic extracurricular physical activity on university research more, but most studies involving female students in the state with over always saying: fewer girls than boys or poor. For the current sports or academic research on the lack of female college students, hoping to pass on Female College Students Physical Training of analysis to understand the female students' sports consciousness and behavior, physical activity status, from a realistic point of view, a strategic vision and a practical need to explore how to improve the awareness of female students physical exercise.

2 RESEARCH OBJECT AND METHOD

2.1 *Object of study*

Object of this paper is to Nanchang, the university first, second and third-year female students, a 296-year female students, 32.1% of the total number, 315 sophomore female students, the total number of 34.2%, three-year female 311 students, 33.7% of the total number.

2.2 *Research methods*

2.2.1 *Literature*
Based on the research process, inspect and collect a lot about sports sociology, pedagogy, sports psychology, statistics and the Students' Health and physical exercise, and other related disciplines, literature and information, and data collation and analysis of each screening for this study provide strong theoretical basis and reference materials.

2.2.2 *Questionnaire*
Questionnaire distributed to female students entrusted to the hands of teachers, and to guide and supervise the students fill out questionnaires recovered. The questionnaires were distributed and 1,000 were returned 922 response rate was 92.2%, 900 valid questionnaires, accounting for 97.6 percent efficiency.

Questionnaire validity test validity refers to the survey findings illustrate the effectiveness of the described problems. To ensure that the questionnaire be able to reflect the contents of the study, the questionnaire "very effective, effective, basically valid, invalid" the overall evaluation of four kinds of scoring methods. In order to improve the reliability of the test, according to the logic analysis and inspection requirements, experts invited to participate in the audit of the audit assessment questionnaire, and then based on expert opinions and suggestions to make the necessary additions and modifications. Experts believe that the questionnaire was designed to meet the requirements, are valid.

Questionnaire reliability test reliability refers survey findings reflect the actual situation of credibility. The survey questionnaire reliability test used the test-retest method, sell its stability factor. In the survey sample within a small range, the first payment in 13 days and returned questionnaires will be sent again to the same batch test questionnaire, please fill in a similar questionnaire it. After the survey questionnaires counted twice in the same variable correlation coefficient and a significant test, the results show correlation coefficients were greater than 0.9, indicating a higher degree of credibility questionnaire, in line with the requirements of sociological surveys.

2.2.3 Mathematical statistics

In this study, the conventional statistical methods, all of the data processing in Excel and other software on your computer system uses the appropriate statistical processing to complete.

3 SURVEY RESULTS AND ANALYSIS

3.1 Health survey of self-awareness

According to the survey, female college students in their health status satisfactory 74% of the total number of people, only 11% very satisfied, 15% dissatisfied, consider themselves superior physique 15%. Think better and generally accounted for 38%, respectively, and 38%, more than 90% of female college students consider themselves physique without any problems. 94% of female students that health is very important, but there are 11% of the students that no disease is health. For a long time, conventional wisdom has been that no disease that is healthy, but with social progress and scientific development, people's understanding of health tends science.[3] Students' awareness of the importance of physical exercise level, to a certain extent, a reflection of its participation in physical activity habits ideological foundation.[4] Female students at school think that health is very important, very confident of their own health, but most of the students' physical condition to be improved.

Few female students' awareness of health there is a deviation, that no disease is health.

3.2 Extracurricular physical exercise purpose Survey

Data show that: most of the girls during their leisure time to participate in regular physical exercise, but the motivation to participate in sports, but there is a big difference (Table 1). Comprehensive analysis: In the regular exercise of those, because i like sports and participate in exercise accounted for 41% of the total number of surveys, to improve their fitness, exercise for sports 21% of the total number, in order to shape the body, including weight loss and free time for independent exercise of the total number of 20% pure spend leisure time physical activity with the possession of only a small percentage of 19%.

3.3 Physical exercise intensity and duration survey

Physical exercise intensity and duration of physical exercise is the core issue of the size and duration of exercise intensity is to determine the length of the key elements of good and bad effects of exercise, and only know how to control the timing and intensity of exercise in order to achieve the effect of exercise science. Survey are shown in Table 2, 48.8 percent of female college students each time to ensure the exercise of 30 minutes or more, 51 percent of female students each exercise duration of 30 minutes or less, only 26% of the students during the physical exercise conscious control of exercise intensity and duration, and occasionally and very little control exercise time and intensity, respectively, 39% and 36%. From the statistical results, participation in extracurricular physical exercise female college students have a more aggressive behavior, but the exercise capacity of less than scientific requirements, exercise is not high quality. Scientific training requirements are: moderate intensity, each lasting 20 to 30 minutes; and exercise regularly in order to maintain the necessary fitness level.[5] The author believes that universities

Table 1. Causes physical exercise regularly participate statistics.

	Like sports	Enhance physical fitness	Shape the body	Spend time
Number of people	260	131	126	119
Percentage	41	21	20	19

Table 2. Physical exercise intensity and duration survey.

	Participate in physical exercise duration		Exercise intensity control		
	More than 30 min	Following 30 min	Conscious	Occasionally	Seldom
Number of people	450	472	235	359	328
Percentage	49	51	26	39	36

Table 3. Physical exercise methods source.

Source	Television	Teacher	Literature	Network	Else
Number of people	150	558	249	97	294
Percentage	16	61	27	11	32

Table 4. Exercise precautions survey (E: exist; N: negate).

	Preparatory activities		Brine refill		Relax		Sports injuries	
	E	N	E	N	E	N	E	N
Number of people	124	798	238	348	458	206	222	700
Percentage	13	87	26	38	50	23	24	76

should increase the female students in extracurricular physical exercise participation rates, based on trying to increase female students of physical exercise intensity, in other words, to solve the problem of the quality of their physical activity.

3.4 *Methods of cognitive exercise survey*

Scientific training methods are very important to understand the scientific method can exercise detours, fewer sports injuries.[6] If the right way, we can get a multiplier effect, and the parties may often be caused by inappropriate methods of unexpected injuries, sports injuries mostly because they do not carry out preparatory activities and events caused by improper methods. As can be seen from Table 3, 61 percent of female college students the scientific method is derived from the physical training physical education teachers, physical education teachers in the student seen sporting cognitive aspects of scientific knowledge has played a positive role.

From Table 4, the students' regular physical exercise need to pay attention to understand fully: Physical exercise preparatory activities when only 13 percent of people; exercising care brine inattention and 38%, respectively, supplemented; carelessly relax and do not mind a total of 23%; sports injuries have been 24%.

3.5 *Physical exercise findings of project selection*

Survey shows that female students often participate in sports activities as the ratio of highest to lowest: ballroom dancing (18%), badminton (16%), walking (15%), hiking (12%), running (9%), fitness operation (6%), female college students favorite sports sort is badminton, ballroom dancing, walking, aerobics, running, climbing. Overall, the students on fitness means not demanding technical factors, while too much is the pursuit of its fitness factor, especially for some easy to carry out, without space, equipment limitations before public health projects single bell. Such as badminton, walk, run etc. These are all different aspects of contemporary college student's physical fitness screening tool changes and features.

3.6 *Select the time period and group exercise situation survey*

Survey results shown, female students selected for the morning. Exercise time 22% of the total number, 35% of student's workout time of uncertainty in the evening up to 43%; their exercise alone accounted for 13%, and exercise with a friend accounted for 87%. 15:00 to 5:00 Physical Training after Class is the best time. After a day

Table 5. Select the time period and group exercise questionnaire.

	Exercise time			Exercises	
	Morning	Uncertain	At night	Self	With friends
Number of people	205	319	398	122	800
Percentage	22	35	43	13	87

of learning, the brain and nervous system are in a state of intense work, this time not only to enhance the physical workout, you can also make the nerves to rest. From human physiology and after school to see the purpose of physical exercise, this time period is the best, but most female students chose to exercise at night, probably due to the school's crowding out other arrangements this time period. From the point of view of scientific training, this situation should arouse the attention of school authorities should try to free up time for the afternoon to allow students the freedom to organize in order to exercise a little more spare time.

4 CONCLUSIONS AND RECOMMENDATIONS

4.1 Conclusion

Most of the girls from the independent exercise of consciousness have recognized the importance of physical exercise, and for after-school physical activity have higher interest. While girl's beauty psychological, as shape the body, including weight loss but also inspired the girls actively involved in extracurricular physical exercise to go.

Female college students in physical exercise on both the quantity and quality meet the requirements, specific performance: short duration of exercise and exercise intensity is small, etc.

From time to participate in physical exercise, physical exercise different grades in college female students over three-grade girls, two grade girl's workout time to be poor.

4.2 Advice

Physical education teachers in the teaching should actively encourage students to exercise; consciously strengthening exercise for female college student's personal temperament, physical fitness, physical health, future development has an important role.

Reforms to make it to entertainment, sports teaching direction.

Continue to increase efforts in building sports equipment, mobilization and suggestions society organizations, public sports venues to facilitate students to participate in sports activities, while increasing physical activity after school students the best time to provide protection.

REFERENCES

[1] Fu Yi, Yu Fang, Liu Ding-yi. Mental Health and Physical Education Related research [J]. China Sport Science and Technology, 2006, 45(5):120–125.
[2] Hao Shu-yuan. On the Physical Fitness and Health [J]. 2002, 9(2):124–127.
[3] Jiang Shi-quan, Guo Hong-bo. Mental health factors and countermeasures [J]. Shanghai Institute of Physical Education, 2003, 27(6):144–145.
[4] Liang Jian-chun. Factors affecting the formation of College Students study habits [J]. Physical Education, 2001, 20(7):29–31.
[5] Yan Ning, Mao Rong-jian, Mao Zhi-xiong. Physical activity and emotional effects of physical exercise [J]. Beijing Sport University, 2003, 26(1):30–32.
[6] Yang Jian-xiong, Jiang Li-qi. Higher Normal Students' Physical Exercises workout crowd crowd with non-comparative study of mental health [J]. Beijing Sport University, 2003, (26)5:613–614.

Computer, Intelligent Computing and Education Technology – Liu, Sung & Yao (Eds)
© 2014 Taylor & Francis Group, London, ISBN 978-1-138-02469-4

An application of computer in sports management of school

J.W. Han
Handan Polytechnic College, Handan, P.R. China

H.J. Wang
Hebei Vocational College for Correctional Police, Handan, P.R. China

ABSTRACT: This paper gives a research on the application of computer in school sports management based on literature data, observation and interviews, analyzed application situation of computer technology in university physical education management, management of extra curricular activities, student health management, sports equipment and facilities management and sports files and intelligence information management, providing the reference for enhancing college sports management efficiency and strengthening the effectiveness of school education management.

Keywords: PE management; computer application; teaching; education management

1 INTRODUCTION

With the development of science and technology economy, IT has become an important pillar of social development in the era of knowledge economy. Computer technology which is scientific and efficient in all of life has been widely used. School education management is one of them. Physical Education (PE) management is an important part of the school education management which plays an important role in the overall development of students. Enhancing the efficiency of PE management has important significance to achieve goals of PE and coordinated development of school affairs. So, it is very necessary to promote the scientific and the efficiency of PE management. The departments of PE management should use modern tools, such as computer and network, to manage the practice work of PE management and promote PE management work implemented effectively.

2 THE MAIN CONTENTS

2.1 The application status of computers in school sport management

PE management is an important component of education management and is based on human resource and materials, which uses the most effective means and methods according to the development law of PE development for the work of the school in various sports planning, implementation and inspection evaluation. PE management is systematic, complex and independent. Many schools use computer, network or multimedia technology to make PE management, but due to some PE educators' traditional ideas and knowledge structure, IT work is constrained to apply in sports management, and auxiliary management function of computer and network technology has not been fully exploited.

Computer technology in Physical education management needs the hardware facilities, such as computers, multimedia and projectors. Different levels of economic development in different regions differs the application of computer-aided management. The lower level of economic development has less hardware facilities, so a certain restrictions will be subject to computer-aided PE management. The relatively high level of economic development in schools area makes a basic configuration of the facility, but the traditional concepts of education and economic makes PE management software relatively scarce, and lack of computer knowledge of some physical education teachers, some developed PE management software can not function effectively. Some schools in economically developed areas actively carry out a number of practical activities of computer applications, such as multimedia sports Courseware presentations, computer-assisted physical education teachers in the majority of the sports center, but the computer-aided management theory is little and plays little role in the practice teaching research.

2.2 Application research of computer in PE management

Computer Application in Physical Education: Application in Teaching schedule Management. Teaching schedule Management in physical education management is mainly based on existing human and material resources for periodic review or temporary checks of physical education schedule program to ensure fulfilling the requirements of the teaching plan teaching programs such as lesson plans throughout the year and semester schedule unit lesson plans. This management is often inefficiency, and computer aided management will greatly improve facilitate management effective. In recent years, computer network management in school education is widely used in many schools in order to enhance the efficiency of management. Many schools have opened a campus network and LAN, and physical education teachers can put various teaching programs through a computer network into the computer store, and then through the computer related to the campus of the online file-sharing. So that it not only can be used for sport managers to view timely review of the teaching plan, but mutual exchange between teachers can be learnt. It promotes the management of PE efficient.

Computer application in teaching management: Recently, Multimedia Technology is applied widely to make courseware in PE teaching. The Multimedia Technology could show the writing, audio and video at the same time, and show the physical action or single action in the way of pictures or cartoon to the students to make the students understand easily. For example, some complex physical action could be replay again and again, the students could master the key more quickly and the teaching could be efficient. After the lesson, exchange information between the students and their teachers or between the teachers could be easily by email or bbs. Some schools in poor areas can also get the latest teaching resources and information by computer technology from developed areas to achieve efficient use of physical resources.

The application in theory test scores assessment and summarizing feedback management: The traditional theory test method requires a lot of manpower and resources, but using computer network technology by building an online theory test system, can achieve real-time and statistical hand-on and score, so that it not only improves the management efficiency but reduces emotional aspect to be more objective and realistic. The assessment of semester or academic year to the overall quality of teaching, including teaching ability, teaching level and teaching comprehensive, can be put in the computer in a timely manner, and it will be summer when the summary of teaching quality, according to the evaluation criteria, to give an objective assessment. After a comprehensive analysis and summary of the results, it will make timely feedback to accurate and comprehensive improvements in teaching management to improve management efficiency.

2.3 Computer application in extracurricular activities

The application in the collective extracurricular activities: The collective extracurricular activities are frequently Morning exercises and calisthenics. The management adds up the quantity and quality, and then put them in to make the graphs showing to assess the results. With this, it could be easily to monitor the exercises. PE management could arrange the schedule, the content and the guide of exercises by the campus network, and inform the class timely. And the manager could summer and add up the data to do the preparation for research.

The application in team training and athletic competition management: The computer plays an important role in the team training and athletic competition management. In many junior and senior schools, the coaches often train students based on their intuition and experience during training. The emotional aspect is too much, and the rational aspect is too little. The coaches could record the daily test results about the players' physiological and psychological qualities, and then make a scientific analysis through the computer. According to this, the coaches could make the schedule more reasonable. Computer application in the athletic competition could make the Organization of the competition more orderly, such as, the making of Official Program of the choreography, the collection of the data, and the release of the race results and so on.

2.4 Computer application in students' health test management

The health of the students is the key of the education. The health of the students could reflect the effect of the physical education directly. The improvement of the health plays an important role. Now every student has his health files, and schools do regularly a comprehensive physical test to students. After the test, the results needed to be added up artificially, and then be stored in the health files. That is a huge workload. With the application of computer, the electric files could be built, and the data could be stored and searched easily. The assessment and the solution could be done easily, and the targeted advice could be given convenient.

2.5 Computer application in the management of sports equipment

Sport equipment management is main of the acquisition and maintenance of sports equipment and the construction of the stadium. Application of computer technology to the management of sports venies is main through the campus network to public timely of the configuration of sport equipment and sport costs. So as to it achieves financial management and transparency of the school. In the sport equipment management, it must be classified according to the assets, materials and consumables. Meanwhile it sounds the management system in equipment purchase and maintenance. If simply relied on manual management, it is easy to result oversight in management, and management efficiency will be greatly reduced. Application of computer technology will greatly improve work efficiency. Computer classifies and statistics the purchase time of equipment type, which managers can easily access to relevant information. So as to make a deal for the specific questions, meanwhile it can be through the campus network to announce the equipment loaned by which class and student. Students not only easily choose to borrow, but also improve equipment utilization, and promote school sport to carry out.

2.6 Computer applications in PE work files and intelligence information management

Work files and intelligence information management are an important contents of PE management, faced with a large number of complex work files and intelligence information accumulation and sorting statistics, computer applications makes it a powerful information storage and feedback features to be fully exploited through the application computer technology, and timely information on the files and collect intelligence data processing aggregate storage and so on. The higher education sector and the PE department issued various documents, work rules and regulations, training program, teaching program and students' health, etc, which would be through the characters or graphic scanning, then the data entry method to classify had been stored in the computer. That not only files and intelligence information achieve reasonable and orderly management and ease to look up information. The rapid development and popularization of the Internet, which allows us easier to access to a large number of the latest sports information, and timely to collect and store materials. That not only promotes the smooth development of school sport, but also helps to raise the level of sports research.

3 CONCLUSIONS

The use of computers improves the efficiency of PE management, through computer networks, the management of PE working papers and the public of other information, such as schedules and decisions will be more quickly and convenient, which greatly enhances the timeliness of PE management. The storage and retrieval the information of PE management by using computer is conducive to the orderly management. With the application of computer technology in PE management, the physical education will develop scientifically and efficiently, and the computer will also play more and more important role in PE management.

REFERENCES

Bai Wei. 2009. Sports school computer management system development and implementation. Liaoning Sport Science and Technology, (5):96~97.

Lin Yingsui. 2006. Thoughts on application of computer to the PE teaching management in our college. Science, 11:33~34.

Liu Huaijin, 2011. Zhou Cibao, Zheng Weitao. Management and practice of open computer room in college sports laboratory. Bulletin of Sport Science & Technology, 5:16~17.

Pang Li, Niu Jianjun. 2012. Discussion on school sports management informatization. Bulletin of Sport Science & Technology, 3:125~127.

You Genghui. 2010. Preliminary study on computer-aided management of physical education. Management Observer, 15:206~207.

Wu Tao. 2008. College Sports Computer Applications Management System. New curriculum research, (3):125~126.

Xu Miao. 2013. The integration of computer technology and the university sports teaching research. Electronic Test, 18:161~162.

Computer, Intelligent Computing and Education Technology – Liu, Sung & Yao (Eds)
© *2014 Taylor & Francis Group, London, ISBN 978-1-138-02469-4*

English teaching under the guidance of innovative thinking

J. Wang & Y. Zhu

School of Foreign Language, Wuhan Bioengineering Institute, Hubei, China

ABSTRACT: Modern English teaching requires that English classes must face all students and focus on the quality-oriented education. This paper dwells on how to walk into English classroom and experience a new teaching mode that makes English "alive". This paper, discussing the two major deals—teachers and the classroom, teachers and students, amply demonstrates innovative thinking can make English class "alive" so as to better achieve the effectiveness of English teaching.

Keywords: english teaching; innovative thinking

1 INTRODUCTION

There is no fixed method in teaching. Educators have been exploring, pursuing and striving for effective teaching method. Modern education requires teachers to establish characteristic sense, and form individualized instruction. It also requires that teaching methods avoid simplification, modeling, formulation, and classroom teaching should be student-centered, giving full play to students' initiative and creativity. Therefore, by using a variety of teaching activities to make the classroom really "alive", we must create a pleasant learning environment to stimulate students' interest in learning and a strong desire for knowledge. We must cultivate students' enjoyable learning emotion and develop learning ability to let them seek happiness and development during learning procedure. Thereby, while students form autonomously learning, teaching quality is also improved. To achieving these goals, it is necessary to give full play to the innovative thinking in the teaching process. So, what is innovative thinking?

The so-called innovative thinking is that people use existing knowledge and experience to enlarge and develop thinking skills in new areas. That is, the original thinking in pursuit of the best and latest knowledge in the field of people's thinking. As Albert Einstein said, "The innovative thinking is a kind of thinking ability which is novel and valuable, unconventional, with high mobility and persistence, but also clearly drawing the outline and solving the problem." innovative thinking does not come naturally, and it continues to nurture and develop through people's learning and practice. Recent years, in my own groping in teaching English, I used this way of thinking to guide students to learn English, and the effect is gratifying!

2 TEACHER AND CLASSROOM WITH INNOVATIVE CONSCIOUSNESS

As we all know, the classroom model in the United States, Britain and Canada and other countries is quite different from our Chinese. They have small class size, and their teaching styles are very free and lively. While, with the large number of students in our Chinese classrooms, many teachers still hold outdated concept, requiring students to behave in the classroom, so that in this classroom students tend to produce a sense of depression, or psychological disorders, and often have a feeling of being led by the nose, easy to produce irritability, emotional weariness and psychological conflict. In fact, as long as we use our brains, think more ideas, students' psychological barriers can be eliminated, and students' high level of enthusiasm can be cultivated. That is, we need to update the concept, using innovative classroom consciousness to enable students to learn in amusement.

2.1 *Utilizing warming-up activities as lead-in part before class*

If English classes coincide with the domestic and foreign holidays, such as Women's Day, Trees-Planting Day, May Day, Mother's Day, Christmas Day, etc., teacher or students can make presentations and introductions about these holidays. If there are non holidays, activities can be performed like singing English songs, speaking an English news, telling an English humorous story, practicing some English tongue twisters, introducing the related knowledge you read online that associated with the character or the information in the text to lead in the new lesson. In short, there are plenty and flexible ways to practice English before class.

2.2 *Utilizing the auxiliary tool for situational teaching*

The new English textbook prints with illustrations, providing a lot of information for students to learn. But these illustrations are static, its connotation has certain hidden meaning. If teachers can make static illustrations "moving up", namely, use computer-assisted instruction or slide show, then the classroom will be enriched with large-capacity, multi-information, multi-interest and efficiency. In order to develop students' thinking, cooperative interaction approach can be taken. That is, under the guidance of teachers, students' hands and brains are activated to perform in cooperation, and thus they play each person's strengths, compensate for each other, learn from each other, inspire and coach each other, forming a three-dimensional network of interacting thinking.

While students are in the cooperation in drafting, teachers should encourage students to develop their innovative thinking and combine components in illustrations, giving full play to students' intrinsic motivation and creativity. In the production of illustrations, there are several requirements: 1. Flexible production. Another illustration should be faithful to, but can not be bound by, the original design, its content may have reasonable additions or deletions to serve for the purpose of the teaching material. 2. Aesthetic education. Proportions between the screen required coordination. So students are learning and at the same time geting aesthetic education. 3. Broad participation. Allowing students to participate in recreating illustrations can reduce the burden on teachers, but also cultivate students' innovative spirit and practical ability. In the classroom, with a large number of listening and speaking practices, students should follow teachers' instructions by placing small puzzles to the command position. All these are beneficial to inspire students' thinking and develop students' intelligence.

Facts have proven that, only with one mouth and not using any tools, teacher is much more difficult to create a happy atmosphere and its effect is far worse. In English classes, with simple and graceful posture, we can increase the dynamic teaching; with images and humorous brief strokes, photos, etc., we can increase vitality of the blackboard; with advertising posters made from waste, we can add color to the classroom; with the use of multimedia courseware, we can enrich students' eyes and ears; with homemade poster, we let students experience and appreciate the beauty and expand the space of learning; with pasting students' masterpiece on the wall, we can let the walls speak for the students. These all reflect the application of aesthetics in teaching, in which teachers' starting point and students' feeling are both wonderful, and the pleasure of learning emerges naturally.

2.3 *Utilizing the plot in the textbook to do role-play*

Language acquisition aims at communication, which requires teachers simulate various scenarios according to the teaching goals, social culture and customs of English-speaking countries to develop students' communicative ability, making them correctly and appropriately use language. Then the podium becomes a stage for communication, we can decorate the classrooms as the bedrooms to live; decorate the classrooms as the stores to shop; decorate the classrooms as the hospitals to see a doctor; decorate the classrooms as the restaurants to dine; decorate the classrooms as the squares to play, etc.

For example, in the unit of *Visit*, I ordered students to use words such as bathroom, kitchen, living room and other room facilities. Students could do the design of their imagined future house in small groups, and each team member was asked to explain to the class. Groups competed with each other. I then set Best innovative Award, Best Choreography Award, Best props Award, Best Actor, Best actress, Best group Award, the effect of the game was very successful, much more than I expected. This will not only allow students to firmly grasp related words, but also let students play the spirit of cooperation and imagination. Teacher transforms different forms of teaching according to teaching materials with ornaments, hand puppets, pictures, to help students create a scene to do role-play, in which students will dedicate themselves to unconsciously reinforcing the old knowledge and memorizing the new content, and classroom is full of festive atmosphere.

2.4 *Continuous improvement of teaching to develop innovative thinking*

With the reform of modern education, exploring the future of education must be based on scientific selection of teaching materials and teaching methods. To achieve the creation of classroom education, teachers need to do everything possible to broaden the students' knowledge, create plenty of interesting topics to stimulate students' curiosity to stimulate students' innovative thinking. However, to stimulate student interest and improve the efficiency of classroom teaching, we shall start from the reform of teaching methods. 1. innovative retelling. Retelling process is actually the brain thinking process, which can train students' thinking ability. In text teaching, therefore, leading the students to do innovative retelling. On the basis of the content and form of the original, with grasping the original theme and story development, after processing, sorting, inducting, and rewriting, students repeat the text daringly and reasonably. In so doing, we can promote the rapid transformation of the student's ability of language knowledge. It is beneficial to develop students' intelligence and cultivate students' rich imagination to develop their innovative thinking. Innovative retelling can be divided into three types: 1) Variable retelling. It enables students to transform person, tense, voice or article. 2) Sequel retelling. According to the changes that may occur, using existing knowledge and imagination to tell the story with possible outcomes. This retelling help students develop imagination and innovative awareness. Such as, in Unit 3, Reading II, *A letter of complaint*. We can let students expand the association to tell *What would he do while the manager received this letter?* 3) General retelling. It is based on the content of the material presented to analyze, generalize, conclude main ideas of the text or paragraphs. This is a high level of retelling, and students need a strong inductive capacity. Such as, in Unit 6, Dialogue I, *Work Ethics*. We can let students tell *What is the work ethics?* 2. Impromtu speech. During the practice of listening and speaking, teacher shall try to give students time in class, so that they can fully show themselves to fight for a chance to speak. Such as, in Unit 2, Reading I, *Stunts in the cinema*. After students finishing retelling the text, I organized them to have a debate—*To be a stuntman (stuntwoman)/Not to be a stuntman (stuntwoman)*. Students' high enthusiasm and the warm scene fully demonstrated their language skills and thinking imagination, putting the ability of thinking imagination to a new height.

As stated above, retelling and speech are a kind of effective teaching methods to train students' pragmatic competence, to stimulate students' innovative thinking. Therefore, in the process of teaching, teachers should teach students in accordance with their aptitude. And according to students' actual level, teacher should choose the appropriate method to achieve the ideal effect in teaching English.

3 TEACHER AND STUDENT WITH INNOVATIVE CONSCIOUSNESS

As we all know that only reaches a certain quantitive level, things will have a qualitative leap. It is certainly true in learning English. Students need to learn the basics of the books to lay the foundation of knowledge, as the basis offers the possibility and foundation for the training of thinking ability. As the saying goes, knowledge provides the raw material for thought. In English teaching, it should be based on the basic teaching and training, striving to achieve students' learning being developed, alive, and thorough. There are two points needed to be attentioned. Firstly, it requires students to apply knowledge in practice with the full understanding rather than rote memorization. Secondly, it focuses on the mastery of knowledge on thinking. Based on the students' characteristics and ways of thinking, through various channels, by asking questions and inspiring and coaching to guide and encourage students' thinking, the knowledge structure should pave the way for students' ways of thinking. Learning while thinking, and knowledge learning should be guided by thinking.

3.1 *Achieving the equality between teachers and students and teaching democracy*

We all know that in the foreign classroom, teachers and students talk about each other's point of view. It is a strong democratic atmosphere, so the students think actively and question boldly. While in our classroon, because of our attention to behavior, students are very cautious and fearful for teachers, not daring to speak English. With the pass of time we created a number of "dumb English" learner. To change this situation requires that we shall change the concept of teachers, encourage students to expand multiple thinking, promote student-teacher interaction. Teachers, as the true participants, should change their roles flexibly, and make integration with students, so that students are more free to think and are inspired with intrinsic interest in learning. Meanwhile, we should correctly treat mistakes students made in the learning process. Blindly blaming can make students have psychological shading and disorders, resulting in students daring not to speak English in afraid of making mistakes. Therefore, teacher should actively and skillfully groom the errors occured in students' homeworks, papers, especially in spoken language, to ensure students' enthusiasm and confidence.

3.2 *Building harmonious teacher—student relationship after class*

Harmonious teacher-student relationship is the lubricants for teachers to impart knowledge and the assurance of English teaching quality. Therefore, the positive emotional communication can induce harmonious classroom atmesphere, playing a catalytic role to stimulate students' curiosity. So how to build harmonious teacher—student relationship? We have to study students. Study their psychology, remain open, emotional communication with students, strive to make friends with each student, and generate goodwill and trust between teachers and students in the subtle manipulation, leading students to show initiative and enjoyment to learn in order to facilitate our effective teaching.

3.3 Equally treating achievers and underachievers

In teaching, often there is a phenomenon of a serious breach of ideological education—students are artificially divided into superior and inferior camps. This leads to the haughty achievers and underachievers bearing huge psychological pressure and severe inferiority complex, worse still, severe mental illness. The symptoms showed in their jealous for achievers, hatred for teachers, poor discipline, and being destructive. In fact, everyone has self-esteem, and is potentially ingenuity. Converting underachievers, firstly, we need to respect and care for underachievers. Now students are sensitive to teachers' and outside evaluation. It calls for teachers to improve their teaching methods and ideas, giving every student full of eternal love from the bottom heart, no blaming, no rebuking, and believing they are malleable, at the same time, giving every student more successful experience. If we consider the level of underachievers in all aspects of preparations of lessons, teaching procedure, correcting, assisting, always concerning about their progress and more encouragement and affirmation, giving them the chance of success, then their interest will gradually emerge and will leap to achievers step by step, and our teaching quality will be largely improved. Thus, the fraternity and warm words of teacher will be a magic key to eliminate the psychological barriers, and motivate underachievers.

4 CONCLUSION

Practice has proved that teachers need to let boring teaching content reside in amusing, desirable situation by means of a combination of a variaty of teaching methods, making classroom interesting, communicative, full of activities and vitality. That enables students to devote all their energy both to experience the fun of participation and to learn to live, to cooperate, to learn, to overcome the difficulties, to establish the confidence of winning a campaign, to enjoy the joy of success.

In short, if innovative thinking is properly used in college English teaching in universities, there will be more beneficiaries—our students, because they will feel learning English is relaxed and happy and efficient.

REFERENCES

Babalis, T. & Xanthakou, Y. 2012. Research Attitude and Innovative-Creative Thinking: Differences between Undergraduate Male and Female Students. Social and Behavioral Sciences. 69: 1452–1461.

Barbot, B. & Randi, J. 2013. From perception to creative writing: A multi-method pilot study of a visual literacy instructional approach. Learning and Individual Differences. 28: 167–176.

Craft, A. & Cremin, T. 2007. Teacher stance in creative learning: A study of progression. Thinking Skills and Creativity. 2(2): 136–147.

Cropley, A.J. 2011. Teaching Creativity. Encyclopedia of Creativity (Second Edition): 435–445.

Davies, D. 2013. Creative learning environments in education—A systematic literature review. Thinking Skills and Creativity. 8: 80–91.

Jaarsveld, S. & Lachmann, T. 2012. Creative reasoning across developmental levels: Convergence and divergence in problem creation. Intelligence. 40(2): 172–188.

Özcan, D. 2010. Contributions of English teachers' behaviours on students' creative thinking abilities. Social and Behavioral Sciences. 2(2): 5850–5854.

Wang, A.Y. 2012. Exploring the relationship of creative thinking to reading and writing. Thinking Skills and Creativity. 7(1): 38–47.

Computer, Intelligent Computing and Education Technology – Liu, Sung & Yao (Eds)
© 2014 Taylor & Francis Group, London, ISBN 978-1-138-02469-4

Exercises item bank design of microwave course for fostering student's ability

Y.Y. Liang, Y.F. Mcng & G.Zh. Lv
Department of Electrical and Optical Engineering, Mechanical Engineering College, Shijiazhuang, China

ABSTRACT: With student as the center, with arousing the curiosity and fostering the ability of student as a starting point, exercises item bank that lay stress on the engineering background of the knowledge and the internal relations of courses content is designed in this paper. And the exercises item bank management and service technique is studied to fit learning depth and scope of the students. Purposes of the study is inspiring and enlightening the wisdom of the students, taping their potential, and fostering their ability of comprehensive using knowledge, engineering practice, and scientific researching innovations.

Keywords: microwave course; effective teaching; exercises item bank

Fundamental of microwave engineering course mainly consist of electromagnetic field theory, microwave technology, and antenna. These contents are important foundations of engineering technology for radar, communication, guidance, and electromagnetic countermeasure. In order to heighten the quality of teaching, fostering student's ability of microwave theory, technology, and engineering practice, a lot of work was down to improve teaching idea, content of courses, teaching method and aid in recent years. In this paper, exercises item bank of microwave coursc is designed and serviced, in order to fostering student's ability of mastering and applying microwave knowledge.

1 PROBLEMS AND COUNTERMEASURES IN MICROWAVE COURSE TEACHING

In educational reform of microwave course in recent years, we centre on students closely from beginning to end. Teaching quality was heightened by all means. Material object like waveguide, transmission line, kinds of microwave component and antenna are shown to visualize the abstract content. Animations like wave propagation, working state of transmission line, directional diagram of antenna are made to simplify the complex content. Network course is designed to make self-learning convenient for students, and strengthen experience exchanging to them. Undeniable, these measures achieve some good results, but it is not remarkable enough compare to the desired results. When a lecture is given, some students remain indifferent. So the teaching model needs to be studied to achieve good teaching results.

Linying Zhang studied that learning result is interfered with student's learning characteristics, and learning motivation is variable influenced by teaching behaviour.[2] The new student-centered point promote that student is the center of education. Learning of the student should learn on their own, not just absorb knowledge. Student's learning process is self-fulfillment.[1] Student need be given correct guidance to enhance the teaching effect.

While communicating with students, we also conducted a survey to be more targeted. We find that lack sympathy from learning and teaching is the key problem. From student's questionnaire, from selection of "lecture, self-learning, discuss each other, and do more exercise", 60% of them like lecture, and 70% of their learning gains are from classroom lectures. From selection of "some depth question, discuss questions between classmates, discuss questions with professor, thinking by yourself", they like "some depth question" best. Obviously, most students are used to professor lectures. Question guide and thought deep interaction should focus their efforts in teaching.

Students prefer acquire knowledge by their own to cramming passively by professor from their questionnaire. However, they don't like self-learning which need more time to learn. That tells us that when thinking and designing some topics, we should put ourselves in the mindset from students rather than knowledge. This is even harder work undoubtedly. Well-designed question is hard-earned precious. They are the daughters of hardworking and wisdom of professor. They should be recorded and accumulated to form exercise item bank to provide valuable information for the later teaching.

2 EXERCISES ITEM BANK DESIGN FOR FOSTERING STUDENT'S ABILITY

Up till now, studying and discussing of item bank are mainly about exam item bank. They consider the question from the separation of teaching and assessment.[3] They are interested in paper management and program of automatic papers generation.[4] There are several studies of exercise item bank development. They converted relevant requirements of syllabus into exercises, established "JTQB" teaching mode based on question.[5] There are many exercises in the back of each section of microwave materials. There are also many materials of exercises and answers. They play invaluable role in helping deepening microwave knowledge understanding, knowledge permanent and expanding student's thinking. We use the ripe exercise directly. But it isn't the key point of this paper. In this paper, designing of exercise item bank that stimulate students interest in learning and improve students' innovation ability is concerned. The former is realized by create contexts, and the latter needs cross functional knowledge.

2.1 Create contexts to stimulate student's interest

Babies have great powers of learning. They are very interest in everything. They are filled with curiosity and exploring spirit and never tired. Let's observe their learning. When they see a fresher thing, they observe it, gauge it, and explore the mysteries of it. Then they understand, and use it in their life experience. The same applies to students. As learning, understanding phenomenon should be introduced first. This can be done. In fact, any professional knowledge is used to solve actual problems in life or in engineering. When teaching materials are made, the specific issues and the solution will be distillated and abstracted to knowledge of formula and principle.

If the principle and formula are explained in teaching, supplemented with a certain amount of traditional exercises, students may grasp ways to work problem, but they don't understand them necessarily. They even fell boring very likely. However, if the initial engineering process is restored, the knowledge discovery and technology invention process is returned, students will have the knowledge, increasing their engineering ability, gain a sense of achievement in the process of independent thinking and problem-solving. Their thirst for knowledge will be aroused to make further improvement on learning and exploring. Start from student's known interested thing, lead to what they have learnt, allures them learning actively. Our exercise item bank is designed based on this train of thought.

For example, when polarity is learned, this question can be introduced: observe the antenna of radio and television, if the horizontal antenna is turned to vertical or vise versa, observe it, and think its reason. Thus vertical polarization and horizontal polarization of the wave can be introduced. Then the identification method of linear polarization and reciprocity of antenna directivity can be summarized.

2.2 Cross functional knowledge to form network

As other courses, teaching of microwave course is given lectures one by one according to chapter, section and knowledge point. In fact, one course or even several courses of a discipline, knowledge points are interconnected each other. It is a whole system for studying or solving a practical problem in a field. It is separated into different materials and knowledge module artificially according to knowledge attribution to learn in proper order. Like the course of "fundamental of microwave engineering", it can be transmitting, receiving and transmission wave in the entire communication system, it can also be antenna and feeder line of radar system. The fundamental theory can solve many problems in electromagnetic countermeasure, radar imaging and signal processing. Therefore, if teaching knowledge point just by knowledge point, no matter how well students learn, they couldn't see the wood for the trees.

After a stage of teaching, comprehensive exercise need be designed. A big system and a complete knowledge network can be formed by relating each knowledge point organically. Students then understand why they learn the knowledge, what they will accomplish, and what position they are in knowledge system and engineering application. By learning like this, can students solve problems applying microwave knowledge freely when they meet similar or related situation.

For example, after waveguide and antenna principle are learned, they can be synthesized together. Analysis from field distribution to wall current distribution in waveguide, and from wall current distribution to radiation characteristic of slotted waveguide, then the appropriate slot location and size can be gained for effective radiation. Then quantitative analysis can be done by corresponding software such as Matlab or HFSS. Next, analyze how to design the slot and slots array to get really need radiation field pattern. In the end, content of waveguide system, wall current distribution, radiation field calculation of antenna, principle of pattern multiplication, phased-array antenna is brought together organically.

3 EXERCISES ITEM BANK MANAGEMENT AND SERVICE TECHNIQUE

How to use the exercise that long-term accumulated is another problem before us. If it is improper used, may get little effect, or even counterproductively, strike the enthusiasm of the students. This is because that student will lose interest if the exercise is too simple, and lose confidence if it is too difficult. The degree of difficulty should be controlled to be challenging, and could do it after careful thinking and hard working. Students will have a sense of achievement when the problem is solved. Consider that student's knowledge and ability improve continuously with learn, exercises item bank should be managed and serviced according to cognitive rules.

Study of item bank now available is mostly realization of automatic generating test paper for examination.[4] Distribution of knowledge points, question types and degree of difficulty is the main consideration. We study it from another angle, i.e. design of exercise item bank by proceeding in an orderly way and step by step. The exercise is considered comprehensively in accordance with depth and width of knowledge according to the students' learning process. For every question of item bank, the main concern parameter properties are: difficulty coefficient and comprehensive.

The difficulty coefficient is divided into nine grades from easy to difficult according to the exercise difficulty. The comprehensive means that every question belongs to which knowledge point or covers which knowledge points. When they use it, the exercise item bank system will extract a question meet the requirements if only the student select difficult grade and knowledge module. When students accomplish a question and submit it to system, it is generally judged automatically. The complex discussing problem will be judged by teacher.

The initial state of student user is locked except difficulty grade one. When the student done at least one question of grade one correctly, grade two will be unlocked automatically, and so on. Complex question with multi knowledge points need certain foundation, the related single knowledge point need to be unlocked at least to grade five. Such interesting and game design inspires students overcome difficulties and become aggressive person.

4 CONCLUSIONS

Exercise item bank development need long process and hard work. It is integrated through accumulated of wisdom in teaching, collected of relevant information, used the effective arrangement of science and technology history, and focused summary of student's question. It need enrich, revise, and perfect. It is used to inspire and enlighten the wisdom of the students, tape their potential, and foster their ability of comprehensive using knowledge, engineering practice, and scientific researching innovations.

ACKNOWLEDGEMENT

This work was supported by the College Foundation (No. JX1X1346).

REFERENCES

[1] Yanxiang Zheng. *Efficacy Guarantee of Education Normal Form Changing* [M]. Shanghai Education Press. 2006.
[2] Linying Zhang. *Research of the Formation Mechanization of Teaching and Learning Quality, Evaluation of Teaching and Learning, and QMS in High Education* [D]. Nanjing University of Science & Technology. Nanjing, China, 2008.
[3] Donghua Yuan. *Thinking of Item Bank & Examination Paper Bank Building in College* [J]. Heilongjiang Education (Higher Education Research & Appraisal). 2013/04.
[4] Yuye Zhang. *Design and Realize of Universal Item Bank Manage System* [J]. Journal of Jinan Vocational College. 2013/01.
[5] Hongbo Gao. *"JTQB" Innovation Model Approach of Classroom Teaching Based on Item Bank [J]*. Forestry Education in China. 2013/03.

Computer, Intelligent Computing and Education Technology – Liu, Sung & Yao (Eds)
© 2014 Taylor & Francis Group, London, ISBN 978-1-138-02469-4

Research of "Double Subjects" teaching mode based on the digital platform

Y.Q. Shi, H. Li & Z.P. Ren
Institute of Command Information System, PLA University of Science and Technology, Nanjing, China

ABSTRACT: The new "Double Subjects" teaching mode based on the digital platform is an effective teaching mode. It has broad application prospects in the teaching about computer which based on practice. According to the analysis of the current situation of the database course teaching, combined with years of teaching experience, the author deeply researches and analyzes how to use the "Double Subjects" teaching mode based on the digital platform in the database course teaching.

Keywords: the digital platform; double subjects; database

Currently, many domestic universities take database management systems based on visual programming technology as the database course teaching content, such as Visual FoxPro. However, the biggest problem in the actual process of practice teaching is the "paying attention to theory and slighting practice". The teachers lay particular stress on explanations about teaching basic theory and basic grammar. That causes unbalance between theory and practice, also causes divorce of practice and application. The real database course teaching must strengthen the training of students' autonomous and practical ability to encourage students to ascertain, analyze, summarize and innovate. How to solve the common problem of discrete of theory and practice in database course teaching is the most important thing in current database course teaching research. It makes students have a comprehensive and complete understanding of the development process of the database management system and skillfully master the Visual FoxPro database and visual programming design.

1 INTRODUCTION

1.1 *What is the "Double Subject" teaching mode based on the digital platform*

"Double Subject" is a new teaching mode which takes the teachers as led subject and students as active subject. It takes student independent practice as the main line of teaching. The teaching mode's goal is maximizing teachers' and students' enthusiasm and initiative to develop students' innovative awareness, innovative spirit, innovative ability and the ability to solve practical problems (Zhao 2004). "Double Subject" is insufficient to accommodate basic computer courses' characteristics, such as huge amount of information and fast update rate. And thus it is difficult to reflect the advantage of modern education. While the teaching mode innovation team integrating modern information technology and basic computer courses, it proposes the "'Double Subject' mode based on the digital platform". Under the precondition of "Double Subject" teaching, it introduces a wealth of teaching resources to each teaching session by using the network environment (Xu 2010), and then restructures and improves the courses system to ultimately realize the reform of teaching concept, teaching mode and teaching management. It has provided accurate and convenient services for creating conditions for the reform of personal training, improving management efficiency and deepening teaching reform and students' self-learning.

1.2 *Features of "Double Subject" teaching mode based on the digital platform*

Some traditional teaching modes overemphasize leading role of teachers' and ignore students' autonomy, initiative as learning subjects. Some exaggerate subjectivity of students and ignore the leading role of teachers. "Double Subject" is fundamentally different from the traditional modes. "Double Subject" teaching mode emphasizes teachers' leading role as a subject in the teaching process and students' active participation and self-development as a subject. "Teaching" and "learning" always exchange the center position in the teaching process. Teachers and students constantly exchange subject role of the activity. So that, the two subject role play the maximum. This teaching is a two-way interactive and learning combining with teaching.

"Double Subject" is a qualitative transcendence to one subject. It has three characteristics:

a. Equality between teaching and learning dialogue. "Double subject" teaching mode advocates the "subject—subject" relationship of teachers and students, rather than the "master—slave" relationship either part oriented. The change means that teachers and students recognize each other in the teaching implementation process. They recognize that they have the same status and rights which means that both parties have equal opportunity to participate in the teaching and tangibly embody equality between teachers and students in teaching.

b. Interactive in the teaching and learning process. "Interactive" exists in any teaching mode, but in the "Double Subject" teaching mode which focuses on equality between teaching and learning, the dominant position of students is undoubted confirmed and students' initiative can be fully mobilized. "Interactive" is changed from "passive" to "active". Classroom atmosphere is active and teaching effect is obvious.

c. Integrity between courses and "Double Subject". Computer Courses maneuverability is strong and especially the database course combines with project practices closely. So it is needed to reconstruct the contents of courses according to project-driven and then coordinate with the subjectivity position of teachers and students in teaching interaction and finally achieve the coordination and integration between courses and "Double Subject".

2 THE DATABASE TEACHING PRACTICE USING THE "DOUBLE SUBJECT" TEACHING MODE BASED ON THE DIGITAL PLATFORM

2.1 *Problems in traditional database teaching*

Currently, most institutions only take Visual Fox-Pro as a universal basic database teaching, so there are the following general questions in the teaching process:

a. The amount of information is not enough. Most students are first in touch with database. The database is a computer professional course with extremely rich contents, including database basic theory, basic concepts, basic operations, and basic development based on the Visual FoxPro database management system. But it is not only just "four basics". The most important feature of the course is linked with the application and associated with the practice. Therefore, the existing "teaching and operating" in class of traditional teaching is insufficient to meet the huge amount of information of database course.

b. Operation is neglected. Restricted to the limitations of classroom teaching hours, the existing database course is theory-based. The final written examination also will make students focus on book knowledge. Operation is just taken as a superficial approach to verify the theory. The final result of ignoring operation is that after the ending of the course the students' hands-on ability involved database is still not improved.

c. Teaching stays on the surface. Current database teaching is theory-based and operation—supplemented in general. And the operation just stays on the surface of a simple operation, such as how to create a database, how to create a table, how to insert data, how to create a simple form and so on. Students only master "fragmented" operation about the system development. And the ultimate purpose of teaching of developing a unified complete database management system is still unable to achieve. As for the theory, because the operation cannot be deep enough, theory cannot be understood thoroughly. And ultimately teaching stays on the surface and the depth and breadth do not meet needs of the modern university database teaching.

d. The whole concept of the project development cannot be understood. The amount of teaching information is not enough. Operation is ignored. Teaching stays on the surface. After students have learned database course systematically, apparently they only get "fragment" but not the "whole" and obviously. So they cannot understand the whole concept of a database project development.

2.2 *How to use "Double Subject" teaching mode based on the digital platform to teach database*

The teaching process of "Double Subject" teaching mode based on the digital platform is generally divided into four stages: task setting, autonomous learning, and collaborative learning and stand-up and promotion. Combined with the characteristics of big amount of information, paying attention to practice and operation, easy to learn and hard to go deep into and integration of project of database course, the teaching mode innovative team enriches and restructures teaching contents according to Visual FoxPro project development process. The actual teaching arrangement of the various stages is shown in Figure 1 Specifically.

In the task setting stage, teachers set classroom tasks according to specific teaching plan, actual teaching progress and students' current situation

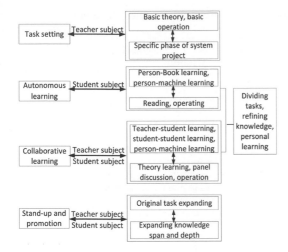

Figure 1. The teaching process of "Double Subject" teaching mode based on the digital platform.

about a week before each classroom. This task is not only the "problem solving", but also basic theory and basic operation of the current teaching plan will be mapped to a particular stage of the specific project based on the Visual FoxPro system. Each task setting is expanded around a stage and the completion of the whole system project is the symbol of the end of the course. This stage is mainly teacher-principal.

In the autonomous learning stage, under the premise of the task proposed in the first stage, students carry out "person-book learning, person-machine learning" as the subject. Scilicet the students read their textbooks and related paper or electronic materials to achieve self-awareness, and then grope to practice and operate by computer. The ultimate goal in this stage is that students decompose tasks by their self, refine knowledge and learn individually for the first round. It establishes self-awareness foundation for subsequent collaborative learning.

In the collaborative learning stage, the dominant position of teachers and students is significantly reflected. This stage includes three steps: traditional "teachers-students learning" of teachers teaching and students listening; "students-students learning" of students researching, analyzing and discussing for each other; "person-machine learning" of students deeply interacting with computer again and integrating the theory study, panel discussions and operation practice with each other under the guidance of teachers. Meanwhile, the stage is also the exacerbation and systematization of "self-decomposition of tasks, refining knowledge and personal learning" in the first round. Teachers' scientific summary, theoretical induction, operation and demonstration etc. with an open manner

can let students make a self-evaluation for the early self-awareness from the heart and thus from their own knowledge system.

In the stand-up and promotion stage, going through the three stages before, the students' interest to learn database is greatly stimulated and their initiative has also been greatly improved. In this stage teachers appropriately adjust the direction and the difficulty of the task to expand based on the situation of students task completion. For example, teachers guide students to acknowledge "computational thinking" according to Visual FoxPro teaching combining with students Prerequisite (the C programming language), and ultimately achieve optimization of breadth and depth of students' computer literacy.

"Digital platform = network environment + teaching resources". In the field of network environment, the teaching mode innovation team carries out a full range of interactive with the students in the classroom in the database teaching by "Polar electronic classroom system". While taking advantage of the convenience of the campus network, combining with their own reality, they self-build resources and have developed their own database repository and create conditions for students self-learning outside the classroom. Now the syllabus, implementation plans, course plans, electronic courseware, experimental outline, experimental instruction manual, exercises library, second level question bank, teaching software, domestic and foreign related electronic books such teaching resources have uploaded to intranet for students to view. So that students can more clearly understand and master the content, the framework, the focus of course. They can choose network resources suiting independent learning according to their own characteristics and receive the best learning effect. Simultaneously, the use of online tutoring answering system also extends the students' way of "eliminating doubts". Soon after, we will continue to upload teaching videos and operating demonstration such teaching resources to intranet to provide visualize teaching materials for teachers and students.

3 THE ANALYSIS AND RESEARCH OF "DOUBLE SUBJECT" TEACHING MODE BASED ON THE DIGITAL PLATFORM

Database is a basic computer course by which students can master the latest technology of information management and improve software development capability. It is intended to enable participants to master the necessary database basic knowledge while developing various database application systems and can develop database

Table 1. The comparison between the "Double Subject" based on the digital platform teaching mode and the traditional teaching mode.

Innovation aspect	Traditional teaching mode	"Double Subject" teaching mode based on the digital platform
Subject	Single subject	Double subject
Resource	Single teaching material constructing	Integration of various resources
Thinking	Discuss course according to the course	Introduce computer thinking
Content	The textbook knowledge	Combination of practical training and competitive training
Method	Teaching + demonstrate	Choose analogy teaching, project driving, group by group practicing according to specific course content
Medium	Blackboard + multimedia	Omnibus and multi-angle introduce digital platform
Process	Introduce textbook knowledge	Introduce teaching reform results and the latest development and professional application of the area technology

application system with practical value combined with their specialty. Introducing "Double Subject" based on the digital platform in this course is a kind of teaching model innovation. The comparison with the traditional teaching mode is shown in Table 1 Specifically.

4 CONCLUSIONS

Database course which used the "Double Subject" teaching mode based on the digital platform compares with the traditional teaching mode. It carries out innovative reform in teaching subject, content, resources, forms, methods and other aspects. This educational reform fully reflects the characteristics of database course, including combination of theory and practice, association between practice and application and emphasizing application and operation of course. Practice has proved that "Double Subject" teaching mode based on the digital platform adapts to the specific requirements of educational reform of basic course and reflects the philosophy of innovative education personnel training.

REFERENCES

[1] T.Y. Zhao, Teaching Mode Reform and Practice of Remote Open Education Management Courses [J], Jilin Engineering and Technical College jouanal. 2004 (11).
[2] Y. Xu, On the computer network environment of online teaching [J], China-school education (theory), 2010 (16).

Computer, Intelligent Computing and Education Technology – Liu, Sung & Yao (Eds)
© 2014 Taylor & Francis Group, London, ISBN 978-1-138-02469-4

Service design blueprinting for stray animals—concept of establishing joint adoption platform for stray animals

Ya-Han Tu & Wen-Huei Chou
National Yunlin University of Science and Technology, Yunlin, Taiwan

ABSTRACT: Aiming to improve the method of adoption in dog shelters, this research is people-orientated, analyzing people's adoption needs and willingness through a service design concept and user's research methods. It re-constructs current adoption service procedure and concept, and incorporates the notion of joint adoption and also creates an abstract service value. The notion applied in this research uses the adoption system and methods from World Vision, which enables the adopters to share the feelings of supervision, joy and belonging. Apart from dog lovers, it may also influence potential adopters to become more active, because of the newly changed system and methods.

Keywords: stray dogs; joint adoption; service design; stray dog shelter

1 INTRODUCTION

Around the world many countries are devoted to promoting animal welfare. These countries have established animal welfare organizations and stroked a balance between caring and damaging in terms of policy and morality in mercy killings and neutering (Srinivasan, 2013). In Taiwan, however, the promotion of animal welfare has yet to exist in form. In 2009, according to statistics from the animal protection information website of the Council of Agriculture, Executive Yuan, for every 100 people there exists 0.37 stray dogs in Taiwan, and in July 2013, 39.34% of the dogs in public shelters were put down. Some people impulsively purchase pet dogs, but the dogs then are treated with abandonment when the interest fades away. Others are superstitious and misunderstands the meaning of setting captive animals free in religion, which also turns into another factor escalating the number of dogs on the street (Ou Ru-Huei, 2006).

When stray dogs become a social issue and an underprivileged group, there are areas which the law does not cover, like abuse. While the number of stray dogs has reached saturation point and become a threat to people's safety. The current solution is to catch and send the dogs to shelters to be put down or adopted. The system operates to deal with the situation and to ensure quality of life for people; nevertheless, the welfare of dogs on the street and in shelters still needs attention and big improvements (Tung Meng-Chih, 2010).

The main goal of this research is to improve the adoption service for stray dogs. It applies the design to redefine the adoption procedure, to raise the adoption opportunities for dogs, seek a positive impact on society, and improve the treatment of stray dogs. By setting up a friendly adoption practice, and turning the adoption concept into a collective consciousness and an ongoing active process (Chuang Chia-yu, 2012), the adoption system will be better and stray dogs will no longer be a social problem or an underprivileged group.

The service design includes people, merchandise and environment, along with service quality, features and atmosphere (Kuo Tzu-Jui, 2011). It focuses on the users and bases itself on service framework or construction. It searches for the key to a breakthrough and contains empathy, which enables people to obtain a more practical, efficient service. By embracing approaches, skills and an integrated, technical platform with cross-field cooperation (Kuk & Janssen, 2013), it creates an innovative, comprehensive solution, and enhances the connection between the users' sensory perception and experiences in order to upgrade the quality of service. Moreover, through service blueprint, the service system is then visualized which allows the abstract service concept and the operation in front of and behind the scenes to be completely conveyed to the users. It also goes further to apprehend and analyze the complexity in the service procedure (Chang Hsu-Hwa & Lu Pin-Wei, 2010).

Therefore, this research hopes to boost people's contribution to the society via the concept of service design, and examine the adoption service through a transparent procedure. With inspiration among one another, a cooperative relationship is formed to make an impact on people's values and behavior and to even become a common belief within the nation.

2 DEFINITION AND CREATION OF STRAY DOGS

"Stray dogs" is a broad term, referring to a single situation in which dogs illegally exist except as pet dogs. People determine if dogs are worthy of living and have the right to demand under the circumstances that the dogs have a "home" and fit the specifications set by humans, and that sometimes they have to be a property of humans' (Srinivasan, 2013). The main four triggers creating stray dogs in Taiwan are abandoning pets for personal reasons, lost pets, escaped dogs and breeding outdoors. On the other hand, one of the social factors is that business people import a great number of foreign dogs for sale and breeding. It creates unfit dogs by in-breeding and over-reproduced and weak female dogs that are deserted (Hsu Ya-Chu, 2009; Tsai Shin-Yun, 2008). Therefore, the fate of stray dogs, being mistreated and killed, can be altered. The core of the notion is to prevent stray dogs from mercy killing, and to encourage people's kind contributions to the society in an attempt to take stray dogs away from shelters and settle them in a better "home". In addition, it narrows the distant gap and prompts an interaction between people by means of mutual help along with resources.

3 STRAY DOGS AND RABIES IN TAIWAN

Street dogs attack people for survival and self-protection, and a great number of them at the same time results in numerous social problems. It directly or indirectly causes accidental deaths of stray dogs, accidents involving humans and issues of environmental protection. Recently rabies has broken out in the Formosan ferret-badgers population. Because of the general public lacking sufficient knowledge of disease prevention against epidemics, people have started to fret about the infection of rabies among dubious street dogs and even their own pets. Consequently, more pets have been abandoned in a short period of time. Gukeng Township, in Taiwan, even encouraged people to catch stray dogs and to take them to the shelters in exchange for rice to bring rabies to a halt. These treatments originate from humans' selfish angle, destroying the survival right of other living creatures on the planet and brutally culling the species that constantly and loyally accompany humans. Therefore, the concept in this research expects to apply the mechanism of rewarding in shelters to generate solutions for current obstacles. It can not only suppress the outbreak of rabies, but also encourage friendly rewarding to hinder problems from adoption.

4 CASE STUDY, DESIGN AND DEVELOPMENT OF CONCEPT

The common strategy after catching stray dogs in most countries around the world is to neuter them (Hsu Ya-Chu, 2009). Research conducted in Taiwan discovered that the solution to street dogs lies on a persistent increase of effective adoption and an enhancement of people's morality, responsibility (Chen Chih-Ling, 2009; Fuh Ying-Bin, 2013; Tung Meng-Chih, 2012). Even though it cannot replace mercy killings in shelters, adoption cuts down the number of dogs purchased, inappropriate puppy mills and save more space in shelters. It also improves dogs' welfare, thus hoping to boost their health and survival rate.

The central government in Taiwan supervises and establishes policies in public shelters. Environmental departments are responsible for handling stray dogs after local governments assessing human resources. However, the treatment of street dogs varies across the island. Mercy killings are mainly carried out on stray and deserted animals, and shelters also implement selective culling to control the number in order to meet humans' interest and space management (Hsu Ya-Chu, 2009). Most people think sending stray or abandoned dogs to shelters means their duty for the dogs is fulfilled. In fact, with an aim to decrease the number of dogs and to expand space, shelters performing mercy killings on a big scale within a limited time is one of the must-do procedures for a shelter (Archer, 2013). In other words, a shelter is a temporary place before dogs face the destiny of mercy killings. According to different researches, the way to prevent mercy killings is to put adoption into effect. Purchasing should also be replaced with adoption as it puts an end to buying and selling animals in markets. By doing so, dogs in shelters have a higher chance of survival, and then it lessens cases like puppy mills abusing dogs during breeding and deserting dogs with low fertility rates.

The Internet and relevant documents show that adoption mainly relies on dog lovers constantly keeping track of shelters' websites. As soon as they know which dogs will be put down, they immediately apply for adoption to save the dogs. Dog lovers then act as intermediaries to launch campaigns for adoption with love. However, this kind, proactive behavior is solely from a minority of people, and it actually gives them financial burden. Moreover, many people are very sympathetic about stray dogs, but due to a restriction to their living circumstances, they cannot adopt and look after dogs. As a consequence, this research expects to integrate different forms of efforts and participation to create a social network for street dogs via a service platform. With collective wisdom, more people are able to enthusiastically take part in a task of adopting and taking care of stray dogs. The research further consults the system of adoption and service of public good, as well as the mechanism of rewarding in World Vision and Centers of the Taiwan Fund for Children and Families. By doing so, it hopes to pool and boost the affection and capacity for looking after stray dogs in order to bring down the number of dogs culled. With mutual help and rewarding, it also allows users, who cannot adopt dogs under their personal circumstances, to form a sense of solidarity, trust and caring.

The core values of World Vision Taiwan are respecting children's lives and development, and helping impoverished and vulnerable kids. Their actions are seen in offshore islands and many remote, mountainous areas across the country. Even though the organization is established to serve people, the needs of vulnerable groups are valued and matching relationships between giving and needing help are built through a charitable platform. Donors act as a caring sponsor to contribute a fixed amount of money per month. They can also send gifts, letters and meet their sponsored child, and meanwhile they will receive a reward like an annual report and a video clip on the child's growth. As for the record of their sponsorship and updates on children, the online platform fulfills the needs. Through the Area Development Program, donated money is allocated for improving the lives and environment of children across the globe. Social workers visit children periodically to ensure that they obtain a proper education, health and capability to change their future. Children's lives, therefore, are more meaningful and valuable, no longer filled with suffering. The concept of this research consults the World Vision's child sponsorship program, and it compares and analyzes the program and the adoption system in shelters for stray dogs in Taiwan for a solution. Four major conceptions for implementation are proposed.

1. Establishing joint adoption: The current procedure in effect in Taiwan's public shelters is people, who are willing to adopt a dog, pay a visit and adopt one. They are then responsible for looking after the dog in the future. As mentioned above, a great number of people actually feel pity for street dogs, the problem is they are unable to adopt and take care of the dogs by themselves due to the restrictions. However, they are happy to donate certain sums of money, goods and materials and even time to partially participate in looking after stray dogs. There are other people who have no problem providing dogs with a home, but expenses are beyond their capability. Because of this, joint adoption is initiated for matching networks with different abilities to raise adoption rates by accumulating donations, goods and materials from people and making the contents of participation projects public and transparent.

2. Online service platform: Through public shelters' service platform, people can receive information about adoption, project implementation, rewarding events and stray dogs. Participants include shelters, main adopters and offshoot sponsors, and online adopters. They obtain related information on adopting, caring for and protecting dogs via the platform.

3. Function of rewarding: Donors will receive updates about stray dogs and activities when making a contribution monthly. Combining this feature and identifying items, it brings cooperation, a sense of solidarity and trust in resources to main adopters and offshoot sponsors.

4. Creating additional values: It attracts users to be constantly involved, serving to bring people together.

The structure of the entire adoption system concept is shown in Figure 1. Its objective is to cut down the number of stay dogs that die from mercy killings. Shelters in Taiwan are core strongholds for adoption, and joint adoption projects are promoted on the Internet to make potential groups understand. An online service platform for adoption is also launched for participants to apprehend the implementation of the projects. Via records written by adopters on the platform and information exchange in shelters, an interaction is formed within, and the safety and care of dogs are guaranteed. The function of rewarding is also integrated into the system, for instance free vaccines, events and activities, with which participants are rewarded for contributions within their limits.

The flowchart of the joint adoption concept is illustrated in Figure 2. Via an online platform and the participation from servers in shelters, the service platform for joint adoption include activities of rewarding, identifying items of the project, records of updates on dogs and project counseling,

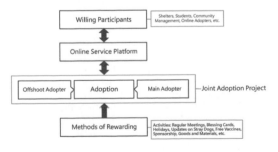

Figure 1.   Structure of entire adoption system concept.

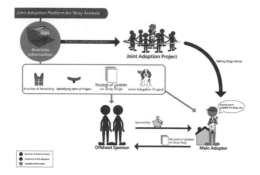

Figure 2. Flowchart of joint adoption concept.

etc. When the joint adoption project is in practice, two or more sponsors support one main adopter. Offshoot sponsors would like to adopt stray dogs, but they cannot because of their circumstances or personal reasons. They instead contribute a fixed amount of money per month and goods and materials to help adopt dogs. Main adopters are willing and able to give dogs a suitable environment; therefore, they adopt dogs in terms of looking after them and offering them a home. Main adopters also keep a record of updates on dogs monthly, which makes it easier to keep track of dogs and to reward people. They cooperate with offshoot sponsors to fulfill the task of joint adoption. The existence of the platform allows them to ensure service and to check financial status. When it comes to the establishment of the rewarding system, it functions to computerize dogs, announce events and encourage interactions, etc. Supervision and scrutiny on the service can also be achieved through the platform.

5 CONCLUSION

The design conception of this research is to seek a new path for the adoption system with the approach of service design. A new service direction is proposed for the online adoption project in Taiwan's public shelters. It attempts to raise adoption rates in shelters, lower the percentage of mercy killings, prompt social participation and contributions from the general public, and encourage mutual help and create mutual trust from the interactions among participants. The online adoption service platform is regarded as a multi-bridge among shelters, participants and stray dogs. It brings out features of consistency and rewarding when they interact with one another, which is then applied to promote new projects to people. Through the exercise of matching by the system, the function of rewarding is designed to help more people take part in looking after and adopting stray dogs within their

capability and circumstances. During the process of the entire adoption service, we hope to satisfy the needs of different users, reach transparency for people involved, and create features of consistency and rewarding. In this research, the framework of a workable service design for solving the problem of stray dogs is drawn by analyzing literature, documents and contents of the interviews. It expects to enhance the needs of application and implement the blueprint for the service design in future research.

REFERENCES

Animal Protection Information on http://animal.coa.gov. tw/html/?main=9h&page=09_resources_a02. http:// animal.coa.gov.tw/html/download/resources/09_ resources_j00_102_7.pdf.

Archer, John, *Why do people love their pets? Evolution and Human Behavior*, 18(4), 237–259, 1997.

Centers for Disease Control, R.O.C. (Taiwan) on http:// www.cdc.gov.tw/diseaseinfo.aspx?treeid=8d54c504e82 0735b&nowtreeid=dec84a2f0c6fac5b&tid=9D2E1B3 A862F06FB.

Chang Hsu-Hwa & Lu Pin-Wei, Using an Integrated Model for Service Design and Service Quality Improvement: A Case Study on Insurance Industry. *Management and Systems, 17*(1), 131–157, 2010. (In Chinese).

Chen Chih-Ling, *A study of the animal populations in animal shelters in Taiwan.* National Taiwan University, 2009. (In Chinese).

Chuang Chia-yu, News Representation and News Discourse of Trap-Neuter-Return Issue in Taiwan. Shih Hsin University, Taipei, 2012. (In Chinese).

Fuh Ying-Bin, A study of the association between animal welfare and zoonoses of abandoned animals. National Taiwan University, 2013. (In Chinese).

Hsu Ya-Chu, *Painful Euthanasia? A Discussion about The Practice of Animal Euthanasia, in Taiwan Public Animal Shelters.* National Taiwan University, Taipei, 2009. (In Chinese).

Kuk, George, & Janssen, Marijn, Assembling infrastructures and business models for service design and innovation. *Information Systems Journal, 23*(5), 445–469, 2013.

Kuo Tzu-Jui, *Transformation of Design Business Under The Development of Service Design.* National Taipei University of Technology, 2011. (In Chinese).

Ou Ru-Huei, *The Legal System and Practice of Animal Protection Focused on Pets and Strays.* Chinese Culture University, Taipei, 2006. (In Chinese).

Srinivasan, Krithika, The biopolitics of animal being and welfare: dog control and care in the UK and India. *Transactions of the Institute of British Geographers, 38*(1), 106–119, 2013.

Tung Meng-Chih, *A study of the no-kill policy in Changhua County public animal shelter. National Chung Hsing University*, 2012. (In Chinese).

Tsai Shin-Yun, *Discussing the Development and Practice of Local Animal Welfare with the Legislation and Evolvement of Animal Protection Law—Regard Dog and Cat as the Illustrations.* National Taiwan University, Taipei, 2008. (In Chinese).

World Vision on http://sponsorship.worldvision.org.tw/ sp/zh_TW/sponsor/plan.

Computer, Intelligent Computing and Education Technology – Liu, Sung & Yao (Eds)
© 2014 Taylor & Francis Group, London, ISBN 978-1-138-02469-4

Diversified and parallel teaching model based on the ability training of computational thinking

Q.J. Zhang, X.F. Jiang & J.R. Liu
Northwestern Polytechnical University, Xi'an, China

S. Jiang
National Computer Network Emergency Response Technical Team, Coordination Center of China, Beijing, China

ABSTRACT: For the cultivation of innovative talents, and relying on the information technology, we begin the reform and innovation of deepening the teaching contents and the teaching methods. According to the cognitive and thinking formation, we have established the participatory, diversified and parallel teaching model based on the computational thinking training, and this mode can improve the teaching efficiency and the students' active learning ability, and then cultivate the students' computational thinking ability.

Keywords: computational thinking; participatory teaching; diversified and parallel teaching; criticism and query

1 INTRODUCTION

Under the new situation, the extensive and civilian computer applications has affected computer education, area difference has make the related basic of computer education uneven, and the connotation of computer teaching has been promoting and enriching rapid and continuously. All these have posed challenges for computer basic education. In university, the computer teaching needs change radically the long existing one-sided understanding, such as "Computers are tools", "Computer is programming" and "Computer is the application of software tools". The pedagogues of university should combine the three means of the modern science development which are computational science, theoretical science and experimental science, and cultivate innovative talents of composite top.[1]

However, the existing mode of computer basic education could not meet the need of the innovative talents' cultivation. In view of this situation, the computer basic education in Northwestern Polytechnical University adheres to the ideas "innovation as the theme, the cultivation of innovative and composite talents as the goal, strengthen the computational thinking training as the way", constructs the teaching platform to the training of innovation, adheres to the teaching system of international, introduces timely the advanced technology into classroom, enriches and develops the experiment content, improves the teaching method by modern education technology method, and has formed diversified and parallel teaching model based on the ability training of computational thinking.[2,3]

2 DIVERSIFIED AND PARALLEL TEACHING MODEL BASED ON THE ABILITY TRAINING OF COMPUTATIONAL THINKING

In diversified and parallel teaching model, the teaching idea has been designed again and the training of the computational thinking ability has been as the teaching core. To make the teaching idea a reality needs both teachers and students to participate in the teaching and the suitable reform. This essay will be carried on in three aspects.

2.1 Teaching idea

In diversified and parallel teaching model, "Students as the main body, teachers as the leading role" are as the teaching ideas. Its goal is the transition of "Students learn" to "Students can learn" and "Students learn hardly" to "Students learn difficult knowledge".

The new teaching ideas strengthens general education in the cultivating of innovative talents, and it thinks calculating the thinking ability as the guidance, improves the general teaching quality, pays attention to dealing with relationship between professional and general, broad and deep, individuality and commonness.

The teaching ideas advocates the concept of case teaching into the teaching, lets the students feel algorithm and computational thinking wonderful, and combines knowledge education and skill education. At the same time, it uses a variety of examples to help students to understand the teaching content and ensures the teaching content and depth. Then, it links all kinds of isolated and fragmentary knowledge together through the teachers rational series, guarantees the whole knowledge structure and system, enhances the practical ability of students to stimulate students' creative thinking, and strengthens the ability of independent thinking and judging ability of students to fully mobilize the enthusiasm of students and arouse their active learning.

2.2 Teachers and teaching

2.2.1 Optimizing teacher resources and absorbing the computer professional teacher

In order to reflect the new teaching idea, carry out the training of thinking ability, at the beginning of the implementation of diversified and parallel teaching pattern, teacher resources are optimized, and absorbed a lot of computer professional teachers. By setting up a teaching team which includes some scientific research persons, we have co-designed and undertake the teaching scheme, combined with the research project to enrich the teaching cases, deepened the students' understanding of professional knowledge and application knowledge based on the teaching of typical case, improved the students' ability of analyzing and solving practical engineering problems.

2.2.2 Broadening the vision, exploring the new mode of resource development and sharing with international cooperation, school enterprise cooperation

The outstanding foreign experts and scholars have been actively invited to school to carry out teaching exchange or teaching to promote international curriculum localization. At the same time, we have hired a number of well-known experts, professors, technical director of enterprise as part-time teachers of school, and take the teaching of the specialized course or as guidance teachers to guide students in the enterprise practice and graduation thesis, then formed a new mode which school and enterprise collaboration and sharing the high quality teaching resources.

In addition, actively building a course taught in English and bilingual courses, carrying out each link in English teaching (training scheme,

curriculum content, practice teaching, quality assurance) are others measures.

For the materials, the improvement strategy is the introduction of international advanced materials, speeding up the textbook upgrading, actively doing a good job planning of teaching material construction, and establishing a scientific textbook, evaluation and selection system. General education encourages the introduction of international mainstream teaching materials and excellent foreign teaching materials, encourages and organize the teachers to write characteristics materials, advanced materials and series materials to highlight college professional competitiveness. Encouraging the teachers which has the subject conditions and rich teaching experience to write textbook based on their research results is another way.

2.2.3 Paying attention to teaching students in accordance with their aptitude, improving the teaching method, relying on information technology and improving the teaching means, exploring actively the heuristic, inquiry, discussion and participatory teaching

1. Constructing course home page and achieving the course's dynamic management
   Carrying out the construction of electronic information platform actively, providing personal space for each teacher, constructing curriculum homepage, releasing the course plan in advance, updating dynamic schedule, implementing the course online sharing, and submitting dynamic course work, all these are effective ways.

2. Outputting the knowledge diversity and implementing the parallel teaching methods
   We have explored to introduce the advanced mobile media into teaching, such as iPad. With the help of advanced information and network technology, the students can not only obtain the teaching contents from the teachers, but also understand other explanations through the network, and fulfill the practice according to the teaching contents timely to deepen our impression and improve teaching effect. So the students' learning process has been translated from the traditional mode in which classroom theory teaching, reviewing, submitting the job and then doing experiment to the parallel teaching mode in which all these steps have been completed all the steps in parallel.

3. Encouraging students to question and cultivating the critical teaching environment
   In the teaching process, in addition to help students understand and master the teaching content, inspiring and encouraging students to question the arguments and reasons for

supporting teaching knowledge, considering whether they are true and the reasoning process is appropriate are others effective modes. The students have been supported the discussion, debate and criticism, questioning to promote thinking, then the teachers asks students why some explanation or strategy be used and to gives good examples in critical thinking.

2.3 Students and "learning"

Students are important participants in the teaching process, and training them to obtain some knowledge and ability is the ultimate goal of teaching activities. So, the teaching mode that lacks the students' active cooperation is unable to achieve good results. Therefore, the diversified parallel interactive mode has done a lot of work, pays attention to participate in teaching, fully mobilizes the enthusiasm of students, and encourages students' autonomous learning.

2.3.1 Improving the design ability by the experimental work of scientific research
To carry out the achievements and ideas of scientific research into the test experiment and the verify experiment, to encourage and guide the students to design the experiment which meets the project' needs in experimental teaching and curriculum design, to enhance the process which understand classroom theory and knowledge again. Through experiment and practice, to improve the students' ability to design and to increase the experimental class interest and knowledge. All these are useful methods.

2.3.2 Realizing the interactive teaching by using the new media network
Students can obtain information through the network media (such as micro-blog, BBS), then they can learn independently and have collaborative learning, and can have diversified feedback and pluralistic development, so the new learning mode which students, teachers and knowledge have multisided interaction in network environment can implement. Desalination of constraints, giving students more inspiration and guidance, letting the students to choose, develop the initiative and consciousness, strengthening the subject consciousness of students, making the students accept the knowledge from the passive to active inquiry, knowledge, and improving the comprehensive quality of students, all these are our useful ways.

2.3.3 Supporting students to participate in research and competition activities, entering early into the topic, the lab and the team
Organizing the outstanding students to enter into the laboratory and participate in the research

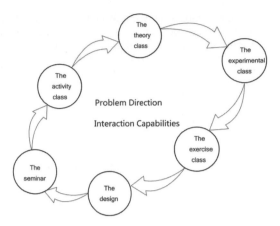

Figure 1. The diversified and parallel teaching model.

projects through the advisor system, engaging in the scientific research and writing the research papers, all these ways are for the cultivation of students' scientific quality and innovative spirit. According to the needs of the laboratory or the team, selecting the students who are interested in the scientific research to act as the research assistants, assisting to carry out the scientific experiments and the management work of instruments and equipments, organizing the students into the laboratory to do graduate design with scientific projects, these are some of the other effective measures.

In Figure 1, the diversified and parallel teaching model has been depicted. As can be seen from the diagram, this teaching mode has linked the theory class with the experimental class, the exercise class, the design class, the seminar, the activity class and others teaching activities together closely, promoted actively these teaching links, feedback layer after layer after layer, then ensured the whole knowledge structure and system, stimulated the students' creative thinking, strengthened the students' ability of judgment and independent thinking, and finally trained the students to achieve the computational thinking.

3 CONCLUSIONS

The diversified and parallel teaching model is a new model that is different from the traditional teaching model, and it is the need for the cultivation of innovative talents. It relies on the information technology, fuses the advanced technology and the advanced education means into the teaching process, and reforms deeply the innovation of the teaching content and the teaching method, then this mode improves the measures of "teaching" and "learning" through adjusting the teaching idea, finally builds up the participatory teaching, diversified and parallel teaching mode based on the ability training of computational thinking.

The mode has realized the real-time interaction between teaching and learning, and has translated the traditional serial education to the parallel teaching process in which every teaching link can carry out simultaneously and can realize the diversified absorption of knowledge in teaching process at the same time, then the cultivating of the computational thinking ability can carry out the whole teaching process in this teaching mode. Because the innovative teaching has been implemented in the basic computer series courses, our teaching mode and implementation schemes have been introduced to the teaching implementation plan of computer science and technology professional core curriculum in Higher School "and" the teaching implementation plan of the core basic computer course in college" of the ministry of education.

REFERENCES

[1] Chen Guoliang, Dong Rongsheng. Computational thinking and computer basic education. Chinese Teaching University University 2011.1: 7–12.
[2] Huang Yufu. Interactive teaching application in distance computer education. Adult education. 2011.1:85–86.
[3] Zhao Jianhua, Zhou Qiuyi. Analysis of the teaching process based on the interactive whiteboard. Chinese audio-visual education 2011.1:92–96.

Computer, Intelligent Computing and Education Technology – Liu, Sung & Yao (Eds)
© 2014 Taylor & Francis Group, London, ISBN 978-1-138-02469-4

Study on application of acoustic pyrometry in coal-fired boiler

S.P. Zhang, G.Q. Shen, Y. Wang, X.Q. Wang & M. Xu
Key Laboratory of Condition Monitoring and Control for Power Plant Equipment Ministry of Education,
North China Electric Power University, Beijing, China

ABSTRACT: The flue gas temperature could be real-timely monitored by an online method based on acoustic pyrometry in boiler furnace, but the domestic studies were limited in simulation and still in the stage of experiment in China. In the paper, one-path acoustic pyrometry system was developed and installed in a boiler of 300 MW. The linear sweeping frequency signal was used as acoustic source signal and the generalized cross-correlation technique for time delay estimation was adopted. The temperature was also measured by K ceramic thermocouples which were specially made for verifying the accuracy of acoustic pyrometry measurement. Research indicates that this signal can be used as sound source signal and the frequencies are from 500 Hz to 3,000 Hz. An improved generally cross-correlation algorithm can be used to get the Time of Sound Flight (TOF) in hot state. The relative error of temperature measured by acoustic pyrometry can be less than 1% compared with it measured by thermocouple, so this technology is stable and reliable. The paper also provides important reference for this technology popularizing application.

Keywords: acoustic pyrometry; linear sweeping frequency signal; generally cross-correlation algorithm

1 INTRODUCTION

Real-time online temperature monitoring for flue gas in power plant boiler furnace has been a hot spot in this field, but a difficulty as well (Zhao et al., 2010; Feron, 2010). As a direct reflection of the stability of combustion process, the temperature of flue gas should be measured accurately so as to achieve effective control of combustion process in the boiler. The commonly used temperature measurement methods for flue gas can be divided into both contact and non-contact (Liu, et al., 2000; Seat, et al., 2002). The former, including thermocouple thermometer, pressure gauges thermometer, optical fibre measurement, mainly uses direct contact between the temperature measurement devices and measured objects to make them in thermal equilibrium (Sarma, et al., 2010; Gam, 1996). For power plant boilers, contact measurement method is very limited, and real-time online monitoring cannot be implemented. The non-contact temperature measurement method includes the optical method and the acoustic method (Mahan, et al., 2008; Ranc, et al., 2005). As a kind of non-contact high temperature monitoring methods, the acoustic method is one of the few technologies that can get a large number of temperature information from fewer input requirements. It is developed in the mid-1980s, and commonly used in the early 1990s. Up to now, based on this technology molded products have been made and put into practical application abroad, among which SEI (Scientific Engineering Instruments) company's products from USA are the most typical, but they use pneumatic sound source. The technology is under basic research and laboratory research stage at home.

This paper introduces a self-developed acoustic pyrometry system for coal-fired boilers. Hot-state experimental researches of acoustic source signal and time delay estimation were tested in a domestic boiler. It provides providing an important reference for this technology popularizing application at home.

2 THE THEORY OF ACOUSTIC PYROMETRY AND SELECTION OF ACOUSTIC SOURCE SIGNAL

2.1 The theory of acoustic pyrometry

Acoustic pyrometry obtains the temperature of the medium indirectly based on the propagation velocity of the acoustic wave in the medium.

The relationship between the two is as follows:

$$v = \frac{L}{\tau} = \sqrt{\frac{\gamma R}{m} T} \tag{1}$$

where v is the acoustic propagation speed of the medium in m/s, L is the distance between the measuring points in m, τ is the TOF of sound in s, R is the universal gas constant in $J/(mol \cdot K)$, γ is the isentropic exponent of gas (the ratio of the heat capacity at constant pressure and at constant volume), T is the gas temperature in K, and m is the gas molecular mass in kg/mol. $Z = \sqrt{\gamma R/m}$ is a constant for a given gas mixture. TOF depends upon the temperature of medium and if it contains temperature variations, TOF is obtained by integrating the temperature-dependent sound speed. Hence, the calculation formula of the one-path temperature derived from Formula (1) is as follows:

$$T = \left(\frac{L}{\tau Z}\right)^2 \tag{2}$$

2.2 Acoustic source signal

The corresponding acoustic source signal uses linear sweeping frequency signal. The mathematical expression of linear sweeping frequency signal is as follows:

$$f(\tau) = f_0 + \frac{f(\tau_g) - f_0}{\tau_g}\tau, \tau \in [0, \tau_g] \tag{3}$$

where f_0 is the instantaneous frequency of the sweeping frequency signal at 0 time point, $f(\tau_g)$ is the instantaneous frequency of the sweeping frequency signal at τ_g time point, and $[0, \tau_g]$ is the signal time of duration.

3 TIME DELAY ESTIMATION

3.1 The Cross-Correlation (CC) method

The signal models of the two channels are:

$$x_1(n) = s(n) + n_1(n) \tag{4}$$

$$x_2(n) = As(n - D) + n_2(n) \tag{5}$$

where $s(n)$ is the signal, $n_1(n)$ and $n_2(n)$ are noises, D is the time delay between the two channels, and A is the attenuation coefficient.

The cross-correlation function is:

$$R_{12}(\tau) = \int_{-\infty}^{+\infty} G_{x_1x_2}(f)e^{j2\pi f\tau}df$$
$$= F^{-1}[\psi_{12}F(x_1)^*F(x_2)] \tag{6}$$

where $G_{x_1x_2}(f)$ is the cross power spectrum of the signal 1 and 2, ψ_{12} is the weighting function of the

frequency domain processing, F is Fourier transform, F^{-1} is Inverse Fourier transform, and $*$ is conjugation.

3.2 PHAT-β weighted

At this point, the weight function is:

$$\psi(f) = \frac{1}{\left|G_{x_1x_2}(f)\right|^\beta} \tag{7}$$

The weighted cross-correlation function is:

$$R_{12}(\tau) = F^{-1}\left[\frac{1}{\left|F(x_1)^*F(x_2)\right|^\beta}F(x_1)^*F(x_2)\right] \tag{8}$$

where F is Fourier transform, F^{-1} is Inverse Fourier transform, and $*$ is conjugation.

4 EXPERIMENTAL RESEARCH

4.1 System development

The temperature monitoring system for flue gas based on acoustic pyrometry mainly consists of acoustic wave generators, acoustic waveguides, acoustic receiving devices, signal conditioner, signal I/O devices, a host, wirings and so on.

The acoustic signals are converted into voltage signals from the microphone installed on the acoustic waveguide, amplified by the signal conditioner, collected by the data acquisition card, and imported by the acoustic pyrometry system in the mainframe computer. After a calculation acoustic pyrometry system shows the measurement temperature.

The function of the software system is to control the emission of acoustic signals, data collection and analysis, and temperature measurement. The software system uses Labview and Matlab for mixed language programming.

4.2 Normal temperature state experimental studies in a boiler furnace of 300 MW

In a 35.4 m-high platform of a domestic 300 MW boiler unit, the acoustic measurement points were installed in the existing short blow holes, point 1 and 2 arranged in the front wall and back wall respectively and the corresponding used channels were Channel 1 and 2. Electro-acoustic source was arranged in point 1. The acoustic waveguide was made to order according to the short blow flange size. The sampling frequency was set at 102,400 Hz, sampling points was set at 65,536 the emitted sound frequency was set at 500 to 8,000 and the linear sweeping circle is 0.1 s.

When the boiler was in normal temperature state, the temperature of the furnace measured by the flue gas probe was 17 °C and the local sound velocity of the furnace was 340.5 m/s. The sound field formed by acoustic pyrometry in the utility boilers is enclosed space sound field. In the boiler furnace, the sound wave is emitted by the acoustic temperature measurement device, spreads to the surroundings, is reflected when coming across the boundary, produces the standing wave in the space after more than once reflection and forms the reverberant sound.

The remote microphone receives the signal with no obvious distortion due to a relatively quiet environment of the normal temperature state and a large signal-to-noise ratio. The normal temperature state experimental cross-correlogram indicates that with the basic cross-correlation algorithm accurate time-delay estimation cannot be obtained due to the effect of reverberant sound in the enclosed space (Fig. 1a). *PHAT-β* method is able to produce the best measuring effect in the reverberant environment with a relatively sharp peak when the corresponding coefficient β is 0.8 (Fig. 1b). The actual distance between the measuring point 1 and 2 is 13.58 m.

4.3 *Hot state experimental studies in a boiler furnace of 300 MW*

The background noise should be analysed first in order to study the TOF of sound in the environment of high intensity noise in the furnace. Background noises mainly include combustion noise, aeolian tone generated by the flue gas across the bundles, burner jet noise and other mechanical noises. The background noise energy is mainly distributed in the low frequency band below 500 Hz.

The sweeping frequency signals received by Channel 2 were completely drowned in the noises due to a too small signal-to-noise ratio. The accurate time-delay estimation cannot be obtained before filtering processing.

The Butterworth filter is selected for filtering processing which has the amplitude characteristic of maximal flat in the passband and decreases monotonically with an increasing frequency.

The characteristic function of N-order low-pass Butterworth filter is:

$$|G(j\Omega)|^2 = \frac{1}{1 + \left(j\frac{j\Omega}{\Omega_c} \right)^{2N}} \qquad (9)$$

where Ω_c is passband width, i.e. the cut-off frequency. When the order N increases, the filter characteristic curve becomes steeper and its characteristics are more close to the ideal rectangular amplitude-frequency characteristic $|G(s)|^2$.

Solving the relevant parameters:
$\xi = (10^{0.1A_p} - 1)^{0.5}$, A_p is the maximum attenuation of the passband.
$\lambda = (10^{0.1A_s} - 1)^{0.5}$, A_s is the maximum attenuation of the stopband.

$$N \geq \frac{\lg\left(\frac{\lambda}{\xi}\right)}{\lg\left(\frac{j\Omega_s}{j\Omega_p}\right)} \qquad (10)$$

The bandpass filter is used the designing method of which is firstly turning the designing technical characteristics of the filter to the technical specifications of low-pass filter, then a low-pass filter transfer function designed based on these performance specifications, finally getting the filter transfer function according to the frequency conversion relationship.

R12 (Normalization)

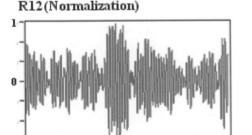

Points/n

(a) Basic cross-correlation

R12 (Normalization)

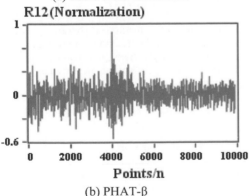

Points/n

(b) PHAT-β

Figure 1. Cross-correlogram in normal temperature state.

The selected filter range is [500, 5,000] Hz and N is set to 3 according to background noise power spectral characteristics so that the low-frequency background noise can be filtered.

With the diverse compositions of the high temperature flue gas, the high temperature and the particles become the most important cause of acoustic attenuation. The energy of high frequency signal over 3,000 Hz attenuates to 0 substantially and the acoustic signal collected by Channel 2 mainly concentrates in a relatively low frequency range from 500 Hz to 2,000 Hz. According to the attenuation characteristic of hot state space, the authors propose that the sound field approximates to a free sound field and although there are reflections from the wall, the energy of the reflected sound waves has been very weak, basically decaying away.

In order to concentrate the acoustic wave energy, the chirp signal the frequency of which is 500 Hz–3,000 Hz and the sweep cycle of which is 0.1 s is used. The filtering interval is [500, 3,000] Hz. Because the stable measurement results cannot be obtained with ordinary cross-correlation method and $PHAT$-β weighted at this time, a new improved $PHAT$-β algorithm is used and the β is taken as 0.6.

Figure 2 shows the $PHAT$-β cross-correlogram on which a sharp peak can be seen. Table 1 shows the 10 measuring values of the temperature on the path, wherein the 8th is an obvious error.

4.4 The temperature calibration by thermocouple

For verifying the accuracy of the measurement, some 10 m-long K ceramic thermocouples, the accuracy of which are 1 °C, are customized. The inserting the thermocouples from both sides of short blowing holes where the measuring points located in simultaneously, it takes 15–20 minutes for each point to reach the thermal equilibrium. The temperature near the furnace wall is around 200 °C

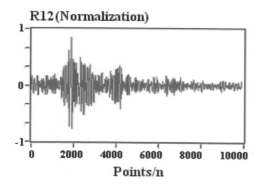

R12 (Normalization)

Figure 2. Cross-correlogram of improved PHAT-β.

Table 1. The temperature of the measuring path (°C).

Number of measurements	1	2	3	4	5
Temperature	1084	1080	1098	1060	1120
Number of measurements	6	7	8	9	10
Temperature	1083	1068	345	1058	1011

while the temperature inside the furnace wall is around 450 °C. The temperature rises from 200 °C to 1,000 °C directly with a large temperature gradient when the thermocouple inserting depth is more than 0.5 m and stables at 1,000–1,200 °C when the inserting depth is over 0.5 m. The measured average temperature of the entire path is 1,072 °C. At the same time the temperature of acoustic pyrometry is 1,063 °C. The relative error of temperature measured by acoustic pyrometry can be less than 1% compared with it measured by thermocouple. The temperature measured by the acoustic pyrometry system meet the requirements.

5 CONCLUSION

1. It is completely feasible to use linear sweeping frequency signal as the acoustic source signal. The proper emission frequency is from 500 Hz to 3,000 Hz when the 300 MW boiler is in hot state.
2. In the normal temperature state boiler and reverberation environment, an accurate time-delay estimation cannot be obtained with the basic cross correlation algorithm while it can be gotten with the $PHAT$-β method. However, with the noise increasing, the accuracy is reducing.
3. With the improved $PHAT$-β method a relatively stable time-delay estimation can be obtained not only in the cold state and reverberation environment but also in the hot state environment. The proper value of β is between 0.6 and 0.8.
4. How to increase the sound pressure level of the acoustic source and find a better time-delay estimation algorithm in the low signal-to-noise ratio will be the focus of the future research work.

ACKNOWLEDGMENTS

This research was supported jointly by the 111 Project of China (No. B12034), the National Basic Research Program (973) of China (No. 2012CB215203), and the National Natural Science Foundation of China (No. 51036002).

We are grateful to the anonymous reviewers whose constructive suggestions have improved the quality of this paper.

REFERENCES

Feron, P.H.M. (2010). Exploring the potential for improvement of the energy performance of coal fired power plants with post-combustion capture of carbon dioxide. *International Journal of Greenhouse Gas Control*, 4(2), 152–160.

Gam, K.S. (1996). A stable microcomputer-controlled heat pipe furnace and test of new noble metal thermocouples. *Measurement*, 18(2), 101–108.

Liu, T., Fernando, G.F., Zhang, Z.Y., and Grattanb, K.T.V. (2000). Simultaneous strain and temperature measurements in composites using extrinsic Fabry—Perot interferometric and intrinsic rare-earth doped fiber sensors. *Sensors and Actuators A: Physical*, 80(3), 208–215.

Mahan, J.R., and Yeater, K.M. (2008). Agricultural applications of a low-cost infrared thermometer. *Computers and Electronics in Agriculture*, 64(2), 262–267.

Ranc, N., Wagner, D. (2005). Some aspects of Portevin–Le Chatelier plastic instabilities investigated by infrared pyrometry. *Materials Science and Engineering: A*, 394(1–2), 87–95.

Sarma, U., and Boruah, P.K. (2010). Design and development of a high precision thermocouple based smart industrial thermometer with on line linearisation and data logging feature. *Measurement*, 43(10), 1589–1594.

Seat, H.C., Sharp, J.H., Zhang, Z.Y. and Grattan, K.T.V. (2002). Single-crystal ruby fiber temperature sensor. *Sensors and Actuators A: Physical*, 101(1–2), 24–29.

Zhao, Y., Wang, S., Nielsen, C.P., Li, X., and Hao, J. (2010). Establishment of a database of emission factors for atmospheric pollutants from Chinese coal-fired power plants. *Atmospheric Envronment*, 44(12), 1515–1523.

Computer, Intelligent Computing and Education Technology – Liu, Sung & Yao (Eds)
© 2014 Taylor & Francis Group, London, ISBN 978-1-138-02469-4

Development of coupled tactual communication tool

Yasuhiro Matsuda & Tsuneshi Isomura
Kanagawa Institute of Technology, Atsugi, Japan

ABSTRACT: The purpose of this study is the development of a tactual communication tool that conveys emotional communication during an oral conversation. In the present study, one novel tactual communication tool (the coupled tactual communication tool) was developed and oral communication using the tool was examined. As a result, the subjects mainly used the tool to respond to the talk by the other subject; the way of gripping the coupled tool was more varied than the one of the previous tool; the maximum air pressure change of the coupled tool was significantly larger than the one of the previous tool. Thus, the coupled tool was used more actively than the previous tool.

Keywords: multimodal communication; emotional communication; communication tool

1 INTRODUCTION

The most primitive form of communication is tactual communication (interpersonal touching). Tactual communication between people familiar to each other can express various positive emotions. But a social distance exists between unfamiliar people, and there is a tendency to avoid the touch of unfamiliar people. Varying kinds of communication disorders are caused by aging. Some of the hospitalized or institutionalized elderly persons have difficulties not only of verbal communication but also of emotional (nonverbal) communication. Thus, a kind of communication support system between the hospital or institution staffs and elderly person is expected.

We have developed the tactual communication tool with the concept of "using tactual communication but keeping a social distance" (Matsuda et al. 2010). The tool consists of two soft rubber balls and a hose (see Fig. 1 upper). A hole was made on the surface of each ball (diameter: 60 mm) so that both balls could be connected by the hose (inner diameter: 6 mm, length: 1200 mm). Two users each hold one ball during an oral conversation (see Fig. 2 left). When one ball is gripped, air is pumped out of that ball and into the other. Thus, a user can grip the ball in different ways, and the other user can recognize the different pumps (pressures) of the ball. We analyzed the effectiveness of this communication tool during oral communication (Matsuda et al. 2010) and the features of emotional communication by using the tool (Matsuda et al. 2011 & Matsuda et al. 2013). The result showed that the subjects mainly used the tool to respond to the grip and talk by the other

subject and intended to emphasize their talk when they expressed emotions; surprise was characterized by unique strong and short one-time grip; both joy and anger were characterized by strong multiple grips with constant short intervals; sad-

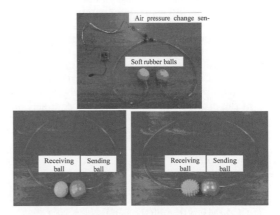

Figure 1. The previous tool (upper), different-sized tool (lower left) and knobbed tool (lower right).

Figure 2. Oral communication using the previous tool (left) and different-sized tool (right).

ness, disgust and fear were characterized by weak grips with constant short intervals and similar to each other; the coincidence ratios of surprise, joy and anger were higher; the coincidence ratios of sadness, disgust and fear were lower. The receiver frequently misrecognizes sadness, disgust and fear that expressed by weak grips.

Next, we improved the tactual communication tool (Matsuda et al. 2012). To increase the pump of the receiving ball, we change the sending ball into a bigger ball (diameter: 76 mm). The receiving ball is same as the previous tool. Figure 1 lower left shows the tactual communication tool with different-sized balls. To stimulate senses of the receiver, a knobbed ball (diameter: 66 mm, including knob height 4 mm) is adopted as the receiving ball. The sending ball is same as the different-sized tool. Figure 1 lower right shows the tactual communication tool with knobbed ball. The balls of these communication tools are separated into the sending ball and receiving ball. Then two users each hold two tools during an oral conversation (see Fig. 2 right). We analyzed the features of emotional communication by using these two tools (Matsuda et al. 2012). The results showed that the different-sized tool could emphasize the pump of the receiving ball and improved the coincidence ratios of sadness and fear; the knobbed tool could stimulate the senses of the receivers, but it could not improve the coincidence ratios of sadness, disgust and fear.

Using these three tools, the subjects could express the emotions by gripping, but there was only one channel of gripping-pumping. If the channels of gripping-pumping are expanded, the expression by gripping can be more varied.

In the present study, to expand the channels of gripping-pumping, we developed a coupled tactual communication tool (hereinafter called the coupled tool) and oral communication by using this tool was examined.

2 DEVELOPMENT OF COUPLED COMMUNICATION TOOL

To expand the channels of gripping-pumping, we coupled two pairs of tactual communication tools. The novel tool consists of four small soft rubber balls and two hoses (see Fig. 3). A hole was made on the surface of each ball (diameter: 53 mm) so that both two balls could be connected by the hoses (inner diameter: 6 mm, length: 1200 mm). The interfaces between the balls and the hose were sealed by adhesive bond. The both hoses were bound and the two balls of both ends were coupled. Two users each hold the coupled balls during an oral conversation. If one user grip only the upper ball, the upper ball of the other user is pumped;

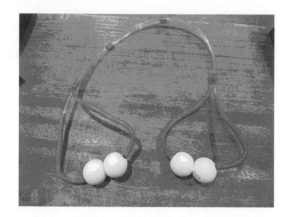

Figure 3. The coupled tactual communication tool.

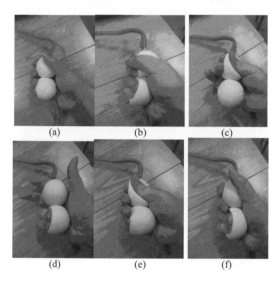

Figure 4. Classification of way of gripping. The holding form (a), grip two balls at once (b), grip only upper ball (c), grip only lower ball (d), grip upper ball consciously (e) and grip lower ball consciously (f).

if one user grip only lower ball, the lower ball of the other user is pumped; if one user grip both balls, the both balls of the other user are pumped. Thus, the expressions by gripping are more varied than the previous tools. Figure 4 shows the holding form and the classification of way of gripping.

3 METHOD

The subjects were seven male and one female college students (subjects 1–8). All subjects gave their informed consent after hearing a description of the study.

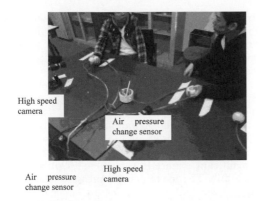

High speed camera

Air pressure change sensor

High speed camera

Air pressure change sensor

Figure 5. An experiment.

The communication tolls were the previous tool and coupled tool.

Two subjects participated in the round. The order of the subjects of each round was predetermined. The experiment using two communication tools (the previous tool and coupled tool) was conducted in the round. The order of the tools of each round was also predetermined and counterbalanced. In the first session, the subjects sat face to face and held one tool, respectively. The subjects communicated using speech about the specific theme (e.g. favorite foods, favorite music, favorite books, etc.) and gripped the tool freely. Each session was conducted for three minutes. In the second session, the subjects held the other tool, respectively. The subjects communicated using speech about the other specific theme and gripped the tool freely. The experiment consisted of 28 rounds by round-robin system.

Each hose had a third branch in the center. These branches were connected to air pressure change sensors (FKS-111, Fuji ceramics) (see Figs. 1 left and 5). The air pressure change sensors and two high-speed video cameras (DEWE-CAM, Dewetron) were connected to a data logger (DEWE-800, Dewetron). The data logger measured the air pressure change as a result of the grip and simultaneously recorded the images of the grips by the subjects. The measurement range of the air pressure change was 1 Pa–133 kPa and the sampling frequency was 10 kHz. The image was 640 × 480 pixels and the sampling frequency was 70 Hz. Another digital video camera (HDC-TM300, Panasonic) recorded the entire appearance of the experiment.

4 RESULTS

First, we classified the way of gripping the two tools (N = 56, respectively). The ratios of the way of grip-

ping the previous tool were as follows: gripping by all fingers and palm 85.8%; gripping by the finger pulps 7.1%; other 7.1%. The ratios of the way of gripping the coupled tool were as follows: gripping the lower ball consciously 76.7%; gripping the two balls at once 12.5%; gripping the upper ball consciously 3.6%; gripping only the lower ball 3.6%; gripping only the upper ball 1.8%; other 1.8%.

Second, we analyzed the air pressure change during the experiment session. Figure 6 shows the sample data of air presser change as a result of the session (for 180 seconds) of the coupled tool. We divided the data into 18 segments, so that each segment consists of the data for 10 seconds. Figure 7 shows the air pressure change of one divided segment. In this segment, the subject gripped the lower ball consciously two times. We calculated the maximum air pressure changes of the upper and lower balls in each segment (Fig. 7). Then the mean of the maximum air pressure change of the both balls of each segment was calculated. Figure 8 shows the sample data of air presser change as a result of the session (for 180 seconds) of the previous tool. Figure 9 shows the air pressure change of one divided segment. The maximum air pressure changes of the previous tool of each segment were also calculated in the same way (see Fig. 9). Figure 10 shows the means

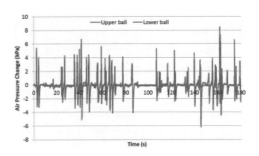

Figure 6. Air pressure change as a result of the session (for 180 seconds) of the coupled tool.

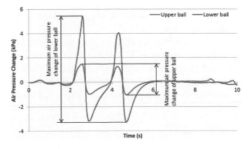

Figure 7. Air pressure change of one segment (for 10 seconds) of the coupled tool.

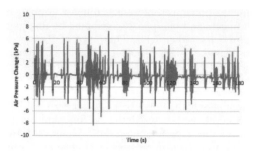

Figure 8. Air pressure change as a result of the session (for 180 seconds) of the previous tool.

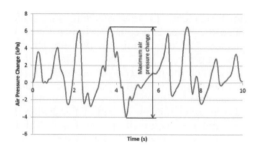

Figure 9. Air pressure change of one segment (for 10 seconds) of the previous tool.

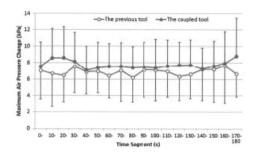

Figure 10. Mean of maximum air pressure change as a function of the time segments and tools (error bars represent standard deviations).

of maximum air pressure change as a function of time segments and tools.

After the experiment, the subjects were asked how they gripped the tool. The subjects answered that they mainly used the tool to respond to the talk by the other subject; they were more tired from gripping the coupled tool than gripping the previous tool.

5 DISCUSSION

The ratio of gripping the previous tool by all fingers and palm was 85.8%; the ratio of gripping

the lower ball of the coupled tool consciously was 76.7%; the other 5 kinds of way of gripping the coupled tool were confirmed. Thus, the way of gripping the coupled tool was more varied than the one of the previous tool.

To analyze the grip strength of the coupled and previous tools, we conducted an analysis of variances. The dependent variable was the maximum air pressure change. The variable composed a 2×18 within-subjects design of tool and time segment. A 2×18 Analysis Of Variances (ANOVA) revealed a significant main effect: tool ($F(1,896) = 14.94$, $p < 0.001$). The maximum air pressure change of the coupled tool was significantly larger than the one of the previous tool. Because the subjects gripped the coupled tool strongly, it was considered that the coupled tool was used more actively.

The subjects answered that they mainly used the tool to respond to the talk by the other subject. This answer was same as the result of the experiment of the previous tool (Matsuda et al. 2010). The subjects also answered that they were more tired from gripping the coupled tool than gripping the previous tool. Considering the hand structure, the upper small ball of the coupled tool should be replaced with the previous soft rubber ball.

6 CONCLUSION

In the present study, to expand the channels of gripping-pumping, we developed a coupled tactual communication tool and oral communication by using this tool was examined. As a result, the way of gripping the coupled tool was more varied than the one of the previous tool; the coupled tool was used more actively. The subjects mainly used the tool to respond to the talk by the other subject. To prevent tiredness, the upper small ball of the coupled tool should be replaced with the previous soft rubber ball.

REFERENCES

Matsuda, Y., Shimbo, T. & Isomura, T. 2010. Tactual Communication Tool for Emphasizing Emotional Communication. *Journal of Rehabilitation Medicine*, Suppl. 48: 162.

Matsuda, Y. & Isomura, T. 2011. Emotional Expression by a Person's Grip on a Tactual Communication Tool. *Communications in Computer and Information Science (CCIS)*, 174: 247–251.

Matsuda, Y. & Isomura, T. 2012. Emotional Communication by using Novel Tactual Communication Tool, *Proceedings of 2012 International Congress on Engineering and Information*: 327–338.

Matsuda, Y. & Isomura, T. 2013. Emotional Communication by using a Tactual Communication Tool, *International Journal of Computer Theory and Engineering*, 5 (2): 279–283.

Computer, Intelligent Computing and Education Technology – Liu, Sung & Yao (Eds)
© *2014 Taylor & Francis Group, London, ISBN 978-1-138-02469-4*

Lean construction in the process of the implementation of standardized management performance evaluation system

Jing Wang
China Construction Eighth Engineering Bureau Workstation of Postdoctoral Scientific Research, Shanghai
Management Science and Engineering in Shanghai Jiao Tong University Post-Doctoral Research Station, Shanghai
Northwest University of Politics and School of Economics and Management, Xi'an

Rong-Quan Ma
China Construction Eighth Engineering Bureau Workstation of Postdoctoral Scientific Research, Shanghai

ABSTRACT: the quality of construction projects related to the effect of the construction project investment, construction engineering applicability, more directly affect people's life and property safety. Based on the reflection of equalization in lean build standardized production management, this paper designed the lean construction in the process of the implementation of standardized management performance evaluation system. To reinvigorate the standardization of the trinity "quality, cost, time limit for a project" management idea, to achieve reunification of the project quality and economic benefit.

Keywords: lean construction; standardized management; the performance evaluation system; realize the path

1 INTRODUCTION

Quality of construction engineering project is related to the effect of the construction project investment, construction engineering applicability, more directly affect people's life and property safety. For a long time there are many factors affecting the quality of construction projects, mainly in project management lag, the project technology is complex, long construction period, thus cause project quality fluctuation. Therefore, improve the level of standardization of project management, performance evaluation system to study the effects of lean construction standardization management is significant. Take the performance evaluation system is the realization of the value of construction projects, to ensure that construction projects play a necessary link in the process of practical utility.

2 THE REFLECTION OF EQUALIZATION IN LEAN PRODUCTION TO BUILD STANDARDIZED MANAGEMENT

Lean construction according to the theory of lean production and construction production theory

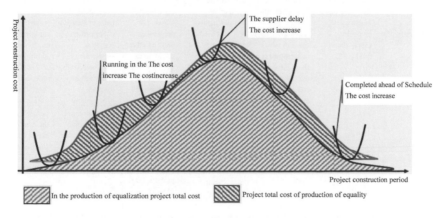

Figure 1. In "equalization" and "production of equalization" under the engineering project cost.

The project	Level (score) 0	level (score) 1	Level (score) 2	Level (score) 3	Level (score) 4	Level (score) 5
Flexible workers	No skills, flexible, typical state is a corresponds to a machine.	Multi-motor operation consciousness, cross training has begun.	Cross training table establishment, training records documented, workers began to machine operation.	Cross training table widely used, > 75% of the workers has been cross training, basic operational workers less than 2 working procedure.	Workers in all areas of the existing cross training, training table record showed, basic process can run 3 or more workers.	Comprehensive flexible workers, all the workers can run all processes or so, basic training and cross training into daily work.
Kaizen supervisor/manager	Inside are not Kaizen activities.	Kaizen activities under the top drive to improve the backward phenomenon occurs frequently or file work is not done, no plans for the future.	Kaizen activities must has the support of consultants, and launched by two managers, improvement plan has been established.	Improvement activities have been completed, the remaining items are normal, the coordination state is steadily improved, the normal workers participate in improvement activities.	Weekly improvement plan finish, initiate and implement most activities based on demand.	Team to carry out continuous improvement activities every day, spontaneous team work to solve the problem, achieve the goal.
Balance production	Takt time concept is not understanding and application, therefore, cycle time and takt time is used to balance the production process.	Training is completed, managers and workers to master the principles and concepts, but the balance of production operation has not yet start.	Takt time start is used to control the output, takt time is the working area to understand, to post, but often does not lead to work overtime or advanced production implementation.	Know the cycle time and the relationship between the takt time, and is used to balance work, standardize enterprise reflected in balance and change, in overtime and still occur in order to satisfy the demands of production, advanced production but improved substantially.	Factory through normal plan can meet the production requirements, not to work overtime, unit of work and basic production coordinated takt time.	All process is consistent with the takt time, single piece flow based on the beat and daily production each kind of components of the mixed type production.
The production plan	Push this plan leads to shortage of parts, excessive inventory or a longer cycle, inventory supply days (DSI > 75).	Promote the planning system still in use, dependent on MRP planning workshop production, have the consciousness of the Kanban/pull, there have been some signal system used in the schedule. (DSI < 75)	Push for MRP planning system is reduced, the dependence of most of the manufacturing process based on consumption and user orders use kanban CARDS added signal, output balance aggregation. (DSI (35)	Plan at some point in the production chain equilibrium output, all processing parts based on consumption and user orders, through Kanban pull signal added. Supplier system began to build, MRP is used to drive most supply parts ordering process. (DSI < 25)	Plan based on equilibrium mixed type production, manufacturing parts of Kanban change often, supply a supplement use Kanban signals and MRP for long-term procurement negotiations, is not used for issuing of order. (DSI < 15)	Factory production is completely based on the user's signal, in order to realize the completely mixed model output, continuous production process is controlled by a worker in the unit, only when the customer pull signal can supplement. (DSI < 5)

Figure 2. The implementation of standardized management performance evaluation system path graph (a).

The project	Level (score) 0	level (score) 1	Level (score) 2	Level (score) 3	Level (score) 4	Level (score) 5
5S	There is no improvement and monitoring level of 5 s system. (5 s score = 0)	5 s rating existing, awareness training is completed, the project implementation in the early. (< 5 s score > = 0 and 5)	The first level and keep sorting and cleaning is finished, use the red logo, some storage area is established. (< 5 s score > = 5 and 10)	Only work area must be items, all must be placed orderly and visual identity, have maintained good, clear daily work task clear. (5 s score > = 0 and < 15)	Keep the practice of the level 1, 2 & 3 standard has been posted, every day. (< 5 s score > = 15 and 20)	Area has ability to maintain 5 s project, create the rules and standards, staff systematic training, abide by the management to take the lead. (5 s score > = 20)
Visual control	The organization and running, there are no visual instructions product flow is not obvious, the implementation of plan not shown.	Supervisors and workers set up some information board, and maintain.	Floor mark, storage areas and visual organization method to establish, message board message clear and up to date.	Normal and abnormal easy visual detection, landmarks, product/process flow visual, inventory placed in use, tools and visual information board latest obviously.	Visual plan posted by production and equipment maintenance workers and maintenance, information used for point-of-care team and management meeting.	Form the visual workplace, work information exchange, fully visitors don't need to explain can clearly understand the operation, continuous improvement action plan has been established, to improve the results were presented.
Poka Yoke	Without a sense of complete mistake proofing training.	Awareness training has been completed, some mistake proofing devices begin to use.	Mistake proofing device is applied to the key working procedure, immediately stop line and feedback system, into the next process to be effective in preventing defective products.	Mistake proofing device is established and is used for defects may occur most of the process, accompanied by detecting defects and stop process method.	Mistake proofing device layout in all process, used to prevent defects, all of the original testing, self-checking and inspection methods start to constitute a complete method of zero defects.	Culture of zero defect, mistake proofing devices for all tools and with the original detection, self-checking and check together, effectively eliminate the defects.
Standardized operations	Operation method depends on the individual, personal and other parts have no coordination in class, in the past there were large variations in manufacturing and assembly time.	Kaizen activities began used to improve some methods of implementation, there is still no standardized procedures, individual and team.	Standard operating table began to establish and effective implementation, need to do further ways to improve, work standardization goes further.	Standard operating table and standard work merge table in all working procedure, establishing standardized operations defined beats, sulfur, between process standard work packages, as well as the cycle time, these standards are workers understand and execute.	Workers to reduce the cycle time, adjust the time, and implement the standard work on improvement Suggestions, workers to create, maintain and training standard operating procedures.	Posted a standardized operations for 100% of the station, at the same time, the relationship between the load of takt time and cycle time all posted, improvement has been completed and updated every day, everyone according to standardized operation.

Figure 2. The implementation of standardized management performance evaluation system path graph (b).

as the theoretical basis to build the entire project delivery system [1–3]. Standardization management is to point to in the engineering project implementation, the proposed standardization requirements, in addition to implement the standardization requirements, plans for organization, coordination, control, and the personnel, funds and standardized authentication facilities management [4–6]. Production of equalization is the important embodiment of lean construction of standardized management. In "equalization" and "production of equalization" under the engineering project cost comparison, as shown in Figure 1.

3 LEAN CONSTRUCTION IN THE PROCESS OF THE IMPLEMENTATION OF STANDARDIZED MANAGEMENT PERFORMANCE EVALUATION SYSTEM

Based on the above research, the implementation of standardized management performance evaluation system design path, its function is to: summarize, prediction, improvement. As shown in Figure 2 (a) and (b).

4 SUMMARIZES

"Quality is life", the standardization management by attaches great importance to the society, especially the standardized management of the construction project, is the social focus problem. Project to achieve the desired goal, in the process of lean construction must be standardized management performance evaluation system was applied to organic coordination of construction quality, cost, time limit for a project, do as much as possible of the three objectives optimization, reach to the "quality, cost, time limit for a project" the trinity management concept of a new understanding,

to realize the unification of the engineering project quality and economic benefits.

ACKNOWLEDGEMENTS

1.54 batch on China postdoctoral science foundation projects "ecological assessment and comprehensive management paradigm of manufacturing supply chain research", number: 2013 m541552. 2.2013 annual shaanxi province social science fund research project "manufacturing and logistics industry linkage development mode study", number: 13 d085. 3.2014 postdoctoral funding annual Shanghai pudong new area of science and technology development fund project "China building industry chain and ecosystem coupling: factor and the model and mechanism study. 4. China construction eighth engineering co., LTD. Science and technology research and development project "construction production line based on the theory of lean construction theory research and practice", number: 2012-28.

REFERENCES

[1] Jiang Shuhong Su Zhenmin. Lean build: an advanced construction of the system [J]. Journal of infrastructure optimization, 2004.6 (3): 11~14.
[2] James womack, Daniel t. Jones. Lean thinking: elimination of waste, to create wealth [M]. Shen Xijin, et al. Beijing: the commercial press, 2002.113~120.
[3] MinYongHui Su Zhenmin. Lean construction system mode of construction management research [J]. Journal of building economy, 2007. (1): 52~55.
[4] Koskela L.A. n Exploration forward a Production Theoryandits Applicationto Construction [M]. ESPOO: VTT Publications, 2000.57~61.
[5] Womack J P, Jones D T.L ean Fhinking [M]. New York: Simonand Schuster, 1996.215~219.
[6] Ohno t. Toyota Production System, Beyond Large—Scale Production [M]. Cambridge, Massachusetts: the Productivity Press, 1978.162~168.

Reform practices on environmental protection conspectus in local colleges and universities

L.X. Li, Z.W. Song, Y. Zhan & K.J. Luo
School of Environment and Chemical Engineering, Heilongjiang University of Science and Technology, Harbin, China

Y. Liu
College of Life Science and Technology, Harbin Normal University, Harbin, China

ABSTRACT: Environmental protection conspectus is one of the general courses open to some local colleges and universities students, who's major is non-environmental specialty. This paper described the reform practices of knowledge system on environmental protection conspectus in Heilongjiang Institute of Science and Technology. After studying relevant literature, a module was formulated, which lead to the commencement of short courses. Through these courses students were informed on the importance of environmental protection.

Keywords: environmental protection conspectus; knowledge system; reform practices

1 INTRODUCTION

It's known that environmental problems are generated with the economic and social development, thus, the nature of environmental problems is one of most important economic and social issues. The traditional model of economic development led to global environmental pollution, ecological damage and threat to human survival and development. The students in colleges and universities are advanced expertise of social construction and management in the future, from the view of comprehensive quality education, learn the course "environmental protect" is very important for them. In 1996, the Ministry of environmental protection, the Central Propaganda Department, the ministry of education clearly stated "environmental protect compulsory course or elective course should open to students of non-environmental specialty in colleges or universities (Zhou 1999). According to the survey, teaching environmental protection conspectus to students of non-environmental specialty was not an easy work, some problems existed such as fewer classes, no suitable textbooks, students paid no attention to an elective course and so on (Xu et al. 2005). Since, environmental protection conspectus should be offered to students of non-environmental specialty. How to give more information in limited classes, how to foster the interest of students to this course?

Environmental protection conspectus had been taught to mining engineering, safety engineering and related majors in Heilongjiang University of Science and Technology for seven years. The authors, with years of experience in teaching this course, made great effort to improve the current system of curriculum knowledge and analyze the existing education system. The aim of revolution were to make students know more knowledge of environmental protection, foster their awareness of environmental protection and teach them how to apply the knowledge of environmental protection in their further job. The authors intended to provide a useful reference of the specific teaching activities for brothers college by this article.

2 THE NATURE, STATUS AND FUNCTION OF ENVIRONMENTAL PROTECTION CONSPECTUS

Environmental protection conspectus was public elective courses in many colleges of science and engineering, which comprehensively expounded the basic knowledge about environmental protection. It was an basic course of an introduction to the environmental major. Environmental problems are the important issues which human beings are confronting today, environmental protection is a research hotspot in the world. How to protect the human environment? We must know the environment problems firstly and understand the resource of pollution, then learn how to restore ecological damage. Therefore, strengthening environmental education, learning environmental regulations to raise the environmental awareness is an important approach to solving environmental problems (Zhang et al. 2009). The purpose of this course is make environmental education for students who majored in non–environment, introduce environmental protection knowledge, improve the environmental protection consciousness of them of (Yuan et al. 2011).

3 PROBLEMS IN KNOWLEDGE SYSTEM AND TEACHING METHODS OF ENVIRONMENTAL PROTECTION CONSPECTUS

3.1 Textbooks contents do not meet training requirements

Recently, many teachers adopted the textbook environmental protection conspectus which was edited by Lin and published by the Higher Education Press. Our university used this textbooks for several years, but with the increase of teaching experience and strict demands of students on the content there are two problems with this version of textbooks: First, it was difficult to stimulate interest of students, the content is systematic and detailed, but writing style are not very interested; Second, the knowledge content update so slowly, although this book is a reprint, and has been published for more than 10 years, new theories and knowledge did not update in time, it is difficult to meet students requirements for the new knowledge, new theories and new methods of environmental protection.

3.2 The single teaching methods, it was difficult to meet the requirements of students

Due to the limits of the syllabus of curricula and the content of textbook, teaching is still in the old mode of one-way teaching. In the theory part, most of the teachers using blackboard and multimedia, students listen and take notes passively, "Teaching" and "Learning" was isolated, students had no the opportunity to actively thinking. It might result in students grasp of knowledge rigid, dogmatic, it is difficult to arouse students' interest (Dong et al. 2011).

4 REFORM MEASURES OF KNOWLEDGE SYSTEM ABOUT ENVIRONMENTAL PROTECTION CONSPECTUS

4.1 Optimization and reorganization of theory teaching content

The textbook is the vector of the course, it is the basic guarantee of the talents cultivation quality.

The most important thing for the teacher is how to select a suitable textbook for students. So authors summarized new technologies, new methods and progress of environmental protection in the last ten years combined with teaching experience of environmental protection conspectus course, wrote the textbook of environmental protection conspectus printed by Chemical Industry Press in 2010. This textbook not only added lots of new knowledge, new technologies and new methods in the field of environmental protection, but also optimized the course content, removed some old knowledge, included abundant content and complement environmental issues which students was interested in. It also included some environmental protection cases as extracurricular reading materials.

In our university, only 32 class hours were give to this course, the content was made major changes and updated. The content was highlighted as follows: sustainable development strategy, water environment and water resources, air pollution and prevention, soil pollution and prevention, solid waste pollution, and environmental management chapters, which made students more impressive of the knowledge.

4.2 The research project combining with theory knowledge

In this class, the achievements of our environment specialized teachers in the relevant fields was introduced, such as when teaching water environment and water resources section, introduced Dr. Song's research work on granular sludge and biofilm, Dr. Ren's research work on treatment of oil wastewater; when teaching air pollution and its control section, introduced Professor Liu's research work on harm and analysis of atmospheric particles; when teaching soil pollution and its prevention section, described associate professor Yang's research work on repair of soil heavy metal pollution, Dr. Gu's research work on soil reclamation in mine area; when teaching environmental impact assessment and environmental management sections, introduced professor Zhan's research work on environmental impact assessment and environmental management in mining area. The measures mentioned above not only offered students an opportunity to understand the teachers' achievements but also inspire their interests, enhanced their pride for our university.

5 CONCLUSIONS

This article discussed the achievements in the process of the course system reform and practice of environmental protection conspectus in local colleges and universities, represented by Heilongjiang University of Science and Technology. Environmental protection conspectus course was elective course for some specialist in our university, there has always been some problems for many years, such as more content with the contradictions of teaching hours less. By construction and practice of course system of environmental protection conspectus, updating the contents of the textbook, combining case teaching with scientific research project, students' environmental knowledge and application skills were improved, and students could apply what they had learned.

Classroom teaching is an important way of imparting knowledge to students. With the aim to teach well, the comprehensive understanding of the nature and content of the course must be done. The teacher should make ongoing exploration and research on the teaching content and teaching methods (Zhang 2008).

ACKNOWLEDGEMENTS

This research was supported by Heilongjiang province higher education association "Twelve-Five" educational science planning project (HGJXHB1110866); Educational science "Twelve-Five" planning project in Heilongjiang province (GBB1212050); Reform and research project of academic degrees & graduate education in Heilongjiang province (JGXM_HLJ_2012102); 2014 educational research project of Heilongjiang University of Science and Technology.

REFERENCES

Dong, Y.H., Feng, Z.Y. & Lin, J.W. 2011. Preliminary Studies on Teaching Reform of "Environmental Protection Conspectus" Public Basic Course. *Journal of ShenYang College of Education* 13(5): 42–45.

Xu, S. & Chen, S.M. 2005. Teaching Reform and Practice of The Public Course of Environmental Protection Conspectus. *Sun Yatsen University Forum* 25(1): 138–142.

Yuan, X.M. & Wang, B.Y. 2011. Teaching Research on Environment Protection Introduction to Non-environment Specialty Students. *Journal of Luoyang Institute of Science and Technology (Natural Science Edition)* 21(3): 70–71.

Zhang, D.J. 2008. How to Teach a Course very well, *China University Teaching* (11): 17–19.

Zhang, J. & Zhang, X.F. 2009. Reform and Practice of Environmental Protection Conspectus. *Science and Technology Information* (22): 335.

Zhou, X.F. 1999. Preliminary Probe into Course Content and Teaching Method of Environmental Protection Conspectus. *Journal of South China University of Tropical Agriculture* 5(1): 66–68.

Computer, Intelligent Computing and Education Technology – Liu, Sung & Yao (Eds)
© 2014 Taylor & Francis Group, London, ISBN 978-1-138-02469-4

An empirical study on influential factors for real estate enterprise core competence in Western Region

J.G. Chang, F.Z. Luo & Y.H. Han
Xi'an University of Architecture and Technology, Xi'an, China

ABSTRACT: Through the questionnaire survey on the real estate enterprise managers in Shanxi province, an empirical analysis is carried out by the use of the factor analysis approach based on the principal component analysis to find out the influential factors for real estate enterprise core competence in Western Region. The research shows the influential factors are property products, capital planning and management, human resource, project profit, social relations, organizational management, strategic management, market promotion, enterprise culture in accordance with the size of the influence degree to the core competence. The research result, which is of the theoretical and realistic significance, will provide directions on how to establish the core competence for the real estate enterprise in western region.

Keywords: real estate enterprise; core competence; influential factors; factor analysis

1 INTRODUCTION

When the industrial environment and market structure cannot explain the source of an enterprise's competitive advantage, the perspective has turned to the internal part of an enterprise. The research on the influential factors of the real estate enterprise core competence mainly starts from the perspective of concept (Li Shihong, 2001), characteristics (Ma Dongsheng, Du Changhua, Shang Guobei, 2007), conceptual model (Fan Huanling, 2009), value chain (Tong Yan, 2003) and so on. The research results above are mostly based on the understanding of the connotation of the core competence or based on the enterprise practice, which lead that it is difficult to make a convincing explanation. Based on the survey of the real estate enterprises' managers in Shanxi, the factor analysis method is taken to further understand the structure of the real estate enterprise core competence and to play a guiding role of finding key points in cultivating the core competitiveness of the real estate enterprises in western areas of China.

2 DATA SOURCE AND RESEARCH METHOD

2.1 *Data source*

The research data are obtained by the questionnaire survey that is designed using the Likert five-points-scoring-method. The 10 real estate enterprises of level 1 qualification are randomly selected in Shanxi, level 2 and 3 qualification respectively for 15 and 20. The paper is mainly by the above middle managers of real estate enterprises and proper number of low-level managers should be considered in order to ensure access to a more comprehensive and actual situation. According to the level of qualification and scale of real estate enterprises, 6 to 10 questionnaires are given out to each real estate enterprise, and a total of 300 questionnaires are out, 276 valid questionnaires of which are recycled.

2.2 *Research method*

This study takes the literature research method and factor analysis. Through the review on the literatures about the elements or the influential factors of real estate enterprise core competitiveness, the influence factors of real estate enterprise core competitiveness are preliminarily determined. And after interviewing experts and scholars in theoretical and practical circles, the collection of influencing factors are finally determined.

The factor analysis method is a kind of data reduction technique. It explores the basic structure of the observed data, and a few hypothetical variables to represent its basic data structure by studying the internal dependencies among mass variables. The hypothetical variables can reflect main information of original variables. The original variable can be observed, and the hypothetical variables cannot be observed, known as the factor (Huang Qiong, 2006). The version 17.0 of SPSS software is adopted to finish the research. Empirical Study

2.3 Correlation test

The premise condition of Factor analysis is that there is correlation between different variables and the correlation coefficient of the correlation matrix must be significantly greater than zero. Now the KMO statistics and Bartlett's sphericity test is used to make a decision. KMO statistics is used to detect partial correlation between variables, the value range of which is 0 to 1. Generally it is considered best when KMO is greater than 0.9, well when above 0.7, very poor when 0.6, and not suitable for factor analysis when 0.5.

The Table 1 shows that KMO statistic is 0.714, so it is suitable for factor analysis. The significance level of chi-square statistic is 0.000, which is smaller than 0.05, suggesting that there is high correlation between each index. Both the KMO statistics and Bartlett's spherical test show that the selected indicators are suitable for factor analysis.

2.4 Total variance explained

The factor extraction and factor rotated results are shown in Table 2. Based on the principle of the eigenvalue greater than 1, 10 common factors are

Table 1. KMO statistics and Bartlett's sphericity test.

Kaiser-Meyer-Olkin measure of sampling adequacy		0.714
Bartlett's test of sphericity	Approx. Chi-Square	256.438
	df	76
	Sig.	0.000

withdrawed, and their cumulative variance contribution rate is 94.729%, which shows that the 10 common factors can extract 94.729% of the original data information and have good explanatory power.

2.5 Factor named and discussed

The eigenvalue in the correlation coefficient matrix of the Table 2 can measure the important degree of various factors. According to the comprehensive analysis of Table 2 and 3, 10 common factors are as follows.

The first common factor is named as property product guarantee ability, including the planning and design and project quality. The planning and design play a basic and prevailing role, and it determine the project positioning, the division of niche market and development cost, etc. It is directly related to the implementation of the subsequent project development degree and consumer recognition, and in turn affects the return on investment. The project quality control is to finish the implementation of planning and design by the quality control of construction stage, including civil engineering, equipment installation, decoration, outdoor landscape and so on, and determines the safety, reliability, applicability and durability of the property.

The second common factor is named as capital management ability, including capital resource, market analysis and investment ability, capital operation and land resource. Because the real estate industry objectively requires a lot of money resources and the financial market is imperfect, real estate enterprises need to broaden the financing

Table 2. Total variance explained.

Component	Initial eigenvalue			Extraction sums of squared loadings			Rotation sums of squared loadings		
	Total	% of variance	Cumulative (%)	Total	% of variance	Cumulative (%)	Total	% of variance	Cumulative (%)
1	7.56	24.41	24.41	7.56	24.41	24.41	3.93	12.70	12.70
2	4.40	14.20	38.62	4.40	14.20	38.62	3.64	11.74	24.44
3	3.51	11.33	49.95	3.51	11.33	49.95	3.60	11.62	36.07
4	3.28	10.58	60.54	3.28	10.58	60.54	2.99	9.65	45.72
5	2.64	8.52	69.07	2.64	8.52	69.07	2.94	9.50	55.23
6	2.27	7.33	76.40	2.27	7.33	76.40	2.94	9.50	64.73
7	1.81	5.83	82.24	1.81	5.89	82.24	2.51	8.11	72.85
8	1.45	4.68	86.92	1.45	4.68	86.92	2.36	7.61	80.46
9	1.33	4.29	91.22	1.33	4.29	91.22	2.34	7.56	88.03
10	1.08	3.50	94.72	1.08	3.50	94.72	2.07	6.69	94.72

The factor load matrix after the orthogonal rotation through the maximum variance method is shown in Table 3. Each principal component has larger load on a handful of indicators.

Table 3. Rotated component matrix.

Potential impact factor	Component									
	1	2	3	4	5	6	7	8	9	10
Planning and design	0.88									
Project quality	0.78									
Capital resource		0.68								
Market analysis and investment ability		0.67								
Capital operation		0.60								
Land resource		0.53								
Staff's professional skills			0.81							
Entrepreneur ability			0.75							
Human resource			−0.71							
Consciousness and spirit of innovation			0.53							
Project cost control				0.94						
Project schedule control				0.83						
Cooperative partnership					0.76					
Customer relationship					0.69					
Government relationship					0.68					
Information resource					−0.55					
Organization structure						0.93				
Operating mechanism						0.69				
Operating and management philosophy						0.61				
Enterprise system						0.75				
Enterprise vision							0.81			
Strategic plan							0.67			
Property management								−0.83		
Marketing network								0.79		
Brand influence								0.56		
Staff cognition									0.92	
Cohesive force									0.52	
Enterprise core value									0.94	
Project safety									0.94	
Knowledge sharing mechanism										0.68
Learning atmosphere										0.57

channels and to strengthen the financing ability. The land resource is still scarce and is the strategic resource in the real estate development, now the system of bidding, auction and listing determines that the land resource acquisition tests the enterprise's financial strength in essence. Real estate development requires high level of market analysis and a clear and correct understanding of the real estate market, then you also need to have the consciousness and the ability of capital operation, only in this way can find good investment opportunities, laying a foundation for higher returns.

The third common factor is named as human resource ability, including the staff's professional skills, entrepreneur ability, human resource, consciousness and spirit of innovation, which can mainly be divided into two kinds, one kind is entrepreneur's quality and ability, and the other kind is the enterprise's technical personnel and management personnel. The strategic development of the enterprise depends largely on entrepreneur's quality and ability, and on the other hand, the real estate development cycle is long, and the business is multifarious, which needs to integrate the internal and external resources, and to coordinate the relationship between the parties, so the high requirement of the employees' quality and ability is put forward. Under the condition of new economy, if enterprises want to achieve sustained competitive advantage in the fierce market competition, the innovation of various aspects of implementation technology, management, system, product and so on is the basic guarantee, and the innovation of real estate enterprises depends on human resources' innovation consciousness and spirit.

The fourth common factor is named project profit guarantee ability, including the project cost control and project schedule control. The land price, the price of building materials and equipment and labour is constantly rising, and there is also a large number of the cost of financing and related taxes and fees, which makes the real estate project development costs that directly determines the project's profit margins rise faster in recent years, the project cost control. The project progress is closely related to project quality, safety, cost and so on, and influences the project product's time node to market, so the project progress control and the project profit have a close relationship. Customer relationship is directly related to the consumer's attitude to real estate enterprises, and the benign interaction between the customer that can win the trust and praise of customers, is an effective method to set up real estate enterprise's brand.

The fifth common factor is named as social relation ability, including cooperative partnership, customer relationship, government relationship, information resource. The handling capacity of social relations is the premise of effective integration of external resources, and real the competition among real estate enterprises has evolved into the competition of the real-estate-enterprises-center supply chain, which requires different units to assist in the development of the whole cycle and means that establishing a long-term cooperative partnership can effectively reduce the cost of integration of external resources. From the land obtainment to each link of the examination and approval for the record, etc., it needs to have relations with a dozen relevant government departments. Secondly though the real estate market is developing rapidly in China, there are still many imperfections, so it needs government regulation and control, which shows that the government relationship is especially important.

The sixth common factor is named as organization management ability, including organization structure, operating mechanism, operating and management philosophy and enterprise system. The suitable organization structure, advanced management concept and enterprise system are the foundation of effective management of enterprises, which concerns effective allocation of resources and the enterprise's operating efficiency and is the guarantee to reduce operating costs. From the existing research, the more the enterprise organization management ability is prominent, the more beneficial to cultivate the core competitiveness of enterprises and to improve performance (Ding Weibin et al., 2005).

The seventh common factor is named as strategic management ability, including enterprise vision and strategic plan, strategic management refers that the enterprise, according to the external environment and internal conditions, sets the enterprise strategic target and carries out the correct implementation and realizes the goal in order to ensure the progress plan, which is a dynamic management process in the process of implementation (Zhuang Dongmei, 2011). Strategic management makes enterprise's positioning and developing direction become clearer, enhances the risk resistance ability to face the uncertainty outside, and is conducive to the sustainable development of the enterprise.

The eighth common factor is named as marketing ability, including property management, marketing network and brand influence. Good property management can not only prolong the service life of the property, but promote property appreciation by providing thoughtful service for the owners. Smooth marketing network plays an important role in the success of the marketing planning, image packaging and advertising. A strong brand appeal is an effective weapon for marketing. Marketing is the effective measure to expand the property products into the market for consumer recognition and to recover the investment. Under the environment of more and more homogenizing in product, strong ability of marketing is the enterprise's essential requirements.

The ninth common factor is named as enterprise culture ability, including staff cognition, cohesive force, enterprise core value and project safety. Enterprise culture is a kind of soft power, which has a subtle influence on enterprise staff's consciousness and behavior, and thus makes the behavior of staff meet the needs of the development of enterprises, so the cohesion of enterprises will be greatly enhanced, which makes the power of the staff and enterprise's development form the same direction together. Identifying enterprise culture can promote the informal organization to form, which will reduce the management cost of enterprise, form the features of enterprise.

The tenth common factor is named as organization learning ability, including knowledge sharing mechanism and learning atmosphere. Learning enterprise can ensure to follow closely the pulse of the times in the external environment of rapid changes, draw knowledge from the technology and management experience summary and the practice of imitating from others, and then spread it quickly in the enterprise. Learning new knowledge and skills can not only keep the enterprise competitive advantage, but also to cure internal consensus and values for the enterprise and make it become a kind of enterprise culture.

3 CONCLUSIONS

Based on the data collection from the investigation, an empirical study on influential factors for real estate enterprise core competence in western region—by the example of Shanxi province, is carried out, considering the regional characteristics

1036

of the real estate industry so that the results are property product guarantee ability, capital management ability, human resource ability, project profit guarantee ability, social relation ability, organization management ability, strategic management ability, marketing ability, enterprise culture ability and organization learning ability. The operators and managers of real estate enterprises in the western region can refer to the conclusion and combined with the enterprise's developing condition, tilt resources to the influential factors needed to strengthen, improve the efficiency of the resources use and promote to cultivate the core competitiveness of enterprises. This conclusion also has reference significance for the real estate policy.

ACKNOWLEDGEMENT

First please allow us to thank all the authors whose article we find information from to do some research. We also wish to appreciate the organizers of CICET2013 and the anonymous reviewers for their hard-working. I would particularly like to thank Shanxi province soft science research plan project (2013 KRM03) for her funding.

REFERENCES

Ding Weibin, Rong Xianheng, Gui Binwang, 2005. An empirical analysis on the factor choice of the core competence in Chinese SMEs, Studies in Science of Science 5:651.

Fan Huanling. Discuss on the core competence structure of real estate development company, Productivity Research 19:165–167.

Huang Qiong, 2006. The Application of the Factor Analysis Method in the Grades Evaluation of Higher Vocational Students, Journal of Hubei Vocational-Technical College 1:35.

Li Shihong, 2001. Discuss on the core competence of real estate enterprise, China Real Estate 12:56–57.

Ma Dongsheng, Du Changhua, Shang Guobei, 2007. Analysis on factors of the core competence of real estate enterprise, Commercial Times 8:58–59.

Qiu Haozheng, 2011. Quantitative research and statistical analysis, Chongqing: Chongqing University Press 326.

Tong Yan, 2003. Core competence structure of real estate development company, Economic Management Journal 5:72–74.

Zhuang Dongmei, 2011. Study on the relationship between the enterprise culture and enterprise strategic management, Oriental Enterprise Culture 16:50.

Computer, Intelligent Computing and Education Technology – Liu, Sung & Yao (Eds)
© *2014 Taylor & Francis Group, London, ISBN 978-1-138-02469-4*

The development of data recording function in intelligent meter with AVR MCU's self-programming technique

Y.Z. Zhai

North China Institute of Science and Technology, Yanjiao, East of Beijing, China

ABSTRACT: The record function of the monitored information is usually adopted in portable intelligent meters. The recording way by means of the MCU's Flash is characterized with the more simple hardware, higher effective software and lower power dissipation. The technical requisition and realization procedure of self-programming is described with the MCU of ATmega64A as an example; the application is also introduced in connection with the development of record function of an intelligent monitor meter.

Keywords: intelligent meter; MCU; self-programming

1 OVERVIEW

In recent years, profound changes have taken place in MCU world, product types become rich, the performance is becoming more and more powerful, more opportunities are provided for the development and application.

A handheld meter based on microcontroller makes itself popular with the application of field monitoring by the characteristic of portability, low power consumption, battery power. Etc. Its functions usually include the following aspects. 1) Monitoring: implement information collection through the interface circuit of sensor; 2) Function settings: the display of information and operation management is achieved by man-machine interface; 3) Information management: recording the collected information in the instrument; 4) Instrument information access and viewing online: that is meter's local access by itself and online communication check.

Recording and reading are specific functions for the handheld meter based on MCU, and the medium and methods of implement recording are various, this paper will introduce a method by MCU chip Flash to realize the information recording.

2 CHARACTERISTICS OF INFORMATION RECORDING

1. Chip memory: different from automatic timer recording of on-line monitoring instrument, the information is saved on the upper computer hard disk; hand-held instrument can just save the information on the instrument internal chip.

2. Power off memory: monitoring information saved in field must be non volatile. Even if the battery is depleted or meter is shutdown, information should not be lost, that is the recording medium of information should be EEPROM or Flash.

3. Recording trigger: recording function of information is triggered by manual operation, this mode of operation determines the recording frequency is limited, and so is the recording capacity required.

4. The removal or covering of recording information: because of the limited storage capacity, the invalid information need to be removed or covered, so that the meter may be applied for a long time.

5. Recording information poll: for the saved information, the meter itself should be able to review, that is conducive to management in the field and beneficial to verification of recording information.

3 THE SCHEME TO REALIZE

Usually in the intelligent meters based on single chip computer, due to limited EEPROM capacity of single chip itself, the information is saved in the expansion of the EEPROM chip for the non volatile information memory. Usually Serial interface chips, for example I2C, TWI, SPI, are used to implement, such as ferroelectric FMC256 chip. While Software is running, because of the serial mode, information reading and writing speed is slow, and takes up the running time of the MCU, therefore Reduces the operation efficiency of the MCU, increased power consumption, so it is not suitable for the design of the handheld meter where power consumption is concerned closely.

Correspondingly, using the free Flash resources on chip of MCU, the collected information are saved directly in the Flash of MCU itself, it can realize the non volatile memory of information just as program memory also. There are two advantages doing like this, firstly expanded EEPROM device is no longer needed, secondly the software is simple, high efficiency, fast running speed, that is because the internal reading and writing Flash are in parallel operation mode, so it is clearly a better solution. Of course the premise that this solution can be implemented is the MCU selected must support this function.

Justly AVR Series MCU is a kind of monolithic that can be programmed on the Flash space by itself, i.e. Read-While-Write Self-programming function, of course, to satisfy a extent of recording capacity requirements, some microcontrollers with larger storage capacity are required as ATmega64\128\256, this paper will give an introduction with ATmega64 as example.

4 REALIZATION OF SELF PROGRAMMING FUNCTION WITH AVR MICROCOMPUTER

4.1 The storage resources of several typical ATmega's MCUs

ATmega's MCU which is produced by ATMEL company belongs to a kind of the Reduced Instruction Set (RISC) series MCU. Because it owns 32 general-purpose registers that can be used as accumulators, the high efficiency can be easily achieved with the code realization for software functions. Comparison of several typical ATmega series of MCSs storage resource is shown in Table 1.

For handheld intelligent meters, if the development is based on the assembly language, the soft-

Table 1. View of the storage resources of ATmega's several MCUs.

	ATmega64	ATmega128	ATmega256
EEPROM	2K	4K	4K
FLASH	64K	128K	256K
Internal SRAM	4K	4K	8K
Write/erase cycles	10,000 flash/100,000 EEPROM		

ware code capacity usually is limited. Provided as 20Kbytes, remaining space will get at least 40K even if ATmega64, so it is considerable to achieve information recording with the storage resource of MCU, nevertheless the Flash memory space of ATmega's MCU just can be erased or written the quantity of not more than 10000 times, otherwise it can't be guaranteed the reliability of writing, but the quantity of times is enough for the lifetime of the most intelligent meters. This paper takes ATmega64 as an example to illustrate.

4.2 The realization mechanism of self programming function

1. ATmega Series MCU's Flash space, is divided into two parts of the application area and the loading area, Flash self programming code must be stored in the boot area, the object of Flash self programming is limited to its application space, two space size distribution is allocated by the fuse bit set.

2. ATmega Series MCU provides SPM instruction and SPMCSR register specialized for self programming operation. The SPM instruction execute various operations to the Flash according to the type of the SPMCSR register specified, after register SPMCSR execute page erase, page write and page loading etc., SPM instructions must be executed within the next 4 instruction cycles. Oppositely the LPM instruction can be used to read any byte in Flash without any cycle limit.

3. MCU's flash memory is organized in the form of page, the program counter pointer can be considered as combination of two parts: one is the lower part for word addressing within page; another is the high part for page addressing. Flash self programming is conducted by page, for different types of MCU, the page space may differ in size, and the page space size of ATmega64 is 128 bytes.

4. The Z-pointer is used to address the SPM commands. The Z pointer is a 16 bits register. The high part of 15-7 is specified the programming corresponding page, lower part 6-1 specified operation word. Self programming page operation includes: page erase, page write, page loading, the pattern is set in the SPMCSR register.

5. MCU's self programming mechanism is provided with a temporary page buffer, the data need to be loaded to a temporary page buffer before it can be programmed to write to the page, and the page must be erased. The implementation process of self programming to specific Flash application space is suggested as follows, first to perform a page erase, then to fill temporary page buffer, finally to perform a page write.

6. Flash page write operation costs about 4 ms, only after the page write operation is fulfilled, the software code in applications space can be executed. So we should query SPMEN (self programming enable bit) in the SPMCSR register, self programming routines can't be exit until it is reset.

4.3 A sample of self programming application

During the data recording process of collecting information of the meter, each record information may not just occupy a whole page space, there may be part of last recording information in the programmed page yet, which requires the last record first saved, then be erased, finally rewritten. Here gives an idea: first the reserved page content loading to the temporary page buffer, and then let the programming content to be loaded to the rest of the temporary page buffer, and then as a whole page programming. To summarize the Flash self programming mechanism is as follows:

1. Retaining the content of the current page and save in the temporary page buffer;
2. Adding new content into the page buffer space temporary rest;
3. Executing the current page erase operation;
4. Executing the current page write operation.

An assembly subroutine sample for Page erase is gives as follows, here the Z pointer has be set:

```
; spmcrval set the pattern of operation
;for SPM instruction
ldi spmcrval, (1<<PGERS) | (1<<SPMEN)
; check if the previous programming operation
;has fulfilled or not?
Wait_spm: lds temp1, SPMCSR
sbrc temp1, SPMEN
rjmp Wait_spm
in temp2, SREG //preserve the scene and signs
cli            //close the interrupt,
;the SPM instruction set
; followed by the SPMCSR instruction
sts SPMCSR, spmcrval
spm
; restore interrupt and original status
out SREG, temp2
ret
```

5 MCU'S SELF PROGRAMMING TECHNIQUE APPLIED IN INTELLIGENT INSTRUMENT

5.1 Application background

In coal mine shaft and underground subway bypass channel freezing construction, to grasp and control the freezing works process, the status and changes of the freezing temperature field must be monitored. Because the temperature sensors to be placed is more in quantity, and mostly behaves linear distribution, the 1-wire bus technology usually is used to monitor the environmental temperature at the temperature sensors in practice.

Compared with the on-line monitoring, the monitoring with the hand-held intelligent meter is of many advantages; 1) Not necessary for an external power supply, 2) Not necessary for laying communication lines, 3) Not necessary to install device and artificial maintenance. Its applied ways is incomparably superior to on-line monitoring, so it is necessary for the development of 1-wire bus handheld temperature measuring meter.

As the hand-held meter of a 1-wire bus temperature monitoring, multiple functions is needed to realized to the temperature sensing cable, such as search, monitoring, inspection, setting number and other functions, the meter can be connected with more than several wire of temperature sensing cable, then all the freezing temperature sensing cable can be monitored by only one meter. The meter is applied not only in the performance of temperature monitoring in the field, but also in the information records of the temperature sensing cable so that the analysis and summary to the information is conducted easily, therefore the record function of the meter is one of the indispensable content.

To reduce power dissipation in the meter and to simplify hardware design, the expanding serial EEPROM scheme is abandoned in the design, we make use of the remaining space of the MCU's Flash to record monitored temperature information, that is, self programming technique is used to realize the recording of the temperature sensing information.

5.2 Hardware design overview of the meter

According to the storage space needed in the temperature record information, An ATmega64 microcontroller is selected as core chip in the hardware design of the meter, the circuit structure is shown as in Figure 1.

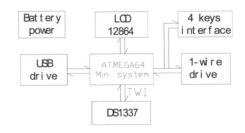

Figure 1. The principle diagram of handheld 1-wire bus temperature meter.

The meter is powered by 3V battery, the DC/DC chip is selected for battery circuit boost to supply 5V power for the whole circuit. 1-wire bus driver interface circuit is used for connecting to an external temperature sensing cable; the information of temperature sensor on the temperature sensing cable is get by the MCU under software control. The USB driver is used for connecting with the computer, which is used to transmit the recorded information to connected PC, and also can be used to set some parameters to the meter. There a real time clock chip DS1337 is used to identify the record time of temperature information; it is directly connected to the ATmega64 bus of TWI. The meter is also designed with a liquid crystal display and keyboard interface circuits, they are used to realize the interactive function of operation meter.

5.3 Recording function design of temperature sensing cable

Based on the actual application, maximum of 60 digital temperature sensors are permitted to lap on a temperature sensing cable by the meter, the temperature information of each temperature sensor occupies 2 bytes, in addition of recording time of year, month, week, day, hour, seconds, milliseconds, and a null byte total 8 bytes, each record of temperature sensing cable takes up to 128 bytes, or 64 words, then ATmega64 Flash can store 2 records per page. According to the calculation of each cable distribution 2K storage space, all twelve cables each can continuously record 16 times, that is enough to meet most application needs.

In software design, each temperature sensing cable is allocated a number L_num (its value is 0 to 11). In the Flash 12 temperature sensing cables will be allocated 2K FLASH record space in continuous way, totally 24K. Records number of each temperature sensing cable temperature acquisition information is signed as R_num, its value ranges 0–15. Each record is also continuously saved in the assigned 2K space. The temperature record operation of the temperature sensing cable is triggered by the button, when the function key is pressed, the temperature monitoring information of the cable is acquired, and at the same time the real time tag is get and altogether saved in the microcontroller's internal RAM, then call record subroutine to save the information to the assigned Flash zone.

5.4 The software design of meter record subroutine

The software design flowchart of the meter recording subroutine is shown as in Figure 2, the key elements of software design is shown.

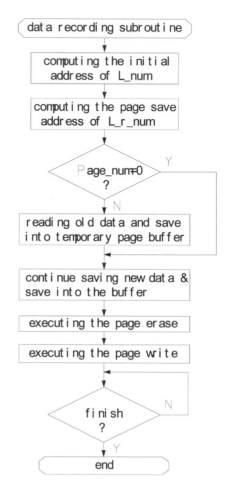

Figure 2. Record information flash self programming flow chart.

1. Set the cable number as L_num, initial storage address of records as Rt_addr, the initial storage address of the cable is calculated as follows:

   L_num_addr = Rt_addr + 2048× L_num

2. According to the record number L_R_num, Page_num, the corresponding record page number, is calculated, and the page address Page_addr is computed as follows:

   Page_num = L_R_num / 2

   Page_addr = L_num_addr + 128× Page_num

3. Calculation the remainder of L_r_num divided by 2, the remainder is 0. That means the storage will happen in a new page, not necessary to retain the original content, the new record information can be directly saved to the page buffer. If the remainder is not 0, it means there exists reserved for content in the being programmed page, we should read it first and write it to page

buffer, and then a new record information can be written to the successor position of the page buffer.

4. To execute page erase and page write operation.

6 SUMMARY

Implementation of information record with the MCU's internal Flash, is of a simple hardware design, high efficiency software, fast processing speed. Comparison with the serial, byte by byte operation mode of E²PROM chip, MCU's Flash self program operation is in parallel, page mode. To realize the recording function the large storage space may be required, the selection of available MCU types should be made by the specific situation. In the development of portable meter, due to the power consumption and simple hardware design thought, the application of the MCU Flash resources is a good choice.

REFERENCES

Arthur J.D. 2007. *Atmega64A Data Book*. ATMEL Corp. http://www.atmel.com

Sun Q.Y. & Lin Y.J. & Yang C.L. 2011. The realization of the single-chip computer program remote upgrade based on GPRS. *Instrumentation and monitoring & analysis*. (3):14–17.

Wang C.Z. & Zhang Z. etc. 2008. AVR Atmega series microcontroller source code remote rewriting *The Journal of Jilin University (INFORMATION SCIENCE EDITION)* 26(11).

Zhai Y.Z. & Xu S.R. 2008. The design and application of Ground freezing remote monitoring system. *Coal science and technology*. (10):68–71.

Zhai Y.Z. & Zhao Y.M. 2011. 1-wire bus monitoring system development for the deep ground freezing. *Coal science and technology*. (11):104–107.

Computer, Intelligent Computing and Education Technology – Liu, Sung & Yao (Eds)
© *2014 Taylor & Francis Group, London, ISBN 978-1-138-02469-4*

The application of concept map in the modern educational technology course

L. Xu
College of Computer Science, Sichuan Normal University, Chengdu, China

W. He
College of Information Technology, Sichuan Normal University, Chengdu, China

ABSTRACT: Concept maps organize and represent knowledge and their relationship with graphical method, which could help students complete the assimilation of new knowledge, and achieve meaningful learning. Give the specific application of concept map in the course of modern educational technology.

Keywords: concept map; the modern educational technology; application

1 CONCEPT MAP AND ITS IMPLICATIONS FOR TEACHING

Concept map was put forward earliest by professor Novak of Connell university in America, Novak says the concept map is the graphical representation of a theme's concepts and their relationship, the concept map is a tool to organize and represent knowledge. It usually puts related concepts about a theme into the circle or box, and then connect the correlative concepts and propositions by lines, mark meaning relationship between two concepts. Thus, concepts, propositions, cross connection and hierarchical structure to constitute the four elements of the concept map. Among them, Concept is the rule properties perceived of the things, usually marking with a proper noun or symbol; proposition is the statement about phenomenon, structure and rules of the things, in a concept map, the proposition is the meaning relationship between the two concepts through a connecting words; cross connection indicate relationship between different concepts of knowledge domain; hierarchical structure is a way of showing the concept. Therefore, the concept map is the space network structure represent of the relationship between concept and concept, is a kind of visual semantic network.

Concept map is based on Ausubel's meaningful learning theory. Ausubel thinks, "students' learning, if you want to have value, it should to be meaningful as much as possible". The meaningful learning has two prerequisites: First, students showed a significant learning set, which shows a tendency to establish contact between a new content and their knowledge. Second, the learning content has potential significance to students,

which can link up with their existing knowledge structure. In particular, the "contact" refers to a kind of substantive contact, rather than arbitrary, non-literally contact. That is to say, meaningful learning is achieved through assimilation process of the new and old knowledge.

The modern educational technology course is a compulsory course for normal school students, is an interdisciplinary course, relates to the teaching and learning theory, teaching equipment, various media software, teaching design etc. More content, more concepts, less lessons. Therefore, students are often confused of the concepts and terms in the curriculum, can't understand the content about information technology, influence the students' interesting in learning the curriculum. How to help the students understand and grasp the concepts and terminology, assimilation of new knowledge and old knowledge, forms the systematic concept framework, so as to realize the application of the concept, these problems have been solved effectively by applied concept map into the curriculum teaching.

2 THE APPLICATION OF CONCEPT MAP IN THE MODERN EDUCATIONAL TECHNOLOGY COURSE

2.1 *Visualize the abstract knowledge*

With the aid of graphic function of the concept map, some of the more abstract concepts can be represented with intuitive graphical, at the same time, with the aid of metaphor and association, helps to understand the relationships among concepts.

For example, in order to make the students understand the several basic parameters' meanings of digital sound, help students to process and use digital sound, the students require to understand the digital sound process: sampling, quantization, coding. But for the non computer professional students, to understand the meaning of each step is not easy, so make concept map, as shown in Figure 1, the comparison between sound digital process and production process of uniform, the sample can be seen as measuring the height of each student, quantization can be considered as the height of students are classified, such as student height from 1.46 meters to 1.50 meters will be in accordance with the size of 1.50 meters, code is finally the uniform cutting and manufacturing. In this way, not only to form the specific meaning of each step of the process of digital voice, and by comparing the use of each step, so as to help students understand the process of digital voice, so as to master the sampling frequency and sampling precision's meaning of the parameters. Implement visualization of the abstract concept, help students understand and master the concepts effectively.

2.2 *As a knowledge organization tool*

In knowledge representation, concept map can easily construct a clear knowledge network, help the students to master the knowledge framework, promote students' intuitive thinking formation and knowledge transfer.

The course of modern educational technology involves many knowledge fields, so it is related to many terminology and concept. How to clarify the relationships between concepts and concepts, terminology and terminology, clarify the knowledge context, concept map provides us a good way.

For example, in the chapter of acquire and use of digital media material. This chapter relates to the knowledge of acquisition, storage, processing and utilization about sound, graphics, image and multimedia in the computer. There are a variety of type name and file name, students are particularly vulnerable to confusion, to this, can also be through drawing concept map, vividly the relationship

between the concepts and terminology. Sound media as an example, draw concept map as shown in Figure 2. Put the classification, concept, characteristics, common application of sound media into one concept map, concentrate dispersed terminology together, shown each term's hierarchy and relation of meaning. On this basis, graphics, image and multimedia are also in the same way to draw the concept map, and then merging several concept maps into one concept map, will have the integrated concept map about digital media material acquisition and use. In this way, students' intuitive comparison of similar concepts can be promoted further, to master the concept. At the same time, in such a process, in accordance with the meso—the micro—the macro sequence organization concepts, can promote students' structured knowledge of concepts, form structured conceptual framework, promote systematic awareness of the knowledge.

2.3 *As the knowledge expand tools*

Along with the development of information technology and the combination of education, the modern university advocated the teaching mode of teach only the essential and ensure plenty of practice. Therefore, teaching hours is less often, in the classroom the teacher only can teach basic contents, students need more after class through self-study and explore the expansion. However, if the lack of the guidance of teachers, students' self learning and inquiry will often have no clear purpose, easy to lose the direction. To this, with the aid of the concept map, showing the research content and steps of students to self-study, thus, students have a clear study and research direction, it will not get lost in the ocean of information. For example, in the chapter of the integration of information technology and curriculum, professional features prominent, very practical, therefore, Inquiry learning and Group collaborative learning are adopted, the study and inquiry content express

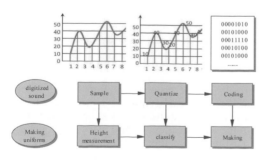

Figure 1. The process of digital sound.

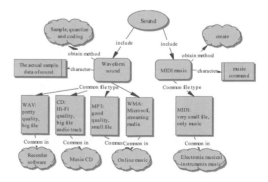

Figure 2. Sound media knowledge framework.

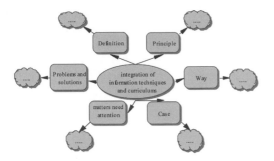

Figure 3. Integration of information technology and curriculum.

by concept map shown in Figure 3. Obviously, in this way, students can learn and inquiry around several aspects, with more purpose and direction, to avoid the confusion problem easily occurred in the massive cyber source environment.

2.4 *As an evaluation tool*

The initial purpose of concept map is to test the students' knowledge, so it can be used as an evaluation tool. In the process of teaching, teachers can advance through drawing concept map to explain the concept, but also by requiring students drawing concept map to learn and examination the students' situation on concept comprehension. The ways are as follows:

- Given a set of concepts, ask students to drawing concept map;
- Showing a concept map, ask students to judge the right and wrong;
- Ask students to Answer questions by concept map.

Through the students' drawing concept map, can test students' knowledge structure as well as the understanding of the relationship among knowledge, or the right or wrong understanding of knowledge, analysis of the causes according of misunderstanding concepts and knowledge, and correct timely. In addition, teachers can be aware of students' thinking activities and timely diagnosis through the process of students' making concept map.

3 CONCLUSION

Knowledge point is the foundation of the knowledge framework. By concept map, we can organize many knowledge, clear the knowledge context and the relationship, structured and systematic scattered knowledge, and promote the transfer of knowledge.

Concept map organize information in a logical way, can be very convenient to contact the old knowledge and new knowledge, help learners to absorb new information and new ideas. It can also help learners reflect and evaluate of the learning process, and promote the development of students' advance thinking.

"Visual representation of concept map implemented the overall understanding which use of words alone can't do." Therefore, the concept map is an important tool of communication. One concept graphs represent a kind of information organization or way of thinking, can be shared with others. The process of drawing concept map is not only a process of organization concept, but also the process of combing relations according to the problem, so as to solve the problem. Therefore, the use of concept maps is useful for cultivating students' problem solving ability.

Concept map is a kind of teaching strategy, can also help teachers teaching effectively. By ask for students draw concept map, let the students learning new knowledge on their own initiative, organizing and understanding knowledge on their own initiative, developing students' subjectivity of study. It is advocated by constructivist learning methods, which helps the students' learning ability and innovation ability.

At present, there are many concept map software, bring great convenience for drawing concept maps. For example, in Inspiration, you can easily insert graphics where needed, realize the visualization of knowledge; in MindMapper, you can choose the branch direction and branch shape according to the relationship between concepts characteristics, which making concept map more vivid, and more intuitive.

ACKNOWLEDGMENT

The paper is a research result of project "Practical teaching reform on modern educational technology ability of normal school students based on social software", which is a part of Sichuan provincial quality project of higher education in 2011.

REFERENCES

Shi, L.F. 2001. *Theory of learning*. Beijing: people's education press.
Wang. D.P. & L, X.G. 2004. Concept map theory and its application in Teaching. *Modern Educational Technology*. (6):45–48.
Zhu, X.Q. 2002. The knowledge of the concept map and its research summary. *Shanghai Research on Education*. (10):31–34.
Zhang, Sh. & Huang, T.H. 2004. *Modern Education Technology*, Beiging: Higher education press.
Zhang. Q.W. 2002. Concept map and its application in teaching, *Journal of Educational Development*. (11):25–27.

Computer, Intelligent Computing and Education Technology – Liu, Sung & Yao (Eds)
© 2014 Taylor & Francis Group, London, ISBN 978-1-138-02469-4

Based on the peer mutual aid "grouping" teaching method of college physics experiment teaching and research

Zhu-Qin Liu

College of Physics and Electronic Information, Yan'an University, Yan'an, China

ABSTRACT: According to the characteristics of the university physics experiment course, peer mutual aid "grouping" teaching method is proposed. From the experiment of preparation before, classroom organization teaching and some problems that should be paid attention to in teaching, students' grasp of the course and learning interest and so on many aspects are analyzed, the results show that the teaching method not only improves the students' interest in learning, and improve the students' ability to analyze problems, solve the problem.

Keywords: "group peer mutual aid" teaching method; the university physics experiment; cooperative learning

1 INTRODUCTION

Physics experiment is a science and engineering is an important basic course for college students, is a scientific experiment training for students, raises the student beginning ability important link, its for high quality has an irreplaceable role in the cultivation of innovative talents, with the rapid development of science and technology, the progress of the society, puts forward higher requirements to the cultivation of the talent, physics experiment teaching must also keep pace with The Times, constantly reform to adapt to the society for talents knowledge structure and the scientific quality is higher and higher request [1–4]. In recent years, we refer to the practice of brother institutions [5–7], test in traditional physical experiment teaching, integrated into "group peer mutual aid" teaching method, so that can not only stimulate students' interest in learning, and to improve students' ability to analyze problems, solve problems, thus greatly improving the teaching effect.

2 IN THE UNIVERSITY PHYSICS EXPERIMENT TEACHING USING OVERVIEW "GROUP PEER MUTUAL AID" TEACHING

2.1 *Preview before the experiment*

"Group peer mutual aid" teaching method is the whole class is divided into several experimental group, each group choose a team leader, feel free to contact the teacher. Each experiment for three teaching links of the project: the first part

is the preparation before the experiment. Students mainly use the campus network resources, preview the content of the teacher assigned, let the student to the class experiment contents have a preliminary understanding first, at the same time can also review the theoretical knowledge, the physical basic knowledge was applied to the experiment, through the preliminary preparation, students find out the physical experiment target, the proposition of thoughts, used formula, which is to be directly measured quantities and record the data table, etc. Student after preliminary review, the teacher use the Internet at any time to the students put forward a series of questions related to this study, let students have the opportunity to reflect on their own to prepare 'understanding of the content, find out the deficiency of their preparation and have difficulty in understanding. On the other hand, for teachers, can also be a more accurate understanding of the preparation situation of students, students are expected to do the experiment of difficulties and problems, can be more reasonable, more scientific and efficient teaching organization. Specifically: the teacher asked the students to prepare the related experiment content, and complete the previewing notebooks of corresponding, previewing notebooks of students through the network to submit before the class, the teacher by looking at the students' feedback, understand students' preview, experiment, common problems and difficulties students have experimental skills. Teachers select students feedback problems, timely modify classroom organization of teaching content, in order to most effectively use of classroom teaching time to better organize the teaching.

2.2 Operation experiment class

The second part is the operation experiment of college physics experiment. Class, the students according to the group discussion, free debate, experimental operation and other activities, in the process of these activities, teacher's role is only activities of the organizers, guides and coordinator, and students are real master, they want to acquire knowledge, you must actively participate in the activities. Because the student is prepared by fully preparation experiment, so the enthusiasm of participation is more high than the traditional teaching way, the students' interest in learning thicker, the learning effect is more obvious. In class, some students take the initiative to stand up to the same group of students patiently explain, hands-on demonstration, the speaker is very strong, the listener is very attentively, some students in order to a dispute, please the teacher to decide, the students' learning is active, the content of the teacher's teaching completely based on students as the starting point. On the same physical quantity measurement, the students put forward different experiment scheme, such as "metal specific heat measurement" this experiment project, some students hybrid method is presented in this paper, some students electric heating method is presented in this paper, some students put forward by cooling method, students can use different methods to complete the experiment project. Students operation while recording original data, the data record is the most important physical information obtained from the experiment, the most precious materials, each student must prepare original record of paper on the experimental data, the experimental design good record form, before everything seriously records and data, can't alter or torn off. Shouldn't be frightened by "bad data", only through the analysis of the data to determine whether you need to improve the experiment instrument or operation, etc. The original experimental data by the end of the class, students will check record to teachers, if the measurement data conform to the requirements, the teacher wants to sign, if the measurement data does not conform to the requirements, students need to fill do, until it meets the requirements, to achieve the teaching effect.

2.3 Experiment report writing after class

The third step in university physics experiment is writing lab reports, the contents of the experiment report usually includes: the experimental subject, experimental apparatus, experimental principle, experimental steps, data record, data processing, expression results, error analysis, the results are discussed, and put forward a new scheme, etc. Students according to their own written report on the experimental data, the first fellow students and then compared the results are discussed and analyzed the advantages and disadvantages of various measuring scheme, the final experiment presented by the team leader is responsible for the project summary report. Project requirements of designing experiment to the format of the thesis writing, in order to make the student's thesis project to achieve standardization, teachers use a unit of time to the students briefly introduce the basic knowledge of experimental science and technology thesis writing, its main contents include: (1) the basic characteristics of experimental science and technology thesis, namely the thesis should be innovative, authenticity, feasibility and practicability. (2) the structure of the experimental science and technology thesis format, i.e. general papers should have title, signature, abstract, key words, introduction, body, conclusion, references, etc. (3) the experimental steps of writing scientific paper: the first is to collect data. Sources of information has two aspects, one is the directly obtained by experimental measurement data, the second is through the indirect through the literature data. For sorting and analyzing these data. The second is to formulate the title, writing written. To the student to the chart of the paper, the standardization of the symbols, units and formula representation. By telling students can according to your own design content, the selected measuring instruments, complete each physical quantity measurement, obtain the relevant data, to consult the relevant references, and finish the complete experimental paper. Teachers according to students submit the test report or dissertation project, understand the students' mastery of knowledge, in order to further organize teaching.

3 "GROUP PEER MUTUAL AID" TEACHING METHOD

3.1 Improve the students' autonomous learning ability

Along with the increase in the number of university experiment, make teachers and students one-on-one communication problem, grouping peer mutual teaching method to solve this problem. Because all this teaching method is given priority to with students, set up a series of mutual learning, thus it can be more exert students' initiative, group students initiative to acquire knowledge and experimental skills to each other, this kind of teaching method helps to establish a mutual help study atmosphere of mutual trust, in the process of complete a series of experiments project to achieve a common goal, to improve the students' ability of communication and participation enthusiasm, thus improve the students' ability of autonomous learning.

3.2 To cultivate the students' unity cooperation ability

In today's era of economic globalization, people at the same time in the competition is more and more need to cooperate, how to make students learn to learn, learn to care about, learn to cooperate, learn to be responsible for, cultivate them to form a sound personality, innovative consciousness and innovative spirit, has become a mainstream consciousness education. Grouping the essence of the peer mutual teaching method is to let students learn to cooperate, encouraging students to actively participate in the whole process of experiment teaching, to make them become the master of teaching, exercise their cooperation at the same time, the ability to learn from each other.

3.3 Improve the teaching effect

Traditional experiment teaching is a teacher, first clear the experiment principle, experiment method, experiment steps and matters needing attention, etc., according to the requirement of the teachers and students, step-by-step operation experiment, the teaching method with teachers as the main body, injection students the only way to learn is through the teachers, the teaching in the teachers spread knowledge and experimental skills at the same time, to suppress the cultivation of students' innovative ability. Grouping and peer mutual teaching method provides students with more space for independent learning, from the preparation before, operate well in class and write test report and so on each link is independent, 2012, 2013, the university physics experiment teaching, we have adopted group peer mutual teaching method, and the teaching effect of this teaching method is studied. Half semester of 2012 a total of 15 university physics experiment course in the class, we investigated the telecom 11 (120), 85% of the students think this kind of teaching method is very good, while 15% of students think that this method is general, 2012 in the second half of the semester, a total of 13 class university physics experiment course, we randomly surveyed oil 11 (84), 95% of the students think this kind of teaching method is very good, while 5% of students think that this method is general, half semester of 2013 a total of 16 university physics experiment course in the class, we investigated the oil and gas 12 (85), 90% of the students think that this teaching method is very good, while 10% of students think that this method is general, in 2013 the second half of the semester, a total of 15 university physics experiment course in the class, we randomly surveyed mathematics 12 (101), 96% of the students think this kind of teaching method is very good, while 4% of students think this way. We counted the students' attendance situation over the past two years, none of the students absent without cause, can be seen from the survey and the classroom attendance, this teaching method enhanced students' interest in learning, improve the teaching quality. Our study also found that the teaching method students can get more information from peers, more experimental skills, and more creative thinking.

4 CONCLUSION

After nearly two years of teaching practice shows that in the university physics experiment teaching using peer mutual aid "grouping" teaching method, changed the traditional one-way teaching pattern of physical experiment, to enhance the accountability of the teacher, to enhance the students' learning initiative, promotes the student class inside and outside of mutual learning, improve the students' autonomous learning ability, cultivate the students' unity cooperation ability, to cultivate the students' innovative thinking and innovative ability of science, improve the students' ability to analyze problems, solve problems, so as to improve the teaching quality of college physics experiment.

REFERENCES

[1] Song Weixing. [1] design experiment teaching process standardization of thinking and exploration [J]. Journal of experimental technology and management, 2009, 26 (7): 125~130.
[2] Liu Xiaogong, Yang construction, etc. To cultivate undergraduate physics experiment "four abilities", the research and practice of teaching model [J]. Journal of experimental technology and management, 2008, 25 (12): 125~130.
[3] Zhang yong, li yan, etc. Design of university physics experiment research and practice of multidimensional evaluation [J]. Journal of experimental technology and management, 2008, 25 (9): 125~130.
[4] Wang Xiaoyi Bai Guangmei etc. Innovative experiments and innovative thinking and practice of talent training [J]. Journal of experimental technology and management, 2008, 25 (11): 125~130.
[5] Pagen A p, Crouch C H, said Mazur E. P investigate the instruction: Results from A range of classroom [J]. Phys., called the 2002 (40): 206.
[6] Zhao Yujing. Analyze the peer mutual teaching method in the teaching the important role of [J]. Journal of accounting of township enterprises in China, 2011 (5): 163.
[7] Said Mazur Eric. Peer teaching method—university physics teaching guide [M]. Zhu, Chen Xianfeng, eds. Beijing: mechanical industry publishing house, 2011.

Research of cloud storage and data consistency strategies based on replica redundant technology

Hong-Xia Mao, Kun Huang & Xiao-Ling Shu
Sichuan TOP IT Vocational Institute, Chengdu, Sichuan, P.R. China

ABSTRACT: Cloud storage is an ideal way of data storage, so cloud storage has been widely used. But the data security in cloud storage must be solved. Cloud storage must ensure that data is not lost or damaged. Most cloud storage systems use replica redundancy technique to solve the problem of the loss of data. The consistency strategy of the replicas is worth studying. The commonly used strategies include: the consistency strategy based on replica chain, the consistency strategy based on multi-version control, the consistency strategy based on timestamp. The consistency strategies will be the focus in the cloud storage research.

Keywords: cloud storage; replica; data consistency; redundant technology

1 INTRODUCTION

At present, cloud storage has become the optimal choice to store huge amounts of data, therefore, more and more users pay attentions to the cloud storage. When enterprises and personal users use cloud storage to store data, the data security problem must be solved. The user will worry about whether data will be lost. Therefore, whether cloud storage can guarantee the security of data storage has become a barrier restricting its development. Most cloud storage systems use redundant technology to ensure that the user data will not be lost. But there is also a problem must be solved, that how to ensure data consistency problem of all the replicas. The data consistency strategies in the most of the cloud storage systems are researched and analyzed in this paper.

2 CLOUD STORAGE

2.1 *The concept of cloud storage*

Cloud storage is the extension and development from the concept of cloud computing. Cloud storage system is a new type of structure of cloudy storage system. It is composed of multiple storage equipments, using the application clusters, distributed file systems, or grid technology, and other functions. Cloud storage can connect a large number of various types of storage devices in the network together to provide access and business services, by applying the software and certain common external applications or interface. Cloud storage is also a cloud computing system whose core is the data storage and data management.

2.2 *The structure model of cloud storage system*

From the architectural model, cloud storage system has a storage layer compared with cloud computing system. Cloud storage also has a lot of basic management functions related to the data management and data security. In the cloud storage system, the users don't need to know the system, even don't need to know the specific locations of their data, all of equipments in cloud storage are completely transparent to the users. The users don't need to maintain the hardware and software update, don't need to make their own data backup. The specific cloud storage service providers will provide the services which the users need to pay. For small and medium enterprises, they can greatly save the investment in hardware, and get the required storage space and computing power with a low-cost.

Compared with the traditional storage devices, cloud storage is not only refers to the hardware resources used to store data, but also a complex system composed of multiple parts, such as network devices, storage devices, servers, applications, public access interface, access network and the client program. The structure model of cloud storage system is shown in Figure 1.

The structural model of cloud storage system is composed of four layers.

2.3 *Storage layer*

The storage layer is the most basic part of the cloud storage. In this layer, different types of storage devices are connected together via WAN, Internet or FC Fiber network to realize the centralized management of the storage devices,

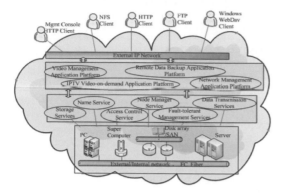

Figure 1. Structural model for cloud storage.

condition monitoring and the dynamic extension of the capacity.

2.4 *Basic management layer*

Basic management layer is the core part of the cloud storage. This layer provides the unified view of public management of different services. The layer use cluster, distributed file systems and grid computing technology, to implement the cloud data disaster & recovery and data access. This layer can also realize the logic virtualization management, multi-link redundancy management of the storage device, as well as hardware status monitoring and fault maintenance of the storage devices.

2.5 *Application interface layer*

The application interface layer is the most flexible part of cloud storage. Different cloud storage operating units can develop different application service interface and provide a variety of application services according to the actual type of business.

2.6 *Access layer*

Any authorized user can login cloud storage systems through a common and standard application interface, and enjoy cloud storage service. With different operating units of cloud storage, cloud storage provides the different access types and access methods.

3 THE REPLICA REDUNDANT TECHNOLOGY

For a long time, the development data storage has encountered many problems, the most worthy of them is the data availability. The availability of stored data is worthy to be solved. Stored data may

be lost because of artificial reason or some physical causes such as engine room fire, natural disasters, etc. Therefore, the cloud storage system must solve the problem of data loss. Cloud service providers must ensure the user's data security and ensure that users can upload and download the data is really their own. In the most cloud storage systems, the replica redundant technology is used to ensure the data is not lost.

Replication redundancy technology is one of the most simple. The principle is very simple. Through the file system, the copies are distributed to various nodes. As long as one replica of these nodes is effective, we can obtain the file. The number of replica about the file, the data availability is better, and the reliability is higher. Due to replication does not involve coding arithmetic, file creation and read without decoding operation, the efficiency of reading and writing is very high. Replication method in distributed storage includes two levels: the entire file level (whole-file-level), and the file block level (fragments-level). The method of entire file level is very simple, which stores multiple copies of the original data. Each copy is stored on different physical storage nodes. So, if data on one node is damaged or lost, the user's data integrity and availability does not be affected. This backup method is simple, has high stability. Most cloud storage systems adopt the entire file level replica redundant technology, such as: Pastry, Tapestry, OceanStore and CFS. The HDFS architecture is shown in Figure 2.

The file block level replica technology is that the data file is divided into many blocks each of which is S the size of a block. Each block has N copies which are stored in different storage nodes, such as HDFS.

The NameNode maintains the Name space, and controls the client access to the files in the file system and manages the DataNode; Sencondary NameNode store the backup system information

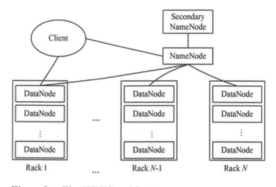

Figure 2. The HDFS architecture.

files of the NameNode; DataNode store the user's data and provide user interaction and read or write operations, under the control of the NameNode.

4 THE DATA CONSISTENCY STRATEGY BASED ON THE REPLICA REDUNDANT TECHNOLOGY

Using multiple replicas storage, the stability of storage system and the availability of data files is greatly improved, but the negative effect of the inconsistency between replicas is also brought. When one replica of the file is updated or deleted by the user, this replica is different from other replicas. But this will have very serious consequences. The purpose of consistency management is that the users always use the latest version of the file. Consistency control strategy is designed to make replica of the file system transparent to users. For users, they can get any replicas of file which are always the same version.

So, storing multiple replicas of data, the consistency among the replicas is inevitable. The consistency is divided into two kinds: strong consistency and weak consistency. Strong consistency is that data-change must be applied to all other replicas of this data, which ensure that all replicas have the same content at any time.

4.1 The replica consistency strategy based on replica chain

Using the consistency strategy based on replica chain, the system establishes the replica chain to transmit the update message. The replica chain is created dynamically. Assuming that one replica on ith node in the chain is the start to update data.

The ith node sends the update message along the chain forwardly and backwardly. When one node is updated, the identity bit is set to 1, otherwise is set to 0. When the node receives the update-message, then updates its own data, and sends the update message in the same direction. When the data on all nodes in the chain has been updated, the process is end.

HDFS is used to store the mass data. In HDFS, the file is divided into the different blocks, these blocks are stored on different DataNode. When users access the HDFS, firstly users make communication with the NameNode to get the DataNode list on which stored the needed data. Then the users directly manipulate the data with the DataNode. The whole process, NameNode is only responsible for processing metadata information, not for user data transmission. In order to ensure the consistency of the data, all the DataNode which stored

user's data block replicas build a data chain, as shown in Figure 3. Only all the DataNode have succeed, the user will accept the acknowledgment messages for write one block. Then, the users send the next data block, until all data blocks are sent.

For reading every data block, the users need to send request to the NameNode to find the list of the DataNode of data blocks. Then the users can read the data from the correct DataNode.

From the analysis of the above, in order to maintain the consistency of the data, the technology of pipeline is used in the writing process. Although for each DataNode in data chain, the advantages are improving the efficiency of data forwarding, facilitating management for the nodes from the source and destination for the packet. But, every write operation must be done in each DataNode, then, return the success message, it reduces the performance of system. For some data blocks, the number of replications is big, the number of nodes in the transmission chain also increases. Due to any node failure on the data chain, it will cause interruption of data transmission. So data access latency will increase.

4.2 The replica consistency strategy based on multi-version control

In order to reduce the traffic in the process of write operation and solve the problem of Byzantium, multi-version control strategy is proposed. This strategy needs to maintain multiple versions for each data. In the process of the write operation, the system does not update the old version of data, directly write the new version into the system. Each file may have multiple versions, so the system must provide a mechanism to distinguish between different versions. The method can provide a time mark for each version, the new version of the timestamp is larger than the old version. When a client requests to read, the system needs to find the latest version of relevant data, and then sends the data to the client. When the server receives the client's written request, system will first need to find the biggest time tag of relevant documents in the old versions. Then, the system generate a new time mark for the new version, each storage node stores the new version of the data.

Since each write operation will generate a new version, and the quantity of version will consume

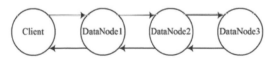

Figure 3.   The replica chain of HDFS.

more hard disk space. Multi-version control will adopt the garbage collection mechanism, when the system of the data in the version number to a certain extent, the garbage collection mechanism will be started to delete the old versions which are not be needed. The objects for recycling are the incomplete data versions. Many systems use multi-version control, mainly include the PASIS, SWALLOW, Past, CFS and Farsite and Ocean-Store storage layer.

4.3 The replica consistency strategy based on timestamp

The replica consistency strategy based on timestamp is that if the data on one storage node in the system is changed, the update messages will be not transmitted to other nodes. But the changed data is marked with a current timestamp. When the data on a node needs to be changed, it will submit the request and the timestamp of the replica through the broadcast form. Then the node informs all the nodes in the system which data block need to change and its version. When a node receives the broadcast information, determine whether it have the replica of the file, if not then do nothing. If the node has the version of the replica, then the order of timestamp is compared with the timestamp of the broadcasting information. If the version of the node is latest, then send the replica to the source node. When the source node received many versions of the replica, the newest replica will be the replacement, and then the data is changed. The main advantage of this strategy is that the network load is low. But this strategy will appear the following problems: there is a node updated the data, if the node is disconnected with other nodes, so it will cause the dirty data.

5 CONCLUSIONS

The concept and model of cloud storage is researched in this paper. Most cloud storage systems use replica redundancy technique to solve the problem of the loss of data. The replica consistency strategy is worthy to study. The commonly used strategies include: the replica consistency strategy based on replica chain, the replica consistency strategy based on multi-version control, the replica consistency strategy based on timestamp. The replica consistency strategy will be the focus in the cloud storage research.

REFERENCES

Cloud Storage [OL], http://en.wikipedia.org/wiki/Cloud_storage.

Garth R. Goodson, Jay J. Wylie, Gregory R. Ganger, and Michael K. Reiter. 2003. Efficient Consistency for Erasure-coded Data via Versioning Servers. Carnegie Mellon University Technical Report CMU-CS-03-127, April 2003.

Kubiatowicz J, Wells C, Zhao B, and Rhea S. 2000. OceanStore: An architecture for global-scalepersistent storage, In Proceedings of the 9th Int'L Conf. on Architectural Support for Programming Languages and Operating Systems, 2000:190–201.

Pamies JL, Garcia LP, Sanchez AM. 2008. Rewarding Stability in Peer- to- Peer Backup Systems [C]// Proceedings of 16th IEEE International Conference on Networks (ICON'08), 12–14 Deceber, 2008, New Delhi, India. Piscataway, NJ, USA: IEEE, 2008:6.

Rochwerger B, Breitgand D, Levy E, et al. 2009. The Reservoir Model and Architecture for Open Federated Cloud Computing [J]. IBM Journal of Research and Development, 53(4):1–17

Zeng WY, Zhao YL, OU KR, et al. 2009. Research on Cloud Storage Architecture and Key Technologies[C]// Proceedings of the 2nd International Conference on Interaction Sciences: Information Technology, Culture and Human (ICIS'09), Nov 24–26, Seoul, Republic of Korea. 2009:1044–1048.

Positive transfer of Sichuan dialect on english pronunciation teaching

Hong Yun

School of Foreign Languages, Sichuan University of Science and Engineering, Zigong, Sichuan

ABSTRACT: It is a new breakthrough in English pronunciation teaching to take advantage of the students' dialect. By comparing the pronunciation system of Sichuan dialect and English, this paper illustrates that Sichuan dialect can help the students be aware of some similar English phonemes and use positive transfer on their pronunciation learning so as to arouse their study interest and improve their English pronunciation efficiently.

Keywords: sichuan dialect; english pronunciation teaching; positive transfer

1 INTRODUCTION

Chinese students learning English is on the basis of good command of their mother tongue. The influence of their mother tongue in English learning is inevitable. Therefore, in Sichuan dialect area, students learning English pronunciation must be influenced by Sichuan dialect. In the past, many scholars focused on the effect of negative transfer of Chinese, ignoring positive transfer effect in English pronunciation learning. This one-sidedly exaggerated the negative effect of the mother tongue. Actually by using the positive transfer of the students' dialect as their learning English pronunciation tool the students' interest can be not only promoted, but the teachers' teaching difficulties also can be reduced. Undoubtedly it will be a new breakthrough, and is worth discussing.

2 THE THEORY OF LANGUAGE TRANSFER

"Transfer" in psychology is also named "Learning Transfer" or "Training Transfer". It refers to the phenomenon that a formed knowledge will affect the gaining of a new knowledge. "Transfer" is not only to take effect in a certain experience, but also between different experiences. For example, the knowledge about Mathematics will ease the learning of Physics and Chemistry. Transfer has its positive effects on learning, and also negative ones. As the name suggests, positive transfer occurs when the learner's previous knowledge, skill or ability facilitates his learning of new ones, while negative transfer refers to the impediment of the acquired knowledge, skill, or ability exerts upon the new learning.

In the guidance of transfer theory, Lado, one of the founders of Second Language Acquisition Theory, proposed "language transfer theory" in his "Contrastive Analysis" where he compared mother tongue and the second language. He believes that in the process of language acquisition, learners tend to transfer their native language knowledge to the learning of the second language. Such transfer in the process of language acquisition can be divided into positive transfer and negative transfer. Transfer will be positive when their native and second language habits are the same. When the two languages are different in structure, negative transfer, also called interference, occurs. Thus differences between the first and second languages create learning difficulty which results in errors, while the similarities between the first and second languages facilitate rapid and easy learning.

In the field of second language acquisition research, phenomenon of negative transfer from mother tongue attracts the attention of many scholars and their studies. Many scholars believe that the mother tongue to a large extent will interfere the learning of foreign languages. Because the vast majority of people tend to use their native characteristics in learning a foreign language which let many different kinds of errors occur. Many scholars state and analyze the disadvantages when the Chinese students learn English pronunciation in the influence of their mother tongue, and give out some ways to overcome the negative transfer in English pronunciation teaching and learning. Actually, English and Chinese belong to different language families. English is classified as a member of the Indo-European family, while Chinese belongs to the Sino-Tibetan language family. Therefore, there are great differences between English and Chinese in phonetics, grammar and vocabulary.

For this reason, many scholars notice more about the differences between the two languages, and excessively emphasize the interference of the students' native language in learning English or the effect of negative transfer of the mother tongue. They believe that mother tongue interference is the main obstacle to acquire correct English pronunciation. However, we should realize that it is impossible that the Chinese students are not subject to their native language during they learn English. In fact, it is useless to avoid the intermediary function of the mother tongue in the second language or foreign language learning. If we can make good use of the intermediary role of the mother tongue, and give full play to the positive transfer of mother tongue, we can teach and learn English pronunciation better.

3 THE COMPARATIVE ANALYSIS OF THE SICHUAN DIALECT AND ENGLISH PRONUNCIATION

According to the theory of Comparative Phonetics, we know that in any two languages there are always similarities and differences. There are also many similarities in segmental phonemes and supra-segmental phonemes between Sichuan dialect and English pronunciation.

Sichuan dialect is a dialect of southwestern mandarin in North Group. It is the basic dialect of Standard Chinese (Putonghua) which is used as a common language by modern Han people. There is a great deal of consistency in pronunciation, vocabulary and grammar between Sichuan dialect and Putonghua. But there still exists different characteristics. There are 48 phonemes in English International Phonetic Alphabet (IPA), including 20 vowels and 28 consonants. Chinese Pinyin is the phonetic system used to transcribe Chinese characters. It has adopted Latin alphabet, and can be divided into Shengmu (Initials) and Yunmu (Finals). There are 21 Shengmu and 39 Yunmu in Putonghua, but 20 Shengmu and 36 Yunmu in Sichuan dialect with retroflexization of Yunmu. For the convenience of teaching English pronunciation in Sichuan dialect area, teachers can compare the phonology of Sichuan dialect and English pronunciation. Ma Chuandong et al. pointed out that there are 9 similar consonants and 10 vowels between Sichuan dialect and English pronunciation according to their research. This indicates that the Sichuan people can find similar phonemes from their dialect to learn some English phonemes well during their English pronunciation learning. It is also helpful for teachers to use the knowledge of Articulatory Phonetics to do comparative teaching of English pronunciation.

4 THE USE OF POSITIVE TRANSFER OF SICHUAN DIALECT ON ENGLISH PRONUNCIATION TEACHING

The author notices that many of the students in the colleges of Sichuan area are Sichuan locals. They all communicate with each other in Sichuan dialect in their daily life. Here the paper takes Chengdu dialect and Zigong dialect as examples to explore the similar manners and places of articulation between Sichuan dialect and English pronunciation so as to help those students grasp correct English pronunciation.

A main sign of dialect in Sichuan is that it has no distinction between the blade-alveolars and the retroflex sounds. Most of Sichuan people do not distinguish between /z/, /c/, /s/ and /zh/, /ch/, /sh/. For example, they pronounce /shi/ as /si/. Retroflex sound is prominent in Shengmu system of Zigong dialect, so Zigong people can pronounce /zh, ch, sh, r/ in Chinese Pinyin system well enough. People who come to Zigong like to learn this feature interestedly. The students attending to Sichuan University of Science and Engineering in Zigong all try to learn this kind of "retroflex sounds". The imitation behavior can enable the students to better experience/D3/, /tʃ/, /r/ in English pronunciation. In English phonetics, /D3/, /tʃ/ are palato-alveolar affricates. When producing them, the soft palate is raised and the nasal resonator is shut off, and then presses the tip, blade and rims of the tongue against the back part of the alveolar ridge and side teeth to stop the air behind the closure. The front of the tongue is raised in the direction of the hard palate as for /ʃ/. Lips are rounded and protruded slightly. Lower the tongue slowly, keeping the sides of the explosion of air out over the tongue, allowing a corresponding fricative to be heard. In producing/ tʃ/, the vocal folds do not vibrate. In producing/ D3/, the vocal folds should vibrate. /zh/ and /ch/ in Zigong dialect are produced by first curling up the tip of the tongue against the hard palate and then loosing it and letting the air squeeze out through the channel thus made. /zh/ is unaspirated while /ch/ is aspirated. We can see that in producing Zigong retroflex affricates, the tip of the tongue is curled up to form a closure with the rear edge, and of course the centre of the tongue is hollowed. But in the case of the English palato-alveolar affricates, the closure is made between not only the tip and the upper alveolar, but also between the blade, and the rims of the tongue and the side teeth. Although the manners of articulation are different, the places of articulation are similar. The students can find out the correct places of articulation by comparing them to their dialect. Thus their interest can be aroused to contrastively study English pronunciation. But it must be stressed that using dialect phonemes to replace English pronunciation should be prohibited during teaching and learning.

One of features of Zigong dialect differing from other dialects in Sichuan is that Zigong people can distinguish the two Shengmu of /n/ and /l/. This is why most of Sichuan students find it difficult to catch the differences between articulation of life [laif] and that of knife [naif], while Zigong people can pronounce these two sounds well enough. For example, Zigong people pronounce "Bull" as "Niu", "you" as "Ni". The mouth is fully closed. This experience can help students understand the English alveolar nasal /n/, which is produced when the tongue forms a closure with the alveolar ridge and upper side teeth and then the soft palate is lowered so that the air can escape through the nasal cavity. But when producing the alveolar lateral /l/, we must raise the soft palate so that the nasal resonator is shut off completely. The tip of the tongue is in contact with the upper alveolar ridge, allowing the air to escape over the sides of the tongue. So when producing /l/, we can not let the air escape from the nasal cavity, but from the tongue side. We can also try to pinch the nose with hands so as not to let air escape from the nasal cavity when practice this sound. With this method, we can associate to pronounce /l/ sound. too.

Chinese students have difficulty in grasping velar nasal [ŋ], which is lack in Chinese Pinyin system. But if teachers tell them that this nasal sound frequently appears is Sichuan dialect, such as wo "/ŋo:/", "an yi /ŋ ai i/", "e yi /ŋo: i/" in Zigong dialect, the students will realize as soon as possible to the manner and place of articulation of this sound. It should be noticed that this velar nasal can occur in initial of Zigong words but can not appear in the first of English words.

The pronunciation of English front vowel /æ/ is a major difficulty to most of Chinese students, because there is no this sound in Putonghua. But it is worthy of noticing that Chengdu people pronounce /an/ of Putonghua as /æn/, such as man tou /mæn təu/; Tian An Men /tiæn æn men/. This feature of Chengdu dialect differing from other features of Sichuan dialect is precisely what people in other parts of Sichuan like to imitate. Teachers can grasp this point of interest of the students to do contrastive teaching of English pronunciation.

5 CONCLUSIONS

In the process of pronunciation teaching, inspiring students to find which phonemes in their dialect are similar in articulatory manners and places to English sounds can stimulate students 'interest in learning and improve their learning efficiency. Teachers should do well about the guidance work and point out the different pronunciation methods by comparing the pronunciation habits and articulation positions, so as to find a proven method of teaching English phonetics to help students' acquisition of English pronunciation.

Through the comparison of phonetic features between English and Chinese, if teachers can systematically transfer the students' familiar pronunciation knowledge and capacity to learning English phonetics, follow the principle of seeking common ground while keeping differences, take good advantage of Chinese positive transfer, they can do more with less effort in their teaching.

REFERENCES

[1] Brown, H.D, Principles of Language Learning and Teaching (Fourth Edition) [M]. New York: Pearson Education, 2000.
[2] Gao Wenjing Analysis on the Influence of the First Language Transfer on English Learning [J]. Literatures 2010 (7).
[3] Lado, Robert. 1957. Linguistics across Cultures: Applied Linguistics for Language Teachers [M]. Ann Arbor, Michigan: University of Michigan, 1957.
[4] Ma chuandong, Tan Lunhua. Preliminary Comparative Study on Sichuan Dialect and English phonetic System [J]. Journal of Sichuan Normal University (Philosophy and Social Science Edition), 1998 (5).
[5] Niu Jie. The Influence of Dialects on English Phonetic Learning [D]. The Central University for Nationalities, 2011.
[6] Oxford Advanced Learner's English-Chinese Dictionary [M]. The Commercial Press, Oxford University Press, 2003.
[7] Zhang Fengtong. British English Phonetics and Phonology [M]. Sichuan: Sichuan University Press, 2002.

Computer, Intelligent Computing and Education Technology – Liu, Sung & Yao (Eds)
© 2014 Taylor & Francis Group, London, ISBN 978-1-138-02469-4

Developmental recommender systems for learning

D. Fu

Yunnan University of Nationalities, Kunming, P.R. China

ABSTRACT: On-line open educational resource is changing the model of learning and teaching. To benefit from this huge educational resource, many recommender systems have been proposed for peoples who want to learn something from these on-line courses. These recommender systems offer much help for on-line learners however most of them focus only on the similarity between on-line courses. In this paper, more attention is paid on the hierarchical structure of on-line educational resource. By introducing the hierarchical structure of on-line educational resource, the knowledge map could be offered for on-line learners which will improve the efficiency of learning on-line.

Keyword: Recommender system; Graph learning; Knowledge map; High-dimensional feature

1 INTRODUCTION

On-line open educational resource is a new opportunity for peoples who want to improve themselves. Since the first on-line open educational resource is available, we could find almost any we want to learn from internet world. For example, many high quality courses which cover social science, mathematics, engineering, etc. are offered by many prestigious universities such as MIT, Stanford University, Oxford University, Cambridge, HEC, etc. Facing these voluminous educational resources, a sweet trouble is there how we find out what we need from these on-line educational resources.

Fortunately, recommender systems provide much help for peoples who want to benefit from these on-line educational resources. Recommender systems which are borrowed from the field of machine learning are efficient tools for on-line learners to search what they need. In some sense, they are a special searching tool just like Google or Baidu. Some of known recommender systems [Baloian et al. 2004, Berri et al. 2006, Chen et al. 2008, Helou et al. 2010, Schirru et al. 2010, Stern et al. 2010, Yau et al. 2007] could help people to find a lot of on-line educational resources which correspond to the keywords that learners offered. Some recommender systems such as [Lonsdale et al. 2004, Petersen et al. 2008, El-Bishouty et al. 2007, Rogers et al. 2005, Santos et al. 2008] even could offer some on-line educational resources which are similar to the resource that learners have learned.

The technique behind these recommender systems is the technique of ranking which is an important branch of machine learning. The core of ranking is to measure the similarity between the on-line resources and what the learners need. Therefore, it is the key problem of learning a similarity measure for developing an efficient ranking algorithm. For more technical details on learning a similarity measure, please see [Tang et al. 2011, Maurer 2008].

More and more researchers on educational technique have noticed that some shortcomings are there for these existing recommender systems for educational resources. For example, Ververt et al. have pointed out in [Ververt et al. 2012] that there are seven problems for existing recommender systems:

1) Context Acquisition Challenges
   They pointed that a large gap between the learners and the dimension of educational resources, where the dimension of educational resources means the number of the features of some educational resources such as action, current topic of interest and the tasks. Recommender systems should capture the similarity between learners and the dimension of educational resources.

2) Context Representation Challenges
   Representation of educational resources is the base of developing recommender systems. Held et al. [Held et al. 2002] indicate that various educational resources should be structured, interchangeable, compossible, uniform, extensible, and standardized.

3) Evaluation Challenges
   In order to prove the successful application of contextual recommender systems in TEL, the evaluation of this technology needs to be further strengthened.

4) Data Set Sharing Challenges

A collection of data sets is needed to compare the results of different recommendation algorithms and the influence of contextual data on the recommendation process [Drachsler et al. 2008].

5) Privacy Challenges

Privacy and legal protection rights are a major challenge that needs to be tackled when capturing and using contextual data for recommendation.

6) Interaction Challenges

Usability evaluations of the LIP [Schmidt 2007], MOBIlearn [Lonsdale et al. 2004], and TANGO [Ogata et al. 2004] systems indicate that the development of user interfaces is critical for context-aware recommender systems. Among others, people are often confused because they do not understand why certain recommendations are made and why these recommendations change.

7) Towards Global Data Infrastructures

As it has been pointed out by D. Rehak in his Digital Content Manifesto [Rehak 2010] that is driving the US-based Learning Registry initiative, the information world is fragmented but still an abundance of learning information exists. For any learning activity, it can be suspected that somewhere relevant digital content can be found.

Noticed these challenges, the special recommender systems which focus on educational resources recommending should be rethought based on existing recommender systems.

In this paper, the hierarchical structure of on-line educational resource is considered in developing recommender system. Specially, the purpose of the proposed recommender system in this paper is providing systematic curriculum but fragmented courses. In other words, the recommender system will help on-line learners approaching from entry-level courses to higher-level courses.

For developing such recommender system, more complex machine learning techniques are employed here. For distinguishing the level of educational resources which are similar in context, the ranking techniques [Chen et al. 2013] are used. Based on the ranking results, graph cut [Boykov et al. 2001] techniques are employed to find the knowledge map contained in these ranked educational resources. Finally, the needing of learners is offered by comparing the similarity between the structured educational resources and the interesting of learners. Here similarity learning techniques are used. By integrating these entire machine learning techniques, a novel recommender system is developed for recommending structured on-line educational resources.

2 THE FRAMEWORK OF DEVELOPMENT RECOMMENDER SYSTEMS

In this section, a novel framework of development recommender system is proposed. Different from the traditional recommender systems, the proposed recommender system will help learners to find structured on-line educational resources which could offer learners from entry-level courses to higher-level courses.

2.1 Ranking of on-line educational resources

The base of the development recommender system proposed here is to distinguish the levels of different on-line educational resources. In this subsection, ranking algorithms are employed for treating this problem.

Given a set of labeled educational resources, a ranking algorithm could provide a model for comparing the level between two different courses which belong to similar topics. Technically, denote (x, x') as a pair of educational resources. If x is higher than x', the label is set to be 1. On the contrary, the label is set to be -1.

To model the relation between different educational resources, a non-linear regression model is used. In detail, a kernel function

$$k(x, x') = \exp\left(-\frac{\| x - x' \|^2}{\alpha} \right)$$

is used to define the level difference, where a > 0 is a kernel parameter. If, $k(x, x') - \tau < 0$, the label of the pair of (x, x') is set to be -1. Others, the label is set to be 1.

It is clear that the parameters α and τ determine the relation model between educational resources pair. Therefore, the model could be learned by the optimization problem

$$(\alpha^*, \tau^*) = \arg\min_{(\alpha, \tau)} \sum_{i=1}^{n} \exp(-y_i(k(x_i, x_i') - \tau))$$

where $(x_i, x_i'; y_i)$ is a labeled sample from training set.

To minimizing the risk of the model defined by (α, τ), the gradient descent method could be used. For more details about the gradient descent method, please refer [Chen et al. 2013].

2.2 Developing knowledge map with graph cut

When the ranking model is learned, the bi-relation between both educational resources could be determined by using ranking function. However, the bi-relation between both educational resources could not provide explicitly complete picture of developing some capability. Therefore, it is very important to develop a global structure of given educational resources, which will lead learners to select apposite group of courses.

Technically, it is a task to generalize the bi-relation defined by ranking function. In this paper, manifold is used to describe the global relation among all educational resources we could obtain from the internet. More detail, a graph Laplacian matrix is used to represent the global relations among different levels educational resources. Mathematically, the Laplacian matrix of a simple graph G is defined as

$$L = D \mid A,$$

where D is a degree matrix of the given graph G, and A is an adjacency matrix of the given graph G. Explicitly, the element of Laplacian matrix L is defined as

$$l_{i,j} = \begin{cases} \deg(v_t), & i = j \\ |1, & i \mid j \text{ and } v_t \text{ is adjacent to } v_j \\ 0, & \text{otherwise} \end{cases}$$

By using the Laplacian matrix L, the global relation among all educational resources we have could be represented numerically. It should be noticed that the Laplacian matrix L is a sparse matrix with high probability because should be zero if the level difference between both educational resources is larger than 2. Therefore, the sparse Laplacian matrix L will lead learners to find the optimal path of teaching themselves by using a graph cutting techniques.

2.3 Recommending with similarity learning

Finally, learners should select the best matched path to teach them.

It is clear that a lot of candidates are generated by using graph cutting techniques. The task of the last process is selecting an optimal path for learners. Therefore, it could be thought as a similarity measure learning problem which means developing an appropriate similarity measure to define the gap between the needing of learners and the educational plan.

To learn an appropriate similarity measure, the unsupervised learning techniques are needed because the label information is rarely available for on-line learners. In other words, on-line learners almost obtain less information about how to learn a subject before they begin to learn. Therefore, the

unsupervised learning model is more appropriate in this situation.

For all probable educational plans which are generate by Laplacian matrix, the features of these plans could be represented by eigen-decomposition of L. Here, denote the feature of some plan as a vector p. Given a set of plans $\{p_t | t = 1, 2, |, n\}$, a sparse and low-rank decomposition technique could be used to find the optimal plan among the set of plans. In detail, all possible plans are put into a matrix

$$P = (p_t)$$

and then, the plan matrix is decomposed into a sparse matrix S and a low-rank matrix R

$$P = S + R.$$

This decomposition model enables learners to find the best plan from all possible plans by using the low-rank matrix R. Ideally, the low-rank restriction of R means a plan is selected from all possible plans. It should be noticed that the selected plan is the main part shared by all plans because the difference part is just a sparse error.

3 CONCLUSION AND DISCUSSION

In this paper, a novel development recommender system is proposed by combining several machine learning techniques including ranking techniques, graph learning techniques and unsupervised sparse and low-rank matrix decomposition techniques. All of these machine learning techniques helps to distinguish the level of all available educational resources, develop teaching programs and selecting the optimal teaching plan belong to special on-line learners.

It is clear that the proposed framework of development recommender system is just a concept model. There is a long distance to apply this recommender system in real world. In future, more effort should be paid on technical details of developing a practical recommender system. For example, develop more efficient ranking algorithms for large scale educational resources, construct more efficient large Laplacian matrix eigen-decomposition algorithms, and look for more efficient sparse and low-rank decomposition techniques.

REFERENCES

Baloian N., Galdames, Collazos P.C. & Guerrero L. 2004. A Model for a Collaborative Recommender System for Multimedia Learn-ing Material. Groupware: Design, Implementation, and Use, vol. 3198, pp. 281–288, Springer.

Berri J., Benlamri R. & Y. Atif. 2006. Ontology-Based Framework for Context-Aware Mobile Learning. Proc. Int'l Conf. Wireless Comm. and Mobile Computing, pp. 1307–1310.

Boykov Y., Veksler O. & Zabih R. 2001. Fast approximate energy minimisation via graph cuts. IEEE transactions on pattern analysis and machine intelligence, vol. 29, pp. 1222–1239

Chen G.D. & Chao P.Y. 2008. Augmenting Traditional Books with Context-Aware Learning Supports from Online Learning Com-munities. Educational Technology and Soc., vol. 11, no. 2, pp. 27–40.

Chen H., Tang Y. Li L.Q., Yuan Y., Li X.L. & Tang Y.Y. 2013. Error analysis of stochastic gradient descent ranking. IEEE Transactions on cybernetics. Vol. 43, no. 3, pp. 898–909.

Drachsler H., Hummel H. & Koper R. 2008. Personal Recommender Systems for Learners in Lifelong Learning Networks: The Requirements, Techniques and Model. Int'l J. Learning Technology, vol. 3, no. 4, pp. 404–423

El-Bishouty M.M., Ogata H. & Yano Y. 2007. PERKAM: Personalized Knowledge Awareness Map for Computer Supported Ubiquitous Learning. Educational Technology and Soc., vol. 10, no. 3, pp. 122–134.

Held A., Buchholz S. & Schill A. 2002. Modeling of Context Information for Pervasive Computing Applications. Proc. Sixth World Multiconf. Systemics, Cybernetics and Informatics, p. 6.

Helou S.E., Salzmann C. & Gillet D. 2010. The 3a Personalized, Contextual and Relation-Based Recommender System. J. Universal Computer Science, vol. 16, no. 16, pp. 2179–2195.

Lonsdale P., Baber C., Sharples M., Byrne W., Brundell P. & Beale R. 2004. Context awareness for MOBIlearn: Creating an Engaging Learning Experience in an Art Museum. Proc. World Conf. Mobile and Contextual Learning (mLearn '04), pp. 115–118.

Maurer A. 2008. Learning similarity with operator-valued large-margin classifiers. J. Mach. Learn. Res., vol. 9, pp. 1049–1082

Ogata H. & Yano Y. 2004. Context-Aware Support for Computer-Supported Ubiquitous Learning. Proc.

IEEE Second Int'l Workshop Wireless and Mobile Technologies in Education, pp. 27–36

Petersen S.A. & Markiewicz J.K. 2008. ALLAS: Personalised Language Learning on Mobile Devices. Proc. Fifth IEEE Int'l Conf. Wireless, Mobile, and Ubiquitous Technology in Education, pp. 52–59.

Rehak D.R. 2010. Digital Content Manifesto. Proc. Invited Talk of the Fourth Int'l Workshop Search and Exchange of E-Le@rningMaterials, http://www.learningregistry.org/news/digitalcontentmanifestosem2010.

Rogers Y., Price S., Randell C., Stant D., Fraser O., Weal M. & Fitzpatrick G. 2005. Ubi-Learning: Integrating Indoor and Outdoor Learning Experiences. Comm. ACM, vol. 48, no. 1, pp. 55–59.

Santos O.C., Granado J., Raffenne E. & Boticario J.G. 2008., Offering Recommendations in OpenACS/dot-LRN. Proc. OpenACS/.LRN Conf., pp. 37–46.

Schirru R., Baumann S., Memmel M. & Dengel A. 2010. Extraction of Contextualized User Interest Profiles in Social Sharing Platforms. J. Universal Computer Science, vol. 16, no. 16, pp. 2196–2213.

Schmidt A. 2007. Impact of Context-Awareness on the Architecture of E-Learning Solutions. Architecture Solutions for E-Learning Systems, C. Pahl ed., ch. 16, pp. 306–319, IGI.

Stern H., Kaiser R., Hofmair P., Kraker P., Lindstaedt S.N. & Scheir P. 2010. Content Recommendation in Aposdle Using the Associative Network. J. Universal Computer Science, vol. 16, no. 16, pp. 2214–2231.

Tang Y., Li L.Q. & Li X.L. 2011. Learning Similarity With Multikernel Method. IEEE Transactions on systems, man, and cybernetics-part B: cyvernetics. vol. 41, no.. 1, pp. 131–138.

Verbert K., Manouselis N., Ochoa X., Wolpers M., Drachsler H., Bosnic I. & Duval E. 2012. Context-Aware Recommender Systems for Learning: A Survey and Future Challenges. IEEE Transactions on learning technology. Vol. 5, no. 4, pp. 318–335.

Yau J. & Joy M. 2007. A Context-Aware and Adaptive Learning Schedule Framework for Supporting Learners' Daily Routines. Proc. Second Int'l Conf. Systems, pp. 31–37.

Computer, Intelligent Computing and Education Technology – Liu, Sung & Yao (Eds)
© *2014 Taylor & Francis Group, London, ISBN 978-1-138-02469-4*

Discussions on the relationships between musical education and the emotional creativity cultivation for P.E. majors in college

Hong-Qiang Qu

Institute of Physical Education, Luoyang Normal University, Luoyang, China

ABSTRACT: Through literature, expert interviews, it makes logical analysis on the following issues: music and sports are intrinsically related; musical education plays an important role in promoting creativity for P.E. majors in colleges; the Feasibility and ways of how the musical education should be carried out for P.E. majors in Sport Department.

Keywords: musical education; relationships; emotional creativity; P.E. majors

1 INTRODUCTION

Music and sports are highly similar with each other in the origins and forms. Musical education is an important way to the emotional and creative cultivation, especially for P.E. majors. Therefore, P.E. Teachers and scholars should actively think about how to carry out the musical education for the students in sports colleges.

2 THE RELATIONS BETWEEN MUSIC AND SPORTS

2.1 *Music and sports are universal human culture*

Music as an aural art, is known as human language without borders, so is the sports, they are both cosmopolitan cultural forms. Music, through the sound transmission of information, with the expression of emotions, has a unique aesthetic characteristic and educational functions, meanwhile, sports as a form of exercise, is also with the principles and internationally accepted method and rules, so they are both universal human culture.

2.2 *Music and sports have the same educational functions*

Music and sports have a lot of similarities in the educational functions: Firstly, both are able to raise the level of human intelligence and promote the formation of good moral character; secondly, musical and sports activities are able to meet the aesthetic needs of people and to improve their aesthetic capacity. As the ancient Greek philosopher Aristotle had proposed: the body, with the sports, right mind, with music.

2.3 *Music and sports have the same form of expression*

Musical and sports activities are similar in the form of expression: the rhythm and the strength to grasp the intensity. The difference between the two is that music has to go with the sound, while sport is through physical activity. Sports and music can be integrated with each other well, for example, dance is a perfect combination of art forms, completed by physical activity in the accompaniment of music.

3 THE IMPORTANCE OF EMOTION AND CREATIVITY TRAINING FOR P.E. MAJORS IN COLLEGES

3.1 *The meaning and importance of emotion and creativity*

Emotion is one of objective things, it not only meets peoples' needs and experiences but also generates attitude and a person's own mental state and self-feelings. Furthermore, it may affect the recognition process. Generally speaking, positive emotional power promotes awareness to the tenacity of things to solve the problem: health, positive emotions can inspire the students to challenge and persevere. Because the blazing emotions can produce tremendous power, motivate students to make greater achievements in the professional learning experience with more fun in life, so being rich in healthy emotion is a critical psychological quality.

Creativity refers to a person's knowledge of existing elements, re-integration, and the ability to produce new social value of things. The nature of creation is to explore and discover the unknown: on the national level, innovation is the soul, which in the modern international competition, in the sport fields, the majority of sport workers' innovation capability is also important to the development of sports.

3.2 *Physical characteristics of the P.E. students' moral emotion*

Professor Deng-Song Zhou, who worked for Beijing Sports University said in an interview, based on years of managing experience, personal observation and related survey results: P.E. majors, as part of the students, after years of professional training and school education, the vast majority of them may have the correct values, worldview, can consciously safeguard public morality, but in the emotional aspects, many students have a boring life, apathy, they are difficult to be moved, hardly excited. Professor Zhou further noted: college students are in the formation of a critical period of life, they have been relatively stable physically and psychologically. During this period, if timely and effective manner is taken to exert a positive influence on their spiritual world, it will help to improve their emotion, enthusiasm for learning and creativity.

3.3 *Emotions and creativity training plays an important role in promoting the overall development of the P.E. majors*

Suhomlinski once said: "emotions are moral beliefs, principles and spiritual strength of the core and if the flesh goes without the emotion, morality becomes empty". Positive emotions can improve people's physical and mental strength "Thus, the attitude of emotional experience as a principal", ethical and responsible support for sports majors, whether it is motivation expertise, technology, or the life of social responsibility, all derive from their inner feelings.

Modern society requires the overall quality of human intelligence, psychological, creative ways of thinking. The fundamental aim for higher education is to help the students to get a positive attitude to life, with the right values and morality, with the ability to adapt to modern society, with the sense of innovation and creativity, rather than educating them only to achieve money rewards.

The academic studies show that: the relationship between moral, intellectual, physical and aesthetic education is not a simple overlay, but an organic fusion: the beauty of music and arts education lies in the rhythm, intensity of feeling and imagination.

In the field of higher education in the West, whether it is a comprehensive professional colleges or universities, arts and social science courses are 20% of the total hours of the curriculum: for example, the Massachusetts Institute of Technology, the school sets 360 credits for the undergraduate students, clearly stipulates that 72 credits are set for art courses. Tsinghua University in China uses the formulation " 8-1 > 8" to illustrate the image that if you spend an hour a day on arts education, you can make the rest seven hours of learning more efficient than full eight hours only to study.

According to the reality in China, in the first reform process of primary and secondary school with the new P.E. curriculum standards, due to the lack of the specific contents and standards as references. Many P.E. teachers seemed at a loss, they do not know how to start. One of the reasons is that they are weak in practical ability to innovate, without a thorough understanding of the "New curriculum Standard", they can not independently arrange for Physical Education activities. Therefore, the fact has shown: the reform of primary and secondary education in the process of promoting new sports curriculum was not successful. The majority of P.E. majors in colleges lack creativity, so they need to continuously improve their professional adaptability for future teaching work which might be very creative.

4 FEASIBILITY ANALYSIS: THE IMPLEMENTATION OF MUSICAL EDUCATION IN SPORTS DEPARTMENT

4.1 *The school's educational philosophy and school leaders support*

Philosophy and concept of education at a school play an important role in commanding, especially for colleges. Therefore, the introduction of music education in the Physical Education Department, firstly, the department leaders need to abandon the old view that musical education is no more than "singing and dancing". As the leaders, their support is the first import factor.

4.2 *The school hardware facilities and time to devote*

In the history of China's modernization and development of higher education information technology progress, the vast majority of colleges and universities have been equipped with multimedia audio-visual equipment, the hardware facilities are external conditions for carrying out musical education, but even if hardware conditions permit, musical education also takes some time, especially for the teachers, the arrangement of teaching content, and even participate in relevant training and learning to be musical, it may take some extra time.

4.3 Teachers' own cultural knowledge and artistic aesthetic ability

Teachers as the leaders of educational activities, need to have some common knowledge of arts and culture and the aesthetic ability to appreciate the musical education resources, so that they will be able to guide students in music appreciation and learning effectively.

4.4 The students' cultural foundation and musical appreciation ability

Most sports majors are relatively weak in cultural knowledge, with relatively limited understanding and appreciation of the arts, after a long time be trained for sports, most of them cline to take "muscle movements" not "spiritual activities", so the teachers must patiently cultivate their related interests for music and arts, encourage guide and entertain them, to make the students gain the motivation through the happy experiences.

5 CONCLUSIONS AND SUGGESTIONS

Music and sport are both part of the worldwide human culture, they are similar with each other in origin and the form of expression and educational functions; musical education has great effects in training on human emotion and creativity.

For the current weak side of college sports majors overall psychological characteristic, measures should be timely taken to develop their emotional health through musical education and to stimulate their creativity.

The factors that affect the implementation of musical education in sports department are: the recognition and support of from the faculty leaders, school time commitment and hardware facilities, teachers' and students' appreciation for music and acceptability.

Musical Education in Physical Education Department may be conducted by the following ways: into general course or optional course, cooperation between departments, cultural activities on campus under a musical theme.

REFERENCES

[1] Lu-Sheng Chen. Horse Sword New Psychology [M] Beijing Normal University Press, 2002.
[2] Qiu-Ling Liu. On the role of arts education in the overall development of the people of [J]. Education and occupation, 2006, (17):124–125.
[3] Fan-Shao Chu. "Psychological education" and "moral" Integration [J] big reference quality education, 2007, (5):28–29.
[4] Guangxi Arts College of Education, 2005, (4):33–35.
[5] Of normal enhance students' musical aesthetic education Analysis [J] education and career, 2006, (32):149–150.

Computer, Intelligent Computing and Education Technology – Liu, Sung & Yao (Eds)
© 2014 Taylor & Francis Group, London, ISBN 978-1-138-02469-4

Heritage tourism development of the new situation intangible sports

Jun-Biao Tu & Ming-Hua Zhou
Institute of Physical Education, Luoyang Normal University, Luoyang, China

ABSTRACT: Development and utilization of intangible cultural heritage is currently the subject of an international paper through literature, mathematical statistics, research methods, the study believe that there are a lot of excellent national traditional sports culture, only the beneficial development of these traditional sports culture, especially sports non-material cultural tourism project development, not only to promote economic development, while improving people's cultural awareness and appreciation of the level, to improve China's cultural soft power sports.

Keywords: sports; intangible cultural heritage; travel

1 THE CONCEPT AND FEATURES OF THE INTANGIBLE CULTURAL HERITAGE AND SPORTS TOURISM

1.1 *Leisure and aesthetics define the concept of intangible cultural heritage*

UNESCO world cultural heritage in order to improve protection system, in October 2003 formally adopted "Safeguarding of the Intangible Cultural Heritage", a non-material cultural heritage is defined as "communities, groups and, sometimes, individuals recognize as an integral part of their cultural heritage of various social practices, ideas expressions, knowledge, skills and related instruments, objects, artefacts and cultural spaces." China authoritative definition of the concept of intangible cultural heritage from the State Council in March 2005 issued "on the strengthening of China's intangible cultural heritage protection work opinions", the file will be expressed as intangible cultural heritage "of our peoples from generation to generation Cheng, closely associated with the life of the masses of the various traditional cultural forms (such as folk activities, performing arts, traditional arts and cultural space)."

1.2 *Sports non material cultural heritage tourism concept definition*

Sports culture as a kind of intangible cultural heritage, in reproduction and progress of all ethnic groups, experienced the vicissitudes of life has been retained, showing a strong vitality and capacity for sustainable development. The reason is that this kind of culture is rooted in the national mass production life, deep in people's behavior, language and thought, reflection the nation's mental and spiritual, is human creativity, imagination, profound wisdom and hard work of the true portraiture and inheritance. Its value in the modern tourism industry is increasingly showing the attraction and the potential for the development of strong. In the protection of intangible cultural heritage, inheritance and development. Under the background, the rich and colorful, fascinating and bloom the history culture and sports, tourism industry with it will create a new form of industry, namely the non sports tourism industry material culture, which is mainly based on folk sports and cultural tourism. As a special kind of folk custom sports, has a strong national colors, body attribute it is essence of folklore. The combination of folk sports and tourism, and more reflected in the leisure, entertainment, ornamental and participation features. Non material cultural heritage of sports tourism as a new tourism projects and sports industry part, is a tourist to attract the folk sports resources, exotic or alien culture unique, on the condition of a certain folk sports tourism facilities, to leave their home, go to the folk custom sports tourism destination is a cultural life the way of folk sports consumption. It is composed of folk sports tourism resources, folk sports tourism products, folk sports tourism market (folk sports tourism providers and consumers) composed of 3 elements.

2 FAVORABLE EXTERNAL CONDITIONS FOR SPORTS AND NON-MATERIAL CULTURAL HERITAGE TOURISM A GOOD OPPORTUNITY

2.1 *International and domestic sports tourism boom set off*

In 2001 February 22–23 day, CO sponsored by the world tourism organization and International Olympic Committee "world sports and Tourism

Conference" held in the Spanish city of Barcelona, for the sports and the sports industry to develop the huge development space, but also can provide a sustainable use of tourism resources and motivation to the development of the tourism industry. In recent years, sports tourism has gradually become a kind of fashion, according to statistics, the number of golf tourism abroad in Britain each year up to 3000000 passengers; German bicycle tourism travel agency has more than 200, each year about 12000000 people participated in the bicycle tourism.1994 years of sports tourism in China, sports tourism is showing a rapid, sustained, coordinated development the momentum, the annual growth rate reached 30%–40%, the sports tourism industry and other industries, the development of integration of sports and tourism phenomenon. In 2001 the tourism theme: China sports tour. 2011 year in November 11th to 14 China Sports Tourism Fair held in Haikou City, Hainan Province, this theme is: sports tourism, fashion life.

2.2 Changes in consumer attitudes, enhance health awareness

The development of sports tourism policy introduced by the government, provides a good policy environment for the development of sports tourism. "Eleven five" period, struggling to achieve the rise of central China "golden development period" in our province, the development of tourism is facing the opportunity to hitherto unknown. With the implementation of the "Twelfth Five Year Plan" period of China's "outline of national tourism and leisure", will pay more attention to the sustainable development of sports tourism industry policy of government support. The central government puts forward the grand goal in 2020 to build China into a world tourism power, the State Sports General administration and the State Tourism Bureau decided to start the national sports tourism special investigation, in order to further research clearly the future two to jointly promote the development of sports tourism ideas, basic framework and policy measures, provide the basis for the formulation and implementation of two material documents related to sports to accelerate the development of tourism. In order to implement the national policy, local governments can stage a series of in line with the actual situation of the local sports tourism development policy.

3 TOUR OF SPORTS INTANGIBLE CULTURAL HERITAGE AND THE INFLUENCING FACTORS

With the improvement of living standards, more tourists seeking new, unique, curiosity, experience of psychological needs. This stimulated the local tourism industry continues to heat up, the humanities landscape more and more popular, especially the intangible culture heritage resources was developed to take advantage of the growing trend, the local people for generations pass continued and long-term preserved primary sports folk arts and culture, there are more and more tourism activities and human development in the. Although has obtained the enormous economic benefits, but also suffered varying degrees of damage, loss and variation. Due to the lack of awareness and the protection measures, drive plus interest, a lot of folk traditional sports cultural artifacts and works of art is not the careful design and was randomly into tourism commodity, which seriously distorts the artwork. Many sports national folk art and folk custom and etiquette, festivals, due to blind development, many performing art is not the real people in the transmission performance, and even some performances also added some unhealthy content, thus losing the original flavor and culture ancestor continued, become dull business performance.

Due to the development of culture of folk sports tourism adverse, many places appeared tourism places and similar content and crudely made trend, these no grade and follow the same pattern of tourism activity, really makes visitors feel boring. All of these, not only make the passenger authenticity of non-material cultural misleading and twisted in the understanding, but also to have the value of the intangible cultural heritage caused the native state of destruction and the normal damage, at the same time, but also damage the Chinese nation for thousands of years to make excellent traditional culture precious. If things go on like this, the tourism activities of natural loss of the original attraction so as to make the economic benefits greatly reduced, plus the incorrect utilization of intangible cultural heritage tourism resources, will also make the intangible cultural heritage can not effectively protect and inherit, the living culture of endangered and disappear, leading to not sustainable development.

3.1 Sports intangible cultural heritage tourism resources survey inadequate

Sports tourist resources of intangible cultural heritage is one of the basic work of planning of tourism development, tourism development in the investigation, it is the prerequisite for the development of marketable tourism products, plays an important role in the whole process of tourism development. Investigation of tourism resources in tourism developers, previous just focus on tangible tourism resources collection, but despise the invisible and intangible cultural heritage resources, especially the top secret, hidden in the folk non matter cultural, make its value has not been fully utilized, even distortion in the tourism development process is simple, the. This will inevitably affect people more aware of its value, to realize its precious nature, in order for the intangible cultural heritage resources in the development process is not conducive to better protect.

3.2 Sports inheritors of intangible cultural heritage inadequate attention, inadequate protection

Heritage protection and tourism administration departments at all levels to sports intangible cultural heritage is not enough, the lack of inheritors, many places are not the culture and heritage protection were put into important schedule of tourism development. Sports intangible cultural heritage mostly people carrier, strengthen the protection of sports intangible cultural heritage items is a key link for its protection. As everyone knows, cultural tourism can become tourists preferred target, is because there are many folk inheritance people involved in tourism activities, so that visitors to this tour will leave a deep memory, to revisit and drive people to travel to lay a good foundation. But some tourism destination in order to meet the passenger curiosity psychological, in the development of sports tourism in some national customs is transformed, exaggerated, or even barbaric, vulgar, commercial atmosphere over the serious destruction of the connotation and meaning of culture, and ethnic stability of spiritual beliefs and the cohesion of the Chinese nation will be impact.

3.3 Sports intangible cultural heritage protection system of laws and regulations lag

Damage to the scale of the intangible cultural heritage, and the destruction of the intangible cultural heritage should bear the legal responsibility and other issues, so far there is no law more perfect. To protect the work is not strict system, especially the standard and target management protection is not standard. All sectors of society to participate in the not to coordinate, encourage and safeguard measures, the lack of legal policy. Therefore, to change this situation becomes the current policy making and legislative practice is objective and inevitable requirement.

3.4 The way the government administrative protection of non physical cultural heritage need to be improved

The so-called administrative protection refers to the government, the state in the protection of non material cultural heritage of sports administrative

act on, such as to carry out the census, archiving, research, preservation, inheritance, carry forward, as well as the realization of these protective behavior and fiscal, administrative, technical and other measures to provide the. Administrative behavior is the social organization and management behavior is mandatory in the general sense. But the administrative protection behavior is different from other administrative acts of the biggest characteristic, is to achieve effective protection or save the object by this behavior. So basically it is a service behavior or security behavior. Administrative protection cannot be simply equated with the administrative examination and approval or improper intervention. Non material cultural heritage for thousands of years is mainly dependent on the folk soil natural existence, handed down, once the administrative means too much or rude intervention, thus undermining the survival of the social environment, the results are often run counter to one's desire. In practice, many similar problems have arisen. Therefore, we should emphasize an important nature of administrative protection is the administrative guarantee, namely administrative department provides protection to the work of the finance, policies, such as security.

3.5 Sports non between government departments at all levels of material cultural heritage tourism and inconsistent interests

Tourism departments involved more, because of the tourism related departments have their own interests, such as cultural departments to emphasize the protection of tourism development, that will cause damage to the non—material cultural, not aware of tourism development will bring economic benefits to its, more conducive to the protection of. While the tourism sector too commercial, blindly pursuing economic benefit, it ignored the protection, not to realize that only seriously for the protection of the intangible cultural heritage, to the sustainable use of. In addition to the government staff subjective constraints, as well as the duties of each department is not clear, cause local and overall, inferior and superior multiple interests intertwined, lack of coordination mechanisms, resulting in no dislocation of government functions and responsibilities, is not conducive to the protection and utilization of sports intangible cultural heritage.

4 SPORTS INTANGIBLE CULTURAL HERITAGE TOURISM DEVELOPMENT CONCEPTION

4.1 Relying scenic, showcasing

Mainly to folk dance, traditional theater, acrobatics these three categories of intangible cultural heritage using stage performances in a particular way to showcase area, audio-visual enjoyment to tourists, such as "The Dream of Dunhuang", "Silk Road" "Yunnan Impression", "bagui great song" and a number of excellent music and dance based on the genre of local folk, ethnic, religious, cultural, and quickly opened the domestic and international markets, and achieved widespread success, so that national resources been effectively utilized.

4.2 Development and innovation, enhanced experience

Folk music and dance for sports tourism development, innovation can be from the costumes, props, form, content, style. As widely welcomed Younger farmers can undertake publicity through the transformation of new ideas, educate the masses, the task of creating a harmonious social atmosphere. In the development of philosophy, should pay attention to the mental and psychological meet visitors, increase visitor experience. Product Development prominent tourist participatory, interactive, allowing visitors to participate in sports such as folk dances, music, folk art and other activities, to enhance its "experience" consciousness.

4.3 Repair school field trips, savor the true

At present, some folk art courses sports college training set, because out of the original ecology of the cultural environment, students can not directly feel truly national style characteristic, folk art, on which the image features, body movement, ethos, regional style, rhythm rhythmic understanding and perception will naturally be affected. Therefore, the university arts education can be combined with repair school field trips to arts education as a medium to academic studies as a means, through personal contacts and experience the original ecology of folk art to inspire thinking, students observation, perception, expression. By Xiuxue folk songs, savor the true national culture conducive to pass, and to promote sustainable development of the performing Intangible Cultural Heritage Tourism Development.

Computer, Intelligent Computing and Education Technology – Liu, Sung & Yao (Eds)
© *2014 Taylor & Francis Group, London, ISBN 978-1-138-02469-4*

Analysis of value factors leading innovative "Land Volleyball" sports in leisure sports

Ming-Hua Zhou & Jun-Biao Tu
Institute of Physical Education, Luoyang Normal University, Luoyang, China

ABSTRACT: Using the method of literature, the study of value to volleyball sports in leisure sports. Research shows that: the volleyball is a collection of sports, leisure, entertainment, new sports soluble public fitness programs and competitive sports in one, regardless of the venues and facilities, environmental conditions, their idea of leisure sports and sports culture personality and other aspects are more suitable for the learning of students engaged in leisure sports. Volleyball sport can become a new bright spot in the national fitness activities; it ingenious combination of personal skills and teamwork, has a unique charm of movement, and the ball of light and soft, no harm to the fingers. Its activities at the venue, lax rules, in various forms, flexible technology, whether it is used for physical fitness, entertainment, or as to improve the auxiliary volleyball practice will make participants feel heart steadfast, can give full play to individual skills, to improve the sensitivity, judgment, reaction ability of the individual, has a positive effect on enhancing sports, nerve, blood circulation, respiratory system with the ability to work. It can also make the participants felt the collective wisdom and strength, to enjoy the fun of collective cooperation, to experience the joy of winning the game.

Keywords: Land Volleyball; leisure sports; leading value

1   INTRODUCTION

Reviewing the development of volleyball, William Morgan was originally invented volleyball, because people need a moderate amount of exercise, new confrontation is not high, prominent characteristics of entertainment. But the volleyball movement development so far, in the athletic forward while gradually divorced from the masses, has become a must have a certain height, skilled, have good fitness sport participation. In the center of the national fitness sports development strategy to tilt shift today, how to promote the mass sports mass effectively, is the direction of development of sports of our country at the present stage and the trend, the further implementation of the national fitness strategy is imminent, this problem is before us, we often think, how to change the current not for the situation of volleyball, and seek to meet different sports people in need through the reform of the existing sports form. After years of teaching practice, we found that the combination of volleyball and tennis, to inject new vitality to the volleyball sports, to produce a new, more lively and interesting forms of exercise—"Land Volleyball".

The volleyball and tennis with, to inject new vitality to the volleyball sports, to produce a more lively and interesting forms of exercise—"Land Volleyball". Development of "Land Volleyball"

can make up for the traditional volleyball in the actual popularization of breaking the bottleneck restricting the development of the existing, Land Volleyball, also has the value of exercise and entertainment value good in reducing entry difficulty at the same time, will be accepted more people and love. At the same time "Land Volleyball" movement is a new fitness ball games project has good prospects for development, through research and explore constantly, which is easy to be popularized, entertaining and competitive, the development of sports industry, will bring considerable economic value. The current trend of volleyball sport for continuously towards popularization, diversification, and "Land Volleyball" sports development research, complying with the development trend, the sports big family added a new member, also to the role of reference and guidance for the future research of the same type.

2   THE ORIGIN AND INFLUENCE OF LAND VOLLEYBALL

2.1   *The origin of Land Volleyball*

Through the long-term teaching practice, on the basis of literature, the research group in 2005 began to explore a new way of volleyball, and continue to explore and experiment, study and research activities through the volleyball course 2008 sports college group, we conducted a thorough exchange of views on the reform of the existing pattern, volleyball to promote the development of mass sports view, the colleague opinion is highly unified, research meaning through this, combined with previous related studies of the Beijing Sport University Professor Ge Chun lin for reference, strengthened the confidence we reform the existing volleyball. In the volleyball teaching practice, we pay special attention to the volleyball and tennis are combined, the reform of the existing form of volleyball. After careful design, verification data, comparative analysis, the preliminary motions. Because the sport is volleyball are closely associated with tennis, changed venues specifications, change the basis of its height, provision of equipment material properties, competition system and the number of entries have done related reform movement, a new form of birth. Because of this activity is to volleyball as the main form of exercise, combined with the characteristics and play tennis, the ball has remarkable characteristics rebound after the ball, so they called it "Land Volleyball".

2.2 *The value of leisure sports lead*

Development and research of "Land Volleyball" movement, which belongs to the completely independent innovation. "Land Volleyball" movement is a good development prospects of the new fitness ball games project, it is not only easy to promote, and entertaining and competitive, it can be for the development of sports industry, bring considerable economic value and. "Land Volleyball" movement is better combination of movement forms and characteristics of volleyball and tennis, and broke through the bottleneck restricting the development of the volleyball movement, also has the value of exercise and entertainment value good in reducing entry difficulty at the same time, so that it can be accepted more people and love. "Study on the Land Volleyball movement" innovation development, will enable the new members added sports big family, in the promotion of volleyball movement toward the development of popularization, diversification of the road further, to the role of reference and guidance for the future research of the same type.

The development of sports tourism policy introduced by the government, provides a good policy environment for the development of sports tourism. "Eleven five" period, struggling to achieve the rise of central China "golden development period" in our province, the development of tourism is facing the opportunity to hitherto unknown. With the implementation of the "Twelfth Five Year Plan" period of China's "outline of national tourism and leisure", will pay more attention to the sustainable development of sports tourism industry policy of government support. The central government puts forward the grand goal in 2020 to build China into a world tourism power, the State Sports General administration and the State Tourism Bureau decided to start the national sports tourism special investigation, in order to further research clearly the future two to jointly promote the development of sports tourism ideas, basic framework and policy measures, provide the basis for the formulation and implementation of two material documents related to sports to accelerate the development of tourism. In order to implement the national policy, local governments can stage a series of in line with the actual situation of the local sports tourism development policy.

3 UNFAVORABLE FACTORS AND BOTTLENECK ANALYSIS PRESENTVOLLEYBALL

Volleyball games more exciting, more intense, attracting more and more attention and love of volleyball. But because the volleyball entry threshold is too high, the popularity of Volleyball in Colleges and universities, have to face the volleyball skills high, comprehensive technology, the fierce confrontation and the hardness of the ball and facilities of higher requirements, these adverse factors have doomed the volleyball sports existing restricted by different degree in the promotion.

All participating in volleyball sports people must face a fact: the three big ball sports tradition, volleyball entry is difficult, the beginning of the volleyball beginners too high. Moved by the beginner is brilliant volleyball game, giving them is frustrated, because volleyball has skills high, all the ball part of the technology are in the air, and to the technical requirements is very comprehensive, not only will serve, spike attack, but also master the rapid and efficient defense reaction technology, and in the volleyball match, beginners often becomes the "pick up the ball game" or "ball game", one of the important reasons of losing all these will cause the volleyball lovers.

Even if according to the existing standard volleyball new rules reduce the ball pressure and used a relatively soft material, but for beginners, the ball hardness too. When a lot of girls face the first rapid reaction to the ball all Dodge, even brave beginners after a period of practice, their arms will appear different degree of epidermal damage phenomenon. The teacher continued to encourage them, to continue to adhere to the courage to overcome difficulties, but really insist on practice and can fully realize the volleyball fun does not see more.

Volleyball is a three-dimensional, not only has the plane in outside air, and the height and the Internet are the definition of the mark rod, for beginners, too complicated, and Volleyball Ground boundary constraints on people and the ball is too cumbersome, the offensive line not only limits the attackers also limits the spike height, the midline and network is very important in some cases, but in some cases it can touch the stampede, volleyball line limit the ball, but can be hit and the ball out of bounds, which are different from the basketball and football is relatively simple and easy to remember rules. When scholars first stood on the volleyball court, always feel be at a loss what to do.

4 INNOVATION AND VALUE OF LAND VOLLEYBALL

4.1 Characteristics of Land Volleyball

"Many characteristics of Land Volleyball" movement and has a volleyball and tennis, and volleyball technology, equipment and play closer to. "Field and Land Volleyball Games volleyball" are broadly similar, but the biggest different volleyball and traditional volleyball project is, allow the ball landed in the limited area once, can pick up a rebound after landing, both as a stroke, according to the rules in the 3 hit the ball over the net; at the same time the spike and site, the competition method have made bold improvement, let "Land Volleyball" game easier, more interesting, and the ball more often, the game more exciting, at the same time physical exercise effect is greatly enhanced, it can be said that the "Land Volleyball" movement is a movement characteristics and advantages of a one of the new sports.

The volleyball and tennis with, to inject new vitality to the volleyball sports, to produce a more lively and interesting forms of exercise—"Land Volleyball". Development of "Land Volleyball" can make up for the traditional volleyball in the actual popularization of breaking the bottleneck restricting the development of the existing, volleyball, also has the value of exercise and entertainment value good in reducing entry difficulty at the same time, will be accepted more people and love. At the same time "Land Volleyball" movement is a new fitness ball games project has good prospects for development, through research and explore constantly, which is easy to be popularized, entertaining and competitive, the development of sports industry, will bring considerable economic value. The current trend of volleyball sport for continuously towards popularization, diversification, and "Land Volleyball" sports development research, complying with the development trend, the sports

big family added a new member, also to the role of reference and guidance for the future research of the same type.

4.2 "Land Volleyball" movement development in leisure sports value

To Land Volleyball is a new sport fitness and entertainment. The ingenious combination of personal skills and teamwork, has a unique charm of movement, and the ball of light and soft, no harm to the fingers. Its activities at the venue, lax rules, in various forms, flexible technology, whether it is used for physical fitness, entertainment, or as to improve the auxiliary volleyball practice will make participants feel heart steadfast, can give full play to individual skills, to improve the sensitivity, judgment, reaction ability of the individual, has a positive effect on enhancing sports, nerve, blood circulation, respiratory system with the ability to work. It can also make the participants felt the collective wisdom and strength, to enjoy the fun of collective cooperation, to experience the joy of winning the game.

To the Land Volleyball movement has the advantages of novel design, wide application range, strong interest, especially its height is reduced, increasing the number of spike increased competition, a volleyball landing opportunities, reduce the dead ball situations in the game, improve the fierce competition and ornamental. Whether exercise or game, people can enjoy, field there is always "make the dead come back to life", the ups and downs of the warm scene, the fitness people also feel the joy of the game of shin and reproduction. People acquire fitness effect at the same time, to entertain, to perfect personality. So, Land Volleyball has strong entertainment and ornamental, undoubtedly plays an important role in the quality education and mental health education.

In today's increasingly competitive society, to the volleyball movement can let people return to nature, feel childlike joy, promote interpersonal affection and friendship, just the harmony between teachers and students, students and students' feelings, cultivate interpersonal health, unity and coordination.

Teenagers are the future of our country, they have to Land Volleyball, rules, to experience more Land Volleyball made them happy at school, will influence other members of the family and the people around, so that more people join the volleyball movement. To Land Volleyball ages, in various forms, at the venue, economical and practical characteristics and in conformity with the mass entertainment needs and consumer level, in line with the status quo of public sports facilities in our country, which decides the Land Volleyball sports participation will be very large population base. From school to society, from the playground to the green, from the family to the community, it will actively promote the nationwide fitness campaign in-depth, extensive.

Groups and members of society realize the socialization, and the social stability and development, but also the value of their own. In the process of human's socialization, Land Volleyball sports can play an important role in. Land Volleyball has certain technical specifications and rules of Land Volleyball activities, there is a certain constraint of social activities, regulate and restrain behavior among participants with enhanced role in this process. At the same time, to participate in the Land Volleyball activities constitute a temporary places of social interaction, in the process of moving between individuals, individual and collective, collective and collective interactions between frequent, direct. Land Volleyball movement to promote the coordination, promote unity and cooperation, and personal time, which provides an opportunity for them to conduct self-education. To in Land Volleyball, participant's social function, social adaptability and observe social norms consciousness, are highly developed, in the entertainment and fitness effectively realized the individual socialization.

The rapid development of modern society, exacerbated by the intense competition between the members of society, work intensity, resulting in heavy mental burden, interpersonal relations have undergone tremendous changes. Therefore, the modern society requires the social members have good psychological quality, in order to adapt to the high degree of social life. To Land Volleyball on the psychological status and improve the human, has a unique role in the development of the individual psychological quality. Many people because

of high self expectation, once encounter difficulties and setbacks, will lose confidence and confused, often low self-esteem, fear of failure, dare not face competition. Land Volleyball with its rich activities so that each participant in the activities are likely to success and failure, to know themselves, give full play to their potential, enhance self-confidence and the ability to withstand setbacks, constantly honed willpower, see the hope of success in failure, accept new challenges in the success of. People due to various reasons, temporarily lost their mental balance, depression, apathy, play Land Volleyball, in a relaxed, passionate atmosphere, the joy, freedom, autonomy of participants, passion, to negative emotional buffer and catharsis, a positive role in the regulation of mood, emotion plays.

In the Land Volleyball match, the athletic field situation the myriads of changes, in a short period of time to analyze and judge accurately in complex situation, and the two sides in a tense, intense confrontation in the battle of wits, courage, rely on the brain flexible and creative thinking, which is the development of the human brain has a great role in promoting the comprehensive thinking.

Because of the influence of other fashion movement, it is difficult to improve the development of volleyball, try various devices to a person with breadth of vision is, actively promote volleyball sports in the masses, especially to develop "Land Volleyball" movement is a pressing matter of the moment of the task. In volleyball sports big family, project derived often carry out soft volleyball, beach volleyball, volleyball classes, age appropriate development, help to increase the population of Volleyball in Colleges and universities in our country, to improve the overall level of grass-roots volleyball, contributing to the sustainable development to promote China's volleyball sports career.

Computer, Intelligent Computing and Education Technology – Liu, Sung & Yao (Eds)
© 2014 Taylor & Francis Group, London, ISBN 978-1-138-02469-4

Research on optimization of resource distribution and scientific management of laboratories in colleges and universities

Hai-Bo Lun, Hai-Yun Qi & Ying-Ting Zhang
Environmental Management College of China (EMCC), Qinhuangdao, Hebei, China

ABSTRACT: The optimization of resource distribution and regulatory, scientific management of laboratories is necessary and vital to give full play to laboratories in improving teaching, research and talent cultivation of colleges and universities. The thesis gives an analysis of common problems existing in resource distribution and management of in colleges and universities. The problems include decentralized construction, enclosed management, lack of plans for resource distribution, not full use of labs as well as not enough maintenance of equipments. In the end, the thesis gives advice on optimization of resource distribution and regulatory, scientific management of laboratories.

Keywords: laboratories/labs in colleges and universities; resource distribution; scientific management

1 INTRODUCTION

Labs are important for improving teaching, talent cultivation and doing scientific research in colleges and universities. Conditions of labs reflect those of teaching, management and scientific research. They are the means to measure school level and whether a school is qualified. Problems such as how to optimize resource distribution, avoid invisible waste and give full play to labs in improving teaching, talent cultivation and doing scientific research, have been urgent for us to solve.

2 COMMON PROBLEMS EXISTING IN RESOURCE DISTRIBUTION AND MANAGEMENT OF IN COLLEGE AND UNIVERSITIES

Colleges and universities are developing and expanding fast. Experiments and practical trainings are becoming widely used. More and more importance is placed on lab construction in colleges and universities. Lab construction does achieve more progress. However, in real work, problems still exist. Bad resource distribution and management are two of the worst.

2.1 Decentralized construction and enclosed management of labs

Labs and all departments in colleges and universities design experiment courses according to majors and teaching programs. As a result, lab management is comparatively independent, small-scaled, with less cross-use. Teachers have no idea about lab resources in their own college or university. Problems may go to extreme, either in great demand or left unused, which causes low efficiency of resource use and thus invisible waste[1]. In addition, unrealistic competitions between labs on purchasing equipments lead to unnecessary investment and a lack of whole-picture vision. This lack of coordination further worsens the resource distribution, resulting in a lack of variety of lab resources, though they are rich in amounts. It also adds to a tight budget. In this case, lab equipments are being made full use of, which does harm to exploration of research programs as well as application for large-scale experiment projects[2].

2.2 Lack of plans for resource distribution

Lab instruments and equipments should meet the needs of teaching and scientific research. In terms of teaching, scientific and regulatory distribution standards have not been formed with reference to the teaching system. Equipment purchasing is simply based on personal impression or requirements of certain courses, which will easily cause imbalance and huge gaps between labs. In terms of scientific research, due to a lack of a long-term and overall scheme, equipment purchasing is to satisfy urgent needs and focus on present benefits, without thorough consideration on the equipments' practical use, leave alone any optional plans. As soon as the project is finished, the equipments are left unused[3].

2.3 Not full use of labs in a complete teaching period

At present, lab construction is an attachment to theory teaching. With theories outweighing practice, experiment courses are designed with reference to theory teaching as a supplement. Labs are not given full use in helping training students' practical skills, scientific research and social service. As a result, labs are only used in the later stage of the whole teaching period, for the rest of which, they are vacant. Furthermore, teachers come to use the labs almost at the same time. This has led to a shortage of lab resources, which does harm to cultivating students' creativity, improving teachers' qualities, as well as maintenance of lab equipments.

2.4 Maintenance and service of lab equipments

Maintenance and service and lab equipments are not placed enough importance on. After being used, equipments need maintenance in time, which however has been done enough. As a result, the lifespan is greatly shortened. Once problems come up, lab staffs have to contact factories for home repair or scrap the equipment, because they lack basic knowledge related to maintenance or lack confidence to fix it on their own. This has added to the cost of using equipments. On the other hand, teachers know little about how to use the equipments properly. They do not follow the instructions when using the equipments. Problems caused by errors in operation are one of the most serious[4].

3 HOW TO OPTIMIZE LAB RESOURCES AND CARRY OUT SCIENTIFIC AND REGULATORY MANAGEMENT

As far as the above problems are concerned, when constructing labs in colleges and universities, related departments should take realistic conditions into consideration and give an in-depth analysis in detail. At the same time, factors, such as majors, department construction, and teacher resources, should be added. The followings are ways of optimizing lab resources and regulate lab management.

3.1 Reform management system of labs

Distribute lab resources on a basis of experiments and majors. Those labs, which are built mainly for teaching, should be given a big picture and abandon the idea of building labs according to majors. Combine small experiments of several related majors and build comprehensive labs based on types of subjects. Coordinate teaching schedule and prevent experiments from flocking together in the same period. In this way, efficiency of lab resources are improved and repeated investments can be avoided. Those labs, which are built for practical trainings and scientific research, should take into consideration teaching abilities and qualities of teachers and features of schools' teaching. Try to maximize favorable factors and minimize unfavorable ones in order to make the best use of budget for purchasing equipments and avoid buying some expensive but less used equipment.

3.2 Establish a sound system of applying for and purchasing equipments

Strengthen the management on the start on purchasing lab equipments. Show respect to teachers' views and take into full consideration the number and use rates of present lab resources. Prove the necessity of purchase as well as the rationality of amount from the points of experiment courses, class hours, course plans and students. In terms of purchase for certain people, periods or needs, prospective use of later stage should be taken into consideration. If it is just to meet temporary needs, the application should be rejected and be solved through external assistance, in order to avoid a waste of money and resources. All in all, when purchasing lab equipments, colleges and universities should have a bigger picture and comprehensive consideration. In order to prevent repeated investment in the best way, an overall management system should be built. First, teachers apply. Second, conduct a research into present situations. Third, analyze prospect and future use. Finally, prove the details by experts.

3.3 Further explore lab resources and give full play to potential of labs

Labs should first of all meet the demands of teaching. Colleges and universities should encourage teachers with better academic and research abilities to take an active part in developing scientific research projects, in order to improve scientific research abilities of teachers. At the same time, perfect lab construction using research budgets. Use high-end instruments to carry out social service. It can improve teachers' practical skills and use rates of lab equipments. Money got from the service can be used to maintain lab equipments, buy components, upgrade lab equipments and add in more functions. Furthermore, cooperate with external companies and conduct explorations and researches on projects with common interest. It will save investment form the school, enrich teaching resources, provide a training platform for teachers and students, as well as to help external companies solve problems in production. It will result in a win-win situation.

3.4 Carry out various training programs and improve lab staffs' management skills

Colleges and universities should provide regular training for lab staff to improve their practical skills. This training will get them to understand theories, structures, conduct and maintenance of lab equipments in order to increase lifespan of them. At the same time, give training courses to teachers on how to use lab equipments properly. Conduct a strict check before acceptance of precision instruments. Assign specialists to check. Make clear their responsibilities. Establish a perfect system to ensure everyone is doing their jobs. As long as lab equipments are well managed and maintained can their precision be ensured and their lifespan extended.

4 SUMMARY

Optimization of lab resources and scientific and regulatory management of labs are important aspect of lab construction in colleges and universities. During this process, features of schools should be kept. Basic teaching demands should be satisfied. Cooperation between schools and external companies should be strengthened.

Further explore the potential of labs and improve practical skills of lab staffs. In this case, labs will be made best use of in improving teaching, research and talent cultivation. Input-and-output rates can be improved, too. Efficiency and benefits can be given full play to.

ACKNOWLEDGEMENT

Corresponding Author: Hai-Yun QI, Environmental Management College of China, E-mail: qihaiyun322@foxmail.com.

REFERENCES

[1] Y. Wang & X.L. Li, Optimizing the allocation of laboratory resources and supporting innovative talent cultivation[J], Experimental Technology and Management, 2010, 27(12):221–223.
[2] C.F. Ma, Development and Opening of Laboratory resources[J], hExperimental Technology and Management, 2010, 27(12):1–3.
[3] M.C. Lin, Deepening Reform and Strengthening Management to Promote Sustainable Development of Laboratory[J], Research and exploration in Laboratory, 2009, 28(3):260–263.
[4] R. Wang, Optimizing the Configration of Laboratory Resources and Inproving the Efficiency of Laboratory Applications[J], Research and exploration in Laboratory, 2011, 30(10):400–402.

Computer, Intelligent Computing and Education Technology – Liu, Sung & Yao (Eds)
© 2014 Taylor & Francis Group, London, ISBN 978-1-138-02469-4

The study on interaction of English class in vocational colleges based on S-T analysis method

N. Liu
Foreign Languages School, Tianjin University of Technology and Education, Tianjin, China

ABSTRACT: The major of English in vocational colleges mainly develop students' ability of "language + profession", the feature of which is different from common colleges. This paper makes use of S-T analysis method and selects the English courses in vocational colleges as the subjects. The interaction in the English class is analyzed, reflected and optimized, so as to better satisfy the need of developing the talents with comprehensive and practical ability.

Keywords: S-T analysis method; interaction; vocational colleges; english major; teaching mode

1 INTRODUCTION

The teaching and learning in class is an integrity combining the interaction between teachers and students. It is also a multidimensional enlightening platform of teachers' and students' thoughts in and out of class. It extends along with the dimension of time. Recently, teachers in vocational colleges pay more attention on reflection of teaching behaviors and class interaction. S-T analysis method provides an effective method to observe class teaching and learning. This paper observes and analyzes features of English class interaction in vocational colleges based on S-T analysis method. The advantages and disadvantages are concluded in order to improve the effect of class teaching and learning and satisfy students' needs. Thus, the goal to develop application-oriented talents is eventually achieved.

2 WHAT IS S-T ANALYSIS METHOD

In S-T analysis method, S is short for students, which means students' behaviour, while T is symbolizes teachers, namely, teachers' behaviour. S-T analysis method is a quantitative method taking teachers' and students' behaviour in class as the target (Fu Derong & Zhang Huimin, 2001). Researchers observe and record teaching process, present the results in quantitative form. The interaction in class is directly perceived. Teachers can observe the proportion of teachers' behaviour and the converting between teachers' and students' behaviour. All the results are organized into four teaching type—practice type, lecture type, dialogue type and mixed type.

In S-T analysis method, the key step is to collect data and select samples. Observers collect data by observing teaching and learning behaviour in class or from the video, then select samples every certain time and identify the sample to be teacher's or student's behaviour. The sign "S" or "T" is noted down.

3 LITERATURE REVIEW

In October, 2010, the Education Ministry published "National Education Reform and Development of Long-term Planning Programs", which proposes the significance to "develop a large amount of talents with international view, knowing about international regulations, capable to participate in international affairs and competitions". In 2011, the Education Ministry published "Several Opinions about Developing Excellent Engineers by the Education Ministry", which delivers that the talents should be faced with the industry, the world and the future and they should be developed to be creative and high-qualified, with international communication and competition capacity. How to develop the talents as required by the Education Ministry is an urgent task to be dealt with by vocational colleges. No matter which perspective it is to examine the function of vocational education, colleges take the majority role (Cai Jigang, 2013).

The education in vocational colleges serves two purposes. One is to build up solid knowledge foundation. The other is to develop application-oriented talents with certain major. At present, the classes in vocational colleges are with no obvious features. Especially in classes, the teaching and learning situation and class interaction are not satisfactory.

Nowadays, as for the research based on S-T analysis method, more national researchers pay their attention on advanced mathematics (Huang Sujuan, 2008) and college English (Huang Yun & Lin Wen, 2012). After 2010, the research on video becomes popular, such as the open class video of American colleges and the open class video on the Internet. The particular research on vocational colleges classes is rare. Actually researchers including those majoring in educational technology and the major of target class make use of quantitative and objective method to observe the target class. It is helpful and beneficial for teachers to improve class teaching and learning and optimize the teaching mode.

4 CASE STUDY

This study selects three courses of English major in a vocational college in Tianjin. They are the course of integrated skills of English, reading course and listening course. Students in grade two are taken as the subjects. Course teachers are of full-time job.

In the study, nine videos are taken from three courses for three times. Teachers and students are not noticed previously, but researchers just negotiated with them and entered into class after permission. The video lasts 45 minutes since it is the same as one period of class. In the observation of the video, the sample is selected every 30 seconds. The S-T data are obtained in this way and the total number (N), the number of teachers behaviour (Nt), ratio of teachers behaviour out of the total number (Rt) and the interaction ratio (Ch) can be calculated (Table 1).

According to the features of data, the interaction type can be determined and analyzed. If, in the class, Rt is more than 70%, the interaction type is lecture-typed class. If Rt is between 30% and 70% and Ch is less than 0.4, the type is mixed. Under the consideration of interaction type,

teachers can objectively know about teaching and learning behaviour, reflect the advantages and disadvantages of teaching and furthermore revise and optimize the class mode.

As for the integrated skills of English course, two samples are of mixed type and one is lectured-type. To take sample one of integrated skills of English course as the example, the S-T chart of teachers and students behaviour is drawn (Fig. 1). The vertical axis is behaviour in class while the horizontal axis is time. The crossing point of two axises is starting point of class. From the chart it is seen clearly that in the whole class, the teacher and students keep interacting with each other. The teachers often proposes questions so as to enlighten students to interact with the teacher and push the class forward in the atmosphere of smooth and harmonious interaction.

The integrated skills of English course focuses on training the integrated skills of languages. In the class, teachers can discuss a relevant topic with students together so as to improve English skills. Thus, a good interaction in class can arouse and protect students learning interests and improve the effects of teaching and learning.

According to the data, three samples of listening course are of lectured-type. It is shown that in listening course, students are in negative position to receive teachers requirements, with less interaction. The teaching type is mainly listening to the video and explaining reference answers. Students have few chances to interact with the teacher. In reading course, the three samples include lectured type and mixed type, in which, the lectured type takes majority role. In class, teachers behaviour is giving note or explaining text, with few questions delivered to students. The lectured-type class has its own advantages, namely, to deliver knowledge and information directly and systematically to students. However, students are in the position to negatively receive what is given but not to positively think independently. It is not beneficial to develop the application-oriented ability.

Table 1. Data of samples.

Sample class	N	Nt	Rt	Ch	Interaction type
Integrated skills of English 1	90	50	56%	15%	Mixed
Integrated skills of English 2	90	56	62%	19%	Mixed
Integrated skills of English 3	90	70	78%	13%	Lecture-typed
Listening 1	90	74	82%	17%	Lecture-typed
Listening 2	90	66	73%	11%	Lecture-typed
Listening 3	90	81	90%	12%	Lecture-typed
Reading 1	90	51	57%	18%	Mixed
Reading 2	90	64	71%	20%	Lecture-typed
Reading 3	90	78	87%	14%	Lecture-typed

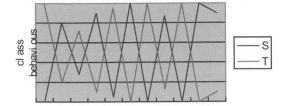

Figure 1.   S-T chart of teachers and students behaviour.

In total, among all the nine samples, three of them are of mixed type and six are of lectured type. The lecture type takes 66%. It is revealed that in class, teachers tend to take the center role while students tend to just listen and take notes. According to the researcher's personal observation, on one hand, teachers behaviour in class is informative; on the other hand, teachers also try to propose questions to interact with students. However it is a pity that students fail to react to teachers behaviour. When one particular student is required, he can just give several words can fail to interact with the teacher.

5   EVALUATION ON CLASS INTERACTION

In this study, the samples can be the representative of the present situation of learning and teaching in vocational colleges. As for the results, the features are concluded as follows.

Firstly, teachers behaviour takes more proportion. In class, teachers give the lecture individually, as is informative and systematically. However, teachers behaviour takes the majority while the ratio of students behaviour is low. Students fail to express themselves and fully participate in the class interaction.

Secondly, the transformation rate between teachers and students behaviour is low. The questioning and answering between the teacher and students is rare. With the interaction not enough, the atmosphere of teaching and learning is not active. Students fall into passive reception from the teacher.

Thirdly, it is not enough to apply multimedia and various teaching strategies. The traditional teaching method is taken, that is, blackboard and chalk. Teachers just focus on textbook but ignore the extension of knowledge and the interaction with students.

As for the reasons, it is out of various aspects. Teachers are lacking of ideas of applying new media, new technology and new methodology. Students are different from other colleges. They are passive in class to receive teachers lecturing, with different English knowledge foundation.

6   SUGGESTIONS

Vocational colleges are the main front to develop application-oriented talents for social construction, while teachers are the main force here. As for how to arrange a class and how to develop and evaluate students so as to satisfy the social needs, it requires teachers to possess comprehensive knowledge and to know about the social needs. Therefore, in class, teachers are able to prepare by screening and reorganize the teaching material out of certain purpose. The class interaction is the utmost important step to consider.

Firstly, teachers should modify their behaviour and give more chances to students so as to enhance students behaviour ratio. Students should take the majority role, as the center of class, to realize the meaning construction of learning. In the teacher-student, student-student interaction, the multi-dimension environment of language communication is constructed, to avoid teacher solo performance. It is not only to obey the language learning regulations but also provide more chances for students to practice language.

Secondly, it is to improve class design and create more chances of interaction in class. In the active interaction, student can be able to think independently and creatively, but not to passively receive what is given by teachers. The integrated skills can be developed and the implicit knowledge can be transformed into explicit knowledge. In the interaction, students keep brainstorming, with the innovation sense and teamwork spirit to be inspired. Students can be more motivated, whose need to be communicated and respected can be forced.

Thirdly, the textbook and the practice, on-line off-line study can be combined together. Scope of teaching and learning can be enlarged. More English Departments in vocational colleges in China apply the mode of "language + profession" to develop talents, such as translation, commerce, tourism and so on. Students should learn to use proper and professional language in certain professional environment. Teachers should create more chances of practice to imitate the professional environment.

On one hand, the learning in and out of class can be combined together. Teachers can extend the teaching and learning content in the form of topic and project which are carried on by students. In this way, students can sense how to apply English in practical and professional situation. If it is possible, students can do intern job to improve the integrated skills and practice ability. On the other hand, the new media can be applied with the on-line and off-line learning combined. Students can learn how to collect, select, judge and use the information. It is important for students to learn actively and independently. In the meantime, the communication space is enlarged with no limitation of time and space.

Fourthly, teachers should focus more on class analysis based on information and education technology. It is essential for teachers of different major to spend some time in learning information and education technology, especially about how to evaluate a class from a quantitative perspective. Teachers can relate their own major and a class design with education technology. It is advantageous for teachers to analyze a class quantitatively and independently, to avoid any subjective elements so as to improve teaching and learning.

7 CONCLUSION

The English major in vocational colleges is different from other standard colleges. The class teaching and learning should satisfy the social need, with theory and skills developed together. The class mode can be improved with the interaction type observed based on S-T analysis. Teachers behaviour is revised and it can serve the development of application-oriented talents. The future study is expected to take larger number of samples and education technology analysis method can be widely applied.

ACKNOWLEDGEMENT

This paper is part of the fruit of the programs. They are "Study of Internet-discussion-type learning and teaching based on the mind map" (the Twelfth Five-year Plan Program of Tianjin Educational Science and Research) (project number: VE4048), 2012 "Integrated Skills of English" course innovation program of Tianjin University of Technology and Education, social science program of Tianjin University of Technology and Education (sk11-15), program of Foreign Languages School in Tianjin University of Technology and Education (wyk201301).

REFERENCES

[1] Fu Derong, Zhang Huimin. Education information processing [M]. Beijing: Beijing Normal University Press, 2001:94–108.
[2] Cai Jigang. Adjustment of foreign language teaching and learning against the background of education internationalization [J]. Foreign Languages Electronic Learning and Teaching, 2013(1):3–8.
[3] Huang Sujuan. The S-T analysis of Advanced Mathematics [J]. The Journal of Education College of Jiangxi Province, 2008(6):76–79.

Computer, Intelligent Computing and Education Technology – Liu, Sung & Yao (Eds)
© 2014 Taylor & Francis Group, London, ISBN 978-1-138-02469-4

Short distance transportation tools design with "problem-solving theory"

H.Y. Zhang & W.J. Hu
Hunan University of Technology, Zhuzhou, China

ABSTRACT: In this paper, taking "problem-solving theory" as the theoretical basis, around short-distance handling tools in the business district for the design of objects, for short-distance handling tools present situation, the problems, the influence of time and space, environmental, this paper propose a general design way from the colors, materials, structure and function of other aspects.

Keywords: problem-solving; short-distance; handling tools; design

1 GENERAL INTRODUCTION

The so-called transportation refers to withstand the load to get through a long distance, and transport (such as cargo) from one place to another. Transportation tool is the tool needed when doing the transporting work. Transport is an important component of the human lifestyle, and short-distance transport is very common in our life. In human practice, the use of tools can relieve body fatigue, so a tool symbolizing the extension of human limbs emerged at the right time, and along with human development, the general category of tools is constantly enriched.

2 GETTING STARTED

2.1 Problems of short distance transportation tools

The transporting process of cargo includes the following procedures: loading cargo, bundling cargo, delivering cargo, untying bundles and unloading cargo, and the main problems existed are:

1. Problems Caused by the Tools to Users
   Impact on the users caused by transportation tools mainly presents on the operating of porters, major problems are as follows: the inconvenience of loading and unloading goods; the low position of handlebars, causing the uneasy of griping; the inconvenience of taking a break halfway; the hardness of controlling speed, when coming to a downhill, if a person push heavy goods, it will be difficult to walk; the trouble of tying and untying the goods, and the main way of tying is by a single rope; the

bothering of washing; the insecurity of cargo handling process; handlebars is too low, not conducive to grip; and the increasing difficulty of transporting goods up and down stairs.

2. Problems Existed in Transportation Tools Themselves
   Problems existed in transportation tools themselves mainly show in their internal structures, belonging to internal factors. These include: most transportation tools are bulky, heavy weighted; not pretty in modeling, single color, and with no unified image; slow, lacking flexibility; with no brakes, uneasy to operate when climbing and descending, the safety parameter is not high; the design of the handlebars are not humane; the corners are too stiff, and people easily get hurt; with no automatic loading and unloading cargo device; after delivering goods, too much parking space is occupied, and the space can not be reduced; the body of transportation tool has no warning alert device (parts or color); its body is constructed mostly bare steel welding, basically no painting, and rusty; no device, when loading and unloading cargo, to prevent the collision and deformation, absorb shock, or resist skid; technical material and standard is low, material is not environmentally friendly, lacking mobility in using process.

3. Environmental Impacts of Transportation Tools
   Transportation tools as an essential element of the business environment, while they have inherent problems, and also have some impacts on the external environment. The main problems to the environment are: most transportation tools with no unified plan, and the style is very old and unsightly, so they greatly influence

the appearance of the city; most handle tools' volume is large, inconvenient to place, and they can be seen at sidewalks, roads and anywhere, occupying a large amount of public space; transportation tools are slow and inflexible, which often leads to traffic jam (The writer learned in the investigation, in Lusong business district, Zhuzhou, there is an average of at least four times daily traffic jams), increasing traffic pressure on the city.

4. Problems of Transportation Tools at Different Time

There are a series of problems associated with handling tools in different using time, and the details are as follows: danger to pedestrians and vehicles when driving at night and there is a lack of the necessary lighting and warning device; lacking the necessary rain cover equipment impacts on people and goods at rainy day; can not reduce fatigue effectively of porters who are having a rest, because there is no necessary device for drinking water.

2.2 The problems analysis and improvement ideas of short distance transportation tools

According to the general method of "problem-solving theory", the stage of analyzing problem is the understanding of its essential characteristics, and it is the key step to solve the problem. Human is the research object of product design, and the goods is the creation. The essence of design is to improve products according to the way of people's life, and its study is the combination of the study of people and products.

1. The Analysis and Improvement Ideas to the Design Object—Transportation Tools

The design object, from the perspective of designer, is namely product. As a kind of product, transportation tool, the same as other products, has various internal factors which influence design. These internal factors including function, structure, material, power, color, human engineering, and several other aspects of the product, as Table 1.

Table 1. The problems and improvement ideas of handling tool.

Elements	The problems existed	The improvement ideas
Function elements	①No unload and braking functions; ②Low speed, uneasy to control, lack flexibility in use; ③No equipment to prevent collision and deformation, absorb shock, or resist skid; ④The main power is the power of people, (electricity, new energy etc. can be considered); ⑤There is no anti-theft function;	①Foldable, stretchable, angular transformation etc, setting emergency brake system; ②The frame type, folding and dismountable (Convenient for loading and unloading cargo), set the controlling and speed regulating device; ③Increase the collision and deformation prevention, shock absorption, anti-skid function; ④Add other power, reduce the human power; ⑤Increase the anti-theft alarm device;
Structure elements	①The grip and hold design is not humane enough, it is inconvenient to grasp and grip, handlebar is too low to hold, it is not convenient to push and pull; ②High shock rate of wheel has effects on goods, the uneven stress leading to the rollover; ③Without necessary device when bundling; ④Inconvenience of Cleaning; ⑤No device assisting to go upstairs, no component to display kettle; ⑥The parking space is too large, so the placing space can not be reduced, and the placing area cannot be adjusted;	①Set up anti-skid structure (body handle), install push and pull handlebar design; ②Improved wheel (flush bonding) avoid wheels friction and bond with the large cargo, let the whole body bear stress by increasing the load-bearing area, to reduce rollover; ③Hooks are added at the edge of tool (convenient to fix rope); ④Detachable for cleaning; ⑤Increase the sliding resistance device for upstairs and the kettle is placed at the edge of the tool; ⑥Using the design of foldable, removable, and compassable, and device which can set the mutual combination (Different positions, different functions);
Material elements	①The corners are too stiff, and people easily get hurt; constructed mostly bare steel welding, basically no painting, rusty; ②Tools are large and heavy weighted; ③Technical material and standard is low, material is not environmentally friendly; ④The selection of the handlebar material;	①The alloy can be applied to replace common iron materials, so as to reduce the weight, and not easy to rust; ②Using the folding, light weighted materials, environmentally friendly and recyclable, lighter, greater bearing capacity; ③Using new and environmental protection materials; ④Adopt anti-sweat and anti-slip material for the handlebar;
Color elements	①The style is not pretty, single color, no unified image; ②No color warning device in handling process.	①Bright color, pure color series, unified image recognition; ②The body of tool should add bright yellow warning line.

The internal problems of handling tool analyzed above are from the aspects of function, structure, material, power, color and user-machine, and then, the improvement ideas and methods for these problems are put forward. The writer designed this transportation tool as Figure 1. In this design the aspects of handling tool color, shape and user-machine elements are mainly considered.

2. The analysis and improvement ideas of handling tool in different time and environment
According to the feature of the problem which existed in handling tool in different time and environment mentioned above, the writer proposed the following improvement ideas, as Table 2.

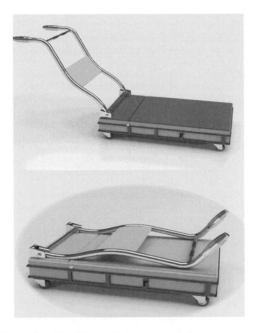

Figure 1.   Handling tools improving design.

Figure 2.   Telescopic upright handling tools.

Table 2.   The problems and improvement ideas of handling tool in different time and environment.

External factors	The problems existed	The improvement ideas
Time factor	①It is not convenient when driving at night because there is a lack of necessary lighting device; ②Lacking the necessary rain cover equipment which has influences on people and goods at rainy day; ③No warning and reminding device, which is danger to pedestrians and vehicles when driving; ④There is no necessary device for drinking water to reduce fatigue effectively of porters who are having a rest;	①Using fluorescence (easy to identify, and avoid unnecessary collisions with motor vehicles at night) or night lighting device; ②Designing shielding parts, working as sun visor in the sunny day, and umbrella in the rainy days; ③Designing sound or color warning, reminding around pedestrian to give way in order to avoid accident; ④Designing a block for rest, and certain storage space to store water etc;
Environment factor	①Most handle tools' volume is large, inconvenient to place, occupying a large amount of public space; ②Transportation tools are slow and inflexible, which often leads to traffic jam, increasing traffic pressure on the city; ③Most transportation tools with no unified plan, and the style is very old and unsightly, so they greatly influence the appearance of the city.	①The think of using foldable, hanging, removable, compostable and scalable methods etc. to reduce the space occupation; ②Design of specific acceleration and deceleration device, so as to control easier; ③Uniform color, keep harmony with the environment, unify visual image, coordinate volume, size, measure.

Based on the impacts of transportation tools on environment and improvement ideas of handling tool in different time, the writer designed a scalable and upright placed handling tool shown as Figure 2.

3 CONCLUSION

According to the analysis above, from the sides of product (handling tool), user (porter), and operating environment etc., this design mainly improved the following aspects: firstly, to ameliorate its impacts on the environment (blocking traffic, occupying the sidewalk and public space etc.), from the size, volume, size and quality of handling tool, the ideas such as using foldable, hanging, removable, compassable and scalable etc. are applied; secondly, considering about the use of handling tool, the convenience of use is increased, and the handle tool is more light, more environmentally friendly, more beautiful, more humane, and more convenient for loading and unloading; lastly, emphasizing form follows function, unnecessary decoration and other components are removed, extravagance is reduced, accidents is decreased, cost is cut down etc. Porter is the user of handling tool, and they belong to the low income earners of city. Designers should improve the problems in the use of this product based on the decrease in design cost. So that this can not only reduce the economic burden of porters, but also solve the current problem of transportation tools.

ACKNOWLEDGMENT

This article is a Humanities and Social Science funded project of Ministry of Education in China, project label: 13YJC760116.

REFERENCES

[1] Zhong Zhixian. *A Problem Solving Theory [J]. Distance Education*, 2005, 18(1):p38.
[2] Xu Yingting. *Research on Problem-oriented Creative Design Process* edited by Package Engineering, 2009, 30(6):p105–107.
[3] Zhang Zongdeng. *Re-discusses the Objective of Design* edited by Journal of Zhengzhou University of Light Industry, 2009(4):p33–34.
[4] Zeng Shan, Guan Huiyuan. *Research on the Complexity Problems of Ergonomics* edited by Package Engineering, 2011, 32(4):p88–91.
[5] Liu Zheng, Sun Shouqian. *Determined Element of Product Design Cognitive Strategies and Its Applications in Design* edited by China Mechanical Engineering, 2007, 18(23):p3–7.
[6] Kruger C, Cross N. *Solution Driven Versus Problem Driven Design: Strategies and Outcomes* edited by Design Studies, 2006, 127(5):p527–548.
[7] Zhang Hongying, Zhang Zongdeng. *Geometric Shape Applying to Modern Furniture Design* edited by Packaging Journal, 2011, 3(6):p81–84.
[8] Bryan L. Decode Design: *How to Think of Designers* edited by Yang Xiaodong Translate. Beijing: China Machine Press, 2008, p88–89.

Computer, Intelligent Computing and Education Technology – Liu, Sung & Yao (Eds)
© 2014 Taylor & Francis Group, London, ISBN 978-1-138-02469-4

Analysis of industry-university-institute cooperation from network perspective—a case study of Honyar

L. Mei
School of Public Affairs, Zhejiang University, Hangzhou, China

ABSTRACT: The article analyzes the industry-university-institute cooperation of Honyar from the network perspective. By using "diamond-amber model", it argues in the context of network, traditional analytical model of industry-university-institute cooperation should take into account role of government, financial institutions and intermediary service organizations and pay attention to interaction between them, to promote practice of industry-university-institute cooperation and innovation emergence on network level.

Keywords: industry-university-institute cooperation; diamond-amber model; Honyar company

1 INTRODUCTION

The "National Eleventh Five-Year Plan" puts indigenous innovation into an important strategic position. It emphasizes the importance of original innovation capability, integrated innovation capability and the capability of introduction-absorption and re-innovation, and also advocates clearly the establishment of a business-based, market oriented, and industry-university-institute integrated technological innovation system. Under the background of globalization and networking era, no business is an island (Hakansson, 1989). Duo to the complexity of technology and environment, innovation becomes more and more difficult, networks of collaborative relationships among firms and other institutions are widely recognized as an important organization form of innovative activities (Orsenigo, Pammolli & Riccaboni, 2001). A company should cooperate with university, research institute and so on, interaction between universities and industry is seen as a strategy to strengthen innovation in the economy (Thune, 2007).

The conventional industry-university-institute cooperation is based on the actors—industry, university and research institute—and their cooperation. There is an increasing awareness of the lack of this narrow understanding from researches and practices and we should introduce more extensive cooperation. As the comparison from China top ten university-industry coopertation cases of 2006 and 2008 on scientific and technological innovation, industry-university-institute cooperation gradually develops from "point-to-point model" such as cooperative development, commission development and R&D collaborative construction to "point-to-chain model" and "network model" that the public technological innovation platform is built by multi-actors to drive the integration of industry-university-institute (Chen Jian'an, 2009).

Therefore, this article analyzes industry-university-institute cooperation from the network perspective. By using the diamond-amber model, it discusses industry-university-institute cooperation condition of Hangzhou Honyar Company.

2 THE CONNOTATION OF INDUSTRY UNIVERSITY-INSTITUTE FROM THE NETWORK PERSPECTIVE

Different scholars give definition of the industry-university-institute connotation. Taran Thune indicates university-industry collaboration is a tie formation where knowledge-intensive firms' strategic needs for new knowledge and universities's need for research funding creats interdependence (Thune, 2007). Yuan Shengjun indicates that industry-university-institute cooperation is a useful method to achieve the superior resources integration of firms, universities and research institutes (Yuan S.J. et al. 2006). Zhu Guilong indicates that industry-university-institute cooperation is a cooperation for market demand and common interests, which includes economic cooperative activies like R&D, production, marketing, consultation services on the basis of the advantage complementary principle and market economic mechanism (Zhu G.L., 2003). Zhang Yongan indicates that it refers to a series of development or operation activities that under the market demand and common interest, firms, univeristies and research institutes do research, technical development, production, market exploitation according to their own resources (Zhang Y.A., 2008). Chen Chunang discusses industry-university-institute cooperation innovation and indicates that it is a cooperation mechanism for firms, universities and research institute to realize their own value (Chen C.Y., 2008). As the discussion of connotation above, the conventional connotation of industry-university-institute cooperation mainly refers to the three actors and cooperation relationship is market demand oriented and common interests oriented to realize the complementary of resources. However, under the network perspective, the range of actors involved in innovation is expanded. Researches also pay attention to the role of government, intermediary organizations and financial institutions. Xu Qiang argues that industry-university-institute cooperation should consider the role of government (Xu Q., 2008). Chen Shijun indicates that the connotation of industry-university-institute cooperation should also include the influences of government, intermediary organizations and financial institutions and so on (Chen S.J. 2008). Wu Wei develops the connotation of general industry-university-institute cooperation which is known as "industry-university-institute-government-finance cooperation" (Wu W., 2007). Under the discussion above, this article considers that the connotation of industry-university-institute cooperation from network perspective is in line with Wu Wei's definition. Under his definition, the connotation of industry-university-institute cooperation refers to four aspects: first, actors of industry-university-institute cooperation include firms, universities, research institutes, government, financial institutions and intermediary organizations; Second, industry-university-institute cooperation is a innovation system composed of all the actors (Zhu G.L., 2003); Third, industry-university-institute cooperation includes all cooperative and exchange activities for industry, academia and research community to achieve the common innovation goal (Hua W.Y., 2008); Finally, industry-university-institute cooperation must be market-oriented (Zhu G.L., 2003).

3 ANALYZING OF INDUSTRY-UNIVERSITY-INSTITUTE COOPERATION FROM NETWORK PERSPECTIVE

3.1 Model initiation

Hakansson first indicates that the basic elements of network include actors, activities and resources (Hakansson, 1987). From the network perspective,

actors (network nodes) of industry-university-institute cooperation contain firms, universities, research institutes, government, financial institutions and intermediary organizations; Activities refer to knowledge, technology and information flows within an actor or between actors and corresponding transactions in network (Wu W., 2007); Resources are composed of available capital, material basis and human resource condition that network members can use in innovation cooperation process. By cooperation, network members contact each other to make use of resources effectively and achieve innovation emergence. However, the model proposed by Hakansson does not in-depth reflect the dynamic mechanism of contact between actors (network nodes). Chen Shijun (2007) proposes a "diamond-amber model" (see Fig. 1) from cooperation dynamics perspective, which represents the function and linkage dynamic mechanism of network nodes in the situation of China.

3.2 Analyzing of nodes and their linkages

In the diamond-amber model, industry denotes firms and institute denotes research institutes. Firms are principal sector of innovative activities, which directly connect the market, gain profits from products and services and creat value for customers; University and research institutes engage in knowledge, technology creation and personnel training, which are basic for the transformation of science and technology to productivity; Intermediary organizations refer to talent exchange market, talent agency, productivity center, various types

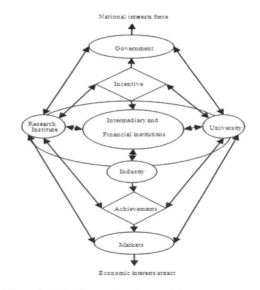

Figure 1. The diamond-amber model.

of incubators, consulting firms and so on, which mainly provide information support for enterprises to develop innovative activities (Hakansson, 1987). Financial institutions which include innovation funds, venture capital firms, state-owned or commercial banks and securities market, provide financial supports for enterprises' innovative activities (Wu W., 2007). Government here provides effective policy supports and some capital supports. It becomes the defender of innovative environment and helps enterprises improve capability of searching market information and innovation capbility through technology, talent deployment and management support.

The effective establishment of industry-university-institute cooperation from network perspective not only requires network nodes play individual role, but also require synergy of them to achieve sustainable innovation. The shorter product life cycles, diversification of customer demand, development of new technologies make a single enterprise more difficult to respond to market-oriented activities. In order to gain competitive advantage, they need service and investment supports from intermediary organizations and financial institutions, and rely on technical supports from universities and research institutes to realize product and technology development and application. For firms, universities and research institutes to achieve their common interests, they rely on their products and push products into market to generate innovation and profit return. In addtion, cooperation realizes the interaction of knowledge, technology and market, which not only promotes the application of scientific and technological achievements but also promotes the spread of tacit knowledge by the movement of personnel; For intermediaries and financial institutions, they obtain profits through information, funds support; Government on one hand encourages actors of industry-university-institute cooperation network by certain policy incentives to play a better role and on the other balances the whole interests from national level to coordinate the arrangement of resouces and policy support efforts.

4 CASE OF HANGZHOU HONYAR COMPANY

Hangzhou Honyar Electric Appliance Co., Ltd., a state-controlled unit, was established in 1984. It belongs to the China Putian Group and grows with more than 20 years of professional production of various types of building power distribution products. At present, Honyar is famous for building electrical products production in China and also becomes application engineering business model of National 863 Program CIMS (Computer Integrated Manufacturing System). The main business products are involved in industry of electrical machinery and equipment manufacturing. As the development of national economy, electrical machinery and equipment manufacturing industry has experienced rapid growth and structural transformation. Take the statistics of electrical machinery and equipment manufacturing industry in 2008 as an example, the three quarters of Gross Industrial Output Value growth of electrical machinery and equipment manufacturing industry are 27.16%, 29.09% and 27.07%, Ratio of Total Assets to Industrial Output Value of Industrial Enterprises above Designated Size is 14.55%, Proportion of Products Sold is 97.42% which is up to 98.13% in Zhejing Province. The statistics shows that electrical machinery and equipment manufacturing industry develops well and is on relatively high level in manufacturing industries. Industry environment provides the basis for the development of enterprise.

After decades of growth, now Honyar forms a relatively complete five pillar industries of "Honyar electrician", "Honyar Power Tube Industry", "Honyar smart", "Honyar lighting" and "Honyar cable". About the product R&D, Honyar lives in the forefront of industry. It was awarded "the High-tech Research and Development Center of Hangzhou" in 2004, "National Accredited Laboratories" in 2005, the title of "Enterprise Technology Center" and "Innovation Advantage Enterprise" in 2006, "China Red Star Design Award" and "the Provincial High-tech R&D Center" in 2007 and "Provincial Science and Technology Progress Award" in 2008. As a representative of the electrical industry in Zhejiang Province, Honyar treats innovation as the driving force for sustainable development of enterprises. Through scientific and technological progress and indigenous innovation, the company's performance maintains 20%–30% annual growth rate. And while promoting the total innovation strategy (Mei L., 2009), the establishment of industry-university-institute cooperation and innovation network play an important role.

In recent years, Honyar has completed the primitive accumulation. The level of informationization continues to improve and it gradually becomes the industry leader. With the increasing diversity of market demand, gradual reduction of the production cycle, Honyar pays more attention to the establishment of cooperation networks outside and considers industry-university-institute cooperation as an important business mean to build innovation networks. Table 1 summarizes industry-university-institute cooperation events of Honyar from 2005–2011.

Table 1. Industry-university-institute cooperation events of Honyar from 2005–2011.

Content	Actors	Cooperation mode	Details
Purchase agreement	TongCe Estate. Honyar	Inter-firms cooperation	Installation, procurement and distribution of Low-voltage equipment (low-voltage cables, switches, wall pipes and so on)
Market-management cooperative agreement	Vietnam KOVA company and Honyar	Inter-firms cooperation	Honyar's semi-finished products are sold in Vietnam and KOVA company assembles them to sale in Vietnam In addition. Honyar provide KOVA with total solution on product R&D production management marketing
Industry cooperation summit	Guangzhou Electric Research Institute. Honyar. Panasonic corporation. TCL-Legrand corporation	Physical mode of industry-university-institute cooperation	Compare notes of joint ventures, business operation, production and management experience, sum up experience of the brand and core competence, build and sign cooperation plans
Information platform and marketing network construction	Alibaba, Honyar and intermediary organizations	Virtual mode of industry-university-institute cooperation	Professional website development. e-commerce building, development of online store and online market
Creative fair	Industry experts, business representatives	Market traction mode of industry-university-institute cooperation	Cooperation: sharing on product line, information knowledge and technology
New materials and R&D projects	Zhejiang University. research institutes. Honyar. Science and Technology Agency	Market traction mode and base mode of industry-university-institute cooperation	"PA6/ABS alloy development and application" project Establishing "joint laboratory of Zhejiang University and Honyar"
R&D cooperative projects	Technology Bureau of Hangzhou. Zhejiang Commerce University. Zhejiang Science and Technology School. Zhejiang University	Market traction mode of industry-university-institute cooperation	"Manufacturing flexible distribution system-basing on Machine Vision for Autonomous Vehicles" project
Information system project of industrial enterprises	Hangzhou Economic Commission. Development and Reform Bureau. Zhejiang University. banks. Enterprise Information Techology Service Center. 52 Research Institute of China Electronics Group	Market traction mode and virtual mode of industry-university-institute cooperation	"Online collaborative construction of virtual enterprise basing on modern management techniques and computer communication technology" project
Innovation research project	Hangzhou Economic Commission. Development and Reform Bureau. Zhejiang Universtiy. Bank Enterprise Information Technology Service Centrer. 52 Research Institute of China Electronics Group	Market traction mode of industry-university-institute cooperation	Research on a multi-function testing machine which is based on a rotary switch on test accessories
Creative design competition	Enterprises. universities in Hangzhou Intellectual Property Bureau	Techno-Park mode of industry-university-institute cooperation	"HonyarCup" creative Hangzhou architectural design competition to establish cooperation platform for integration of ideas
Establishing academica Center	Enterprises. Research institutes. Universities in Hangzhou	Base mode of industry-university-institute cooperation	Establishment of business and industrial R&D platform

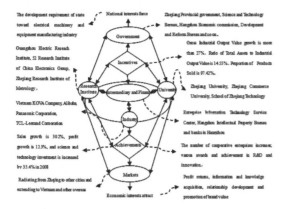

Figure 2.   The diamond-amber model based on Honyar's industry-university-institute cooperation.

Based on the summary of Table 1, this article constructs the diamond-amber model Hangzhou Honyar's industry-university-institute coopera- tion, shown in Figure 2.

Under the analysis framework of "diamond- amber model", the condition of industry- university-institute cooperation of Honyar is shown comprehensively. As seen in Figure 2, the cooperative actors of Honyar is no longer limited to traditional upstream and downstream firms and research institutes which support production, however, under the guidance of market demand, the actors of industry-university-institute coop- eration of Honyar refer to firms, universities, research institutes, government, intermediary serv- ice organizations and financial institutions. These actors interact each other and constitute an syn- ergistic network of industry-university-institute cooperation.

5   CONCLUSION

The article analyzes industry-university-institute cooperation from the network perspective. It discusses the industry-university-institute coop- eration of Hangzhou Honyar Company by using the "diamond-amber model". As the extension of future study, we should explore the research problems like interaction mechanism of coopera- tive actors, mode selection of industry-university- institute cooperation and further track the cooperation condition of Honyar. The establish- ment of industry-university-institute cooperation model from network perspective and analyzing of cooperative actors and their linkages help to

promote industry-university-institute cooperation, provide development proposals to Hangzhou Honyar and other companies, enhance cooperative actors' innovation capability and ultimately stimu- late innovation emergence on network level.

REFERENCES

Chen Chunyang, "Specific Forms, Characteristics and Development Trends of Industry-University-Institute Cooperation of China," Industrial Technology and Economy, vol. 27(6), pp. 24–27, 2008.
Chen Jian'an. (2009, September 2). "Reflection from China top ten university-industry coopertation cases of 2006 and 2008," from http://iurchina.whu.edu.cn/ news/llqy/cxypj/2009-09-02/367.html.
Chen Shijun and Liu Zhou, "Diamond-amber Model of Industry-University-Institute Cooperation and Its Inspiration," Science of Science and Management of S.&T., vol. 29(2), pp. 14–18, 2008.
Chi Renyong. Theory and Practice of SMEs' Innovation Network. Beijing: Science Press, 2009.
Hakansson H. Industrial technological development: a network approach. London: Groom Helm,1987.
Hakansson. H, and Snehota. I, "No Business is an Island: The Network Concept of Business Strategy," Scandi- navian Journal of Management, vol. 5, pp. 187–200, 1989.
Hua Wenying, "Strategy Design of Industry-University- Institute Cooperation," China Scienceand Technology Information, vol. 2, pp. 236–239, 2008.
Orsenigo L., F. Pammolli and Massimo Riccaboni, "Technological change and network dynamics Les- sons from the pharmacrutical industry," Research Policy, vol. 30(3), pp. 485–508, 2001.
Taran Thune, "University-industry collaboration: the network embeddedness approach," Science and Public Policy, vol. 34(3), pp. 158–168, 2007.
Wu Wei and Chen Liping, "To Analyse and to Construct of the Cooperative Innovation Networks of Industry- University-Research Institution Network," Value Engineering, vol. 26(1), pp. 32–35, 2007.
Xu Qiang and Ge Limin, "Comparative Cases Analysis of Foreign Government-Industry- University-Insti- tute Cooperation," Economic Tribune, vol. 19, pp. 90–93, 2008.
Yuan Shengjun, Huang Liping and Liu Zhongying, "The Problems and Solutions Analysis on the University- Industry Cooperation," Scientific Management Research, vol. 24(6), pp. 49–52, 2006.
Zhang Yong'an and Zhang Meng, "Innovation Mode of Industry-University-Institute Cooperation of China," Chinese University Technology Transfer, vol. 7, pp. 28–31, 2008.
Zhu Guilong and Peng Youfu, "The Research on Organi- zation Mode and Operation Mechanism of Innova- tion Network in Cooperation of Industry University and Research Institute," Soft Science, vol. 17(4), pp. 49–52, 2003.

Computer, Intelligent Computing and Education Technology – Liu, Sung & Yao (Eds)
© 2014 Taylor & Francis Group, London, ISBN 978-1-138-02469-4

Enterprise Intranet management system

Chun-Mei Du, Chang-Ming Dai & Xiao-Jun Xu
Hebei University of Architecture, Zhangjiakou, Hebei, China

ABSTRACT: This paper introduces the application of network management system of enterprise development situation and background, and then established the enterprise internal management network system. This system is divided into two major modules, a leading management module, the other is a staff use module. Through this system can greatly improve the automation of enterprise management.

Keywords: Intranet; management system; module; enterprise, enterprise

1 INTRODUCTION

With the development of the Internet, e-commerce has become an important foundation of enterprise management [1]. E-commerce is a network era, is the product of modern network technology, computer technology and communication technology and combining traditional business mode of crystallization [2]. E-commerce can quickly adapt to the changing market, along with the change of the market adjusting its business strategy, in the shortest possible time to adapt to new change means can occupy the market one-upmanship, wins the customer [3].

According to the use of network to the type of classification, e-commerce mainly divided into: based on EDI networks based on Internet, e-commerce and e-business, network based on one (enterprise Intranet) network of electronic commerce [4]. This paper mainly studies enterprise Intranet management system. Intranet management system based on the Internet is a enterprise internal management operation for sharing information, provide decision support, project management and cost control system. It can strengthen the communication between the colleague, improve work efficiency, regulating the work flow, the control project progress and timely summaries in financial and other important information on the basis of the points that managers can effectively obtain prediction and decision support, make enterprise entered modern scientific management, in the market competition advantage [5].

2 SYSTEM DESIGN

2.1 *System design goal*

The design of the enterprise Intranet management system mainly realizes the following goals.

Workflow management: to design a highly automated, work schedule and work report of the examination and approval process control system. Through this system, make it clear division of work, does not happen again due to convey the delay caused by link.

Project management: the system makes the enterprise managers can master the schedule of business enterprise at present, performance appraisal, guiding the work.

Information sharing: to improve internal information flow velocity, the realization enterprise internal information knowledge comprehensive and effective communication and sharing.

Other daily management: can effectively improve the enterprise internal office work efficiency, fully embodies the efficient internal management.

2.2 *System function module design*

Based on the target system of function module design are as follows:

1. Employees submit for higher self summary notation;
2. Company staff, to deliver timely aware of company operation;
3. Company staff, to deliver timely aware of company operation;
4. Fully automatic and not for others view of personal logbooks;
5. All company customer resources storage, products and customer contact material.

2.3 *Product order details*

The departments and personnel management and add online; Working experience in communication and discussion.

According to the above functions are divided into two module system, i.e. ordinary users

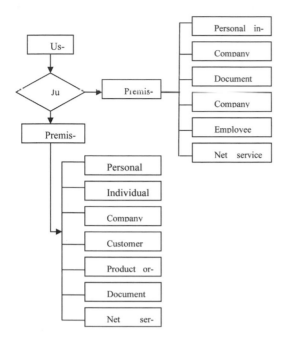

Figure 1.   Main function modules.

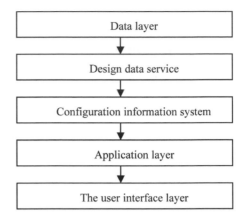

Figure 2.   System framework.

module and advanced users module, through in the program of the size of the setting permissions. Permissions for greater than or equal to three of the ordinary. The main function modules, as shown in Figure 1.

3   DATABASE DESIGN

This system USES SQL Server2000 as a database management system. According to the function of the system, including the development of four basic database table, each basic table and contains a tall information.

1. Personnel data tables: including management information data, the corporate sector, company staff information data table.
2. Experience exchange data table: including exchange of experience and restore data topics.
3. Company work tables: include the company summary information, company product orders, customers, they conclude, etc.
4. Company website basic information data table: include the company name, company website url, etc.

3.1   Detailed design

This system is use ASP and SQL Server with Macromedia Dreamweaver8.0 for development.

The detailed design, including website design system login design etc. This system USES data from the application layer to the user interface layer. Overall structure is shown in Figure 2:

3.2   Web design

The Active Server mix (ASP) is server-side scripting writing environment, use it can create and dynamic, interactive [6]. Can use ASP script commands HTML pages, combined with the creation of the components interact with ActiveX Web pages and based on the Web's powerful application.

3.3   Advanced users and general user

Advanced users include company general manager, vice President and general manager assistant, senior user login system can enter personal information management module, the company business module, document circulated module, company management module, staff management module, this service module. Besides the advanced users other position for the staff, general average users have access to such record after the user.

4   CONCLUSIONS

The continuous and steady development of network to our country electronic commerce environment improvement, the foundation. In the modern enterprise, the Intranet information management will play more and more important role, a highly efficient and practical Intranet system for enterprise. Company adopts the network management of enterprise, many employees in management of the dynamic information, add, delete, modify, On the other hand, it can be employees from daily affairs liberates, improving the internal operation efficiency and quality. E-commerce sites use, can reduce the cost, improve efficiency, enhance the competitiveness of enterprises, Also increased automation degree of the enterprise management.

ACKNOWLEDEMENT

This project won the 2013 Hebei Institute of Architecture and Civil Engineering youth fund support, thanks.

REFERENCES

Bao Rong. 2002. Based on the three-layer structure of Web courses of study and realize FuDaoZhan [D] *nanjing university,* 53–55.
ChenLin. Based on B/S and C/S mode of hybrid library invoicing system design and implementation [D] east China normal university, 2002.
Dong Yong Jian. 2008 Unicom customer relationship management system in some problems. east *China normal university.*
Jiao Fangyuan, 2006.5 The electronic commerce network in the shortest route to search a simple method, *CAAC flight college journals,* 121–123.
Shi Yong, 2007.5 Based on the electronic commerce environment in China enterprise ERP implementation and management, *Modern mall,* 22: 50–52.
Xie, X.K. 1981. *Modern control theoretical Basis.* Shenyang: Liaoning People Publisher. 12–13.
Xie, X.K. 1981. *Modern control theoretical Basis.* Shenyang: Liaoning People Publisher.
Zhao, Mingzhan. 2005. Generalized kalman filter signal modeling for airborne targets. *Aircraft Design.* 4: 77–80.
Zhao, Mingzhan. 2005. The research of the minimum mean square error of the generalized Kalman filter. *Journal of Shenyang Institute of Aeronautical Engineering.* 22: 47–49.
Zhao, Mingzhan. 2006. Deductive proof of generalized kalman filter recursive formula. *Journal of Shenyang Institute of Aeronautical Engineering.* 23: 82–84.
Zhao, W.C. 2007. Parameter varying generalized kalman filter based on generalized linear model. *Control Engineering of China.* 14: 21–23.
Zhao Wentao, Chang Hongxing. 2008.(02) Asp.net based on B/S architecture project management system of network security pattern design [J]. Computer science.

Computer, Intelligent Computing and Education Technology – Liu, Sung & Yao (Eds)
© 2014 Taylor & Francis Group, London, ISBN 978-1-138-02469-4

The reformation and innovation of the course of comprehensive environmental experiments oriented by the work process

Fang Liu, Li-Hai Zhou & Wei Jin
Environmental Management College of China (EMCC), Qinhuangdao, China

ABSTRACT: Through positions of the professional environmental engineering and technology research, and analysis of typical tasks, identify areas of study, learning environment and integrated use of various teaching methods and tools, design mission of professional skills and the curriculum reform of comprehensive quality and effective promotion methods were designed.

Keywords: fields of study; learning environment; teaching methods

Comprehensive environment experimental is a professional offering experimental courses for all environments categories. This course consists of water quality monitoring, sewage treatment, air monitoring and control experiment, noise monitoring and management of laboratory and other components. It is one of the core courses of environmental engineering and technologies, environmental monitoring and control technologies, environmental industries and equipment, environmental planning and management, environmental monitoring and other majors. This course is a very strong technical and practical courses which is established under the demands of cultivation of environmental talents, it will be learned after students finish the study of theoretical learning and hands-on learning of water pollution control and treatment, air pollution control and treatment, environmental monitoring and so on. Its focus is different because of different majors. Well completion of comprehensive environmental experiments course teaching has important implications for enhance the environment students' employability. Currently, this courses is not strong at courses system, teaching methods, such as teaching mainly rely on teaching units, poor comprehensive, contaction with practical work is not enough and so on. In order to train more technical talents to adapt to market demand, improve the course system and comprehensive, this article uses environmental engineering and technology major as an example, relys on the comprehensive experimental environment of the National Excellent Course platform, references to the curriculum development method of Germany learning field, and finally reforms and innovates the coures according to the design method based on working process.

1 ANALYSIS ON ENVIRONMENTAL ENGINEERING AND TECHNOLOGY JOBS

The main content of this investigation includes the production technology and process of the companies, the main environmental position and the corresponding personnel, the main contents and tasks, the environmental technology, work norms, standards and methods, the quality requirements and occupation abilities for the environmental practitioners.

The results of the investigation show that technical talents of environmental technology are in short supply for the moment. Environmental engineering and technology students of Environmental Management College of China (EMCC) have solid basic knowledge, they have got approval and favorable comment of the employing companies for their mastery condition of professional knowledge of water, atmosphere, noise and so on. But, at the same time, the companies pointed out that the students lack the abilities of comprehensive analysis and their adaptation is not strong, generally they lack practical work experience.

We can see from the results that jobs for graduates of environmental engineering and technology mainly include: sewage treatment facilities in operation, waste gas treatment facilities operation, environment monitoring, indoor gas detection, environmental protection equipment installation commissioning and sales. Among them, the operation of sewage treatment facilities management operator, is one of the main jobs of environmental engineering and technology professional employment, the job description as shown in Table 1.

Table 1. Running wastewater treatment facility operator job description.

Major name	Position	Work task	Professional ability
Environmental engineering and technology specialty	Sewage treatment equipment operation management operator	1. Sewage treatment equipments operation and maintenance management 2. Sludge treatment and disposal	1. The ability to install, debug all kinds of sewage treatment equipments; 2. Various types of sewage treatment equipments operation and management ability; 3. The ability of monitor water-quality index; 4. Have the knowledge of environmental microorganisms; 5. The ability of analyze and solve failure process in operation according to the monitoring data.

2 DETERMINE THE LEARNING FIELD

Based on the analysis of the results of post operation of sewage treatment equipment operation management operator and practice conditions, determine the operation of the sewage treatment facilities for typical tasks, and as a basis for determining the learning field.

Field of study:wastewater treatment facility operation and management, second term of the second grade, recommended duration is 120 class hours.

2.1 Target description

- Familiar with the basic process flow, wastewater treatment works, process the basic unit of structure and function
- Master monitoring methods, principle and steps of parameters and indexes of wastewater treatment system
- Have a certain degree of basic knowledge of sewage treatment equipments operation
- Master the sludge sources, methods of sludge conditioning and sludge treatment equipment maintenance and management
- Familiar with excess sludge pump, dispensing device, performance, operation and maintenance technology of dewatering room
- Have the ability of data processing and analysis, and can independently write complete monitoring reports.

2.2 Content description

- The basic technological methods, process and working principle of sewage treatment
- Collection of sewage treatment process sample: sample collection, sample collection of sewage sludge

- Determination of water quality index (COD_{Cr}, BOD_5, ammonia nitrogen and total phosphorus, etc) and the preparation of the monitoring reports
- Determination of process parameters of activated sludge process: the sludge concentration, sludge settlement ratio etc
- Analysis and solve the common problems in the process of operation of sewage treatment equipments
- Maintenance and management of operation of sludge treatment equipments.

3 DESIGN OF LEARNING ENVIRONMENT

According to the study field of content, practice conditions and the actual work set conditions, the existing comprehensive environment experimental content has been combinationed. Use typicality, coverage, comprehensive as the principles, the learning environment is designed, the learning situations corresponding the job of sewage treatment equipments operation and management is constructed, as Figure 1.

Each learning situations depending on the teaching content teaching has one or more than

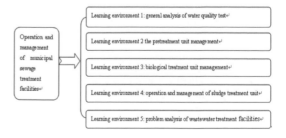

Figure 1. The design of learning situation.

one program tasks, and a program task can consist of several learning situations.

4 TEACHING METHODS

At present, the traditional experimental teaching method basically is that write the experiment purposes, the principle and the procedure on the blackboard, than explained with appropriate presentation by the teachers, and after the teachers emphasize the matters needing attention, then the students will finish the experiment according to the established pattern. Preparation of the whole experiment and the method of design are all set by the teachers, the students operate the experiment according to the requirements of teachers or program instructions. This single teaching method can train students to a certain ability, but it is not good for creativity and independent learning ability of students.

The teaching method of this course include: project teaching method, scene teaching method, simulation teaching method, situational teaching method and so on, these methods can be selected according to the different areas of study. For example, biochemical treatment unit operation management is complex, changeable. In order to enable students to master the ability well, teaching methods in this case will chose project teaching method.

To sewage treatment facilities abnormal phenomenon as an example, in the teaching process, to the sewage treatment plant as the main carrier of teaching, teachers set up sewage treatment device operating system situation, teachers give students one or several sewage treatment case, or the determination of water indicators (such as COD, BOD, DO) experiment, students through analyzing the case, discuss, and discuss how to solve the problems, teachers can give proper guidance. Case teaching method is to cultivate students' ability of analysis and critical thinking skills. At the same time, the introduction of the production line personnel into the campus, the actual production and campus learning organic combination, make the students understand the course of advanced technology. Case teaching method make it difficult to understand the concept of simple, visualized effectively, fully arouse the learning interest and initiative of students, and put forward the problems, to cultivate students' ability to analyze problems, problem-solving and creative thinking.

In the teaching, pay attention to give full play to the positive role of fault setting teaching method and brain storm method of teaching. The formation of students' knowledge and skills is a progressive process from cognitive, imitation to skilled, innovative. Teaching for sewage treatment experimental device existing students, can adjust the amount of water, aeration, sludge recycle flow rate and residual sludge discharge and a series of problems so that the sewage treatment system, such as sludge bulking, floating, floating sludge, foam, stimulates the student to analysis of the reasons, troubleshooting with theoretical knowledge search problem, learned. In fact, these failures are common and personality, is the best material skill training. Causes of failure analysis of the right of some students, the corresponding method that can eliminate the fault, then, failed to exclude the estimation of the students also unwillings to lag behind, to think, to find the correct troubleshooting method. Teachers should grasp this opportunity, in the light of its general trend, guide the inner link between the students how to correct analysis of the related process parameters, process parameters, according to the analysis of process parameters cause failure, troubleshooting and fault. In this guide, to enable the students to accumulate practical experience at the same time, training students to use existing knowledge to analyze and solve problems. Although students encounter "frustration", but this "frustration" is the cornerstone of the success of the chain. At the same time, enhance the mutual interaction between students, strengthen mutual cooperation, improve the occupation accomplishment.

5 CONCLUSION

Through the reform and innovation of "reform and innovation environment experiment course oriented by the work process", learning and working successfully combine together, "learning from working, and working from learning", the concept of teachers and students get change, learning interest of the students get inspired, teaching process in the formed has good interactive, and students enjoy the pleasure from analysis problems and solve the problem of in the process of learning. And students learn how to apply theoretical knowledge into practice, their independent inquisition ability and the innovative spirit have been trained further. Whether as a student of environmental professional or non environment professional students, the role of the reformation and innovation of the course cannot be overlooked. At present, the teaching research which based on the working process is still in its infancy in China, to introduce and popularize this teaching mode in occupation colleges, make it play a positive significance due, we also need to explore and improve in practice constantly.

ACKNOWLEDGEMENTS

This work was supported by the project of Qinhuangdao 2012 science and technology research and development plan (2012023A230).

REFERENCES

Ce Wang. On the combination of working and learning in the teaching of road and bridge construction. Value engineering, (2010): 243.

Houyuan Lu & Xiang Wang & Zhiqing Fan. Analog electronic technology teaching method based on process analysis. Shiyan vocational technical college, 2009, 22 (5): 107–109.

Nuna & Rigen Mo. Traditional disadvantages and reform of organic chemistry experiment teaching model. Journal of Inner Mongolia University for nationalities, 2009, 15 (4): 45–46.

Computer, Intelligent Computing and Education Technology – Liu, Sung & Yao (Eds)
© 2014 Taylor & Francis Group, London, ISBN 978-1-138-02469-4

The study on current situation and countermeasures of developing traditional physical education of minority colleges in China

Fei Wu
School of P.E., Minzu University of China, Beijing, China

ABSTRACT: The current situation of traditional physical education of minority in colleges in China is: 1) in the sports meeting of minority, it develops in college and people exercise; 2) it lacks systematic textbooks and teaching staff, not emphasized in the curriculum of various grades of schools. The suggestions are: policy should be taken to focus on the micro control by the education management offices; some of the PE items of minority, which are easy to apply and full of cultural features, should be emphasized and adopted into the education system; the major of the teaching staff should be improved, so as to ensure the courses; socialization is necessary to take minority PE into the system of national entertainment and form the industry of modern tourism.

Keywords: minority; traditional physical education; development; countermeasure

The traditional Physical Education (PE) of Chinese minority, is the treasure created and developed by the people of minority in the historical development. With the ages passing by, the content of minority PE is extended.[1] How to develop it and exert the value is one of the most important research items for the relevant experts after Beijing Olympic Games. People's spiritual needs, some sports which are suitable for the people of different ages develop in the region of minority. Such sports are part of their entertainment life, such as martial arts teaching and learning organized by martial arts clubs, fans dance, national dance and drum dance, dragon dance, lion dance, Double Ninth climb, dragon boats game etc. All the activities are developed and passed on, as part of the life of minority.[2]

knowledge of history, customs, production, life, economy and culture in that. It is also the combination of sports and nationality dance, folk music, nationality poems.[3] Thus, it is the tendency that traditional PE of minority becomes part of school education. The colleges of minority in China take the traditional PE of minority (Shuttlecock, Wood Ball, Kick ball, Dragon-lion dance, High-stepping Horse, Wrestling among minorities, Spinning Top and so on) class for entertainment, body building and competition. The PE class in colleges is enriched and extended in space and time.

In sum, the traditional PE of minority should be taught and learned in school. It satisfies the need of its development and becomes the product of PE course renovation and development.

1 THE CURRENT SITUATION OF TRADITIONAL PE OF MINORITY IN CHINA

1.1 *Achievements*

1. The traditional PE of minority is one of the most important parts in their life. In the 21st century, with the development of human society and the blending of minor nationalities, the functions of traditional PE of minority develops into multi-dimensions, with more social and practical value.
2. The traditional PE of minority is taught and learned in school courses. There is abundant

1.2 *Problems*

1. The traditional PE of minority does not take a high proportion in curriculum. Nowadays, in the PE curriculum, most of the items are western style, such as track and field, gym, balls etc, which are lacking of connection with Chinese traditional sports. Although the purpose is the same, that is, to develop the health, the traditional style and national features cannot be revealed. Reflecting on the traditional PE of minority, a few of sports items, such as Shuttlecock, Wood Ball, Pearl Ball, Wrestling among minorities, Dragon-lion dance, are played in some of colleges of nationalities, taking up

10% in curriculum (except some colleges and minority schools).[4] In fact, the multi functions of traditional PE of minority accord with that of new curriculum. Therefore, to raise the percentage of traditional PE of minority in PE curriculum is the need of new curriculum and satisfies the requirements of students physical and psychological development.

2. The textbook of traditional PE of minority is not enough.

    In school PE courses, the traditional PE of minority is developed to accord with the principles of human being the center and health being number one, focusing more on students participation and interests.[5] As for the present teaching and learning content of traditional PE of minority, it lacks systematization and consistency, influencing the smooth development of traditional PE of minority in school PE course. At present, some schools set up the PE lesson of Shuttlecock, Pearl Ball, Wrestling among minorities, Martial art. However, most of students have not participate in those sports items before. Thus, the textbook is in urgent need to be edited and modernized.

3. The teaching staff of traditional PE of minority are not in shortage in school. Firstly, it should be realized that the development of traditional PE of minority does not just rely on several teachers in minority schools. There is no doubt that most of teacher in the field of PE should be involved. Secondly, the present situation is that the western sports take the majority so as to bring up the talents of western competing sports. Therefore, the number of talents of traditional PE of minority is insufficient. Finally, school is the cradle of PE and the leading path of traditional PE of minority as well. The quality of teaching staff determines the consistent development of traditional PE of minority. Nevertheless, in most of schools, there is a great shortage of teaching staff in the field of traditional PE of minority. Most of teachers in other fields of PE are lacking of training as well. It shows that in teaching, the example of actions is not on standard, without clear explanations and teaching purpose, which basically influences the development of traditional PE of minority.

2 COUNTERMEASURE TO DEVELOP TRADITIONAL PE OF MINORITY

1. The education management department should strengthen the micro readjustment and control, with the policy to develop traditional PE of minority. The law of PE in PRC says that it is encouraged and supported by the national government that the traditional sports of minority should be explored, sorted out and improved. The PE curriculum in colleges regulated in Education Ministry shows clearly that it is necessary to combine the essence of worldwide sports achievements and traditional PE of minority in China. However, as for the specific policy and laws, it is not published yet. It is suggested that the official government should strengthen the micro readjustment and control, with the micro control to the major form, leading and guiding as the principal method, so as to develop traditional PE of minority well.

2. The core of education should be established to focus on the sports with more cultural features. After the establishment of new China, with the efforts of the Party, government and researchers and relevant working staff of minority, thousands of sports items are exploited, collected and sorted out. It is admitted that we just embark on the education career, with no level development and various problems. Thus, it is required that in the process of developing education, we should follow the truth and tell the truth. According to the regional features, some typical sports items with cultural features and benefit for improving health of students and folk people should be emphasized and built as the core of education. Thirdly, the text book should be systematized and adopted into the standard and formal system of school courses, with the insurance of teaching hours. The major part of traditional PE of minority is not competing. Competing is on the minor position. It focuses on entertainment and body building. If schools choose and reconstruct some minority sports which are adopted into the course system according to the practical situation, the PE course can be enriched greatly. As for those students who are not good at competing sports, the western style sports cannot satisfy the various needs. The main contradiction in PE course is the one between various needs of all the students to join in sports and competing sports taking the major role in PE course. It is suggested that traditional PE of minority should be adopted into the PE course system. Experts and researchers should check and determine the sports on the aspect of skills and sport culture with applicability, readability and renovation. The complete teaching plan and curriculum should be edited as well. Traditional PE of minority should be adopted into the PE course system in school, teaching hours ensured. It is better to carry it out in parallel with other PE courses.

3. It is necessary to construct a high-leveled teaching team and improve the quality and

ability of teaching staff, to ensure the teaching and learning. In June 1995, the outline of people exercise plan passed by national government suggests that: "it is to develop traditional PE of minority and in minority region carry out the sports activities of minority. It is to establish the clubs and societies of minority sports and bring up the talents in the field." It is no doubt that teaching staff are the major topic in PE in schools, as the leaders to develop talents with comprehensive ability. Therefore, it is in urgent need that the teaching staff should improve their ability of teaching and quality.

4. The traditional PE of minority should be socialized and mixed into the entertainment system of the whole people. The traditional PE of minority is favored out of its unique style, rich content and forms, to be an important part of the leisure life. The features such as being healthy, entertainment, being funny, being full of culture and thoughts, meet people's physical and psychological need and get people pleasant emotion. As people have more leisure time, with the tides of people exercise, entertainment becomes an important part of everyday life.[6] It is a trend for traditional PE of minority to be emphasized and favored by people. Thus the traditional PE of minority should be socialized. It should be developed not only in the particular region by particular minority but also by all the nationalities all over the world. It needs to strengthen the education and propaganda so as to mix into the entertainment system of all the people.

3 CONCLUSION AND SUGGESTIONS

3.1 Conclusion

1. With the history proceeding and the society changing, the tradition PE of minority develops into part of people's life and part of education content with great features of minority.
2. The traditional PE of minority is not emphasized by relevant departments. It takes lower proportion in the PE curriculum and lacks systematic textbooks with inefficient teaching staff. Problems are not solved.

3. The traditional PE of minority cannot be satisfied since it occupies weaker position compared with competing sports.
4. The traditional PE of minority should follow certain standards, keeping the features, faced with the world, developing with the western competing sports. Besides, it should develop with times and innovate actively, with the old kept and the new created.

3.2 Suggestions

Firstly, the management department of education should focus more on the micro readjustment and control, with policies developing traditional PE of minorities. Secondly, the core of education should be established to focus on the sports with more cultural features. Thirdly, the text book should be systematized and adopted into the standard and formal system of school courses, with the insurance of teaching hours. Fourthly, the quality of teaching staff should be developed, with the improvement of their major and working ability.

Fifthly, the education of traditional PE of minorities should be socialized and melted into the entertainment system of the folk people.

REFERENCES

1. H-T Yuan, W-Shuai. On the current situation and perspective of traditional cultures of China's Ethnic Minorities. Journal of Wuhan Institute of Science and Technology, 2007(4):121–124.
2. W-Zhao, X-M Hu. Thoughts of Developing Folk Sport. Sports & Science, 2000(5):18–20.
3. Y-Z Lu. Introduction to Social Sports. Higher Education Press, 2007:12–15.
4. X-P Yu, Li W-Shuai. Research on How to Culture the Learning Interests of University Students in Shuttlecock Teaching. Journal of Jilin Institute of Physical Education, 2008,24(6):143.
5. H-T Yuan, X-P Yu, H-C Zhang. The Value and Significance of Promoting "Qingjiang Dance" in P.E. of College & Universities. Journal of Harbin Institute of Physical Education, 2008,26(5):133–135.
6. X-D Xu, L-Yang. Reflections on development of Chinese Wushu after Beijing Olympics. Sports Culture Guide, 2008(3):90–92.

Computer, Intelligent Computing and Education Technology – Liu, Sung & Yao (Eds)
© 2014 Taylor & Francis Group, London, ISBN 978-1-138-02469-4

Discussion on personal protection in university chemical laboratory

Hong-Yan Zhong

Qilu University of Technology, Experimental Management Centre, Jinan City, Shandong Province, China

ABSTRACT: Chemical laboratories in the universities, are the places of potential safety hazards. In our country, it is generally weak in personal protective work of chemical experiments. Therefore, it's worth our learning from the laboratory safety management mode of the University of Oxford and better reflecting on chemical lab safety accidents in colleges and universities both at home and abroad. Safety education should be incorporated into all experimental teaching processes, especially chemical experiments. On the basis of learning from personal protective work in chemical laboratories of well-known colleges and universities at home and abroad e, this paper puts forward proposals on the basic protection of chemical experiment personnel in colleges and universities of our country.

Keywords: chemical laboratory; safety; personal protection

1 INTRODUCTION

Chemistry is a subject based on experiments. Compared with laboratories of other subjects, such as those of physics, electricity and electronics, information and technology, etc., chemical laboratories in universities are places of potential safety hazards. In chemical experiment, plenty of drugs and reagents endangering personal safety are often used, such as inflammables, oxidizers, explosives, easy infectious and corrosive items, also involving the ultrahigh frequency radiation, high frequency electromagnetic field, power frequency electric field, the laser radiation (including ultraviolet, visible light, infrared and far infrared rays), microwave radiation, ultraviolet radiation, high temperature operation, noise and hand-transmitted vibration and other risk factors. People-oriented as well as ensuring the safety of teachers and students are the basis and premise of all education and teaching in universities. It is of great responsibility to ensure experimenters' life safety in university chemical laboratories of higher security risks. For individuals of experimenters, personal protection work is crucial, and prevention outweighs disaster relief. However, the current situation of our laboratories in our country, the writer will take preliminary discussion on the personal protective work in university chemical laboratories based on investigation and research.

2 THE CURRENT SITUATION OF PERSONAL PROTECTIVE WORK IN DOMESTIC UNIVERSITY CHEMICAL LABORATORIES

So far, there have been no relevant policies issued concerning the safety standards of personal protection in university laboratories in our country. For general colleges and universities, they all have security department which is mainly responsible for teachers' and students' personal safety, and property safety of the university. Due to the small number of security personnel, mostly temporary staff, and their extensive business responsibility, security efforts are not so meticulous that the protective work of experimenter is almost uncovered. For ordinary colleges, they are short of teaching and scientific research budgets which are for the procurement of large instruments and equipment. Therefore, protective work of chemical experiments is funded in a very small amount, just purchasing some experimental isolation clothes.

Overall, it is vulnerable in the personal protective work of chemical experiments in our country. Currently, many colleges and universities in our country have set up experimental teaching demonstration centers of basic chemistry, and most general chemical labs are "emphasizing on science over security". Project groups in demonstration centers are aiming at their task of pursuing the experiment results to achieve their expectation, and generally lack of experimental security concept and humanistic concern. They seldom implement risk assessment on experiments, or prepare corresponding emergency plans, or incorporate the personal protective work as a laboratory regulation. In a word, chemical laboratories in universities of our country are lack of perfect, relatively systematic safety education and management measures, while the personal protective work in chemical experiments starts even later.

At present, with the constant expansion in the scales of college chemical labs, colleges have gradually increased requirement over experimental teaching staff as well. The number of comprehensive and innovative experiments has also increased dramatically, and more and more teachers, doctors, post-doctors, and masters are accessible to labs for research, so that the times of exposing to toxic and harmful substances and the personnel of that can be increased. To strengthen the security of chemical laboratory environment, improve the experimenters' personal protection, and to take preventive measures, have now become a problem in urgent need of addressing.

3 THE LABORATORY SAFETY MANAGEMENT MODE OF THE UNIVERSITY OF OXFORD

The University of Oxford attaches great importance to the laboratory safety work. According to the establishment of its organization, it is the vice president that takes chief responsibilities for the safety management of the university; the Health and Safety Management Committee of the University of Oxford (hereinafter referred to as "management committee") has been specially established and chaired by the vice president who is in charge of security matters. The management committee takes the obligation of making safety management principles and policies. Meanwhile, it also has the Health and Safety Advisory Committee (hereinafter referred to as "advisory committee"), whose members are representatives of various professions, and the duties thereby are offering proposals for health and safety policies, with the management committee chairman doubling as its chairman as well. The advisory committee offers proposals exclusively for radioactive protection, biological safety and occupational health. The University of Oxford sets up office of security, which is fully in charge of all the matters related with security. Besides, the university implements the budget related to security projects. Each laboratory has clear responsibility, and the director of each department is in full charge of security of all the faculty and laboratories within their respective jurisdictions.

The University of Oxford has made clear and detailed stipulations on personal protection in its laboratory safety rules and regulations, including protective regulations on working equipment, protective equipment management regulations on personal safety, radioactive protection regulations, accident protection regulations, and especially the safety and protection of chemical experiments is highlighted for instruction.

The University of Oxford particularly emphasizes tutors' responsibility in security. Tutors should guarantee students' safety, and the requirements on them are extremely specific and detailed. A tutor should first ensure the security of all the instruments, equipment and labs involving in the students' experiment designs, and meanwhile, they should know and master the students' ability of security protection, give students systematic security guidance, and arrange relevant safety training to be recorded on file. Students' experiments should be under tutors' supervision at any time. Before experiment, tutors not only check students' safety protection carefully, but also wear protective gear more seriously for modeling first. They should arrange the corresponding work in advance in case of going out on business, and check if the following safety work is done well after students' experiments.

4 REFLECTION ON SAFETY ACCIDENTS OF CHEMICAL LABORATORIES IN UNIVERSITIES BOTH AT HOME AND ABROAD

There are numerous chemical laboratory accidents caused by improper protection, not only domestically, but also in developed countries such as the United States. Despite that their chemical protective work started earlier than us, and is quite mature and complete now, there are still loopholes in existence. These harrowing lessons deserve our profound reflection and issue warnings to the personal protective work of our country.

On July 11, 2008, an explosion occurred when a doctor of a university in Yunnan conducting chemical experiment, who didn't wear any protective gear in the process of operating inflammable and explosive drugs, which resulted in his serious injury, blown blurred facial condition, and only thumb left in its left hand, absolutely appalling scene.

On December 29, 2008, a fire occurred at the University of California, Los Angeles. The local fire department and occupational safety and health management department investigated the accident and found it was the chemical experimenter who caused the fire in the process which killed himself. Data showed that the chemical synthesis experiment conducted by the experimenter had a lot of risks itself, and the experimenter wore no fire-resistant experiment insulating clothes in the whole experimental process, but a polyester shirt, and there was no other protective gear in him.

Hain Rules are initiated by German aircraft turbine inventor Hans Joachim Pabst von Ohain for flight safety, which say that behind every serious accident, there must be 29 minor accidents, 300 harbingers uncompleted, 1000 hidden accidents. Although the issue of university chemical laboratory safety can't be compared with the flight afety, safety deserves first guarantee. Hain Rules highlights the following ideas to the people: the occurrence of any accident is the result of quantity accumulation; human quality and sense of responsibility can't be replaced by any perfect technology or system; preventing troubles before happening and correcting errors immediately are basic principles to be abided by in the area of safety work.

5 STRENGTHENING SAFETY EDUCATION

Safety education is the most important work in preventing accidents as well as the precondition of all education activities. Classes of chemical experiments in universities should incorporate safety education into the normal teaching content. Safety education of chemical experiments should be completed in a full course, full range and multi-level. Full course refers to putting the safety education through the whole teaching process ever since students in primary-school period; full range refers to proceeding the safety education in all experimental teaching, especially experiments in chemistry, biology which are easy to cause safety accidents; multi-level refers to the specific implementation of safety education should be fulfilled step by step rather than overnight.

Safety education covers a very wide range in content from the national safety production laws and regulations, to common sense of safety in daily lives, such as the relevant security regulations of chemical labs, chemical experiment operation procedures, the use and storage of dangerous chemicals, self-help, common sense of personal protection, etc. Promoting safety culture and education should be a part of daily life of college teachers and students. The safety education can be taken through vivid and interesting activities, such as lectures on safety knowledge, competitions thereof, and safety accident analysis, etc. to create a safety culture atmosphere in colleges. Only enhancing the safety consciousness, can education be put into implementation actively.

6 SUGGESTIONS ON BASIC PROTECTION OF UNIVERSITY CHEMICAL LABORATORIES

According to the actual situation of chemical laboratories in universities of our country, we put forward the following suggestions on the basic protection of chemical experimenters in universities or our country by learning from the personal protection of chemical laboratories in domestic and foreign well-known universities.

6.1 Clothing first

Chemical experimenters are required to wear protective suits appropriately and take them off as well as other protective gear before leaving the lab to avoid polluting other non-experimental areas.

In the operation of general chemical experiments, it is suggested wearing long-sleeved cotton or cotton/polyester work clothes with long gowns or other experimental clothes wearing outside. The covering gown is suggested being fastened by textiles which can be quickly unfastened. Safety helmets should be carefully selected, while nylon products are not suggested for they are easy to be damaged in hot or acidic conditions. Many synthetic fibers are poor in anti-permeability, and liquid can seep through but very small amounts are absorbed or even unabsorbed. Similarly, in the fire, synthetic steel products are easy to melt and burn people, at the same time, electrostatic hazards in synthetic material clothes should be also taken into consideration.

6.2 Eyes & facial protection

When there are risks of damage to eyes or to the human body through eyes, eye-protective gear is required in experimental work. According to different damage sources, including mechanical damages, such as impact and splashing liquid, foreign objects into eyes or radioactive damage and so on, different eye-protective gear can be chosen. When there are risks of damage to eyes by liquid splash or damage to bodies through eyes, professional eye-protective gear is required. Under any circumstances, wearing contact lenses or other optical glasses can't replace eye-protective gear. What is especially worth noting that when the dust and harmful liquid or vapor enters eyes, contact lenses will increase the damage to the eyes. Generally, optical glasses are not good enough to prevent the flying objects or particles into eyes, sometimes can cause even bigger damage.

For those staff that need both vision correction and eye protection, regulated eye-protective gear can provide low impact protection. Peripheral glasses protective gear, goggles or masks can be worn outside the ordinary optical glasses; proper eye-protective gear can also be worn outside contact lenses.

It's better to use facial protective gear (such as masks) in the following situations: deflation, inflation or pressurization of glassware; dumping corrosive substances; using of cryogenic liquid, combustion operation; risk existence of explosion or implosion; using chemicals which may cause direct damage to skin; using chemicals that can be quickly absorbed by human bodies through skin, eyes, nose or other channels. For some certain job, it's better to use masks with forehead protection or maxillary protection or the combination.

6.3 Hearing protectors and gloves

In chemical labs, staff members often use ultrasonic waves to clean equipment. So, when the noise can cause hearing damage or weakness or when it is under rules or regulations, hearing protectors are required in order to protect hearing from damage. For most chemical experiments in operation, it's better to use gloves with suitable materials, length and weight, such as processing ultra-low temperature materials. In some cases, the skin protective agent for workers can provide adequate protection, but not for replacing glove-protection. Gloves can temporarily stop the skin allergy, and effectively prevent dust and fiber.

6.4 Other protective equipments

The minimum requirement of using protective equipment in chemical labs is wearing experimental clothes and close-ended shoes, when necessary, wearing eye-protective glasses. When hazardous dust, fog, smoke, and vapor exist in chemical experiments, proper respiratory protective equipment is required. Certain hazards require the application of special safety shoes. Safety helmets should be worn in case of risks of falling objects or possible impact on heads. In certain harmful operations (such as sampling or handling hazardous substances from large containers), other additional protective equipment should be adopted, such as boots, leggings, aprons, sheathings, shoe covers, or elbow gloves, etc.

We should identify and determine the needs of protective equipment for university chemical laboratories, and equip them with adequate protective equipment. Suitable protective equipment should be chosen according to experimental classes, and performance of protective equipment. Experiment management personnel should check individual protective equipment on a regular basis to ensure its good condition, and avoid using expired and ineffective protective equipment. Full training should be provided for users before its application.

"Safety and Protection are the Top Priority" is an accepted management concept of safe production. Universities should play high importance on individual safety protection work, to prevent troubles before occurring, strengthen the adversity consciousness, and eliminate potential safety dangers in the bud. Understand safety protection work of chemical labs correctly and act positively, to ensure the accomplishment of safe experiments, and make contributions to building a peaceful and harmonious campus.

REFERENCES

[1] L. Yang: Personal Protection in Chemical Laboratories. Research and Exploration in Laboratory. 32(9), (2013):248–250.
[2] R. Shi, L.J. Li, and J. Li: Action of laboratory opening in teaching of higher education [J]. Experimental Technology and Management. 26(12), (2009):144–145.
[3] Y.F. Luo, Y.W. Tang, and F. Sun: Discussion on Safety Management of Chemistry Laboratory in Colleges and Universities [J]. Experimental Technology and Management. 26(4), (2009):147–149.
[4] Y.H. Liu, D. Xiang, and S.H. Chen: Importance of the Operability in University Laboratory Safety Management. Research and Exploration in Laboratory. 30(8), (2011):181–185.
[5] M.H. Zeng, X.L. Hong, and C.H. Peng, etc.: By Sino-US Comparision on the Experiemental Safety Regulation to Reflect on the College Chemical Laboratory Safety Administration in Our Country. Research and Exploration in Laboratory. 30(1), (2011):310–313.
[6] Q.M. Liao: Concerning the Security Management in University Laboratory [J]. Research and Exploration in Laboratory. 29(1), (2010):168–170.
[7] C.Z. Liu. Safety Status and Management Policies in University Laboratory [J]. Laboratory Science. (2006).
[8] M.Q. Bao, Y. Zhang, and S.C. Zhang: Analysis of College Chemistry Laboratory Safety Problems and Exploration of Safety Management Measures. Experimental Technology and Management. 29(1), (2012):188–191.
[9] Z.Y. Liu, Y.C. Guo, C.L. Ran, Z.P. Zhang, and Z.H. He: Exploration of Safety and Environmental Protection Management in Chemical Experiment and Teaching Demonstration Centre. Research and Exploration in Laboratory. 32(6), (2013):434–436.
[10] S.M. Zhang and S.P. Liu: Primary Exploration of Safety Management Work in University Chemical Laboratory. Laboratory Science. 10(5), (2006):102–103.
[11] B. Wang and W. Zhou: Reflections on the Strengthening of Laboratory Safety Management in Colleges and Universities, Research and Exploration in Laboratory. 31(8), (2012):187–189.
[12] W. Xu: System Research on Safety Index of Laboratory Hazardous Chemicals—Laboratory Case Research of Shanghai Petrochemical Research Institute. Shanghai, Fudan University. (2008):16–1.

Analysis on development of retail e-commerce

Jing-Wen Guo & Jing-Jing Wang
Changchun Institute of Technology, Changchun, Jilin Province, China

ABSTRACT: With the rapid development of information technology in China and the wide spread of the Internet, mobile terminals and other electronic tools, e-commerce has become an important tool of marketing retailing. Although it has been just 20 years, China has achieved great development of retail e-commerce, and there is a huge potential, at this stage there are still many questions that need to improve and boost.

Keywords: retail; e-commerce; the status quo; analysis

1 THE STATUS QUO OF THE RETAIL E-COMMERCE

With the rapid development of information technology, the growing number of Internet users surge through the Internet, mobile networks online shopping, trading, and payment which are the rapid development of e-commerce model. The retail e-commerce features as efficient, convenient, safe with low cost, which not only affects the consumption habits of residents, but is changing the pattern of retail and business model. Therefore, more appliances and commercial enterprises continue to gush, and there are more and more traditional to test the waters of e-commerce retail business.

Although the pace of retail e-commerce in China has developed rapidly in recent years, emerging as Ali Baba, Suning, easy fast mainstream commercial enterprises, compared with foreign retail e-commerce, we have a lot to fill in the gap. Because of our late start of retail e-commerce, management, technology, transaction size, and transaction scope are far behind the level of developed countries, and the retail e-commerce market, which takes up the market share of the total retail sector is still relatively small. Facing shortage of retail e-commerce, we also saw the presence of the retail e-commerce which also has a very large development space, and its turnover is much higher than the average growth rate of the market, presenting the rising momentum.

2 THE PROBLEMS EXISTED IN E-COMMERCE RETAILING

2.1 *Unreasonable operating mode*

Currently, a lot of traditional department stores, its own brands and other companies have "net", but the majority of the shops did not bring benefits to the business. The reason, is owing to the irrationality of business mode, for example, many electricity suppliers provide only the function of the display of goods, without ability to sell online. The biggest advantage is that e-commerce can achieve shopping without leaving home, and this convenient consumption patterns has attracted more and more consumers to choose online shopping way, which led to rising corporate sales. But many companies did not use the advantage effectively; and there are some companies still use online marketing strategy to associate offline mode. The profit model of electricity providers is completely different from the traditional physical store, for online sales of goods has its own unique kind of choice, more efficient logistics and distribution capabilities and network marketing strategies requirements. Therefore, companies need to further changing the business model to adapt to the needs of the retail electric providers.

2.2 *Backwardness of IT*

Under the new formats of retail, IT has become a basic ability of modern retail business, and information technology, and became important technical support to capture consumer demand, evolve to meet the individual needs of consumers and look for the potential consumer market. But the overall level of IT retail sector is still very low, which seriously hampered the construction and development of traditional retail business and retail e-commerce. Although there are many number of companies that completed the construction of information management systems, basically just internal inventory information on statistics, data isolated single, and the lack of effective information analysis and knowledge of limited value are still existing. Therefore, we should play to the role of enterprise information systems, and information technology level must be strengthened to meet the needs of retail e-commerce development.

2.3 *Weakness in logistics and distribution sectors*

According to Research Center data shown in 2008, the number of shipments due to the occurrence of e-commerce is up to 500 million, accounting for the shipment quantity is 1/3, and by 2009, the singular express driven by the Taobao has more than 1 billion pieces. According to the Express Logistics Advisory Network statistics, it shows that the first half of 2012 the amount of National Express is up to 2.65 billion, of which, the shipment volume of online shopping has been around 60% of the total shipment volume.

These data suggest that improving logistics and distribution capabilities have become important issues facing the development of the electricity supplier, but at this stage, China's logistics still in its infancy, has yet to form a more complete logistics platform preliminary and logistics system, both from the national infrastructure investment is China development of the logistics industry itself is also self-built logistics or electricity are far from meeting the development needs of the electricity supplier, logistics and distribution scale can not afford spending which has become a bottleneck of retail electricity supplier development.

2.4 *Shortage in e-commerce*

The rapid expansions of electronic commerce enterprises are facing serious shortage of talent, and talent becomes another bottleneck problem of retail e-commerce development.

The retail e-commerce because of its own characteristics have greater demands for talent, we must have "electronic" but also have "business" knowledge of the compound talents who become scarce talent in development of retail electric providers. Currently, due to the shortage of compound talents, a considerable number of retail businesses rely on computer professionals to conduct e-commerce, which is differentiated business model for solving the problem of the traditional retail business online sales and physical sales line which is extremely unfavorable, it is innovation and development that is difficult to achieve the desired effect, but also talent shortage has seriously hampered the healthy development of retail e-commerce.

3 IMPROVEMENTS TO THE E-COMMERCE DEVELOPMENT OF CHINA'S RETAIL INDUSTRY ISSUES

Period of rapid development of China's economy has entered in this background, e-commerce has been a single show, shining and continue to maintain the momentum of high-speed development, and such a huge increase in the retail space also makes electronic Business Development become a consensus. But at this stage, e-commerce development of China's retail industry still exist some problems, in respond to recommendations and the problems are followed.

3.1 *Change ideas, and create new model of retail operations*

First, to restructure and develop e-commerce, companies must change the thinking of traditional retail concepts. Traditional retail and e-commerce business model with the retail sales experience and a high level of distinction are under essential difference. For example, th e traditional retail business through years of development has relatively fixed channel resources, rich line service concept. But with different traditional retail, e-commerce more focus on the accumulation of customer data, sales channels, and marketing is also completely different from the traditional retail, which pay more attention to online marketing. Therefore, if the traditional retail sector aims to develop e-commerce, the premise is to change ideas, and need to rethink the organizational structure of enterprises, profit model and a variety of marketing tools.

Secondly, because of the differences in development scale, industry type, market positioning, it determines the retail business can not blindly copy someone else's successful model, but should develop e-commerce with its own characteristics. Take the smaller companies for examples, because of funding, the scale's limitation, weakness of competition, they can rely on Taobao to create a distinctive service, personalized product customization and other small-scale network platform; whereas for some large-scale independent brands with solid chain, when developing the e-commerce, they should also think about how to achieve organic sales interactions differentiation and integration of online and offline, that is innovative marketing model.

3.2 *Improve cooperation with logistics companies such as logistics and distribution capabilities through a variety of ways*

China's logistics development has lagged seriously the development of retail e-commerce. At present, China is actively promoting the pace of construction of logistics infrastructure. In our environment that logistics system is not sound, the development of retail e-commerce should not be stagnant, and standstill, so retail enterprises should actively explore mechanisms for the enterprise logistics according to their characteristics. For example, retail businesses could cooperate with comprehensive ability of logistics enterprises to achieve e-commerce enterprise operation mode, and get a good logistics service capabilities. As the enterprise with the advantages of funding, warehousing and other conditions they can set up logistics and distribution systems, and then get online signed orders to stop marketing the product delivery mode; while for regional enterprises, they can adopt retail business associated logistics model to take advantage of the resources in different areas to improve logistics and distribution capabilities.

3.3 Increase investment in information technology & Improve the comprehensive competitiveness of enterprises

With the rapid development of the Internet and the information technology era, the factors to decide the retail core competence are no longer just good or bad for empty-supply relations, but the level of information. We should promote the use of information flow, logistics, driven by virtual entity which will become the trend of retail development. For example, we can use information technology to achieve optimization of logistics and sorting of goods, and the best distribution route selection, etc., to improve logistics efficiency, and reduce operating costs and maximize profits; consumer demand for mining use of information technology to achieve product mix demand configuration, produced on demand business model, in order to address the backlog of business goods, shortages of goods, and improve the utilization of funds for enterprises to gain more profits.

3.4 Strengthen personnel training and complex management

Currently, many reasons resulting in China's retail industry complex talent shortages, such as; graduates because of lack of work experience without being corporate attention. What's more, the lack of a complete enterprise talent training mechanism talent shortage has become another factor. Therefore, we should strengthen personnel training and management to improve personnel management mechanism. For graduates and other basic talent, you can set up professional training institutions in order to enrich the social experience of personal experience. Meanwhile, enterprises should establish as soon as possible to improve the personnel training system, and strengthen job training of staff in order to ease the problem of lack of business talent.

4 CONCLUSION

Development of Internet technology will advance to another stage of development of retail, and e-commerce has become an inevitable trend in the development of retail development. Although there are still many problems in daily advancement of technology improving electricity providers, supporting mechanisms, e-commerce is bound to bring a brighter prospect to retail trade.

REFERENCES

[1] Zhang Lei. New retailing evolution theory—the theory of conflict Fusion [J]. Chinese e-commerce, 2010 (12).
[2] Guo Yanfang. Retailers composite channel model to explore the e-commerce environment [J]. Commercial Times, 2013 (10).
[3] Sun Li, Zhang Liqun. Leading multi-channel retailing new IT revolution—Ninth China's retail CIO Summit magazine reported [J]. Information and Computer, 2012 (7).
[4] Sun Zhou, Xu Lin. Reasons for the slow development of electronic commerce retailing and strategic analysis [J]. Modern electronic technology, 2005 (9).

Computer, Intelligent Computing and Education Technology – Liu, Sung & Yao (Eds)
© *2014 Taylor & Francis Group, London, ISBN 978-1-138-02469-4*

A modified Capacitance-Resistive Model for estimating waterflood performance

W.J. Sun
School of Earch and Space Sciences, Peking U., Beijing, China
Research Institute of Petroleum Exploration and Development, CNPC, Beijing, China

H. Chen
CNOOC Research Institute, Beijing, China
State Key Laboratory of Offshore Oil Exploitation, Beijing, China

M.H. Zhou
School of Earch and Space Sciences, Peking U., Beijing, China
Research Institute of Petroleum Exploration and Development, CNPC, Beijing, China

Z.Y. Miao
Shengli Oilfield Drilling Technology Research Institute, Dongying, Shandong, China

ABSTRACT: CRM is an important method to match and predict production in oil industry. In this study, we modified the existing CRM for matching and predicting oil production with greater accuracy than the existing model. Production data from chosen oil reservoirs were analyzed using both existing and modified approaches and the results were compared. The results showed that the modified CRM approach could fit the production performance better than the existing CRM in many cases. The physical significance behind this was proposed and explained.

Keywords: Capacitance-Resistive Model; prediction of oil production; water flooding

1 INTRODUCTION

Numerical simulation, traditional decline curve analysis, and generalized nonlinear multivariate regression model (or refer as to Capacitance-Resistive Model, i.e., CRM) are mainly three types of approaches to matching and predicting production performance. The capacitance-resistive model is rooted in signal processing, and can be used to predict the total production rates of oil reservoirs, in which water injection rates are treated as input signals and production rates are output signals. The model parameters may reflect the connectivity between each injector and producer. CRMT is a widely used analytical solution to differential equation of CRM, that is, capacitance-resistive model with one time constant for field represented by a single producer and a single injector as a tank [1,2]. Liang and Weber et al. [3,4] used the fractional-flow model to maximize the oil production rates.

One of the main problems in the existing CRM is that the fraction of injection rate of injector i flowing toward producer j, f_{ij}, was usually assigned to unity when a reservoir is represented by a single producer and a single injector as a tank. This might not be true in many cases. Another problem in applying CRM is the poor accuracy of matching and predicting oil production. In this study, we modified the CRM to improve the accuracy of matching and predicting oil production.

2 THEORY

2.1 CRMT model

In the case of reservoir-control volumes, by combining all production and injection rates, we can assume all injectors and producers as a tank which has only one injector and one producer. Assuming the connectivity factor f_F is equal to unity, CRMT model is expressed as:

$$q_F(t_k) = q_F(t_{k-1})e^{\frac{-\Delta t_k}{\tau_F}} + I_F^{(k)}(1 - e^{\frac{-\Delta t_k}{\tau_F}}) \tag{1}$$

where τ_F is the time constant of reservoir; $q_F(t_k)$ is the total fluid production rate at time t_k; $I_F^{(k)}$ is injection rate of reservoir during time interval t_{k-1} to t_k.

2.2 Oil production model based on fractional-flow model

Oil fractional-flow model can be written as:

$$f_o(t) - \frac{1}{1 + F_{wo}} = \frac{1}{1 + a_j W_i^{b_j}} \qquad (2)$$

where a_j and b_j are constant, which can be determined by matching the oil production history. Once the constant a_j and b_j are known, we can apply Eq. 2 to predict oil production rates of the reservoir.

For CRMT, the oil production rates of reservoir can be written as:

$$q_{oF}(t_k) = \frac{q_F(t_{k-1})e^{\frac{-\Delta t_k}{\tau_F}} + I_F^{(k)}(1 - e^{\frac{-\Delta t_k}{\tau_F}})}{1 + a_F W_i^{b_F}} \qquad (3)$$

where $q_{oF}(t_k)$ is the oil production rate of reservoir at time t_k; $q_{oF}(t_{k-1})$ is the oil production rate of reservoir at time t_{k-1}; a_F and b_F are constants of the field.

2.3 Modified CRMT model

The connectivity factor f_F of reservoir is usually assumed to unity, as shown in Eq. 1. However, some of the injected water or other fluids may not reach the producer because of faults or fractures. Taking this into consideration, the connectivity factor f_F may not be equal to unity and is then an undetermined parameter. Its value is usually between 0 and 1 in many cases and may be greater than one in some other cases. The modified CRMT model can be represented as:

$$q_F(t_k) = q_F(t_{k-1})e^{\frac{-\Delta t_k}{\tau_F}} + f_F I_F^{(k)}(1 - e^{\frac{-\Delta t_k}{\tau_F}}) \qquad (4)$$

where
$0 \le f_F < 1$ in the case of open reservoir boundary with out flow flux;
$f_F > 1$ in the case of open reservoir boundary with in flow flux;
$f_F = 1$ in the case of completely closed reservoir boundary.
Note that Eq. 4 includes only two fitting parameters τ_F and f_F. The values of f_F may depend upon the condition of the reservoir boundary: f_F is less than one if the reservoir boundary is open with out flow flux and is equal to one if the reservoir is completely closed. f_F may be greater than one if the reservoir boundary is open with in flow flux.

2.4 Modified oil production model based on fractional-flow model

The following oil production model can be derived by combining the modified CRMT model and fractional-flow model:

$$q_{oF}(t_k) = q_{oF}(t_{k-1})e^{\frac{-\Delta t_k}{\tau'_F}} + f'_F I_F^{(k)} \frac{q_{oF}(t_{k-1})}{q_F(t_{k-1})}(1 - e^{\frac{-\Delta t_k}{\tau'_F}}) \qquad (5)$$

where $q_{oF}(t_k)$ is the oil production rate of reservoir at time t_k ($k = 1, 2, \ldots, n$); $q_{oF}(t_{k-1})$ is the oil production rate of reservoir at time t_{k-1}; $q_F(t_{k-1})$ is the total production rate of reservoir at time t_{k-1}; $I_F^{(k)}$ is the injection rate of reservoir during time interval t_{k-1} to t_k; f'_F is the parameter of modified oil production model, which is relevant to f_F of CRMT, but may not be equal to f_F; τ'_F is the time constant in modified oil production model, which is relevant to τ_F of CRMT, but may not be equal to τ_F.

3 RESULTS

3.1 Application of modified CRMT to oil reservoirs

In order to verify the modified CRMT model, we applied it to an oil reservoir in China. This oil reservoir is characteristic of low permeability, high density of fractures, and great heterogeneity. The results of these applications are presented and discussed below.

Figure 1 shows comparisons between the estimated total production rates using the existing CRMT model (Eq. 1) and that using modified CRMT model (Eq. 4) for this oil reservoir. One can see from Figure 1 that the modified CRMT model fits the production history better than the existing CRMT model. The total production rates

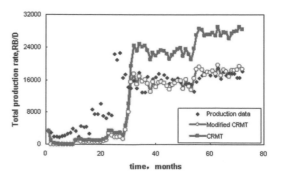

Figure 1. Comparison of CRMT and modified CRMT for total production matching of reservoir.

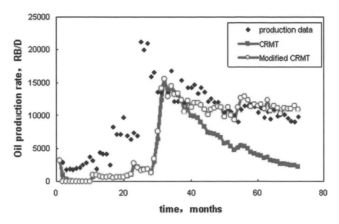

Figure 2. Comparison of existing oil production model and modified oil production model for oil production matching of reservoir.

estimated using the existing CRMT model are greater than the production history data in this reservoir. The value of f_F is 0.6579, less than one. It is obvious that the connectivity factor f_F may not be equal to unity in reservoirs with open or partially open boundaries because the injected water may not fully arrive or affect the producers. In another word, the injected fluids may leak out from the boundary of oil reservoirs ($f_F < 1$) or flow into the reservoir ($f_F > 1$).

3.2 Application of modified oil production model to oil reservoirs

The comparison of oil production matched using the modified oil production model (Eq. 5) and the existing model (Eq. 3) is plotted in Figure 2. The modified oil production model matches the history data more satisfactorily than the existing model.

4 CONCLUSIONS

The following conclusions may be drawn from the present study:

1. The assumption of unity connectivity factor f_F in CRMT has been relaxed. The values of f_F may depend upon the condition of the reservoir boundary: f_F is equal to one if the reservoir is completely closed; it is less than one if the reservoir boundary is open with out flow flux and may be greater than one if the reservoir boundary is open with in flow flux.

2. The case study demonstrated that the modified CRMT by removing the assumption of unity connectivity factor f_F could match the production history more satisfactorily than the existing CRMT.

3. A modified oil production model was proposed and the calculated results showed that the new model matches the production history data better than the existing fractional flow model in the case studied.

REFERENCES

[1] Eberhart, R.C. and Kennedy, J. A new optimizer using particle swarm theory. Proceedings of the sixth international symposium on micro machine and human science pp. 39–43. IEEE service center, Piscataway, NJ, Nagoya, Japan, 1995.

[2] Gentil, P.H. 2005. The Use of Multilinear Regression Models in Patterned Waterfloods: Physical Meaning of the Regression Coefficients, M.S. Thesis, The University of Texas at Austin.

[3] Liang, X., Weber, B., Edgar, T.F., Lake, L.W., Sayarpour, M., and Yousef, A.A. 2007. Optimization of Oil Production in a Reservoir Based on Capacitance Model of Production and Injection Rates. Paper SPE 107713 presented at the SPE Hydrocarbon Economics and Evaluation Symposium, Dallas, Texas, 1–3 April.

[4] Sayarpour, M., Zuluaga, E., Kabir, C.S. and Lake, L.W. 2007. The Use of Capacitance-Resistive Models for Rapid Estimation of Waterflood Performance and Optimization, SPE 110081 presented at the SPE Annual Technical Conference and Exhibition, Anaheim, California, 11–14 November.

Analysis on characteristics of precipitation and runoff production on slop land at Western Yunnan Plateau in China

Z.Q. Liu
Southwest Forestry College, Kunming, China

ABSTRACT: At western Yunnan plateau in China, the characteristics of precipitation and runoff production on slop lands can provide a foundation data for vegetation recovery research and slop management. Characteristics of precipitation and runoff production on slop land were studied with the method of runoff plots. It showed that the distribution of one year rainfall is uneven; the rain keeps on heavy in the rainy season and results in water and soil erosion. Based on the three characteristic values of rainfall: precipitation, rainfall intensity and duration, the rainfalls in the study area were classified into three regimes through K-means clustering in SPSS 15.0 software, The order of runoff coefficients induced by rainfall was regime A > regime B > regime C. However, The order of scale effect on runoff induced by rainfall was regime C > regime B > regime A.

Keywords: western Yunnan plateau; rainfall regime; slop land; scale effect

1 INTRODUCTION

In the process of vegetation construction and ecological environment interaction and mutual influence, hydrological process is the most important aspect, is also one of the central topics in hydrological research.[1,2] Slope is a medium scale system between "point" and "Valley". In information transfer between different scales of the problem Scale issues is a difficult problem in the key issues in ecology, soil science, meteorology and hydrology research field.[3] At the same time, overland flow characteristics and scale effect are the key and hot point in the geology and hydrology research.[4,5] In recent 40 years, study on overland flow and hillslope processes at home and abroad, combining hydrology geomorphology, made some significant achievements, and hillslope Hydrology edited by Kirkby has milepost sense.[6] With the experience of soil and water conservation prediction model for process model gradually replaced the physical mechanism, slope flow and runoff generation process has attracted more and more attention.

2 THE RESEARCH CONTENTS AND METHODS

2.1 *The general situation of research area*

Shangri-La belonging to the Diqing Tibetan Autonomous Prefecture located in the north-west of Yunnan, southeast margin of the Qinghai Tibet Plateau. The county belongs to the mountain cold temperate monsoon climate. The soil is mainly composed of brown forest soil, dark brown soil, yellow brown soil and dark red soil. The main forest vegetation is widely distributed *Picea asperata* forest, *Pinus densata* forest *and Quercus semecarpifolia* forest.[7] Research area is in Diqing Shangri-La County west northwest corner, between latitude 27° 45′–28° 25′, longitude 90° 20′–99° 45′, its transportation is convenient and Yunnan-Tibet Highway (State Road 214) from south to north go through the project area.

2.2 *The layout of runoff plot*

According to the forest ecological hydrology observation standards, horizontal projection area of 100 m² runoff plot was set. Precipitation rainfall duration, rainfall intensity and 30 min maximum rainfall were measured by siphon recording gauges of DSJ2. The soil water content was measured by oven drying method, determination of soil bulk density, porosity of soil physical properties with the ring knife method (as showed in Table 1).

2.3 *Statistical analysis methods*

In order to study rainfall characteristics on runoff impact, the precipitation types were classified based on rainfall, rainfall duration and maximum rainfall intensity with K-means clustering analysis in SPSS15.0. The correlation between rainfall

Table 1. The physical properties of soil in runoff plot.

Soil thickness (cm)	Bulk density (g/cm³)	Capillary porosity (%)	Non-capillary porosity (%)	Total porosity (%)
0–20	1.32	47.31	11.32	58.62
20–40	1.37	40.41	11.46	51.87
40–60	1.53	20.51	7.94	28.45

characteristic and runoff coefficient was analyzed by Pearson correlation analysis in SPSS15.0.

3 THE RESULTS AND ANALYSIS

3.1 The characteristics and changes of precipitation

According to the observed statistical results of Shangri-La weather Station for nearly 30 years, the annual average rainfall is 618.4 mm. The rainy season begins in June average, from November to May of the next year about seven months of drought season, the precipitation of May accounted for 40.2% of the entire dry season rainfall. The highest monthly average temperature throughout the year is also in May, the temperature began to fall after the start of the rainy season, the rainfall distribution in one year shown in Figure 1.

In the rainy season there 42 rainfalls were observed and the total rainfall is 423.96 mm, the rainfall of this season accounted for only 68.56% of the average years. The distribution of rainfall during the year is uneven, and the rainfall of July and October were only 76.1 mm, 15.3 mm, so it caused severe drought. But the rainfall of June and September were 110.75 mm, 114.95 mm, which accounted for 26.12% and 27.11% of total precipitation during the rainy season respectively, and easily formed a continuous heavy rain, resulted in a large surface runoff and soil erosion.

3.2 Analysis of rainfall types

During the experiment rainy season from June to September there was 25 times rainfall that produced runoff. Use SPSS15.0 K-means classification; based on the three characteristic values of rainfall, rainfall intensity and duration, the recorded rainfall in 25 times were divided into three group's rainfall patterns. According to rain fall depth, rainfall duration, and rainfall intensity, the rainfalls in the study area were classified into three regimes through K-means clustering in SPSS 15.0 software, i.e. rainfall regime A with high rainfall intensity, short duration and high occurring frequency, rainfall regime C with low rainfall intensity, long

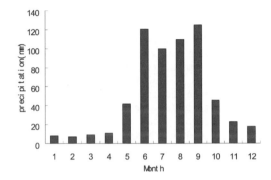

Figure 1. Chart for relationship of precipitation and month.

duration and low occurring frequency, and B the medium (as is showed in Table 2).

P, D, and I30 represent rainfall, duration and maximum 30 min rainfall intensity; the units were mm, min, and mm/min.

As can be seen from Table 2, in the 25 rainfalls there were 14 regime A rainfalls, which is 56% of the total number of rainfall frequency, cumulative rainfall reaches 117.6 mm; there were 7 regime B rainfalls, which is 28% of the total number of rainfall frequency, cumulative rainfall reaches 179.83 mm; there were just 4 regime C rainfalls, the maximum rainfall intensity in 30 minutes of rainfall regime A is 0.27 mm/h, and the maximum rainfall intensity in 30 minutes of rainfall regime C is the lowest, only 0.11 mm/h. However, the duration and precipitation of regime A are relatively minimal, and those of regime C are max. These rainfall values reflect the general characteristics of rainfall. Therefore, it can be considered that regime A has the characteristics of large intensity, short duration and high frequency; and regime C has the characteristics of small intensity, long duration and low frequency, The characteristics of regime B are between the regime A and B, namely, the rainfall intensity is less than regime A but larger than regime C, the duration is less than regime C but greater than regime A.

The rainfall of regime A before the runoff occurrence is generally 2–5 mm, accounting for about

Table 2. Statistical features of the rainfall regimes in the study area.

Regime	Values	Mean	Standard deviation	Coefficient of variation	Total	Frequency
A	P	8.40	4.75	0.61	117.60	14
	D	155.30	113.94	0.58	2174.20	
	I_{30}	13.56	5.64	0.58	189.84	
B	P	25.69	22.46	0.79	179.83	7
	D	621.40	187.46	0.42	4349.80	
	I_{30}	8.47	10.38	1.12	59.29	
C	P	29.37	31.24	1.13	88.11	4
	D	1224.54	157.51	0.21	3673.62	
	I_{30}	6.26	7.56	1.23	18.78	

Table 3. Pearsonian correlation coefficient between runoff coefficient and rainfall.

	Precipitation	Precipitation	Average intensity	I_{10}	I_{30}
Runoff coefficient	1				
Precipitation	0.703**	1			
Average intensity	0.394*	0.262*	1		
I_{10}	0.476*	0.612**	0.781**	1	
I_{30}	0.654**	0.732**	0.764**	0.983**	1

10% of the total rainfall and the intensity in 5 min range between 17.5 mm/h to32 mm/h; the rainfall in the runoff occurrence is generally accounted for about 80% of the total rainfall and the average intensity is generally above 8 mm/h, which is lower than the intensity when the runoff occurs; The rainfall of regime A after the runoff occurrence is generally 0.5–2 mm, accounting for about 5%–10% of the total rainfall and the intensity range between 0.8 mm/h to1.97 mm/h.

The rainfall of regime B before the runoff occurrence range form 2 to 5 mm, accounting for about 10% of the total rainfall and the intensity in 5 min range between 14.5 to 24 mm/h; the rainfall in the runoff occurrence is generally accounted for about 60% of the total rainfall but the actual runoff rainfall is accounted for about 28%–60%; The rainfall of regime B after the runoff occurrence is generally 10 mm, and the intensity range between 0.4 mm/h to 2.5 mm/h. From the rainfall duration, the rainfall duration before the runoff occurrence is in the 30–600 min, and the real cause runoff rainfall duration range form 40 to 100 min.

The rainfall of regime C before the runoff occurrence range form 5 to 50 mm, accounting for about 33%–50% of the total rainfall, As long as there is no high intensity rainfall, the rainfall is also likely to continue to grow. The rainfall in the runoff occurrence is generally accounted for just 20%–30% of the total rainfall. From the rainfall duration, the rainfall duration before the runoff occurrence can last tens of minutes.

Influence of rainfall characteristics on Runoff. Rainfall is the direct source of runoff yield, and also has great influence on runoff.[8–10] The Pearson correlation of the characteristics of rainfall and runoff coefficient was analyzed in Table 3. The results show that the characteristics of rainfall were highly correlated with the runoff coefficient ($P = 0.01$). The relevance between Rainfall, maximum 30 min rainfall intensity and runoff coefficient is more than 0.612. The difference of scale effect of runoff of three kinds of rain type influence is mainly caused by the rainfall intensity.[11] From the analysis above can be learned, the rain intensity of regime A is big and the runoff soon reached the stable stage; under heavy and strong rain, crusts on slope form easily, and the stable period time accounts for a large proportion of the entire duration; runoff production scale is small, so that the runoff loss is reduced on slope, and in the same slope the runoff capacity of regime A is largest. In contrast, because of small rain intensity, regime B especially regime C last for a long time, and the crust is not easy to form, the stable period of rainfall runoff accounted for a little proportion of the entire duration of rainfall, runoff production scale is big, so that the runoff loss is increased on slope, and the capacity of overland flow is relatively low.

4 CONCLUSIONS

1. The distribution of rainfall in the year is uneven, the rainfall of June and September were great, and it easily formed a continuous heavy rain, resulted in a serious runoff and soil erosion.
2. The rainfalls were classified into three regimes through K-means clustering, i.e. rainfall regime A with high rainfall intensity, short duration and high occurring frequency, rainfall regime C with low rainfall intensity, long duration and low occurring frequency, and B the medium.
3. The rainfall and rainfall intensity, especially the maximum 30 minute rain intensity are the key factors to influence the surface runoff capacity. The order of runoff capability induced by rainfall was regime A > regime B > regime C. However, the order of scale effect on runoff induced by rainfall was regime C > regime B > regime A.

ACKNOWLEDGMENTS

This work was supported by the National Natural Science Foundation of China (31160048).

REFERENCES

[1] M. Bonell, B.K. Purandara, B. Venkatesh. The impact of forest use and reforestation on soil hydraulic conductivity in the Western Ghats of India: Implications for surface and sub-surface hydrology[J]. Journal of Hydrology, 2010, 391(1–2): Pages 47–62.

[2] Yong Lin, Xiaohua Wei. The impact of large-scale forest harvesting on hydrology in the Willow watershed of Central British Columbia[J]. Journal of Hydrology, 2008, 359(1–2): 141–149.

[3] Liu Zhiqin, Wang Keqin. Research Advances on Slope Runoff Generation by Artificial Vegetation[J]. Journal of Southwest Forestry University, 2004, 24(2): 65–69.

[4] Bloeschl G, Sivapalan M. Scale issues in hydrological modeling: A review[J]. Hydrol Processes, 1995, 9: 251–290.

[5] Liu Zhiqin, Wang Keqin, Li yanmei. Analysis on Characteristics of Precipitation and Runoff Production on slop land in dry-hot valley of jinshajiang river[J]. Journal of Shihezi University, 2010, 28(2): 227–231.

[6] Kirkby M.J. Hillslope Hydrology[M]. New York: John Wiley & Sons, Ltd, 1978: 235–425.

[7] Wang Luolin Zhu Ling. Choice of development path of latecomer regions—case study in Yunnan Tibetan areas[M]. Beijing: Economic Management Press, 2002: 62.

[8] L. Turnbull, A.J. Parsons, J. Wainwright. Runoff responses to long-term rainfall variability in a shrub-dominated catchment[J]. Journal of Arid Environments, 2013, 91: 88–94.

[9] Nu-Fang Fang, Zhi-Hua Shi, Lu Li. The effects of rainfall regimes and land use changes on runoff and soil loss in a small mountainous watershed[J]. CATENA, 2012, 99: 1–8.

[10] Xu J.X. Hyperconcentrated flows in the slope-channel systems in gullied areas on the Loess Plateau[J]. China Geografiska Annaler, 2004, 86: 349–366.

[11] Vande Giesen N, Stomph T J, de Ridder N. Surface runoff scale effects in West African watersheds: modeling and management options[J]. Agriculture Water Management, 2005, 72: 109–130.

Computer, Intelligent Computing and Education Technology – Liu, Sung & Yao (Eds)
© 2014 Taylor & Francis Group, London, ISBN 978-1-138-02469-4

Causes and preventions about eccentric-wear of suck-rods in the polymer-flooding directional wells

L.L. Liu
Petroleum Engineering Department, Northeast Petroleum University, Daqing, Heilongjiang, China

Q.P. Wang
The 5th Oil Production Factory of Daqing Oilfield Company Limited, Daqing, Heilongjiang, China

S.R. Yang
Petroleum Engineering Department, Northeast Petroleum University, Daqing, Heilongjiang, China

L.H. Wang
Daqing Petroleum Equipment Group, Daqing, Heilongjiang, China

D. Xu
Petroleum Engineering Department, Northeast Petroleum University, Daqing, Heilongjiang, China

ABSTRACT: In order to solve the problem about eccentric-wear of suck-rods in the polymer-flooding directional wells, the force acting on the rod was analyzed, the differential equation and calculation formula about sucker-rod deflection were established, the causes and preventing measures about eccentric-wear of the suck-rods were given, and a method was also proposed to optimize the centralizer. Results show that radial load is the main factor of the eccentric-wear, eccentric-wear usually occurred in stage of big slope segment, which should take measures of centralizer encryption.

Keywords: polymer-flooding well; directional well; suck-rods; centralizer; eccentric-wear

1 INTRODUCTION

As the number of water-flooding to polymer-flooding wells increases, oil recovery is improved markedly, but at the same time new technology problems in the production process have gradually emerged. One of the most serious problems is, after taken the anti-eccentric wear measures of whole well rod centralizing, eccentric-wear of the suck-rods in big slop segment is still serious. Therefore, it is necessary to further study on stress and deflection calculation methods of directional well suck-rods, thus to put forward to the effective measures to prevent the eccentric-wear. Based on the analysis of the stress on suck-rods in the polymer-flooding directional wells, the force on directional well suck-rods in detail and the reasons of eccentric-wear of sucker rod in polymer-flooding directional wells were analyzed, the optimization method of anti-eccentric wear measures were proposed. The results show that: polymer flooding pumping rod in directional well is suffered by the force of the longitudinal force such as fluid drag force and inertia force, and at the same time it is also suffered by the force of the lateral force such as gravity force and radial force. The lateral force will make the deflection of sucker rod increases, which cause aggravation of rod tube eccentric-wear. The proposed optimization methods of anti-eccentric wear and software system have been achieved good economic results.

2 ECCENTRIC-WEAR MECHANISM OF SUCK-RODS IN POLYMER FLOODING DIRECTIONAL WELLS

There are two major differences on force between suck-rods in polymer-flooding directional wells and water-flooding directional wells. First of all, the polymer-flooding produced liquid contains elasticity as well as viscosity. The visco-elastic fluid flowing in the eccentric annulus between the well-bore and suck-rod will inevitably produce radial forces [1–5]; secondly, there is a certain inclination in the directional wells, gravity on directional well suck-rods inevitably contains the transverse component. In the direction perpendicular to the axis

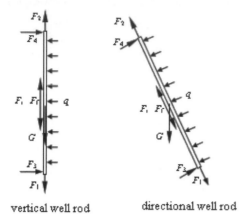

vertical well rod   directional well rod

Figure 1.   Force on suck-rods.

direction. Take out a suck-rod in polymer flooding wells and directional wells respectively, the stress conditions is as shown in Figure 1. In Figure 1, q represents the radial force of suck-rod, which is uniform load; G represents suck-rod gravity, and is also the uniform load; F_i represents the inertia force of suck-rods in the process of movement; F_f represents the frictional resistance acting on suck-rods, the inertial force and frictional resistance are in alternating state in a campaign period [6]; F1 and F2 represent the forces of the other suck-rods on lower and upper side acting on this suck-rod; F3 and F4 represent the forces of the other centralizers on the lower and upper side acting on this suck-rod.

As polymer flooding wells, under the force of radial force caused by visco-elasticity, the suck-rod is bound to the certain bending deflection, when the deflection is large enough to make the suck-rod into contact with tubing wall, they will produce wear. Because the wear is on a specific site and a specific direction, so it is called eccentric wear. But as the polymer flooding directional wells, the suck-rods is not only suffered by the force of radial force, but also by the transverse component of gravity, and the bending deflection will be greater. Therefore, the transverse component of gravity is also a main cause of eccentric wear. Eccentric wear of the polymer-flooding directional slope wells will be more serious than that of the vertical wells.

3   SUCK-ROD DEFLECTION CALCULATION AND ECCENTRIC-WEAR JUDGMENT METHOD

Because the lateral force acting on suck-robs may produce deflection, and when the deflection to a certain extent can cause eccentric-wear, so

calculations on the suck-rod deflection is the key to judge whether eccentric-wear occurs. The polymer-flooding directional wells suck-rod can be simplified as simply supported beam under the action of uniform load and axial pressure, which is shown in Figure 2. q is uniform load, including both the radial force of gravity transverse component, N/m; F is longitudinal load, N; ω is deflection, m; δ is maximum deflection, m; l is the length of the beam, m. The bending differential equation [5] is:

$$EI\omega^{IV} - F\omega^{II} = q$$

It can come to the beam deflection curve equation [6]:

$$\omega = \frac{EI_z}{F^2}q\left(\tan u\sin kx + \cos kx - 1\right) - \frac{ql}{2F}\left(lx - x^2\right)$$

Since the beam supports and loads are symmetrical to the midpoint of the beam cross, therefore, the maximum deflection of the beam occurs at the midpoint of the beam cross. The $x = l/2$ taken into the above equation can get maximum deflection:

$$\delta = \omega_{max} = \omega\big|_{x=l/2}$$

$$= \frac{EI_z}{F^2}q\left(\tan u\sin u + \cos u - 1\right) - \frac{ql^2}{8F}$$

$$= \frac{q}{k^4 EI_z}\left(\sec u - 1\right) - \frac{ql^2}{8k^2 EI_z}$$

$k = 2u/l$ taken into the above equation can be:

$$\delta = \omega_{max} = \frac{5ql^4}{384EI_z}\left[\frac{24}{5} \times \frac{\left(\sec u - 1 - \frac{u^2}{2}\right)}{u^4}\right]$$

Then do the series expansion and ignore the items above the third-order can obtain the maximum deflection calculating formula:

$$\delta = \frac{5ql^4}{384EI_z}\left[1 \pm \frac{12.2}{30}u^2\right]$$

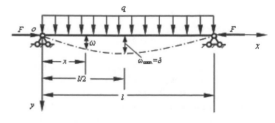

Figure 2.   Simply supported beam under the action of uniform load and axial pressure.

Wherein $u = kl/2$; $k = (F/EI_z)^{0.5}$; $q = G\sin\theta/l$; $I_z = \pi d^4/16$; E is the elastic modulus, Pa; I_z is the centroid moment of inertia of suck-rod, m⁴; G is the gravity of rod per meter, N; θ is inclination of wells, d is the diameter of rod, m. It should be focused on that the sign of the maximum deflection calculating formula. In the course of suck-rod reciprocating neutral point exists, longitudinal force subjected by rods above the neutral point is axial tension, the sign in formula shall be taken as negative; while longitudinal force subjected by rods below the neutral point is longitudinal pressure, the sign in formula should be taken as positive.

Polymer-flooding directional well suck-rod under the action of lateral uniform pressure q will have a certain amount of deflection. From Figure 3 it is clearly that, when the maximum deflection is larger than the centralizer diameter and the tubing centralizer radius difference, it will occur eccentric-wear. Therefore, the critical bending deflection grinding can be expressed as

$$\delta_{cr} = \frac{D - d}{2}$$

Wherein, D is the pipe diameter; d is the diameter of rod. When $\delta < \delta_{cr}$, tubing is rod out of the reach of rob, and will not cause eccentric-wear; when $\delta > \delta_{cr}$, rod will contact with tubing, when pumping for 6 times, the annual contact between rod and tube is up to 3.15×10^6 times, that frequent contact and friction is bound to cause rod and tube wear–eccentric-wear.

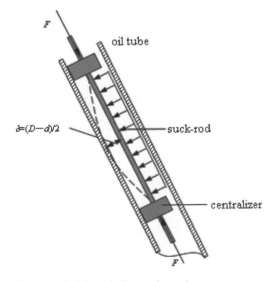

Figure 3. Judging of oil pumping rod.

4 CENTRALIZER ENCRYPTION PRINCIPLE

Currently, the most effective measure to prevent polymer-flooding vertical wells' eccentric-wear is to right the whole well, namely install centralizers on rod couplings, after taken measures, the average pump inspection period can be increased to 800 days or more, [5] but according to the Oil Recovery Plant No. 5, Daqing Oil Field Corp. Ltd. polymer-flooding directional wells work data, the average pump inspection period is only 280 days, the suck-rods in high angle section which deviation angle above 10° get a more serious eccentric-wear. The main cause of this problem is that rods in high-angle section by force of gravity component as well as radial force caused by visco-elasticity of produced fluid, the maximum deflection of this well is far more than that of the polymer-flooding vertical wells. Therefore, further measures should be taken at high-angle section to reduce its maximum deflection. It is not difficult to see from the calculating formula that the best way to reduce the maximum deflection is to reduce vertical and horizontal bending beam span, which means taking technical measures of secondary encryption centralizer on the basis of whole well righting. This is because the suck-rod deflection is proportional to the fourth span deflection, after the installation of a centralizer deflection is reduced to the 1/16 of original deflection, after the installation of two centralizers deflection can be reduced to 1/81 of original.

Installing centralizer can reduce the deflection of rod and prevent rods from eccentric-wear, it would also bring other negative effects such as pumping unit load and increase the cost of production. So which suck-rod centralizer should be done secondary encryption, and how many should be installed? Computer software worked out by the above theory and criterion, first find out rods that exist eccentric-wear, install a centralizer in suck-rod, and then determine whether eccentric-wear will occur in this rod after the encryption, if eccentric-wear still exists then install two centralizers in these rods until none eccentric-wear exists. Arrange centralizers according to the calculation results of software can avoid leakage of centralizer, and can also be avoid of blind encryption, this reaches the goal of centralizer spacing optimization.

5 CONCLUSION

1. The force acting on the polymer-flooding directional well suck-rod were analyzed, causes for eccentric-wear in the polymer-flooding directional well suck-rod were found out, a formula

of complex rod bending deflection was derived, and the measures of judging polymer-flooding directional well suck-rods were given.

2. In directional wells, gravity transverse component of suck-rods in high deviation angle section is big, where gets the highest probability of generating eccentric-wear, which should take technology measures of centralizer encryption.

3. Centralizer spacing optimization method for anti-eccentric wear was proposed, where the software for polymer-flooding directional well centralizer spacing optimization method had been applied in oil field, after taken measures, the pump inspection period can be extended one or more times.

REFERENCES

[1] YangShuren, WangChunsheng, YangYing. Eccentric Annulus Velocity Distribution of Viscoelastic Fluid Axial Movement in Inner Cylinder [J]. Journal of Daqing Petroleum Institude, 2005. Vol 29. No 1:110–111.

[2] YangShuren, YangYing, WangChunsheng. Forces on Polymer-flooding Suck-rods by Viscoelastic Fluid [J]. Journal of Daqing Petroleum Institude, 2005. Vol 29. No 1:112–113.

[3] YangJing, YangShuren, WangChunsheng. Causes and prevention of polymer-flooding well eccentric-wear [J]. Journal of Daqing Petroleum Institude, 2005. Vol 29. No 1:114 115.

[4] Wang Yan. Technology for Controlling Eccentric Wear of Sucker Rods and Tubing in Pumping Wells Lifting Fluids Containing Polymer [J]. SPE89927.

[5] Yang SR, Cui HQ, Wang CS. Numerical simulation on steady flows of viscoelastic fluid in an eccentric annulus with inner rod moving axially [J]. Journal of Hydrodynamics, Ser. B, 2005. Vol 17. No 4:514–518.

[6] Chen Taoping, HuJingbang. Petroleum Engineering [M]. Beijing: Petroleum Industry Press, 2000:216. Ship Structural Mechanics [M]. Shanghai: Shanghai Jiao Tong University press, 2000:37.

Computer, Intelligent Computing and Education Technology – Liu, Sung & Yao (Eds)
© *2014 Taylor & Francis Group, London, ISBN 978-1-138-02469-4*

Discussion on metallogenic environment, mineralization and genesis of Dahongshan Iron-Copper Deposit, Yunnan

M.G. Deng, R. Xu, P. Wang, F.B. Cang, L. Zeng, C.L. Lv & W. Liu
Faculty of Land Resource Engineering, Kunming University of Science and Technology, Kunming, Yunnan, China

ABSTRACT: Dahongshan Iron-Copper Deposit (Hereafter to be shorted as DICD) is located to the northeast of the Honghe fault at the western margin of the Yangtze Paraplatform, and at the southern end of the Kangdian Axis. DICD is composed of a large-scale high-grade iron deposit and a large-scale high-grade copper deposit, hosted in the Pre-Sinian palaeomarine volcanic rocks. DICD is a combination of various deposits, which are interactive in genesis, approximately centered around a volcanic intrusion activity center. These deposits constitute a typical plaeosubmarine volcanic eruption-sedimentation metallogenic series. The study on the Early Proterozoic Dahongshan Group meta-volcanic rocks indicates that the volcanic rocks have typical nature of ocean-ridge tholeiite and that the magma sources have the features of little enriched transitional mantle (T-type MORB). Combined with the palaeotectonic study, we consider that the volcanic rocks are the product of marginal basins during the process of extension. Rifting caused the relatively enclosed reducing marine basins, in which the well-known "Dahongshan" iron-copper deposit was formed under the volcanic eruption-sedimentation-superimposition.

Keywords: early proterozoic; Dahongshan Iron-Copper Deposit; tholeiitic magmas; volcanic eruption-sedimentation; the deposit genesis; Yunnan

1 INTRODUCTION

Dahongshan iron-copper deposit, which is located in Xinpin County, Yunnan, is one of the well-known iron-copper deposits in China. Its metallogenic geological setting and genesis, ore-forming regularity, prospecting potential, as well as its techniques and methods of prospecting have been concerned by the geological academic circles all the way. However, there exists a great divergence in the cognition of its causes of formation, which mainly includes the concepts of Enrichment of Metamorphic Hydrotherm (Yingxuan yang, 1972), Vulcanian Eruption (exhalation)-Depositional Metamorphic Deposit (Jinhe Qian, Yuanen Shen, 1983), Metamorphous Vulcanian Exhalation-Sedimentary Deposit (Yingxuan Yang, *et al.*1988), as well as Volcano and Subvolcano eruption-sedimentation, Metamorphic and Late Reformation (Jiacong Sun, Dexian Qin, *et al.*.1993). The discrepancy, to a certain extent, has restricted and affected the prospecting orientation of the deposit. Therefore, it is of practical significance to strengthen and deepen the study of the genesis of the typical deposit, and to establish a reasonable metallogenic model guiding the exploring, predictinging and evaluating of the deep, peripheral and similar deposit areas.

2 GEOLOGIC CHARACTERISTICS OF THE DEPOSIT

Dahongshan iron (copper) deposit, which occurred in the Dahongshan Formation of Early Proterozoic Dahongshan Group, is surrounded by volcanic lavas. The major copper (iron) ore beds of the deposit are located in the third segment of Manganghe Group and their rocks is mostly tuffaceous marbles. The volcanic rocks, which are of typical submarine ridge tholeiite series, extend in EW direction of strike and constitute EW-trend volcanic eruption zone. Six subvolcanic apparatuses have been found in the section of 18 km in length with spreading axis. The subvolcanoes have formed extremely distinctive proximal volcanic and distal volcanic conduit phases. The lavas are rich in sodium due to intense water-rock exchange. Original magmas show an obvious iron-rich tendency with a high mafic content, corresponding to spilite and keratophyre. The main copper ore bodies of the deposit are large-scale to very large-scale thin platy and stratoid ore bodies, of which copper-iron association can be seen commonly. The main iron ore bodies are thick and big lenses or stratoid large-scale ore bodies, and the copper ore bodies are composed of chalcopyrite-magnetite ores with higher tuffaceous and carbonaceous content. The majority of iron ore bodies are

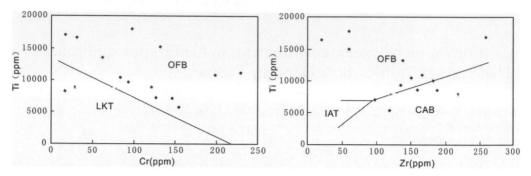

Figure 1. Ti-Cr and Ti-Zr diagrams of basalts (after Pearce, 1975, Garcia, 1979). OFB—ocean-floor basalt, LKT—island arc low-K tholeiite, CAB—calc-alkaline basalt, IAT—island arc tholeiite.

single magnetite or a combination of chalcopyrite and magnetite, while the great thick iron-rich ore bodies are composed of hematite-magnetite-quartz combination. The upper and lower sections and the surrounding area of the copper ore bodies are generally transited into siderite (-magnetite) association. The Ores in the copper ore bodies are of sparsely disseminated and banded structures; the ores in the iron ore bodies generally are of flow, massive, leopard and phyric-banded etc. structures. With dominantly sideronitic texture. The wallrock alteration of the deposit includes albitization, silification, chloritization, biotitization and carbonatation and the regional metamorphism occurred in greenschist facies and low amphibolite facies. Late-stage faults have no control over orebodies with indistinctive damage.

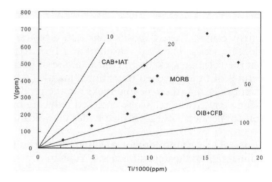

Figure 2. V-Ti/1000 diagram of basaltic rocks (after Shervais, 1982). MORB—Mid-ocean ridge basalt, OIB—Ocean island basalt, CAB—Calc-alkaline basalt, CFB—Continental flood basalt.

3 TECTONIC ENVIRONMENT OF THE FORMATION OF THE DAHONGSHAN GROUP METAVOLCANIC ROCKS

Basaltic rocks are effective for indicating the tectonic environment of the formation of volcanic rocks. Various available diagrams can be used for discriminating the tectonic environment of basaltic rock formation. So the discretion of metamorphic and altered volcanic rocks should be made by immobile component discrimination diagrams. According to the Ti-Cr and Ti-Zr diagrams (see Fig. 1); the meta-volcanic rocks of Dahongshan Group mainly fall into the Ocean-Floor Basalt (OFB) region, while the V-Ti/1000 diagram (see Fig. 2) shows that they all fall in the Mid-Ocean Ridge Basalt (MORB) region. The term of MORB with a broad sense in concepts, includes ocean-floor ridges in the marginal sea basin under extension as well. The palaeotectonic study shows that the protolith of the Dahongshan Group metavolcanic rock is mid-ocean ridge tholeiite, which was

formed in the marginal-basin ridge environment. The MORB type can be further indentified using N b-Zr and Y-Zr diagrams (see Fig. 3), which obviously show the protolith is of T type and MORB type, i.e., the tholeiitic magma are sourced from transitional mantle characterized by little enrichment. Besides, the Y-Zr diagram indicates that the loss of Y during alteration leads to the lower Y content, and partial samples fall into the enriched mantle region (P-MORB), and the phenomenon is especially distinct in the mineralized volcanic rock samples with strong alteration. The study on massive volumes of volcano-metamorphic sedimentary deposits of different periods and modern ocean-floor hydrothermal activities indicates that they were all formed in various tensional environments, such as mid-ocean ridge, continental rift zone, back-arc basin and intra-arc basin zone etc.; however, the mid-ocean ridge and the island arc formed volcanic deposits of extremely different types, respectively. The volcanic deposits formed in mid-ocean ridge are characterized by Cu, Cu-Zn

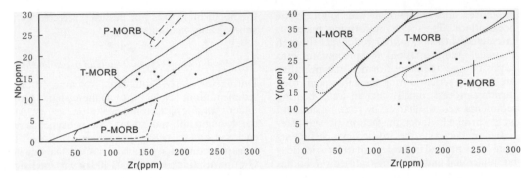

Figure 3.   Nb-Zr and Y-Zr diagrams of basaltic rocks (after LeRoex et al, 1983). The straight lines represent primitive mantle.

and Cu-Fe types. The reason is that the mid-ocean ridge crust is composed of basaltic rocks relatively rich in Cu and Fe, which can provide more Cu and Fe during water circulation and water-rock reaction. Dahongshan volcanic deposit is rich in Cu and Fe and poor in Pb and Zn, which is consistent with the ocean ridge (the general mid-ocean ridge) environment where the deposit originated.

4   THE FUNCTION OF DEPOSIT FORMATION

4.1   Ocean-floor sodium-rich volcanic eruption-sedimentation function

1. Function of Volcanic eruption-segregation: In magma chamber, the primitive sodium magma, rich in volatile and iron after differentiation, gradually evolved into two kinds of magmas: the upper magma which was poor in iron and the lower magma which was rich in iron; after that, the upper magma overflowed first under tectonic stress, followed by the overflow of the upper magma; then the magmas formed the volcanic eruption-segregation deposit by crystallization and differentiation near the volcanic crater.

2. Function of volcanic ore magma eruption: In regard to the deposit formation of the iron ore magmas, most scholars hold the view that iron-rich silicate magmas were liquated from magma chambers in the deep crust under strong differentiation. The magmas in the area have a relatively deep source and its parent magmas are probably tholeiitic magmas. The strong differentiation of this kind of magmas formed light gray meta-sodium volcanic rocks of the lower cycle of the Hongshan Formation and segregated ferruginous magmatic melts or iron ore magmas. The pulsation of crust activities led to the periodicity of magma evolution and rhythmicity and the

cyclicity of ore magma eruption. In the beginning of each cycle, the magmas of lower-degree differentiation overflowed from the volcanic crater under lateral pressure, then the sodium magmas rich in iron and volatile components in a plastic state were broken, torn, included, flowed and cooled, etc. by the later overflowed magmas; these overflowed magmas condensed into iron-rich meta-sodium lavas; subsequently, iron-bearing materials gradually enriched in the magma chamber and formed disseminated iron-poor ores; as further differentiation of parent magma residual melts, an immiscible, ferruginous fluid-magma was segregated and formed iron-rich ore horizons with compact massive structure rightly on the disseminated iron ore bodies.

3. Volcanic eruption-sedimentation function: In the Early Proterozoic, the area was in the continental margin, and a marginal rift type eugeosyncline was formed parallel to the active continental marginal zone; the eugeosyncline with a series of depressions alternating with uplifts, generally strikes from north to south. These depression basins, striking nearly from east to west, formed a secondary tectonic zone at the rift bottom, which was controlled by the nearly EW directional faults in the Ailaoshan Group crystalline basement. A great number of eruptions and overflows of magmatic melts of marine-facies tholeiite series occurred within these depression basins at the bottom of these rift zones, which was associated with paroxysmal activities, and thus formed a multi-cycle and multi-rhythm ocean-floor volcanic eruption-sedimentary series. At the later or dormant stages of volcanic eruptions, a large-scale magma eruption weakened, but exhalation and hydrothermal activities were still intense; these gas and fluid containing rich mineralized materials moved upward along fractures and

interstices, and continuously overflowed to the ocean floor. Then the ore-forming materials interacted with ocean-floor sediments through chemical sedimentation to precipitate into deposits, and therefore, formed the primitive ore-bearing series. During the subsequent rock forming process, much water in water-bearing sediments were discharged by compression and were shrinked; under the action of sulphate-reducing bacteria, the iron-copper sediments were concentrated in the deposit to form lenticular, phacoidal and stratoid-stratified ore bodies with striped and banded structures. In this way, the primitive concentration and positioning process of mineralization was accomplished.

4. Function of Low temperature hot-water deposition: The excalation of the volcano and the dissolution of the seawater to the ejectamenta (i.e. volcanic ash, volcanic rubble and volcanic lava etc.) and maceration of submarine rocks and sediments in the late stage of the palaeo-submarine volcanic eruption, are main source of the massive volumes of mineralized materials (i.e. iron, copper, sulphur and carbon dioxide etc.); seawater dissolved a great amount of afore-mentioned ore-forming materials, and transported them to a distant place from the volcanic eruption center. As physical and chemical conditions varied, a series of chemical reactions occurred in the environment with rich carbon dioxide and poor oxygen, which resulted in the direct deposition of iron carbonates. Later siderite deposits were formed through mineralization and regional metamorphism.

4.2 *Function of subvolcanic gas-fluid metasomasis (filling)*

At the late stage of the submarine volcanic eruption activity in the area, the volcanic crater collapsed and was plugged (the northern collapsed boundary is roughly located near the current F_2) after the eruption generally finished due to the pressure of the magma chamber decreased. In this process, the residual magmas (porphyritic diabase magmas) of the magma chamber in the deep went up along the volcanic conduit but unable to erupt to the surface and thus injected into the sodium volcanic rocks in the form of collapsed blocks, forming iron-bearing lavas and low grade iron ores in the volcanic chimney. Subsequently, a great number of associated iron-rich subvolcanic gas-fluids were strongly filled to or made Metasomatic Replacement with iron-bearing lavas in the volcanic pipe and lean iron ore stratum, forming the thick and large-scale II_1 hematite-magnetite rich ore body. Generally corresponding to horizons II_3, II_{5-1} and II_{5-4}; However, due to the plugging of collapse faults, the area to

the north of F_1 was not basically affected by the sub-volcanic gas-fluids.

4.3 *Modification effect of regional metamorphism*

During the Early Proterozoic volcanic eruption-sedimentation cycle, the Dahongshan Group underwent a long tectonic evolution history. After the Xiaoguanhe movement, the geosyncline was enclosed, and the rift disappeared and returned. The volcanic-sedimentary rock series of Dahongshan Group with thickness up to 2 400 m was intensively folded and metamorphosed. The Jinning movement and associated magma activities caused the sodium replacement of ore bodies to occur, which made the iron-bearing materials of disperse or low-grade iron ore bodies reconcentrated to form iron-rich ore bodies. In addition, further intense metamorphism made the preformed iron-copper ore layers and bodies together with other wallrocks metamorphosed as garnet greenschist, garnet-plagioclase amphibolites schist, albite-chlorite-biotite schist and scapolite, dolomite marble. Regional metamorphism produced greenschist-amphibolite facies. Ore bodies were originally controlled by folding and faulting; after dynamometamorphism, the orebody underwent complicated change of shape, swell-pinch of thickness and branch-complex of shape. Moreover, local veinlets that cross-cut the bedding were formed and iron mineral crystalloblasts became larger in size, resulting in the secondary enrichment and position.

5 GENESIS AND METALLOGENIC MODEL OF THE DEPOSIT

According to the aforementioned descriptions, the DICD is a suite of deposits interconnected in time, space and genesis, a submarine volcanic metallogenic series. The deposit should be of composite genesis, and was formed by submarine sodiumvolcanic eruption-sedimentation-superimposition. Its metallogenic model can be developed and identified by the following characteristics:

1. Rifting created the primary rift-trough environment for the Dahongshan area, and provided favorable enclosed reducing basin environment for the mineralization of the Early Proterozoic submarine sodium-rich volcanic eruption sedimentation.

2. Volcanic eruptions provided sufficient deep or mantle-derived mineralized materials. The Early Proterozoic submarine sodium-rich volcanic eruption sedimentation formed four types of iron-copper deposits, i.e. volcanic overflow-segregation type, sub-volcanic metasomasis ore-rich magma type, volcanic eruption-sedimentation type and

low temperature hot-water sedimentation type. Subsequently, sodium metasomasis occurred under the regional metamorphism and basic magma intrusion; and affected by the late-stage activization-orogeny tectonic superimposing, mineralized elements were reactivated, transported, and further concentrated into ore bodies. Certainly, massive sulphurs in the submarine environment are also originated from the restoring of sea water sulfates.

3. Volcanic eruptions provided enough heat energy for the mineralization of the volcanic eruption-sedimentation in the Dahongshan area, and driving force came from convection induced by groundwater in seawater and mineralized elements leached from rocks along flowing conduits. While the Late Proterozoic Jinning hydrothermal event provided necessary thermal power and mineralization media for the late-stage metamorphic mineralization, promoting the mineralized elements to be activated and transported.

6 CONCLUSIONS

1. The DICD, which was occurred in the Dahong-shan Formation of Early Proterozoic Dahong-shan Group, is hosted by volcanic lavas, with major copper (iron) ore horizons being located in the third Member, Manganghe Formation. Main iron ore bodies are large-scale thickly lenticular bodies parallel to bedding or straitoid bodies. Main copper ore bodies are thinly platy and stratiod bodies with large to super-large scale.

2. The Dahongshan Group meta-volcanic rock is composed of typical ocean-ridge tholeiite series. The volcanic iron-copper deposits are formed by the meta-volcanic rocks in marginal basin ridge environment and have Cu-Fe metallogenetic specialization.

3. Ocean-floor tholeiitic magmas provided ore-forming fluids, materials and heat; mineralization occurred in relatively closed and reductive marine facies basin ore-forming enviroment which were formed under rifting. Volcanic eruption and sedimentation provided sufficient deep or mantle-derived ore-forming materials, which contribute to the formation of the stratiform ore bodies of the Dahongshan iron-copper deposit. Sub-volcanic gas-fluid replacing (filling) made hematite-magnetite ore bodies formed; the late rifts disappeared and returned made the deposit intense folded and regional metamorphized. Therefore, the orebody underwent complicated change in shape with branching-compound phenomenon and formed cross-cut bedding veinlets and stratiform ore bodies.

ACKNOWLEDGEMENT

It is a project supported by the National Basic Research Program of China (No. 41363001). The corresponding author is Mingguo Deng.

Computer, Intelligent Computing and Education Technology – Liu, Sung & Yao (Eds)
© 2014 Taylor & Francis Group, London, ISBN 978-1-138-02469-4

Material flow analysis of titanium resources in China

Y.F. Zhang, G.S. Wang & Q.S. Chen
Institute of Mineral Resources, Chinese Academy of Geological Sciences, Beijing, China

Y.S. Zhou
China University of Geosciences, Beijing, China

ABSTRACT: Titanium is a widely used metal of many great properties. Sponge titanium and titanium dioxide are the two most important products of titanium. Unlike other common studies of titanium by separating them into two major production categories, we focus on titanium as a whole in the analysis. In this article, by analyzing the supply and demand trends, import and export trends, titanium scrap recovery and other aspects, we established a simple framework of titanium material flow in China to provide data based support for future development in titanium.

Keywords: titanium resources; material flow analysis; scrap recovery

1   INTRODUCTION

Titanium, also call "The baby metal" by the Japan Titanium Association according to its application history, has many excellent qualities such as the combination of low specific gravity (only 60% of iron) and high strength (more than twice of iron, 6 times of aluminum), anticorrosion, biocompatibility and non-magnetic. Due to many of its property advantages and a broad application in aerospace, shipbuilding and automobile industry, Titanium has been given names like "Space metal", "Marine metal" and "Smart metal".

China is one of the world's largest titanium industrial country. In 2012, 50% of the world's sponge titanium production (productive capacity: 148,500 tons/year) and 37% of the world's titanium dioxide production (productive capacity:

2.6 million tons/year) are from China. However, current studies intend to separate Chinese titanium industry into two distinct industries of sponge titanium and titanium dioxide causing the absence of a comprehensive view of the titanium element flow in the entire industrial chain (Wang X.D. et al. 2011, Wang X.D. et al. 2013, Deng J. 2013 Bi S. 2010). Based on this, we established a basic framework of titanium material flow in China by analyzing the titanium industry supply and demand trends, import and export situation and the recovery of titanium in China in the past 10 years. The titanium material flow framework is made for early stage quantitative based support for further research on sustainable development of Chinese titanium industry.

The text should fit exactly into the type area of 187 × 272 mm (7.36″ × 10.71″). For correct settings of margins in the Page Setup dialog box (File menu) see Table 1.

2   SUPPLY AND DEMAND

2.1   Titanium resource

Titanium is widely distributed in the Earth's crust, whose abundance is 6320×10^{-6} just after iron, aluminum and magnesium. Ilmenite and rutile are the two most important titanium-bearing ore. From statistics provided by USGS, ilmenite with a world reserve of 650 mt (TiO_2, the same below) in 2012 (Fig. 1) is mainly located in China (200 Mt), Australia (100 Mt), India (85 Mt) and South Africa (63 Mt). The total global production of

Table 1.   Import and export of Titanium products in China from 2006 to 2012 (Units: kt).

Time	Mineral concentrate im	Sponge titanium im	Sponge titanium ex	Processing material im	Processing material ex	Titanium dioxide im	Titanium dioxide ex
2006	880	1.6	1.9	4.7	4.6	257	194
2007	1220	1.1	5.6	4.0	8.0	276	138
2008	1100	1.2	6.3	6.4	8.6	251	98
2009	1480	3.6	0.4	5.5	4.5	249	104
2010	2030	3.4	3.6	6.1	7.6	269	266
2011	2270	0.2	8.7	6.4	11.3	229	398
2012	2890	0.1	4.5	5.0	12.3	163	385

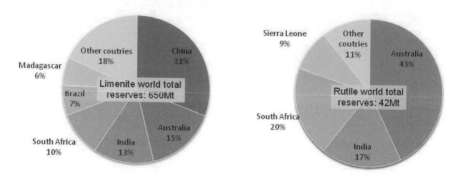

Figure 1. Distribution of reserves limenite and Rutile Reserve in 2012.
Date source: USGS.

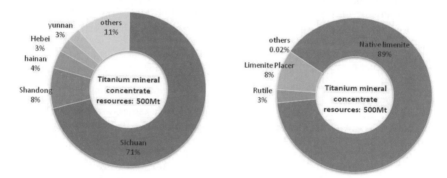

Figure 2. Distribution (left) and type (right) of titanium resources and in China.
Data sources: China Reserves Bulletin in 2012.

ilmenite in 2012 is 6.2 Mt (only 1/105 of its total reserves) implying its rather large reserve supply. On the other hand rutile, with a world reserve of 42 Mt mainly located in Australia (18 Mt), South Africa (8.3 Mt) and India (7.4 Mt), has a comparably low amount of resources especially the high-grade rutile used for titanium dioxide production.

China is a country rich of titanium resources. Among the over 500 MT resources 88% are vanadium-titanium magnetite deposit ilmenite. Other than vanadium-titanium magnetite deposit ilmenite titanium is also commonly found ilmenite sands and rutile (Fig. 2). These titanium-bearing resources are mainly distributed in Sichuan, Shandong, Hebei, Hainan (placer) and Yunnan (placer). Although China is sufficient in raw titanium resources, the domestic titanium-bearing ore supply still cannot match the demands caused by the enormous production capacity of titanium dioxide and sponge titanium. Therefore in China a great proportion of titanium mineral concentrate comes from importation.

2.2 Production and capacity

In recent years with the rise of the titanium industry there has been a rapid increase in the titanium market of new producers bringing in more products (Fig. 3). 2012 Chinese production of titanium mineral concentrates (700 kt), titanium sponge (81 kt) and titanium dioxide (1871 kt) expanded 0.75, 19 and 3 times compared to the statistics in 2003. Moreover, the mining efficiency has also grown with more ores coming out of each mine. Products like sponge titanium and titanium dioxide have grown 34 and 5 times since 2003. Thus with such high production the usage rate of the mineral is at its new low of 55% for sponge titanium and 67% for titanium dioxide. Now the titanium industry is facing its new problem of "too much Ti" especially for sponge titanium (70% rutile-type, 30% anatase-type).

2.3 Consumption and consumption structure

Titanium consumption increased simultaneously with the development of national economy and the expansion of Chinese titanium industry (Fig. 4).

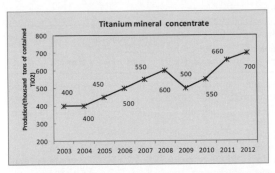

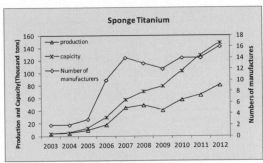

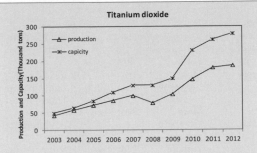

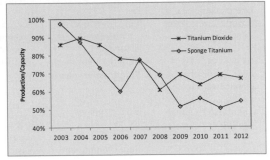

Figure 3. Production and productive capacity of titanium products in China.
Data sources: USGS, Development Report on China Titanium Industry in 2003–2012.

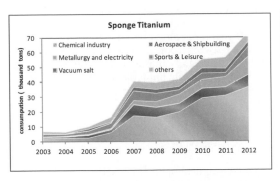

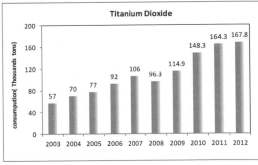

Figure 4. Consumption of sponge titanium and titanium dioxide in China.
Data sources: Development Report on China Titanium Industry in 2003–2012.

For example sponge titanium consumption in 2012 hit a record high of 73 thousand tons which is 9 times the amount of 2003. These sponge titanium are used to produce titanium ingots and titanium processing material. Of which the titanium processing material will be carried on in the further use of fields such as chemical industry (including petrochemical and mineral industries, etc.), aerospace, shipbuilding, metallurgy, electric power, vacuum salt, and sports and leisure industries (such as golf clubs, spectacle frames and watches and other goods), etc. Other than sponge titanium, the consumption of titanium dioxide also has a significant

amount of 168 thousand tons (2 times of 2003) in 2012. Consumption structure of titanium dioxide is roughly as 58% ~ 62% in paint, 21% to 25% in plastics, 6% to 8% in making paper, 3% to 5% in ink and 6% in others (Jia D.M. 2010).

3 IMPORT AND EXPORT

China played an important role in the titanium trades importing titanium resources (mainly mineral concentrates) while exports sponge titanium and titanium dioxide (Table 1). Despite the

Table 2. Titanium recovery status in China.

Application products	Product form	Recyclable products	Recovery cycle (year)	Current Recovery rate	Remark
Aircraft, rockets (engines, airframe)	Various alloy (Ti-6 Al-4V, etc.)	Waste engine Scrap Aircraft	10 20	0%	Possible in future
Thermal power, nuclear power (condenser tubes, turbo)	Titanium tubes, plates, plating, etc.	Scrap tubes, discarded equipment	30	0%	Possible in future
Petroleum and other chemical industry (pipe towers, vessels, heat exchangers)	Titanium tube, titanium	Scrap tubes, discarded equipment	More than 20	Not clear	Between producers and users
Electrode, electrolyzer	Pure titanium sheets (with Pd, Ru, Ta), tubes	Scrap tubes, discarded equipment	3~10	70%	Between producers and users
Plate heat exchanger	Pure titanium sheets	Waste sheets	5~10	60%	
Construction, civil engineering (root house, exterior, tube)	Pure titanium sheets	Waste sheets	More than 50	0%	Rare in China, only Japan and United States
Vacuum Salt making equipment	Various alloy	Scrap tubes, discarded equipment	More than 20	Not clear	Between producers and users
Products for sports and leisure	Pure titanium or Various alloy	Various forms	Years or permanent	Not clear	Uncertain forms, difficult to recycle

abundance of titanium resources, China still has to import great amount of advanced mineral concentrates, which are used to produce higher-quality titanium dioxide a form of titanium that consumes more than 90% of the mineral concentrate production every year. Therefore, the import of the titanium mineral concentrates (2891 kt in 2012) has been increasing recently. For sponge titanium, titanium processing and dioxide china have taken a role as an exporter. However, the quality of titanium dioxide products made in China is not qualified enough to compete with those international companies like DuPont and the average export price is much lower than the average import price. Also the high-end titanium dioxide products are still dominated by foreign markets (Deng J. 2013).

4 SCRAP RECOVERY ASSESSMENT

Titanium industry has a short history in China, likewise the recovery market of this metal is still in its preliminary stage. The titanium used in paint and plastic industry are hard to recover making it non-profitable to form a market. Aerospace and nuclear facilities have a long life cycle; few retired facilities can be found now. Similarly, titanium tubes and bricks used in the chemical industry have a recycling period of 20 years (Table 2); and the recycling process has been monopolized by their

producers and users. For electrode and palladium alloy titanium plate, the recycling period is short (3–10 years) making it possible for recovery agreements between cooperatives. Other miscellaneous products like golf clubs and glass frames are insignificant and with unpredictable recycling period making it difficult to sustain a market.

5 MATERIAL FLOW ANALYSIS FRAMEWORK

The titanium mineral flows (shown in Fig. 5) is a process of Titanium bearing-ore turning into sponge titanium and titanium dioxide, then turning sponge titanium and titanium dioxide into titanium ingot, titanium powder and other titanium material, afterwards using them on consumer goods. This article is based on the process stated above has analyzed imports and exports, domestic production and consumption and recovery of titanium metal.

In international titanium trades, china is both an exporter and an importer: exiting sponge titanium, titanium materials and low tech titanium dioxide products, while entering titanium resource. Titanium resource relies deeply on import: sponge titanium and titaniumtim are only used domestically; titanium dioxide even with a net export still has many problems. The production process of titanium

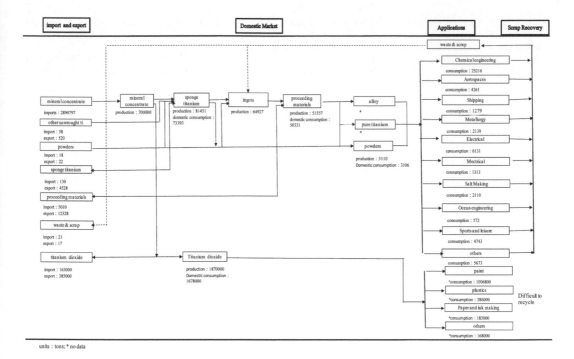

Figure 5. Material flow analysis framework of titanium resources in China.

dioxide in china is a sulfuric acid method which is a non-environmentally friendly and low efficiency method that has been long abandoned in many countries. Due to its low-end qualities the products are not competitive worldwide and china still has to import high-end titanium dioxide while exporting low-end ones. Also China has an import price of 3343CNY per ton while the international average titanium dioxide price is 2946CNY per ton.

In the domestic production sector sponge titanium has a great market potential whereas titanium dioxide shows the opposite. Sponge titanium has many the special properties used in core parts if many mechanics, airplanes, automobiles and experiments. However with high cost this metal of great capabilities is still needs to be promoted into many other fields. Titanium dioxide on the other hand has already surpassed its peak and its high pollution sulfuric acid process for production needs to be replaced by chlorination process.

In the consumption and recovery process, China and Japan have similar applications where both countries mainly use their titanium in civil and industrial sectors. Moreover the titanium usage in construction and automobile industries still needs to be explored. To prevent future environment crisis and increase material usage recycling associations and second hand markets should be built before hand.

As the author I believe titanium metal will be accompanying the development and evolution of the Chinese economy. From the current titanium situation of unprofessional statistics, insufficient titanium supply and unnecessary surplus of titanium dioxide we know china still needs to improve the titanium industry. Regulations must be made in all the sections of the titanium mineral flow from its mining process to its recycling market. As this new strategic industry begin to dominate of future products this framework of mineral flow will assist us to understand more about this industry.

75%. Therefore, 9 point should be the minimum size of the lettering. Lines should preferably be 0.2 mm (0.1″) thick. Keep figures as simple as possible. Avoid excessive notes and designations.

ACKNOWLEDGEMENT

It is a project supported by the Geological survey project funding (12120113091800). The corresponding author is Gaoshang Wang.

REFERENCES

Bi S. 2010. Resuscitation of China titanium dioxide industry in 2009 and the prospect: China coatings. Vol. 25, p40–44.

Deng J. 2013. Titanium dioxide operation in China in 2012 and Forecast: China coatings. Vol. 28, p13–20.

Information on http://www.usgs.gov/.

Information on http://www.jogmec.go.jp.

Jia D.M. 2010. Market analysis of titanium dioxide: Chemical industry. Vol. 28, p20–22.

Wang X.D., Lu F.S., Jia H. & Hao B. 2013. China titanium industry in 2012: China titanium industry. Vol. 1, p. 3–9.

Wang X.D., Lu F.S., Jia H. & Hao B. 2011. Development report on China titanium industry in 2010: Materials China. Vol. 30, p14–20.

Computer, Intelligent Computing and Education Technology – Liu, Sung & Yao (Eds)
© 2014 Taylor & Francis Group, London, ISBN 978-1-138-02469-4

Optimal short-term hydrothermal scheduling based on harmony search algorithm

P. Ren

School of Information Engineering, Shenyang University, Shenyang, China

N. Li

Shenyang University, Shenyang, China

ABSTRACT: In this paper, the nonlinear optimal control problem is formulated as a multi-objective mathematical optimization problem. Harmony Search (HS) algorithm is one of the new heuristic algorithms. The HS optimization algorithm is introduced for the first time in solving the optimal short-term hydrothermal scheduling in power systems. A case on consisting of 9 buses, 11 transmission lines, four thermal plants and three hydro plants in Indian utility system is presented to show the methodology's feasibility and efficiency. Compared with the optimal short-term hydrothermal scheduling of power systems, the search time of the HS optimization algorithm is shorter and the result is close to the ideal solution.

Keywords: short-term hydrothermal scheduling; harmony search algorithm; optimal

1 INTRODUCTION

Short-term hydrothermal scheduling of power systems aims at determining optimal hydro and thermal generations in order to meet the load demands over a scheduled horizon of one day or a week while satisfying the various constraints on the hydraulic and power system network. The goal is to minimize total operation costs of thermal plants. The problem is a complex mathematical optimization problem with a highly nonlinear and computational expensive environment.

Several methods have been developed to solve this problem, including Dynamic Programming (DP) [1], Network Flow Programming (NFP) [2], Non-Linear Programming (NLP) technique in combination with NFP [3], Decomposition Approach (DA) and Linear Programming (LP) [4] method etc.

Harmony Search (HS) algorithm has been recently developed [5] in an analogy with improvisation process where musicians always try to polish their pitches to obtain a better harmony. Music improvisation process is similar to the optimum design process which seeks to find optimum solution. The pitch of each musical instrument determines the certain quality of harmony, just like the objective function assigned to the set of variables. The HS algorithm has been successfully applied to many real world optimization algorithms in terms of solution quality [6].

The organization of this paper is made as follows. The optimal short-term hydrothermal scheduling of power systems is formulated in section 2.

Section 3 describes HS algorithm. A case is studied in section 4. Section 5 draws the conclusion.

2 PROBLEM FORMULATION

The time span of the day is subdivided into 24 equal hourly intervals and the load is assumed to remain constant over each interval. The reservoir inflows, correction factors for head variations and generating units available for scheduling each interval are assumed as deterministically known. In all hydro plants, evaporation, water travel time and spill over of water in the hydro reservoirs are neglected.

The one-day hydrothermal scheduling problem is stated as [7]: Determine the water discharge D_{ij} for the ith reservoir, $i = 1, 2, ..., NH$ during the jth discrete time interval, $j = 1, 2, ..., N$ and the corresponding generation schedule of the hydro plants, PH_{ij} and the generation schedule of the thermal plants, PT_{mj}; $m = 1, 2, ..., NT$ so as to minimize the total fuel cost during the day

$$TPC = \sum_{M=1}^{NT} \sum_{j=1}^{N} F_{mj}\left(PT_{mj}\right) \qquad (1)$$

subject to: the power balance constraints

$$\sum_{m=1}^{NT} PT_{mj} + \sum_{i=1}^{NH} PH_{ij} = PD_j + PL_j; \quad j = 1, 2, ..., N$$

$$(2)$$

the water balance equation

$$Y_{i,j} + 1 = Y_{ij} + AL_{ij} - D_{ij}; \quad i = 1, 2, ..., NH;$$
$$j = 1, 2, ..., N \tag{3}$$

the active power generation of hydro plants

$$PH_{ij} = \left(\frac{H_{oi}}{G}\right)\left[1 + \frac{C_i\left(Y_{ij} + Y_{i,j} + 1\right)}{2}\right]D_{ij};$$
$$i = 1, 2, ..., NH; \quad j = 1, 2, ..., N \tag{4}$$

the limits on water storage level in reservoirs

$$Y_{i,\min} \le Y_{ij} \le Y_{i,\max}; \quad i = 1, 2, ..., NH; \quad j = 1, 2, ..., N \tag{5}$$

with $Y_{i,1}$ and $Y_{i,N+1}$ fixed for $i = 1, 2, ..., NH$ the limits on water discharge

$$D_{i,\min} \le D_{ij} \le D_{i,\max}; \quad i = 1, 2, ..., NH; \quad j = 1, 2, ..., N \tag{6}$$

the limits on active power generation of hydro units

$$PH_{i,\min} \le PH_{ij} \le PH_{i,\max}; \quad i = 1, 2, ..., NH;$$
$$j = 1, 2, ..., N \tag{7}$$

The optimal power flow problem for jth interval with transmission security constraint is formulated as:

$$TFC_i = \sum_{\substack{m=1 \\ m \ne s}}^{NT} (a_m PT_{mj}^2 + b_m PT_{mj} + c_m)$$
$$+ a_S PT_{sj}^2 + b_S PT_{sj} + c_S; \quad j = 1, 2, ..., N \tag{8}$$

the power balance constraints

$$\sum_{m=1}^{NT} PT_{mj} = PD_{th,j} + PL_j; \quad j = 1, 2, ..., N \tag{9}$$

where

$$PD_{th,j} = PD_j - \sum_{i=1}^{NH} PH_{ij} \tag{10}$$

the limits on active power generation of thermal plants

$$PT_{m,\min} \le PT_{mj} \le PT_{m,\max}; \quad m = 1, 2, ..., NT;$$
$$m \ne s; \quad j = 1, 2, ..., N \tag{11}$$

the slack bus constraint

$$P_{s,\min} \le P_{sj} \le P_{s,\max}; \quad j = 1, 2, ..., N \tag{12}$$

the transmission line flows

$$\phi_{k,\min} \le \phi_k \le \phi_{k,\max}; \quad k = 1, 2, ..., NL \tag{13}$$

the power flow equations

$$F_i(X, U, C) = 0; \quad i = 1, 2, ..., NB \tag{14}$$

The state vector X comprises of the bus voltage phase angles and magnitudes. The control vector U comprises of all the controllable system variables like real power generations. The parameter vector C includes all the uncontrollable system parameters such as line parameters, and loads.

3 MATH ANALYSIS OF HS ALGORITHM

The Harmony Search (HS) algorithm, proposed by Geem and Kim [8], is a nature inspired algorithm, mimicking the improvisation of music players. The harmony in music is analogous to the optimization solution vector, and the musician's improvisations are analogous to the local and global search schemes in optimization techniques. The HS algorithm uses the concept, how aesthetic estimation helps to find the perfect state of harmony, to determine the optimum value of the objective function. The HS algorithm is simple in concept, few in parameters and easy in implementation. It has been successfully applied to various optimization problems. The optimization procedure of the HS algorithm is as follows:

Step 1: Initialization.

In this step, the optimization problem is specified as follows:

$$M \inf(x) S.t. g(x) = 0 \, x_{k,\min} \le x \le x_{k,\max}$$
$$k = 1, 2, ..., N$$

where $f(x)$ is the objective function, $g(x)$ is the equality constraint, x is the set of decision variables, x_{min}, x_{max} are minimum and maximum limits of decision variables and N is the number of decision variables. The HS algorithm parameter are also specified in this step. These are the Harmony Memory Size (HMS) or the number of solution vectors in the harmony memory, Harmony Memory Considering Rate (HMCR), Pitch Adjustment Rate (PAR), Bandwidth Rate (BW) and the Number of Improvisations (NI) or the stopping condition.

Step 2: Initialization of harmony memory.

The Harmony Memory (HM) is a memory location where all the solution vectors (sets of decision variables) are stored. The HM is similar to the number of population in other evolutionary algorithms. The HM matrix (15) is filled with as many randomly generated values between its minimum and maximum limits.

$$HM = \begin{pmatrix} x_1^1 & \cdots & x_N^1 \\ \cdots & \cdots & \cdots \\ x_1^{HMS} & \cdots & x_N^{HMS} \end{pmatrix} \quad (15)$$

Step 3: Improvisation of a new harmony from the HM.

Generating a new harmony is called as improvisation. In the memory consideration, the value of decision variables X' for the new vector are selected from $(x^1 - x^{HMS})$. The Harmony Memory Considering Rate (HMCR), which varies between 0 and 1, is the rate of choosing one value from the historical values stored in HM, while $(1 - HMCR)$ is the rate of randomly selecting one value from the possible range of values as

$$x_i' = \begin{cases} x_i' \in \left\{ x_i^1, ..., x_i^{HMS} \right\} if rand \leq HMCR \\ x_i' \in X_i \; otherwise \end{cases} \quad (16)$$

where rand is the uniform random number in the range between 0 and 1 and X_i the set of possible range of values for each decision variable, that is $x_{i,min} \leq X_i \leq x_{i,max}$. This operation uses the PAR parameter, which is the rate of pitch adjustment as follows:

$$x_i' = \begin{cases} x_i' \pm rand \times BW if rand \leq PAR \\ x_i' otherwise \end{cases} \quad (17)$$

where BW is the arbitrary distance bandwidth.

To improve the performance of the HS algorithm, PAR and BW are changed during each generation as follows:

$$PAR(g) = PAR_{min} + \frac{PAR_{max} - PAR_{min}}{NI} \times g \quad (18)$$

where PAR(g) is the pitch adjusting rate of current generation, PAR_{min} is the minimum pitch adjusting rate, PAR_{max} is the maximum pitch adjusting rate, g is the current generation number and NI is the number of improvisations.

$$BW(g) = BW_{max} \exp\left(\frac{\ln\left(\frac{BW_{min}}{BW_{max}} \right)}{NI} \times g \right) \quad (19)$$

Table 1. Comparison of cost and time of HSA and GA in [7].

GA		HSA	
Time (s)	Cost (Rs)	Time (s)	Cost (Rs)
4.906	5.390731×10^6	4.158	5.321796×10^6

where BW(g) is the bandwidth rate of current generation, BW_{min} is the minimum bandwidth rate and BW_{max} is the maximum bandwidth rate.

Step 4: Updating the harmony memory.

Updating the harmony memory in HS algorithm for multi-objective optimization problem differs from that of basic HS algorithm. In this work, non-dominated sorting and ranking scheme, proposed by Deb et al. [10], is used to find the Pareto optimal solutions. The new harmony memory, generated by improvisation process, is combined with the existing harmony memory to form $2 \times HMS$ solution vectors.

Step 5: Stopping criterion.

The HS algorithm is stopped when the Number of Improvisations (NI) has been met. Otherwise step 3 and 4 are repeated.

4 A CASE STUDY

This study is aimed to find the optimal solution for the optimal short-term hydrothermal scheduling as shown in [7]. It consists of nine buses, 11 transmission lines, four thermal plants and three hydro plants. In order to avoid the misleading results due to stochastic nature of the HS, 10 trial runs were made with each run starting with different random populations. The population size was 50 genotypes in all the runs. The simulation was carried out on a Pentium(R) D, 5.00 GHz processor. Table 1 gives the comparison of execution time and cost of a 9-bus in Indian utility system. The cost of the proposed HS is comparable with that of the method in [7] of the literature and the execution time of the HSA are very less as compared with that of other method.

5 CONCLUSION

Short-term hydrothermal scheduling problem of power systems is a multi-objective mathematical optimal problem, which should be solved by a multi-objective mathematical model. In this paper, a new approach is developed using the HS algorithm. The proposed method is employed to solve the model, which is shown to be suitable for the multi-objective optimal problems. Result from a practical case on the nine buses, 11 transmission lines, four thermal plants and three hydro plants in Indian utility system is presented to show the methodology's feasibility and efficiency, and the IIS algorithm should require less computational burden and time compared to trial and error approaches.

REFERENCES

[1] Wood AJ, Wollenberg BF. Power generation, operation & control. 2nd ed. John Wiley & Sons, Inc.; 2003.
[2] Li C-A, Jap PJ, Streiffert DL. Implementation of network flow programming to the hydrothermal coordination in energy management systems. IEEE Trans Power Syst 1993;8:1045–1053.
[3] Sjelvgren D, Brannlund H, Dillon TS. Large-scale non-linear programming applied to operations planning. Int J Elec Power Energy Syst 1989;11:213–217.
[4] Mohan MR, Kuppusamy K, Khan MA. Optimal short-term hydro-thermal scheduling using decomposition approach and linear programming method. Int J Elect Power Energy Syst 1992;14:39–44.
[5] Geem ZW, Kim JH, et al. A new heuristic optimization algorithm: harmony search. Simulation 2001(76):60–68.
[6] Fesanghary M, Mahdavi M, Minary-Jolandan M, Alizadeh Y. Hybridizing harmony search algorithm with sequential quadratic programming for engineering optimization problems. Comput Methods Appl Mech Eng 2008(197):3080–3091.
[7] V. Senthil Kumar, M.R. Mohan. A genetic algorithm solution to the optimal short-term hydrothermal scheduling. Electrical Power and Energy Systems 2011(33):827–835.
[8] Geem ZW, Kim JH, et al. A new heuristic optimization algorithm: harmony search. Simulation 2001(76):60–68.
[9] S. Sivasubramani, K.S. Swarup. Multi-objective harmony search algorithm for optimal power flow problem, Electrical Power and Energy Systems 2011(33):745–752.
[10] Deb K, Pratap A, Agarwal S, Meyarivan T. A fast and elitist multi-objective genetic algorithm: NSGA-II. IEEE Trans Evolut Comput 2002(6):182–197.

Computer, Intelligent Computing and Education Technology – Liu, Sung & Yao (Eds)
© *2014 Taylor & Francis Group, London, ISBN 978-1-138-02469-4*

Study on dynamical behavior of Sturmian System

L.H. Sun & E.L. Zhao
School of Science, Shenyang Jianzhu University, Shenyang, China

C.T. Wang
School of Information and Control Engineering, Shenyang Jianzhu University, Shenyang, China

ABSTRACT: Symbolic dynamics is an iterative system that is generated by a shift on a finite symbolic space. It is a special kind of dynamics. Symbolic dynamics has a lot of theoretical and practical applications in many fields such as physics, computer and so on, so it is important to study its dynamical behavior. Sturmian System is the least complex kind of symbolic dynamics. In the present paper it proves that Sturmian System is a minimal system that has zero entropy and is not chaotic. According to some concepts on Symbolic Dynamics and properties of minimal nonchaotic on Sturmian System, we make a kind of subshift that generated by a nonperiodic recurrent orbit and study its properties. If a period point exists a subshift generated by a nonperiodic recurrent orbit, it is not certain that the subshift contains an uncountable scrambled set.

Keywords: Sturmian Systems; chaos in the sense of Li-Yorke; minimal set; subshift

1 INTRODUCTION

Symbolic dynamical system originated from J. Hadmard [1] and M. Morse [2] in the nineteenth Century and twentieth Century. It has a wide range of applications, including chaos in physics, meteorology, computational complexity, coding, computer science and the general dynamical system. In dynamical system, it is not only an important research object, also is to provide examples, proving the existence, a powerful research tool to reveal the chaotic phenomena in some systems. There is a strict mathematical description of it and its application on theory research in dynamical system in [3].

Sturmian System is the least complex kind of symbolic dynamics, so it is important to study its dynamical behavior. In the present paper the properties on Sturmian System are studied. It proves that Sturmian System is a minimal system that has zero entropy and is not chaotic. We provide an example that responds to the problems whether the subshift generated by a nonperiodic recurrent orbit contains an uncountable scrambled set. According to some concepts on Symbolic Dynamics and properties of minimal nonchaotic on Sturmian System, we make a kind of subshift that generated by a nonperiodic recurrent orbit and study its properties. If a period point exists in a subshift generated by a nonperiodic recurrent orbit, it is not certain that the subshift contains an uncountable scrambled set.

2 DEFINITION AND SYMBOLS

Definition 1 let $S = \{0, 1, 2, ..., N-1\}$ for some integer $N \geq 2$,

$$\Sigma_N = \{x = (x_0 x_1 \ldots) \mid x_i \in S, i = 0, 1, 2, \ldots\}.$$

Let $\rho : \Sigma_N \times \Sigma_N \to R$ such that for any $x = (x_0 x_1 \ldots), y = (y_0 y_1 \ldots) \in \Sigma_N$,

$$\rho(x, y) = \sum_{n=o}^{\infty} \frac{d(x_n, y_n)}{2^n}, \quad d(x_n, y_n) = \begin{cases} 0, & x_n = y_n \\ 1, & x_n \neq y_n \end{cases}.$$

It is easy to verify that (Σ_N, ρ) is a compact totally disconnected metric space. We say that (Σ_N, ρ) is a one-side symbol space of N-symbol.

Definition 2 Let (X, f) be a compact system with metric d. For any $X_0 \subset X$, two points x and y in X_0 form a chaotic pair for the map f, if the following conditions hold:

$$\limsup_{n \to \infty} d(f^n(x), f^n(y)) > 0, \tag{1}$$

$$\liminf_{n \to \infty} d(f^n(x), f^n(y)) = 0; \tag{2}$$

(X, f) is called chaos in the sense of Li-Yorke if there exists an uncountable set $S \subset X_0$, so that for any $x, y \in S$ with $x \neq y$, (x, y) is a chaotic pair of f. S is called a chaotic set of f.

Definition 3 A set $M \subset X$ is called a minimal set of the compact dynamical system (X, f) if $M = orb(x)$ ($orb(x)$ is the closure of orbit of (x) for any $x \in M$.

Definition 4 A point $x \in X$ is called an almost period point of f, if for any $\varepsilon > 0$ there exists an integer $r > 0$ which for any $q \geq 0$, $q \leq r < N + q$ holds such that $\rho(f^r(x), x) < \varepsilon$.

We denote by $A(f)$ the set of almost period points of f on X.

Proposition 1 [3] Let $x = (x_0 x_1 \ldots) \in \Sigma_N$. Given $n > 0$.

$x \in A(\sigma)$ holds if there exists $k > 0$ such that

$$x_0 x_1 \ldots x_n \prec x_i x_{i+1} \ldots x_{i+k}.$$

Let $x \in \omega(x, f)$ be ω—limit set of a point $x \in X$ under f.

Proposition 2 [3] Let $x \in X, x \in A(f)$ if and if only $x \in \omega(x, f)$ and $\omega(x, f)$ is a minimal set of f.

3 PROPERTIES OF STURMIAN SYSTEM

Definition 6 Sturmian words are infinite sequences over two-letter alphabets that have exactly $n + 1$ factors of length n for each $n \geq 0$.

Let $x \in \Sigma_2$ be Sturmian words and $\Omega = (orb(x), \sigma)$, then we denote by Ω a Sturmian System.

Theorem 1 [5] There do not exist chaos in the sense of Li-Yorke in Sturmian System.

Theorem 2 Sturmian System Ω has zero entropy.

Proof: From proposition 3 and the definition of Sturmian System we can obtain

$$ent(\sigma|\Omega) = \lim_{n \to \infty} \frac{1}{n} \ln(n + 1) = 0,$$

that is the entropy of Sturmian System is zero.

Theorem 3 Sturmian System is minimal.

Proof: From proposition 2, $x \in A(\sigma)$ if and only if $x \in \omega(x, \sigma)$ and $x \in \omega(x, \sigma)$ is the minimal set of σ, we have $orb(x) = \omega(x, \sigma)$ by the definition of minimal set. There remain x to be an almost periodic sequence.

First it can be proved that the occurrences of any stable finite sequences in x infinitely.

Suppose there exists a sequence $a_m a_{m+1} \ldots a_{m+n-1}$ which occurs finitely in x. There exists an integer p such that $\sigma^p(x)$ does not contain $a_m a_{m+1} \ldots a_{m+n-1}$.

Definition 6 claims N-sequences differ by at most n in $\sigma^p(x)$. Since this is impossible we infer that the hypothesis is false.

Thus for any $j > 0$, there exists $i \geq 0$, such that $(a_0 a_1 \ldots a_j) < (a_i a_{i+1} \ldots a_{i+N})$ for N large enough.

From proposition 1, x is an almost periodic point.

The proof of the theorem is complete.

Theorem 4 Let $R(\sigma)$ is a set of recurrent points, then for Ω, we have

$$A(\sigma) = R(\sigma) = \overline{orb(x)}.$$

It can be proved according to Theorem 3.

In 2000, Robert S. Mackay [6] presented two problems:

1. Suppose $a \in R(\Sigma_N, \sigma) - P(\Sigma_N, \sigma)$
   $\Sigma(a) \cap P(\Sigma_N, \sigma) \neq \varnothing$. Take $p \in \Sigma(a) \cap P(\Sigma_N, \sigma)$, and denote its period by k. Does the set $cl\{\sigma^{kn}(a), n \geq 0\}$ contain an uncountable scrambled set?

2. Assume that a is a nonperiodic recurrent point and $\Sigma(a)$ contains a periodic point of σ, i.e. $a \in R(\Sigma_N, \sigma) - P(\Sigma_N, \sigma)$ and $\Sigma(a) \cap P(\Sigma_N, \sigma) \neq \varnothing$. Does the set $\Sigma(a)$ contain an uncountable scrambled set for the subshift σ?

4 CONSTRUCTION AND PROPERTIES OF SUBSHIFTS

Denote by $\Sigma(a)$ be the closure of the orbit starting at point $a \in \Sigma_N$, and M be a Sturmian System. By Theorem 1, Theorem 2, there does not exist an infinite minimal set $S \subset M$ in which any two different points are a chaotic pair for the subshift σ, i.e. M is not an infinite minimal scrambled set for the subshift σ.

Take $x = (x_0 x_1 \cdots) \in M = \Sigma(x)$

Let $A_1 = 01x_0 x_1$,

$$A_2 = 0101x_0 x_1 x_2 x_3 A_1,$$
$$A_3 = 010101x_0 x_1 \cdots x_5 A_1 A_2,$$
$$A_4 = 01010101x_0 x_1 \cdots x_7 A_1 A_2 A_3,$$
$$\ldots \quad \ldots \quad \ldots$$
$$A_n = 0101 \cdots 01x_0 x_1 x_2 \cdots x_{2n-1} A_1 A_2 \cdots A_{n-1},$$
$$\ldots \quad \ldots \quad \ldots$$

Thus $A_1 A_2 = A_1 0101 x_0 x_1 x_2 x_3 A_1$,

$$A_1 A_2 A_3 = A_1 0101 x_0 \ldots x_3 A_1 010101 x_0 \ldots x_5 A_1 A_2,$$
$$\ldots \quad \ldots \quad \ldots$$
$$A_1 \cdots A_n = A_1 0101 x_0 \ldots x_3 A_1 \ldots 0101 \ldots$$
$$\qquad 01x_0 \ldots x_{2n-1} A_1 \ldots A_{n-1}$$
$$\ldots \quad \ldots \quad \ldots$$

where $|A_1| = 4$,

$$|A_2| = 2|A_1| + 4 = 12,$$
$$|A_3| = 2|A_2| + 4 = 28,$$
$$\ldots \quad \ldots \quad \ldots$$
$$|A_n| = 2|A_{n-1}| + 4,$$
$$\ldots \quad \ldots \quad \ldots$$

Let $a = (A_1 A_2 A_3 \cdots) \in \Sigma_2$.

Theorem 5 $a \in R(\Sigma_2, \sigma) - P(\Sigma_2, \sigma)$.

Proof Take a subsequence of $N \{n_i\}_{i=1}^{\infty}$ such that

$n_1 = |A_2|,$

$\sigma^{n_1}(a) = A_1 010101 x_0 \ldots x_5 A_1 A_2 \cdots,$

$n_2 = |A_3|,$

$\sigma^{n_2}(a) = A_1 A_2 01 \ldots 01 x_0 \ldots x_7 A_1 A_2 A_3 \cdots,$

$\cdots \quad \cdots \quad \cdots$

$n_i = |A_{i+1}|$

$\sigma^{n_i}(a) = A_1 \cdots A_i 01 \ldots 01 x_0 \ldots x_{2i+3} A_1 A_2 \ldots A_{i+1} \cdots,$

$\cdots \quad \cdots \quad \cdots$

$\sigma^{n_i}(a) \to A_1 A_2 A_3 \ldots$ as $i \to \infty$, i.e. $\sigma^{n_i}(a) \to a$.

Thus $a \in R(\Sigma_2, \sigma)$. It is obvious that a is a nonperiodic point.

So $a \in R(\Sigma_2, \sigma) - P(\Sigma_2, \sigma)$. The proof of the theorem is complete.

Theorem 6 Let $P = \{(010101 \ldots), (101010 \ldots),$ then $P \in \Sigma(a) \cap P(\Sigma_2, \sigma)$.

Proof Take a subsequence of $N \{n_i\}_{i=1}^{\infty}$ such that

$n_1 = 0, \sigma^{n_1}(a) = a = 01 x_0 x_1 \cdots,$

$n_2 = |A_1|,$

$\sigma^{n_2}(a) = 0101 x_0 \ldots x_3 A_1 010101 x_0 \ldots x_5 \cdots,$

$\cdots \quad \cdots \quad \cdots$

$n_i = |A_1| + |A_2| + \ldots + |A_{i-1}|,$

$\sigma^{n_i}(a) = 0101 \ldots 01 x_0 \ldots x_{2i-1} \cdots,$

$\cdots \quad \cdots \quad \cdots$

$\sigma^{n_i}(a) \to 0101 \ldots 01 \ldots$ as $i \to \infty$,

i.e. $(0101 \ldots 01 \ldots) \in \Sigma(a) \cap P(\Sigma_2, \sigma)$.

The same proof to

$(1010 \ldots 10 \ldots) \in \Sigma(a) \cap P(\Sigma_2, \sigma)$.

The proof of the theorem is complete.

Let

$N = N_1 \cup N_2,$

where

$N_1 = \{y = (\underbrace{0101 \ldots 01}_{2k} x_0 x_1 \ldots) : y \in \Sigma_2, k \geq 1\},$

$N_2 = \{y = (\underbrace{1010 \ldots 1}_{2k-1} x_0 x_1 \ldots) : y \in \Sigma_2, k \geq 1\},$

$N_1 \cap N_2 = \varnothing,$

$Q = \{y = (x_i x_{i+1} \ldots x_n 01 x_0 x_1 \ldots) \mid y \in \Sigma_2, i \geq 0, n \geq i\}.$

Theorem 7 $\Sigma(a) = P \cup M \cup N \cup Q$.

Proof Take any $b \in \Sigma(a)$. If $b \in orb(a), b \in N$ or Q.

If $b \in (orb(a))'$ $(orb(a))'$ is the set of derivate of $(orb(a))$, there exists a subsequence of $N \{n_i\}_{i=1}^{\infty}$ such that $\sigma^{n_i}(a) \to b$.

It is obvious that $\sigma^{n_i}(a) \in N \cup Q$.

If $\sigma^{n_i}(a) \in N$, by the definition of limit for any $\varepsilon = 1/2^k$, there exists $i_0 \geq 0$, such that $\rho(\sigma^{n_i}(a), b) < 1/2^k$ for $i \geq i_0$ and as $k \to \infty, b = (0101 \ldots)$

$b = (1010 \ldots) \in P;$

If $\sigma^{n_i}(a) \in Q$, similarly
$b = (x_i x_{i+1} \cdots x_n 01 \cdots) \in Q, i \geq 0$, as $k \to \infty$ or
$b = (x_i x_{i+1} \cdots x_n \cdots) \in M,$

Therefore we have $\Sigma(a) \subset P \cup M \cup N \cup Q$.

It is obvious that $P, N, Q \subset \Sigma(a)$.

Take a subsequence $N \{n_i\}_{i=1}^{\infty}$ such that

$n_1 = 2 \times 1, \sigma^{n_1}(a) = x_0 x_1 \ldots$

$n_2 = |A_1| + 2 \times 2,$

$\sigma^{n_2}(a) = x_0 \ldots x_3 A_1 010101 x_0 \ldots x_5 \cdots,$

$n_3 = |A_1| + |A_2| + 2 \times 3,$

$\sigma^{n_3}(a) = x_0 \ldots x_5 A_1 A_2 \cdots$

$\cdots \quad \cdots \quad \cdots$

$n_i = |A_1| + |A_2| \cdots + |A_i| + 2i,$

$\sigma^{n_i}(\alpha) = x_0 \ldots x_{2i-1} A_1 A_2 \ldots A_{i-1} \cdots,$

$\cdots \quad \cdots \quad \cdots$

$\sigma^{n_i}(a) \to x = (x_0 x_1 \ldots) \in M$ as $i \to \infty$,

So $x \in \Sigma(a)$, that is $M \subset \Sigma(a)$.

So $P \cup M \cup N \cup Q \subset \Sigma(a)$.

We thus obtain $\Sigma(a) = P \cup M \cup N \cup Q$.

By theorem 5–7, $\Sigma(a)$ satisfies the condition in [6] and its period of periodic point is two,

$cl\{\sigma^{2n}(a), n \geq 0\} \subset P \cup M \cup N \cup Q = \Sigma(a),$

which N, Q is a countable set and M is not an infinite scrambled set, thus $cl\{\sigma^{2n}(a), n \geq 0\}$ can not contain an uncountable scrambled set.

5 CONCLUSIONS

Sturmian System is the least complex kind of symbolic dynamics. In the present paper it proves that Sturmian System is a minimal system that has zero entropy and is not chaotic. According to some concepts on Symbolic Dynamics and properties of minimal nonchaotic on Sturmian System, we make a kind of subshift that generated by a nonperiodic recurrent orbit and study its properties. If a period point exists in a subshift generated by a nonperiodic recurrent orbit, it is not certain that the subshift contains an uncountable scrambled set.

REFERENCES

[1] Hadmard J., J. Math. Purce. Appl., 1889, 4, pp. 27–73.
[2] Morse M., Recurrent geodescs on a Surface of negative curvature, TransAms., 22(1921), pp 84–100.
[3] Zuo-ling Zhou. Symbolic Dynamics. Education Press of Shanghai science and technology, 1997.
[4] Sun Li-hua, Zhao En-liang. Study on properties of Sturmian System [J]. Jilin Normal Univerity Journal, 2006(3):46–47.
[5] Xi Liqun, Chen Gang. Substitution Sequence, Strongly Nil Property and Chaos. Journal of Mathematics, 17 (1997).
[6] Fu X C, Fu Y B, Duan J Q, Rokert S Mackey. Chaotic properties of subshifts generated by a non-periodic recurrent orbit [J]. Inter. J. Bifurcation and Chaos, 2000(5):1067–1073.

Computer, Intelligent Computing and Education Technology – Liu, Sung & Yao (Eds)
© 2014 Taylor & Francis Group, London, ISBN 978-1-138-02469-4

The equation establishment for early selection of excellent *Paulownia* clones based on Richards function curve

W. Meng, C.W. Yang, X. Xia, Y. Luo, W. Duan & B.P. Wang
China Paulownia Research and Development Center, Zhengzhou, China

ABSTRACT: To selection excellent clones at seeding stage in *Paulownina*, the equation was established based on Richards function curve. We studied the height and diameter of nineteen kinds of one-year *Paulownia* clones and CK, and builded dynamic simulation with eight growth parameters. The results showed that the annual growth process could be modeled reliably by Richards function. The height fast-growing period of *Paulownia* clones begin late and last long. The height of *Paulownia* clones are between 375.06 ~ 478.10 cm, and not significant difference with CK. The fast-growing period of diameter begin late and the growing period was short. The increments were not high. The growths of *Paulownia* clones were lower than CK, except 1, 2, 11, 16, 18 and 19. Through cluster analysis, we find that 1, 2 grow faster than CK, and the growth characteristics of 3, 4, 11, 12, 16 and 18 were similar with CK. They are all excellent varieties of *Paulownia*. The equation establishment based on Richards function curve is suitable method for early selection of excellent *Paulownia* clones.

Keywords: *Paulownia*; clones; Richards function curve; early selection breeding

1 INTRODUCTION

Paulownia belongs to *Paulownia* genus, and *Scrophulariaceae*, Deciduous trees, Native to China [1], are importance fast-growing timber trees, widely distributed in south Asia [2]. The wood lubricious shallow, uniform structure, unique texture, warped crack, sound insulation, moisture proof, flame retardant, good paint adhesion, widely used in furniture, musical instrument manufacture, is an important export products [3–5]. The breeding objective has been fast-growing, so, how to select the excellent clones in huge clones at early stage has been the main problem. We put forwarded the solution based on Richards function curve was the obvious effect and suitable for application in production.

2 MATERIAL AND METHOD

2.1 Study area

The study area belongs to Yuanyang county, Henan province. The location between the geocoordinate 34°53′~35°05′ North latitude, and 113°34′~113°52′ East longitude. The warm temperate zone and continental monsoon climate zone, at the Yellow River communist-held, Soil type is sandy soil, the nutrient is lower, and pH value is alkali (7.5~8.5), the average content of organic matter, effective nitrogen, effective phosphorus were 8.79%, 20.53 mg/kg, 2.75 mg/kg, respectively.

2.2 Sampling methods and treatment design

All the samples were collected from every site at past 10 years in China, and the 19 clones (Table 1)

Table 1. The name and number of *Paulownia* clones.

Clones	Number	Clones	Number	Clones	Number	Clones	Number
C020	1	Zhong 3	6	Su807	11	YZ	16
85802	2	8508-2	7	9502	12	C137	17
Shan 4	3	Su70	8	78-08	13	9504	18
8508-3	4	9501	9	Su3	14	Shan 3	19
C161	5	Mao 16	10	TS 2	15	C125	CK

were studied by the re-collection in this study. The CK is Maobai 33 that was hybrid by *P. tomentosa* with *P. fortunei 33*. The experimental layout was a complete randomized plot with three replicates of 15 sampled trees per treatment. In each replicate, perimeter trees used as guards, planting density is 4.0 m × 5.0 m. The data of seedling height, stem diameter, the annual growth process of instantaneous days growth (AGR), the max days of growth (AGRmax), the average days of growth (Am), the time of fast growth point (t0), the time of start fast-growth point (t1), the time of end fast-growth point (t2) and the date of growth stage (Dg) were recorded, respectively.

2.3 Data analysis

The equation "Y = A(1 + e − kt)−1/v" used to in forestry research. The parameters AGR, AGRmax, Am, t0, t1, t2, t and Dg were join into the equation, and the results was derivative from 1 to 3 times, and make its 0. The softwares were used in this study including SPSS 19.0 and Office Excel 2007.

AGR = k A e−kt/[v(1 + e−kt)(1 + v)/v]; AGRmax = k A(1 + v) −(1 + v)/v; Am = A k/(2v + 4); t_0 = −1/k inv; tl = −1/k In[0.5v2+1.5v +0.5 v(v2 + 6v +5)0.5]; t2 = −1/k in[0.5 v2 + 1.5v −0.5v (v2 + 6v + 5)0.5]; t = t2 − tl; Dg = 2/k(v + 2).

3   RESULTS AND DISCUSSION

3.1   The analysis of height growth rhythm among Paulownia clones 19

The growth parameters reflect the longitudinal growth of the clones 19 kinds of *Paulownia*. The t0 was late, but had long sustained growth, and the biomass was not high, except clones 1, 3, 16 and 17 were lower than CK.

The results of plant height showed very significant level between treatment and CK (Table 2). Comparing the growth parameters and CK analysis, the results show that compared with CK, but 11 extra, the seeding high-speed period not only at start stage but also end stage, and t0 were later 1 ~ 7 d than CK. The t0 between CK and clone 11, the earliest start date from 6 to 8th in June, and the latest date was appeared from in June 27, the t2 from 1 to 10 in August, and clone 8 is the latest plant. The t0 value of every clone was appeared from 7 to 18 in July, later than CK but clone 11, the latest also is clone 8. The Am value is between 4.34 and 5.40 cm, the largest is the clone 1, and the minimum is 5, the results showed that the high of 19 clones were not significant difference than CK. The AGRmax of 19 clones were between 6.38 and 7.93, the largest is the clone 1, and the minimum also is 5, the results showed that the AGRmax but clones 1, 3, 16 and 17 were lower than CK, meanwhile, the difference was not significant.

Table 2.   The simulation results of seedling high in Paulownia clones 19.

Clones	A	k	v	f	r	t0/d	t1/d	t2/d	t/d	Am/ (cm·d^{-1})	Dg/d	AGRmax/ (cm·d^{-1})
1	488.21	0.04	0.01	5450.70	0.99	95.90	74.10	117.70	43.50	5.39	90.50	7.93
2	482.59	0.04	0.02	3147.50	0.98	98.50	73.20	123.70	50.40	4.60	104.80	6.77
3	443.86	0.05	0.01	2120.10	0.98	98.20	77.50	119.00	41.50	5.15	86.30	7.57
4	434.79	0.04	0.01	2650.00	0.98	98.70	76.00	121.40	45.50	4.60	94.50	6.77
5	422.83	0.04	0.02	2000.30	0.96	97.70	74.20	121.10	46.90	4.34	97.50	6.38
6	418.29	0.05	0.01	2504.60	0.98	99.10	78.40	119.80	41.40	4.86	86.10	7.15
7	404.94	0.04	0.01	1378.90	0.96	100.70	79.00	122.40	43.40	4.49	90.30	6.60
8	414.60	0.04	0.01	2195.70	0.98	102.90	80.90	125.00	44.10	4.53	91.60	6.66
9	401.31	0.04	0.01	2841.00	0.97	101.70	79.70	123.80	44.10	4.37	91.70	6.44
10	431.39	0.04	0.02	1979.10	0.97	98.80	75.80	121.90	46.10	4.50	95.80	6.63
11	443.74	0.04	0.02	2807.30	0.97	94.50	72.20	116.80	44.70	4.78	92.90	7.03
12	440.67	0.04	0.02	3329.40	0.97	96.60	73.10	120.00	46.90	4.52	97.50	6.65
13	421.27	0.05	0.01	1748.10	0.95	98.60	77.20	120.00	42.70	4.74	88.80	6.98
14	383.99	0.05	0.01	1440.10	0.96	102.20	82.20	122.20	39.90	4.63	83.00	6.81
15	402.41	0.05	0.01	1900.00	0.97	99.90	79.50	120.20	40.70	4.75	84.70	6.99
16	463.15	0.04	0.01	2363.20	0.97	97.30	75.30	119.30	44.00	5.06	91.50	7.45
17	425.80	0.05	0.01	2091.60	0.99	100.70	80.50	121.00	40.50	5.06	84.20	7.44
18	442.87	0.04	0.01	1826.00	0.96	99.60	76.90	122.30	45.40	4.69	94.40	6.91
19	415.10	0.05	0.01	1739.00	0.99	98.10	77.30	119.00	41.70	4.78	86.80	7.04
ck	451.12	0.04	0.01	2959.00	0.97	95.00	73.30	116.60	43.30	5.01	90.00	7.38

3.2 The analysis of stem diameter growth rhythm among Paulownia clones 19

The stem diameter parameters reflect the cross growth of the clones 19 kinds of *Paulownia*. The time of start growth of stem diameter was earlier than seedling high, and t_0 and Dg were longer, and the biomass were not significant difference than CK (Table 3).

3.3 The analysis of annual biomass among Paulownia clones 19

The seedling hight biomass was not significant difference than CK (F = 1.0591 < F0.05 = 1.7625, d_f = 19, 60). But the stem diameters was significant difference (Table 4) among *Paulownia* clones (F = 4.8042 > F0.01 = 2.2231, d_f = 19, 60).

The twenty clones were divided three groups when the distance was limited to 0.12 by clustering analysis (Fig. 1). The first group was including clones 5, 6, 7, 8, 9, 10, 13, 14, 15, 17 and 19. There seedling high were appearance between 11th and 18th in July, later 8 days than CK results in the longitudinal growth lower than CK. Meanwhile, the stem diameter were later from 2 to 37 days than CK results in the cross growth was lower than CK. So, all of the characters in the first group was lower than CK will result in the breeding aim decline.

The Second was including clones 3, 4, 11, 12, 16, 18 and CK. In this group, clones 3, 4, 11, 12, 16 and 18 were clustered to the CK showed that

Table 3. The simulation results of seedling stem diameter in Paulownia clones 19.

Clones	A	k	v	f	r	t0/d	t1/d	t2/d	t/d	Am (mm·d⁻¹)	Dg/d	AGRmax (mm·d⁻¹)
1	80.23	0.03	0.09	1812.50	0.94	88.50	51.30	125.80	74.40	0.52	155.30	0.76
2	74.58	0.03	0.12	1169.00	0.93	82.80	44.00	121.60	77.60	0.46	162.10	0.68
3	67.74	0.03	0.09	1388.20	0.95	90.70	53.30	128.10	74.80	0.43	156.10	0.64
4	67.55	0.03	0.11	1675.30	0.89	87.80	48.40	127.30	78.80	0.41	164.70	0.60
5	60.25	0.03	0.11	851.20	0.89	82.90	44.80	120.90	76.10	0.38	158.90	0.56
6	62.19	0.03	0.09	724.40	0.91	86.50	51.30	121.60	70.20	0.42	146.50	0.62
7	56.48	0.03	0.10	498.40	0.85	86.80	49.10	124.40	75.30	0.36	157.30	0.53
8	60.25	0.03	0.09	1477.60	0.94	91.80	54.20	129.40	75.30	0.38	157.00	0.56
9	63.41	0.03	0.09	1314.80	0.94	92.40	53.70	131.00	77.30	0.39	161.30	0.58
10	50.52	0.03	0.10	1289.20	0.94	84.70	47.70	121.80	74.10	0.33	154.60	0.48
11	68.25	0.03	0.09	1565.40	0.93	85.70	50.10	121.20	71.10	0.46	148.40	0.68
12	67.27	0.03	0.10	605.40	0.88	87.90	49.00	126.90	77.90	0.41	162.60	0.61
13	64.21	0.03	0.09	488.70	0.88	88.90	51.50	126.30	74.80	0.41	156.20	0.61
14	59.87	0.03	0.06	655.50	0.88	93.60	59.80	127.40	67.60	0.42	140.90	0.63
15	59.90	0.03	0.09	821.30	0.95	91.10	53.40	128.70	75.30	0.38	157.20	0.56
16	81.13	0.03	0.09	1229.50	0.93	88.60	51.10	126.00	75.00	0.52	156.40	0.76
17	61.48	0.03	0.07	970.70	0.93	90.60	56.20	125.00	68.80	0.43	143.40	0.63
18	73.31	0.03	0.09	1406.90	0.94	90.20	52.00	128.30	76.30	0.46	159.20	0.68
19	57.96	0.03	0.06	1287.20	0.98	84.40	54.10	114.60	60.50	0.46	126.00	0.68
ck	74.56	0.03	0.11	1122.30	0.91	87.40	48.20	126.50	78.30	0.46	163.50	0.67

Table 4. The results of multiple comparison among *Paulownia* clones.

Clones	Different levels	Clones	Different levels	Clones	Different levels
1	76.68abAB	8	57.06cdABCD	15	56.98cdABCD
2	71.46abcABC	9	59.96abcdABCD	16	77.78aA
3	65.09abcdABCD	10	48.69dD	17	59.48bcdABCD
4	64.44abcdABCD	11	65.87abcdABCD	18	70.20abcABC
5	57.99cdABCD	12	63.90abcdABCD	19	55.89cdBCD
6	60.28abcdABCD	13	61.37abcdABCD	CK	71.28abcABC
7	54.11cdCD	14	57.37cdABCD		

Notes: Different letters at the same row means significant level, uppercase letters showed significant 1% level, and lowercase showed 5% level. The method was Tukey test.

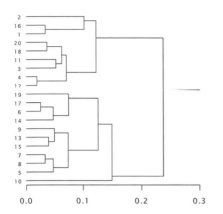

Figure 1. The clustering analysis among *Paulownia* clones based on growth index.

there had the same most characters, so, the higher fast-growing varieties was not appearance in this group.

The third group was including clones 1 and 12, there showed the excellent trait than CK. The value t0 and Dg of seedling were later from 1 to 3 days than CK, but Dg and AGR were longer 7 days and 14 days than CK, respectively. However, the t0 and AGR of stem diameter in according with CK, but the Am was higher than CK, and the AGRmax reached to 0.52 mm results in the annal AGRmax reached to from 71.46 to 76.68 mm, was clearly higher than others clones.

4 CONCLUSION

Recently, Clones 1 and 12 showed good character in clonal test plantation. We are putative the equation "$Y = A(1 + e{-}kt){-}1/v$" based on richards funtion curve was applied for *Paulownia* selection breeding. It was benefited for early selection of excellent *Paulownia* clones from huge clonal materials.

ACKNOWLEDGMENTS

It is a project supported by the National Forestry Public Welfare Profession Scientific Research Special (201104049). The corresponding author is Prof. Bao-ping Wang.

REFERENCES

[1] J.P. Jiang. *Paulownia* Cultivation (China Forestry Press, Beijing, 1990).
[2] Z.H. Lv. Studies on growth characteristics in *Paulownia fortune* in young period of different provenances. (The Master Degree of Central South University of Forestry and Technology, Changsha, 2013, 5).
[3] Morenos, Martinjp and Ortizjm. Inter-simple sequence repeats PCR for characterization of closely related grapevine germplasm, EuPhytiea, Vol. 1 (1998), p. 117–125.
[4] R. Liu, Y. Dong, G. Fan, et al. Discovery of genes related to witches broom disease in *Paulownia tomentosa × Paulownia fortune* by a *De Novo* assembled transcriptome, PLoS ONE, Vol. 8 (2013): e80238. doi:10.1371/journal.pone.0080238.
[5] H.W. Wang, J.M. Duan, P. Zhang, et al. Microsatellite markers in *Paulownia kawakamii* (Scrophulariaceae) and cross-amplification in other *Paulownia* species, Genet Mol Res, Vol. 12 (2013), p. 3750–3754.

Computer, Intelligent Computing and Education Technology – Liu, Sung & Yao (Eds)
© 2014 Taylor & Francis Group, London, ISBN 978-1-138-02469-4

Study on the teaching methods of engineering college physics and experiments

Z.Q. Xu & K.G. Qian

Department of Physics and Technology, Kunming University, China

ABSTRACT: Physics is the foundation of all natural sciences except for mathematics, as well as Foundation of all engineering technology. The establishment of many new disciplines, many important inventions in the engineering technology and the development of physics are inseparable. College Physics and Experiments is an important basic theory of University engineering professional course. However, students have prevailing difficulty in learning College Physics and Experiments, thinking physics and experimental concepts, regularity, difficult to understand and master. In order to help students master the basic concepts of the subject, the basic laws to enhance the students 'ability to analyze and solve problems, on the basis of many years of teaching experience in research, teaching methods of College physics and Experiments have been studied.

Keywords: physics and experiments; teaching methods; research

1 INTRODUCTION

At present, many countries in the world are competing fiercely with each other to occupy a strong position on the stage in the 21st century global economy and military. The key of the competition is in science and technology, which is the science and technology talent competition. As engineering professional students, they must have a solid theoretical basis, broad knowledge of natural science, rigorous style and innovation consciousness to become the backbone in 21st century science and technology, to keep pace with the increasing pace of the new technological revolution, and strengthening basic theories. So methods of College physics and Experimental learning is particularly important for them. Students can not only learn the law of nature in the form of basic movements and have access to a more comprehensive, more awareness of the system, but also be trained in experimental skills and abilities to work independently. It lays the foundation of learning professional knowledge and modern science and technology.

2 MAKING EFFORTS TO MOBILIZE THE STUDENTS' ENTHUSIASM FOR LEARNING AND CREATION

2.1 Student of physics history

All that can promote students 'wisdom and touches students' minds is the education of humanities education. This requires teachers put teaching materials to the teaching of physical culture in the context of understanding and design, combined with the current reality of social life, college students' development to explore the physics of the knowledge contained in scientific, social, and life of enlightening. Turn a static imparting to a dynamic evolution of knowledge and inspiration, cultivate students 'view of history and development, cultivate students' active participation in experimental operations and strengthen the ability of exercise consciousness, as well as students in a subtle sense of observation, analysis and scientific innovation. For example, in the teaching of "thin lens", in order to stimulate students' interest and curiosity, the teacher can first present to the students: "What is the first application of lens in scientific research?". Then the teacher describes how Galileo used the telescope with which he himself invented to observe and study the sky for the first time to discover a series of significant astronomical phenomena, showing Galileo's extraordinary dimensional real, truth-seeking, innovative scientific spirit; describing the role which physics and experiments play in the development of the natural science; introducing the value of scientific research which Galileo created by combining experiments and mathematics, and its influence on the development of science. In this way, vigor and vitality can be integrated with the history of science in the teaching activities. Not only the scientific qualities and cultivation of humanistic quality can be achieved, but also reflects the qualities and skills of education to new ideas.

2.2 Creating new situations, combining theory with practice

The traditional teaching of physics stresses theory of integrity and systemic, student exercises are often designed for the idealized model. Learning physics for the students is to learn some flat physical symbols and formulas. Students cannot always link the physical knowledge to life worlds, while new situations put actual physical knowledge and life closely combine to enhance the application of physical problems and practice. Let physics go into the life of students, into the students to face the world, into the students belief that high-tech is inscrutable: the military situation in the United States of the waging war in Afghanistan; using satellite technology to capture the Taliban; blues over the Yellow River, China's construction in Shanghai maglev train rear-end events, which will stimulate a strong desire to learn for the students. When students really know that he is living in a world of physical phenomena, they will be interested in the power for studying physical knowledge and the use of physical knowledge to create a great desire, thus it will greatly enhance students' creative learning.

2.3 Encouraging students enrichment activities, reading

To encourage students to participate in various extracurricular activities, teachers can suggest extnsively reading, taking physics section knowledge as the core, and forming a broad range of knowledge. Science is highly differentiated and integrated, making the whole of science and technology an independent structure, criss-crossing system. It requires students transit from the study of things to the system, from the study of single values to a multi-value research and from the uni-direction to network. Students must explore the nature in a mutidimensional way. In this situation, in order to solve a acertain physical problem, not only some related physical disciplines of knowledge and method are needed, but also a lot of knowledge and methods including natural science, social sciences, and thinking science are required. Just as Taylor pointed out: "People who have rich knowledge and experience are more prone than those who have only one kind of knowledge and experience of Lenovo and insights," Nobel Physics Award winner Giaever, has a formal background in machinery, electricity, military, and philosophy. When he became fascinated with physics, he boldly and decisively affirmed "Let tunnel effect and phenomenon of superconductivity unite". He discovered superconducting electron tunneling effect and theoretically predicted suppercurrent through a tunnel barrier layer possiblity.

3 EXPLORING EFFECTIVE AND HIGH—QUALITY TEACHING METHODS

3.1 The key to teaching—scientific and reasonable questions

The problem is the beginning of creation. Nothing would be created without problems. From the ancient times to the present, the starting point of scientific research and innovation is not from the exsist problems, but from finding problems in the phenomenon and practice. Finding problems is an important part of scientific research. Once a person asks himself a question, generates the desire to solve it, forms the problem of consciousness, he is able to feel and detect keen and precise information. Problems make the point with selsctive attention on the ongoing. The objective thinking, and exploration activities form a significant function. Juch as Hisheen Fort once said: "Asking the right questions often solves the problem of most." One famous physicist Li Zhengdao said: "For researchers, the most important thing is that whether they will be able to ask the right questions or not." The problem consciousness is a human instinct, so it is the same with humans' creation. If traditional teaching modle is adopted for a long period of time, students rarely ask questions, character of students will be affected, obliterating the personality development of students. The students no longer have the deep-seated awareness of futher exploration.

3.2 Going into the essence through specific issues

Studying physics is not just skillfully use the formula to solve the problem, but having a certain amount of judgment before you begin to calculate. Therefore, when studying a specific content or doing an exercise, focusing on the result only means staying on the surface of the question. Students will only know the physical phenomena instead of physical nature. Only in further process or results of solving problems and tracing the physical nature of preoblems can the physical facts be understood and wisdom be enhanced. For example, in a typical example of simple harmonic motion in spring oscillator, textbooks are arranged to use previously learned knowledge of the kinematics and dynamics to analyze a spesific sport. We start with the physical abstract idealized model—spring oscillator, then force analysis, and use Newton's Second Law to list the dynamic differential equations and solve equations to the general equation of motion. Then substituts into the initial conditions, determine the kinematic equations. The information of the spring oscillator motion can be known. From this content, we should be aware of: The force of the object dominates the sports, and once the initial conditions to determine the state of the motion of the object are to determine the movement of the object. In this way, we will recognize from a specific problem to a general conclusion.

3.3 Changing abstract non-type into an intuitive type by using images

Images are a "number" and "shape" combination of products, which is "specific" and "abstract". It combines comprehensive embodiment. It not only intuitively and generally reflects the relationship between the two relevant physical quantities, but also contains physical phenomenon, physical process, physical state, and physical laws which can not be expressed clearly in some abstract and mathematical ways; it is the rich carrier of physical information, as well as the tie of imagination and abstract thinking; it is widely used in scientific experiments in the analysis of experimental data, and is one of the theoretical means of study. In university physics and experimental teaching process, the image can vividly express the laws of physics, intuitive desciption of the physical process, clearly show the relationship between the physical quantities. The intuitive and accurate experimental results can be drawn by using the images. In the process of problems solving, it is good to simplify. When solving some problems, it is hard to solve problems in a comprehensive, logical or mathematical way. If images methods are used, an unexpected effect is often achieved. Therefore, the image method is indispensable for university phsics and experimental teaching aids, Reasonably using images canachieve a multiplier effect. Regardless of particle kinematics, particle dynamics and thermodynamics, or in electromagnetics, wave mechanics, optics, physical images play an important role in order to uniform spherical electric field, for example, to make the first ball, the ball outside the Gaussian surface, using the Guass theorem to find the electric field, and then take distance as abscissa, electric field strength, the size of the vertical coordinate to draw the electric field intensity distribution curve analysis, explain, will cause the best results. Images are a "number" and "shape" combination of products, which is "specific" and "abstract". It combines comprehensive embodiment. It not only intuitively and generally reflects the relationship between the two relevant physical phenomenon, physical process, physical state, and

physical laws which can not be expressed clearly in some abstract and mathematical ways; it is the rich carrier of physical information, as well as the tie of imagination and abstract thinking; it is widely used in scientific experiments in the analysis of experimental data, and is one of the theoretical means of study. In university physics and experimental teaching process, the image can vividly express the laws of physics, intuitive desciption of the physical process, clearly show the relationship between the physical quantities. The intuitive and accurate experimental results can be drawn by using the images. In the process of problems solving, it is good to simplify. When solving some problems, it is hard to solve problems in a comprehensive, logical or mathematical way. If images methods are used, an unexpected effect is often achieved. Therefore, the image method is indispensable for university phsics and experimental teaching aids. Reasonably using images canachieve a multiplier effect. Regardless of particle kinematics, particle dynamics and thermodynamics, or in electromagnetics, wave mechanics, optics, physical images play an important role in order to uniform spherical electric field, for example, to make the first ball, the ball outside the Gaussian surface, using the Guass theorem to find the electric field, and then take distance as abscissa, electric field strength, the size of the vertical coordinate to draw the electric field intensity distribution curve analysis, explain, will cause the best results.

4 MAKING THE EXPERIMENT COURSES PLAY AN IMPORTANT ROLE

The professional curriculum of college physics tests are substited by in—class testing, and theory teachers undertake the teaching. They are not enough professional teachers in testing, their guidance cannot help a lot. On one hand, teachers have to correspond to much more experimental topics, they can be busy with the experimental content explanation and experimental failure exclsion, it's impossible for them to guide each student effectively throughout the process of the experiment, resulting in irregularities that some students have and problems which cannot be timely resolved. Thus the experimental data is inaccurate, affecting students' experimental capabilities. On the other hand, teachers have to guid too many students. It is not easy for them to manage the implementation of each student. It sometimes occurs that ndividual student's experiment is not serious, the occurrence of phenomena such as experiment data is not real, affecting the improvement of the quality of experimental teaching. It will curb students' creative thinking, students will reduce emphasis on experimental course. It's not conductive to nurture the abilities of students and abity to innovate. How to resolve these problems? In addition to making efforts to mobilize students' learning and creative passion, students can be divided into several large groupsaccirding to different experiments. The team leader is the direct assistant to the teacher, and then divide them into small groups according to the instruments. The team lead can be the indirect assistant to the teacher. The team leaders can understand the actual situation otf the students in the experiment. The feedback of requirements and recommendations of students will be given to the teachers timely. Teachers target answers to the problems which students encounter in the experiment, adjust teaching concepts, improve teaching methods. Manwhile the requirements and the intent of the teachers can also be fed back to the students. It enables students to complete the experiment better. For example, if some students do not seriously deal with the experiment preview report, the assistant may suggest checking the preview circumstances by ask questions before the experiment, and the sore is included in the usual grade. The adoption of this proposal results in an increase of "usual question" assessment, greatly increasing the enthusiasm of the students. The exchang between teachers and students becomes easier, smoother, and more harmonious because of the assistants. Besides, it is more conductive to play the main role of teachers and the leading role of the students in the experiment teaching. In addition, assistants help teachers mark lab reports, assess, and manage the experimental of the students. Teachers can be freed from the onerou task of teaching. They are able to focus on experimental guidance and difficult questions. Teachers can also concentrate on experiment designs and completing of innovative experimental subjects.

5 SUMMARY

In many years of teaching practice, through constant learning from other colleges and the experience of their predecessors, according to the professional training objectives and characteristics, the use of modern teaching methods are distinguished. Combined with the actual situation of engineering specialties, teachers highlight a general pinciple, the method of teaching and training. Be sure to clarify the concepts of physics, actively study the teaching methods of practical as well as high quality and efficient teaching methods. Try to stimulate the enthusiasm of students to learn in this course. Students can master the basic concepts, understand the basic theoretical system, and at the same time understand the application, the most important is that students can get the access to basic theoretical analysis and problem—solving abilities. I hope the research on teaching methods and reform has a certain theoretical and practical significance fo the promotion of engineering professional university physics and experimental teaching.

REFERENCES

[1] Zhang Dasong. Physics basic tutorial. Beijing: higher education press, 2008.
[2] Zhou Fengfan, Wang Haocheng. Values reconstruction of College physics demonstration experiments. University Physics [J]. 2011,30 (8): 46–50.
[3] Lv Zhiyuan. Humane education into the university physics teaching and practice [J]. 2011,30 (8): 55–58.
[4] Su Yafeng, Xu Zhongfeng. On China's university physics teaching reform in university physics teaching characterustis from the University of Illinois at Urbana-Champaign, United States [J]. 2011,30 (10): 48–51.
[5] Zhang Libin, Zhang Gong, Li Guangping. Analysis on Harvard University initiative to enhance teaching quality of physics [J]. 2011,30 (12): 48–53.
[6] You Shanhong, Wang Minxiang, Cao Lihua, Wang Guanghuai. Quantum mechanics of engineering specilties teaching method [J]. 2008,27 (8): 45–47.
[7] Lv Zengjian, Chen Xiaomin. History of science into the physical exploration of experimental teaching [J]. 2011,30 (6): 38–41.
[8] Lu Hui, Yinqijun, Qian Shuitu, Zhu Yong. Exploration and practice of the experimental combination of teaching and research [J]. 2008,27 (8): 48–51.

Empirical study on the self-management of higher vocational college students

X.Y. Zhang

School of Management, China University of Mining and Technology, Xuzhou, China
Xuzhou College of Industrial Technology, Xuzhou, China

ABSTRACT: This study constructed the items of self management of Higher Vocational College Students which through the interview and Delphi approach based on the generic model method. Based on the students in Xuzhou College of Industrial Technology. The dimensions and factors of self management were constructed by the means of cluster analysis and Exploratory Factor Analysis (EFA). To test the direct effects of the EFA, structural equation modeling was employed to conduct the Confirmatory Factor Analysis (CFA) based on the data investigated from the Xuzhou College of Industrial Technology. The models demonstrated good fit so, it was confirmed that the self management consist of 4 dimensions, including 17 items. Finally it puts forward the related counter measure to enhance the self-management of college students from individuals, families and schools.

Keywords: college students; self management; empirical study

1 INTRODUCTION

Since ancient times, there have existed abundant thought of self-management in the society. For example, the *Book Of Changes* contains the idea that *the gentleman constantly strive to become stronger*. Confucius *self-cultivation*, Socrates *understanding one's own ignorance*, Delphi's motto in ancient Greek temple *knowing yourself*, and the self-management influenced by Modern Renaissance humanism.

At present, the existing research results of self management mainly focus on the clinical treatment, education and industry. The foreign research on self—management mainly concentrate on the following aspects:

First, from the perspective of organizational behavior, Manz defines self-management as a set of cognitive and behavioral strategies. And Frange thinks it is an individual effort on certain aspects of their own decision or behavior.

Second, based on the physical and mental health, Kenneth thinks self-management behavior is to take action to prevent the occurrence of complications and improve health.

Third, from the Angle of pedagogy research, the self management ability is the goal of education development in the future. Zimmerman regards self-management as a process through initiative regulation of individual status, learning behavior and environmental to achieve the learning objectives. From the viewpoint of behavior modification, Cole defines self-management as achieving the goal of change or protecting a certain behavior, based on the analysis of individual behavior and the control of causes and effects. Long thinks Self-management is to achieve the target objectives by goal setting and regulation of time and related resources. Albert Bandura's social cognitive psychology on the definition of self-management is attended by scholars. He believes that self-management is that the individuals actively set goals, take action, monitor and evaluate their performance and make the corresponding adjustment to shape the process of their own fates.

Research on self-management in domestic academic circles is mainly based on the following three aspects.

First, psychological perspective, Wang Yiming, Jin Yu (2002) define self-management, namely an individual adjust their psychological activity and behavior, control improper impulse, overcome the unfavorable situation, actively seeking to develop and achieve good psychological qualities.

Second, philosophy perspective, Guo Hailong (2007) argues that self management is the dynamic activities, in which during the certain social history condition, an individual with self consciousness, independent consciousness and ability of freedom, through reasonable design, self education, self coordination and self control and so on, obtains personal self realization and all-round development and promotes social progress and human liberation under the premise of correct understanding and the environment.

Third, management perspective, Wang Yongming, Pan Huixiang (2008) define self-management as a management practical activity, in which an induvial having self consciousness, independent consciousness and ability of personal freedom, under the precondition of correct understanding of their own, achieves the individual self realization and all-round development, through reasonable design, self learning, self coordination and self control. Yang Yongjie (2006) argues that self-management is that individuals or groups plan, organize, coordinate and control their own activities, in order to better achieve their goals. Fang Weibo, Xiao Pei (1988) argues that self management refers to the complete process of self awareness, self evaluation, self development, self education and self control, where people in a certain social relation effectively mobilize their initiative, plan and control their behavior, train and develop their thinking, improve and mediate their psychological activity and, to achieve personal goals.

Self management of university students is that college students fully mobilize the initiative of their own, fruitfully use and integrate their resources (physical, psychological, time and thought), use scientific management methods and carry out the self understanding, self planning and organization, self-monitoring, self development and self-education and a series of activities, in order to achieve the goal of higher education and to meet the growing qualities of individual requirements of the society[1–2].

In this paper, we study higher vocational college students' self management. Based on the training objectives of vocational education and the perspective of social demand for skilled talents, we explore the content of higher vocational college students' self management. Through the investigation and analysis of the present situation of college students' self management in vocational colleges, we put forward the corresponding countermeasures.

2 DESIGN

This research mainly uses the structured interview, Delphi method, questionnaire survey, exploratory factor analysis and confirmatory factor analysis method and so on.

2.1 Questionnaire revision

In order to be able to focus on the research problem and guarantee openness, we deeply interview vocational college students from different grades, different majors, different sex. For example, list the specific consciousness and behavior of College Students' self management, as much as possible, combined with observation and experience. And we give examples 1) I give myself goals and tasks systematically arranged weekly, daily. 2) I will adjust their depressed mood, when I meetwith frustration in the study, life and work, and let myself go out from the shadow of failure.

Through interviews, 56 items are collected. Using Delphi method to screen the items, finally we get 26 items, and then we work out the formal questionnaire. It includes two parts. The first is the basic personal information, including academic discipline, the one-child, gender, position, origin, learning achievement, comprehensive quality assessment, prize grades, work implementation situation etc. The second is the closed question, including target management, plan management, organization management, incentive management, control management, development management, method management, innovation management, physical, psychology, social activities, student cadre, social part-time, material resources, information resources, human resources, time resources. It involves 4 levels and 17 indexes. Fill in the answer mode using Likert-type method. It is divided into "(1) nothing (2) a little accordant (3) uncertainty (4) accordant (5) full accordant. "The respondents choose one from five answers, and were given 1, 2, 3, 4, 5.

2.2 Objectives

In this study, using the method of cluster sampling, in Higher Vocational Colleges we deliver 1000 questionnaires. The professional includes

Table 1. Sample summary.

Item	Type	Total	Percent	Item	Type	Total	Percent
Gender	Male	497	56%	Only child	Yes	319	36%
	Female	381	44%		No	557	64%
Grade	Freshman	313	36%	Birthplace	Country	620	71%
	Sophomore	475	54%		County	134	15%
	Junior	90	10%		City	98	11%
Discipline	Arts	239	27%		Capital	20	2%
	Science	245	28%		Metropolis	6	1%
	Engineering	394	45%				

marketing, accounting, housing market, processing, chemical, safety, environment supervision, computer, application of polymers, materials engineering, mechanical and electrical, mechanical, Numerical Control, electric, communication, etc. After recycling, we eliminate invalid questionnaire, get 878 valid questionnaires. The recovery rate is 87.8%. A sample survey is shown in Table 1.

3 THEORY MODEL DISCUSSION

3.1 *Exploratory factor analysis*

Validity is the accuracy of measuring variables with measurement method, namely the accuracy or correctness. We adopt the method of factor analysis to test the structure validity of the questionnaire. A random sample of half of the data namely 439 is regarded as exploratory factor analysis. First, we examine KMO and Bartlett and determine whether the scale is suitable for factor analysis. After calculation, KMO of self-management characteristics is 0.915, χ^2 of Bartlett is 2617.308 up to $(p < 0.001)$. It suggests that there is a common factor between correlation matrix, and it is suitable for factor analysis.

Then we analyze 26 items by principal component analysis in combination with oblique rotation for the first time. According to Kaiser $\lambda > 1$, w extract four factors. After examining the classified

subject, we remove the topics which are not in accord with intention and a little interpretation, and delete nine questions (A4, A5, A9, A12, A14, A18, a19, a25, A26). We use principal component analysis method to analyze 17 items secondly, KMO is 0.936, χ^2 of Bartlett is 7529.900 up to $(p < 0.001)$. It suggests that there is a common factor between correlation matrix. Pattern matrix is shown in Table 2. In addition, among at least 0.551 in part commonality, 65.952% of the total variance can be explained by the four factors extracted, so the scale has good construct validity.

3.2 *Confirmatory factor analysis*

Through exploratory factor analysis, we believe that self-management consists of academic development management, physical and mental health management, social activity management, resource development management. And the four potential factors are made up of 17 observation variables. Using half the sample data to do confirmatory factor analysis. In the fit test of self-management and data, though further analysis of two order factors and the measure of indexes correction value, we assume that the errors are not independent of each other, so on the basis of the index and confirmation of the original formal questionnaire items, it is partially modified, as is shown in Figure 1.

The model fit index is shown in Table 3.

Table 2. Analysis of the surface self management pattern matrix factor scale.

Type	No.	Factor extraction Factor 1	Factor 2	Factor 3	Factor 4	Commonness	Explained variation	Total
Academic	a1	0.540				0.594	20.185	20.185
development	a2	0.569				0.660		
management	a3	0.623				0.632		
	a6	0.766				0.708		
	a7	0.794				0.740		
	a8	0.745				0.683		
Physical and	a10		0.681			0.551	18.282	38.467
mental health	a11		0.664			0.593		
management	a13		0.575			0.566		
Social activity	a15			713		0.689	14.551	53.018
management	a16			0.804		0.764		
	a17			0.670		0.639		
Resource	a20				0.694	0.653	12.934	65.952
development	a21				0.743	0.708		
management	a22				0.721	0.674		
	a23				0.714	0.696		
	a24				0.655	0.662		
Characteristic value		7.675	1.477	1.059	1.001	–	–	

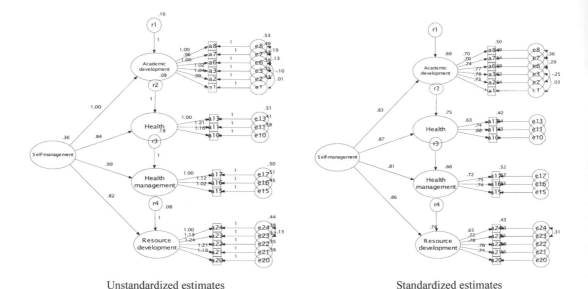

Unstandardized estimates   Standardized estimates

Graph 1.   Self-management features of confirmatory factor analysis models after correction.

Table 3.   Self-management of two order confirmatory factor analysis to test the fitness of table.

Indicator	χ^2	P	GFI	AGFI	RMR	RMSEA	NFI	RFI	IFI	TLI	CFI	PGFI
Standard	Smaller	>0.05	>0.90	>0.90	0.05	0.08	>0.90	>0.90	>0.90	>0.90	>0.90	>0.90
Model	590.507	0.000	0.934	0.908	0.041	0.064	0.933	0.917	0.946	0.933	0.946	0.671

4   RESULT ANALYSIS

Through the exploratory factor and confirmatory factor analysis of theoretical model, construction of higher vocational college students' self-management is divided four dimensions, namely academic development management, physical and mental health management, social activity management and resources development management. We will further analyze all sample data to understand college students' self-management present situation.

4.1   Reliability analysis

Internal consistency Cronbach α of the scale is shown in Table 7, Cronbach α is 0.860, academic development management is 0.881, physical and mental health management is 0.711, social activity management is 0.781, resources development management is 0.858, all are higher than 0.70. It shows validity analysis is good, combined of the previous sample reliability, the scale can reflect the condition of self management of Higher Vocational College students.

4.2   Evaluation of the present situation of vocational college students self—management

Using the Delphy method, we weigh various component of college students' Self-Management (SM), and get Academic Development Management (ADM) (0.4), physical and mental Health Management (HM) (0.3), Social Activity Management (SCM) (0.1), Resource Development Management (RDM) (0.2), the results is shown below.

By computing Higher vocational college students 'self-management' score is 3.33 (total score 5 points). It can reflect that the students' self-management is relatively weak, especially the score of physical and mental health management is the lowest, followed by resource development management. Research results show that students' self-management ability is lack.

4.3   Descriptive statistical analysis

Though further analysis of the mean and standard deviation of 17 three-level index in self-management scale, we get the following results. It is shown in Table 4.

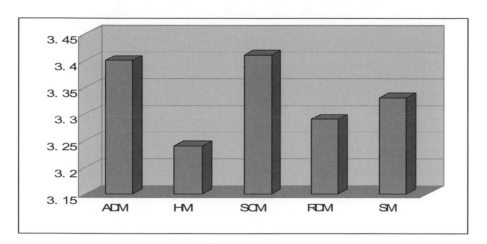

Graph 2. The overall evaluation of the current situation of college students' self management.

Table 4. Descriptive statistical analysis.

Index	N	Minimum	Maximum	Average	Standard deviation	Order
Target management	878	1.00	5.00	3.4146	0.96878	12
Plan management	878	1.00	5.00	3.4579	0.95744	10
Organization management	878	1.00	5.00	3.3872	0.96124	13
Incentive management	878	1.00	5.00	3.6686	0.88864	4
Control management	878	1.00	5.00	3.5103	1.04156	8
Development management	878	1.00	5.00	3.3064	0.98367	14
Method management	878	1.00	5.00	3.2175	0.99454	16
Innovation management	878	1.00	5.00	3.2494	1.02220	15
Physical management	878	1.00	5.00	3.4913	0.81734	9
Psychology management	878	1.00	5.00	3.6310	0.82950	5
Community activities	878	1.00	5.00	3.6082	1.00127	6
Student cadres	878	1.00	5.00	3.4282	1.09053	11
Social part-time	878	1.00	5.00	3.5444	1.01739	7
Material resources	878	1.00	5.00	3.7506	0.88596	2
Information resources	878	1.00	5.00	3.6693	0.77486	3
Human resources	878	1.00	5.00	3.8793	0.79816	1
Time resources	878	1.00	5.00	1.8622	0.45093	17

Through the study of each index of self-management, we found time management (1.8622), method management (3.2175), innovation management (3.2494), development management (3.3064), organization management (3.3872) are in the end. However, human resources (3.8793), material resources (3.7506), information resources (3.6693), incentive management (3.6686), psychology management (3.6310) are in the top. Research results show that time management, innovative consciousness of the higher vocational college students are weak, relatively speaking, more emphasis is put on human resources, material resources.

5 CONCLUSION AND COUNTERMEASURES

This study explores the structure and dimensions of self-management of higher vocational college students, respectively, academic development management, physical and mental health management, social management and resource management. Through the empirical study on the current situation of vocational college students' lack of self-management, it focuses on the lack of time management and innovation management, the improper learning methods management. In order to effectively improve the comprehensive quality of vocational college students and the personality accomplishment, students themselves, family and school need make the joint efforts. Therefore, in this paper we put forward the corresponding countermeasures from individual, family education, school education to improve the college students' ability of self management.

5.1 Academic development management recommendations

School level, teachers should change the traditional teaching mode, increase the interactive teaching methods, such as group discussion, demonstration and so on. Teachers had better also guide the students to think actively, encourage students to innovate bravely, fully develop students' initiative and creativity. In addition, teachers should communicate with students, listen to their ideas.

Household level, parents should instruct students academic management development and put forward high requirements. They help establish clear learning plans, regularly supervise their children's study, and keep contact with teachers. High requirements can help students recognize learning objectives, understand the employment and social situation now, then students will make more efforts to accomplish the goals. Rewards and punishment for students must be clear in order that students get fruit harvest through the material, spiritual encouragement. It can make the students know the severeness of the error, which is beneficial to students.

Students learn to manage their studies. After entering the university, students should learn how to set goals, especially the long-term objective, conform the targets first, then optimize and improve them constantly. In the process of achieving the goal, students should put their goals into practice, timely adjust themselves. Students should have self-innovation spirit, cultivate their own curiosity, observe tiny things around and find rules and mystery.

5.2 Physical and mental health management advice

Schools should strengthen students' mental education and establish students' mental health files, carry out various forms of psychological counseling activities, establish a psychological consultative room, to understand the student's basic situation in time. And then we can help students to eliminate confusion on psychology, study and life, alleviate their pressure. Students can also find a place to vent their anguish. It can help students adjust and relax their minds.

Parents should be concerned about students' physical and mental health. Parents urge their children to develop a good habit of diet and time during the vacations. Once their emotions change, parents should choose a suitable opportunity to help them resolve mental pressure. At school, parents often call to ask their diet, listen to the children and help them solve problems. Parents' care can help students to get rid of the bad habits, and gradually develop good habits. Students should pay attention to their own physical and mental health, it is beneficial to the healthy growth of students.

Students must strengthen the physical exercise and take an active part in sports activities in their daily life. According to their situation, they decide daily exercise time and item, and then stick to the plan. Attention should be paid to the daily diet, they arrange reasonably their own meals and rest time. It is beneficial for students to plunge into learning in high spirit. Encountering problems and a competitive environment, students must have a positive attitude, learn to adjust and control their emotions. Students should participate actively in school's psychological activities, and learn more about the psychological knowledge. If there is a lot of psychological problems, students must consult with the teachers who can help to alleviate psychological pressure.

5.3 Social activity management advice

Students' thought is changeful, active, and have strong desire for knowledge. Therefore, in the spare time, school can organize students to participate in beneficial social activities, such as work study, community service, volunteer service and other forms of social practice, let students truly understand the social, increased social experience.

Parents can use the social resources to arrange children to carry on the social practice in the enterprise during the summer and winter vacations. This can exercise their social practice ability and interpersonal communication skills. In addition, parents can introduce their children to their friends or colleagues, let children communicate with them, or make children deal with an emergency. It can exercise their eloquence ability and the ability of dealing with affairs.

College students should actively participate in community activities and social practice, to improve their ability to balance learning and life and enhance their comprehensive management ability. It can make them adapt the society better in the future.

5.4 Resource development management recommendation

Schools should create a good network environment, pay much attention to the construction of the campus network resources to form a rich and colorful network community. Schools can increase the amount of books, take the students' demand consideration fully. In the daily teaching and activities, schools timely imparts the concept of cherishing and using time to the students. Besides, school should increase the course about finance, how to use time, collection and use of information resources and interpersonal communication, to broaden the students' knowledge. The combination of theory and practice can help students learn how to manage resource development.

Parents guide students to allocate the resources rationally, train their ability to manage resources, such as financing ability, etc.

Students should make schedules in their spare time, reasonably distribute their learning, life and other things. For the external interference factors such as games, leisure and recreational activities, students should resist them, they need not spend a lot of time in the entertainment. Unless students make use of time reasonably and effectively, it is not beneficial to improve the qualities of students' culture and spirit. At the same time, it can help students obtain more skills certificates and knowledge outside the textbook, it also can help students improve their employment ability.

In conclusion, this study explored the structure and dimension of self-management of higher vocational college students. Through the analysis of questionnaire and SPSS and AMOS, we study the present situation of vocational college students' self management, and put forward the corresponding countermeasures for the existing problems. The deficiency of this study mainly lies in the limitations of sample selection, we only select the vocational college students. In the future we will widely collect higher vocational colleges from different areas and different types, in order to explore the content of higher vocational college students' self-management deeply.

ACKNOWLEDGEMENT

This project is supported by the 2012 year Jiangsu province higher philosophy and Social Science Research Fund (2012SJB880079), Thanks.

REFERENCES

[1] Li Hongyan, Shao Cailing, An Tao: Study on Students Ability of Self-management [J]. Journal of Agricultural University of Hebei, 2008.

[2] Chang Xin, Li Huimin. Study on How to Improve the Students' Ability of Self-management [J]. China Market, 35th. 2010.

[3] Zhao Yiyin. Study on Knowledge Employee Self-management and Innovation Motivation Mechanism [D]. Tianjin University of Commerce, 2007.

[4] He Qing: Study on Training and Evaluation of the Innovation Ability of Graduates [D]. College of education in Huazhong Normal University, 2010.

[5] Miao Chunxia: College Students' Life Quality and Its Evaluation Based on The Concept of Harmony [D]. China University of Mining and Technology, 2010.

[6] Yang tingfang: Study on Knowledge Employee Self-management Structure and the Related [D]. Jinan University, 2010.

[7] Wu Minglong. Structural Equation Model—AMOS operation and application. Chongqing University press, 2009.

[8] Wu Minglong. Statistical Analysis of the Questionnaire—SPSS operation and application. Chongqing University press, 2009.

[9] Fang Weibo, Xiao Pei. Self management [M]. Beijing: People's Liberation Army Publishing House, 1988: p19.

[10] Guo Hailong. Modernization and self management research [M]. Beijing: China Social Sciences Press, 2007: p10.

Computer, Intelligent Computing and Education Technology – Liu, Sung & Yao (Eds)
© *2014 Taylor & Francis Group, London, ISBN 978-1-138-02469-4*

Study on the construction of the quality assurance system of bilingual teaching

Q. Xiong, Q. Han, W. Zhou & J. Peng

School of Electrical and Information Engineering, Chongqing University of Science and Technology, Chongqing, China

ABSTRACT: In order to acclimate to the trend of internationalization of education, bilingual teaching in Chinese University is in the ascendant, but due to various factors, there are still many problems in bilingual teaching and the teaching quality could not be guaranteed. Therefore, a full range of bilingual teaching quality guarantee system, which consists of research, management and evaluation, should be constructed. To establish a scientific and reasonable bilingual teaching quality guarantee system, will be beneficial to improving the quality of bilingual teaching.

Keywords: bilingual teaching; quality assurance; access mechanism; supervision system; incentive mechanism

1 INTRODUCTION

In recent years, bilingual teaching in Chinese universities is developing very quickly, because it is requirements for the internationalization of education and talent. All colleges and universities has made some achievements in promoting bilingual teaching process, but also face a variety of problems, these problems have a direct impact on the bilingual teaching effect. At present, there are many researches about bilingual teaching, many of which are discuss the problems in bilingual teaching and the specific measures to solve these problems from the point of view of teaching, but ignore the role of college teaching quality management to ensure and improve the quality of bilingual teaching.

This paper analyzes the necessity of bilingual teaching quality assurance system, puts forward the research and thinking in three aspects: bilingual teaching study, management system and quality evaluation system, so as to ensure and improve the quality of bilingual teaching in Colleges and universities.

2 THE NECESSITY OF BILINGUAL QUALITY ASSURANCE SYSTEM

The practice of bilingual teaching in universities for several years, has made many achievements, but there are still many problems, such as the administrative department and teachers' understanding of bilingual teaching is not yet complete, theoretical research is not thorough, teaching objectives are incorrect orientation. Bilingual teaching management system is not perfect, mainly displays in: the bilingual curriculum is not perfect, the number of bilingual course is still of a small number, lack of qualified teachers, bilingual teaching materials and connection of teaching contents lack, bilingual teaching skills need to be improved, the interaction of teacher and student is poor, the students' ability to study is uneven. Because the lack of a scientific and reasonable bilingual teaching evaluation system, teachers' and students' efforts are not objective evaluation. Therefore, constructing bilingual teaching quality guarantee system of scientific and reasonable to ensure and improve the quality of bilingual teaching is very necessary.

Bilingual teaching quality assurance system's establishment and the consummation to strengthen the understanding of the goal of bilingual teaching, and can provide a correct orientation for universities. Management system aim at bilingual teaching is constructed, which is carried out guaranteeing the quality and quantity. Bilingual teaching quality guarantee system can acquire and timely feedback various elements, each link and the working state information of bilingual teaching, and its quality was controlled.

The so-called quality guarantee system refers to the school to continue to meet the individual needs and social needs as the goal (to achieve personal and social requirements of the bilingual talents standard), the factors inside and outside the university system as the background, the practice of bilingual teaching and management system as the foundation, the bilingual teaching evaluation as the means, the various departments of the link, the quality of bilingual teaching management activities closely together, forming a clear tasks, responsibilities, authority coordination, promote each other organic whole.

3 CONSTRUCTING THREE LEVELS OF BILINGUAL TEACHING RESEARCH SYSTEM

The universities, schools, teachers, three levels of bilingual teaching research system is built to do in-depth research on various aspects of bilingual teaching. In universities, Office of Educational Administration, Personnel, International Cooperation Department, Higher Education Research, the Steering Group and other relevant units set up a special team of bilingual teaching research group to study bilingual teaching content, objectives, principles, concepts, working principle and methods. Relevant documents of bilingual teaching are developed and various aspects of bilingual teaching strict regulations are set to strengthen the institutionalization. In schools, all teachers should be organized to learn national, provincial and school-related documents and teachers with bilingual teaching ability should be encouraged to open bilingual course. Teachers themselves have the responsibility and obligation to continue to conduct research and teaching reform, exploring our students' bilingual teaching mode.

4 CONSTRUCTING COMPREHENSIVE BILINGUAL TEACHING MANAGEMENT SYSTEM

4.1 Establishing bilingual curriculum and teacher access mechanism

Bilingual courses are allowed to be open required to be reviewed by the school supervision expert. In order to better the quality of bilingual education, Office of Educational Administration and schools organize experts to supervise the bilingual program will be open for scrutiny. Courses have no conditions or unsuitable are shut out, and the courses are ensure to carry out bilingual teaching is the right decision at the very beginning.

Bilingual teachers must have bilingual teaching qualification. In seniority, bilingual teachers should be the professional backbone teachers, must have strong language skills, and master standard spoken English, familiar with the English vocabulary. Bilingual teachers should have overseas study or work experience, or full-time foreign language training. In addition, Office of Educational Administration shall organize the bilingual teachers giving one bilingual lectures and supervision experts evaluate and secretly ballot to determine the qualified bilingual teachers. After that, university issue a "bilingual teacher qualification certificate" to bilingual teachers, and who have not obtained the qualification certificate could not carry out bilingual teaching.

4.2 Establishing particular bilingual supervision system

Office of Educational Administration arranges two or three supervisor to guide each bilingual course, asking every supervisor to listen lectures not less than two times. Teaching experts earnestly perform their duties, to thoroughly research, check all the teaching links of classroom, found the problems and immediately solved them. Problems found in the lecture are put forward some suggestions to the teacher for improvements, and common problems are given guidance. This is the most direct part in bilingual teaching quality control.

4.3 Holding bilingual teaching competition regularly

Bilingual teaching competitions are held regularly and through the contest, bilingual teachers can show their elegant demeanor, exchange experience and improve their level of bilingual teaching. Through the competition, management department can understand the teaching level and teaching method of bilingual teachers, and give the corresponding certainty, consequently improving the quality of bilingual teaching.

4.4 Constructing effective encouragement mechanism

Universities should give necessary financial support to bilingual course. Bilingual teaching reporting and filing system should be established. Teachers who will open bilingual course declare annually to the school during the arrangement of the teaching plan, and fill in the "registration form of bilingual teaching", audit contents including textbook, syllabus, teaching plan, courseware and exercises. After project approval, bilingual course is given the necessary financial support by Office of Educational Administration.

An effective incentive mechanism should also be established, by increasing the class fee and the workload calculation, by bilingual teaching reform project being given priority, and by having the priority to give one's professional title and awards. As a result, acknowledge their hard work and encourage them to constantly improve their own quality and have passion in bilingual teaching.

5 CONSTRUCTING SCIENTIFIC AND REASONABLE QUALITY EVALUATION SYSTEM

5.1 Establishing the quantitative quality evaluation index system

The construction of teaching quality evaluation system, first of all a reasonable, measurable and operable evaluation index system should be developed, so that all aspects of bilingual teaching can be made an objective evaluation.

This evaluation system should cover all aspects of the bilingual teaching and two level indicators can be quantified. First level index includes six aspects: curriculum, teachers, students, resources, and management, Second level index are more detailed and each index is given a weight. In the process of evaluation, each second level index is given a mark, and finally total weighted mark is got to be the evaluation of the bilingual course.

5.2 Improving the quality feedback mechanisms

The teaching quality feedback mechanism consists of students, experts and teachers themselves. Evaluation of teaching feedback mechanism is established by three aspects. Teachers evaluate students' learning, timely contact with counselor, and timely correct students' style of study, attendance and other problems. Students evaluate teaching ability, classroom organization ability and multiple aspects of teacher's ability online, and make assessment on teachers' teaching. Experts' evaluation and feedback is very important because their evaluation opinions are more objective and justice. Therefore, evaluation of teaching feedback mechanism needs comprehensive opinions from three aspects of the people, and only in this way, the true level of teaching can be really reflected.

The quality of bilingual teaching information feedback platform needs to be improved. Colleges and universities should pay attention to ask bilingual teaching supervisors, college (department) leaders and students to feedback on the quality information in whole process of bilingual teaching. The preparation of teaching materials, teaching content, teaching methods, teaching order maintenance, the implementation of bilingual teaching effect, students' bilingual consciousness and ability and other aspects of the information feedback need to be reviewed and summarized, providing a sufficient foundation to improve bilingual teaching in the next step.

5.3 Joining the student self-evaluation

In the process of bilingual teaching, the teacher is usually the center gravity of management and evaluation while the students is less required, then students relax own management, this greatly influences the effect of bilingual teaching. Therefore, students' self-evaluation should be joined in the assessment, and students are helped to understand their role in the bilingual teaching, discover learning problems, and rethink on their learning attitude profoundly, so as to be better at bilingual learning.

6 SUMMARY

Based on the analysis of present situation and existing problems of bilingual teaching in colleges and universities, this paper proposes to build the bilingual teaching quality guarantee system, to carry out bilingual teaching research on three levels, to establish the comprehensive management system and the quality evaluation system. Next, further study can be carried out in the quantitative quality evaluation index system.

ACKNOWLEDGEMENTS

This work was supported in part by "Data Structure and Algorithm" project, included in the National Bilingual Education Model Curriculum in 2009, in part by "c programming" Experimental Teaching and Research Project of Chongqing University of Science and Technology (No. 201318), in part by Teaching & Research Program of School of Electrical and Information Engineering (No. 201305, No. 201309).

REFERENCES

[1] Lou Lingyan, Wang Ge, The Necessity of Building a Quality Assurance System for Bilingual Courses at Higher Educational Institutions, Shangye Jingji, 2012(9).
[2] Liu Fa-gong, Quality Is Supreme for Bilingual Teaching in Colleges and Universities, Journal Of Zhejiang Gongshang University, 2010(6).
[3] Wang Guo-li, An Analysis on Quality Control of Bilingual Education in Newly-upgraded Local Universities, Journal Of Education Institute Of Taiyuan University, Vol.28 No.4, Dec.2010.
[4] Wang Fei, Chen Dongling, How to Improve the Quality of Bilingual Education in Ordinary Universities, Social Sciences Education, Oct.2011.
[5] Li Haiyin, Quality of teaching and countermeasures of university bilingual education in Henan province, Journal of Shangqiu Teachers College, Vol.27 No.9, Sep.2011.
[6] Zhou Zhi-xia, Study on Channels to Improve Bilingual Teaching Quality for Economic and Management Spcialty, Journal of Weifang University, Vol.12 No.1, Feb.2012.
[7] Xu Hai-Yan, Zhang Feng-jun, Li Dong-cai, Xu Ling, Li Yan, Exploring into Improving Bilingual Teaching Quality of Introduction to Materials Science, Journal of Hefei Normal University, Vol.29 No.6, Nov.2011.

Computer, Intelligent Computing and Education Technology – Liu, Sung & Yao (Eds)
© *2014 Taylor & Francis Group, London, ISBN 978-1-138-02469-4*

How the humanities influence on the college students' engineering quality

J.Q. Zhao
College of Liberal Arts, Beihua University, Jilin City, China

D.X. Geng
Engineering Training Center, Beihua University, Jilin City, China

ABSTRACT: In this paper we have a study on how the humanities influence on the college students' engineering quality, aiming at the absence of engineering quality of college students. And then we put forward that the point that the humanities is the foundation and the premise to cultivate and improve students' engineering quality. Meanwhile, we think that both the scientific spirit and humanistic spirit are the souls of engineering quality, and the combination of both is the effective way to improve the engineering quality.

Keywords: humanities; human spirit; engineering quality; science spirit

1 INTRODUCTION

The high-quality engineers are the driving force in technology to accelerate industrialization stably, positive and high-speed. Yet at present, the engineering qualities of practitioners are seriously absent in china. They are weak in systematization of engineering knowledge and lack of innovation and application in engineering, especially; they are short of engineering awareness on responsibility, quality, safety and environmental protection.

How to improve this situation as soon as possible? I believe that, in reality, humanities are the important base and premise of developing and enhancing the engineering quality of colleges' students. If our society pays special attention to both humanities and engineering qualities, we will obtain effect getting twice the result with half the effort.

2 HUMANITIES AND ENGINEERING QUALITIES

Humanities are the intrinsic natures of man, which mainly include humanistic knowledge, social mentality, humanistic spirit and human behavior etc. The specific expressions may be found in individual quality of human, such as thought level, moral, psychological quality, mode of thinking, interpersonal communication, emotion, and outlook on the world and life and so on. The core of humanities is spirit of humanity, concern of human life, the value and significance.

Humanities are the essence of the culture which is refined from cultural created by human beings, and they reflect both the seeking to the human nature and the care of the destiny of human beings. On the view of macroscopic, the humanities embody in the national spirit, and in micro presentation, they appear as the temperament of the people and the value orientation, such as caring for life, pursuing ideal, praising of moral, yearning for the perfect personality, loving of truth and nurturance the manner of scientific thinking and so on. At the same time, the scientific spirit of "be careful, responsible a, realistic and creative in studies" is also the important part of humanities. As we known, the absence of humanities will lead to the inanity, even loss of conscience; in the same way, the humanities are imperfect if it is lack of scientific spirit. As Yang Shuzi said, the famous mechanical engineering specialist, educators, and an academician with the Chinese Academy of Science, "Without technology, a play on the collapse; But not human, not playing since the collapse."

Engineering quality is the inside character, specialization and the style of work of people in the face of the engineering problems. And they are the inner quality, manners of occupation and professional level when they facing engineering problems, which reflect the ability to follow the engineering rules, the consciousness to pursue scientific spirit and humanities in specific.

Engineering quality includes engineering knowledge and skill, engineering consciousness, innovative capabilities and so on. Engineering consciousness is the awareness, knowledge and concern to the engineering problem, and it is consists of sense of duty, safety awareness, quality awareness, cost consciousness, awareness of environmental conservation, management, etc. The spirit of science is the core of the engineering quality. And the engineering quality has the character of internality, stability, plasticity and unity. Internality means that the structure, characteristics and level of engineering quality can not be directly observed, but it can be reflected from the engineers' efficiency, quality and capability. Stability refers that it is not easy to change in short time, and it has relative stability and often repeatedly in engineering activities. Plasticity means that, engineering quality can be developed and improved through adscititious learning. Unity refers that engineering quality is a multi-level integrated system, the components of system both independent and mutual constraints. The engineering quality depends on each element and the equilibrium relationship between them. The unbalance of development of each element has a serious effect on the cultivation of the engineering quality. For example, the lacking of quality awareness and lower insurance ability will seriously impede the development of engineering quality. The unity of the engineering quality testifies to the combination of scientific spirit and humanistic spirit.

Most college students today are not lack of the cultivation of engineering knowledge, skill and innovative ability, but they are short of the cultivation of humanistic spirit, and which seriously affected the comprehensive cultivation of the engineering quality of college students.

3 THE RELATIONSHIP BETWEEN HUMANITIES AND ENGINEERING QUALITY

First of all, humanities are the base and premise for the development of the engineering quality. The humanities, such as language literacy, thinking character, the capability of self-knowledge and views on life and values, are base and premise for the development of the engineering quality, and which have a great influence on the cultivation of the engineering quality.

Language in education plays an important role in healthiness development of students' personality and promotion of development fully and harmoniously of students. Language literacy includes Chinese knowledge, reading ability, logical thinking ability, writing ability and oral expression ability and so on. These abilities are directly related to our thinking character, cultural quality, aesthetic values, vision and knowledge, attitudes and feelings,

mind and views, etc, and which have a significant role on acquiring engineering knowledge, forming engineering capacity, cultivating engineering consciousness.

Moreover, as we known, learning from history can warn and inspire the thinking method, macro speculative philosophy point out the moving direction, the prohibition imposed by law establishes the rules of conduct, the public opinion from the standpoint of morality and ethics can can exert great pressure on policy. And above these play the unreplaceable important role in the engineering quality cultivation and which can also enlighten and regulate the behaviors and way of thinking of engineers.

Secondly, the engineering quality blocks the further development of humanities. The core of engineering quality is science spirit which can promotes development of humanities.

Modern engineering, internet information technology and the high-tech products not only change the self surviving method and the thinking as well as concepts created by human beings, but also directly affect the humanity.

Science and technology are the important part of the advanced cultures as well as the important basis for major policy and legislation. And they are not only the major contents of science education, but also the cornerstone of the human survival and development, but also the most important resource to develop continuously of human civilization. Throughout history science have changed the person's worldview, Darwin's theory of evolution undermined the Western creationism, the discovery of the gene in humans offered evidence of the rule of heredity and variation, the proposition of astrophysics and the big bang theory changed the human view of the universe. In general, science influences a person's value system, and knowledge as well as information is the treasures of priceless worth. Along with that, efforts are intensified to conserve and improve the ecological environment. At the same time, the science changes human' view of development, the Development of Geoscience in the New Century eliminates the fear of nature, and which also warn the people the complexity and frangibility of the earth and alert humans to care for the earth. The development of science make human' view of development come through the perception and development nature, and then construct a road for the harmony of human beings and nature, which lead to the idea of sustainable development.

Thirdly, humanities and engineering quality help each other forward. The engineers or the managers who are lack of good humanities tend to lose their credibility, justice and profession ethics in front of people's lives and property, as well as the interests of the individual and the group. On the contrary, the person with good engineering quality who pursue engineering quality and safety as well as focus on the environmental protection, showed good personality and temperament, correct views on life and values. Accordingly, it can be thought that both science spirit and humanities are the soul of engineering quality, and the higher engineering quality is difficult to cultivated without the combination of two, even if they are well-read and have outstanding ability.

4 THE EFFECTIVE METHOD TO IMPROVE THE ENGINEERING QUALITY OF COLLEGE STUDENTS

4.1 Make greater efforts to cultivate the humanities

The university and college should strengthen the construction of the human environment, and provide more courses about humanities education. The teachers in higher engineering education should have good humanities, and they should have rich experiences and capabilities of engineering practice besides of the theory knowledge and scientific research. In short, only the person with good science spirit and humanities can adequate to the duty and mission of engineering education.

4.2 The spirit of science be combined into humane quality education

The humane quality education courses such as literature and history, music and art, cultivation of ideological morality, should focus on the cultivation of science spirit for students. For instance, in language teaching, students should use of Chinese language Skilled, cultivate the ability of thinking in images step by step, inherit the national spirit and heritage of humankind, and consequently cultivate the healthy psychology and sound personality. On the other hand, the teachers should combine the humanities with science spirit to arouse students' enthusiasm in learning, encourage students to explore and innovate for the unknown world. Especially, the teachers should focus on the cultivation of scientific way of thinking and comparative analysis ability for students.

4.3 Foster the conception of humanities in the cultivation of engineering quality

To a big manufacturing country be concerned, the society needs the college students with good engineering quality urgently to satisfy the further development of nation. According to the direction of talents training, the grade, standards and requirements of engineering quality cultivation to different disciplines such as liberal arts, science, engineering and business administration, can be divided into different levels. Among these, students in science and engineering are the designers and implementers of the future projects as well as the products manufactures; their engineering quality has to do with the people's basic confidence and feelings to the products. Thus it is need to grasp the knowledge and skill of engineering and the innovation capability in depth.

Thus, the teachers should combine the engineering knowledge, science spirit with the humanities in engineering education, and let the educatee solve the practical engineering problems agilely applying the engineering knowledge. At the same time, the teachers should help them establish strong engineering consciousness of responsibility, quality, cost, security, management, and environmental protection and so on, cultivate innovation ability and good characters, and form the good engineering quality finally.

In the course of the theory and practice of engineering technology, or in technology contest and scientific research, we should attach importance to humanistic education besides strengthening cultivation of scientific spirit. Through the humanities education, the students known that the product quality is close related to the living quality and feelings of human beings, as well as the social confidence; the cost and manufacturing process have respect to the rational use of resources, environmental conservation and sustainable development; safety for product is connected to the life security and social stability. And anyway, the teachers should cultivate the students' awareness of self supervision in human nature; let them understand the truth in life from the heart, impress on students the importance of one's character and deeds accord with words. A person should be provided with caring and loving society and nature of responsibility on the basis of cherishing their own lives and conscience.

REFERENCES

[1] Jinsheng Zhou, Shuxiong Peng: Humanities and Humanistic Quality (Guangming Daily, Beijing 2004).
[2] Yajun Shi, Zhanyan Xie, Bing Wen: Humanistic Quality Theory (China Renmin University Press, Beijing 2008).
[3] Yajun Shi, Zhanyan Xie, Bing Wen: Humanistic Quality Theory (China Renmin University Press, Beijing 2008).
[4] Qingwen Fan, Shengqin Liu, Jiyong Ma: Experimental technology and management Vol. 21(2004), p.5–8.
[5] Dejing Zhang: China University Teaching, Vol. 3(2010), p.4–6.

Computer, Intelligent Computing and Education Technology – Liu, Sung & Yao (Eds)
© 2014 Taylor & Francis Group, London, ISBN 978-1-138-02469-4

Analysis and discussion of cultural landscape for college campus

Yan-Ning Zheng & Fang Jiang
Shunde Polytechnic, Foshan, China

ABSTRACT: This essay would discuss the representation of college spirit and creation of campus culture and multi-layered contact space by the combination of idea of high education and campus landscaping. By means of the expression of landscaping factors, regards to environment and culture, creating the beautiful campus of a modernized, informationised, humanized and socialized top college and its school culture, is the main topic of following.

Keywords: campus landscaping; campus culture; placeness spirit

The college landscape is composed by the constructions, gardens and other structures altogether. The planners, architects and landscape architects integrate their philosophy into the landscaping. By the way of conception, planning and design, they use efficient materialization and representational form to express and deliver the thoughts and cultural connotation [1].

The campus landscaping culture is the kind which is embodied by the natures of the architecture style and campus sceneries. It is in a way a kind of reflection of the mental outlook, esthetical sentiment and value orientation of the school. According to this, the landscaping design of the riverside park in Shunde Polytechnic is also going to represent the regional characteristics of Shunde city as "Land of Dragon boat", and put spurs to the dragon boat festival and dragon boat culture. Depending on the unitary planning of New Urban Area in Shunde, the design would take the water area of Guipan River as the core section, so that to form an open gallery with unique landscaping structure and greening space—a riverside park reflecting the characteristics of the time and regional culture. Furthermore, the design would combine with the progress of the school cultural construction, and sown the seed of ideal realization to all students and staffs of Shunde Polytechnic [2].

1   BACKGROUND

Shunde government proposed the requirements as "High-level origin, New organization and Distinctive features" to the college, and Shunde Polytechnic rooted the educational philosophy of "Endemic, Humanism, Aesthetic, Characterization" as echo. Shunde is a famous waterside country locating on the south of Five Ridges. The Dragon Boat Festival is an activity which has a long story. The Dragon Boat Competition represent put up the Chinese people's heroic spirit of solidarity, combatant spirit and fearlessly marching. This is the essence of Shunde spirit as well. The government and school intend to imtroduce the Dragon Boat competition to the riverside park in the campus. By such way they integrate the regional culture and Dragon Boat spirit into school cultural construction, so that to cultivate the heroic spirit on the heartlands of students and staffs [3].

2   LANDFORM

The riverside park of Shunde Polytechnic is locating on the west of the campus and east of the Guipan River. It is the main route of the campus traffic which means advantageous location. Its position faces water in east, west and south sides that makes it an open viewing site with broad horizon. Currently the green land is occupied by the nursery garden, and also because of the frequent replacement of nursery stocks, the plant landscape is very unstable that has interfered the environment of Office Building.

3   THEME

How to carry the school cultural construction through the design, and fully excavate the potential vigour of the school, hence to create a synthesis park integrating leisure, sightseeing and waterside amusement altogether—is the main theme that the design intend to discuss. The discussion depends on the natural geographical conditions of Guipan

River bank and the regional culture of Dragon Boat spirit and explores the future of the Dragon Boat culture with the educational philosophy. By centring on the spirit of solidarity and forward marching that are advocated in the Dragon Boat traditional culture, the design makes its greatest efforts to perform the spiritual space of campus with noble sentiment, cultural depth and regional characteristics.

4 PRINCIPLES

Depending on the theme we discussed above, the design is basically supervised by the principles as following.

4.1 *Ecology*

Taking the inheritance of regional culture of Shunde as foundation, the design joins the sustainable concepts and modern ecological standpoints into the synthetic and integrated ecological methodology. Under the conditions of natural geographical environment, the landscaping factors of the park would be required to be consistent with the surrounding area and make the best to promote the ecological environment. Hence then, the entire design would obtain the uniformity and coherence.

4.2 *Landscaping*

As for the landscape spaces, increasing and extending the enjoyable and participatory spaces, is a key aspect of the progression of enriching the space layout of the park and the campus cultural activities. In order to create the enjoyable and relaxing areas in the limited spaces, the area and other kinds of spaces must penetrate into each other. The riverside belt is a zonal space in the park. It directs the penetrability and mobility of the space. People they might favour a walking in such a place, or stand to look into the distance, or talk besides the water… Polymorphous space styles would derive multiple human behaviours. And such diverse styles would develop the continuation of moving and connectivity of sights.

4.3 *Utility*

The design must take the demands of functions as first place. Under the preconditions of maximising the ecological benefits, natural surrounding and structure of the green space, it should specify the essence and content of the park in order to increase its functionalities. Hence so, it can achieve the functional convenience, formal suitability and

beautiful landscape, and endow us the unlimited imaginable spaces on sense of feeling, viewing and hearing. Fully utilising by men in the site makes the true meaning to the space. Therefore, how the design could create the beauty combining with the people's demands in the college, and how the space could become the sharing wealth by continue acceleration and management, are the most precious meaning of such the space.

4.4 *Region*

"The local cultural characteristics are the synthetic reflections of the regional natures and local customs, and the most important cultural background of all the spaces in the school." While the students and staffs could feel the local cultural atmosphere in the communication spaces, they would swiftly cognise, and immediately approve this environment. "Thus, it is vitally important to represent the local cultural characteristics while promoting the sense of approval of the space." Hence then, the design would take the Shunde local Dragon Boat culture as the regional culture factor with the inheritance of the native's spirits [4].

4.5 *Culture*

The school culture is usually formed by the emotion, and reversely, the school culture could also impact the mental world and impact more via the emotions. Encouragement, is just the mental progress of urging the birth of some thoughts, expectations and behaviours. Hence, as the school culture, no matter it is in the form of materials or of spirit, if it obtains healthy contents and vivid emotions, it would be the nice encouragement for students.[11] The design of Shunde Polytechnic is constructing brand landscaping—new school culture that is supervised by the educational philosophy of "Endemic, Humanism, Aesthetic and Characterization".

5 SPACE STRUCTURE

5.1 *Space layout*

In the design of the space layout, it consists seven themes, as memorial space, surpassing space, associate space, unitive space, pondering space and yearning space.

6 FUNCTIONAL STRUCTURES

Depending on the ideas of principle of utility, the design divides the space into six functional areas, as square area, riverside sightseeing area, ecological preferring area, open activity section and reading jungle area.

7 TRAFFIC SYSTEM

All the roads make themselves an integrated and orderly system with clear distinctions between its primary essentials and the lesser one. It deploys the layouts depending on human traffic of daily life and great activities. Meanwhile, it also takes the safety and smooth moving of motor vehicles into considerations. The design would add more garden surrounding walk lanes. They would connect each garden area, and make them stand alone as well.

8 PLANTING ON THE GREEN LAND

The entire leisure green land would use appropriate design of ecological community. Except the proper selections of native trees, it would also introduce a large amount of landscaping trees in all kinds of species, so that to make the ecological landscapes of the plants full of variety, and create a true ecological leisure area with abundant vegetation, limpid water, balmy blossoms and quality soil. The plants collection forms the steric layouts in the vertical space by the order of tall arbours—medium arbours—flowering shrubs—ground covers—humidogene—marshy vegetation—aquatic vegetation. Dense quantity of trees makes a more peaceful environment with better ecology. Hence this would create the harmony of land and water, dynamic and static, artificial scenery and natural landscapes.

9 EPILOGUE

Nowadays, all kinds of demands in the campus environments have become more and more polymorphous. How to find out a campus environment which can fit the diverse society in the future development[9]; how to combine the campus planning and high education philosophy and reflect it on the campus landscaping; how to represent and college spirit in the landscaping design, so that to construct the beautiful campus and noble school culture of a top college that faces the new age with modernity, informationization, humanism and socialisation; and how to reflect the principles of humanistic and ecological on the landscaping design—In the current tide of the revolution of high education colleges, all of these are the sensitive and challenging global topics which are about both high education school culture and landscaping planning.

REFERENCES

[1] Liu zhi-Jian. The campus culture construction of theory of multicultural background. J. (2005). Theory Horizon, (10), p.138–139, in Chinese.
[2] Cai Han-Jun. The basic connotation of university culture and the construction of the way. J. (2005) Heilongjiang Researches on Higher Education, (4), p.6–7, in Chinese.
[3] Li Duo, Wu Jiang. Universitytown—A kind of humanism campus design idea. J. (1999). Time + Architecture, (1), p.45–47, in Chinese.
[4] Wang Yue. Campus environment design study regional culture characteristics. D. (2004). Northwestern Polytechnic University, in Chinese.

Computer, Intelligent Computing and Education Technology – Liu, Sung & Yao (Eds)
© 2014 Taylor & Francis Group, London, ISBN 978-1-138-02469-4

The discussions on the standardization of the Tibetan text

B.J. La, H.Z. Yu & R. Dou
Ministry of Education Key Laboratory for Chinese Ethnic Minority Language,
Northwest University for Nationalities, LanZhou, China

ABSTRACT: The standardization of the Tibetan text is to analyze the contexts through a whole text of Tibetan language, and to identify the numbers and the symbols in simplified form and/or the peculiar semantic chunks, and to give the standard writing form of them under the controlled vocabulary of Tibetan language. This paper explains the definition of the standardization of Tibetan text that targets the problems of the Tibetan text during the speech synthesis of Tibetan language and gives the data structures and flows of the sort algorithms of Tibetan lexicon. This paper also studies the types and patterns of non-standard Tibetan text, the analyser of Tibetan text, the structures of Tibetan documents, the format of semantic chunks, and the flows of data. The non-standard Tibetan texts are split by text block and implement the standardization of Tibetan text by using lexical analyzer and semantic recognizer.

Keywords: Tibetan text; standardization; sort algorithm of lexicon; lexical analyzer; semantic recognizer

1 INTRODUCTION

Tibetan Language is classified Tibeto-Burman that belongs to Chinese-Tibetan, which is mainly divided into three dialect areas: Dbus Gtsang (latin transliteration), Amdo and Kang. Dbus Gtsang refers to Tibet Autonomous Region, Amdo mainly refer to Qinghai, Gansu and Aba Tibetan and Qiang Autonomous Prefecture in Sichuan, Kang is mainly refer to Ganzi Tibetan Autonomous Prefecture in Sichuan Province, Yushu Tibetan Autonomous Prefecture in Qinghai and some other regions. There are some differences in the spoken language in the three dialects, but the characters are generic.

This paper studies the Tibetan texts standardization issues in connection with the Tibetan speech synthesis encountered for discussion.

2 THE DEFINITION OF TIBETAN TEXT NORMALIZATION

2.1 *The standard text of Tibetan*

Tibetan text normalization refers to all of the text that consist of the modern Tibetan characters or Sanskrit Tibetan characters.

The errors of Tibetan spelling or typographical can be corrected by labor or machine; Tibetan non-standard phrases can be confirmed or regulated by Tibetan dictionary, Tibetan grammar and Tibetan rule base. After correcting or rectifying, the non-standard writing forms of Tibetan belong to Tibetan text specification category.

2.2 *The non-standard text of Tibetan*

There are some other characters in Tibetan texts which do not belong to Tibetan characters, such as numbers, dates, phone numbers and other characters written by Arabic numerals, mathematical formula and the number of symbols in technical manuals, emoticons, currency symbols, or other shorthand symbols in Email texts, the domain names or IP addresses usually are used in the Web pages, etc. There are many conventional notations in Tibetan text, for example, French quotes and quotes are non-standard Tibetan text. These non-standard texts can correctly determine their pronunciation after converted to the standard written form and become standardized text.

2.3 *Tibetan text normalization*

Selecting any of the special and complex sentences from non-canonical Tibetan text to do the Tibetan text normalization, the text contains numbers, time, special symbols, currency, dates, telephone numbers, punctuation, IP address, E-mail address and other types.

3 THE NON-STANDARD TIBETAN TEXT BLOCKS

3.1 *The classification of non-standard Tibetan text blocks*

By directly using the Chinese punctuation marks, Arabic numbers, letters and other special symbols, there list common classification of non-standard Tibetan text blocks below:

1. Punctuation marks
   ་ གཅས་འདུག་ངགས་ ("Zhi Zhe Ming Yue")
2. Phone number, such as follows
   The Arabic numerals are used directly to record phone numbers in Tibetan texts, for example 0931-2938541.
3. Numbers, such as follows:
   Numbers have different ways of writing, different meanings, and different ways of reading. For example: Whether "3726951" should be standardized phone number: three seven two six nine five one (གསུམ་བདུན་གཉིས་དྲུག་དགུ་ལྔ་གཅིག) or be standardized numbers three point seven two million six thousand nine hundred and fifty one (ས་ཡ་གསུམ་དང་འབུམ་བདུན་ཉིས་ཁྲི་དྲུག་སྟོང་དགུ་བརྒྱ་ལྔ་བཅུ་ང་གཅིག), which needs to be determined by the semantic of the context.
4. Dates, such as follows:
   2007 ཟྱ་ཟླ་6 ཚེས་ 18 ཉིན
5. Time
   Time may consist of hours, minutes, seconds, or the time interval and so on. Such as 8:10.
6. Other digital
   There are many other forms of digital. The system of Tibetan text can add new digital block identification rules constantly based on the need. Rules can set a certain priority level. When there are events of conflict rules, the rules with higher level will be used to identify. Such as £200, 1.25% and −5°C.
7. The mixed category
   The difficulty lies in the type of texts whose process is endless in the standardization of the text, and no system can cover all the possible cases. So it is necessary to establish the appropriate rule bases which allow to add new rules. There are some other text types which are worth considering, besides digital, numbers and other types. Such as follows:
   Mathematical expressions, such as $27 \times 60 = 1620$, $\sin30 = 0.5$.
   Web sites and Email address, etc. For example:ss@sina.com.
   Emotions symbols appear online, such as ☺ and ☹.

3.2 *The mode of Tibetan non-canonical text blocks*

The mode of Tibetan non-canonical text blocks called the rules which generate and recognize Tibetan word as pattern, elements identified by a pattern (rule) is token, and the word lexeme is the value of the identified elements.

Numeric types (token): 3.12

The regular expression mode which is matching: (\\d+)(\\.(\\d\\d))?

Currency types (token): $25.68

Mode (pattern): \\$(\\d+)(\\.(\\d\\d))?

Phone number types (token): 0931-2938541

Mode (pattern): (\\d+)(\\-) (\\d+)

Mathematical expression type (token): $3 + 5 = 8$; $27 \times 60 = 1620$

Mode (pattern): (\\d+)(\\+) ?(\\ ×)? (\\d+)(\\=) (\\d+).

4 INFORMATION PROCESSING AND TIBETAN TEXT NORMALIZATION

4.1 *Tibetan text analyzer*

Analyzing Tibetan text is the front-end of conversion system in Tibetan text and speech, analyzing and processing the inputting texts, and providing the necessary information to the back-end speech synthesizer, such as pronunciation, pause, etc.[3] The ideal Tibetan text parser is the ideal Tibetan natural language understanding program.[2]

4.2 *The analysis of Tibetan document structure*

Tibetan document structure is divided into the structure and the input Tibetan text. Identifying the boundaries of sentences and paragraphs is extremely important for all Tibetan documents. Sentences or paragraphs are the large rhythm units, too. If entering Tibetan texts has the marked format, document structure analysis is doing the interpretation of the marks. Tibetan text input is a part of the texts in buffer, the text may be an ordinary Tibetan text, it also can be formatted and marked text, Figure 2 shows the structure diagram of the text analyzer.

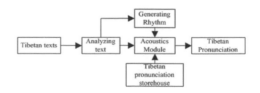

Figure 1. The role of Tibetan text analyzer.

Tibetan dictionary is an essential resource for text analysis, and is the knowledge database stored Tibetan linguistic. Tibetan dictionary modules are relatively independent, and query interface can be defined. Word segmentation is word module. English word segmentation is very clear, words are divided by the space. Tibetan syllables are connected together in written Tibetan sentences, there is no word boundary indicator, and therefore, word segmentation in the Tibetan language information processing is essential. Grammar analysis is to determine the composition Tibetan words, phrases and sentences. There are not only adhesion, but also twists and turns in Tibetan sentences, as well as Tibetan ambiguity discern, and all of them add the difficulty of Tibetan Word segmentation. Tibetan lexical analysis is obtained Tibetan basic grammar information by dividing words from the dictionary and tagging the words, which is part of speech; Tibetan syntactic analysis is knowing the relationship between the words, based on a grammar, and using the small grammatical syntax of the sentence to form a large one. The text information extracted from sentences includes Tibetan texts

rhythm, rhythmic structure, accent and intonation. Word and pronunciation conversion is converting the writing form of expressing the meaning of the text into the phonetic form of writing. It should be the phonemes form for Tibetan language.

Tibetan text analysis module can be modified, according to the progress of research.

4.3 Data streams

The inputted Tibetan text remains in the buffer, Tibetan text as a character stream will be recorded to an internal structure, internal structure as a pointer passed to each module in turn. The internal data structures will be added into new information when each module complete their work.

Enter a sentence ཚེས་བརྒྱད་ལ་ང་པེ་ཅིང་དུ་འགྲོ། ("I'm going to Beijing on the 8th"), after text analysis the process are written in Table 1.

4.4 The semantic form of Tibetan standard text block

1. The standardized form of digital:
   0, 1, 2, 3, 4, 5, 6, 7, 8, 9

   ཟིག་ གཉིག་ གསུམ་ བཞི་ ལྔ་ དྲུག་ བདུན་བརྒྱད་ དགུ

   Ten, Hundred, Thousand, Ten thousand, One hundred thousand, one million, ten million, one hundred million

   བཅུ་ བརྒྱ་ སྟོང་ ཁྲི་ འབུམ་ ས་ཡ་ བྱེ་བ་ དུང་ཕྱུར

2. The Standardization form of various digital:
   10 ༡༠
   11 ༡༡
   20 ༢༠
   1.25% བརྒྱ་ཆའི་གཅིག་དང་ཉི་ཤུ་རྩ་ལྔ་གཉིས་ཤུ།

3. 2938541 can represent two types of digital:
   Phone Number: Two nine three eight five four one
   ༢༩༣༨༥༤༡།

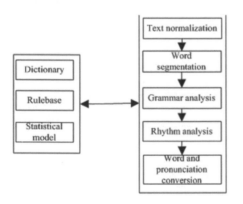

Figure 2.   The structure diagram of the text analyzer.

Table 1. The data flow of text analysis table.

Tibetan	English comparison (for reference)
To enter Tibetan: ཚེས་ལ་པེ་ཅིང་དུ་འགྲོ།	To enter English: I'm going to Beijing on the 8th
Document analysis: ཚེས་ལ་པེ་ཅིང་དུ་འགྲོ།	Document analysis: I'm going to Beijing on the 8th
Tibetan word: ཚེས་ལ་པེ་ཅིང་དུ་འགྲོ།	English word: I'm/going/to/Beijing/on/the/8th
The phrase of Tibetan rhythm: ཚེས་ལ་པེ་ཅིང་དུ་འགྲོ།	The phrase of English rhythm: I'm/going to Beijing/on the 8th
Lhasa tone IPA: ŋa^{12} tɕe^{53} cɛ^{14}la^{12}pe^{55} tɕiŋ^{55} thu^{12} tso^{14}.	English phonetic or IPA: [aɪm] [ˈɡəʊɪŋ] [tə] [beidʒiŋ] [ɒn] [ðə] [eɪtθ].

Figure: Two point nine three million eight thousand five hundred and forty one

ཚལ་གཉིས་དང་འབུམ་དགུ་དང་ཁྲི་ཉི་བརྒྱད་སྟོང་

ལྔ་བརྒྱ་བཞི་བཅུ་ཞེ་གཅིག

4. The canonical form of Tibetan: year, month, day, hour, minute, second:

ལོ ཟླ ཉིན དུས་ཚོད སྐར་མ སྐར་ཆ

5. Date:
2007 ཟླ་ཀྲུ༌s ཚེས 18 ཉིན

༢༠༠༧ལོའི་ཟླ་༥ཚེས་༡༨ཉིན

6. Time14:20:10

ཆུ་ཚོད་དུས་ཚོད་བཅུ་བཞི་དང་སྐར་མ་ཉིས་ཤུའི་སྐར་ཆ་བཅུ

7. Mathematical expressions:
$$27 \times 60 = 1620$$
Twenty-seven multiplied by sixty equals one thousand six hundred and twenty

ཉིས་བདུན་ལ་དྲུག་བཅུ་སྒྱུར་ན་སྟོང་གཅིག་དྲུག་བཅུ་ཉི་ཤུ

ཡིན

8. Phone number 010-62775212

ཀྲིག་གཅིག་ཀྲིག་དྲུག་གཉིས་བདུན་བདུན་ལྔ་གཉིས་གཅིག

གཉིས

9. Punctuation
《ལྷ་གཞས་འཇུག་རྟགས》 ("Zhi Zhe Ming Yue")

ལྷ་གཞས་འཇུག་རྟགས་ཞེས་པའི་གཞུང

10. Other numbers
1.25% བརྒྱ་ཆའི་གཅིག་དང་ཕྱེད་ཆ་གཉིས་སུ
–5°C དྲུའི་ཐང་ས་སྟེག་མ་ལྔ
£200 (Two hundred pounds) དངུལ་པར་ཉ ཞེ་བརྒྱ

5. THE DESIGN AND IMPLEMENTATION OF THE TIBETAN STANDARDIZED TEXT

5.1 *Problem need to be solved*

1. Determining non-standardization Tibetan text block type.
2. Converting the non-standardization of Tibetan texts into a standardized format depending on the type.

5.2 *The solution of Tibetan text specifications*

Token (text blocks) at least contains two information: one is the type of the mark, such

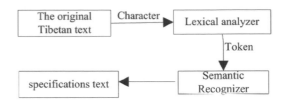

Figure 3. Text specifications steps.

as: ལྷ དང་ཡིག་གི་རྩ་དུས་ཚེས་ཉུ་དས (Date of Tibetan); the other is the value of the mark, such as: ༢༠༠༧ལོའི་ཟླ་ཕ་འའི་ཙ ཟ་༡༨ (May 18, 2007). It's identifying a text block type rather than a specific block of text values essentially, so called the sequence identified by the lexical analyzer as a stream of tokens.

Token contains at least two parts: the type and the semantic information. Token type can identifies a class of tokens uniquely, so called the token type as class mark and in the case, that can not confusion.

Text specifications steps:

1. Segmentation of Tibetan sentences, cut into several text blocks: Tibetan characters blocks, punctuation, word points and carriage return character.
2. Using the lexical analyzer to achieve text blocks (mark) identification based on regular expressions (pattern) rules, in order to determine the type of the text block.
3. Using regular expression to search engine to achieve regular expression matching in the lexical analyzer, and to determine the exact type of the text block when matching text blocks and regular expression successfully.
4. Forming the Tibetan standard text by Tibetan recognizer which needs to use the context requires.
5. Lookup: Digital lookups digital table, symbols check symbol table.

5.3 *The sorting algorithm of Tibetan word*

Using the Tibetan dictionary sort regulations to carry out the sorting of Tibetan word. Through the program computer can sort Tibetan words automatically to identify the Tibetan's root letter, superscripted letter, subscribed letter, prefix, suffix, secondary suffix, and then recognition, judgment, calculations, sorting, sorting Tibetan vocabulary.

5.4 *The implementation of Tibetan text normalization module*

Tibetan text normalization identifies non-normalization Tibetan text blocks through analyzing the Tibetan text context, and then finding out the standard format corresponding specification table of Tibetan, Tibetan text normalization process is shown in Figure 4.

Through the analysis of Tibetan text, the non-standard types of text blocks are split. The lexical analyzer achieve identifying the block of text (mark) and determining type of the text block. Using regular expression search engine to achieve a block of text matching with the regular expression in the lexical analyzer, and then determine the exact type of the text block expression. Finally, form the Tibetan standard text by the semantic identifier based on the context of the Tibetan.

5.4.1 Lexical analyzer
The main work of lexical analyzer are:[3]

1. Filter out the unwanted ingredients, such as spaces, carriage returns
2. Distinguish mark and the semantic identifier.
3. Without error handling. Such as: illegal character, Tibetan words with misspelled characters.
4. Lexical analyzer work with semantic recognizer in parallel, the lexical analyzer inputting according to the original text, the identified text block as stream of tokens.

5.4.2 Semantic recognizer
Blocks of text identified by lexical analyzer output to identifier semantics by the form of token stream, semantic identifier processing the token and then obtain the final value of a block of text, which is canonical form.

6 CONCLUSIONS

The biggest problem of Tibetan text standard is Tibetan word segmentation. The reason is that there are a few researchers doing the study of Tibetan natural language processing and the foundation is weak. The establishment of electronic dictionaries, determination of the standard system, the development and study of the rule base and the design of statistical models, all of which had to be started from the bottom, and there is still a situation which is a lack of a large sample of Tibetan corpus. To solve the problem of the Tibetan characteristics of adhesion and twists, what should be done is the from the innovation from information technology.

In addition, to structure Tibetan word lexical analyzer and semantic identifier matching the characteristics with Tibetan words, the research of engine algorithms should be done, for automatic theory is needed.

With the development of information technology and Internet, Tibetan text will not be standardized, more and more non-standardization and complex texts will appear. Therefore, the Tibetan text standardization is an important and necessary work in technology of Tibetan information processing.

ACKNOWLEDGEMENT

It is a project supported by the national natural fund regional fund of China (61262054). The corresponding author is hong zhi yu.

REFERENCES

[1] Gesangjumian, Gesangyangjing. Introduction of Tibetan dialects (M). Beijing. Nationalities Press. 2002.
[2] Hockett, C.F. Tutorials of Modern phonetics (M). Beijing. Peking University Press. 2003.
[3] Cai Lianhong. Fundamentals and Applications of Modern Speech Technology (M). Beijing. Tsinghua University Press. 2003.

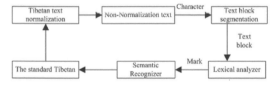

Figure 4.   Tibetan text normalization process.

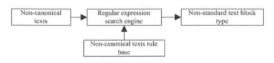

Figure 5.   The workflow of lexical analyzer.

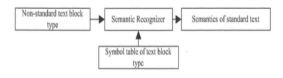

Figure 6.   The workflow of semantic recognizer.

Computer, Intelligent Computing and Education Technology – Liu, Sung & Yao (Eds)
© 2014 Taylor & Francis Group, London, ISBN 978-1-138-02469-4

Composition and function of the digital micro-teaching system

G.Q. La & Y. Wang
Department of Education, Yunyang Teachers College, Shiyan, Hubei, China

ABSTRACT: Microteaching became an effective means of training teachers' professional teaching skills, but continue to promote information technology in the education process, the traditional micro-teaching training requirements have been gradually unsuitable for modern teaching skills, along with computer, network comprehensive development of information technology, digital micro-teaching system came into being, and has become an important means of teachers' professional skills training.

Keywords: microteaching; digital micro-teaching system; IT

1 INTRODUCTION

Microteaching made since the 1960s and the introduction of teaching practice, it is pre-service teacher training teaching skills to provide a simulated environment to practice, it will complete a part of the teaching curriculum teaching broken down into fragments, for a pre-service teacher training a specific teaching skills, because of its clear training objectives and scientific performance evaluation for teacher training plays countries can not be ignored effect. However, with the development of computer, networking and other information technology, the traditional micro-teaching a certain extent have been behind the times, with increasingly high degree of digitization, digital micro-teaching system onto the system as a mainstream teacher training skills stage of history.

2 THE CONCEPT OF DIGITAL MICRO-TEACHING SYSTEM

Concept of digital micro-teaching system, until now there is no authoritative definition. The author based on its performance, features will be summed up as: digital micro-teaching system is the use of modern computer technology, network technology, video and audio capture and compression technology, digital transmission and storage means and built with video and audio on-demand and production, multimedia storage and edit and broadcast live in one of the other functions for normal students or teachers teaching job skills training network system.

3 THE COMPOSITION OF THE DIGITAL MICRO-TEACHING SYSTEM, FEATURES AND FUNCTIONS

Composed of a digital micro-teaching system. Early micro-teaching system mainly consists of a blackboard, cameras, monitors, recorders, switchers, microphones, amplifiers, and mixers and other equipment elements. Most micro-teaching system in recent years has added projectors and multimedia computers and other equipment, and between the control room and any micro classrooms televised dialogue, to carry TV broadcasts will be a micro screen broadcast live classroom training to other micro classrooms, but also realize insert explanations, real-time recording and other functions [1]. For the traditional training of pre-service teachers teaching skills structure and function of this system is fully able to cope, but in training how to carry out teaching activities in the information environment based on professional skills, how to use multimedia computers and networks to carry out collaborative learning skills such as aspect has become powerless. In order to better solve problems related to the latest digital micro-teaching systems are generally multimedia computers, high-definition video camera, a digital projector (or digital TV), an interactive whiteboard, network switches, pickup intercom, transfer sound mixer, amplifier, speaker systems, video and audio encoder, VGA encoder, HD Encoder, automatic tracking camera system, multimedia network switching control systems, servers and other components.

Features (two) digital micro-teaching system. The level of educational resources collected through multimedia network teaching system and micro-teaching system and other systems to capture classroom video, video recorders, VCD, DVD, multimedia computers and other teaching information. Educational resource classification management level, to achieve automatic teaching resources through resource classification system based on automatic classification of student ID identity preservation, save the original system administrators tedious work.

In the service-level educational resources, the establishment of learning resource library system by teachers and students an online learning platform, through distance education system to provide a platform for distance education for teachers and students not in school and other institutions to offer online learning, exam, guidance and other services.

System uses a distributed network architecture, business process micro-teaching, recording and other quality courses in the classroom terminal to complete. Real-time monitoring through the network video status of each classroom; through classroom management software systems to real-time control deployed in each classroom training host; through the deployment on the classroom PC and the control room video category management server's video classification management software for video uploading and category management.

3.1 The video and audio capture and control system in a distributed deployment, unified by the central control management software

1. Improving the reliability.
   Under normal circumstances, each business process separate classrooms can watch each other through a network, but do not interfere with each other. Distributed computing allows to reduce the server load, reliability and service life of the entire system are improved.
2. A high scale.
   Due to the use of distributed business processes within the classroom structure, making the future of new multimedia network classroom costs dropped significantly. The traditional center of the control structure, the new network classrooms, upgrade the server must re-wiring cumbersome.
3. Vertical high scalability.
   All videos are stored in the video category management server, are recorded in the database operator, time, class, school and other information, laid a good foundation for building the future of micro-teaching credit management, teaching resource library.

3.2 Multi-channel video motion synthesis, automatic classification

Dynamic synthesis of multi-channel video, save managers late heavy editing; based on student identity information to classify video intelligence, the traditional way, students need to be information input, if the system is carrying the full load, classify and post-production the workload is huge.

3.3 Convenient system operation, system administration efficient and reliable

Control signals and traffic signals independently of each other and prevent the misuse of trainees in the control room and the resulting micro classrooms can not communicate, making the system efficient and reliable management; based touch-screen control, simple and practical interface, making the system easy to operate, easy to use and strong.

3.4 Integration and good scalability

System uses open architecture, open the database and application program interface, easy micro-grid system is called institutions related data to other systems.

4 FUNCTION DIGITAL MICRO-TEACHING SYSTEM

4.1 Courseware synchronous generator

Each digitized multimedia courseware teaching system can be trained on teaching their teaching situations to use, and a range of IT applications simultaneously recording operation, and generate the appropriate network-on-demand courseware and upload it to the server, to facilitate trainees and other users post-demand and download.

4.2 Real-time and non-real-time feedback evaluation

1. Real-time feedback evaluation are: the completion of the training the trainees within the micro classrooms can be made to guide teachers, students conduct a comprehensive analysis between the evaluation of their situation through video playback training site, and suggest improvements; also available through a network for remote video and audio transmissions way to start the remote analysis and evaluation; trainee trainee can also play video through their own identify problems, analyze problems, self-correction and evaluation.
2. The evaluation of non-real-time feedback. Non-real-time feedback to guide the evaluation mainly other trainee teachers or students to watch online video on demand or by downloading and courseware, rationalization proposals and evaluation.

4.3 Trainees IT applications continues to increase capacity

As the digital micro-teaching system itself is using the most advanced computer, communications and other IT network generated, the application of such systems trained personnel practice activities sure to take some of the information technology applications in the entire course of their training through the relevant operations, information technology and curriculum integration of trainees throughout the entire process will be recorded and application of information technology to improve the ability of trainees in large part through constant reflection [2].

4.4 E-resume support

Many graduates have a job when the parties to resume recruitment also shows their professional capacity, digital micro-teaching system can be trainees during the training of teaching cases recorded and stored in the network database, they can at the time of job own success stories download dials presented to the employer, the employer can also access the trainee's performance during the school through the network, which greatly facilitates the mutual recognition process appointee with the employer, contribute to a comprehensive understanding of the required the overall quality of human resources, the paper resume play an irreplaceable role.

5 CONCLUSION

Digital micro-teaching system in teacher education and training process, especially in the training process of gradually teaching skills than the traditional teaching of the irreplaceable role of skills development, has become an important means of training teachers in specialized construction. Therefore, as a Teachers College to train future teachers should focus on students' ability to apply information technology to train more educators to adapt to the information age.

Fund: This article was fund by Hubei Provincial Department of Education Humanities and Social Sciences project, project number: 2011jytq205.

REFERENCES

[1] Zhang Zishi. New teaching skills of digitalm icro-teaching system [J]. China medical education technology, 2008, 12.
[2] Wang Jing. Development of professional skills of teachers' college students based on the micro-teaching system [J]. China medical education technology, 2013, 06.

Computer, Intelligent Computing and Education Technology – Liu, Sung & Yao (Eds)
© *2014 Taylor & Francis Group, London, ISBN 978-1-138-02469-4*

New democratic revolution period individual educational function of revolution music

D. Cheng
YunYang Teacher's College, China

ABSTRACT: Ideological and political education individual refers to the ideological and political education in the promotion of education full development impacts and effects. For individual survival function, individual development and individual enjoyment function. Individual function of Ideological and political education is the activity directly to performance, is the work of Ideological and political education's main body function.

Keywords: new democracy revolution period; music function; individual education

1 INTRODUCTION

The period of New Democracy revolution music thought political education individual function refers to the historical period for the educated in the survival function, individual development function and individual enjoyment function three aspects of promotion.

2 INDIVIDUAL SURVIVAL FUNCTION

Ideological and political education of the individual survival function refers to the ideological and political education in guiding the human individual follow objective law; obey the principle of survival in order to obtain a better survival state role. For individual survival in physiology and psychology in two dimensions, the physiological aspect of life refers to the individual through effort or their labor practice meet their basic necessities of life such as basic physiological needs, psychological survival refers to the individual through interactions with others gain respect, sense of belonging, love to reach the humanistic psychologist they will (advocate) self realization.

Music as a kind of spiritual works, apparently it to the individual psychological impact on survival is greater, but the period of New Democracy revolution music is not a lack of promotion the individual survival works. These songs are mainly concentrated in satisfying people's food and clothing problem above, such as: after the uprising of Pingjiang, general Peng Dehuai arrives for many times to the local people, spreading this song: Peng Dehuai, to my country, to open the gentry Ootani Kura, the poor eat revolution. The Red Army

had win. The song directly shown to participate in the revolution can solve the problem of dress warmly and the majority of farmers. If say before a revolutionary songs mentioned just for working people and temporary solution, then in 1930 June, the Soviet land allotment movement like a raging fire to spread the "Tian Ge" let people feel for the problem of dress warmly and revolutionary masses system solution. The lyrics written, workers and peasants riots, and big landlords and local tyrants share Mo, field. The "down with the local tyrants and everyone for having heard it many times" and many other songs. These songs by the broad masses of the propaganda, calling them to join the revolution, thus enabling them to find a reasonable and effective to solve the problem of food and clothing of the road itself, thus manifests the revolutionary music the individual survival function.

Maslow believed that individuals to meet the physiological needs then gradually produce security needs, belongingness and love need esteem need and the need for self-actualization. Revolution music can also meet the individual variety of psychological needs; make the individual with full enthusiasm into the work and life to achieve its psychological survival function. Is the most representative, was born in 1935 by Tian Han lyricist, Nie Er music "March of the volunteers", the song is almost involved in all aspects of individual psychological survival. The lyrics for "up! Do not want to be slaves! Our flesh and blood let us build our new the Great Wall! The Chinese nation to the most dangerous time, everyone was forced to issue a final roar! Up! Up! Up! We million people united as one man, braving the enemy's fire forward, braving the enemy's fire forward! First of all, the Chinese nation to the most dangerous moment, we are forced to issue a final roar, the statement is to wake up and meet the broad masses of the people's sense of security (personal security and national security), secondly," the Chinese nation, the new the Great Wall, million people united as one man is not only meet the individual words such as a sense of belonging, let them get a strong sense of national identity, but also to arouse individual consultation (safety) needs. In addition, braving the enemy's fire forward, forward, forward into the! The lyrics called on people to fight against imperialist aggression and oppression makes the majority of the people who are actuated by high ideals, is willing to national survival and revival as his lifelong pursuit of the goal, to meet their needs of self. Thus the new Pearl (Democratic) during the period of revolutionary music achieved promotion for the survival and development of the function of individual psychology.

Revolution music not only effective for individual physical survival pointed in the right direction, but also to meet the individual psychological survival in a variety of needs. Realization of individual survival function.

The individual development function. Ideological and political education individual development function refers to the ideological and political education inmolding the moral character and promote the development of the positive role played by the. Revolutionary music ideological and political education function of individual development function is a revolutionary music for individual moral accomplishment and individual development plays a positive role. In different historical periods of human development meaning and goal although somewhat different, but adapted to the social development of individual generally has a corresponding political orientation, have normative behavior ability, have a positive and progressive spirit power and perfect personality. The revolutionary music the function of Ideological and political education will also benefit from these four aspects.

The political guiding function of revolutionary music refers to music through revolution, inspired, mobilization and education, the education of thought and behavior to meet the requirements of social development to the revolutionary cause; it is a revolutionary aim of music education and the transcendence of embodiment. During the period of new democratic revolution, revolutionary music ideological and political education is the main task of improving the people's ideological and political quality prompted them to form and maintain support the revolution of the Communist Party the correct political direction. During this period of revolutionary music through goal orientation, policy guidance and guidance of public opinion

completed the political guiding function. Such as "Communist children round the song" in "ready, we are the children, the owner must be our future". These lyrics to the young people to establish the goal of communism, actively devoted to the revolutionary cause plays a positive guiding role; at the same time by Zhao Qihai lyricist, composer Xian Xinghai's "revolution" to go to the rear of the war the majority of teenagers set specific goals. In addition to this kind of goal oriented songs, there are a large number of songs is to publicize the policy of our party as, publicize the party's land revolution policy of "land revolution song", "Tian Ge"; to promote the party's army song "three disciplines and eight points for attention"; to promote the party's anti-Japanese policy in Taihang Mountain. These songs to make the broad masses of the people to understand the party's policy, raised for different period revolution in the recognition task, to mobilize the broad masses of the people actively. The political guiding function of revolutionary music is mainly reflected in its opinion, revolutionary songs in a large number of works in different periods of the reactionaries songs such as "critical Kuomintang reactionaries", "is", "down with the local tyrants White-Haired Girl" these songs exposed Kuomintang, landlords and local tyrants and ferocity of the reactionary nature of faces, there is also lots of songs is to establish and maintain our party and army of the glorious image. Such as "East is red", "Jiefang District day", "Nanniwan", win universal praise song for our party's fine tradition and good style to give publicity to our party, the revolutionary work to create a good atmosphere, play a positive role in guiding public opinion.

Revolutionary songs of normative behavior function. Revolutionary music ideological and political education can help people understand and agree with the correct behavior, so that the broad masses of the people's behavior consistent with the revolutionary development of form and revolutionary specification. Revolutionary music ideological and political education through the revolutionary music to the people to the social norms, affirmation and praise the revolutionary act, negation and criticism not revolution and counter-revolution behavior. Throughout the period of New Democracy revolution, our party faces expansion team mission, this time to participate in the revolutionary ranks becomes a positive and correct behavior. A large number of revolutions music in the promotion of the broad masses of the people in the revolutionary ranks the correct behavior plays an important role in. Some revolutionary propaganda team goal, such as "a strong and strong." "The sun comes out according to the

Quartet, Nanshan gas just hero. Not for money to official, specifically the local tyrants open barn." The leadership of the Communist Party of revolutionary, Nanshan Mountain Red, overthrowing warlords reactionaries, the eradication of the landlords and the gentry of the revolution, knife, farmers branch and sent cropland; "a propaganda and revolutionary army discipline and excellent style of "three main rules of discipline and eight note", have reflected the army glorious" ten these Lang brother "Song Lyric" these Lang brother, when the Red Army yo, about the most glorious. There are "from the song", star accompanies me to fight and other songs have inspired the majority of youth to devote into revolutionary army. In addition, in the enemy's blockade of Jiefang District during the period of production data are scarce, the correct behavior is actively involved in production, and the revolutionary music exists in a lot of calls and praised the production work. The army and the people such as "production" of the army and the people to carry out production cooperation, DIY, have ample food and clothing so contagious Lyric greatly mobilized the masses to join in the revolutionary enthusiasm, in addition "spinning line", "Nanniwan" and many more revolutionary songs are played a similar role. Visible revolutionary songs can serve to guide and standardize the behavior of the individual function.

Individual enjoyment function. Ideological and political education individual enjoyment function, by means of Ideological and political education, enables each individual to realize it's a need and desire, and from experience to meet, the joy and happiness, so as to obtain the enjoyment of the spirit. Revolutionary music ideological enjoyment function mainly refers to promote individual, he wishes to experience a revolution, revolution of joy and happiness, to enjoy the glory and joy. This function is mainly reflected in the individual thought quality improvement. Revolution music through its positive elements, beautiful and cheerful melody for the majority of the revolutionary masses ideological and moral quality has played a positive role.

Good thought personal character formation including knowledge-sentiment will ability four aspects. The first revolution music continued to wake up and improve the revolutionary masses of moral cognition. For example, in 1921 Beijing Xindian labor Tutorial school teachers and students sing the song "five one anniversary song", the song mentions "the world, sacred labor", put forward "to power system all destroyed as" slogan, the performance of the Chinese working class consciousness. And the birth of the Communist Party of China, spread in Guangdong sea area of Lufeng Germany (the) "international worker's Day", "Tian Gong", "Tsai called the song" and other songs, singing to teach farmers, impoverished farmers in propaganda and revolutionary truth. These revolutionary songs gradually improve the majority of working people's ideological and moral accomplishment. In addition, revolutionary music is another important role in training for the majority of the toiling masses of sympathy and nationalism, patriotism and other senior moral emotion. Such as opera "the White-Haired Girl" inspired profound sympathy to the farmer. The song "the dockers" through the lyrics "from North Korea, from night to night to move toward, eyes blurred, bones are scattered, to two meals a day to eat meal blood, sweat all day" on dock workers difficult situation description to arouse the people to the bourgeois actively take the dog hates and workers class sympathy. In addition, "March of the volunteers" as described in "the Chinese nation to the most dangerous moment, we million people united as one man, braving the enemy's fire". "The Eight Route Army Song" in "once strong s Kou frontier, chant in a heroic but mournful tone towards the battlefield" these songs can greatly improve the broad masses of the people's national emotion and intense patriotic passion. In addition, a large number of revolutions music inspired by the broad masses of the people actively participate in the revolutionary masses in the revolutionary life solidarity exhibited more moral behavior. Songs such as "unity is strength" on the people's mutual understanding mutual solidarity, singing songs such as "cowherd" through the revolutionary hero praise makes more people actively committed to national independence and liberation of the motherland to the revolutionary cause in. Embodies the revolutionary music on moral cognition enhancement, have noble moral emotion and moral behavior, protect our homes and defend our country to join the revolution.

It is not difficult to see that the revolutionary music can not only promote the individual survival and development, but also can enhance the individual ideological and moral qualities, to meet the individual needs of music art, reflect the individual enjoyment function, but the individual function of Ideological and political education function of music is revolution part, although each member of society must first meet the individual development embodied individual, but his ultimate goal is to realize the socialization of the individual, the social attribute. Revolutionary music as well, and his individual function compared to what is more important is its social function.

REFERENCES

[1] Wang Yuling On the modern history of the Revolutionary War and Revolution music [J] Journal of Cultural Studies, 2009, (01).

[2] Ao Haihua of Red Tourism ideological and political education innovation [J]. Guizhou Normal University, 2006.

[3] Bian souvenir Technology detonated music revolution from the music producer of the Beijing Olympic Games [J]. Musical instruments, 2010, (05).

[4] Choy to. Marx of Music [J]. Musical Research, 1998, (10).

Computer, Intelligent Computing and Education Technology – Liu, Sung & Yao (Eds)
© 2014 Taylor & Francis Group, London, ISBN 978-1-138-02469-4

Aerobics exploratory stage performances and design from the CCTV spring festival evening aerobics program perspective

A.H. Zhang
Yunyang Teachers College, Shiyan, Hubei, China

ABSTRACT: With aerobics rapid development in our country, people are aerobics aerobics theoretical aspects of a lot of research, but for aerobics stage performance aspects are few. In this paper, literature, video analysis, induction, and logical analysis and other methods, aerobics stage performances, stage design (including music, costumes, lighting, background, and many other elements) analysis and study, trying to make aerobics. Enjoy the performance of this platform by the stage, while giving viewers more ornamental value presented aerobics show works.

Keywords: aerobics spectator; stage design; stage performances

1 INTRODUCTION

Aerobics is a set of gymnastics, dance, music in one, a reflection of "force" and "beauty" a sport, with fitness, heart health, entertainment effect. Aerobics three main categories: Aerobics, Fitness Aerobics and performative aerobics. Fitness Aerobics also includes general aerobics, aerobics, hip-hop, wrestling, yoga, Latin aerobics, step aerobics, dumbbell exercises, etc. [1]. Its contents, selectivity, respectively, for different aspects of people of different ages and gender selection. Aerobics its unique charm loved by the masses, universal strong. As people's living standards improve, as people's increased awareness of fitness, aerobics rapid development, from the square to the school and the gym, to the CCTV Spring Festival Gala (hereinafter referred to as Spring Festival) stage. CCTV Spring Festival is an annual celebration of the Lunar New Year's Eve variety of Lunar New Year gala held, is the highest rated, longest performances, the actors most variety show [2]. Aerobics can be on the show that it has a place in people's minds, that it is really the fire. This article from the calendar year the Spring Festival Evening performances aerobics program started, the program of performances and stage design analysis and study, fully embodies the spirit of essential characteristics aerobics principle, adding lighting, costumes, music, background and many other artistic elements, the use of a variety of performances and modern high-tech means, aerobics stage performances for processing and transformation. Make aerobics aerobics stage performances through technical content, profound cultural connota-tion, sincere feelings, vivid scenes and stunning visual, auditory effects, allowing viewers to enjoy the artistic beauty; experience healthy, lively, cheerful, positive spirit of sport; feelings of joy, happy, peaceful atmosphere.

2 AEROBICS STAGE PERFORMANCES

Stage is the stage for performers [4]. Performances, the actors on the stage and the audience in creating the next stage watching the entire process. While performing aerobics should be: to aerobics for the material, blending elements of integrated arts stage, limited to the theater stage space, consistent performance characteristics aerobics performances [5]. Aerobics performances based on program needs, according to the choice of the specific content of aerobics and characteristics required, complex chart a calendar year the Spring Festival Evening aerobics stage performance charts, performing aerobics can be seen from the following three main performances

3 AEROBICS WITH SONG PERFORMANCES

Aerobics song performances with the highest frequency. Such performances or to sing Hit-based, supplemented by performing aerobics, embellishment, foil singing. Such as "youth season", "Love Thirty-Six", "we are all one people," and so on. Or singing, aerobics equally important, are the main programs of the protagonist. Such as "jump", "health song." "Healthy Song" from the lyrics written specially to match aerobics action choreography, the singer is the star Xie Xiaodong, Mavis, who is leading the fitness industry know that exercise instructor MCA. "Healthy Song" either from the program scheduling or actor's choice, can be clear that the director's intentions. The results showed "healthy Song" gave rise to an unprecedented influence: that year, the streets, men and women almost always shook his head twisted hip singing "... left three times, right three times, the neck twist, ass twist, sports ... we do together." Between today, "gold partner" products are still borrow this program to advertise. The protagonist is good supporting role worth mentioning, aerobics performances are to stage performances in this way show their unique value: to bring healthy, progressive, spiritual joy, vision, hearing, spiritual enjoyment of the arts and so on. Also let more people know and understand the aerobics. 2.2 musical performances.

This stage musical art form combines singing, dialogue, performances and dance and other artistic elements, through lyrics, language, music, and other body movements closely, the story and the emotions inherent in them, meaning vivid performance out [6]. Such performances straightaway, very popular with the public welcome. Aerobics performance also in such a form of artistic performances on the stage at the show, such as "Sunshine gym." "Sunshine gym" living the gym moved to the Spring Festival stage: a jump general aerobics, step aerobics, dumbbell exercises, there are barbells and riding a cycle ergometer training, as well as show muscle fitness training, the content is very rich, the scene is very spectacular, fun. "Sunshine gym" is about a group of love fitness, the pursuit of healthy living, caring urban men and women gathered in the gym with degrees Eve story. Allen Lin plays a fitness coach, "the number one beauty show business," Jiang Qin Qin plays a return from abroad, relatives are not around lonely girl, Xie Yuxin is playing a fitness enthusiast. Its story line with the modern pursuit of health, fashion, lifestyle, showing contemporary lofty spiritual qualities. Good story, the story of profound meaning, vivid sensational performances, as well as the star effect, so that the "sunshine gym" became the year "Spring Festival" dance class program in the main event, presented to the audience a perfect musical. Aerobics performances by musical performances performances, relatively speaking, the effect is stronger than the aerobics with song performances, its songs, dialogue, aerobics, performance and other factors to give absolutely the same attention. People enjoy the whole works but also on the more impressive performances aerobics.

4 PURE AEROBICS PERFORMANCES

From sports performances on stage performing trend is not difficult to see that the use of more and more rich artistic elements, sporting element is relatively small, the pure sporting character performances have been eliminated, such as pure Aerobics Competition—style performances, pure martial arts routine style performances. Instead, with a high artistic features stage performances. Aerobics is a set of gymnastics, dance, music is one of the emerging fashion sports items, content is very rich. Aerobics meet the contemporary stage performance requirements of the times, with strong performances, especially hip-hop, aerobics, etc. Aerobics aerobics performances in pure form through processing stage art performances is entirely feasible. 2011 Spring Festival, Shenzhen migrant hip-hop group performing "Our workers have the power" is a form of performing such a model. "Our workers have the power" through the actor solid basic skills, such as small joints and small muscle groups; difficult skill moves, such as earth movement, throwing and catching; and the profound meaning of the formation, the shape of the arrangement, together with the action-packed music, free-spirited action style, showed a positive and cheerful vigor, reflecting the movement of sport implies beauty, spiritual beauty, artistic beauty and physical beauty to harmony manifested, heighten the atmosphere, and enhance the performance results, to audience huge visual impact and spiritual sense of shock that reflects modern life of migrant workers, and it inspires! This pure aerobics choose the right performers such as content, organization science, creative, and then give profound meaning, the use of modern high-tech means to the stage performances, such works must have been like, "We workers have the power", as is the audience expectations and favorite works.

5 STAGE DESIGN AEROBICS PERFORMANCES

Specifically, stage design, including stage equipment, lighting, music, backgrounds, props, costumes and other aspects of the design. Stage equipment, lighting, background and other non-professional aspects aerobics designed by the professional experts. They are expert in this area, especially the Spring Festival variety show such an important level. Therefore, it is natural to do well. Such as "healthy Song", in the center of the stage and circular designs can lift a cylindrical stage, Xie Xiaodong, Mavis led some actors sing in the following jump, MCA coach with some actors jumping on top of both layers can focus. Coupled with the mobile lighting, sound effects and other artistic elements combine to make the program more ornamental, in vision, hearing, feeling, by the all-round shock spectators. Music, costumes, props and other aspects of the design professional aerobic: First, costume design changed. Before almost all leotard or sportswear, then the program is based on the characters and story design clothing. Such as "Love Thirty-Six" in the assembly design beautiful short boots, "We workers have the power" to design clothes to wear helmets. This change in the actor at the same time to facilitate movement to meet the needs of stage performances, make the program more ornamental. Second, the props are designed to make the program richer image. Such as "Sunshine gym" in the use of scarves: decorative worn around the neck, to get hands aerobics and jump immediately to make actors into a general aerobics aerobics equipment. Both beautiful and practical, and gave the audience a sense of magic to the vagaries of the mystery. "Our workers have the power" in the towel and bricks are designed so that migrant workers more in line with the image of actor. Finally, talk about aerobics music. Aerobics without music, it is a strong sense of rhythm, giving the desire to want to jump. But it is the soul of aerobics, Aerobics Aerobics and still did not go far enough, is not the same performative aerobics. Such as "healthy Song", "We workers have the power," the two music programs, action, scene, atmosphere, and many other coordination, and truly embodies the soul of the music is aerobics. Stage performances of contemporary works of art in large part on the overall effect of the decision in stage design and modern high-tech [7]. Modern design stage performances aerobics music, costumes, props, etc. keeping with the times change, and bold innovation; in sound, light, electricity, screens, King and other aspects of the use of modern high-tech means. A high level of stage design can strengthen the shock effect of the program, the program's artistic atmosphere rendering, enhanced program ornamental. Aerobics show true.

6 CONCLUSIONS AND RECOMMENDATIONS

6.1 Conclusion

1. Through various forms of aerobics to increase publicity and promotion, so that more people understand aerobics, aerobics appreciate performances to raise awareness of aerobics performing aesthetic.

2. For works want to express intent, choose a more suitable form of performance more scientific and more innovative content, in order to better highlight the theme, to achieve the best performance results.
3. Update the study concept, bold innovation and design. Without violating the principle of the premise, if necessary, to break some traditional concepts (such as aerobics performances must wear a leotard, etc.), the times, the needs of the development of the times, the use of modern high-tech means to design vision, hearing, feeling, shocked the audience by various aerobics better perform the work.

7 RECOMMENDS

Spring Festival playbill in the calendar year, unless "We workers have the power" clearly marked hip-hop, the other programs are written dancers or simply just write songs to sing, and dance aerobics will confuse a clear concept of aerobics is not enough emphasis In recent years, overall development of our country better Aerobics: our athletes in sports aerobics has made impressive achievements; Fitness Aerobics much favored people; performative aerobics back in twenty years before boarding Gala.

In the future, I hope to give the community more and greater attention aerobics, aerobics to bring the healthy, happy, but also can promote the vigorous development of aerobics.

REFERENCES

[1] Zhang Ying. Aerobics instructor coaches training materials [M]. Gymnastics State Sports General Administration of Sports Management Center published. 2004.
[2] Juan. Spring Festival Evening Pieces Cultural Values tendency of eleven characters in the show skit set an example [D]. Postgraduate master's thesis, 2012.3.
[3] The most complete CCTV Spring Festival Evening program from previous live and video information.
[4] Wang Yan, Yang Huixin. Discussion on Wushu competition performance market [J]. Harbin Institute of Physical Education, 2002.4.
[5] Wu Jing. Stage martial arts compose research [D]. Postgraduate master's thesis, 2010.5.
[6] Website http://baike.baidu.com/view/9921.htm
[7] Yang Yujie Zhu Bin. Feast of sound and light to create a 09 TV Spring Festival Evening.

Computer, Intelligent Computing and Education Technology – Liu, Sung & Yao (Eds)
© *2014 Taylor & Francis Group, London, ISBN 978-1-138-02469-4*

The visual entertainment design based on IM micro emoticons

M.J. Yu

College of Art and Design, Wuhan University of Technology, Hubei, China

ABSTRACT: Micro emoticons externally show human emotions and act as a quite direct and effective information exchange form in non-verbal communication. Micro expressions are not simply equivalent to facial expressions, but serve as new signs resulting from expression symbolization. Based on basic principles in linguistics, communication studies, and design art studies, this research profoundly investigated the effect of micro emoticons on entertainment. Obviously, combination of multiple disciplines was reflected in this paper. Besides, this paper can also promote further studies on micro emoticons and research development. In this way, real entertainment in the design can be interpreted more clearly.

Keywords: micro expressions; entertainment; visual design; IM

1 GENERAL INTRODUCTION

Albert Mehrabian, a psychologist in USA, argued that the whole impression a person has on a communicatee consists of three parts: the impression on his verbal language (7%), the impression on his voice (38%), and the impression on his facial expressions and other body language forms (55%).[1] Presently, under the influence of natural and social environment in which we entertain others and are also entertained by others, the interactive exchange forms among people include not only simply traditional face-to-face communication mode, but also man-machine exchange interaction mode. "Micro" reminds people of the American drama *Lie to Me*. Since the hero Dr. Cal Lightman in this drama was very experienced and cautious, he fully demonstrated the theory and practice of micro expressions. In a broad sense, micro emoticons refer to symbols for emotion expression on network. They make language in exchange interaction easier to understand (as displayed in Fig. 1). At present, there are few research literatures related to micro expressions in China. Besides, relevant research subjects are not focused and in most existing researches, only network expressions are investigated. There are 4 main research areas: (1) Integrated surveys and cultural studies associated with network language are conducted, in which character expressions play the leading role. (2) Based on visual design, the development trend of graphic network emoticons is analyzed from different angles. (3) Network expressions are investigated from the perspective of linguistics. (4) From diverse aspects of cultural studies, network expressions are analyzed. This paper started with micro expressions and took the communication process in IM as the basis, while visual design for entertainment acted as the main line. In this research, current visual information with the entertainment effect was focused. At the same time, theories and principles in semiotics, psychology, design science, communication studies, etc were also taken into account to conduct multi-angle and wide-field analysis. This research can provide partial theoretical basis for design method development and application of visual graphic language for entertainment.

2 MICRO EMOTICONS AND VISUAL ENTERTAINMENT DESIGN

2.1 *Micro culture and micro emoticons*

As a product in the micro age, the micro culture on network is actually a language used on internet that has developed rapidly in recent years. In the great age, there are many things whose names contain the meaning of "micro", from "micro blog" to "hint fiction" or "micro film". Thereby, the great age seems to be more similar to the micro age.

Humans' micro expressions are displayed unconsciously and then discovered by researchers.

Figure 1. The abstraction process of facial expressions.

Usually, Humans' micro expressions are very private to some degree and people attempt to hide them. Mr Lv Jingren's view is presented as follows: the same cluster can also be encountered in SMS (short message service) and on internet, that is, the currently popular expression characters called emoticons. They are virtually graphs resulting from the combination of horizontal characters and symbols; people try to use them as an easier communication form, compared with characters. If symbolic elements of these expression characters are arranged in a more compact pattern, they are more similar to Chinese characters. To avoid monotony of letter arrangement, the worldwide computer space also shows compound and multiplicity that are similar to Chinese characters.[2]

2.2 *Visual entertainment design in postmodernism*

With the formation of post-modern society, that is, consumer society, the emergence of social pan-entertainment, and the gradual development of design science, entertainment elements play an unprecedentedly large part in design. It is stated that we should extremely enjoy entertainment. Actually, acting as a cure for mental stress, entertainment has become an indispensible element in life. Consequently, visual entertainment design develops into a product in the perceptual consumption age and is widely applied in various design fields. Entertainment effect that can bring economic benefits is thereby generated. As pointed out by Fredric Jameson, culture acts as an element in consumer society and unlike other societies, consumer society shows so many signs and images. In the current screen-reading age and image times, dry words are replaced by numerous images and graphic symbols. Since entertainment is taken as the primary attribute of visual entertainment design, it is required that visual entertainment information must generate entertainment effect during the process of content transmission. So, current micro expressions show obvious entertainment significance. There are few theories of visual entertainment design. Visual entertainment information is mostly dismissed with a laugh and few people conduct in-depth analysis on such information. Consequently, cultural metaphors and social influence that visual information implies are ignored.

3 THE VISUAL ENTERTAINMENT EFFECT OF MICRO EXPRESSIONS

3.1 *Entertainment communication of modern micro emoticons*

Abstracting images from viewing is the basic mode of early humans' visual generalization. In all ages,

graphic symbols are broadly used and develop continuously in various countries. Early humans handed down plenty of highly symbolic languages in traditional image system. They not only show humans' spiritual demand, but also serve as visual presentation of mental happiness pursuit. For example, facial expressions of rapper on ornamental sculptures in Eastern Han Dynasty are caved carefully; eyes and brows show humorous and vivid expressions. The technique of expression presents high artistic appeal and entertainment.

Visual entertainment signs are undoubtedly classified as symbols, and specifically, at the same time, they are closer to artistic symbols. The humorous expression is an important expression way of entertainment communication. As stated in *The Cultural Contradictions of Capitalism* written by Daniel bell, it is an absolutely true fact that the contemporary culture tends to become a visual form, not a printed form. The humorous effect of micro emoticons is largely reflected in their contents and implied meanings. In a sense, they can be taken as integration of various smile forms such as hearty laugh, giggle, etc. The conveyed spiritual essence is to reflect the humorous effect. The striking entertainment effect results from Humans' natural emotions whose specific characteristics are subjected to certain exaggeration and transformation. Obviously, due to their iconicity, emoticons become more vivid and also show humorous expression effect (as demonstrated in Fig. 2). It is expected that designers can have the ability to know these design essentials in advance when people's real needs and unknown needs have not been expressed completely. In this case, audience's emotion system can also be activated positively, that is, receivers can acquire real pleasure from design works for entertainment. When people chat with friends or make some comments, they mostly aim to entertain and relax themselves. So, humor counts most. For instance, p(^o^)q implies the same meaning as working harder, taking more efforts and all; •_• and (T_T) represent a sad face and a tearful face. The inherent anti-tradition feature facilitates the visual culture to replace character culture and obtain the position of hegemony. At the same time, the visual culture rapidly dominates the cultural field exclusively.

Figure 2.   The graphic symbolic system Emoji in Apple.

3.2 Entertainment originality and visual reading-leads to emotional entertainment experience and high-level ego-involvement

Albert Einstein claimed that imagination is more important than knowledge. Bill Gates also proposed the following thesis: originality is just like atomic fission; only an ounce can produce countless business benefits. In visual entertainment design, originality implementation should synchronize with visual reading to achieve harmony and unity between the two. In the information age, under the influence of modern life styles, cultural ideas, and entertainment attitudes, people show stronger desire to express their personalized opinions to the outside world. As the basis of humans' visual cognition, micro emoticons are characterized by international cognitiveness.

Interpersonal communication took various symbols as the medium. That is, one interprets the meaning of symbols standing for the other side' action and then responds to these symbols. In this way, the interaction between the two is realized. Since humans are both natural and social, it is inevitable for people to present endless relations with others. In 21st century, humans can interact with others freely and conveniently through the man-machine communication mode on network. During communication, by using micro emoticons, intimacy and the sense of identity can be generated more easily to achieve the entertainment effect of communication. Humans' various expressions show strong expressive force and at the same time, they also play an inductive role in communication. Hence, when an image expression for entertainment is displayed on network, we are prone to study it and associate it with the emotional concepts available in the brain.

High-level ego-involvement refers to highly-focused attention individuals pay in cognition process. As a result, it has an impact on individuals' psychological reaction and behavior tendency. Due to their design originality, iconicity, and good effect for conveying ideas, emoticons on network can induce two communicative sides to unknowingly focus on them and show strong interest. Then, individuals are internally motivated to have better understanding of corresponding symbol meanings and the other side's attitudes. During the process, interaction in emotional experience is generated and excitement of brain activity is improved. Meanwhile, the entertainment experience effect becomes better.

4 THE COMMERCIAL POPULATION VALUE OF ENTERTAINMENT DESIGN FOR MICRO EXPRESSIONS

4.1 Popularization and democratization

Visual entertainment design causes people to be relaxed and cheerful. Its humorous visual style arouses the same emotion in people's inner world. The visual entertainment design reveals humans' demand and desire for spiritual enjoyment. Their need in seeking visual stimulation and psychological liberation is not necessary to be hidden in reality. Under democracy and mass demand, visual entertainment starts with ideology and displays modern life styles and attitudes from multiple angles.

As can be inferred from the development process of emoticons abovementioned, the addition of emoticons to IM communication tools indicates that users' demands for personalized emotional expression on network are satisfied. Those demands drive users to utilize convenient, speedy, and personalized IM tools to exchange ideas on internet. Users' choice of IM tools shows that they are satisfactory with this platform. Apple designed the emoticon Emoji in the keyboard of IOS5 system in 2011 and Users can add it to the keyboard. In February, 2011, Facebook realized that its traditional emoticons showed no originality. So, with the aid of the illustrator Pixar, Facebook designed brand-new emoticons. But at that time, it was hard to express various detailed emotions in tiny digital images. To solve the problem, a research team under UDC designed an emoticon namely, "Tiny flowers". "Tiny flower can be either a male or female". So, it can be designed more easily and freely.

4.2 Consumer society and era requirement

In the perceptual consumption age, people pay more attention to external individuality and fashion. The value of entertainment plays a more and more important role in people's consumption. In the process, people gradually form their views in entertainment consumption. In practical application of emoticons, net citizens naturally select their favorite images as carriers to express their personal emotions. If audience like one image very much and frequently use it, then it is no doubt that its derivatives can also become a very important component in the whole link. During popularization of entertainment, micro emoticons can improve their own popularity. In turn, companies also fully use the popularity of micro emoticons on network to promote their commercial products. Based on its advantage in visual reading of graphic symbols, visual entertainment design can display the entertainment effect during the process of information transmission.

5 CONCLUSIONS

Visual entertainment design shows the capacity to activate inner emotions of audience. In terms of the transmission mode and the design form, it can communicate with human minds through particular entertainment transmission ideas. As a result, multilevel and interdisciplinary visual communication mode is formed. Meanwhile, as the basis for exploring visual entertainment design in this paper, micro emoticons have become a simple, practical, and creative visual language for emotional entertainment in consumer society with pan-entertainment tendency.

In the process of knowing about nature, intelligence, human motivation, or ideas, it is not their original features, but their manifestation patterns in language that are actually learned. Metaphors acting as our medium form the cultural content. [3] Since the medium is the extension of the human body, micro expressions serving as the medium extend human emotions and limb actions. Micro emoticons display the perceptual pattern of rational human emotions and act as an animate artistic form. Their perceptual charm can exactly satisfy people's demand for spiritual life in current society.

REFERENCES

[1] Chen Yuehua and Wang Yan: Interfaces and bodies in the visual field of communication aesthetics. Beijing: China Film Press, (2008).
[2] Kohei Sugiura: Asian characters in books and their design. Beijing: SDX Joint Publishing Company, (2006).
[3] Neil Postman: Amusing ourselves to death: The disappearance of childhood. Guilin: Guangxi Normal University Press, (2009).
[4] Toyama, K and Dias, M.B: Information and Communication Technologies for Development, 41(6): 22–25 (2008).
[5] Jens Frederik Jensen. Interactivity: Tracking a New Concept in Media and Communication Studies. Nordicom Review, vol.12(1998), P.90–94.
[6] Information on http://www.dolcn.com/

Computer, Intelligent Computing and Education Technology – Liu, Sung & Yao (Eds)
© *2014 Taylor & Francis Group, London, ISBN 978-1-138-02469-4*

An ERP study on the cognitive relation of Tibetan trilingual

A.X. Hu, X. Bai & T.N. Gegen

Key Lab of China's National Linguistic Information Technology, Northwest University for Nationalities,
Lanzhou, China

ABSTRACT: Taking Tibetan undergraduates as subject, the study shows that the error rate of semantic coherent judgment between the second language and the third language is lower than that between the native language and the third language, and indicates Tibetan undergraduates learn English by means of Chinese. Based on ERP signals, it is more difficult for word processing than sound processing in semantic comprehension and it is more difficult to judge English-Tibetan materials than English-Chinese materials. Besides, the English prime words increase the difficulty for the comprehension of target words.

Keywords: behavioral data; ERP signals; trilingual cognition

1 INTRODUCTION

With the growing of trilingual in number among minority nationalities, cognitive study of trilingual has become a key branch in linguistic studies. This paper laid focus on the relationship between the third language and the second language as well as the third language and the native language. The function of speech in semantic understanding, the learning method of the third language and whether the third language acquisition (English) is through the second language (Chinese) or the native language (Tibetan) are discussed and analyzed in detail. It attempts to solve cognitive problems based on lexicon theory and event-related potentials.

2 EXPERIMENTAL METHOD

2.1 Selecting subjects

12 Tibetan undergraduates (7 males, 5 females), average age 24.3, are chosen to be the subject of the experiment. Their eyesight or corrected visions are normal. The subjects' native language is Tibetan, and they begin to learn Chinese at the age of 10–12 and English at the age of 19–22. They are capable of listening, speaking and writing skills in the three languages.

2.2 Experimental material

The study requires four groups of tests for the subjects to judge if the former stimuli are semantically equivalent to the later stimuli. The first group is about English words and Chinese words, the second is about English words and Tibetan words, the third group is about English sounds and Chinese sounds while the forth is about English sounds and Tibetan sounds. The prime words or sounds are English. 30 Tibetan-Chinese-English words that have same meaning and mental representation are chosen as experimental items. Tibetan and Chinese are single words that are also non-living nouns, such as "hand", with the word frequency of 90–217 time/million. Besides, the words are tested by familiarity. In addition, 30 Tibetan-Chinese-English words that have same meaning of animals, such as "cat", are chosen as filler items. The experiment employs Go-Nogo paradigm.

2.3 Experimental design

The experiment is designed by means of single factor and 2 levels classified by judgment types (same or different). A test group is formed by 30 experimental items and 30 filler items, and the stimuli are presented randomly. The single presentation of three kinds of language sounds is separated in random order, and is balanced between participants.

2.4 Experimental procedure and the task

After basic preparation including placing electrodes, the subjects are asked to sit in front of the screen with a distance of 80 cm. Firstly, the instructions are presented followed by "*" to test the fixation point for 500 ms. Then the target words are presented. The speech signal of all three languages has the duration of 800 ms and is normalized by PRATT software. The major task for subjects is to judge whether the target word or sound and the prime word or sound have the same meaning. If they are, press left-click and vice versa. The next stimulus comes out when a response is made or after 2500 ms without any response. Before the experiment, there are 5 to 10 minutes for practicing with different materials. After a group experiment, there are 2 to 3 minutes for resting.

2.5 Data recording

The stimuli are programmed by means of STM2. The behavioral data which consist of reaction time and the correction of judgment is recorded. The EEG signal is collected by ESI-128 (Neuroscan Co., SynAmps 128), the resistance is kept under 5 kΩ and vertex is used as reference electrode. Besides, the filter is set for 0.1–100 Hz and the frequency 250 Hz. Next, after filter the original signal for 30 Hz, we reduce artifact, segment during −100 to 900 ms, make baseline correction and average of the whole brain regions. Finally, we get the averaged oscillogram of each subject under same experimental condition.

2.6 Data analysis

The behavioral data are consisting of reaction time and the correction of judgment. ERP data is set to record with a time range of 1000 ms as soon as the target word is presented and the baseline 100 ms before the target word is presented. On the basis of the overall averaged oscillogram, we take N120 (100 ms–130 ms), P220 (180 ms–240 ms), N300 (250 ms–350 ms) and N400 (350 ms–500 ms) to analyze. Besides, the coordinates of dipole are traced and recorded every 50 ms as traceability data.

3 EXPERIMENT RESULTS

3.1 Behavioral data results

In linguistic cognition study, behavioral data is mainly made of reaction time and feedback error rate, which can reflect the cognitive and comprehension degree of the stimuli. Figure 1 shows behavioral data of 12 Tibetan undergraduates and reflects the reaction time of lexical access, which is Tibetan words take the shortest time to recognize and English the longest.

Chart 1 shows the response time of subjects under eight circumstances. In general, the judgment time of English and Chinese are shorter than that of English and Tibetan. The response time for English and Chinese words or sounds is about 500 ms while that for English and Tibetan words or sounds is about 700 ms. It indicates that the judg-

Chart 1. Response time (ms).

Type	Respond time	Standard deviation
Coherent English-Chinese words	543	56.6
Incoherent English-Chinese words	638	61.3
Coherent English-Tibetan words	807	54.2
Incoherent English-Tibetan words	812	69.3
Coherent English-Chinese sounds	543	56.6
Incoherent English-Chinese sounds	638	61.3
Coherent English-Tibetan sounds	807	54.2
Incoherent English-Tibetan sounds	812	69.3

ment time of the third language and the second language is about 200 ms shorter than that of the third language and the native language. Besides, it takes longer time for subjects to response when the prime presentation and the target presentation contain different meanings. To be specific, the longest response time (812 ms) appears when different English and Tibetan words are presented while the shortest response time (495 ms) appears when same English and Chinese sounds are presented. Moreover, the response time of sounds is shorter than that of words, which accords with former studies. As for standard deviation, the maximum value reaches 69.3 when different English and Tibetan words are presented and the minimum value reaches 28.5 when same English and Chinese sounds are presented. The results illustrate individual variations in semantic judgment.

The data in Chart 1 shows that the response time of the third language and the second language is shorter than that of the third language and the native language. Hence, it can be inferred that Tibetan undergraduates learn English by means of Chinese instead of their native language.

Chart 2 shows the error rate of 12 subjects under eight circumstances. In general, the error rate of semantic judgment of English and Tibetan words or sounds is about 10%, which is much higher than that of English and Chinese words or sounds (5%). The results show that more mistakes are made in semantic judgment between the third language and the second language than between the third language and the native language. Overall, the error rate is lower when the words or sounds have coherent relations, which suggests that it is more difficult for subjects to make correct judgment when it comes to incoherent semantic presentation. Moreover, the judgment of sounds has lower error rate than that of words. Among them, the highest rate (10.74%) appears when different English and Tibetan words are presented and the lowest rate (3.93%) appears when same English and Chinese sounds are presented. The results accord with former studies. As

Chart 2. Error rates (%).

Type	Error rate	Standard deviation
Coherent English-Chinese words	4.82	0.83
Incoherent English-Chinese words	4.99	0.77
Coherent English-Tibetan words	10.35	1.50
Incoherent English-Tibetan words	10.47	1.59
Coherent English-Chinese sounds	3.93	0.65
Incoherent English-Chinese sounds	4.19	0.72
Coherent English-Tibetan sounds	10.18	0.79
Incoherent English-Tibetan sounds	10.21	0.69

Chart 3. Scalp voltage distributions.

Type	English-Chinese words	English-Tibetan sounds	English-Chinese sounds	English-Tibetan words
N120	−6.13	−4.78	0.73	0.66
P220	2.64	5.06	2.57	5.25
N300	−7.68	−7.53	−0.55	−3.13
N400	−5.13	−6.77	−0.32	−4.38

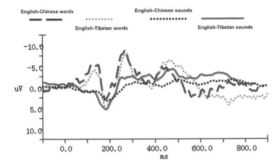

Figure 1. ERP audiogram of CZ.

for standard deviation, the maximum value reaches 1.59 when different English and Tibetan words are presented and the minimum value is 0.65 when same English and Chinese sounds are presented. The results illustrate the differences between subjects is small in individual variations in the case of semantic judgment.

The data in Chart 2 shows that the error rate of the third language and the second language is lower than that of the third language and the native language. Hence, it can be inferred that Tibetan undergraduates learn English by means of Chinese instead of their native language. It is easier for Tibetan undergraduates to acquire a third language by means of the second language.

3.2 ERP data results

This part lays emphasis on analyzing the time process of brain and its features based on ERP signals with regards to coherent or incoherent English-Chinese/English-Tibetan words. Then the discussion of the relationship between three languages in language study and usage is displayed. Figure 1 is ERP audiogram of CZ.

From the Chart 3, it can be seen that with respect to N120, the lowest voltage is −6.13 when English

and Chinese words are presented while the highest is 0.66 when English and Tibetan sounds are presented. With respect to N120, the lowest voltage is 2.57 when English and Chinese words are presented while the highest is 5.25 when English and Tibetan sounds are presented. With respect to N300, the lowest voltage is −7.68 when English and Chinese words are presented while the highest is −0.55 when English and Tibetan sounds are presented. With respect to N400, the lowest voltage is −6.77 when English and Tibetan words are presented while the highest is −0.32 when English and Chinese words are presented. N120 mainly reflexes visual processing; hence it is activated by words rather than sounds. P220, along with N300 mainly reflexes auditory processing; hence it is activated by sounds rather than words. N300 is strongly activated when words are presented indicates Tibetan undergraduates need a processing phrase for sound information before word processing. N400 reflexes semantic processing, and it is activated under all four types of situations. To summarize, it is more difficult for word processing than sound processing in semantic comprehension and it is more difficult to judge English-Tibetan materials than English-Chinese materials.

4 CONCLUSION

This part discusses the semantic processing for Tibetan undergraduates when prime words or sounds are English. Based on behavioral data and ERP data, it can be inferred that Tibetan undergraduates learn English by means of Chinese instead of their native language. Furthermore, it is easier for Tibetan undergraduates to make judgment of English-Chinese materials, which means they acquire the third language by means of the second language. With regards to main components, N120 is activated during word processing while P220 and N300 are activated during auditory processing. The strong activation of N300 during speech information processing indicates direct semantic processing when sounds are received. N400, which normally appears around 450 ms, shows semantic processing. All four types of components are clearly activated and it is more difficult for word processing than sound processing in semantic comprehension and it is more difficult to judge English-Tibetan materials than English-Chinese materials.

REFERENCES

[1] Alvarez, R.P., Holcomb, P.J., & Grainger, J. (2003). Accessing word meanings in two languages: An event-related brain potentials study of beginning bilinguals. Brain and Language, 87, 290–304.
[2] Barber, H.A. & Kutas, M. (2007). Interplay between computational models and cognitive electrophysiology in visual word recognition. Brain Research Reviews, 53, 98–123.
[3] Chauncey, K., Grainger, J., & Holcomb, P.J. (2008). Code-switching effects in bilingual word recognition: A masked priming study with ERPs. Brain and Language, 105, 161–174.
[4] Warrington, E.K. & Mccarthy, R.A. (1994). Multiple meaning systems in the brain: A case for visual semantics. Neuropsychologia, 32, 1465–1473.
[5] Papaioannou, C. & Padilla, A.M. (1982). Bilingual memory of Greek-English bilinguals. Psychological-Reports, 50(3):1047–1054.

Computer, Intelligent Computing and Education Technology – Liu, Sung & Yao (Eds)
© 2014 Taylor & Francis Group, London, ISBN 978-1-138-02469-4

A cognitive study on Tibetan-Chinese-English lexical processing of Tibetan undergraduates

X. Bai, A.X. Hu & T.N. Gegen
Key Lab of China's National Linguistic Information Technology, Northwest University for Nationalities, Lanzhou, China

ABSTRACT: Taking Tibetan undergraduates as the research object, this paper aims at analyzing three different kinds of lexical processing, namely Tibetan, Chinese and English based on ERP. In this way, some conclusions are drawn for Tibetan trilingual in the processing of three different writing systems. In semantic processing, the greatest variation appears in 450 ms, which means the beginning of it. Besides, there exist discrepancies in the processing and the lexical access of Tibetan is clearly earlier than Chinese and English.

Keywords: cognition; lexical processing; event-related potentials

1 INTRODUCTION

As characters are the most efficient way to gain information, the cognitive processing of trilingual is the main emphasis in linguistic study. Different character systems possess disparate visual patterns; hence, in order to explore Tibetan trilingual, the visual pattern needs to be recognized. In writing system, there are three ways to symbolize words: alphabetic, syllabic and ideographic. We use Tibetan-Chinese-English words that have same meaning and mental representation as experimental materials. The subjects are senior Tibetan-Chinese majors who study languages in traditional method and are not proficient in English. The task is divided into semantic judgment and classifying assignment, while electroencephalogram signals are collected by ESI-64 EEG during the process of lexical access for analyzing their processing and cognition.

2 EXPERIMENTAL METHOD

2.1 Selecting subjects

12 Tibetan undergraduates (7 males, 5 females), average age 24.3, are chosen to be the subject of the experiment. Their eyesight or corrected visions are normal. The subjects' mother tongue is Tibetan, and they begin to learn Chinese at the age of 10–12 and English at the age of 19–22. They have all passed CET-4, and are capable of listening, speaking and writing skills in the three languages.

2.2 Experimental material

30 Tibetan-Chinese-English words that have same meaning and mental representation are chosen as experimental items. Tibetan and Chinese are single words that are also non-living nouns, such as "hand", with the word frequency of 90–217 time/million. Besides, the words are tested by familiarity. In additions, 30 Tibetan-Chinese-English words that have same meaning of animals, such as "cat", are chosen as filler items. The experiment employs Go-Nogo paradigm.

2.3 Experimental design

The experiment is designed by means of single factor and 3 levels classified by language types (Tibetan, Chinese and English). A test group is formed by 30 experimental items and 30 filler items, and the stimuli are presented randomly. The single presentation of the three kinds of languages is separated in random order, and is balanced between participants.

2.4 Experimental procedure and the task

After basic preparation including placing electrodes, the subjects are asked to sit in front of the screen with a distance of 80 cm. Firstly, the instructions are presented followed by "*" to test the fixation point for 500 ms. Then the target words are presented and the experiment is officially started. The font and size of all three languages are suitable and the target words are placed in the central of the screen with the visual angle of no more than

2.5 point. The major task for subjects is to judge whether the target word is animal. If it is an animal, press left-click and vice versa. The next stimulus comes out when a response is made or after 2500 ms without any response. Before the experiment, there are 5 to 10 minutes for practicing with different materials. After a group experiment, there are 2 to 3 minutes for resting.

2.5 Data recording

The stimuli are programmed by means of STM2. The behavioral data which consist of reaction time and the correction of judgment is recorded. The EEG signal is collected by ESI-64 (Neuroscan Co., SynAmps 64), the resistance is kept under 5 kΩ and vertex is used as reference electrode. Besides, the filter is set for 0.1–100 Hz and the frequency 250 Hz. Next, after filter the original signal for 30 Hz, we reduce artifact, segment during −100 to 900 ms, make baseline correction and average of the whole brain regions. Finally, we get the averaged oscillogram of each subject under same experimental condition.

2.6 Data analysis

The behavioral data are consisting of reaction time and the correction of judgment. ERP data is set to record with a time range of 1000 ms as soon as the target word is presented and the baseline 100 ms before the target word is presented. On the basis of the overall averaged oscillogram, we take N120 (100 ms–130 ms), P220 (180 ms–240 ms), N300 (250 ms–350 ms) and N400 (350 ms–500 ms) to analyze.

3 EXPERIMENT RESULTS

3.1 Behavioral data results

In linguistic cognition study, behavioral data is mainly made of reaction time and feedback error rate, which can reflect the cognitive and comprehension degree of the stimuli. Figure 1 shows behavioral data of 12 Tibetan undergraduates and reflects the reaction time of lexical access, which is Tibetan words take the shortest time to recognize and English the longest. To be specific, the reaction time of Tibetan and Chinese are similar between 450–600 ms while that of English is longer in about 850–1000 ms. The result means there is a big difference between English comprehension and Tibetan or Chinese comprehension. Figure 2 shows feedback error rate of the three languages. In general, the subjects make least mistakes when the words presented are in Tibetan and the most mistakes when the words presented are in English. The data

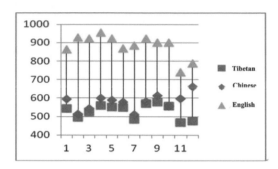

Figure 1. Time distribution of Tibetan, Chinese and English (ms).

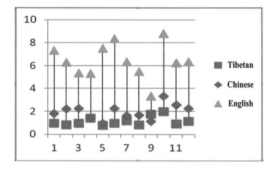

Figure 2. Error rates of Tibetan, Chinese and English.

shows that error rate of judgment of Tibetan and Chinese words is similar between 1%–3% while that of English words is between 5%–8%, which also means there is little difference between Tibetan and Chinese comprehension but great distinction between them and English.

3.2 ERP data results

This section gives analysis of ERP signals collected during Tibetan subjects making judgments of Tibetan, Chinese and English target words. The main discussion is about the variation of voltage in different activated brain regions over time. Furthermore, the data can be used to explain the difficulty of semantic processing in the three languages as well as in the time course.

Compared with standard words, the target words can trigger bigger amplitude. Besides, after comparing three kinds of language stimuli, it can be found that the major disparate area is between 400 ms–550 ms in ERP oscillogram. To make a direct contrast between Tibetan, Chinese and English target stimulus, Figure 3 displays an overall average oscillogram of Pz, Fz, Cz electrodes.

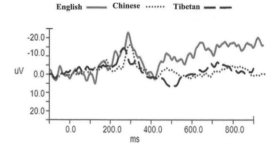

English ———   Chinese ·······   Tibetan — —

Figure 3.   ERP comparisons of Tibetan, Chinese and English.

Chart 2.   The average voltage of CZ.

Language	Tibetan	Chinese	English
N120	0.64	1.45	5.33
P220	2.29	1.98	0.37
N300	−9.86	−11.42	−21.32
N400	6.13	0.77	−9.68

It can be seen in Figure 3 that P300 and N400 differ the most among the three languages. With respect to P300, English words trigger the biggest amplitude while Tibetan words and Chinese words trigger smaller and similar ones. With respect to N400, English target words trigger the biggest amplitude followed by Chinese target words and Tibetan words trigger the least. P300 reflects the processing of speech messages; hence the ERP data indicates Tibetan undergraduates need more cerebral activation when it comes to processing English. N400 reflects the processing of semantic messages; hence the data indicates that English comprehension is hardest for Tibetan undergraduates and Tibetan the easiest.

Chart 1 shows the averaged amplitude of N120 (100 ms–130 ms), P220 (180 ms–240 ms), P300 (260 ms–330 ms) and N400 (350 ms–550 ms) of Cz electrode. After calculation and significance analysis, the results are as follows.

1. N120: According to analysis of variance, the main effect of different language types is not significant, $F(1,18) = 0.836$, $p = 0.574$; the main effect of different electrodes is quite significant, $F(18,324) = 12.647$, $p<0.001$; The interaction between target words of all languages and different electrodes is not notable, $F(18,324) = 0.256$, $p = 0.936$.
2. P220: According to analysis of variance, the main effect of different language types is not significant, $F(1,18) = 0.037$, $p = 0.962$; the

main effect of the same electrode is significant, $F(18,324) = 31.705$, $p<0.001$; the interaction between similar target words of all languages and different electrodes is not notable, $F(18,324) = 0.982$, $p = 0.574$.
3. N300: According to analysis of variance, the main effect of different language types is not significant, $F(1,18) = 0.069$, $p = 0.422$; the main effect of the same electrode is significant, $F(18,324) = 44.29$, $p<0.001$; the interaction between similar target words of all languages and different electrodes is not notable, $F(18,324) = 0.759$, $p = 0.381$.
4. N400: According to analysis of variance, the main effect of different language types is significant, $F(1,18) = 9.163$, $p = 0.01$; the main effect of the same electrode is very significant, $F(18,324) = 17.386$, $p<0.001$; the interaction between similar target words of all languages and different electrodes is notable, $F(18,324) = 1.628$, $p = 0.029$. On the basis of significance analysis of all electrodes, CZ $t(18)=4.216, p<0.008$; P4 $t(18)=2.529, p<0.002$; PZ $t(18) = 5.878$, $p<0.004$; F7 $t(18) = 4.206$, $p<0.003$; T6 $t(18) = 5.752$, $p<0.028$. To conclude, no obvious differences are found in N120, P220 and N300, however, when it comes to N400, difference is significant. The divergence at 400 ms indicates the comprehension processing begins. Figure 4 is a brain electrical activity mapping during 350 ms–450 ms.

It can be found in the mapping above that Tibetan words trigger the left brain while processing Chinese and English words triggers the right brain. The activation of Chinese words is during 450 ms–500 ms and that of English is during 350 ms–400 ms, which means the activation of right brain is effected by studying time and

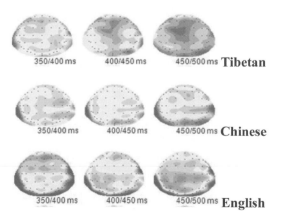

Figure 4.   Brain electrical activity mapping.

1203

familiarity of the language. Less familiarity leads to early activation, inferring more judging activity is involved. What is more, it shows that the semantic comprehension is conducted in the left brain and the judgment of language is conducted in the right brain.

4 CONCLUSION

In summary, it takes Tibetan trilingual much longer time with higher error rate to processing English words, illustrating that the familiarity of language influences cognitive processing. Based on ERP, there is more activation in the left brain when target words are presented. In semantic processing, the biggest divergence appears at 450 ms, which means Tibetan undergraduates start semantic comprehension at 450 ms. In addition, the lexical access of Tibetan is much earlier and much easier achieved than Chinese and English.

ACKNOWLEDGEMENT

It is a project supported by the Graduate Students Innovation Foundation of Northwest University for Nationalities (ycx13153). The corresponding author is Xue Bai.

REFERENCES

[1] Kutas, M., & Federmeier, K.D. (2000). Electrophysiology reveals semantic memory use in language comprehension. Trends in Cognitive Science, 4, 463–470.
[2] Albert, M.L. & Obler, L.K. (1978). The bilingual brain. Neuropsychological and neurolinguistic aspects of bilingualism. New York, Springer-Verlag.
[3] Basnight-Brown, D.M., & Altarriba, J. (2007). Differences in semantic and translation priming across languages: The role of language direction and language dominance. Memory & Cognition, 35, 953–965.
[4] Caramazza, A. (1996). The brain's dictionary. Nature, 380, 485~86.
[5] Fabbro, F. (1999). The Neurolinguistics of Bilingualism: An introduction. Psychology Press Ltd. (PP. 225–254). Lawrence Erlbaum Associates Publishers.

Computer, Intelligent Computing and Education Technology – Liu, Sung & Yao (Eds)
© *2014 Taylor & Francis Group, London, ISBN 978-1-138-02469-4*

Study on cognitive processing of Tibetan-English-Chinese trilingual based on speech

H.Z. Yu, X. Bai, A.X. Hu & N. Ma
Key Lab of China's National Linguistic Information Technology, Northwest University for Nationalities, Lanzhou, China

ABSTRACT: The paper aims at analyzing the cognitive processing of Tibetan undergraduates on Tibetan, English and Chinese on the basis of ERP technology. The main conclusions are as follows. The judgment of speech is more difficult than that of characters as the subjects take longer time to make judgment and make more mistakes, which infers that the processing of characters and speeches is quite different in all three languages. The differences result from the sequence of language acquisition and the features of different language system. Tibetan speech activates more in left occipital lobe than English or Chinese, which accords with the fact that the activation of right brain appears with less familiarity of a language.

Keywords: behavioral data; ERP signal; speech perception

1 INTRODUCTION

Lexical access can be achieved through either character information by visual system or speech information by auditory system. However, as for input signal, spoken language is quite different from written language. During communication, human brain needs to distinguish speech signal and other sounds. Phoneme is the fundamental unit of spoken language that can distinguish meaning. The subjects are senior students who are educated in traditional teaching method and are moderately skilled trilingual. The experiment is designed to analyze time course in phonetic and semantic processing.

2 EXPERIMENTAL METHOD

2.1 Selecting subjects

12 Tibetan undergraduates (7 males, 5 females), average age 24.3, are chosen to be the subject of the experiment. Their eyesight or corrected visions are normal. The subjects' native language is Tibetan, and they begin to learn Chinese at the age of 10–12 and English at the age of 19–22. They are capable of listening, speaking and writing skills in the three languages.

2.2 Experimental material

30 Tibetan-Chinese-English words that have same meaning and mental representation are chosen as experimental items. Tibetan and Chinese are single words that are also non-living nouns, such as "hand", with the word frequency of 90–217 time/million. Besides, the words are tested by familiarity to eliminate the interference of vocabulary frequency. In addition, 30 Tibetan-Chinese-English words that have same meaning of animals, such as "cat", are chosen as filler items. The experiment employs Go-Nogo paradigm.

2.3 Experimental design

The experiment is designed by means of single factor and 3 levels classified by language types (Tibetan, Chinese or English). A test group is formed by 30 experimental items and 30 filler items, and the stimuli are presented randomly. The single presentation of three kinds of language sounds is separated in random order, and is balanced between participants.

2.4 Experimental procedure and the task

After basic preparation including placing electrodes, the subjects are asked to sit in front of the screen with a distance of 80 cm. Firstly, the instructions are presented followed by "*" to test the fixation point for 500 ms. Then the target words are presented. The speech signal of all three languages has the duration of 800 ms and is normalized by PRATT software. The major task for subjects is to judge whether the target word or sound and the prime word or sound have the same meaning.

If they are, press left-click and vice versa. The next stimulus comes out when a response is made or after 2500 ms without any response. Before the experiment, there are 5 to 10 minutes for practicing with different materials. After a group experiment, there are 2 to 3 minutes for resting.

2.5 Data recording

The stimuli are programmed by means of STM2. The behavioral data which consist of reaction time and the correction of judgment is recorded. The EEG signal is collected by ESI-128 (Neuroscan Co., SynAmps 128), the resistance is kept under 5 kΩ and vertex is used as reference electrode. Besides, the filter is set for 0.1–100 Hz and the frequency 250 Hz. Next, after filter the original signal for 30 Hz, we reduce artifact, segment during −100 to 900 ms, make baseline correction and average of the whole brain regions. Finally, we get the averaged oscillogram of each subject under same experimental condition.

2.6 Data analysis

The behavioral data are consisting of reaction time and the correction of judgment. ERP data is set to record with a time range of 1000 ms as soon as the target word is presented and the baseline 100 ms before the target word is presented. On the basis of the overall averaged oscillogram, we take N120 (100 ms–130 ms), P220 (180 ms–240 ms), N300 (250 ms–350 ms) and N400 (350 ms–500 ms) to analyze. Besides, the coordinates of dipole are traced and recorded every 50 ms as traceability data.

3 EXPERIMENT RESULTS

3.1 Behavioral data results

In linguistic cognition study, behavioral data is mainly made of reaction time and feedback error rate, which can reflect the cognitive and comprehension degree of the stimuli. Figure 1 shows behavioral data of 12 Tibetan undergraduates and reflects the reaction time of lexical access, which is Tibetan words take the shortest time to recognize and English the longest. The result indicates the semantic processing of characters and speeches are quite different. The processing activation of Tibetan speeches concentrates on 400 ms–480 ms while that of Chinese speeches concentrates on 490 ms–620 ms. But the processing activation of English speeches starts very late, about 650 ms–850 ms and varies greatly due to subjects. In general, the processing duration of speeches is shorter than that of characters. Figure 2 shows

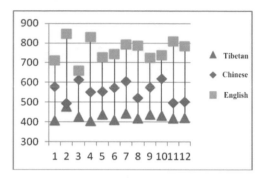

Figure 1. Time distribution of Tibetan, Chinese and English (ms).

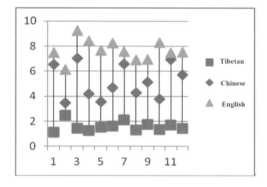

Figure 2. Error rates of Tibetan, Chinese and English.

Chart 1. Response time and error rate (standard deviation).

Type	Tibetan	Chinese	English
Response time	427.75 (20.3)	556.42 (44.7)	762.92 (54.6)
Error rate	1.59 (0.38)	5.15 (1.35)	7.65 (0.83)

feedback error rate of the three languages. The error rate of English is 6%–8%, which is highest. The error rate of Chinese is 4%–7% while the error rate of Tibetan is 1%–3%. Compared with former research, the error rate of Tibetan speech stimuli and Tibetan character stimuli is similar.

T-test is performed to verify the significance of acquired data. The result is listed in the Chart 1.

With respect to response time, the difference between Chinese and English is remarkable, $t(12) = −10.139$, $p<0.05$. The difference between Tibetan and English is very remarkable, $t(12) = −15.216$, $p<0.01$. With respect to error rate,

1206

the difference between Chinese and Tibetan is remarkable, $t(12) = -7.256$, $p<0.05$. The difference between Chinese and English is very remarkable, $t(12) = -5.142$, $p<0.01$. According to the data, we can infer the sequence of language acquisition take important role in cognitive processing. Besides, different language system (ideograph or phonograph) have different impact on language acquisition.

3.2 ERP data results

Compared with standard words, target words can trigger reflection more obviously. It can be seen in the ERP audiogram of CZ Figure 3 that the difference mainly appears during 450 ms–600 ms.

It can be seen in the Figure 3 that P300 and N400 differ the most among the three languages. With respect to P300, English speeches trigger the biggest amplitude while Tibetan speeches and Chinese speeches trigger smaller and similar ones. With respect to N400, English target speeches trigger the biggest amplitude followed by Chinese target speeches and Tibetan speeches trigger the least. P300 reflects the processing of speech messages; hence the ERP data indicates Tibetan undergraduates need more cerebral activation when it comes to processing English. N400 reflects the processing of semantic messages; hence the data indicates that English comprehension is hardest for Tibetan undergraduates and Tibetan the easiest.

Chart 2 shows the averaged amplitude of N120 (100 ms–130 ms), P220 (180 ms–240 ms),

P300 (260 ms–330 ms) and N400 (350 ms–550 ms) of Cz electrode. After calculation and significance analysis, the results are as follows.

1. N120: According to analysis of variance, the main effect of different language types is not significant, $F(1,18) = 0.836$, $p = 0.574$; the main effect of different electrodes is quite significant, $F(18,324) = 12.647$, $p<0.001$; The interaction between target words of all languages and different electrodes is not notable, $F(18,324) = 0.256$, $p = 0.936$.

2. P220: According to analysis of variance, the main effect of different language types is not significant, $F(1,18) = 0.034$, $p = 0.8.55$; the main effect of the same electrode is significant, $F(18,324) = 32.705$, $p<0.001$; the interaction between similar target words of all languages and different electrodes is not notable, $F(18,324) = 0.773$, $p = 0.874$.

3. N300: According to analysis of variance, the main effect of different language types is not significant, $F(1,18) = 0.065$, $p = 0.452$; the main effect of the same electrode is significant, $F(18,324) = 32.705$, $p<0.001$; the interaction between similar target words of all languages and different electrodes is not notable, $F(18,324) = 0.773$, $p = 0.874$.

4. N400: According to analysis of variance, the main effect of different language types is significant, $F(1,18) = 9.163$, $p = 0.01$; the main effect of the same electrode is very significant, $F(18,324) = 17.386$, $p<0.001$; the interaction between similar target words of all

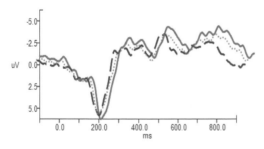

Figure 3. ERP comparisons of Tibetan, Chinese and English.

Chart 2. The average voltage of CZ.

Language type	Tibetan	Chinese	English
N120	0.24	2.56	6.38
P220	1.49	2.04	0.55
N300	−11.26	−13.62	−22.32
N400	7.13	1.79	−8.12

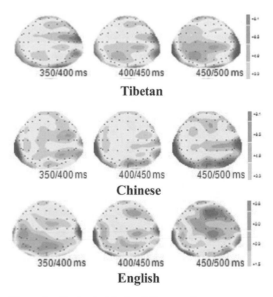

Figure 4. Brain electrical activity mapping.

languages and different electrodes is notable, $F(18,324) = 1.628$, $p = 0.029$. On the basis of significance analysis of all electrodes, CZ $t(18) = 4.216$, $p<0.008$; P4 $t(18) = 2.529$, $p<0.002$; PZ $t(18) = 5.878$, $p<0.004$; F7 $t(18) = 4.206$, $p<0.003$; T6 $t(18) = 5.752$, $p<0.028$. To conclude, no obvious differences are found in N120, P220 and N300, however, when it comes to N400, difference is significant. The divergence at 400 ms indicates the comprehension processing begins. Figure 4 is a brain electrical activity mapping during 350 ms–450 ms.

It can be found in the mapping in Figure 4 that Tibetan words trigger the left brain while processing Chinese and English words triggers the right brain. The activation of Chinese words is during 450 ms–500 ms and that of English is during 350 ms–400 ms, which means the activation of right brain is effected by studying time and familiarity of the language. Less familiarity leads to early activation, inferring more judging activity is involved. What is more, it shows that the semantic comprehension is conducted in the left brain and the judgment of language is conducted in the right brain.

4 CONCLUSION

In summary, it takes Tibetan trilingual much longer time with higher error rate to processing English words, illustrating that the familiarity of language influences cognitive processing. Based on ERP, there is more activation in the left brain when target stimuli are presented. In semantic processing of speeches, the biggest divergence appears at 400 ms, which means Tibetan undergraduates start semantic comprehension at 400 ms. In addition, the lexical access of Tibetan is much earlier and much easier achieved than Chinese and English. From brain traceability data which reflect neural mechanism of Tibetan trilingual before 550 ms, we find Tibetan speech activates more in left occipital lobe than English or Chinese, which accords with former researches.

REFERENCES

[1] Albert, M.L. & Obler, L.K. (1978). The bilingual brain. Neuropsychological and neurolinguistic aspects of bilingualism. New York, Springer-Verlag.
[2] Basnight-Brown, D.M., & Altarriba, J. (2007). Differences in semantic and translation priming across languages: The role of language direction and language dominance. Memory & Cognition, 35, 953–965.
[3] Binder, J.R., Frost, J.A, Hammeke, T.A., Bellgowan, P.S.F., Rao, S.M., Kaufman, J.N., E.T. AL. (2000) Human temporal lobe activation by speech and non-speech sounds. Cerebral Cortex, 10, 512–528.
[4] Fabbro, F. (1999). The Neurolinguistics of Bilingualism: An introduction. Psychology Press Ltd. (PP. 225–254). Lawrence Erlbaum Associates Publishers.
[5] Frazier, L. (1987). Structure in auditory word recognition. Cognition, 25, 157–187.

Ecological tangible metaphor: How to create serene experience in information display

B. Li
Digital Art and Design, College of Computer Science, Zhejiang University, China

F.T. Ying
College of Computer Science, Zhejiang University, China

X.L. Zhao
College of Software Technology, Zhejiang University, China

W.Q. Ying
College of City, Zhejiang University, China

ABSTRACT: This paper aims at exploring a methodology to create serene experience in information display and interactive design. It clarifies the meaning and attributes of serenity in information display. Based on Gestalt cognitive psychology and metaphor theory, this paper proposes Ecology Tangible Metaphor (ETM) method to infuses serene experience within tangible display in information display. Allowing with ETM guideline, 4 designers administered a prototype Plantemp. Through a qualitative contrast experiment between ETM prototypes and normal digital information display prototypes, data analysis of 44 participants questionnaires show that ETM method has a positive effect on serenity arousal.

Keywords: serenity; aesthetics of interaction; implicit interaction; gestalt; ecological tangible metaphor

1 INTRODUCTION

Thanks to introduction of calm technologies and ubiquitous computing (Weiser 1991), many interactive digital products of context-aware and embedded computers fading away from the users' awareness, have been designed and emerge into people's life. Over the past few decades, domain of interaction design has shifted from functionality, usability, to emotional issues (Norman 2002). In interactive design field, it refers to aesthetics of interaction (Petersen, Iversen et al. 2004), such as fluency (Löwgren 2007), efficiency, transparency, playability, seductively (Löwgren and Stolterman 2007), slowness (Hallnäs and Redström 2001), reflection (Kolko 2009), poetics (Lin, Chang et al. 2011), and ludic value (Nam and Kim 2011).

This paper argues serenity as a specific experiential quality (Löwgren 2007) in interaction. Within the fast-tempo society, serenity is one of the most cherishing experiences for modern people. The popularity of relax type APP in Apple Store has provided a strong evidence.

To articulate EMT design method, 4 designers carried out a design prototype named Plantemp. A comparing prototype displaying same information in digital style was set up as a comparing control.

44 participants were recruited to experience and made questionnaires. Statistic results, further discussion and a conclusion close the paper.

2 LITERATURE REVIEW

2.1 *The notion of serenity*

Serenity, noun, means a quality or state of being serene.

Serene, adjective, is marked by or suggestive of utter calm and unruffled repose or quietude.

Serenity's synonyms: calmness, hush, peace, peacefulness, placidity, quiet, quietness, quietude, repose, restfulness, sereneness, calm, still, stillness, tranquility.

–The Merriam Webster Dictionary

Serenity, as a universal emotional experience, usually happens in our daily life. For example, listening to lyric music or immersing ourselves in natural landscapes often brings us peacefulness. It belongs to joy section in basic emotions (Ortony and Turner 1990, Parrott 2001). However, few works have been done on serenity in design domain compared to other basic emotions.

In landscape (Herzog and Bosley 1992) (Pheasant, Horoshenkov et al. 2008) (Lefebvre 1991), costume (Ganguly 2002) and product design (Desmet 2012) fields, serenity is described as a design quality concerning user experience. Some interaction works have also been done to discuss how to arouse serene interaction scenarios. Poetic interaction design (Lin, Chang et al. 2011) provided a method to elicit people's poetic experience with expression making and imagination of both matter and computational things. Slow technology (Hallnäs and Redström 2001) indicated another design exploration of reflection and moments of mental rest. They argued that technology is not only an explicit information delivery method, but also some kind of material to stimulate people's reflection to experience the environment. For example, the experimental design of Soniture (Ibid) took use of sound as a material to make people reflect the specific function of one place. And the reflection would arouse a sense of calm and mental rest.

However, most present researches of serenity are either on psychological theoretical level, lacking of practice operability, or on a layer of design work analysis lacking of theory supports. Few attentions have been paid on the perspective of viewing serenity as an experiential quality in digital information communication. There is still a dearth on serenity creation in interactive domain. So, this paper aims at articulating serenity in interaction, and exploring the methodology to help designers convey information with serenity value.

2.2 *Gestalt and metaphor theory on serenity creation*

Experiential quality is something that characterizes a person's use of a digital artifact to a greater or lesser degree (Löwgren 2007). Designers can manipulate it only through designing conditions to help and lead people to feel it. So two observations' work is deserved to elaborate: first is growing recognition in interaction design which needs to learn from the more mature design disciplines in thinking about the user as a whole person with senses, feelings and desires; second, how to dealing with digital design materials, which are genuinely temporal and spatial (Löwgren 2007). In other words, information transmission process should be bridged to experiential quality.

On one hand, the process of information transmission helps arouse users' emotional experience. Gestalt Psychologists indicated that human beings tend to see things as a whole rather than see them separately (Lehar 2003). Moreover, if the parts that comprise the whole are independent, the whole is not a simple sum of the parts, but a synergistic

"whole effect", or gestalt (Hara 2007). The image formed by material imagination would make people more sensitive to what they feel for the current circumstance (Bachelard 1958).

On the other hand, the form eliciting emotional experience also helps to transmit information. To clarify this, we should apply metaphor theory. Not only in language but also in thought and action, metaphor is pervasive in everyday life. Our ordinary conceptual system, in terms of which we both think and act, is fundamentally metaphorical in nature. Since our universal experience of being in physical environment and manipulating physical objects, orientational and ontological metaphors form spatial metaphors of understanding abstract notions (Lakoff and Johnsen 2003). In this way, to convey incorporeal and abstract information, tangible information transmission with two spatial metaphors shows a promising potential.

What kind of image can be implied in information transmission to elicit serenity? Here, we apply concept of Ecology to summarize and describe natural environments. It includes physical environment, biological environment as well as the relationships between them (Wikipedia 2012). For example, sunlight is the element of physical environment; form of sunflower bloom is a biological environment; sunflower turning towards the sunlight is their relationship. Ecological metaphor is metaphors generates based on ecological phenomenon.

2.3 *What's serenity in interaction design domain?*

According to linguistics interpretation of serenity and reference design research, serenity in interactive domain should be described as a sustained feeling and reflection of calmness and peace, during the whole using process.

To fulfill interactive value, serenity interaction carries two main responsibilities: delivering information, and arousing reflection of serenity. And there are two principles as following:

- The tangible form can clearly convey information.
- The information delivering process should arouse user/customer's reflection about serenity.

In the paper, the author argues that understanding serenity in interaction design calls for investigating the inner experience of a user as he/she experiences serenity. So, it's inappropriate to use quantitative approaches and lab settings for such studies.

3 ECOLOGICAL TANGIBLE METAPHOR

Based on theories mentioned in former sections, author promotes ecological tangible metaphor

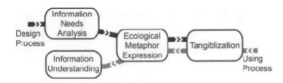

Figure 1. Ecological tangible metaphor.

method to transmit invisible and intangible information, such as environmental or cyber information. For designer, the process is from left to (Fig. 1).

3.1 *Analyze and extract essence of information to help generate idea*

Essence of information is accessible and palpable experience hidden in the digital information, but the precise number itself. For instance, we apply wind-force scale to express wind's power. It's precise but difficult to link with reality, especially for people who are lack of wind scale knowledge.

3.2 *Find out ecological metaphor to transmit the essence of information*

Return to the example of wind force express, a natural way to describe wind power is observe environment changing, such as winging tree and waving water. In this way, invisible and intangible information can be sensed.

3.3 *Abstract and translate ecological metaphor image into tangible form*

In this step, designers should apply ecological phenomenon, focusing on tangible elements such as color, form and movement.

For user, the process is reverse to Design Process. Users should first be aware of device function. Then according to Gestalt and Metaphor theory, abstract tangible information displaying would arouse users' reflection of serene scenery, and help to understand the intangible information.

4 ILLUSTRATIVE PROJECTS

To unfold the notion of serenity and clarify ETM design method, one design prototype was executed. Design topic was to delivery outdoor environment information to indoor users, especially who were in enclosed interior space. 4 students aging from 20–30 year-old whose major covered fields of industrial design, electronic engineering, and mechanical engineering consist the design team.

They chose temperature as the target information, and carried out Plantemp prototype.

Plantemp (Plant+temperature), a temperature displayer, shows outdoor temperature to indoor users. Along with ETM design process, team members focused on temperature perception experience in daily life to analyze the essence of temperature information. They found that besides thermometer, people usually inferred temperature from environment changing, including seasons changing, plant growing as well as color changes of land. Along with season changing, temperature goes up and down, while plants germinate, bloom and languish. So the main idea was to display temperature by referring from seasoning changing and plant growing phenomena.

Based on material collection, three ecological metaphors of temperature were qualitative extracted as Figure 2: color, height, and diameter.

The prototype (Fig. 3) consisted of Temperature Sensing kits, an Arduino Controller Board, LED, four kits of Optical Fiber Movement (Fig. 4). Temperature Sensor tests the temperature information, and sends it to Controller: Arduino Board. Then, according to the temperature ecological metaphors, Arduino Board gives control commands to Display Kits. The most challenge key of hardware implement is the set of Optical Fiber Movement Kits. Every kit consists of Rotation

Figure 2. Ecological metaphor for plantemp.

Figure 3. Plantemp prototype.

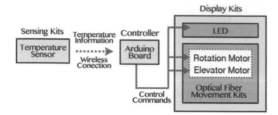

Figure 4. Functional implementation structure for plantemp.

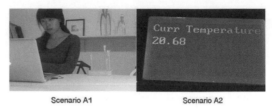

Scenario A1　　　　　　　　Scenario A2

Figure 5. 2 experiencing scenarios.

Motor and Elevator Motor, which in charge of three degrees of freedom: up, down and rotation. All movements designed comply with the ecological metaphors showed in Figure 2.

5 EXPERIMENTS

5.1 Participants

A qualitative experiment was held. 44 Chinese students (M = 19.84, SD = 1.05), from a wide range of academics, were finally recruited. As a return for participation, 30 RMB was paid to each participant. All participants were asked to keep the experiment's content and process confidential.

5.2 Material

1. *Scenario*: Plantemp is named Scenario A1. Paired with A1, Scenario A2 is a LED temperature displayer showing the current temperature as a controlled prototype to deliver the same information but in explicit digital way. For 2 scenarios, there were 4 states changing. Artificial controlling was involved to shift display states to imitate real temperature or weather changing, for the sake of time. For each participant, the 4 states were randomly arranged. According to study topic, all scenarios happened in a no window room to avoid inferences from outdoor environment.

2. *Questionnaire*: It includes 2 sections: experiencing reports and demographics.
   Experiencing reports part consisted 5 questions for each prototype, including information understanding reports, and subjective feeling reports. For information understanding report part, participants were given 4 answers for each state and asked which one portrayed the given state. One of them was expected to describe the given scenario state. For example, participants were asked what the temperature they thought according to prototypes' displaying. Four answers were provided as "hot, warm, cool,

and cold". 1–4 points scores were given to different answers. More points were given if the answer is closer to the expected. For subjective feeling reports part, participants were asked: "(1) Could you totally understand the information transmitted; (2) Did the prototype displaying easily have you reflect any familiar scenario; (3) what was the scenario or scenarios; (4) How serene did you feel when using the prototype." Response alternatives ranged from five-item multiple choices to open-ended answers depending on nature of the items, as well as open questions.
   The demographics portion inquired about the participants' age, gender and major.

3. *Procedure*: For diversity of samples, participants with different majors and genders were recruited in three campuses of a leading university in China mainland. Posters and leaflets were distributed, and advertisements were placed on each local bulletin board, with a clarification of experiment purpose. After indicating an interest in study, all participants were appointed and numbered as "P1", "P2". Participants were recruited over a two-months timeframe from October to November 2012.
   For each participant, the procedure includes 3 steps. First, to understand the background of participants, they were interviewed about their life experiences and habits. Second, scenarios experience. To counteract order effect, participants were asked to make a draw to decide the experiment sequence of 2 prototypes. Before each, the prototype function was explained. The process of experience contained 5 minutes to adjust with the present of prototype, and 15 minutes to experience scenarios. After 20 minutes experiencing, participant should answer the corresponding questionnaire. Then, participants experie nced the next scenario according to the draw made ahead. During the interval of scenarios, participants were free to have a rest.
   At the end of experiment, every participant had an open-end interview about their experience in 2 scenarios. The interview audio was recorded.

6 RESULTS AND DISCUSSION

Intra-and inter-pair comparisons and paired samples t-test were used to analyze questionnaire data.

Consistent with expectation, for information understanding, A1 designed with ETM have the same effect with A2, which is explicit information transmission. This result affirms that ETM method's information transmission do reach users' understanding demand objectively. However, users' subjective experience shows a significant difference. Users subjectively consider information conveyed by A2 is clearer than A1. In other words, users subjectively think that explicit digital information is more efficient than ETM information. The contradictory results of objective and subjective information understanding indicate users' subjective inadaptation to on implicit ETM information. According to interview records, participants stated that they "took a little while to figure out what A1 means", but for A2, they "even lived with" this signals. So, to find out if ETM information, further researches, like a long-term using experiment are required.

Consistent with expectation, design with EMT shows a significant better effect on reflection arousal. Referring to reflections, answers of open-end questions were classified into Ecological Scenes, Artificial Scenes and None. A1 with ETM method were reported arouse more ecological reflection than A2, as percentage shows in Figure 6.

On serenity arousal, EMT method is also demonstrated to have a significant better performance. It shows a consistency with Bachelard's theory that natural environments have the property to arouse serenity.

To move forward a single step, combination with explicit information display would be considerable. In this way, EMT design method could be applied to many types of products, including kitchen appliances, furniture, musical instruments, electronic audio devices, and business products, to create products with serenity.

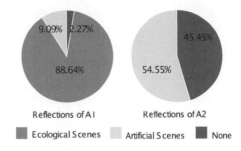

Figure 6.   Reflections of 2 scenarios.

The design experiments with concept generation, prototype implementation and user trials demonstrate that.

To be more successful with this method, a designer needs skill to link information with ecological metaphor and technology. It is also necessary to realize physical interaction for tangiblization and skills for interactive programming. To integrate so many skills, an interesting future research opportunity would be how to combine different kinds of expertise into a complete in a team of integrated designers.

Since the method and cases presented in this paper are initial attempts, we plan to explore other experiential values for meaningful things in future work. At the same time, to further develop our method, a theoretical framework can be further developed by adding deep discussion on each element of the method. For example, theoretical basis on relationships between serenity value and other experiential qualities should also be investigated and discussed. The theoretical framework of ecological metaphor links with information can be explored further by analyzing information property and affective representation. Further investigation is required for effective prototyping technologies used for this kind of tangible interaction. For example, emerging transitive materials, electronic display and sensor technologies can make an impact on the representation of the narratives and the tangible interaction.

Table 1.   Results of paired samples t-test.

Variables	ta	p	d
Information understanding	1.27	0.21*	0.41
Subjective understanding	5.37	NS**	1.43
Reflection arousal	7.35	NS**	1.43
Serenity arousal	14.92	NS**	1.06

df=43. *p<0.05, **p<0.01.
A1 was designed with ETM method; A2 was correspondingly control prototype to A1, designed without ETM method.

REFERENCES

Bachelard, G. (1958). The poetics of space, Beacon Press.
Desmet, P. (2012). "Faces of product pleasure: 25 positive emotions in human-product interactions." International Journal of Design Vol. 1(1).
Ganguly, D. (2002). Rasa: Serenity, valor, love. Master, University of North Texas University.
Hallnäs, L. and J. Redström (2001). "Slow technology: Designing for reflection." Personal ubiquitous computing 5(3): 201–212.

Hara, K. (2007). Designing design, Lars Müller Publishers.

Herzog, T.R. and P.J. Bosley (1992). "Tranquility and preference as affective qualities of natural environments." Journal of Environmental Psychology 12(2): 115–127.

Kolko, J. (2009). Thoughts on interaction design: A collection of reflections. San Francisco, CA, USA, Morgan Kaufmann.

Lakoff, G. and M. Johnsen (2003). Metaphors we live by. Chicago, Univ. of Chicago Press.

Lefebvre, H. (1991). The production of space, Basil Blackwell, Oxford.

Lehar, S. (2003). "Gestalt isomorphism and the primacy of subjective conscious experience: A gestalt bubble model." Behavioral and Brain Sciences 26(0140-525X (Print)): 375–408.

Lin, Y.-C., H.-M. Chang and R.-H. Liang (2011). "Designing poetic interaction in space." Human-computer interaction. Towards mobile and intelligent interaction environments 6763: 559–568.

Löwgren, J. (2007). "Fluency as an experiential quality in augmented spaces." International journal of design 1(3): 1–10.

Löwgren, J. and E. Stolterman (2007). Thoughtful interaction design: A design perspective on information technology. Cambridge, MA, MIT Press.

Nam, T.-J. and C. Kim (2011). "Design by tangible stories: Enriching interactive everyday products with ludic value." International journal of design 5(1): 85–99.

Norman, D. (2002). Emotion & design: Attractive things work better. Interactions. 9: 36–42.

Ortony, A. and T.J. Turner (1990). "What's basic about basic emotions?" Psychological review 97(3): 315–331.

Parrott, W.G. (2001). Emotions in social psychology: Essential readings. Philadelphia, Psychology Press.

Petersen, M.G., O.S. Iversen, P.G. Krogh and M. Ludvigsen (2004). Aesthetic interaction: A pragmatist's aesthetics of interactive systems. Proceedings of the 5th conference on Designing interactive systems: processes, practices, methods, and techniques. Cambridge, MA, USA, ACM: 269–276.

Pheasant, R., K. Horoshenkov, G. Watts and B. Barrett (2008). "The acoustic and visual factors influencing the construction of tranquil space in urban and rural environments tranquil spaces-quiet places?" The Journal of the Acoustical Society of America 123(3): 1446–1457.

Weiser, M. (1991). "The computer for the 21st century." Scientific American 265(3): 94–104.

Wikipedia, (2012). "Ecology." from http://en.wikipedia.org/wiki/Ecology.

Computer, Intelligent Computing and Education Technology – Liu, Sung & Yao (Eds)
© *2014 Taylor & Francis Group, London, ISBN 978-1-138-02469-4*

Strategies of English translation teaching

Y. Zhu & J. Wang
School of Foreign Language, Wuhan Bioengineering Institute, Hubei, China

ABSTRACT: Translation is an independent discipline (Jean Delisle, 1988). With the deepening of translation studies, translation teaching aroused widespread concern among translation academia, and gradually separated from language teaching, being a subject with its own objectives and a special position. This paper, firstly introduces the objectives and content of translation teaching, then points out several common problems in translation teaching. Finally, associated with the basic principles of translation teaching, it analyzes the strategies of English translation teaching.

Keywords: translation teaching; teaching strategies

1 THE OBJECTIVES AND CONTENT OF TRANSLATION TEACHING

1.1 The objectives of translation teaching

The Ministry of Education in 2000 approved the implementation of the "College English Teaching Syllabus". In it, the individual requirements of a preliminary translation subject is to understand the basic theory of translation and similarities and differences between English and Chinese languages; to master common translation skills; to translate moderate difficulty English text or paragraph into Chinese faithfully to the original with fluent language at a rate of 250 to 300 English words per hour; to be capable of translating Chinese discourses of moderate difficulty into English with the same speed and requirements as English-to-Chinese translation; and to be able to serve foreign guests with interpretation of everyday life. In actual operation, teachers can establish periodic teaching objectives depending on the circumstances.

Translation teaching consists of two parts: the College English translation teaching and professional English translation teaching. Despite the differences in terms of teaching materials, teaching purposes, etc., there are still some common points between the two. Both are a method of linguistic analysis, an optimized part of education, and a professional translation training.

In order to meet domestic demand for high-quality translation talents, a lot of universities have carried out bilingual teaching, whose purpose is to train a large number of compound talents to ease the pressure of scarce professional translators. In this process, the College English translation teaching is the foundation and necessary means to train practical, versatile senior translators. Therefore, both professional and College English translation teaching should be gained wide popularity and attention.

1.2 Content of translation teaching

To achieve the above objectives, the content of translation teaching should include translation basic theory, English-Chinese language comparison, common translation skills as well as cultural differences. The content of translation teaching is one dynamic teaching system, whose aim is to achieve faithfully and fluently conveying the original message and to understand the cause and characteristics in all kinds of discourses involved in the two cultures.

2 CURRENT PROBLEMS IN TRANSLATION TEACHING

Translation Teaching is an important part of English teaching. Its effect plays a direct impact on students' overall English learning. At present, there are some problems in China's translation teaching.

2.1 Problems in students' learning

Translation is a comprehensive skill, which to some extent reflects the levels of students' English learning. From the current recognized measures of testing English learning level, it is not difficult to see that there are some problems in students' study of translation.

2.1.1 Excessive use of dialects and colloquial vocabulary

From the student's assignments, we found a high frequency use of dialects, spoken words, etc.

appeared in the translation, which directly affected the quality of the translation. In this regard we must be aware that, in the translation, we shall make full use of Mandarin. Taking the differences between the ancient and current English originals into account, we may appropriately use some dialect expressions which remain strong vitality and have been integrated into Mandarin and are widely accepted around the readers. But the use of these dialects, slangs, etc. must be careful, otherwise excessive, inappropriate use of dialects will make people feel uncomfortable.

2.1.2 *Word for word translation*

Most of the students have the habit of translating the original text by word for word translation. That is, the translation lacks necessary modifications, resulting in the burdensome, long-winded translation. The reason for this problem is that the students do not have a good translation strategy, not good at correspondingly increasing or reducing words according to the actual situation.

In addition, because the obvious differences in the syntax of English and Chinese language, while doing English-to-Chinese translation, some pronouns, prepositions, conjunctions in English need to be changed. In this regard students are clearly in insufficient training.

2.1.3 *Mishandling word order*

Chinese and English have different habits of language expression and word order arrangement. Chinese has a strong logic, its word order is usually described based on a certain logical order from the cause to the effect, from the assumption to the inference, from the facts to the conclusion, from conditions to the results. In contrast, the English word order is generally more flexible, straightly to the point, and explanations are described around the theme of the topic. In expressing multi-logical thinking, English can make use of morphological changes, connecting words, grammatical or lexical tools, to flexibly arrange the sentence structure while necessary. This resultes in its word order being far from Chinese.

2.1.4 *Improper handling of long sentences*

Mishandling of long sentences is one of the most common problems in English translation. There is a lot of sentences containing many prefixes, phrases, attributive clause modifiers. Students are often not able to translate these ingredients into clauses, resulting in the presence of a large number of Chinese expressions that do not comply with the foreign-type long sentences. This makes it very hard to comprehend the translation, giving the feeling of confusion. Therefore, students must take

this issue seriously, correct defects and improve translation quality.

2.2 *Problems in Teachers' teaching*

2.2.1 *Single form of teaching*

Single form of teaching is the common problem in China's current English teaching, which can be seen from the usual three steps in translation teaching: first, doing the translation exercises; secondly, correcting exercises; Finally, commenting exercises. We can see, in the entire teaching process, teachers ignore the contributions of the students' needs and subjectivity. This indoctrination do not let students think independently and do not let them explore cooperation. It is not conducive to cultivate good study habits, and thus not achieve effective teaching.

2.2.2 *Inadequate attention to translation teaching*

In some institutions, some teachers take incomplete, inadequate attention to translation teaching, which is mainly manifested in two aspects: translation capacity requirements are not specific in College English Syllabus; teachers do not pay attention to the learning of the basic theory and the training of translation skills, and just regard translation teaching as teaching methods to understand and consolidate the knowledge of the language, putting too much emphasis on language form, ignoring the language connotations. Many times, the teacher simply gives the standard answer, instead of to explain or to guide students to correct mistakes, which makes the translation teaching very casual. Furthermore, there exists no standard answers in translation practice.

3 PRINCIPLES OF TRANSLATION TEACHING

3.1 *Gradual principle*

Translation teaching activities should follow a gradual, progressive approach, which is consistent with the law of human cognition. Therefore, the levels of selected texts in translation teaching practice should be from easy to difficult. In term of the text content and the subject, it should be the most familiar part to the students; in terms of the language itself, it should be a little plain gradually getting to some difficult. By the transition from simple to complex practice, students are less possible to produce fear of hardship in the translation procedure, but continue to gain confidence in the success, slowly arousing their interest. Therefore, if we use too difficult materials to practice from the start, there is bound to causing obstacles in understanding and interpretation, affecting their interest and enthusiasm in learning translation.

3.2 Succinct training principle

In initial stage of translation teaching, teachers teach translation skills and students learn it. Skills teaching should be closely connected with the students' practice, summarizing and refining on the base of exercises. Before practice, teachers can make a brief introduction with examples of the related skills according to the materials, then let students do the exercises. While correcting students' exercises, teachers should respond to problems in practice and review the proposed use of translation skills. Only in this way can the students really grasp translation skills and the skills training is also being consolidated.

In addition to the teachers' succinct effort outside, we must also strengthen the strength and intensity of the training of the translation. This requires a certain amount of practice of thinking, problem solving, and commenting. Only through constant practice, thinking and summary will students continue to increase capabilities to analyze and solve problems.

3.3 Translation competence + translation criticism principle

The task of translation teaching is not only to improve students' ability to translate, but also the capacity of translation criticism. Translation criticism capacity concludes both the comment on the merits of other translations, but also the criticism for their shortcomings, and even the correction of the wrong place. Cultivating translation criticism capacity is conducive to students in learning the strengths of others, avoiding making the same mistakes of others, and clarifying some understandings. It is a more profound grasp of translation strategies and their applications which will improve the level of translation quality and guide translation practice.

3.4 Speed + quality principle

In translation teaching, while improving translation quality of students, it should also help students improve translation speed. To train students in translation speed, students are required to do a lot of practice in a limited time. Such as English-to-Chinese translation practice can start around 200 English words per hour, and then gradually increased to 250 to 300 words per hour or even more, so that students learn to arrange time effectively in the limited time to gradually improve translation speed, with ensuring the quality of translation at the same time.

4 STRATEGIES OF TRANSLATION TEACHING

Translation teaching is different from the translation theory and the practice of translation. It is a transitional stage between the two, a bridge to connect the two together. In order to effectively carry out the translation teaching, we must take appropriate teaching strategies.

4.1 Guessing strategy

Encountering unfamiliar word is the most common difficulty in translation. Due to poor vocabulary, students are often unable to fully and accurately understand the words, paragraphs, and get feedback from text messages, and thus fall into a panic. In this regard, teachers should guide students to use the guessing strategy to successfully complete the translation. Guessing Strategy can be achieved in several specific ways.

Using word formation. This method requires students to master certain knowledge of English word formation, such as the meaning of roots, prefixes, suffixes.

Using the signal words. Signal words link and indicate the context and tend to have a great indication effect.

Guessing contact meaning. There is often a definite semantic link within sentences and context.

Guessing the meaning based on examples. Sometimes some words will be explained with examples followed.

Presuming by changing words. Sometimes the text is often expressed in different words with the same meaning. Students can use relatively simple words to speculate the meaning of new words.

4.2 Context strategy

Understanding and expressing the translation is performed in the context of specific semantic identification. The choice of words and sentences, discourse structure and language are inseparable from the context. Visibly, context is the basis for the accurate translation. In the process of translation, the translator, in addition to using the existing knowledge of the language to get the original meaning, should also identify the implied intention of the original author based on a variety of information available in the original through speculating and reasoning, then determine the appropriate translation form.

Contexts include macro-contexts and micro-contexts. Macro-contexts, including topics, objects, situations, etc., make a more precise meaning; micro-contexts, the mixed meaning of the words and semantic combinations, make a particular meaning. In the translation process, students must integrate the two in order to accurately understand the original meaning and make appropriate and accurate translation.

4.3 Translation methodology strategy

Translation techniques are fast and efficient ways to improve the translation quality, therefore, they can be effective ways to enhance students' interest in learning translation. Here we briefly introduce several commonly used methods of translation.

4.3.1 Literal translation

Literal translation is a method that maintains the original content, the original form and style with the literal direct translation. The premise is not misleading and comply with the law of the target language. Its efficacy lies in the closer interaction between the reader and the original, and it is easy for readers to directly and accurately understand the original meaning of the source language and culture.

4.3.2 Free translation

In the translation process, when it is hard to find the corresponding words and there are other factors leading to not accurately express the original meaning through translation, free translation would be a good translation method. Due to the differences in the Chinese and English language vocabulary, sentence structure and methods of expression, free translation requires correctly express the content of the original without sticking to the original form.

4.3.3 Transliteration

Some words represent unique things that only exists in the certain source language culture. It is often unable to find the words correspondly in the target language, where the transliteration method can be used. It not only keeps the exotic culture of the source language, while also introduces a foreign language, enriching the national language vocabulary. Transliteration is usually used to translate place names.

It is noted that, transliteration is not available everywhere, but in a limited range. Therefore, teachers should guide students to use transliteration, when names, organizations and buzzwords appear, retaining their cultural shell, reducing the loss of cultural and linguistic misunderstandings arising from the translation process, accurately and fastly disseminating culture. Do not abuse transliteration, otherwise there will be no translation at all.

4.3.4 Conversion

Due to the different expression between the two languages, we often need to convert the speech to meet the needs of the expression or adapt to the habits of the target language, which inevitably turn to use the conversion. Conversion is carried out in speech conversion in accordance with habits of the target language.

4.3.5 Combination and division

To make the translation more in line with the expression habits of the target language, and to make readers easily to read, combination and division are to translate the original words, phrases into a sentence, or to translate the original text of a sentence into two or more sentences.

4.3.6 Structure adjustment

Because of the differences in thinking mode in English and Chinese ethnic nationalities, English and Chinese languages are also different in the expression of word order. Therefore, based on the language habits of the target language, without compromising the basic meaning of the text, structure adjustment is to adjust original sentence structure to make it more in line with the target readers' reading habits.

5 CONCLUSION

With the strengthening of globalization, China is deepening the participation in economy, politics, culture and other fields in the world, making it increasingly important to comprehensively improve college students listening, speaking, writing and translating skills. Especially, College English translation teaching is the objective requirement to fully complete college English teaching work. It is very practical. Teachers should continue the practice of principles and strategies in translation teaching, specifically for the existing problems noted in this paper, to help students understand and master the translation methods and skills in college English teaching, to train and bring up a number of international, practical, senior translators.

REFERENCES

Chen D.H. & Zhang N.F. 2000. *A selection of western translation theory*. Press of City University of Hong Kong: Hong Kong.

Gao L.H. 2008. *Translation teaching: theory and practice*. Zhejiang University Press: Hangzhou.

Zhang, M.F. & Huang, G.W. 2002. Text linguistics and translation studies. *Chinese Translation* 3:13–16.

Variable-slope sampling ADC for compressive sensing

X.J. Li, D.M. Li & S.F. Liang
Institute of Microelectronics of Chinese Academy of Sciences, Beijing, China

ABSTRACT: Random Sampling Slope-ADC (RSS-ADC) has been described as a new Analog-to-Digital Converter (ADC) architecture which can be used for sparse spectrum sensing with its simplicity in hardware realization. However, the sampling instances are signal-dependent and the important prior information contained in the signal is underused. In this paper, a new Variable-Slope Sampling ADC (VSS-ADC) is proposed. The VSSS-ADC introduces the energy criteria to increase the lowest possible sampling intervals. The slope of the reference signal varies with the energy of the input signal and the bigger the input signal energy is the larger the slope is and vise versa. Simulation results show that the VSS-ADC system can acquire higher perfect recovery rate than the RSS-ADC at the same compression ratio and can also reduce the lowest sampling interval.

Keywords: compressive sensing; Analog-to-Digital Converter; random sampling

1 INTRODUCTION

The Nyquist-Shannon sampling theorem which has been generally used as the foundation of signal acquisition and processing systems requires that the sampling frequency must be greater than or equal to twice the highest frequency of the input signal to avoid losing information. However, with the development of information technology, the Nyquist sampling rate is so high that too much data is acquired which will undoubtedly put tremendous pressure on signal sampling, storage, transmission and processing. The recently emerging field of Compressive Sensing (CS)[1,2] can acquire and compress signal at a rate far below Nyquist rate by taking advantage of the sparsity constraint or finite rate of innovations of input signals. Instead of sampling signals at the Nyquist rate, compressive sensing theory first employs non-adaptive linear projections of the input signal which reduces the size of signal space dimension and also preserves the structure of the signal; then reconstructs the signal from these projections by an optimization algorithm.[3]

As CS theory is just a mathematic framework, the key point is how to implement this theory in hardware. There are several architecture proposed to utilize CS theory to reduce the sampling rate: the Analog-to-Information Converter (AIC),[4,5] the Modulated Wideband Converter (MWC),[6] the Periodic Non-uniform Sampling (PNS)[7] and the Random Sampling Slope ADC (RSS-ADC).[8,9] Among all these architecture, the RSS-ADC based on the well-known slope ADC is considered as the simplest hardware implementation. The RSS-ADC takes samples at unevenly distributed points in time domain. For the signal reconstruction, one can employ optimization algorithms from compressive sensing. However, the sampling instances taking from this RSS-ADC architecture are signal-dependent, which means that more samples will be acquired when the amplitude of input signal is near the starting point of the reference slope and samples exceeding the range of the reference slope will be skipped. To solve this problem, a modified Variable-Slope Sampling ADC (VSS-ADC) is proposed in this paper. Instead of comparing the input signal with the same slope ADC, the VSS-ADC can change the reference slope according to the signal energy. That is, the higher the energy is the bigger the slope is. Simulation results demonstrate that the VSS-ADC gets better reconstruction than the RSS-ADC and also reduces the smallest sampling interval.

2 COMPRESSIVE SENSING

The fundamental idea of CS theory is to recover a signal from very few non-adaptive linear measurements by convex optimization, taking advantage of the sparse or compressible structure of the signal. To state this theory mathematically precisely, let $x = (x_i)_{i=1}^{n} \in R^{N*1}$ be our target signal. As prior information, we assume that x is K-sparse which means that it contains only K non-zero coefficients or it can be represented by only K coefficients in a given basis Ψ called sparse basis. In this case, we can design a $M*N$ ($M<<N$) matrix Φ called measurement matrix or sensing matrix to collect non-adaptive linear projections $y = (y)_{m=1}^{M} \in R^{M*1}$ via $y = \Phi x$. Although the reconstruction of high dimensional signal x from low dimensional signal y is an ill-posed problem, the CS theory states that as long as the condition $M=C*K$ is satisfied, where C is an empirical constant, we can reconstruct the original signal x from y by solving the minimum l_0-norm, that is

$$\hat{x} = \arg\min \| x \|_0, \text{Subject to } y = \Phi x \tag{1}$$

A great number of algorithms have been described to solve the optimization problem in (1), such as Basis Pursuit (BP) algorithm,[10] Matching Pursuit (MP) algorithm[11] and Iterative Hard Thresholding (IHT) algorithm.[12]

3 NON-UNIFORM SAMPLING

The basic principle of RSS-ADC is very simple as shown in the upper half of Figure 1. A linear slope with fixed gradient is generated as a reference signal and is compared with the input signal; A counter measures the time when the slope equals the input signal and then reset the slope to its initial state. Let $x(t)$ be the given input signal, the RSS-ADC samples it in the time domain at rate $f_0 < f_N$ with $f_N = 2f_m$ being the Nyquist frequency. The measurements $y = (y)_{m=1}^{M} \in R^{M*1}$ can be represented as

$$y_m = x(t)|_{t=k_m T_0}, \quad k_m \in \{1, N\},$$
$$m = 1, 2, ..., M \qquad k_m > k_{m-1} \tag{2}$$

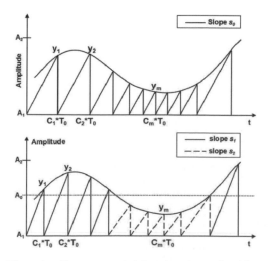

Figure 1. Slopes generated for given input signal in a RSS-ADC (top) and a VSS-ADC (bottom).

As the RSS-ADC is proposed for frequency sparse signals, the corresponding measurement matrix Φ can be represented as a $M*N$ ($M << N$) matrix called partial Discrete Fourier transform (partial-DFT) matrix with each column choosing from a full $N*N$ (N is the length of input signal) DFT matrix.

$$\Phi = \{\phi_{m,n}: 1 \le m \le M, 1 \le n \le N\}$$
$$\phi_{m,n} = \frac{1}{\sqrt{N}} \exp\left(-j2\pi \frac{(k_m-1)(n-1)}{N}\right) \tag{3}$$

where, k_m is the partial-DFT index determined by the input signal and the reference slope of the corresponding system.

3.1 Variable-slope sampling ADC

In order to solve the problem that RSS-ADC can only deal with time domain smooth signals and the smallest sampling interval is large when the input signal is near the starting point of the slope signal, we proposed a new non-uniform sampling architecture called Variable-Slope Sampling ADC (VSS-ADC). Instead of generating a reference signal with fixed gradient, the VSS-ADC compares the input signal to a variable slope reference signal, which means that the gradient of the reference signal generated by the front variable-slope generator is controlled by a limier. The limiter works under the energy criterion. As a result, the gradient of the reference signal is changing with the energy of the input signal: The larger the energy is the greater the gradient and vise versa. For simplicity, we assume that the slope signal raise from A_1 to A_2 and there are only two different kinds of slope s_1 and s_2 ($s_1 > s_2$) as described in the lower half of Figure 1. We can predefine a threshold value $A_0 = (A_1 + A_2)/2$. If the input signal amplitude is larger than A_0, the front slop generator will generate a ramp signal with gradient s_1. If the input signal amplitude is smaller than A_0, the gradient is s_2. In practical application, the amplitude of input signal can be divided into several different intervals.

The hardware schematic of VSS-ADC is shown in Figure 2. The basic building blocks are only a limiter, a variable-slope generator, a comparator and a counter. The ramp reference signal is controlled by the limiter according to the energy of the input signal. The smallest resolvable time is the counter clock period T_0. Here T_0 must be equal to or larger than the Nyquist frequency T_N. The reference signal raising from its initial state. When its amplitude equals the input signal, the integer of counter is recorded and the reference signal is reset to its initial value.

Compared with the RSS-ADC proposed in [8], the VSS-ADC can lower the highest sampling rate

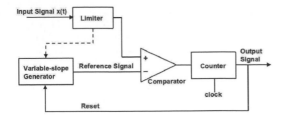

Figure 2.   Hardware schematic of a VSS-ADC.

by reducing the slope of reference signal. In order to reconstruct the input signal from the measurements, we need to record not only the integer of counter when two signals intersect but also the slope of the reference signal. This will increase the storage data. However, the slope can help us recover the input signal more precisely for each slope corresponding to a range of signal amplitude.

3.2   CS reconstruction

The measurement matrix is necessary for reconstructing the input signal from the obtained measurements. As the integer and the slop is recorded in the VSS-ADC, the corresponding sampling instances k_m can be described as

$$k_m = \sum_{i=1}^{m} C_i \tag{4}$$

C_i is the recorded counter integer when input signal and the reference slope signal intersect. With k_m known, the measurement matrix is given by Eq. (3). Assuming the reference slope is ideal and each gradient is s_m corresponding to each measurements y_m, then we have

$$y_m = s_m \cdot C_m T_0 + A_1 \tag{5}$$

T_0 is the counter clock period and also the smallest resolution interval, and A_1 is the initial value of the reference signal. In most applications, the initial state A_1 can be set to zero to simplify the hardware realization.

The reconstruction of input signal is solving the optimization problem of Eq. (1) described in Sec. 2 using Eq. (3), (4) and (5). In this paper, we use the mostly discussed Orthogonal Matching Pursuit (OMP) algorithm[13] to recover the input signal.

4   SIMULATIONS

In order to evaluate the performance of the new proposed VSS-ADC, several simulations have been

done in this section. In all simulations, the input signal is a smooth gas sensor signal which is sparse in frequency domain with length $N = 256$ and sparsity $K = 15$. The perfect recovery rate defined by the $1-Er$ is used as a quality metric. Where, Er is the l_2-norm of the reconstructed signal x_rec and the input signal x calculated as follows:

$$Er = \| x - x\_rec \|_2 \tag{6}$$

The perfect recovery rate takes values from the interval [0,1]. And the bigger perfect recovery rate means the better reconstruction.

Figure 3 is the comparison of reconstructed signal (Fig. 3d) with the original signal (Fig. 3a) when the compression ratio is $M/N = 1/4$. Figure 3b is the representation of original input signal in frequency domain showing commendable sparse characteristics; and Figure 3c is the measurements obtained from the VSS-ADC system. The perfect recovery rate acquired by the matlab simulations is only 97.26%, which means that the VSS-ADC schematic can be used to sample and recover this kind of signals very well.

The comparison of VSS-ADC with the RSS-ADC is also demonstrated in Figure 4. Figure 4

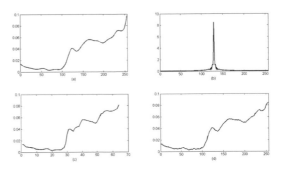

Figure 3.   Comparison of reconstruction signal to original signal with compression ration $M/N = 1/4$.

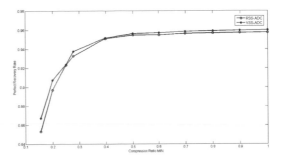

Figure 4.   Perfect recovery rate of the VSS-ADC and RSS-ADC vs. compression ratio M/N.

1221

is the perfect recovery rate acquired by the RSS-ADC and the VSS-ADC system with the compression ratio M/N varying from 0.15 to 1.00. From Figure 4, we can see that not only the RSS-ADC but also the VSS-ADC can get high perfect recovery rate even when the compression ratio is 0.15, which means that both the two architecture can sample and acquire the input signal at a rate far below the Nyquist rate. At the same time, the perfect recovery rate acquired by the VSS-ADC system is higher than that acquired by the RSS-ADC system at the same compression ratio.

5 CONCLUSIONS

In this paper, we proposed a new non-uniform sampling architecture for compressive sensing called Variable-Slope Sampling ADC (VSS-ADC). Different from the RSS-ADC, the VSS-ADC introduces the energy criteria to increase the lowest possible sampling intervals. A limiter is used to vary the slope of the reference signal according to the amplitude of the input signal. The input signal is divided into several different intervals and each interval corresponds to a slope. The large the input signal amplitude is the bigger the slope is and vise versa. This architecture can largely reduce the lowest possible sampling interval. In order to recover the input signal, not only the counter integer when the output of comparator is zero but also the reference slope needs to be stored. This will increase the storage. However, the reference slope can help us recognize whether the reconstruction is correct or not. Simulation results demonstrate that the VSS-ADC can reconstruct the input frequency sparse signal with higher perfect recovery rate than the RSS-ADC at the same compression ratio.

ACKNOWLEDGMENT

Financial support for this work has been provided by "Strategic Priority Research Program" of the Chinese Academy of Sciences (Grant No. XDA06020401) and the National High Technology Research 863 Program of China (Grant No 2013AA030801).

REFERENCES

[1] Candes E J. Compressive Sampling[C]. International Congress of Mathematicians, European Mathematical Society Publishing House, Madrid, Spain, 2006:1433–1452.

[2] Donoho D L. Compressed Sensing[J]. IEEE Transactions on Information Theory, 2006, 52(4):1289–1306.

[3] E.J. Candes and T. Tao. Decoding by Linear Programming. IEEE Transactions on Information Theory, 2005, 51(12):4203–4215.

[4] J. Laska, S. Kirolos, Y. Massoud, et al. Random Sampling for Analog-to-Information Conversion of Wideband Signals[C]. IEEE Dallas/CAS Workshop on design, Applications, Integration and Software, 2006:119–122.

[5] S. Kirolos, L. Jason, W. Michael, et al. Analog-to-Information Conversion via Random Demodulation[C]. IEEE Dallas/CAS Workshop on design, Applications, Integration and Software, 2006:71–74.

[6] M. Mishali and Y. Eldar. From theory to practice: Sub-Nyquist Sampling of Sparse Wideband Analog Signals[J]. IEEE Journal of Selected Topics in Signal Processing, 4(2):375–391, 2010.

[7] M. Mishali and Y. Eldar. Blind Multi-bind Signal Reconstruction: Compressed Sensing for Analog Signals[C]. IEEE Trans Signal Process. 2009 Mar; 57(3):993–1009.

[8] P. Maechler, N. Felber, and A. Burg. Random Sampling ADC for Sparse Spectrum Sensing[C]. In Proc. Eusipco, Sept. 2011.

[9] P. Maechler, N. Felber, H. Kaeslin, et al. Hardware-Efficient Random Sampling of Fourier-Sparse Signals[C]. IEEE International Symposium on Circuits and Systems. 2012 May: 269–272.

[10] Chen S S, Donoho D L, Saunders M A. Atomic Decomposition by Basis Pursuit[J]. SIAM Journal of Science Computing, 1998, 20(1):33–61.

[11] Mallat S, Zhang Z. Matching Pursuit with Time-frequency Dictionaries[J]. IEEE Trans on Signal Processing, 1993, 41(12):3397–3415.

[12] Thomas Blumensath, Mike E. Davies. Iterative Hard Thresolding for Compressed Sensing[J]. Appl and Comp Harm Anal, 2009, 27, 265–274.

[13] Troop J, Gilbert A. Signal Recovery from Partial Information via Orthogonal Matching Pursuit[J]. IEEE Trans on Inform Theory, 2007, 53(12):4655–4666.

Computer, Intelligent Computing and Education Technology – Liu, Sung & Yao (Eds)
© *2014 Taylor & Francis Group, London, ISBN 978-1-138-02469-4*

Exploration on multimedia teaching mode of university English teaching

Yan-Ling Wu
University of Science and Technology, Liaoning, Anshan, Liaoning, China

ABSTRACT: The development of multimedia and network technology brings vigor and vitality to the university English teaching reform, and also brings new challenges to the university English teaching. This paper mainly probes the teaching mode of the university English teaching, proposing that the teaching mode should take "the students as the center, the teacher as the main body, the multimedia technology as the aid".

Keywords: multimedia; teaching mode; university English; teaching efficiency

1 INTRODUCTION

Multimedia teaching refers to the application of computer technology to the different teaching stages, such as the classroom instruction, autonomous learning, after-school tutoring and classroom management, aiming to improve the quality and efficiency of teaching. Multimedia teaching has provided a powerful resource platform, combing voice, image, text with rich, vivid, lively specific information together. In 2007 the Ministry of Education put forward University English Teaching Requirements, which points out that the teaching goal of current university English is "to cultivate the students' comprehensive ability of using English, especially listening and speaking ability so that they can use English to communicate effectively in the future study, work and social contacts, and enhance their ability of independent learning, improve the comprehensive culture literacy in order to meet the needs of our society development and the international exchange... Colleges and universities should make full use of multimedia and network technology, adopt new teaching modes to reform the former teacher-centered single classroom teaching mode." In the university English teaching, reasonable application of multimedia means can provide abundant teaching resources for students, arouse students' interest in learning English, improve the students' learning efficiency, and truly teach students in accordance with their aptitude.

2 ADVANTAGES OF THE MULTIMEDIA TECHNOLOGY IN UNIVERSITY ENGLISH TEACHING

2.1 *Various teaching methods to improve the students' interest in learning English*

English is a practical subject and the integration of multimedia and the English curriculum reform is to arouse the students' subject consciousness, stimulate students' interest in English learning, cultivate students' autonomous learning ability, improve their listening, speaking, reading and writing ability in certain context. The traditional English teaching mode is teacher-centered with exercises focusing on grammar and lots of pattern drills making classroom teaching boring, difficult to arouse the students' learning interest. While in the university English teaching, multimedia technology combines image, sound, text and video information together, giving students more vivid and visual information, stimulating students' senses in multidirections, effectively mobilize students' vision and hearing, providing students relaxing and colorful teaching situation, causing students to obtain optimal cognitive results in a relaxing state and increasing students' interest in learning English.

2.2 *Plentiful teaching contents to improve teaching efficiency in English class*

The traditional teaching in the classroom mainly consists of a piece of chalk, a blackboard, a book and a recorder. To clarify knowledge points, teachers require to write a great deal on the blackboard and make detailed explanation on the blackboard with chalk. The use of multimedia and network technology in the university English teaching has changed this situation. English teachers put into the courseware audio materials, video news, movie clips and the background introduction, text structure analysis, writing characteristics etc., presenting the students one by one, saving a lot of time in writing on the blackboard. At the same time, the teacher can build the courseware settings different font and color, stressing the difficult points and important points in this class, and the students can accept and memorize the new knowledge. In the preparation stage, teachers can also directly search a large number of relevant contents resources through the network, saving time and effort, and making the teacher spend a lot of time and energy on the research, the improvement of teaching methods and declaration of the research projects. Therefore, the application of multimedia and network technology solves the problem of the university English teaching large amount of information in short period of time and improve the teaching efficiency.

2.3 English network platform to promote the communication and interaction between teachers and students after class

Interactive multimedia network makes classroom English teaching extend to the outside of class. Teachers and students can have effective communication and exchanges. Taking University of Science and Technology Liaoning as an example, since the English education online platform was constructed in 2010, more and more teachers have set up courses on the platform, uploaded data, made questionnaire survey, corrected the course assignments, and had online testing. On this platform, with teachers' introduction, students can deepen the understanding about teachers and they become QQ and Micro message friends; through teaching syllabus, students can have access to the teaching goal, the teaching process and the teaching steps; through the teaching materials, students can browse or download the classroom teaching contents and supplementary materials; through course forum, students can discuss and open their views; through the course survey, students can express their opinions and suggestions about teaching to promote the teachers to adjust their teaching. These are effective extensions of the classroom teaching, strengthening the interaction between teachers and students, enhancing students' interest in English learning, and promoting teachers' teaching enthusiasm.

2.4 English network course to cultivate students' autonomous learning and innovation

The students are the subject of learning, and the important goal of multimedia teaching is to stimulate students' autonomous learning. The network course learning is beyond the time and place of traditional learning, enriching the language learning methods and providing more opportunities for students to learn. Through this platform, students can exchange the learning method of network course, becoming independent learners of English learning, finding suitable methods of their own, and raising their awareness of autonomous learning. For our University of Science and Technology Liaoning, Lange Autonomous Learning Platform is introduced and the well-equipped language labs produce excellent conditions for students' individual learning and autonomous learning. According to different levels of their own, students can choose the corresponding stage of learning, learning contents and learning methods. Lange Platform focuses on the students understanding of English sentences and texts, emphasizing the students' speaking and listening, effectively improving students' reading and writing skills, maximizing students' autonomy and creativity.

3 THE ESTABLISHMENT OF THE UNIVERSITY ENGLISH MULTIMEDIA TEACHING MODE

3.1 Improving the ability and level of teachers' applying information technology

The network curriculum resource capacity is unmatched by traditional methods. Abundant teaching materials provide the convenience for classroom teaching. Therefore, the construction and management of curriculum resources are particularly important. For English teachers, in addition to completing listening and speaking tasks, producing teaching video materials according to the teaching goal of each unit, they select video materials, edit, process and design questions. The process of the video material is the most technical, requiring special video editing software. The construction of network curriculum enhances teachers' consciousness of learning modern educational technology, improving their applying level and ability of information technology.

3.2 Correct understanding of the auxiliary role of multimedia and the leading role of teachers

Contrasted with traditional teaching, multimedia teaching has incomparable advantages, but the traditional classroom teaching also has its own advantages. These two have mutually complementary relation and mutual promotion. University English teachers should combine the essence of multimedia and traditional teaching together. We should make full use of modern educational technology, develop the courseware and network English resource, and renew teaching contents. On the other hand, we should inherit preparation step in traditional teaching, taking into full account and adopting the merits of traditional classroom teaching. In the university English comprehensive course, teachers can adopt the mode of multimedia aided teaching and traditional classroom instruction, playing the main role in the classroom teaching to overcome their own weaknesses and effectively improve the teaching quality.

3.3 Establishing the "student-centered" teaching mode and strengthening students' tutoring after school

English is a practical course, with its own learning features, so the solution to the contradiction between the inside and outside of the class is to "delegate to fish, as delegated by the fishing". In the network course, in addition to effective selection, construction and management of curriculum resources, teachers must also keep on learning the teaching theories, making better use of education technology platform. In the university English listening and speaking class, with the help of the advantages of the multimedia means, teachers can adopt the mixing teaching mode of teachers' leading role inside class, and students' autonomous learning outside class. In the limited classroom time not all students can understand audio-visual materials, so teachers can upload information into the network course platform and students can log in the platform, reviewing learning contents to enhance students' ability of autonomous learning and improve their English learning efficiency.

In the network course, teachers should make full use of e-mail, QQ and micro message to communicate with students, encouraging students to participate in teaching activities. Teachers can also, through the platform, listen to the students' opinions on teaching to improve teaching.

4 CONCLUSIONS

In conclusion, the application of multimedia in the university English teaching mode opens up a new way in university English teaching, bringing the vitality and the vigor to the university English teaching reform, and at the same time bringing great challenges. University English teachers should adjust their roles, improve their level of using information technology, make full use of advantages of multimedia in university English teaching, try to combine the advantages of teaching mode of the multimedia technology and the traditional classroom instruction so as to achieve complementary advantage of each other. With the further research on the development of network communication technology and education, network teaching will become a mainstream of teaching, promote the teaching reform and improve the teaching efficiency.

REFERENCES

Gan, Lingling. 2010. A new study on multimedia technology and university English teaching mode.
He, Jianbo. 2009. Internet multimedia technology mode and university English teaching reform.
Yin, Yanlin. 2011. Application of multimedia teaching mode and the reform of university English teaching.
Yu, Dan. 2010. Study in multimedia teaching mode of university English classroom teaching.
Zhou, Mingming. 2011. Application of multimedia technology in university English teaching.

Computer, Intelligent Computing and Education Technology – Liu, Sung & Yao (Eds)
© 2014 Taylor & Francis Group, London, ISBN 978-1-138-02469-4

The level of education technology competence for teacher in vocational college

C.X. Wang & Q.L. Zhan
School of Information Technology Engineering, Tianjin University of Technology and Education, Tianjin, China

ABSTRACT: The educational technology had become one of the capabilities for teachers in vocational college under the information environment of vocational education. In order to understand the ability of educational technology for teachers in vocational college, we divided the level of education technology competence from IT knowledge Theoretical knowledge of educational technology Instructional design Design and development of software in vocational education and Research of vocational education.

Keywords: education technology; vocational college; instructional design

1   INTRODUCTION

Quality of vocational education was the lifeline of vocational education, but educational technology was an important means to enhance its quality and effective way to develop skills composite talents.[1] Therefore, the ability of educational technology had become one of the capability for teachers in vocational college in the information environment, and it also promoted the professional development of teachers in vocational college.

In 2004, China's Ministry of Education formally promulgated the "Educational Technology Competency Standards for Teachers in Primary and secondary schools", which proposed standards of the educational technology ability for teacher in primary and secondary, and explained the content from the awareness and attitudes, knowledge and skills, application and innovation and social responsibility. In 2010, Educational Technology Collaboration Board of universities had also developed "Educational Technology Guide for teachers in universities". After these two standards promulgated, some people began to in-depth study educational technology capabilities for teachers in primary and secondary school and universities. But few people studied education technical capacity for teachers in vocational college.

2   DIVIDING THE LEVEL OF EDUCATIONAL TECHNOLOGY CAPABILITY

There were many common features in educational technology competency for teachers in university and vocational college, but there were some differences in some detail and indicators, due to the special regularity of vocational education. Standard of educational technology ability for teachers in Vocational College was more difficult to construct, because professional features with teachers in vocational college and less research for capacity of teachers professional development in vocational college. Although there were some training syllabus and requirements for IT capabilities for teachers in vocational college, but there were many gaps compared with the competency standards of educational technology. It was necessary to divide the competence level of education technology for the study about educational technology competency for teachers in vocational college. Reference to the relevant literature, we provided the competence level of education technology for teachers in vocational college. As is showed in Chart 1.

3   THE SPECIFIC CONTENT EDUCATIONAL TECHNOLOGY CAPABILITY LEVEL FOR TEACHER IN VOCATIONAL COLLEGE

According to Figure 1, through a lot of research, we developed the specific content and objectives for each level of the ability of educational technology for teachers in vocational technology.

3.1   IT knowledge

IT knowledge belonged to the ability to manipulate levels, including the operation common software and media devices.

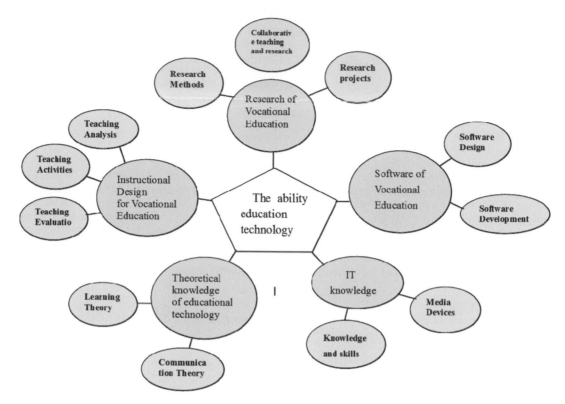

Chart 1.   The level of educational technology capability.

IT knowledge

Basics knowledge	1. Master the basic knowledge of computer hardware and software 2. Learn the basics of knowledge about computer networks and operating principle 3. Learn the basics of knowledge about text, sound, pictures, video and other multimedia
Operating skills	1. Proficiency in multimedia computer, install and use common software 2. Proficiency in multimedia teaching system and related equipment 3. According to the actual needs of teaching, install the appropriate hardware and software configuration 4. Proficiency in word processing software and related software tools of the discipline 5. Familiar with the basic skills of computer networks 6. Using technology to manage teaching 7. Master teaching information management system

3.2 *Theoretical knowledge of educational technology*

The definition of educational technology emphasized on modern educational ideas and theories used in education, theoretical knowledge of educational technology was the important theoretical attainment for teacher in vocational college.

Basics of educational technology

Basic theory	1. Understanding the definition of educational technology, the relationship of education technology and vocational education information 2. Understand the main theoretical basis of educational technology 3. Understanding of the main research methods educational technology 4. Understanding the basic theory of teaching and learning

3.3 *Instructional design*

The purpose of instructional design was to optimize the teaching process, and the ability of instructional design was the core of educational technology and innovation [2].

Instructional design

Analysis and design	1. Proficiency in analysis students, teaching content and teaching objectives 2. Proficiency in designing teaching activities 3. Proficiency in choosing teaching media and teaching strategies

3.4 Design and development of software in vocational education

Information teaching relayed on resources and software, so teachers should have access to the software, design, development and management capabilities.

Design and development of software in vocational education

Design and development	1. Understand the basic process of software development 2. Designing educational software, according to the needs 3. Developing software by tools of software development

3.5 Research of vocational education

Teachers used technology to carry out teaching and research.

Research of vocational education

Research of vocational education	1. Writing papers and teaching reflection by using information technology tools 2. Using new technology in the classroom 3. Using IT to exchange and communicate with students, peers and experts

4 CONCLUSION

The division of levels the ability of educational technology would provide dimensions and behavioral indicators about ability of educational technology for teacher in vocational college, in order to promote teaching ability.

ACKNOWLEDGEMENT

This paper is part of the fruit of two programs. They are "Competency Standards of Educational Technology for Teacher in Vocational College" (the Twelfth Five-year Plan Program of Tianjin Educational Science and Research) (project number: VEXII 2001). And "Study of Internet-discussion-type learning and teaching based on the mind map" (the Twelfth Five-year Plan Program of Tianjin Educational Science and Research) (project number: VE4048). In the course of the study, some literature was referred, thank the authors.

REFERENCES

[1] Yang Guiling. Modern educational technology applied in the field of vocational education [D]. Dissertation of Tianjin University, 2005.
[2] Yuan Dongbing. Status investigation and training Strategy in local university about educational technology's ability [J]. Journal of Shangrao Normal College, 2010, (6).
[3] Hao Dan. Concerned Educational Technology Capacity Building for teachers [J]. China Distance Education, 2006, (6).

Computer, Intelligent Computing and Education Technology – Liu, Sung & Yao (Eds)
© 2014 Taylor & Francis Group, London, ISBN 978-1-138-02469-4

The mathematical model of plant diseases and insect pests and the relationship between the crop growth

Qiang Zhang
WeiFang University of Science and Technology, Shouguang, Shandong, China

ABSTRACT: According to the knowledge model of population will grow crops and pest model of exponential function, similar to the relationship between population on topic given data fitting, under natural conditions, to establish the mathematical model of plant diseases and insect pests and mutual influence between crop growth. Before the data fitting, assuming a linear relationship with pest density and yield of rice, when the pest density tends to infinity, rice yield for negative, so the assumption is not set up. From the population model, the pest density and the relationship between the yield of rice could as index function, when after the fitting, the data is very close, and more practical.

Keywords: green ecological; grow crops; insecticide ozone

In natural state, the farmland has different pests, therefore used in a variety of pesticides to kill insect, insecticidal, however, found that there were a question of cost and efficiency, so, must find a relationship between, and according to the different levels of insect pests of rice paddies, to find a most economic and effective solution. This study is to establish a model, to solve the different levels of pesticides, using time and frequency, so that the cost and the required output to achieve. First of all, establish plant diseases and insect pests and the relationships between the growth of crops. In this problem, it will think of a similar population model, therefore, the use of learned similar population model is established in the topic of the growth of plant diseases and insect pests of crops and model, and then, according to the data of said to respectively to solve out the locust and rice have longitudinal leaf moth on combination of crop growth.

1 THE MODEL ASSUMES THAT

1. In the experiments, in addition to the fertilizer rate, other factors such as environmental conditions, plant density, soil fertility, etc., all at the same level.
2. In the actual problem, production by the crop variety, plant density, climatic conditions, and insect pest resistance to pesticides, such as the role of various factors, and ignore the influence of above factors, only consider the kinds of pesticides and the amount of how much the impact on the growth of crops.
3. Ignore the growth of plants in different stages of the characteristics of various demand for pesticides.
4. Pesticide is not out of date, and effective.
5. Ignore the diseases and pests in different stages of the reproductive cycle and the growth situation, thought it is a constant growth rate.

2 DEFINE THE SYMBOLS

x—pests y per unit area; y—such production rate of crop growth.

3 THE MODEL

Pest and crop growth models, roughly the similar model, therefore, can be used to solve the model some knowledge of the population, for pests and grow crops, the relationship between its still analogy to exponential function.

The density of the Chinese rice locust, due to the Chinese rice locust took rice leaf, cause incision, and can bite the spikes, affect production, so the major effect is it murder rates, ultimately will yield, so the density of the pest, directly reflect the size of the production rate, so the density of pests have inevitable relationship with production rate.

With density and production rate of graphics to be seen:
x = [0 3 10 20 30 40];
y = [0 2.4 12.9 16.3 20.1 26.8];

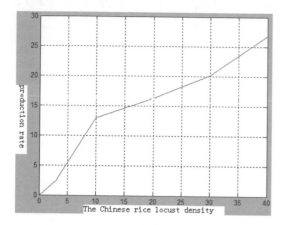

Figure 1. Chinese rice and production rate of locust density diagram.

```
plot(x,y)
grid on
x-label('the Chinese rice locust density');
y-label('production rate');
title('Chinese rice and production rate of locust
density diagram')
```

After many after using different methods fitting, found that it is roughly similar to the exponential function, it verified the previous assumptions.

4 THE MODEL

Fitting according to the following procedure, the production rate of y heart according to the natural production of minus production has the effects of pests. Consider an acre field

```
x = 2000/3*[3 10 20 30 40]';
b = ones(5,1);
y = [780.8 696.8 669.6 639.2 585.6 ]';
z = log(y)–b*log(780.8);
r = x/z
```

Available: $r = -1.0828e{-}005$
So: $y = x_0 e^{rx}$ $(x_0 = 780.8)$
So: $y = 780.8 \times e^{-1.0828 \times 10^{-5} x}$
The Chinese rice locust on rice yield function is:
$y = 780.8 e^{-1.0828 \times 10^{-5} x}$

Due to vertical rice leaf moth harm characteristics in vertical roll rice leaf adult spathe larvae compose silk, larvae of feeding in mesophyll minninth, leaving skin, form a white streak, to rice grain is reduced, immature grain increase, the yield and the effect of rice leaf curl moth longitudinal principle is to reduce to a rice grain, immature grain increased, the yield, so the density of rice leaf curl moth longitudinal, directly affect the rate of leaf, and the rate of shell, which affects the yield loss rate.

Table 1. The data of the Chinese rice locust and rice.

Density (head/m²)	Murder rate (%)	Seed setting rate (%)	Kernels (g)	Production rate (%)
0	–	94.4	21.37	–
3	0.273	93.2	20.60	2.4
10	2.260	92.1	20.60	12.9
20	2.550	91.5	20.50	16.3
30	2.920	89.9	20.60	20.1
40	3.950	87.9	20.13	26.8

Table 2.

Density (head/m²)	Yield loss rate (%)	Leaf rate (%)	Shell rate (%)
3.75	0.73	0.76	14.22
7.50	1.11	1.11	14.43
11.25	2.2	2.22	15.34
15.00	3.37	3.54	15.95
18.75	5.05	4.72	16.87
30.00	6.78	6.73	17.10
37.50	7.16	7.63	17.21
56.25	9.39	14.82	20.59
75.00	14.11	14.93	23.19
112.50	20.09	20.40	25.16

Through the above data shows that the density of pests and there is a link between production, through the image of the two groups of data

```
x = 2000/3*[3.75 7.50 11.25 15.0 18.75 30 37.50
56.25 75 112.5];
y = [794.16 791.12 782.4 770.96 759.6 745.76 742.72
724.88 687.12 639.28 ];
plot(x,y)
grid on
x-label(rice leaf curl moth longitudinal density);
y-label( production rate);
title(vertical rice leaf moth pests and its produc-
tion rate diagram)
```

Can infer its are roughly in line with the exponential function, therefore, with the exponential function fitting

```
x = 2000/3*[3.75 7.50 11.25 15.0 18.75 30 37.50
56.25 75 112.5]';
b = ones(10,1);
y = [794.16 791.12 782.4 770.96 759.6 745.76 742.72
724.88 687.12 639.28 ]';
z = log(y)–b*log(794.16);
r = x/z
```

The fitting available $r = -2.8301e{-}006$
So, the output of rice with rice and longitudinal relationship between leaf curl moth

$$y = 794.16 \times e^{-2.8301 \times 10^{-6} x}$$

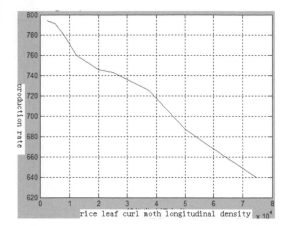

Figure 2. Vertical rice leaf moth pests and its production rate diagram.

5 EVALUATION AND IMPROVEMENT OF THE MODEL

Model is the biggest advantage is that the original data of timeliness, use a variety of methods, to make it more perfect, has the very high fitting precision and suitability. On this basis, the model can get further discussion on a series of reliable and useful information, and the results are in good agreement with the objective facts, thus further suggests that the model is reasonable.

During the process of agricultural production, rice pesticides and the use of ozone greenhouse pest control is more and more widely, and experts and scholars are keen to explore the question is: the strategy is feasible? In fact, the core of the problem can be converted into: "the pros and cons of the use of pesticides size comparison". Obviously, the use of pesticides has both advantages and disadvantages, is not do more harm than good or more harm than good, this determines the feasibility of the use of pesticides or not. Although, the use of pesticides may be contaminated land and air, may also pose a threat to people's health, but can be a reasonable solution to minimize the disadvantages of the use of pesticides.

Scientific data show that without the use of pesticides, the Chinese rice locust and vertical rice leaf curl moth destruction of rice is quite strong, causing serious rice production, also, greenhouses vegetables before without application of ozone in pest control, vegetables not only harvest is poor, and not beautiful appearance.

In the process of agricultural production, the use of the strategy is to make the crop yields increased significantly, appearance beautiful, homogenization of delicious, welcomed by the enthusiasm of the public, therefore, reasonable use of pesticides is feasible. Aiming at the disadvantages of pesticides, below put forward reasonable solution.

5.1 Pesticides in crop residues will endanger people's health

Pesticide sharp strength, although the residue in rice, but its residue will decrease with the increase of time, using almost a month later, the residues of pesticides has become almost zero, so as long as the pesticide use frequency statistics, a good grasp of pesticide fading cycles, in pesticides on crops just harvest after several cycles, this can maximum reduce pesticide threat to people.

5.2 The concentration of pesticides in the damage crops

The biological theory shows that any reagents on the effect of crop restricted by its concentration. When the concentration of pesticides within a certain value, can the insecticidal effect but also can't restrain the growth of the crops, and when the concentration is greater than the value of the pesticide, though can be insecticidal, but also can inhibit the growth of crops. So, can find out an appropriate concentration range for the use of pesticides.

REFERENCES

[1] Jing, but march. Mathematical modeling and mathematical experiment (3rd edition). Higher education press, 2008.1. China.
[2] RanQiKang, zhang zhen yu, Zhang Lizhu. Commonly used mathematical software tutorial, posts and telecommunications press, 2008.10. China.
[3] Zhang Defeng. Numerical analysis and application. National defense industry press. 2007.1, China.
[4] Zheng Handing, diao in narration, mathematical programming [M], shandong education press, 1997.12. China.
[5] Ma Zhengfei. Mathematical calculation method and engineering application of the software. Chemical industry press, 2002.12. China.
[6] Dai Shugui, environmental chemistry (second edition). Higher education press, 2006.10. China.

Computer, Intelligent Computing and Education Technology – Liu, Sung & Yao (Eds)
© 2014 Taylor & Francis Group, London, ISBN 978-1-138-02469-4

The research of MIS construction mode for coal enterprise based on people collaboration

Yi-Fang Fang
Institute of Management, China University of Mining and Technology (Beijing), Beijing, China

ABSTRACT: Focusing on the problems of lack of efficient implementation effects in Information Management Systems (MIS) for core enterprises, the article proposed and elaborated the contents of a new construction model based on people collaboration theory. It then set the OA system construction practice in state-owned core enterprises as an example, and further explained the construction progress and applied advantages of the people collaboration model. It proved that the due construction model has effective application results for MIS developments in core industry.

Keywords: MIS; synergistic effects; people collaboration; information construction

1 INTRODUCTION

With the development of computer science and information technology, the recognition of safe-production and scientific management in mining is constantly rising as the combination files and generated data presents explosive growth. All these have lead to an inevitable tendency of Information Management System (MIS) application in core industry, which could satisfy the efficiency, timeliness and accuracy needs of data processing. However, the problem of lack of efficient implementation effects during the MIS construction has become a hot issue in most coal enterprises. The roots of the phenomenon lie in the shortage of completed collaboration mechanism during the executing process of MIS so that the synergistic effects of MIS don't exhibit its role.

According to the improvement needs above, this work has proposed a new construction model in coal information based on collaboration theory. Through the example of OA system in an coal enterprise, a MIS system which most commonly encountered resistance during implementing process, it demonstrates the model could effectively improve operating efficiency and give full play to synergistic effects of MIS.

2 ANALYSIS OF MIS CONSTRUCTION SITUATION

2.1 *Current construction problems in China's coal enterprises*

For the moment, it's an obvious and inevitable trend for China's coal enterprises to spend enormous funds on the informatization constructions and MIS systems. However, even with the sufficient money and advanced equipment in coal company, the construction effects of various kinds of MIS systems are not satisfying. According to writer's previous scientific research related to informatization work in coal industry, the existed problems in the information constructions could be summarized as below:

i. Most of China's coal companies have brought in the MIS systems as finished goods, and usually lack in preliminary investigation before the constructions get started. As a result, the functions of MIS system cannot meet the expected requirements.

ii. The MIS implementers and clients are lacking of delicate communication about the systems' function details during the construction process, which would easily lead to the inappropriateness of the due systems and misunderstanding of users' demands. And it will cause lots of waste in time and human resources to revise the functions after systems are completed.

iii. Since the mining production activities are often elastic, flexible and diversified formed, it's very difficult to draw up a plan for the MIS projects constructions, and even more difficult to keep up with the plan strictly during the implementation process. So the problems of projecting delays and other obstacles occur when emergency happens, such as equipment overhaul and safety-risks rectifications. As a result, to set up a considerate professional feedback mechanism and official regulation to solve unexpected situations during the implementation process is the key factor to deal with these on-site problems, which is also the problem this article attempts to solve.

iv. Due to the special characteristics of management systems in state-owned coal enterprises, the needs of access control and assignment of authority and responsibility in the MIS systems are flexible. While tradition developing model are based on the workflow management system, the MIS system in coal enterprises need to focus on personnel authority management. The people collaboration construction model would provide a feasible solution to it.

According to the analyses above, information construction in coal companies couldn't achieve intend effects if only relying on the fund investment and MIS systems optimization. In order to save the construction resources and increase efficiency and operation effects of coal MIS systems, this article explores to propose a new developing mode, the people collaboration model, to deal with the issues discussed above to help.

2.2 *Connation of people collaboration*

Collaboration is a management theory rising in the late 1990's, which refers to the process and capability of coordination at least two kinds of different resources or individuals to finish tasks in collaboration. The production and operation management in coal mining MISs, as well as its design in function modules, work requests, business flow and data processing are all around the needs of people/users. Therefore, the establishment of people collaboration mechanism in core companies is the key factor of improving MIS implementation effects.

Collaborative MIS system is a distributed software system based on the advanced Internet technology, through effective resources and information sharing and distribution. It could achieve the purposes of improving work efficiency, reducing labor intensity and duplication of work. It emphasizes on interpersonal and collaborative work among various departments to get effective information exchange and communication from each other.

Coal MIS systems based on people collaboration pays full attention to the role of "people" in the construction process. On the premise that the existing MIS system construction focuses on the transaction processing, the MIS developing model of people collaboration has reinforced personnel operating skills and initiatives during project construction, and sets up personnel centered drive mode of implementation.

3 ANALYSIS OF COAL MIS CONSTRUCTION MODEL BASED ON PEOPLE COLLABORATION

3.1 *Definition of people collaboration construction mode*

There are three types of "people" involving in the process of MIS system construction: the developer (including network designer, database administrator, system designer, programmer, etc.), the implementer and the users, the function of three parties in the system construction process differs from each other. The key to success of MIS construction is to distinguish the roles of three "people", and strictly clarify their duties in the process of system construction.

The people collaboration mode is premised on the demands of system users, which provides insurance for personnel training, communication and coordination work of system designers and implementers. Through the mutual communication and cooperation between developers, implementers and users, the realization of construction mode established in this article aids coal MIS systems to become more suitable for their own developing and clients' needs, and maximizes the cost for the MIS construction.

3.2 *Analysis of people collaboration construction mode*

The implementation effects of MIS system are closely connected with how well the "people" play during the projecting process. As a result, to strengthen the cooperation between working staff, the first and most important thing is to clarify responsibilities of all personnel involved in the process of system construction, as shown in Figure 1.

As is shown in Figure 1, the MIS construction mode based on people collaboration consists of processes as: demand research and system design, operating preparation, launching and mobilization, trial run and training, system operation and debugging, maintenance and optimization.

In each stage of the whole projecting process, the system construction is closely connected with three partners involved. With the help of implementers as the communication intermediary and bridges between developers and users, the three partners are able to complete the construction of coal MIS system through mutual communication, coordination and cooperation, as shown in Figure 2.

The responsibilities of three partners involving in each phase include:

i. The developers: The work of developers mainly concentrates on the developing stage, their

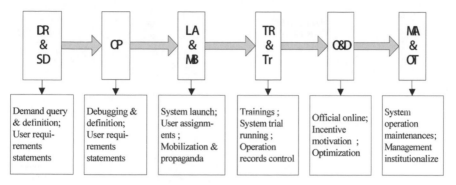

Figure 1. Personnel responsibility in the process of project implementation.

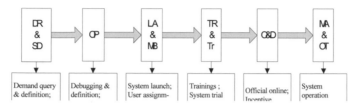

Figure 2. Relationship diagram of people cooperation in MIS implementation.

main responsibility consists of construction planning, system functions analysis (including feasibility analysis, business analysis, data flow analysis, data dictionary, system logic model, etc.), system design (software and hardware configuration, system function design, network design and structure design, system function module and processing design, database design, code design, etc.), system development, system credibility test. The work of developers in the system construction is mostly technical, which determines the quality system construction, and the developer level, as it were, directly affect the quality of the developed system which further affects system implementation effect of coal MIS system.

ii. The implementers: The implementers' main responsibility is to design and write functional specifications, business process diagrams, user manuals and other documents. In the whole process of system construction, they play an important role for system development, operation preparation, systems commissioning and system maintenance. So to speak, the implementers is the medium that connects the developers and users, and the bridge of organizing developers and users in the process of the implementation.

iii. The user: As the ultimate users of MIS systems, the users' main responsibility is to actively participate in the system construction process, and puts forward specific functional requirements and information requirements, review the development and design results and rectify the deviation in the system. It's obvious that the user is the final acceptance of system while the ultimate goal is to achieve customer satisfaction.

4 ANALYSIS OF COAL MIS CONSTRUCTION WORKFLOW OF PEOPLE COLLABORATION

4.1 MIS construction process

The MIS construction mode based on people collaboration has been adopted the informatization developments in Datong coal mine groups. Having clarified the responsibilities of three parties of the staff in the process of MIS system construction, the critical task is to realize the effects of "people" as the core of system construction and give full attention to initiative advantage of "people". By the mutual cooperation and coordination of developers, implementers and users, this could achieve the demands of easy use, fast operation and system flexibility. The process of people collaboration construction mode for coal enterprises is shown as Figure 3.

The figure shows that in the process of the whole system construction, the project schedule control,

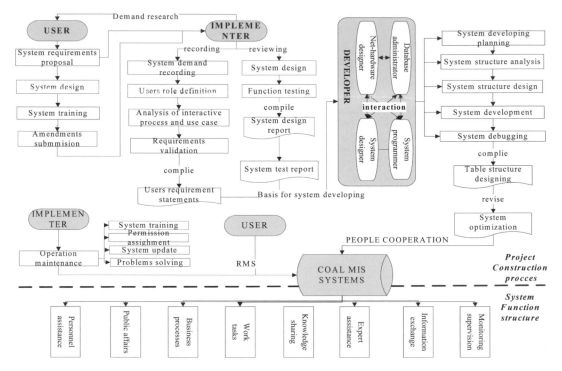

Figure 3. MIS construction process based on people cooperation.

system structure design and function optimization is inseparable from the three partners of common synergy householders. The MIS system mode based on people collaboration affects the developing progress throughout the whole construction process.

4.2 Advantages analysis of people collaboration mode

Comparing with the traditional MIS construction pattern of importing the MIS systems and directly applying them to management practices in coal enterprises, the people collaboration construction mode has kept focus on the role of "people". By ways of controlling the personnel responsibilities, strengthening the collaboration between different parties and reducing error information across working-levels, the collaborative mode helps improve the construction achievements. The main advantages of the mode include the following contents:

i. In the collaborative MIS developing mode, the implementers at the scene could identify user requirements and environment conditions more accurately, which provides the precise building direction and basis for developers and reduces the resources loss caused by developing faults.

What's more, implementers on site provides real-time system trainings that guarantees the users to master operating skills, improves their information knowledge level and the ability to solve the problem by the MIS systems.

ii. The developers in the construction mode ensures the efficient communication between systems implementers and clients which could acquire accurate users' functional demands in order to get practicality and applicability after the system completion.

iii. The close cooperation and sufficient communication among the implementers, the developers and users could effectively reduce resources spent in the MIS system, and the user oriented MIS building pattern offers the customization system which could best fits the practical management requirements for coal companies.

4.3 Implementation effects of people collaboration mode

The MIS construction mode based on people collaboration has obtained good adequate developing effects displayed in the following two aspects:

i. In the view of system application effects, the collaborative MIS systems has fundamentally changed the its information processing mode, and improved the overall information level of coal mining management. The realization of system significantly reduces the transaction costs of business administration, and greatly improves the work efficiency and faculty's operation skills. The mutual communication and coordination between three partners could promote, to a great extent, the system construction process as well as to improve the quality of the MIS application effects. In a word, the people collaboration construction mode develops a system of more fitness and flexibility to real business requirements in coal company.

ii. From the aspects of management effects produced by MIS system, the collaborative construction pattern has brought a new conception of management and control mode within MIS. In order to change the traditional coal administration ways, while coal enterprises used to invest large amounts of equipment, funds to promote the process of MIS construction, the new construction model emphasizes the role of people coordination and communication to guarantee the realization of system management goal, it also subjectively reduces the changing impacts to clients of the system, and helps to accept working conveniences brought by information construction. The construction mode has also built an advanced information construction mode which brings positive influence to the whole coal industry.

5 CONCLUSIONS

In conclusion, the construction process and advantages analysis of MIS projects in coal enterprises have shown that the two core effects brought by people collaboration construction consists of improving management efficiency and reducing the company cost. In addition, the collaborative construction mode has proposed a new way to guide the coal enterprise in the process of information construction. By the means of giving full play to the synergistic effect of information project among the user, implementers and developers, the construction mode successfully improves MIS construction project success rate and system promotion effect.

REFERENCES

Chang Jing ming & Tan Zhang lu. 2013. Analyses of problems feedback and treatment mechanism in process of informatization project implementation. *Journal of Industrial Mining Automation,* 4:95–98.

Feng Dong qin. 2012. Introduction to MIS system selection and implementation. *China Metal Bulletin,* 20:129–133.

Tan Hui. 2007. ERP implementation process control based on project management. *Market Modernization,* 10: 190–192.

Yang Lu. 2012. *The product development and application of management information systems in group corporation,* Jinan: Shan Dong University Press.

Zhang Rui xin. 2012. *Introduction to office automation.* Beijing: Tsinghua University Press.

Zhao Yang & Lv Ke. 2013. Construction and Implementation of Information Resources Allocation System for Collaborative Innovation. *Journal of Information Science,* 9:15–21.

Computer, Intelligent Computing and Education Technology – Liu, Sung & Yao (Eds)
© 2014 Taylor & Francis Group, London, ISBN 978-1-138-02469-4

The analysis of forced oscillation and weak damping oscillation

Meng-Jiao Lv

*School of Electrical and Electronic Engineering, North China Electric Power University (NCEPU),
Baoding, China*

ABSTRACT: The main types of oscillations are the forced oscillation and the weak damping oscillation. The forced oscillation and the weak damping oscillation have different mechanisms and need to adopt different means to control them. Thus, when low-frequency oscillation occurs, the system should quickly and accurately distinguish the type of oscillator. In this paper, starting from the mechanism of forced oscillation and weak damping oscillation, make a comprehensive comparative analysis of these two mechanisms, revealing the nature of the low-frequency oscillations and the root causes of induced oscillations, I do a detailed comparison and distinction in the aspects of waveform, communication, energy and other aspects. And there has a more intuitive verification though the waveform of the Southern network. The results of the study have definite instructive meaning for analysis, monitor and control of low frequency oscillation.

Keywords: power system; the weak damping oscillation; the forced oscillation

1 INTRODUCTION

With the development of power system, the capacity of the power grid is increasing as the voltage grade. Power transmission from the west to east will exceed 100,000 MW [1]. Interconnection of the power grid is the trend of all over the world. It brings great advantages to the power system and also lots of new problems, low frequency oscillation is one of them [2]–[5]. While in the low frequency oscillation, the two most common are the weak damping oscillation and the forced oscillation.

As the generator run in the parallel mode, its rotors may have relative swing under disturbance. if the system damping is insufficient to overcome this disturbance, persistent oscillations will occur. At this point on the power line, the voltage, the current, the power will occur amplified oscillation, this oscillation in the tie-line power interconnection system was especially evident. Because of its oscillation frequency is very low, generally 0.2 ~ 2.5 Hz, so called low-frequency oscillation (also known as power oscillation, electromechanical oscillations).

People have studied the weak damping oscillation, the forced oscillations, bifurcation theory, chaos theory, strong resonance mechanism [6]. Among them, the most mature theory is the weak damping oscillation; the forced oscillations [7–11] successfully explained the actual system's low-frequency oscillations that the weak damping oscillation can not explain [7]. Some other mechanisms have not yet been solved in the theory, some

still remain in the theoretical discussion stage, It is difficult to apply in the project. Using the weak damping oscillation and forced oscillations to explain the power system's low frequency oscillation has a very important significance in engineering applications and the following in-depth study.

2 THE WEAK DAMPING OSCILLATION AND THE FORCED OSCILLATION'S THEORY BASIS

2.1 *The theory of weak damping oscillation*

In the 1960s, F.P. DeMello and C. Concordia and other scholars first proposed the weak damping oscillation mechanism that the modern excitation system's negative damping torque reduces the damping level, due to the excitation system's inertia, with the increase of excitation regulator's zoom multiples, the real value of the rotor mechanical oscillation will be gradually increase from negative characteristic. When the magnification is too large, the real value will increase from negative to positive, thus resulting in an increase of oscillation. After several decades of development, now the theory has been improved and researched more in-depth, researchers have widely accepted.

This is the most important mechanism for the interpretation of low-frequency oscillation problems, the after works mostly are commenced around the mechanism. After years of practice test, the mechanism is relatively mature, recognizing as the authoritative low-frequency oscillation mechanism.

2.2 The theory of forced oscillation

Forced power oscillation theory is deduced by applying perturbation to the classical second-order equations of generator motion. Take the single machine infinite system as an example to illustrate the basic principles of the forced oscillations and power system small disturbance dynamic equation and its solution: Because the model is based on the classic single infinite system as an example for the analysis of the forced oscillation theory. So the linearized equation of motion generators is:

$$\frac{T_J}{\omega_0}\frac{d^2\Delta\delta}{dt^2} + K_D\frac{d\Delta\delta}{dt} + K_S\Delta\delta = F_0\sin\omega t \tag{1}$$

where in; $F_0\sin\omega t$ is a constant periodic small perturbation, F_0 is the amplitude of the disturbance, ω is the frequency of the disturbance; δ is the generator power angle; $\omega = 2\pi f_0$, f_0 is the system reference frequency; T_J is inertia time constant of the generator; K_D is a generator damping; K_S is synchronize torque coefficient of the generator.

Deform the basic mathematical formula can be obtained:

$$\ddot{x} + 2\zeta\omega_0\dot{x} + \omega_n^2 x = h\sin\omega t \tag{2}$$

This is a second order non-homogeneous constant coefficient linear differential equation, its solution divide into the general solution and particular solution:

The general solution is:

$$x_1(t) = e^{-\zeta\omega_n t}[B_1\cos\omega_d t + B_2\sin\omega_d t] \tag{3}$$

where: $\omega_d = \omega_n\sqrt{1-\zeta^2}$

The particular solution is:

$$x_2(t) = B\sin(\omega t - \varphi) \tag{4}$$

So the solution of formula (1) is the sum of two parts: $x = x_1 + x_2$

The first term is transient response. The third term represents the pure forced oscillations caused by the disturbance, that the steady-state response. To steady-state response, when the disturbance frequency is close to or equal to the natural frequency of the system, it will cause significant power oscillations. The power oscillations amplitude not only relate to the perturbation oscillation frequency, but also with the system damping, the amplitude of the disturbance and other factors.

Through the contrast of the two oscillation's mechanisms, it can be seen that they both appear after disturbance, but they are very different in essence after oscillation, the former is due to the system disturbance torque is weakened, becoming weak or negative damping, the later is due to the system disturbance signal's frequency is at or near the natural oscillation frequency, as long as the disturbance source is not removed, there has been oscillation.

3 THE DISTINCTION BETWEEN FORCED OSCILLATION AND WEAK DAMPED OSCILLATION

Forced oscillation and weak damped oscillation mainly distinguish from the following aspects: oscillation waveform characteristics, the oscillation transmission mode, the oscillation energy variation. From these three aspects can clearly identify the type of oscillation.

3.1 Oscillation waveform characteristics

Based on the above characteristics of forced oscillation summary, in the waveform characteristics, in the start-up stage the speed increase very quickly, after a few cycles it will achieve maximum value. After reaching steady state, active power basically showing changeless amplitude oscillation, maintaining zero attenuation. And mechanical power and electromagnetic power occur oscillations simultaneously, and the oscillation frequency and amplitude variation between the two are the same. The biggest difference between weak damping oscillation and forced oscillation is due to the disturbance, the torque will decreases, after the waveform reach a peak it will show low amplitude attenuation, and can not remain constant amplitude oscillation.

And Forced oscillation caused by the periodic disturbance, its frequency and the natural frequency are the same or similar, so the oscillation modes of the whole network units are relatively simple, at steady state was equal amplitude oscillation, damping ratio is 0.

3.2 Oscillation transmission mode

In the mode of oscillations transmission, forced oscillation has a clear source of the disturbance, the disturbance oscillation wave from the starting point, spread to the whole network along the lines, in the start-up process each state of the whole network is not instantaneous, this will take some time. There is some inertia in power system, so for a disturbance on a node, the remote unit does not response immediately reach a steady state value, there will be a transient process.

In summary, the differences between the forced oscillation and weak damped oscillation in the dissemination of formal is: forced oscillations exist propagation process in start-up phase, measuring the different nodes in the same time axis, there is a phase of leading or hysteresis; while weakly damped oscillation does not exist propagation process.

3.3 *Oscillation energy variation*

The multi-machine power system forced oscillations has a clear disturbances source. When power oscillation forced to steady resonance state, exogenous disturbances acting is equal with system damping dissipation energy, the kinetic and potential energy converse mutually, the total energy is conservation, the exogenous disturbance energy can be injected into the system which is bound only by the unit where the disturbance source exist, and the system damping dissipated energy is consumed by all the units and all the damping in the network, that is, where the unit's energy where the disturbance source exist is definitely different to the other units' energy. Due to the exogenous disturbances acting converse into potential energy, it spread through the network, while the kinetic energy of each unit is also reflected in the cyclical changes, the potential energy changes can be seen as two parts: one part is periodic oscillation energy accompanied with oscillation, another part is exogenous disturbances energy that inject system, the system can be proved to satisfy any potential node meet with conservation relations.

4 SIMULATION ANALYSIS

In recent years, China's Southern Power Grid also occur low frequency oscillation phenomenon repeatedly, causing serious damage to the unit equipments. Therefore, we selected Southern Power Grid as the main object of study, to extract low frequency oscillation waveform of its occurrence. First, this is a brief introduction of China Southern Power Grid Interconnection structure, picture shown in Figure 1.

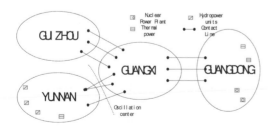

Figure 1. China Southern Power Grid.

4.1 *Differences of waveform characteristics*

When the unit of DAYA Bay power sags, it cause the whole network of China Southern Power Grid low frequency oscillation, where the disturbance side (by the end of the Guangdong Power Grid) and the contralateral unit (sending end Yunnan power grid) power angle oscillations shown in Figure 2a and Figure 2b.

In order to analysis the figure in detail, we obtain the PRONY results in Table 1.

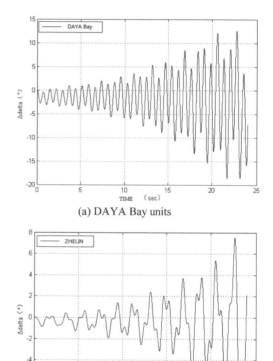

(a) DAYA Bay units

(b) ZHELIN units

Figure 2. Power angle oscillation curve.

Table 1. The PRONY results.

Component	Frequency (Hz)	Damping ratio (%)	Root
1	0.7462	−4.8016	0.2254+j4.6884″
2	1.3171	−2.2868	0.1893+j8.2359
3	0.8855	−0.6447	0.0359+j5.5635
4	0.9334	−0.0776	0.0045+j5.8650
5	0.9886	0.3604	−0.0224+j6.2115

Compare the power angle oscillation curves of the unit where the disturbance exist and contralateral side. It can be found the side of the unit disturbance oscillation's mode is more complex. From the Table 1, we know that DAYA Bay and ZHELIN units contain obviously multiple modes; while in the contralateral side, namely Yunnan side, power angle oscillation mode is single.

4.2 *Differences of transmission mode*

According to the theoretical explanation, In the forced oscillation process, the different nodes exist the presence sequence in response to the disturbance. The disturbance occurs in the Yunnan side of Little Bay units, Yunnan–Guangxi contact line (YAN CHONG line) and Guangxi–Guangdong contact line (YUMAO line) will obtain the start-up oscillation active power graph within 5 seconds, they are shown in Figure 3.

It can be seen from the figure, since YANCHONG line is near from the disturbance point, the oscillation wave began to spread from disturbance source, and then reach YANCHONG line, then reach YUMAO line, YANCHONG line's active power phase is ahead of the phase of Yu Mao line.

When weakly damped oscillations begin, the YANCHONG and YUMAO line active power's curve trajectories almost coincide, the difference of phase between the two does not exist on the start-up process.

4.3 *Differences of energy change characteristics*

Apply a cyclic mechanical disturbance on the DAYA Bay power unit to stimulate the whole network. The forced oscillation frequency is 0.496 Hz. To calculate the transient potential energy on both sides of the contact line, as shown in Figure 4.

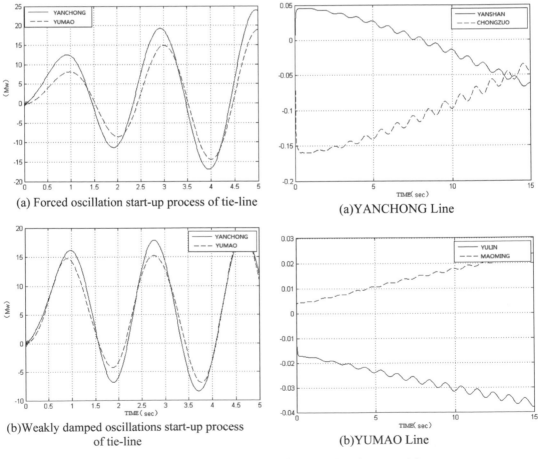

(a) Forced oscillation start-up process of tie-line

(a)YANCHONG Line

(b)Weakly damped oscillations start-up process of tie-line

(b)YUMAO Line

Figure 3.   The start-up oscillation active power graph.

Figure 4.   Transient potential energy curve.

We can see YANCHONG bus that transient potential energy of CHONGZUO bus is increasing, and transient potential energy of YANSHAN bus is decreasing. The trend is potential energy flow from CHONGZUO bus line flows to YANSHAN bus.

5 CONCLUSION AND OUTLOOK

In this paper, weakly damped oscillations and forced oscillations are studied, analyzed and compared both similarities and differences between the two low-frequency oscillation mechanism and the oscillation characteristics. Use China Southern Power Grid verify the conclusion. Studies have shown that weakly damped oscillations and forced oscillation mainly have three differences, like waveform characteristics, mode of transmission, and the change of energy, and these differences may provide the basis for fault identify, locating more accurate and rapid. But for the two both low-frequency oscillations,the best solution is to cut the disturbance source, increasing the system damping are conducive to the two kinds of low frequency oscillation's suppression. And specific measures need to be further study.

REFERENCES

Adamiak, M.G, Apostolov A.P, Begovic, M.M, IEEE Transactionson Power Delivery, 2006, 21(2).

Dong, Jingyuan, Xia, Tao, Zhang, Yingchen, Weekes, Tony, Thorp, James, Liu, Yilu, "Monitoring Power System Disturbances at the Distribution Level," IEEE PES General Meeting, Pittsburgh, July, 2008.

Demello F P, Concordia C. Concepts of synchronous machine stability as affected by excitation control[J]. IEEE Transactions on power apparatus and systems, 1969, 88(4): 316–328.

Dewei Zeng, Electrical Power, 2001, 34(11), pp. 28–33.

Jim Y Cai, Zhenyu Huang, John Hauer, Ken Martin. 2005, IEEE, Transmission and Distribution Conference & Exhibition: Asia and Pacific Dalian, China, pp. 1–7.

John F. Hauer, Navin B. Bhatt, Kirit Shah, and Sharma Kolluri. 2004 IEEE Power Engineering Society General Meeting, pp. 1685–1690.

Magdy E. Aboul-Ela A.A. Sallam IEEE Transaction on Power System. 11(2), pp. 767–773.

Xiaorong Xie, Yaozhong Xin, Jinyu Xiao, Jingtao Wu, Ying duo Han. Power and Energy Magazine, 2006, 4(1) pp. 54–63.

Yixin Yu, Li Peng, Proceedings of the CSEE, 2005, 25(11), pp. 6–11.

Yixin Ni, Shousun Chen, Beijing: Press of Tsinghua University, 2002, pp: 260–262.

Yusheng Xue, Wei Li, David J. Hill, "Optimization of Transient Stability Control, I: For Cases with a Unique Unstable Mode," International Journal of Control, Automation, and System. vol. 3, no. 2, pp. 334–340, June 2005.

Zarghami, Mahyar, Crow, Mariesa, Jagannathan, Sarangapani, Liu, Yilu,"Damping Inter-Area Oscillations by UPFCs Based on Selected Global Measurements," IEEE PES General Meeting, Pittsburgh, July, 2008. Jingtao Wu, Xiaorong Xie, Liding Wang, Jiong Hu, Tao Zhang. Electrical Equipment. 2006. 7(3), pp. 46–49.

Zima M., M. Larsson, P. Korba, C. Rehtanz, and G. Andersson. In Proc. of the IEEE, 2005, 93(5). pp. 980–996.

Zhian Zhong, Chunchun Xu, Bruce J. Billian, Li Zhang, Shu-Jen StevenTsai, et al, "Power System Frequency Monitoring Network (FNET) Implementation,"IEEE Trans. Power Syst., vol. 20, no. 4, pp. 1914–1921, Nov. 2005.

Computer, Intelligent Computing and Education Technology – Liu, Sung & Yao (Eds)
© 2014 Taylor & Francis Group, London, ISBN 978-1-138-02469-4

Research on a new method of unbalanced traffic demand forecasting

Cheng-Bing Li, Min Li, Rui-Xue Guo & Jian-Chao Wang
School of Transportation, Inner Mongolia University, Hohhot, P.R. China

ABSTRACT: The urban traffic supply and demand unbalanced is a special form of supply and demand, to establish an appropriate manner under the disequilibrium between supply and demand to urban traffic demand forecast, and have great significance for traffic management decision-making. This article obtains from the traffic demand and supply, the composition and influencing factors were described, in addition to the urban residents travel vehicles travel choice and the proportion of the urban population quantity analysis, to predict the growth rate of residents travel planning in transport, on the base of the status quo of travel on planning of urban traffic demand forecast. Can provide a new approach for traffic demand forecasting.

Keywords: disequilibrium between supply and demand; traffic demand; a new forecast method; the urban traffic

1 INTRODUCTION

With the rapid development of national economy and people's living standards greatly improved, the urban traffic supply and demand unbalanced problem increasingly prominent, traffic jams often occur. The urban traffic demand forecasting in alleviating urban road problem plays a key role. Not only that, transportation systems or support the development of the social infrastructure and "circulatory system", occupies an important position in the social and economic system.[1] Transportation is good or bad, directly affects the development of national economy and the improvement of people's living standards. In today's society the world exists in every big city traffic congestion problem, therefore, alleviate the urban traffic problem has always been a hot spot in the domestic and foreign experts and scholars.

On traffic demand forecasting method, the experts developed a lot of methods, commonly used have level prediction method, grey correlation method and so on. But the traditional traffic demand forecasting method in the overall planning of the urban planning spatial entity (such as land utilization, population distribution) or travel survey data as the basis, the prediction result is only a reflection of planning space.[2] Literature[3] the kohonen neural network and the summation Auto Regressive Moving Average (ARIMA) model combining forecasting exchange; Literature[4] put forward a kind of wavelet decomposition and reconstruction combined with time series analysis of combined forecasting method, this requires complex mathematical model and the function relation. In 60 ~ 70 s of the 20th century, Murchland[5] and Tomlin[6] for the first time, the scholars such as four stage method needs the combination forecast model research, try to now there are still many imperfections. In this paper, from the Angle of the traffic generated by simple mathematical theory to the urban traffic demand forecast, can for the urban traffic control, management and planning to provide a certain basis.

2 TRAFFIC DEMAND AND SUPPLY

2.1 *Aggregate demand and its components*

Traffic demand is to point to in a certain period of time the total amount of OD flow within an urban area, it contains various purposes of people and objects in the social public space in a variety of ways mobile demands of passenger flow and cargo flow. Sometimes in order to convenient to deal with problems, and according to the needs of passenger OD flow can be according to certain proportion swap.[7] In order to make traffic data is more persuasive, the determination of total demand is usually to obtain data through directly to the survey, investigation methods including stratified sampling survey, field investigation and questionnaire investigation, etc.

2.2 *The description of the aggregate demand*

Plenty of activity in the city of transportation infrastructure on the displacement of the point between the people and goods around the traffic system in the service of all kinds of social and economic activities.[8] It is a convenient and effective transportation, our city will have a healthy development of the security, the people's quality of life constantly improve, at the same time to form the traffic demand. People will not travel without a purpose, in other words, people not to travel and travel, but for travel to achieve a certain purpose, or somewhere, or to take STH. To sp. As a result, people will consider in the schedule of comfort, cost, convenience and travel time, etc., after considering weigh how to travel. In addition, policy factors will also great influence on traffic demand, the more important to have traffic control and the implementation of various traffic policy. City the size of the population, economic level and, of course, such as traffic supply can have influence on traffic demand.

2.3   Traffic supply

Traffic supply is a complex system of urban traffic, a city's transport infrastructure provide greatly affects the efficiency and people's satisfaction with the trip. Urban road traffic to be orderly, not only reasonable signal timing, operations in the intersection of the reasonable planning and construction, etc., must have the relevant traffic control strategy, transportation, service measures, transportation infrastructure construction and management of investment in transport this feature implemented accordingly.

On the transport infrastructure, such as the construction of roads and terminal not only take up a certain land resources, also need to invest a lot of manpower and material resources and financial resources. And the maintenance of transport infrastructure and purchase will need a lot of money. In the intersection of reasonable layout planning and with the corresponding traffic light plays an indelible role in the smooth general characteristic of road. Policy factors are serious, the government, the management of the terminal of the traffic development strategy plan, traffic regulations and rules, etc., for urban transportation development to provide a good development platform. In the modern city, has a convenient public transport is also indispensable, city bus, BRT, subway, taxi, etc., which makes convenient residents needs can be met. Residents if driving, parking has become their most concern, therefore, and services in public places need just the right amount of parking Spaces to meet the needs of residents. City travel, transport supply would have a big impact on the quality of our life. Wanting, rapid and sound development of a city must have a good supply of traffic.

3   TRAFFIC DEMAND FORECAST

3.1   The traffic supply and demand unbalanced degree

Analyze the unbalanced degree and the measurement is to determine the requirements in the planning of traffic planning in aggregate demand. Traffic supply and demand unbalanced degree dd is equal to an area in a certain period of the traffic divided by the total demand D aggregate supply S, namely:

$$dd(t) = \frac{D(t)}{S(t)} \tag{1}$$

The formula shows that when the $dd(t) = 1$, traffic demand and supply in equilibrium, when the $dd(t)$ indicates 1, traffic demand and supply in a state of disequilibrium. When the greater the absolute value of $dd(t)$, the more serious the disequilibrium between supply and demand.

3.2   According to the traffic generation forecast traffic demand

We according to the traffic generated by the method to forecast the traffic demand. Divides into the travel vehicles, non-motor vehicles, private cars and walking three categories. Set traffic generation for U, private cars, non-motor vehicles and walking occupies $a\%$, $b\%$ and $c\%$ respectively. According to the urban population and urban economic level changes is expected to travel transportation choice as follows: Private car $\alpha\% \sim \beta\%$, non-motor vehicles $\gamma\% \sim \delta\%$, on foot $\varepsilon\% \sim \in\%$. For the occurrence of planning in urban traffic and private cars, non-motor vehicles and pedestrian traffic generates Q_1 and Q_2 and Q_3 respectively:

$$Q = Q_1 + Q_2 + Q_3 \tag{2}$$
$$Q_1 = U \times a\% \times [1 + (\alpha\% \sim \beta\%)] \tag{3}$$
$$Q_2 = U \times b\% \times [1 + (\gamma\% \sim \delta\%)] \tag{4}$$
$$Q_3 = U \times c\% \times [1 + (\varepsilon\% \sim \in\%)] \tag{5}$$

According to The Times demand our traffic supply can be obtained as follows:

$$s(t) = \frac{D(t)}{dd(t)} = \frac{Q}{dd(t)} \tag{6}$$

here, the unbalanced degree $dd(t)$ for planning, $s(t)$ for the planning of transportation supply, $D(t)$ for the planning of transportation demand, the $D(t) = Q$.

4 NUMERICAL EXAMPLES

In a certain city transportation mainly rely on private cars, non-motor vehicles and pedestrian, total number of 100000 person-time, private cars accounted for 40%, non-motor vehicles travel 50%, and walking travel accounts for 10%. According to urban population scale and economic development level factors such as comprehensive analysis and forecast, the residents of 10 years is expected to travel rate for the choice of means of transport, the growth of private cars is 120% ~ 140%, the growth rate of non-motor vehicles is 100% ~ 120% and the growth rate of 50% ~ 50% of walk. The unbalanced degree of city are estimated $dd(10) = 0.8$. If want to urban planning, the demand for 10 years of traffic demand.

We can calculate the first 10 years choose transport growth after traveling passengers:

Private cars:

$$Q_1 = 100000 \times 40\% \times [1 + (120\% \sim 140\%)]$$
$$= 88000 \sim 96000 \text{ people/day}$$

Non-motor vehicles:

$$Q_2 = 100000 \times 50\% \times [1 + (100\% \sim 120\%)]$$
$$= 100000 \sim 110000 \text{ people/day}$$

Walking:

$$Q_3 = 100000 \times 10\% \times [1 + (50\% \sim 100\%)]$$
$$= 150000 \sim 20000 \text{ people/day}$$

Therefore, the first ten years of traffic number is: 203000 ~ 226000 people/day.

To measure unbalanced degree of $dd(10) = 0.8$, is required to supply as follows:

$$S(10) = \frac{203000 \sim 226000}{0.8}$$
$$= 253750 \sim 282500 \text{ people/day}$$

So the city was planning the first ten years of cities, traffic supply should be 253750 ~ 282500 people/day to meet the demand of traffic.

Using this method is simple and feasible, does not need complex function relation, just put the choice of transportation and growth statistics calculation, can be based on the combination of planning years population base of traffic demand forecast.

5 CONCLUSIONS

Urban traffic demand forecasting is the precondition of urban planning, is the basis of urban development strategy, the road network planning and construction and organization of scientific management of city traffic has important significance. Urban traffic system is a large complicated system, it is difficult to accurately depict using mathematical function. We want to alleviate the bottleneck restricting the development of urban traffic is to solve the problem of traffic supply and demand. This text set about from urban traffic generation, first elaborated the aggregate demand and structure of the urban traffic and traffic supply and the main factors influencing the traffic supply and demand is analyzed, and combining the unbalanced degree is put forward under the predict disequilibrium in planning of traffic demand forecast method; on the example of the proposed method. Hope to solve the traffic problems have found a new way.

ACKNOWLEDGEMENT

This work was financially supported by the Inner Mongolia Autonomous Region higher school science and technology research projects (Project No: NJZC13030201025009) and the Inner Mongolia University high-level personnel introduction research projects (Project No: 125115).

REFERENCES

Gao Hui, Zhao Jianyu, Jia Lei. Short-term traffic flow prediction method[N]. Journal of jinan university (natural science edition), 2008, 1. 1 (22): 88–94.

He Guoguang, Ma Shoufeng, Li Yu, Based on wavelet decomposition and reconstruction method of short-term traffic flow prediction[J]. Systems engineering theory and practice, 2002, (9): 101–106.

He Jiawei, zhao Qiang. Traffic demand forecasting method based on constraint model research[J]. Computer and communications, 2005, 5 (23): 26–29.

Huang Zhongxiang, Liu An, Li Zuomin. Unbalanced traffic demand forecast[J]. China soft science, 1998; Procedure of 9–105.

Maschavan Der Voort, Mark Dougherty, Susan Watson. Combining kohonen maps with ARIMA time series models to forecast traffic flow[J]. Transportation Research. PartC, 1996, 4(5): 307–318.

Murchland J D. Some remarks on the gravity of distribution and equivalent Maximization formulation[A]. LSETNT-38, Transport Network Theory[C]. London: London Graduale School of Business Studies, 1966: 71–90.

Tang Zhiqiang, Tao Yi, Xu Wuming. Unbalanced highway toll collection forecast a preliminary study[J]. Industry economics and management, 2008; 4 (176): 38–41.

Tomlin J A. Mathematical programming model for traffic network problem[D]. Dept. of Civil Engineering, University of Adelaide, Australia, 1967.

The analysis of the urban agglomeration traffic supply and demand

Cheng-Bing Li, Yi Zhang, Min Li & Xi-Lu Li
School of Transportation, Inner Mongolia University, Hohhot, P.R. China

ABSTRACT: This paper analyzes the various forms of transportation urban agglomeration, detailed description of urban agglomeration transport system and divides the transport system type and composition of it. And through the inner city transport system analogy, integrated various factors, and ultimately draw traffic based on supply and demand in urban agglomerations regression analysis model.

Keywords: urban agglomeration; regression analysis; supply; demand

1 INTRODUCTION

Urban agglomeration is a special form of regional spatial organization arising from the process of urbanization, which is one or two or even more than two cities as the core of regional economic development, relying on certain natural conditions, using modern means of transport and integrated transport network accessibility, to expand and increase the number of cities in the geographical scope of the city, and thus constitutes a social, economic, technological integration of the urban regional.[1]

French scholar Guttmann first proposed "megalopolis" in 1957, had mentioned that a major feature of the group is that "among the city has convenient links via the transport corridor linking the core of the city, is no gap between the city and closely";[2] Professor Wang have pointed out the important reason to promote the rapid develop of urban agglomerations abroad is that "played the role of a well-developed communication and transport network" in the study of development of urban agglomeration conducted abroad.[3]

The traffic problems of urban populations should also be taken seriously. In a city group, with the gradual integration of the economic, social, etc., across the city to work, travel, shopping, tourism, visiting relatives, etc. The ways to travel become more. How to meet the multi-level city group travel needs, and provide fast, convenient transport supply safe and comfortable means of transportation and transportation facilities, and also the development of urban agglomeration economies is the key to building a culture of travelers. Therefore, we need to analyze the transport supply and demand of urban agglomerations to ensure the quality of urban residents in internal traffic group travel.

2 URBAN AGGLOMERATION TRANSPORTATION SYSTEM

2.1 The transport system description of urban agglomeration

With the gradually development of China's urban population, the city's transportation network system of internal group also develop. For long-distance transport, transformed from point to point mode of transport for the domain to domain[4] gradually, the formation of the road network between the cities of urban agglomeration is also becoming more complex.

In a single urban agglomeration, we can point the main trunk roads, rail, aviation, water, etc within the group and other types of road network at all levels for the line, and with a range of administrative and economic regions to establish an urban agglomeration network traffic system.

2.2 Description the external transport links of urban agglomeration transport system

Urban agglomeration is an open system the same as city, so there are outflow and inflow of residents, then, not only to improve the internal transportation network systems group, and, for a relatively high level of development in terms of urban agglomerations, accessible the outbound traffic is also very important. For example, a group of outside urban agglomerations and towns adjacent to the movement of persons and goods, then, we need to improve urban agglomerations have enough external transport system to complete fast, convenient, safe and efficient transport of people and goods to travel. Outbound traffic flow of urban agglomeration is an important factor in urban agglomerations traffic supply and demand analysis.

3 THE ANALYSIS OF SUPPLY AND DEMAND IN URBAN AGGLOMERATIONS TRANSPORTATIONS SYSTEM

3.1 *Analysis supply of urban agglomeration transport system*

3.1.1 *The supply factors analysis of urban agglomeration transportation system*

The factors affecting the supply of urban transportation systems group analyzed from three directions. From the urban agglomeration internal transport systems, the Factors inner city traffic supply is mainly the overall level of economic development of transportation construction, transportation equipment manufacturing industry development level, policy factors, technical factors and market price factors. Inter-city transportation supply factors including overall economic level, the degree of traffic facilities, policy factors, degree of urbanization, technological factors and market price factors. External transport traffic supply urban agglomeration factor is the level of the main urban agglomeration development, urban agglomeration economic level, policy factors, technical factors and market price factors.

We can know that the city's transport system is more complex group than the urban transport system, but we can see the internal factors and external urban and intercity transportation between the three, much the same. And because the ratio between the three different effects, we can create a function-based urban transport system supply urban agglomerations transportation system supply function and analyzed.

3.1.2 *The supply function of urban agglomerations transportation system*

Based on the supply function inner city transport system, analogy the urban agglomerations supply function as follow:

$$S_t = S(y_1, y_2, y_3) \qquad (1)$$

where: S_t—Supply of urban agglomeration; y_1, y_2, y_3—Urban transport supply function within the group, Inter-city transport supply function, External transport supply function; $S(y)$—Urban agglomerations transportation system supply function.

By the analysis of the traffic travel way of urban agglomeration shows that inner-city residents travel mode mainly for urban roads, urban rail transit; main mode of intercity travel between there are roads, railways, aviation; urban agglomerations

outside the main transportation modes roads, railways and aviation.[6]

First, we know that the supply of transportation within the city's function as follows:

$$y_1 = b_0 + h_1 f_1 + h_2 f_2 + h_3 f_3 + h_4 f_4 + \beta \qquad (2)$$

where: y_1—Supply of inner city traffic; f_1—GDP; f_2—Expenditures research and experimental development (R&D); f_3—Transportation price index; f_4—Political factors, β—Random error b_0, b_1, b_2, b_3, b_4—Characteristic parameters.

We also used regression analysis to supply inter-city traffic analysis. By analyzing that supply inter-city mainly by road, rail, aviation and consists of three parts, so we can get the intercity transportation supply function as follows:

$$y_2 = \sum_{i=1,j=1}^{n} H_{ij} + \sum_{i=1,j=1}^{n} R_{ij} + \sum_{i=1,j=1}^{n} A_{ij} + \alpha \qquad (3)$$

where: H_{ij}—The highway transport supply of i-th city to j-th city within the urban agglomeration; R_{ij}—The railway transport supply of i-th city to j-th city within the urban agglomeration; A_{ij}—The Air transport supply of i-th city to j-th city within the urban agglomeration; a—Random error.

Using regression analysis based on various factors, respectively analyzed each of the three main mode of transport intercity factors, can get:

$$T_{ij} = b_0 + \sum_{k=1}^{n-1} b_k A_k + b_n A_n \alpha \qquad (4)$$

where: T_{ij}—The transport supply each part, including H_{ij}, R_{ij}, A_{ij}; $j = 1, 2, 3 \dots n$. b_0, b_j, b_n—Characteristic parameters; A_j, A_n—Various factors; $j = 1, 2, 3 \dots n$.

Similarly, we can draw three main urban agglomeration of external transport supply function.

Therefore, we can get that for a group of urban transportation system supply function expression

$$S_t = \omega_1 y_1 + \omega_2 y_2 + \omega_3 y_3 \qquad (5)$$

where: $\omega_1, \omega_2, \omega_3$—Scaling factor for each part of the traffic within the urban agglomeration.

3.1.3 *The supply factors analysis of urban agglomeration transportation system*

The factors affecting the supply of urban transportation systems group analyzed from three directions. From the urban agglomeration internal transport systems, the main factors affecting the single inner city traffic demand is as follows: the level of economic development, transport services, other modes of transportation competition policy factors, domestic tourism trips, population and city size. The main factors affecting the demand for inter-city transportation as follows: total economic level, the degree of integration of urban agglomeration, policy factors, lifestyle, transportation services, market price factors. Urban agglomeration traffic demand factors external transport include: the level of urban agglomeration development, urban economic level, policy factors, transportation services, market price factors.

We can know the various factors that influence urban agglomeration transport system mainly includes three aspects. Are single inner city traffic demand, traffic demand intercity urban agglomeration between internal and external traffic demand urban agglomerations. Belong to a linear relationship between the three, so we can use to build demand function regression model urban agglomeration transport system, and analyze.

3.1.4 The demand function of urban agglomerations transportation system

We had known that the demand function of city's transport system as follows:

$$
\begin{cases}
D_{1t} = \alpha_{10} + \sum_{i=1}^{m} \alpha_{1i} x_{1i} + \psi_1 \\
\\
D_{2t} = \alpha_{20} + \sum_{i=1}^{m} \alpha_{2i} x_{2i} + \psi_2 \\
\\
D_t = D_{1t} + \kappa D_{2t}
\end{cases}
\tag{6}
$$

where: D_t—The total traffic demand at t time; D_{1t}—Passenger traffic demand at t time; D_{2t}—Freight traffic demand at t time; x_{1i}—Factors affecting demand for urban passenger transport; x_{2i}—Factors affecting demand for urban freight transport; κ—The scaling factor of passenger demand needs into cargo; ψ_1, ψ_2—Random error.

We will be the D_t that demand inner-city recorded as D_1. Since intercity and urban agglomerations are consistent with the external form of the inner city, therefore, can be inter-city and urban agglomerations external transport analogy to inner city traffic demand. We will be denoted D_2 as intercity travel demand, D_3 as the urban population demand for outbound traffic.

From the previous analysis, we can know that the demand for transportation between intercity and urban population in terms of the external aspects, although different transportation needs, but the same can be divided into two categories according to their purpose, one is freight demand, a class of passenger demand. Therefore, we can conclude that the traffic demand function of urban agglomeration as follows:

$$
D_t = \mu_1 D_1 + \mu_2 D_2 + \mu_3 D_3 + \psi
\tag{7}
$$

where: D_t—Urban agglomeration traffic demand; μ_1, μ_2, μ_3—Scaling factor for each part of the urban agglomeration within the city; ψ—Random erro D_1—Inner city traffic demand; D_2—Intercity traffic demand; D_3—Cities outbound traffic demand; r.

4 CONCLUSION

With the accelerating process of urban agglomeration, the future construction of urban population will gradually become the focus, and urban agglomerations in the transport system will also become an important part of the building, so the transportation system of the city groups will become an important direction. Supply and demand model of this thesis the results of urban agglomeration transport system is still immature, and there are inadequacies, I hope the studies to improve a lot in future.

ACKNOWLEDGEMENT

This work was financially supported by the Inner Mongolia Autonomous Region higher school science and technology research projects (Project No: NJZC13030201025009) and the Inner Mongolia University high-level personnel introduction research projects (Project No: 125115).

REFERENCES

Ding, Junhong, Ning, Yuemin. Introduction to Urban Geography[M]. Hefei: Anhui Science Press, 1983: 314–324.

Gao, Yan. Evaluation of the development of urban population intercity transport system[D]. Xi'an: Chang'an University, 2009:4–6.

Gao, Ziyou, Zhao, Xiaomei, Huang, Haijun, Mao, Baohua. Research of complex network theory and urban transportation systems complexity of the problem[J]. Transportation Systems Engineering and Information, 2006, 6(3):42–44.

Liu, Jinjiang. Urban Transportation Planning Research group[D]. Xi'an: Chang'an University, 2004:7–16.

Wang, Naijing. Development model and experience of foreign urban agglomeration New Exploration[J]. Economic and Management Research, 2005, (2):83–84.

Yao, Shimou. New knowledge about the basic concepts of urban agglomerations[J]. Urban Research, 1998, (6):15–17.

Computer, Intelligent Computing and Education Technology – Liu, Sung & Yao (Eds)
© 2014 Taylor & Francis Group, London, ISBN 978-1-138-02469-4

Improved Particle Swarm Algorithm in the power system reactive power optimization

Kai Wang
Department of Economics and Management, North China Electric Power University, Baoding, China

ABSTRACT: According to the characteristics of reactive power optimization of no non convex and having multiple local optima. And PSO algorithm' results have the problems of depending on the initial presence, easy to fall into local optimum. An improved PSO algorithm is proposed in this paper. Through dynamic inertia weight, the speed inheritance pattern of particles is optimized, making the particles have good early divergent and later fine search ability. And the introduction of extreme disturbance operator achieves particle labor migration, getting rid of local optima. The simulation and comparison show that the algorithm is effective and feasible.

Keywords: power system; reactive power optimization; improved PSO algorithm

1 INTRODUCTION

Power system reactive power optimization is not only one of the effective means to assure the safety of electric power system and economic operation, but also an important measure to reduce the network loss and improve voltage quality [1]. And power system reactive power optimization problem is essentially a mixed nonlinear problems with multiple variables and constraints. And it has the characteristics of the convex, the existence of multiple local optimal point. The optimization process is complex.

At present, the reactive power optimization problem solving is mainly divided into classical algorithms, which mainly includes the gradient method, linear programming and nonlinear programming, etc, and modern intelligent algorithm, which mainly includes genetic algorithm, Particle Swarm Algorithm (PSO), etc [2]. Among them, PSO has better effect in solving discontinuous, non-differentiable nonlinear optimization problems. But there are still dependent on the initial values, easily trapped in local optima and other issues.

To solve these problems, an improved PSO algorithm is proposed in this paper. One side, to enhance the searching capability of the algorithm, dynamic inertia weight is introduced to ensure the global divergence and local fine of the particle search, as the algorithm converges and gradually reduces the particles search step length. Meanwhile, using probability method, through the extreme disturbance operator to ensure the particle can be timely and effective to get rid of local optimum extreme, break through the evolutionary stagnation, find the global optimal solution.

2 THE POWER SYSTEM REACTIVE POWER OPTIMIZATION MODEL

Power system reactive power optimization is to improve the voltage quality, reduce network loss, optimize the system running state in a given structure parameters and load conditions, through the reasonable adjustment of "control variables" to change the trend of distribution. Take the minimum active power loss as the target of static reactive power optimization [3]. Its model is:

$$\min f = \min \sum_{k=1}^{N_l} G_{k(i,j)} \left[U_i^2 + U_j^2 - 2U_i U_j \cos(\delta_i - \delta_j) \right] \tag{1}$$

where N_l = the total number of nodes in the network; $G_{k(i,j)}$ = the conductance of the branch i and j; U_i, U_j = the voltage of nodes i, j, respectively. δ_i, δ_j = phase angle of node i, j.

Constraint equation for the corresponding system trend is [4]:

$$P_i = U_i \sum_{j=1}^{N_l} U_j \left(G_{ij} \cos \delta_{ij} + B_{ij} \sin \delta_{ij} \right) \tag{2}$$

$$Q_i = U_i \sum_{j=1}^{N_l} U_j \left(G_{ij} \sin \delta_{ij} + B_{ij} \cos \delta_{ij} \right) \tag{3}$$

where P_i, Q_i, U_i, is the active, reactive power and voltage injecting into the node; G_{ij}, B_{ij}, δ_{ij} is the conductance, electrical susceptance and phase Angle difference between node i and j, respectively. N_l = the total number of nodes.

Constraints of control variables are:

$$T_{imin} < T_i < T_{imax} \tag{4}$$

$$G_{jmin} < G_j < G_{jmax} \tag{5}$$

$$U_{Gimin} < U_{Gi} < U_{Gimax} \tag{6}$$

where T_{imin}, T_{imax} = the upper and lower limits of the transformer ratio; G_{jmin}, G_{jmax} = the upper and lower limits of parallel compensation capacitance; U_{Gimin}, U_{Gimax} = the upper and lower limits of generator terminal voltage.

Constraints of state variables are:

$$U_{imin} < U_i < U_{imax} \tag{7}$$

$$Q_{Gimin} < Q_{Gi} < Q_{Gimax} \tag{8}$$

where U_{imin}, U_{imax} = the upper and lower limits of node voltage; Q_{Gimin}, Q_{Gimax} = the upper and lower limits for reactive power output of the generator.

3 IMPROVEMENT STRATEGY OF PSO ALGORITHM

From the essence of the PSO algorithm we can know, the particle's initial position affects the development direction of the particles. As the particles gradually move closer to the location of the optimal solution, particle iteration speed decreases. And for larger dimension complex issues, often there are multiple extreme value points. Particle swarms are likely to fall into local optimal solution within the neighborhood and can't jump out, losing the ability of global optimization. So in view of the above problems, this paper puts forward the improvement strategies. The characteristics of the model are as follows.

3.1 Dynamic inertia weight

Inertia weight w reflects the degree of particles inheriting the current speed of previous speed. And a large inertia weight is beneficial to global search, while a smaller inertia weight is more conducive to regional development. In order to better balance global and local search ability of the algorithm, the linear decreasing inertia weight is introduced as:

$$\omega(k) = \omega_{start} - (\omega_{start} - \omega_{end})(T_{max} - k)/T_{max} \tag{9}$$

where ω_{start} = the initial inertia weight. ω_{end} = the inertia weight at the time of maximum number of iterations; k = the modern iterative algebra; T_{max} = the maximum iterative algebra.

3.2 Extreme perturbation operator

The essence of PSO algorithm easily falling into local optimum is the existence of particle "over-concentrate" phenomenon in late stage. And the probability of relying on existing pattern to break local optima is small. Therefore, do artificial migration through extreme perturbation operator to strengthen the global search ability of particles [5]. That is:

$$P_{id} = r_3 P_{id} \tag{10}$$

$$P_{gd} = r_4 P_{gd} \tag{11}$$

$$r_3 = \begin{cases} 1, & t_0 \le T_0 \\ U(0,1), & t_0 > T_0 \end{cases} \tag{12}$$

$$r_4 = \begin{cases} 1, & t_g \le T_g \\ U(0,1), & t_g > T_g \end{cases} \tag{13}$$

where P_{id} = individual extreme; P_{gd} = global extreme; t_0, t_g are individual extreme and global extreme evolutionary stagnation step number; T_0, T_g = the need of disturbance stagnation step number threshold for individual extreme and global extreme. $U(0,1)$ = uniform random function.

Therefore, the improved particle velocity equation is:

$$v_{id}^{t+1} = \omega v_{id}^t + c_1 r_1 (r_3 P_{id} - x_{id}) + c_2 r_2 (r_4 P_{gd} - x_{id}) \tag{14}$$

where v_{id}^t = velocity of the particle at time t; c_1, c_2 are learning factors; ω = dynamic inertia weight.

4 ALGORITHM STEPS

Using improved PSO algorithm to solve the reactive power optimization problem, the specific steps are as follows:

1. Input the original data including network node parameters, control variables, state variables and the constraint condition;
2. Initialize the system original parameters;
3. Calculate the system power flow. Get each line of active and reactive power and voltage node;
4. Calculate the particle fitness, and looking for the individual extreme and group's extreme;

5. Using dynamic inertia weight to optimize the particle optimization speed, and update the particle position;
6. Using extreme disturbance operator to judge whether do artificial migration, and recalculate the particle fitness;
7. If the termination condition is satisfied then the algorithm stops, otherwise go to step (3), the iteration continues;
8. Output global optimal solution, the algorithm terminates.

5 ANALYSES OF CASES AND COMPARISON

This paper takes the IEEE 6 node system as an example for analysis. The system's wiring diagram

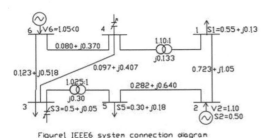

Figurel IEEE6 systen connection diagran

Figure 1.   IEEE6 system connection diagram.

and the corresponding parameters are shown in Figure 1.

The system's parameter of benchmark capacity is 100 MVA, variables are normalized value. And it consists of two generators and two sets of adjustable transformer. Take node 6 as the balance node, node 2 is a PV node, node 1, 3, 4, 5 are the PQ nodes, two adjustable transformer branch. Select the node 3, node 4 as the installation site for reactive power compensation equipment. Specific parameters can be seen in literature [6].

1. Comparing with the literature [7], the initial trend of reactive power optimization and optimized results are shown in Table 1.
2. The iteration figure of optimization process is shown in Figure 2.

Table 1, Figure 2 shows, the initial network loss is 0.1161, node 1 voltage amplitude is $v_1 = 0.854$, less than the lower limit of 0.9, do not meet the safety requirements of the power system. After using the method of optimization in this paper, each node parameters meet the requirements. And the network loss is reduced to 0.0887. Compared with the results shown in the literature [7], the reduction rate of this algorithm is 23.60%, higher than both of them. Therefore, this algorithm has better global searching ability, convergence speed, less time-consuming and better results.

Table 1. The initial trend and optimization results of IEEE6 node system.

Variables	Run limit Min	Max	Initial trend	LP	SGA	This algorithm
Control variables						
V_{G2}	1.10	1.15	1.100	1.140	1.145	1.100
V_{G6}	1.00	1.10	1.050	1.096	1.100	1.000
T_{35}	0.90	1.10	1.025	0.952	0.963	1.0975
T_{41}	0.90	1.10	1.100	0.987	0.988	0.900
Q_{C3}	0.00	0.055	0.000	0.055	0.055	0.055
Q_{C4}	0.00	0.05	0.000	0.052	0.015	0.030
State variables						
Q_{G2}	−0.20	1.00	0.338	0.130	0.191	0.103
Q_{G6}	−0.20	1.00	0.382	0.426	0.403	0.412
V_1	0.90	1.00	0.854	0.996	0.995	1.085
V_3	0.90	1.00	0.930	0.983	0.986	0.958
V_4	0.90	1.00	0.951	1.000	0.999	0.968
V_5	0.90	1.00	0.915	1.000	0.996	1.081
Network loss						
P_L			0.1161	0.0890	0.0899	0.0887

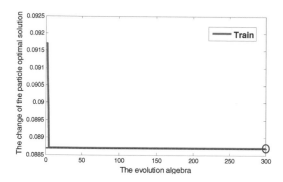

Figure 2. The particle evolution curve of optimal values.

6 CONCLUSIONS

Aim at PSO algorithm's defects, such as the results depending on the initial value, having poor stability and easy to fall into local optimum etc. This paper presents a dynamic inertia weight to optimize particle velocity inheritance mode, strengthening the search ability of particles. And introduce the extreme perturbation operator to achieve particle migration by artificial disturbance, getting rid of local optima, strengthening the global exploration ability of particles. Reduce the influence of particle initial value for the final result in a certain extent.

Comparison can be seen by the example above; improved particle swarm optimization algorithm has better convergence results, which would be of great significance for the study of power system reactive power optimization. In addition, given the POS algorithm to solve multi-variable, multi-constrained mixed nonlinear problems with good results, therefore, the study of the essence of optimization for PSO algorithm in all kinds of literatures and comparison are also the direction of further research in this paper.

REFERENCES

[1] Liu Hongwen, Zhang Gexiang. A reactive power optimization method based on improved quantum-inspired genetic algorithm [J]. Power System Technology, 2008, 32 (12):35–38.
[2] Xu Wenchao, Guo Wei. Summarize of reactive power optimization model and algorithm in electric power system [J]. Proceedings of the EPSA, 2003, 15(1):100–104.
[3] Iba K. Reactive power optimization by genetic algorithm [J]. IEEE Trans on Power Systems, 1994, 9(2):685–692.
[4] Xiong Hugang, Cheng Haozhong, Li Hongzhong. Multi-objective reactive power optimization based on immune algorithm [J]. Proceedings of the CSEE, 2006, 26(11):102–108.
[5] Hu Wang, Li Zhishu. A simpler and more effective particle swarm optimization algorithm [J]. Journal of Software, 2007, 18(4):861–868.
[6] Wang Hongzhang, Xiong Xinyin, Wu Yaowu. Power system reactive power optimization based on modified tabu search algorithm [J]. Power System Technology, 2002, 26(1):15–18.
[7] Xiong Yuhui. The optimization of reactive power flow in power system [D]. Nanchang: Nanchang University, 2005.50–52.

Computer, Intelligent Computing and Education Technology – Liu, Sung & Yao (Eds)
© 2014 Taylor & Francis Group, London, ISBN 978-1-138-02469-4

Application of university technology transfer readiness levels

W. Liu
School of Business Administration, North China Electric Power University, Beijing, China

J. Zhang
Higher Education Institute, North China Electric Power University, Beijing, China

ABSTRACT: In order to provide a relative unified standard to choose technical achievements for technology transfer managers, the weights of the five attributes of technology transfer readiness levels could be determined in advance by using U-shaped weight analysis, and the threshold level standard could be determined by using Delphi method. When there are several technical achievements to be compared, it needs to judge the technical achievements whether accord with the threshold level standards or not first, and then calculate the UTTRLs Index to decide which with the highest readiness level.

Keywords: university; technology transfer; readiness level; U-shaped weight analysis

1 INTRODUCTION

A large number of technical achievements are produced in the Chinese university each year. But a lot of cost is required in the process of technology achievements change into product, so only the advanced technology achievements with good market prospect can be selected to transfer. At present it often depends on experience and subjective judgment of technology transfer manager to select the valuable technology achievements, and the judgment standard therefore varies with each manager. University technology transfer readiness levels can overcome this random by the calculation of the total score according to a series of evaluation index.

2 UNIVERSITY TECHNOLOGY TRANSFER READINESS LEVELS

The University Technology Transfer Readiness Levels (UTTRL) include five attributes, they are Technology Maturity Levels (TMLs), Technology Advancement Levels (TALs), Technology Demand Levels (TDLs), Technology Criticality Levels (TCLs) and Stage of Industry Life Cycle (SILCs). Each level summary for every attribute is in Tables 1–5.

3 APPLICATION IN UNIVERSITY TECHNOLOGY INNOVATION MANAGEMENT

In accordance with different R&D purpose, technology innovation projects can be divided into several

Table 1. TMLs definitions.

	Description
TML1	Innovative ideas is bring forward
TML2	Basic principles observed and reported
TML3	Component validation in laboratory environment
TML4	System validation in laboratory environment
TML5	System model or prototype confirmation in a high fidelity laboratory environment or in Simulated operational environment
TML6	System prototype near or at the actual operational environment
TML7	Performance of actual system satisfy with the requires and system been proven to work in its final form and under expected conditions

Table 2. TALs definitions.

	Description
TAL1	The technology has been mastered by a majority of enterprises in the same domestic industry
TAL2	Only 50% of enterprises in the same domestic industry master the technology
TAL3	Only 20% of enterprises in the same domestic industry master the technology
TAL4	Only 5% of enterprises in the same domestic industry master the technology
TAL5	Initiating at domestic industry
TAL6	Advanced technology, initiating in the world

Table 3. TDLs definitions.

	Description
TDL1	Key demands unsatisfied, system not up to the threshold standard, and there are no acceptable technical alternatives
TDL2	Key demands satisfied, but system performance degraded and there are no acceptable solution
TDL3	Key demands satisfied, but system performance degraded, there are acceptable solution available
TDL4	Key demands satisfied, but existing some minor "fit" issues, there may include some capabilities in the product that are not required, and may represent a potential vulnerability
TDL5	"Perfect" fit between demands and product/technology functions. Requirements for products satisfied: nothing more, nothing less

Table 4. TCLs definitions.

	Description
TCL1	Alternative component/technology can be easily substituted within the target system, without any modification or debugging
TCL2	Alternative component/technology can be substituted; but a simple debugging of the system, or replacement or redesign of its individual component is required
TCL3	Alternative component/technology can be substituted; but a moderately complicated debugging of the system and replacement or redesign of many of its components is required
TCL4	Substitution is possible; but a significantly complicated debugging of the system and changing or redesign of a majority of other components/technologies is required
TCL5	No flexibility: any changes to the product/technology under evaluation would require a complete redesign of the system

types, e.g., cost reduction, performance improvement, new product, etc. The importance of each attributes is not the same for different project types. It is necessary to set a threshold standard for every attributes according to different types. Only when the R&D achievement reaches all the threshold standards, it can enter the process of technology transformation.

UTTRLs Index needs to be calculated to compare two or more technology projects which reach the threshold standard. First, for a certain type of technology innovation project, the weight of every attribute should be determined according to the relative importance of the attributes. U-SHAPED weight analysis method can be applied to deal with the experts' judgments.

Table 5. SILCs definitions.

	Description
SILC1	Decline: market demand significantly decreases because of the lack of resources that the industry depends on or new technological reform
SILC2	Maturity: market demand tends to be stable; Technology is very mature; Industry profitability begins to decline. Developing substitute products is the key point of technological innovation
SILC3	Growth: market demand grows rapidly; Technical Information is clearer; The key point of technological innovation is improve performance and increase product variety
SILC4	Introduction: market demand grows quickly; Technological reform is active; Major users of the industry are committed to opening the market, eager to obtain competitiveness advantages in technology products

Different values are given for each level of each attribute. It is worth noticing that the number of levels for different attributes is not the same, so the highest level of each attribute could be given the same value to solve this problem. For example, we can define the highest level of each attribute as 10, then count the value of other levels, and the formula is 10/n, "n" is the number of levels for different attributes. Then, the corresponding values on each level of each element of the compared projects are weighted, and the UTTRLs index of the target project is obtained. Because each attribute is positive index, the higher the index, the higher the effectiveness. The project with maximum UTTRLs index is the best.

4 AN EXAMPLE FOR DEMONSTRATION

To see how this could work in practice, a very simple hypothetical example is provided to examine in the context. There are five Technology achievements, and they have the following characteristics.

$$A_1 = \{TML_{S1} = 4, TAL_{S1} = 4, TDL_{S1} = 3,$$
$$TFL_{S1} = 4, ILC_{S1} = 3\}$$
$$A_2 = \{TML_{S2} = 6, TAL_{S2} = 3, TDL_{S2} = 3,$$
$$TFL_{S2} = 4, ILC_{S2} = 4\}$$
$$A_3 = \{TML_{S3} = 5, TAL_{S3} = 5, TDL_{S3} = 2,$$
$$TFL_{S3} = 3, ILC_{S3} = 4\}$$
$$A_4 = \{TML_{S4} = 5, TAL_{S4} = 3, TDL_{S4} = 4,$$
$$TFL_{S4} = 5, ILC_{S4} = 3\}$$
$$A_5 = \{TML_{S5} = 6, TAL_{S5} = 3, TDL_{S5} = 5,$$
$$TFL_{S5} = 3, ILC_{S5} = 2\}.$$

4.1 Determining the weight with U-shaped weight analysis

4.1.1 Construct judgment matrix of attribute importance by system comparison method

In this example, six experts are invited to judge the important degree of each UTTRLs attributes. Table 6 is one Judgment results of the experts.

The experts only need to tick "√" in the blank Space according to the important degree of each attribute and the sure degree of each judge. In this paper, in order to make the expert to understand and operate more easily, "Sure degree of your judge" is used instead of "self-confident words score standard" in the U-shaped weight analysis method.

All the questionnaires are collected. "Very sure" is given 10, "Somewhat sure" is given 9, and "Almost sure" is given 8. So the judge results of the six experts can be expressed in terms of self-confident degree evaluation matrix as follow.

$$
C_1 = \begin{bmatrix} 9 & 0 & 0 & 0 \\ 10 & 0 & 0 & 0 \\ 0 & 10 & 0 & 0 \\ 0 & 0 & 9 & 0 \\ 0 & 8 & 0 & 0 \end{bmatrix}
\quad
C_2 = \begin{bmatrix} 10 & 0 & 0 & 0 \\ 0 & 9 & 0 & 0 \\ 0 & 8 & 0 & 0 \\ 0 & 0 & 10 & 0 \\ 0 & 9 & 0 & 0 \end{bmatrix}
$$

$$
C_3 = \begin{bmatrix} 10 & 0 & 0 & 0 \\ 9 & 0 & 0 & 0 \\ 0 & 9 & 0 & 0 \\ 0 & 0 & 8 & 0 \\ 0 & 8 & 0 & 0 \end{bmatrix}
\quad
C_4 = \begin{bmatrix} 10 & 0 & 0 & 0 \\ 9 & 0 & 0 & 0 \\ 0 & 9 & 0 & 0 \\ 0 & 8 & 0 & 0 \\ 0 & 10 & 0 & 0 \end{bmatrix}
$$

$$
C_5 = \begin{bmatrix} 10 & 0 & 0 & 0 \\ 0 & 10 & 0 & 0 \\ 0 & 9 & 0 & 0 \\ 0 & 0 & 9 & 0 \\ 9 & 0 & 0 & 0 \end{bmatrix}
\quad
C_6 = \begin{bmatrix} 10 & 0 & 0 & 0 \\ 9 & 0 & 0 & 0 \\ 0 & 10 & 0 & 0 \\ 0 & 9 & 0 & 0 \\ 0 & 0 & 8 & 0 \end{bmatrix}
$$

4.1.2 Consistency test to a judgment matrix

Whether the difference of the experts' judge result is in the permitted range or not should be examined before weight calculate, and this process is named consistency test. Kendall's concordance coefficient is one of the commonly used methods, and the main steps are as follows.

Step 1: Change the scores of self-confident degree into rank order

The following rules should be according to: if the score is greater than 0, the higher the important degree is, the small the rank order is. If the scores belong to the same important degree, the higher the score is, the small the rank order is. If there are several attributes with the same important levels and self-confident degree scores, the rank order is the average of their rank order positions.

Table 7 is the rank order result changing from self-confident degree evaluation matrix.

Step 2: Calculate Kendall's concordance coefficient

Calculation formula of Kendall's concordance coefficient is in the following.

$$
r_W = \frac{SS_R}{\frac{1}{12}K^2\left(n^3 - n\right) - K\sum T} \tag{1}
$$

Among them, K is the number of experts Participating in evaluation, n is the number of Attributes, R is the total of all rank order of an attribute, and SS_R is the sum of squares of deviations of R, the Calculation formula of SS_R is following.

$$
SS_R = \sum R^2 - \left(\sum R\right)^2 / n \tag{2}
$$

m is the number of the same rank order given by one expert.

$$
T = \sum \left(m^3 - m\right) / 12 \tag{3}
$$

Table 6. Attribute weight evaluation table of UTTRLs.

Attributes	Very important	Important	Normal	Not important	Sure degree of your judge		
	1	0.75	0.50	0.25	Very sure	Somewhat sure	Almost sure
Technology Maturity Levels (TMLs)	√					√	
Technology Advancement Levels (TALs)	√				√		
Technology Demand Levels (TDLs)		√			√		
Technology Criticality Levels (TCLs)			√			√	
Stage of Industry Life Cycl (SILCs)		√					√

Table 7. Rank time table of attribute importance judgment result.

Attribute (n)	Expert (K)						R	R²
	1	2	3	4	5	6		
Technology Maturity Levels (TMLs)	2	1	1	1	1	1	7	49
Technology Advancement Levels (TALs)	1	2.5	2	2	3	2	12.5	156.25
Technology Demand Levels (TDLs)	3	4	3	4	4	3	21	441
Technology Criticality Levels (TCLs)	5	5	5	5	5	4	29	841
Stage of Industry Life Cycle (SILCs)	4	2.5	4	3	2	5	20.5	420.25
Total							90	1907.5

According to Table 7, SS_R in this example can be calculated,

$$SS_R = \sum R^2 - \left(\sum R\right)^2 / n = 1907.5 - 90^2/5 = 287.5$$

There are two same rank orders in the attribute importance judgment result of the second expert, so

$$T_2 = \frac{m^3 - m}{12} = \frac{2^3 - 2}{12} = 0.5$$

Because there isn't same rank order in the judgment result of other expert, $\Sigma T = T_2 = 0.5$

The relevant data is substituted in the formula (1),

$$r_W = \frac{287.5}{\frac{1}{12} \times 6^2 \times \left(5^3 - 5\right) - 6 \times 0.5} = 0.805$$

Step 3: Kendal harmonious factor significance test

$$H_0 : \rho = 0,\ H_1 : \rho \neq 0$$
$$\chi^2 = K(n-1)r_W = 6 \times (5-1) \times 0.805 = 19.32$$

$df = n - 1 = 5 - 1 = 4$, so according to χ^2 value table, $\chi^2_{(4)0.01} = 13.28$. Because $\chi^2 = 19.32^{**} > 13.28 = \chi^2_{(4)0.01}$, H_0 is refused at the significance level of 0.01, and H_1 is adopted. The significance test result means that the attribute

importance evaluation results of the six experts are highly consistent, and the attribute weight can be continued to calculate.

4.1.3 *Calculation of attribute weight*

4.1.3.1 All the self-confident degree evaluation matrix are added together

$$C = \sum_{i=1}^{k} C_i \tag{4}$$

In formula (4), C_i is the self-confident degree evaluation matrix of the i'th expert, C is the sum of self-confident degree evaluation matrix of experts from the 1st to k'th, then the following is obtained.

$$C = \begin{bmatrix} 59 & 0 & 0 & 0 \\ 37 & 19 & 0 & 0 \\ 0 & 55 & 0 & 0 \\ 0 & 17 & 36 & 0 \\ 9 & 35 & 8 & 0 \end{bmatrix}$$

4.1.3.2 Calculation of degree belonging to very important of each attribute

$$e_i = \frac{1}{10K} C_i D',\ (i = 1, 2, 3, \ldots, n) \tag{5}$$

In formula (5), e_i is the degree belonging to very important of the i'th attribute. C_i is the self-confident degree belonging to each important level of the i'th attribute. K is the number of experts. D' is the transposed matrix of importance level parameter.

$$D' = \begin{bmatrix} 1 \\ 0.75 \\ 0.50 \\ 0.25 \end{bmatrix}$$

The degree belonging to very important of the five attributes can be calculated using formula (5).

$$e_1 = \frac{1}{10 \times 6}(59\ \ 0\ \ 0\ \ 0)\begin{bmatrix} 1 \\ 0.75 \\ 0.50 \\ 0.25 \end{bmatrix} = 0.983$$

$e_2 = 0.854$ $e_3 = 0.688$ $e_4 = 0.513$ $e_5 = 0.654$

4.1.3.3 Normalization

$$W_i = \frac{e_i}{\sum_{i=1}^{n} e_i} \qquad (6)$$

The weights can be obtained, $W_1 = 0.266$, $W_2 = 0.231$, $W_3 = 0.186$, $W_4 = 0.139$, $W_5 = 0.177$.

4.2 Determining threshold level standard

Delphi method is used to determine the threshold level standard of university technology transfer, and after several consultations, the threshold level standard tend to be consistent. Only the Technology achievement which meets $TML_S \geq 5$, $TAL_S \geq 3$, $TDL_S \geq 3$, $TFL_S \geq 3$, $ILC_S \geq 2$ at the same time can enter the Technology transfer process.

4.3 Normalization of each attribute level score

See Tables 8–12.

Table 8. The score for each technology maturity level.

TML_s	1	2	3	4	5	6	7
V_{TML}	1.43	2.86	4.29	5.71	7.14	8.57	10.00

Table 9. The score for each technology advancement level.

TAL_s	1	2	3	4	5	6
V_{TAL}	1.67	3.33	5.00	6.67	8.33	10.00

Table 10. The score for each technology demand level.

TDL_s	1	2	3	4	5
V_{TDL}	2.00	4.00	6.00	8.00	10.00

Table 11. The score for each technology fungible level

TFL_s	1	2	3	4	5
V_{TFL}	2.00	4.00	6.00	8.00	10.00

Table 12. The score for each stage in industry life cycle.

ILC_s	1	2	3	4
V_{ILC}	2.50	5.00	7.50	10.00

4.4 Calculation of the UTTRLs Index

In this example, technology achievement A_1 and A_3 don't meet threshold level standard of technology maturity and standard of technology demand separately. The UTTRLs Index of other three technology achievements can be calculated by using formula (7).

$$L_A = W_1 \times V_{TML} + W_2 \times V_{TAL} + W_3 \times V_{TDL} + W_4 \times V_{TFL} + W_5 \times V_{ILC} \qquad (7)$$

L_A is the UTTRLs Index. so,

$$L_{A2} = [0.266 \quad 0.231 \quad 0.186 \quad 0.139 \quad 0.177] \bullet \begin{bmatrix} 8.57 \\ 5.00 \\ 6.00 \\ 8.00 \\ 10.00 \end{bmatrix} = 7.433$$

$$L_{A4} = 7.260, \quad L_{A5} = 7.014$$

Through the comparison, technology achievement with the highest technology transfer readiness level should be transferred first.

5 CONCLUSION

UTTRLs provide a standard for technology achievements choice in university technology transfer management. In this paper an example is given to explain how to apply UTTRLs in the technology achievements choice. In the example, U-shaped weight analysis is used to of technology transfer readiness levels, and Delphi method is used to determining the threshold level standard. Two technology achievements don't meet the threshold level standards, and the UTTRLs Index of the other three technology achievements which meet the threshold level standards are calculated to compare. For convenience, in practice, technology achievements can be divided into several categories such as cost reduction, performance improvement, new product, etc. The attribute weight and threshold level standard for every category can be determined in advance by using the above method, Then the technology transfer manager can judge and choose the best technology achievement to transfer according to the attributes' levels of each achievement. So the method in this paper does not only solve the problem of inconsistent standards, but also save the cost of specialist.

ACKNOWLEDGMENT

This paper was one of the research achievements of education science research project approved by Hebei Association of Higher Education (GJXHZ2013-32) and was financially supported by "the Fundamental Research Funds for the Central Universities" (No. 13MS59).

REFERENCES

Jim Smith. 2004. An alternative to technology readiness levels for Non-Developmental Item (NDI) Software. *technical report. CMU/SEI-2004-TR-013, ESC-TR-2004-013.*

Nolte, William L., et al., 2003. Technology Readiness Level Calculator, Air Force Research Laboratory, presented at the NDIA Systems Engineering Conference.

Qin Ying, 2004. Determining weight coefficients of teaching quality evaluation index by u-shaped weight coefficients analytical method[J]. *Journal of TaiYuan teachers college (natural science edition),*vol. 3, pp. 12–15.

Qiao Junlu, Analyses and Countermeasure of the technology transfer work, http://www.chinatorch.gov.cn/ckzl/llyj.

Zhang Juan, Liu Wei. 2010. Research on technology transfer readiness level and its application in university technology innovation management [A]. *2010 International Conference on E-business and E-government (ICEE2010)[C].* Conference Publishing Services: 1904–1907.

Computer, Intelligent Computing and Education Technology – Liu, Sung & Yao (Eds)
© *2014 Taylor & Francis Group, London, ISBN 978-1-138-02469-4*

IT offshore outsourcing: Development and countermeasures

M.M. Hu
Hunan International Economics University, Changsha, China

S. Xu
Hunan University of Commerce, Changsha, China

ABSTRACT: The shift of global service industry and the worldwide wave of IT outsourcing bring great opportunities and challenges to China's IT outsourcing and industry. Based on the definition of IT offshore outsourcing, this paper makes explanations on the situation of China's IT offshore outsourcing and its impact on China. And then, from the competitiveness analysis of China's IT offshore outsourcing, it puts forth the countermeasures for China to develop IT offshore outsourcing in the future. It specially emphasizes the importance of government support and strengthening the awareness of intellectual property protection.

Keywords: IT offshore outsourcing; China's IT outsourcing; industrial upgrading; government support; intellectual property

1 INTRODUCTION

Compared with domestic outsourcing, offshore outsourcing refers to transnational outsourcing activity carried out by outsourcers and their contractors coming from different countries. Since 1988, Kodak outsourced most of its information system to IBM, IT outsourcing got rapid development. However, in the early 1990s, IT outsourcing is mainly domestic outsourcing. Until the late1990s, because the U.S. economic depression and the arising of "millennium bug" problem, the U.S. outsourced many Information Technologies (IT) to India, which led to the development of IT offshore outsourcing.

The advantages of IT offshore outsourcing include: effectively reducing the cost of outsourcers; obtaining high quality staff and technology from other countries to improve outsourcing project quality; shortening project completion cycles by use of different working teams from different time zones around the world. Of course, IT offshore outsourcing may also increase the complexity of business operation and then may result in outsourcers' loss of management control, which is mainly due to the complexity of multinational remote management. In addition, there exist language barriers, cultural differences, and differences in the protection extent of intellectual property regulations and other issues. However, with globalization of the world economy, it must be certain that IT offshore outsourcing has the advantages

of international cooperation and can help to gain profits from the labor cost differences between different countries. So on one side, IT offshore outsourcing has become a very effective way for outsourcers to improve their core competence and obtain sustainable development. On the other side, according to undertaking IT offshore outsourcing, developing countries obtain important opportunities for their economic transformation and their improvement on countries' competitiveness. To be the main contractors of many outsourcers from developed countries, including the United States and other European countries, China has obtained an important developing opportunity. China's enterprises are cooperating with more and more foreign enterprises and playing an increasingly important role in the global value chain. This paper focuses on the development, influence and countermeasures of China's IT Offshore outsourcing to find effective ways to improve IT offshore outsourcing quality.

2 THE DEVELOPMENT OF CHINA'S IT OFFSHORE OUTSOURCING

Entering the 21st century, IT offshore outsourcing becomes an irreversible and new round trend of global industrial revolution and transfer. It also increasingly becomes an important strategic tool for enterprises to design their multinational business and improve their international competitiveness.

Many multinational enterprises outsource their IT infrastructure services in the global market and save their labor costs up to 60%, or save approximately 30% of their IT infrastructure operational costs. According to statistics, the global potential market size of service offshore outsourcing has reached $465 billion, in which IT application services market is $90 billion and IT infrastructure services market is $85 billion. Because of supply shortages, the market potentials is still far from being fully released. Therefore, the potential market and developing opportunity of IT offshore outsourcing is still quite huge.

China has been an important undertaking country in global development of IT offshore outsourcing. According to the report of International Data Corporation (IDC), the market size of China's undertaking on software offshore outsourcing reached $4.123 billion in 2011. It realized an increase of 22.8% than that in 2010. This figure is expected to continue rapidly rising with a Compound Annual Growth Rate (CAGR) of 25.3%. According to the forecast of the Ministry of Industry and Information Technology of China, at least before 2020, China's IT service industry will be the fastest growing industry from the aspect of output value and is likely to become the top two largest industry in 2020. However, we must also see that there are several problems needed to be solved for China's IT outsourcing industry in the next period of time. In the market share and growth rate of IT offshore outsourcing, China is still significantly behind India. In 2007, the output value of global software offshore outsourcing reached $60 billion, while China just accounted for less than 10% share. Although the growth speed of China's top four IT outsourcing service providers is not slow in the past few years, the annual growth rate of India's top four IT enterprises is twice as that of China's IT enterprises. In 2007, the size of India's top four IT enterprises reached 14 times that of China's top four IT enterprises. In 2011, after the rebound of global software market, some new technology represented by cloud computing, mobile internet and social networking constantly promoted the birth of new business models, which also brought new opportunities and challenges for the development of global IT market. At the same time, it is found that data security and intellectual property has become common weak points. Privacy protection and security protection are still challenges IT offshore outsourcing face.

3 THE IMPACT OF IT OFFSHORE OUTSOURCING ON CHINA

As a main country of undertaking IT offshore outsourcing, China undoubtedly obtains huge economic and social benefits from it. Offshore outsourcing facilitates industrial transfer and upgrade, promotes the optimization of export structure, breaks trade barriers, and produces technology spillover effects. The development of India's software industry well confirms the positive role of undertaking IT offshore outsourcing in promoting India's development. In India, according to undertaking IT offshore outsourcing, IT services exports are expanded and then corresponding exports revenues are also increased, which reduce India's export deficit and improve its international balance of payments. In China, IT offshore outsourcing also produces such effects on its economic development. The IT management level of China's enterprises has been greatly improved. Their core competences are also enhanced. As the same time, IT offshore outsourcing creates employment opportunities for Chinese. It drives China's education development of IT technology and management. Another important benefit for China is saving energy consumption and reducing environmental pollution. However, IT offshore outsourcing is a double-edged sword. Some people think IT offshore outsourcing brings some adverse effects on China. Some enterprises are not good at outsourcing management and risk control, which leads to the failure in IT offshore outsourcing cooperation or loss of intellectual property. In the global value chain, although China is increasingly undertaking IT offshore services, developed countries still regard it as a supplier of cheap labor. Just for this reason, China is still in the low end of the global IT industry value chain. Other analysts believe that IT offshore outsourcing may result in the uneven development in different regions and sectors of China. The income gap will be enlarged. This is due to the fact that the enterprises undertaking IT offshore outsourcing are mainly concentrated in economically developed areas in China and the wage of IT enterprises is much higher than that of other enterprises. In addition, compared with the manufacturing industry, IT offshore outsourcing brings greater culture, values and institutional impacts on China.

4 DEVELOPMENT TACTICS OF CHINA'S IT OFFSHORE OUTSOURCING

Understanding the present situation and the need of development is to better guide the future practice. At present, compared with India, China's total market of undertaking IT offshore outsourcing still remains behind. The organizational structure of China's software enterprises seems small and scattered, and there is not a real big business. According to related statistics of China Software Association, there are over 8000 enterprises engaged in IT outsourcing in China. In these enterprises, there are only 2000 who specialize in software research and development. The rest are mostly concurrently engaged in software and related services. From the point of view of employed persons in an enterprise, enterprises with less than 50 persons approximately account for 55%; enterprises with 50 to 200 persons account for 42%; enterprises with more than 1000 persons are only a few. In addition, although Chinese labor costs are lower, the information technology and management training are still relatively backward, which is embodied in China's international certification on IT and contact center operations; intellectual property protection; labors' language level; and communication skills. Therefore, it is very necessary for China to build development support system of IT offshore outsourcing.

4.1 Increasing government support and building a full service plarform

In order to enhance the international competitiveness of China's IT offshore outsourcing, the most important thing is to increase government support. To this end, the government needs to strengthen the construction of IT infrastructure, simplify work processes, and formulate relevant policies to give more concessions to IT enterprises in regard of finance, taxation, export subsidies, export credit and credit insurance. The government should pay special attention to the construction and improvement of IT outsourcing statistical system, strengthen the research on development trend of IT offshore outsourcing, and grasp the new situation and new features of the development of IT outsourcing industry, which is to provide enterprises the qualitative and quantitative basis to make decision and reduce their possibilities encountering the barriers from policy, law, market, society and technology. As the same time, the government should provide advisory services, IT offshore outsourcing policies, market access, and the project need information for enterprises through the dedicated website to guide enterprises to undertake and develop IT offshore outsourcing market.

4.2 Improving industry integration and service quality

The small-scale of IT enterprises is the main weakness in the development of China's IT offshore outsourcing. Therefore, we must find ways to improve industry integration and expand the enterprise scale. These can be achieved by acquisitions and mergers to integrate business resources to promote the sustainable development of the whole industry. The formation of IT outsourcing industry clusters is also very important. Through industry gathering, rational division of labor and integration of resources within the industry can enhance the enterprises' competitiveness. The association of service outsourcing industry should be given adequate attention. The industry association should play a substantial role in coordinating corporate relations, promoting effective integration within the industry, and promoting orderly competition. Of course, China's IT enterprises should be encouraged to cooperated with those of developed countries to expand business scale through the introduction of foreign capital.

4.3 Promoting enterprises' upgrading on industry value chain

China should learn from the India's successful experiences in IT offshore outsourcing development. Furthermore, China's enterprises should actively seek to cooperate with India's enterprises to achieve complementary advantages and enter into the high-end international IT market. For China's enterprises, such kind of cooperation can help to quickly obtain partners' resource advantages to train project management personnel and enhance the ability to open up international market. China's enterprises can make full use of the marketing network in the U.S. and European markets developed by India's enterprises to develop European markets. This is conducive to the progressive realization of IT enterprises' upgrading on industry value chain.

4.4 Improving education and training system of it talents

Human capital is an important foundation of IT outsourcing development. IT talents are directly involved in the value chain and are the source of customer value creation. At present, there is a large gap of China's software talents. Personnel structure is irrational and unstable. There is still a gap in the language and culture between Chinese and foreigners. Therefore, we should form an effective strategy and management system for IT human resources. A talents training system mainly directed by the national formal education and combined with multi-level schools runed by society and enterprises should be established. The government should give policy support to the society and enterprises for running schools. It is very urgent to cultivate high-end software development professionals and low-end software technical personnels, which is to provide strong intellectual support and personnel protection for the development of IT industry. The IT enterprises should also increase their own internal personnel training and actively attract external technical elites to rapidly establish the human capital base in a technology field or an industrial application field. In addition, we should also focus on the marketers' education and improvement on software knowledge, target market culture, and language ability to enable marketers qualified to explore overseas markets.

4.5 *Strengthening the management awareness on intellectual property*

The intellectual property issues of IT offshore outsourcing mainly relates to the issue of the intellectual property ownership, including patents, trademarks, copyright and related rights. Especially for tenure issues that property ownership is not clear and is not agreed in contract, the protection awareness of intellectual property should be strengthened in particular. For example, in an outsourcing partnership, the contractor may need provide the third part's development tools or softwares to finish their tasks, or the outsourcer permits the contractor to use the third part's intellectual property to finish the tasks. Both of the two situations may constitute infringement. Therefore, in addition to confirming the ownership relegation, the scope of license or authorization is needed to make clear. The contractor must use it in strict accordance with the scope of the authorization. With regard to an intellectual property produced by the contractor in an outsourcing project, The problem of the ownership right should be included in negotiation and contract. In addition to these provisions needed to be clear, enterprises should keep their promises in full accordance with international information security requirements to enhance their credibility and win the sustainable development.

5 CONCLUSION

The development of IT offshore outsourcing not only conforms to the global trend of economic development, but also be in line with China's role in the world economy. More importantly, the development of IT offshore outsourcing will certainly complement with China's established manufacturing advantage. IT outsourcing industry and manufacturing industry will become the twin-engine to promote long-term, balanced and sustainable development of China's economy. From the current competitiveness situation, China is still far behind India on the aspect of comprehensive abilities in undertaking IT offshore outsourcing. There are many reasons for the ability gap, including policy support, quality of human capital, IT infrastructure, cost advantage, and business environment. Government's support is the most important factor to affect the future development of IT offshore outsourcing. If China will grasp the development opportunity in the new round of global service outsourcing wave, the government should serve as a guide and give main support in infrastructure investment to play a full role in macro-guidance, comprehensive coordination, talents cultivation, financial support and service system.

REFERENCES

IDC: Market Scale of China's Offshore Outsourcing Reached $4.1 Billion Last Year. http://tech.sina.com.cn/it/2012-07-24/16427423124.shtml.

Yan, Z. 2008. Comparison of Competitiveness in undertaking IT outsourcing between China and India. *Journal of Jiangxi University of Finance and Economics* 10(3): 11–15.

Zhiqiang, X. 2009. China's Exploration in Software Outsourcing Inflection Point: Learning from India's Reverse-type Growth. *21st Century Business Herald.*

Computer, Intelligent Computing and Education Technology – Liu, Sung & Yao (Eds)
© 2014 Taylor & Francis Group, London, ISBN 978-1-138-02469-4

A study on combination of occupational and educational characteristics of vocational education in teaching reform of basic commonality curriculum

Yu-Guo Fan
Shandong Transport Vocational College, Weifang, China

ABSTRACT: It is necessary for vocational education to focus on its occupational characteristics and also take its educational characteristics into account if it is run with high quality and distinctive features. Occupational characteristics determine aspirations of practical value of educational characteristics while educational characteristics determine knowledge-based approach of occupational characteristics. In teaching reform of basic commonality curriculum, basic commonality curriculum can reflect its true value only to realize the combination of occupational and educational characteristics. This article is to dissert the effective combination of occupational and educational characteristics of vocational education in teaching reform of basic commonality curriculum, taking vocational college English for an example.

Keywords: vocational education; effective combination of occupational and educational characteristics; basic commonality curriculum

1 PREFACE

In recent years, under the guidance of the principles and policies of our country to develop vocational education vigorously, great development and progress have been made in vocational college education, especially a variety of professional curriculum development and construction has been carried out in many vocational colleges, taking national quality course construction and demonstration college building as an opportunity, and vocational characteristics of professional curriculum in some vocational colleges are more distinctive. However, compared to leapfrog development of professional courses, the development of basic commonality curriculum has lagged, even though some reforms of basic commonality curriculum some vocational colleges have made can not still meet the requirements of advanced vocational education concepts, namely to achieve he effective combination of occupational and educational characteristics. In this context, the author is to investigate the effective combination of occupational and educational characteristics of vocational education in teaching reform of basic commonality curriculum, taking vocational college English for an example.

2 THE RELATIONSHIP BETWEEN OCCUPATIONAL AND EDUCATIONAL CHARACTERISTICS IN VOCATIONAL EDUCATION

Vocational and educational characteristics of vocational education are complementary. On the one hand, occupational characteristics determine aspirations of practical value of educational characteristics. Vocational education is career-oriented, and the training of personnel will event-ually face the specific production practices, where it has a specific job requirements, contents, context, etc., which determines it is of great value aspirations for educational process to solve the students' career of confusion. Of educational pursuit, it is difficult to train useful talents adapted to job demand and achieve the purpose of vocational education if it is divorced from value-oriented practice. On the other hand, educational characteristics of vocational education determine the occupational knowledge-based approach. The theoretical knowledge systems in different professional fields and complex individual knowledge building are needed to achieve educational purposes of Higher Vocational Education. The implementation of occupational characteristics is no longer a simple operation of machines or acquirement of skills, but needs the students to know the knowledge well behind specific skills to provide rich possibilities of career transformation. Therefore, the higher vocational education without occupational characteristics can not realize the purpose of developing professional skills of personnel while vocational education lack of educational characteristics is difficult to train professional skills of personnel with a rich cultural heritage, healthy personality characters, and independent thinking and judgment. Occupational and educational characteristics of vocational education are just like "two wings". Only when the coordination resonance and effective combination of the tow sides come into effect will sustainable development of vocational education training be achieved.

3 TEACHING REFORM OF BASIC COMMONALITY CURRICULUM

To adapt to the new situation and development of China's vocational education and realize the effective combination of occupational and educational characteristics of vocational education in teaching reform of basic commonality curriculum, the author thinks that the reforms should be carried out in teaching philosophy, teaching contents, teaching mode, teaching methods and evaluation, etc.

3.1 Teaching philosophy

Vocational basic commonality curriculum should formulate courses based on talent specifications, strive to create a good quality of students and provide satisfactory service for society starting from social needs and student development. The core objective of employment-oriented basic commonality curriculum is to serve employment. Setting the courses and their contents and the choice of methods must focus on the goal of employment services. The theoretical contents of basic commonality curriculum should be appropriate, and it must strictly be in accordance with the requirements of professional positions selection of suitable talents. What professional positions need should be taught and how much it needs should be taught appropriately, focusing on the theory in practice, the scope of application of prominent theoretical knowledge and the introduction of application examples to improve students' ability of applying theoretical knowledge and ultimately the implementation effect should be tested through employment adaptability. During the course of curriculum development and public

settings, general education should be combined with vocational training, that is to say, basic commonality curriculum not only pays attention to the students' learning of theoretical knowledge and the development of humanities and culture and the spirit of innovation, but reflects the vocational students' needs for future career development and job specific requirements for basic commonality curriculum. Taking vocational English as an example, on the one hand, students' comprehensive ability of English language and humanities should be developed mainly in language knowledge, language skills, learning strategies, attitudes and cultural communication. On the other hand, because the goal of vocational education is to develop skilled personnel in the field of production, construction and service, vocational English teaching should be closely linked to occupational teaching based on the industry group and work process and achieve the combination of work and study in vocational English teaching and then apply their knowledge to their work.

3.2 Teaching contents

On the teaching content of basic commonality curriculum, theoretical knowledge should be integrated into operating skills. Vocational colleges should integrate theoretical knowledge into operating skills in order to improve students' ability of knowledge integration and flexibility and lay a solid foundation for the student's career. Also, it is certain to be clear that vocational students not only obtain a professional skill but more importantly obtain a wealth of knowledge and innovation ability. Specific to the vocational English teaching, the author thinks it is a cultural foundation course first, playing the role of training and developing English comprehensive ability, employment, entrepreneurship, and more post migration, sustainable development, comprehensive development and lifelong learning ability. At the same time, vocational English plays the role of supplying career development services and reflecting different stages of job for the students. Therefore, the author believes that depending on English language requirements from the students' different professional career development stages and different stages of work, the curriculum contents of vocational English can be divided into basic English, workplace English, industry English and professional English, respectively based on the language knowledge and language skills of primitive accumulation, pan-Business English for all occupations, industry English based on a typical work process, and professional English based on complete discipline system. Thus, the effective combination of occupational and educational characteristics of vocational education in teaching reform of basic commonality curriculum can be carried on.

3.3 Teaching mode

The design of teaching mode is to complete the teaching content and achieve the teaching philosophy better; therefore, the new mode of basic commonality curriculum should coordinate the relationship between occupational and educational characteristics of vocational education to make it more harmonious and coordinated. It's very essential to optimizing the structure and focusing on innovation in the reforming process. Optimizing the structure of basic commonality curriculum in vocational education should focus on cultivating innovative talents, improving their overall quality of employment, paying attention to the combined effects and the overall effect of basic commonality curriculum and establishing a curriculum system of talent training distinct from Talents disciplinary curriculum system based on the market for high-skilled talents specifications. Emphasis on innovative modular construction of basic commonality curriculum the curriculum should focus on dividing basic commonality curriculum into facilitate various combinations of elements which can be a knowledge unit, an operating unit, and also a situational simulation unit in order to improve students' professional and moral qualities, professional competency and overall professional quality through the training module courses of basic commonality curriculum. In view of the differences between professionals and students' individuals, it is not necessary for the teaching modes of basic commonality curriculum to adopt uniform requirements while the mode of compulsory, specified elective or any elective can be adopted. Basic English, workplace English and industry English can be compulsory courses and some professional English and quality courses can be elective according to the interests and needs of the students. In addition, the students can be divided into three parts depending on their basic level of English language and the needs of students' own development. The teaching mode of vocational English can be divided into A, B, C three levels. Among them, level A is intended for the students who have a good foundation in English and hope to pass CET-4 or go further education after three-year learning of English, and in this level, English is compulsory with basic English being main teaching content; level B is mainly intended for the students who are interested in English learning and have a certain level of English language in the hope of passing PETS-3, and in this level, English learning is compulsory or elective with workplace English or industry English being main teaching content,

focusing on the training of listening and speaking; C-level is mainly intended for the students who almost have no English language foundation and no interest in English learning student population, and in this level, English learning is elective with professional core competencies being main teaching content, focusing on training of professionalism and cultural communication. Therefore, the teaching contents of three different teaching modes from three different levels make vocational and educational characteristics of vocational education combined well. In addition, the second class and the third class can be set up as well as traditional classroom teaching. The second class mentioned here refers to a teaching mode full of various school activities, practice and training in which reasonable and correct English is used in the situations mentioned above; and the third means a kind of teaching mode in which reasonable and correct English is used in internship enterprise, future work and social activities. Thus, in the three stages mentioned above, the progressive combination of work and study is realized in vocational college English teaching, namely the combination of class teaching and job-related English proficiency training, college English teachers and professional teachers in college English teaching and College English learning in classroom and the use of English in work. This teaching model is undoubtedly beneficial to not only students' English proficiency in the practice environment, but also to the effective combination of occupational and educational characteristics of vocational education.

3.4 Teaching methods

The lecture method is the main traditional teaching method of basic commonality curriculum, which makes it difficult to represent vocational characteristics of vocational education in teaching. In recent years, the new teaching methods of task-based teaching and project teaching based on work process which can represent occupational characteristics of vocational education are very popular. These teaching methods emphasize task-centric, put forward a task on the basis of a professional problem and set a scene in which the students are assigned all kinds of roles like in real jobs enabling students to make full use of what they have learned during the course to complete the task. Also taking vocational English teaching as an example, a company is going to participate in an international launches of new products and has set up a team to this, including some members from research and development section, production section and sales section. In the task, the students can be divided into several groups, and each group with members from different parts of the company were

Table 1.

Forms of evaluation	Proportion	Nature of evaluation	Specific contents	Emphases
Class performance and task completion	40%	Formative assessment	File bags	Learning attitude
Performances of practical activities in and outside the school	20%	Formative assessment	Self-assessment and peer assessment	Learning attitude
Results of final examination	40%	Summative assessment	Comprehensive language skills	Learning effect

in charge of the introduction of one part of the product, including the size of the design, material selection, working principle and function, maintenance services and so on. During the process, first, students gather the relevant information, and then a representative from each group is sent to present their work, and last all the students and the teacher make summary and evaluation about the performances of each group. In this process, the students' English language proficiency and comprehensive and professional knowledge related to the product have been made full use of and occupational and educational characteristics of vocational education are effectively combined. Meanwhile, some professionalism such as professional ethics, integrity awareness, realistic and teamwork has also been strengthened.

3.5 Teaching evaluation

Traditional teaching evaluation mode of basic commonality curriculum is mainly based on students' integrated performances of daily academic and final examination. Besides this, the author thinks, students should be guided to concern the learning process of these basic commonality curriculums and the association between the application of some basic knowledge and future occupation. In particular, more attention should be paid to students' performances of the application of some basic knowledge in all kinds of practical activities in and outside the school including proportion, rationality and correctness of the application of some basic knowledge. In view of this, a more reasonable English teaching evaluation mode is designed as follows in Table 1.

4 CONCLUSION

In short, vocational and educational characteristics, which are complementary rather than exclusive, are two indispensable parts of vocational education. So the comprehensive development of the human personality can be promoted and the comprehensive capacity of vocational education and well-being index of students can be improved only if both get attention. Professor Jiang Dayuan thinks that work process is an essential path to integration of practical and theoretical curriculum of vocational education and that basic commonality curriculum should be combined into industry, trade, business, profession and practice, starting from posts and tasks of jobs. Thus, occupational and educational characteristics of basic commonality curriculum can be effectively combined to make it more viable in vocational education reform tide.

REFERENCES

[1] Dayuan Jiang. 2007. New research on vocational education. Beijing: Education Science Press.
[2] Dayuan Jiang. 2008. The basic trend and revelation of vocational education curriculum reform of the world. Beijing: Chinese Vocational and Technical Education.
[3] Junbo Ma. 2010. The reform of vocational English based on vocational education concept. China Modern Education Equipment.
[4] Department of Higher Education. 2000. The basic requirements for vocational English teaching. Beijing: Higher Education Press.

Function of college physical education in quality-oriented education and ways of implementing

Wen-Xi Gao

Transportation College, Inner Mongolia University, Hohhot, China

ABSTRACT: In this paper, Physical Education Teaching Education for improving the quality of students, promote student intellectual development, improve learning efficiency, to develop students of ideological and aesthetic quality, and improve quality education in PE teaching the basic way. Physical quality is an important part of quality education, it is with the ideological and moral qualities, scientific and cultural quality, labor skills and other qualities constitute a relatively complete continuum of quality education. Physical education is to implement the physical quality of the main channel. Physical Education teaching as an important component of basic education, it has unique advantages in promoting the comprehensive development of children and to comprehensively improve the quality of all aspects of the students, when compared with other education disciplines, with great advantage and irreplaceable role in Therefore, the study of physical education and quality education, the relationship of great significance.

Keywords: physical education; physical quality; quality education

1   INTRODUCTION

Quality education is a series of activities for the purpose of full developing and improving students' basic quality for all students. As an integral part of quality education in physical education, PE plays an important role in quality education activities. Correct understanding of the role of physical education in development of quality education is important.

2   THE MEANING OF SCHOOL PHYSICAL EDUCATION AND QUALITY EDUCATION

1. As an important part of basic school education, school physical education is an indispensable element of quality education in the current. "Sports and health courses standard" pointed out that "through learning sports and health courses, students will: enhancing physical, mastering and applying basic knowledge of sports and health and movement skills; training interest and hobby of movement, forming insisted exercise habits; have a good psychological quality, performing out the sense of interpersonal dating of capacity and cooperation spirit; improving on personal health and groups health, and forming health of lifestyle; carrying forward sports spirit, and forming an aggressive and optimistic cheerful of life attitude."

2. The meaning of quality education in physical education

In PE, Connotation of quality education includes five aspects of ideological qualities, cultural qualities, capacity qualities, psychological qualities and physical qualities.

Ideological and political education should run through the entire process of physical education teaching, the key is raising students' sporting values, setting the right goals of value and enhancing students' patriotism, raising right students' consciousness and habits on sports.

Capacity quality is the ability of developing science sport prescription, consciously for exercise by using sports knowledge and combining themselves of actual,: can by using evaluation approach of physique indicators, correctly evaluating themselves' exercise effect, and having the capacity on exercise process for effective control; can by using learn of movement race aspects of basic knowledge to organize small race activities and served as referee work; can by using sports aesthetic knowledge, having the capacity of shaping body beauty and attitude beauty, and the capacity of enjoying sports game. The first goal of the PE training is to make student have above ability, to improve their intellectual curiosity, creativity and self-development ability.

Physical fitness is an important component in PE. Considering to develop "generalist" talent, we should pay attention to differences between different students, so that all pupils to balanced development.

3 THE PRESENT SITUATION OF SCHOOL PHYSICAL EDUCATION

1. Single education situation
   Physical fitness standards of school physical education in China has long been stuck in the levels of economic and technological evaluation, has seriously neglected the importance of physical education in quality-oriented education. This lead to cognitive illusions and even school sports education student on sports tired mood, also formed students to develop sporting values could not be achieved.
2. Teaching philosophy need to be updated
   With the implementation of quality-oriented education, teaching aims of PE has undergone a lot of changes, and in general the purpose of physical education is not about making it as a theoretical knowledge to learn, but to inspire them to sport, master basic sports skills and methods, so that they will actively exercise and have a good body. In such a context, a considerable number of set theory in the PE teaching in colleges and universities links are inappropriate, and many institutions have not fundamentally changing the teaching concept, regarding the PE as "sports knowledge for students", without the correctly positing PE in health care and guidance for the students.

4 THE ROLE OF PHYSICAL EDUCATION IN QUALITY-ORIENTED EDUCATION

As an important component of quality education, physical education has significant advantages in quality education and other disciplines indispensable role. The position and function of physical education in quality-oriented education are determined by the function of school physical education and the requirements of community development roles for school physical education. Mao Ze-Dong's early "Sports Studies" reveals that: Sports is the car of containing knowledge, the house of containing moral, and it not only can make our bodies strong-strengthening, but also have the effects of increasing knowledge, regulating emotions and strengthening will. In addition to following the teaching rules on comprehensive development of students' body, enhancing physical fitness and spreading sports knowledge and skills, sports also can be effective student's education on ideology and moral, develop students' intelligence and cultivate values, develop personality, and promote students' socialization.

1. Sport education function of school physical education
   The first goal of school physical education is the education, followed by sports, which means that sport is education through sports; sport is not just exercising the student's body, more importantly educating students learning to live. Although today live in urban or rural students no longer have to go in the jungle to make a living, but sports and "survival" remained relatively close relationship. Because the change of the living environment and conditions, giving new content to "survival". Modern people may no longer have to fight Doberman or the natural environment, but have to adapt to an increasingly competitive modern society, so that they are not to be eliminated, and preventing obesity, diabetes and other diseases of modern civilization that caused by inadequate sports. With the improvement of people's living standard increasingly, the trends of life-time extension's is increasingly obvious, in order to "survive" and adapt to the rapid development of society, lifelong education came into being, and lifelong sport and physical exercise is especially important. School sports not only lay a solid basis for the lifelong physical education both in body and mind, but developing students 'lifelong physical education awareness, habits, capacities. Such as school sports through teaching means in the situational teaching, training students' survival consciousness; through based teaching makes students master various sport's skills; through game or competitions training students' consciousness, habits and capacity of lifelong sports, while also training students' capacity of groups collaboration, cooperation and competition, and laying solid of body based and good of consciousness quality for adapted increasingly rapid competition of social environment, to achieve school's survival education and features.
2. Life education function of school physical education
   Modern social people except to survival also need to constantly improve quality of survival or life. It is race of consensus that lifelong sports has become an important part of modern civilization life quality, sports in the aspects of educating students to form correct life habits and life skills occupy pivotal status, students educated by various education in the school, sports should be the most "secular" education, they who include of langue, history, philosophy, math, Physical and chemistry are only "homes culture", before students use towards social, and that is difficult to make living for students. On the contrary sports is not like this, it con-

tains which of "playing" education, "beauty" education, "security" education, "health" education, "relationships" education, "life habits" education, "enjoy" education and so on, all of them can immediately "within" and put into students' life, in this meaning, we can not regard sports just as a sport education, but as a carrier of sport, The carrying capacity of the educational life is incomparable to any other education. Sports as a Living education may not be able to directly bring up a remarkable talent of many ages industrial revolution caused, but can lead to generation who knew how to live healthy and civilized.

3. The moral education function of school physical education

    With the development of market economy, inevitably causing some people's moral quality are broke, and under the condition of moral cang mourning phenomenon is not uncommon, ideological and moral education for students is a top priority, but education practice can not become a fait accompli by sitting and prattling about the general principle, and the cultivation of personal moral need students' individual activity. Ethical style often is associated with the interests of the competition and moral upbringing needs in a competitive manner in order to be effective, sport can provide such an opportunity for moral education. One of sport content is the modern competitive sports, continually complete procedures and rule reflect a moral expectations of the community, participation in which will enable people to know how to use the behaviors of social groups to guide and constrain their behavior; the moral function of school physical education also reflect on improve the quality of the entire nation and national cohesion by watching and participating in sports game. Such as during the Beijing Olympics, the whole country was jubilant, cheered for athletes win and prosperity of the motherland, all of that embodied the moral education function of school physical education.

4. Character education function of school sports

    Participation in sports is in itself a personality show, the society of knowledge economy, with particular emphasis on unique, personalized sports knowledge innovation, precisely for the teacher and the student's individual play offers a relaxed and healthy stage. As a sports personality education, on the one hand teachers designed to the shape of student's personality through various situations, on the other hand to provide students with a certain autonomy movement of subjective, unfettered self had cultivated in an environment. Such as endurance in physical training, contributing to the formation and development of student resilience, participation in team sports (football, basketball) movement has contributed to the formation and development of students' resourcefulness and courageous, unity. Willing to work hard and never give up personality, thus enabling students to personality, temperament, ability of positive changes have taken place.

5   WAYS OF IMPLEMENTING QUALITY EDUCATION IN PHYSICAL EDUCATION TEACHING

1. Pay attention to basic education

    Professor Gu Mingyuan noted, quality education can not be exactly the same as the basic education, but basic education must be quality-oriented education, primary and secondary education is basic education, it must be for the students' growth of three foundations: one is to lay a good foundation for the growth of physical and mental health; the second is to lay a good foundation for further learning or life-long learning; three is students into the community lay the foundation. So, school sports teaching in implementation quality education should do: first, training students physique based of while, growing up training students of self-confidence, pride, improving students psychological quality level, for students physical and mental health development hit good based; second, making students awareness and understanding sports and health, personal and social of relationship, improving students of sports consciousness and engaged in sports exercise of social sense; third, making students master sports basic and basic skills, learned science of fitness method, for students' lifelong physical education lay the foundation.

2. Teaching method of strengthening spontaneous activity of small groups

    Quality education is to promote the education of students, at same time it is a personalized education. PE teaching Reform to those education of repressed ideas, content and method in the development of the students' minds, individualized, with the form and content of sports, putting students in the situation of emotional communication, to repeatedly feel success and happiness, in perfecting the process of appreciation of self and others, the personal temperament, intelligence, ability to be fully developed.

3. Laying stress on the development of students' personality

    Physical education is conducted on the premise of collective behavior of students, teachers and students in bilateral of pedagogy played their own enthusiasm. Presently, PE is restricted by equipment and site, therefore, small groups based on interests and hobbies, more generally to replace the traditional class system of command group, this is the trends of school's educational reform and development.

Cultivating and fostering new generation of 21st century with high qulity requires rational thinking and bold exploration of physical education with the thought of quality-oriented education, and truly implementing the principal position of students in physical education and practical features.

6 CONCLUSION

PE plays an important role in quality education, cannot be replaced by other disciplines. School physical education not only laid the foundation for sport, but also with a comprehensive and coordinated way to develop young people, so that allowing students to adapt to the high-paced life, and improving their quality of life. Therefore, we shall actively pursue the construction of campus sports, preaches for the construction of campus sports culture, contributing our meager power to improve comprehensive qualities.

REFERENCES

[1] Zhang Daozhen. Practical physical education [M]. Beijing: Commercial Press, 1987.
[2] Liu Miqing. The innovation of physical education teaching in colleges and universities [M]. Jiangxi: Education Press, 2001.
[3] Liu Luying. Analysis on College physical education [J]. Journal of Chongqing technology and business University.
[4] The CPC Central Committee and State Council's decision on deepening reform and promoting quality education. 1999.6.
[5] Jin Qinchang: Science of school physical education [M]. Higher education publishing press. 1996.4.
[6] Lai Tiande: The quality of the education and reform of school physical education, Issue of the school physical education in China, 1998(1).
[7] Lee Cheung:The school physical education. Higher education publishing press, p. 10.
[8] "Sports and health" curriculum development groups: the interpretation of physical education and health curriculum. Hubei education press, 2001.
[9] Mao Zhenming: the new vision of teaching reform of physical education. Beijing sport press, 2003.1.
[10] Lai Tiande: The quest of the school physical education reform, Beijing sports university press, 2003.1.

Computer, Intelligent Computing and Education Technology – Liu, Sung & Yao (Eds)
© *2014 Taylor & Francis Group, London, ISBN 978-1-138-02469-4*

Factors influencing users' knowledge sharing in enterprise-hosted open innovation communities: The perspective of grounded theory

Liang-Huang Chen & Min Qin
Research Center of Management Science and Engineering, School of Software, Jiangxi Normal University, Nanchang, China

ABSTRACT: Innovation communities have emerged in recent years. There are increasingly being utilized by enterprises as a tool to collect knowledge and to nourish internal innovations. Based on the qualitative method of grounded theory, this paper investigated users in enterprise-hosted innovation communities. Then it formulated a system which consists of 67 keywords, 16 areas and 4 main areas as well as a conceptual model which analyzed these factors. The result showed that enterprise institution was the premise of users' participation, and community technology was the base, and community culture was the core of the whole knowledge activity promoting the realization of knowledge sharing. The summary and some relevant suggestions are given in the last part.

Keywords: innovation communities; grounded theory; knowledge sharing

1 INTRODUCTION

Due to the rapid development of modern information and communication technology plus the formation of knowledge network, more and more domestic and international enterprises set up open innovation communities, aiming to encourage external users to participate in inner-enterprise creative activities. For instance, American Threadless T-shirt Company allows consumers to design their own T-shirt on line, Procter & Gamble Company founded a Connect & Develop online community to encourage the public to take part in the research and development of company products, Dell opened Dell Express blog and Idea storm community to collect consumers' feedback and creative ideas, which in return helps to improve the design of products.

In recent years, innovation communities based on Web 2.0 touch more importance to users' network interaction, the publication and sharing of consumers' creative knowledge, at the same time they put more expectation on users of mutual interests to connect, interact and corporate with each other. Knowledge sharing permeated all innovation community activities. As a creativity resource, the primary task of improving the performance of users' knowledge sharing is to figure out influencing factors affecting creative knowledge sharing, and then make some scientific suggestions on how to build an efficient knowledge sharing innovation community.

2 THEORY REVIEW

At present, it has become a main research direction of informatics and knowledge management field to reveal online community incentive mechanism in terms of analysis and empirical study of influencing factors affecting knowledge sharing in online community, many a foreign scholars have done basic research: Bock et al. discussed the influence of external motivation, social psychological power and organization atmosphere to the inclination of knowledge sharing from the perspective of rational behavior; such factors as confidence, subjective norm, cost, profit, reciprocal relationships and self-efficacy have also been proved to be able to exert influence on the attitude, willingness and behavior of knowledge sharing. The relevant researches of domestic scholars fall on two main perspectives: the first is the researches on organizational factor. These researches focus mainly on exploring the incentive functions of managerial support, equal organization and reward policy in supply chain. The second is researches on psychological inducement. In recent years, professional in informatics and knowledge management borrowed some research variables from social psychology and conducted a series of empirical studies on influencing factors affecting knowledge sharing in virtual communities. For example, there exist some studies, under the framework of social capital theory, analyze the social interaction, mutual trust and reciprocity principles between members of network mobile communities, as well as the promotive function of shared vision and common language to the exchange of information and knowledge between members. There also exist some studies exploring positive effects of self-efficacy, outcome expectation and intention of sharing in social cognitive theory to knowledge sharing behavior. The latest researches demonstrate that sense of community, altruism and sense of identity have positive influence on knowledge sharing behavior. Besides, knowledge sharing depends greatly on situations, for face variable in Chinese culture is also one influencing factor of knowledge sharing in virtual community.

Making a general survey of domestic and international relevant researches, people can find that studies on influencing factors of knowledge sharing in online community are mainly in western culture background which based on western theory, and relevant studies are not limited to single subject but extract influencing factors and indexes of knowledge sharing in virtual communities under the guidance of borrowed sociological, psychological, economic and managerial theories. But at present, there are few researches on innovation community in mainland, this paper sums up and sorts out various factors through interviews and data processing, aiming to build up a relatively complete analysis system of influencing factors of knowledge sharing in innovation community.

3 RESEARCH APPROACH AND DESIGN

3.1 Research approach

Developed by Glaser and Strauss, grounded theory was a research approach based on a great number of detailed materials, which is designed to gradually improve conception and abstraction level like a screw and then form a theory through scientific logic, induction, deduction, contrast and analysis. Grounded theory is a qualitative research method, which is formed on the basis of empiric data, the Figure 1 shows study process.

This method is particularly suitable for situations where phenomenon is short of theoretical explanations or the explanatory power is weak. As long as there exist "process or interaction" and "procedural", the grounded theory can be used to conduct researches. Knowledge sharing in enterprise open innovation community is corporative interaction and harmony allocation between organizations, and existing researches on influencing factors are short of theoretical support, these two sides decide the applicability of grounded theory in this research.

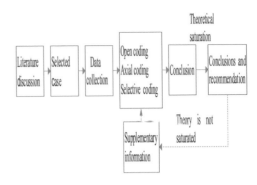

Figure 1. Grounded theory basic processes.

3.2 Theoretical sampling

In order to select more representative enterprise innovation community to do research, this paper considers three aspects: (1) have great influence of the enterprise; (2) existence of creative module in innovation community; (3) have large number of users of that innovation community; (4) have great quantity of posts. Comparing various innovation communities, this paper focuses on Xiao Mi innovation community, a well-known and fast-growing community in China.

3.3 Data collection

According to the coding methods of grounded theory, this paper in the first place encodes materials and different information.

1. Interpreting interviews and questionnaires. The author interviewed 6 administrative staffs of community, sent out 300 questionnaires among which 282 questionnaires were returned, and the effective rate is 94%. This paper at first excludes invalid users, then excludes repetitive interviews and label the rest interview information.
2. Summarizing literature materials. Classify and label theories in literature.

4 ANALYSIS OF INFLUENCING FACTORS OF KNOWLEDGE SHARING IN INNOVATION COMMUNITY BASED ON GROUNDED THEORY

This research uses grounded theory to decode interview materials on three levels (open coding, axial coding and selective coding) and check the saturation, during which conception, areas and model come into being.

4.1 Open coding

At first, this paper conceptualizes interview materials, labels 137 interview information, extracts every

Table 1. Examples of open coding.

Interviews, questionnaires	Conceptualization	Standardization	Areas
a1: I want to take participate in innovation communities derive knowledge; a2: I chose this community because I love this area; a3: I feel this community very good, nice atmosphere activities; a4: Features of this community more powerful, better management; a5: Every day I spend much times to join in the community, learn interesting innovative applications	aa1: Common interest aa2: Motivation aa3: Community management aa4: Community powerful aa5: Members agree	A1: Similarity A2: needs knowledge A3: Influence A4: Community management A5: Group norms	AA1: Community institution AA2: Social value AA3: Image value AA4: Community culture ...... (16 areas)

phenomenon the labels signify and puts up with 113 conceptions; then, this paper conventionalizes the conceptions, and construes 67 top level subject headings; at last, this paper blend them into 16 areas (AA1–AA16), also known as second level subject headings, Table 1 shows some examples of open coding.

4.2 Axial coding

The second step of grounded theory is axial coding. Main areas borrow decoding model to relate various areas and they are constructed on the basis of refinement of subject headings. This paper focuses on four main areas, as Community institution, Community technology, Community culture, Knowledge activities.

4.3 Selective coding

There are distinct paradigm models, characteristics and faces of evidence chain of 4 main areas generalized via selective coding, but the 4 main areas do not cover all contents of materials. The focus area of this research falls on the users' knowledge sharing in open innovation community. See Figure 2.

Community institution supplies members with preliminary confidence, and it is the basis of shaping community culture. Community encourages altruistic behavior and reciprocal behavior, and nurtures members' sense of belonging. In return, members' confidence and sense of belonging improve outcome expectations, and promising expectations and sense of belonging motivate members' to fulfill their need for knowledge. Meanwhile, incentive measures and community culture will promote members' willingness to share their professional knowledge, experience and key technology; will promote exchanges between members on certain issues; will encourage members to give feedback to the solution, thus upgrade knowledge

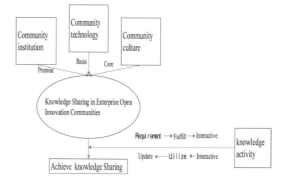

Figure 2. Knowledge sharing model.

in community. Technology in community are tools for members to search for knowledge and share with others. It is an important influencing factor of knowledge sharing's efficiency whether people can quickly and accurately locate the knowledge they need and figure out the person who shared the knowledge. Therefore, community institution is prerequisite for maintaining the normal operation during the early stage, community culture is the core of community's attraction and sustainable development, and community technology is the base for operating.

4.4 Saturation examination

Saturation to certain extent when people cease to collect samples for no more characteristic of one area can be further analyzed. This paper draws materials at random, and no new area is covered, so theoretical saturation is sound and safe.

5 CONCLUSION AND SUGGESTION

All comments this paper studies involve interaction between members. According to sociological theory, one participant has to fulfill the other participant's expectation to the largest degree if they want to hold a sustainable interaction in the long run. The above research shows that members join into community out of various value needs, and only when their needs are meet will they stay in the community. So the establishment of enterprise innovation community should take members' value needs into consideration, and fulfill their needs to the greatest degree via corresponding measures (such as nurturing leads of feedback, community motivation system etc.). People should retain more community members and cultivate more creative talents.

Most international researches on enterprise innovation community are empirical studies, this paper attempts to use grounded theory to construe an influencing factor model of users' knowledge sharing in enterprise innovation community, and give a preliminary description of how major factors influence knowledge sharing, for the purpose of emphasizing the importance of knowledge activity processes. Besides, this paper demonstrates that there are such problems in innovation community as sustainable development, administrative model and performance assessment, these aspects have never been explored in existing researches thus leave room for further study of this paper.

ACKNOWLEDGMENT

This project is sponsored by following Foundation: ①National Science Foundation of China (71262023); ②Science and Technology Support Project of Jiangxi Province (20121BBE50026); ③Social Science Plan Project of Jiangxi Province (13GL23); ④Doctoral Foundation of Jiangxi Normal University.

REFERENCES

[1] CHO, et al. An empirical study on the effect of individual factors on knowledge sharing by knowledge type [J]., Journal of Global Business and Technology, 2007, 3(2):1–15.
[2] Ulrich Lichtenthaler. Outbound open innovation and its effect on firm performance: examining environmental influences [J]. R.D Management. 2009, 39(4): 317–330.
[3] DominikMahr, Annouk, Lievens. Virtual lead user communities: Drivers of knowledge creation for innovation [J]. Research Policy, 2012, 41:167–177.
[4] Simard C., & West J. Knowledge networks & the geographic locus of innovation: Open innovation research a new paradigm [M]. Oxford University Press, 2006.

Computer, Intelligent Computing and Education Technology – Liu, Sung & Yao (Eds)
© 2014 Taylor & Francis Group, London, ISBN 978-1-138-02469-4

The evaluation index system of Geographic Information System in the teaching quality and safety for field practice

Xin-Hui Xu, Jie Chen & Ji-Sheng Xia
School of Resource Environment and Earth Science, Yunnan University, Yunnan Institute of Geography, Kunming, China

ABSTRACT: Field practice is the basic part of the Geographic Information Systems (GIS). It deeply shows the combination of the theory and practice, the class and field. It is also an important way to improve the students' professional skills. The quality of the field practice and the build of the safety evaluation indicators can promote the field teaching to be scientific which leads to the improvement of the field teaching's quality and effect. This paper uses the Analytic Hierarchy Process (AHP) to do research of GIS field teaching quality and safety.

Keywords: field practice; quality; safety; evaluation system

GIS is a strong practical discipline. It must rely on a lot of field practice as well. Our college attaches great importance to the field practice of GIS, taking full advantage of the superior geographical resources in Yunnan province, establishing field practice bases. So, to achieve the aim of practice, establishing the evaluation index system of GIS in the teaching quality and safety for field practice to manage and evaluate the field practice systematically.

1 THE PURPOSE AND MEANING OF RESEARCH

1.1 The meaning of field practice

Field practice is the consolidation and extension of class learning, is an important link to verify the theoretical teaching. Field practice requires students to be personally on the scene, getting the first-hand data and information, and discover, solve a problem in the work, in order to open up the thinking of training students' innovation consciousness and practical ability. So that improving the students' cultural quality and scientific quality[1][2].

1.2 The purpose of research

Through studying the problems of GIS field teaching, the purpose is to establish the field of quality and safety evaluation of teaching standards, reform and innovate field teaching content, configurate field routes, improve the security of field teaching, so as to improve teaching quality and effectiveness.

2 THE PROBLEMS IN THE FIELD PRACTICE TEACHING

2.1 The performance evaluation is lack of a unified and scientific standard, namely: Using a ruler measure student performance

The following situations often appear when evaluating the performance. (1) Sometimes affected by objective factors; (2) Appreciating the results and ignoring the process; (3) Attaching importance to the perceive of theoretical knowledge and ignoring the grasp of practical skills; (4) Handing over practice details repeatedly and ignoring the students' awareness of innovative thinking. In a word, lacking specific quantitative index.

2.2 The practice lines and content need optimize

Now, practice content, using repeatedly, need optimize. We should make full of its superior geographical environment in Yunnan province to establish the colorful and characteristic practice bases. For example, adding the exploration of the Stone Forest karst base, the biodiversity base, the complex geology in the back hill of Qiongzhu Temple (trilobite fossil), landform, vegetational forms to the basis of the original, so as to enrich the practice content constantly. Constantly stimulating the sense of exploration and innovation to our students, only by doing this, can we achieve the ultimate goal of organizing the internship. It means to get ready for students' employment, so as to deliver the qualified senior professional and technical personnel for the country or society.

2.3 Safety education consciousness does not reach the designated position

Regardless of whether due to natural reasons, human reasons or other reasons, the safety of the field practice is very important. But, some may be unexpected danger. In order to avoid such problems in the field practice, security assessment mechanism should be introduced in the process.

3 PRINCIPLES OF EVALUATION

The field teaching quality is affected by multiple factors, when establishing evaluation index system, we must follow the following principles to achieve fairness and objectivity.

3.1 Comprehensive evaluation principle

3.1.1 Pay equal attention to preparation, field and achievements
Field practice including preparation, field practice and field teaching summary. Ignoring the preparation, the grasp of skills in the process and other aspects results that the students are slack, reports are copied. So, using preparation, field and achievements as the evaluation factors at the same time can help to promote students' integrated learning.

3.1.2 Combine with internship units, teachers' and students' evaluation
Complete practice need the good match of the internship units, teachers and students. The three parts evaluate the practice field Independently and combine them, we can evaluate the practice quality objectively and roundly.

3.1.3 Combine with qualitative and quantitative evaluation
Practice technology results, the number of samples, the parties involved in the degree can be quantified assessment. Teachers, students' performance, attitude, initiative, creativeness and so on can be qualitative evaluation. Only by this, can we ensure the objectivity and comprehensive of evaluation[2][3].

3.2 Security principle

Because the field practice has complexity, openness and the internship in complex geography, teachers are required to fully consider the safety of the field practice to eliminate potential safety problems when choosing the practice environment and conditions.

3.3 Representative principle

The evaluation indexes is numerous, so we must guarantee the indexes to be independent relatively and representative, they does not contain each other, cross, overlap. So that the practical teaching quality assessment has comprehensive and reasonable evalucation through the evaluation and summary of the indicators[3].

3.4 Feasibility principle

When specifying index system must make every indicator clear, refined and focused, reduce the difficulty of operation as far as possible. Namely: simple. Ensuring the operability of the evaluation system and improving the efficiency of evaluation.

4 THE ESTABLISHMENT OF EVALUATION INDEX SYSTEM

No practice, no sublimation and innovation of the theory. The field practice plays an important role in the process of teaching. Based on the above, contacting the actual situation of GIS field practice and referring to the relevant information, from the preparation, field practice, field safety and field teaching summary four aspects to establish the evaluation factors and indexes. Finally, establishing a complete evaluation index system of GIS in the teaching quality and safety for field practice through the empirical methods and AHP giving the weights to each evaluation index. Evaluation index and weight as shown in Table 1.

4.1 Preparation stage

4.1.1 Practice mobilization meeting
The mobilization meeting is the key link of GIS field practice. The meeting mainly introduces practice main content and matters needing attention in detail. At the same time, doing a warning job to make the field practice in the state of "zero risk".

4.1.2 Goods preparation
Preparation work before practice focused on the preparation of goods. Among them, practice instrucction helps students to clear the content and goals of each practice place. The practice routes arrangement helps to avoid delaying time because of lost. Through the learning of the preparation stage, it can make the students use the instruments in the field and keep on school property well.

4.1.3 Practice content
The cultivation of innovative spirit and practical ability is the key of quality education. The innovation and the non-repeatability of practice content are one of the indicators of the practice teaching quality evaluation.

Table 1. The evaluation index of GIS in the teaching quality and safety for field practice.

First-grade index	Second-grade index	Third-grade index	Score
(A) Preparation stage	Practice mobilization meeting	A1 the mobilization meeting and a warning job (2′)	
	Goods preparation	A2 the practice instruction (2′)	
		A3 the practice routes (2′)	
		A4 Internship equipments (2′)	
	Practice content	A5 The innovation of practice content (2′)	
		A = A1 + A2 + A3 + A4 + A5	
(B) Field process	Teaching effect	B1 teaching attitude (3′)	
		B2 professional ability (3′)	
	Learning effect	B3 field notes (15′)	
		B4 content grasp (20′)	
		B5 wild ecological consciousness, the consciousness of environmental protection (5′)	
		B6 field innovation ability: find, analyze and solve problem (4′)	
		B = B1 + B2 + B3 + B4 + B5 + B6	
(C) Field security	Field practice and survival skills	C1 the team spirit and organizational discipline (7′)	
		C2 safety problems resulting from students' attitude (5′)	
		C3 safety problems resulting from natural environment and physical fitness (3′)	
		C4 self salvation consciousness (5′)	
		C = C1 + C2 + C3 + C4	
(D) Teaching summary	Teaching report	D1 the teacher's teaching summary reports (5′)	
		D2 the students' practice summary reports (10′)	
	Security	D3 the summary and feelings of security (5′)	
		D = D1 + D2 + D3	
Total score			

4.2 Field process

4.2.1 Teaching effect

The guidance teacher is the only dependence in field teaching. Teaching effect affects the practice quality greatly. It can be evaluated from the two aspects: teaching attitude and professional ability.

4.2.2 Learning effect

The main purpose of field practice is to lead the students to integrate theory with practice, form the geography thinking, and train students to master and improve the necessary geography professional practical skills. At the same time, the protection of local environment can reflect the students' consciousness of environmental protection, and spread positive energy. It can be evaluated from the four aspects: field notes, content grasp, wild ecological consciousness, the consciousness of environmental protection, field innovation ability.

4.3 Field security

4.3.1 Field practice and survival skills

Field security in the geography internship is a inevitable problem. In the field practice, teachers and students must abide by the discipline. In case of the accident, we can use skills to survive flexibly with self salvation consciousness. Safety can be evaluated from these aspects: the team spirit and organizational discipline, safety problems resulting from students' attitude or natural environment and physical fitness and self salvation consciousness and others.

4.4 Teaching summary

4.4.1 Teaching report

The summary report is the most comprehensive summary and evaluation for this practice after finishing the practice. This report reflects the teachers and students' experience and harvest and the practice achievement. It can be evaluated from two aspects: the teacher's teaching summary reports and students' practice summary reports.

4.4.2 Security

Security is essential to successful practice, but also to ensure the quality of practice. It can be evaluated with summary and feelings of security.

Table 2. The evaluation grades of GIS in the teaching quality and safety for field practice.

Comprehensive score: W	100~90	89~80	79~70	69~60	<60
Evaluation grades	Excellent	Good	Medium	Qualified	Unqualified

5 THE TEACHING QUALITY AND THE SAFETY EVALUATION PROCESS

5.1 *Teaching quality and safety evaluation table*

The evaluation of teaching quality and safety will eventually be implemented in each evaluation indicator. To make the teaching evaluation to be simple and easy to operate, we can design the GIS field practice teaching quality and safety evaluation tables based on evaluation system. Evaluation table as shown in Table 1.

5.2 *Evaluating by the roles, and get comprehensive score according to the corresponding weights*

Teachers' evaluation T (60%):

$$T = (A) + (B) + (C) + (D) \tag{1}$$

Teacher representatives' evaluation S (30%):

$$S = (A) + (B) + (C) + (D) \tag{2}$$

Practice units' evaluation P (10%):

$$P = (A) + (B) + (C) + (D) \tag{3}$$

Comprehensive score W:

$$W = 0.6 \times T + 0.3 \times S + 0.1 \times P \tag{4}$$

5.3 *Grade evaluation*

In order to evaluate the field practice teaching quality and safety more easily, comprehensive evaluation is graded into different levels. Grade division as shown in Table 2.

6 CONCLUSIONS

In order to ensure objective, accurate and comprehensive of the internship evaluation results, this article start by the preparation stage, the field work, field safety and teaching summary these four aspects, and combining the specific situation of GIS major, has built index system about the GIS field practice teaching quality and the safety evaluation.

1. On the principle of evaluation methods, to overcome the "eccentric" situation existing in the traditional evaluation. We combine the internship units, teacher and student evaluation method, give same attention to preparation, field and results, strive to the fair and objective of evaluation.
2. Quantify field practice teaching quality and safety, can not only promote scientific field practice, but also regulate the behavior of students' field practice. Moreover, it fully mobilizes teachers' and students' enthusiasm, promotes the communication and cooperation between teachers and students, greatly improves the effect of practice.
3. The teaching quality and the safety evaluation table (Table 1) is simple and feasible. That is to say, by completing this form and simple operation can acquire the teaching quality and safety assessment score. Then by comparison to the evaluation scale table (Table 2) can obtain the evaluation of teaching quality and safety level.

In a word, this evaluation system is based on the summary of specific circumstances in our school's years of GIS professional field practice. The topic is aimed to improve the quality of field practice and effects through teaching reform.

ACKNOWLEDGMENTS

Fund Project:

Yunnan University, School of Resource Environment and Earth Science, Teaching Reform Project (number: 2012CJ005).

Yunnan Province Education Department (number: 2012C109).

Scientific Research Funds, the Ministry of Education "Chun Hui Plan" Research Projects (number: Z2012051).

Yunnan University, School of Resources Environment and Earth Science Research Project (number: 2013CG006).

REFERENCES

[1] Wu Rui. 2010. Study On the Performance Evaluation System of Wenshan Institute of Geography Field Practice[J]. Journal of Wenshan University. 23(3): 98–101.
[2] Wei Lidong, Jia Guoling, Zhang Zeguang. 2008. Construction of the Evaluating System of Geography Field Practice[J]. Journal of Hengshui University. 10(1): 105–107.

[3] Cheng Jiumiao, Zhu Yongheng. 2009. Discussion on Evaluation Index and Method of Performance Practice Field of Geographical Science Majors[J]. Journal of Anhwei Normal University. 32(4): 384–388.

[4] Long Haili, Wang Aihui. 2012. A Preliminary Study on Improving the Teaching Effect of Geography Feld Practice[J]. Journal of Heihe. 179(6): 77–78.

[5] Zuo Panshi. 2010. Quality Control of Geographical Field Practice[J]. Journal of Shaoguan University. 31(8): 144–147.

Computer, Intelligent Computing and Education Technology – Liu, Sung & Yao (Eds)
© 2014 Taylor & Francis Group, London, ISBN 978-1-138-02469-4

The primary discussion of GIS specialty field teaching

Xin-Hui Xu, Yi-Ran Fu & Shu-Cheng Tan
School of Resource Environment and Earth Science in Yunnan University and Yunnan Institute of Geography, Kunming, China

ABSTRACT: Field practice is the indispensable teaching process in GIS specialty undergraduate course teaching, which is the important embodiment of practice teaching. There are many ways to improve and optimize in the content, the route, the practice instruction and other related construction. In view of the above problems, combining with the teaching practice and teaching target, put forward to adapt to the market demand as the guidance, training development thinking, consolidating the professional knowledge, strengthening the ability of field practice and so on, to develop comprehensive quality of talents. At the same time, through the teaching reformation, improve the practice teaching quality and effects.

Keywords: GIS specialty; field; teaching reformation

Geographic Information System (Abbreviated GIS) is nearly 20 years of an new set of geography, computers, RS and Cartography in one discipline, it requires not only proficiency in computer programming languages, but also geology, physical geography, Human Geography, geobotany, cartography, surveying, RS, databases and other courses of study. This professional training personnel can not only in the scientific research institutions, colleges and universities engaged in scientific research or teaching, but also in the city, region, resource, environment, transport, population, housing, land, infrastructure and planning and management and other fields in applied research, technology development, production management and administrative work.

1 REFORMATION PURPOSES

Field practice is one of the important link of GIS professional teaching, trains the student to discover problems, solve the problem, is an effective way to improve the comprehensive qualities and skills. In order to comply with the requirements of the Times, this paper tries to through the teaching reform, to improve the quality of field practice teaching and deepen students' understanding of classroom teaching, therefore, from the field teaching content, circuit protection, configuration, security, and so on aspects to explore.

2 PROBLEMS IN FIELD TEACHING

2.1 *Inferior quality in field teaching and lack of index in the safety evaluation*

Field practice is an essential teaching link of GIS, which is the integration of theory and practice, the combination of indoor teaching and outdoor practice. It is the important way to cultivating students' professional skills. The construction of field practice teaching quality and the safety evaluation index will helpfully improve the quality and the effect of field teaching scientifically and rigorously.

2.2 *Lines, and contents of field practice need optimization*

At present, the practice line and the practice content have been used over times, and did not get supplement and updating in time, after the school enrollment expansion, a large number of students desire for knowledge, so lines and contents of field practice need optimization. There are many geographical advantages in Yunnan province, we should make full use of its superior geographical environment to build abundant and colorful practical bases, so as to achieve the final goal of our practice: to lay the foundation of students' employment, to preferably provide qualified senior professional technical personnel for the society.

2.3 *Practice instruction needs improvement*

Practice instruction is an important handbook in students' field practice. We need to follow the practice content and update constantly, so that students could have a better comprehensive understanding in field practice.

3 REFORMATION THOUGHTS

The GIS field teaching work is still in the exploratory stage because the major in Yunnan University is still young, we put forward the following points about GIS field teaching reformation measures by analyzing about present situation.

3.1 *Transformation of learning style*

We can get some of the reasons affecting the effects of practice through interviewing teachers and students about their experiences of field work. Firstly, there are attitude problems in students, some students could not accurately grasp the importance of practices. As a result, correcting attitude is extremely urgent. Secondly, at present, most of the practice in geological geography field is a kind of cognitive, validation, and equipment application practice, which focuses on the book knowledge field perceptual knowledge and verify the previous conclusion,[1],[2] the students will be psychological slack in the practice process, and lack of active learning and innovation of knowledge, so the process of far than expected effect. In this case, if the earning style can be turned into active model, to explore the learning process, the efficiency of learning will improve and the students' innovative thinking will be developed.

3.2 *Innovation of content, construction of practice base*

On the basis of the original, such as campus measurement, RS, GPS integrated practice, topographic map interpretation. Add JiuXiang or Stone Forest karst landscape base, biodiversity base, complex geology (trilobite fossils) or landscape or vegetation types of the hill in Zhukong Temple, and constantly enrich the content of the internship, construct the practice base to become more scientific, more standardized, more diversified.

In order to fully reflect the GIS's comprehensiveness and cross characteristic and satisfy the requirement of GIS teaching practice,[3] we should pay attention to consider three aspects in the construction of practice base.

"Whole", which is to satisfy the GIS to be completed by the use of GPS, RS interpretation, topographic map reading, geography informational technology teaching; "Wide Covers", is within the scope of the base covers the internship required for various terrain; "More Convenient", the practice base of transportation, accommodations, distance and other objective conditions is suitable for the needs of the field, minimum cost to achieve the best effect.

3.3 *Practical system need improvement*

Practice teaching material construction is constraint, specified, and mature,[4] only in the way of stepping up efforts to the improvement of the teaching materials and the field practice teaching quality and the safety evaluation index set, which can ensure the quality and effect of practice (Table 1).

In addition, we should intern student to carry on the summary after the practice, we can find out the existing problems from two aspects of teachers and students.we shall establish a feedback between teachers and students to improve the quality and promote the effective reformation (Table 2).

Table 1. Teaching quality of practice and safety evaluation scores table.

1st indicators	2nd indicators	Score proportion
Preparation	Mobilization Goods Contents	10%
Process	Teaching effect Learning effect	50%
Security	Practice Survival skills	20%
Summary	Report Security	20%

Table 2. 3S comprehensive practice feedback questionnaire.

Grade: Name:

Performance score (out of 100 points):
What part is preferably well-done in this practice?

Which part of knowledge in the practice is no good?

What is the biggest reward for this practice?

What are your views and suggestions about the practice?

4 THE REFORMATION PATTERN

4.1 Ready to field trip before

1. Before departure, lead teachers should introduce the arrangement, providing detailed schedule, so that we can let practical students know fairly well. lead teachers focus on the point to review on students theoretical knowledge. Using the spare time before departure, at the same time students must listen and record carefully after the completion of a preview teaching, students should avoid field appeared in the practical process at a loss to increase preview test, and the scores will eventually bring in internship score.
2. The lead teacher will distributed to each team according to the specific content, each topic is to be covered wide range to use the knowledge. we will turn the cognition and validation learning types into inquisition type mode. To make the students think with questions, understand consciously in the process of field practice.

The lead teacher must provide life guidance to students according to the arrangement of the location, so as to try to avoid unexpected circumstances such as illness. At the same time, the lead teacher will distribute ≪GIS instruction for field practice≫ to students, and they must abide by it. To improve students' vigilance and consciousness, student will be deducted points if in the event of violations.

4.2 The teaching methods will change

We use "brainstorming" in field practice stage. The so-called "brainstorming" is also called intelligence stimulation method and free thinking method, a kind of motivational thinking method. Which was created by American scientist A.F. Osborn, first proposed in 1939. We can also adopt this method in the field. Teacher ask questions, students will autonomously learn with the destination according to the survey of the problems. It will change the way from "centralized type", to "the teacher's guidance, student led the way".

4.3 The teaching quality and safety evaluation system is built

In order to ensure the evaluation results of objectivity, accuracy and comprehensiveness. Under the condition of GIS specialty in our school, at the same time, we build the GIS teaching quality and the safety evaluation system from preparation stage, field work, safety and summary of four aspects.

5 CONCLUSION

Field teaching will have a pivotal position for GIS Specialty students, we explored basing on GIS Specialty existing problems of field teaching, reformational thinkings and the GIS Specialty teaching pattern of field teaching form after the reformation. We hope that we can create a better learning environment through our reformations, so as to improve the study effect, promoting the students' comprehensive ability.

ACKNOWLEDGEMENTS

First of all, I would like to express my gratitude to School of Resource Environment and Earth Science at Yunnan University teaching reform project (Number: 2012CJ005), Scientific research funds in Yunnan Province Department of Education (Number: 2012C109), The ministry of education "ChunHui Plan" research projects (Number: Z2012051), School of Resource Environment and Earth Science at Yunnan University research project (Number: 2013CG006).

Last my thanks would go to my Correspondence Author Yiran Fu.

REFERENCES

[1] Li Gongquan, Liu Xuefeng, He Zhenming. Geographic information systems specialty field on the teaching mode of comprehensive practice [J]. Journal of Yangtze university institute of technology (natural) volumes. 2012, 9 (11): 176–178.
[2] Xia Lihua, Chen Yingbiao, Feng Yanfen, Wang Dehui. Geographic information systems specialty practice mode exploratory research—GIS in Guangzhou university Industry practice [J]. Journal of geographical information world. 2007, 5 (2): 81–85.
[3] Zhou Wei, Long Yi, Tang Guoan. GIS practical teaching infrastructure construction [J]. Bulletin of surveying and mapping. 2008 (8): 75–77.
[4] Xu Hanwei, Zhang Youjing. Theory of GIS specialty practice teaching system construction [J]. Bulletin of surveying and mapping. 2005 (3): 62–65.
[5] Lu Wenjuan. Information technology support to promote understanding of teaching mode to build [J]. Journal of modern education technology. 2012, 22 (10): 23–26.

Cultivate the students' innovative ability with competition

Guang-Jie Fu
College of Electrical and Information Engineering Company, Northeast Petroleum University, China

Hai-Wei Mu
College of Electronic Science, Northeast Petroleum University, China

Jin-Yu Wang, Shuang Ren, Guo-Bin Tao & Yu-Bo Duan
College of Electrical and Information Engineering Company, Northeast Petroleum University, China

ABSTRACT: The competition between the countries in the world, in the final analysis is the talent competition, the talents are not only traditional the contents of the book to learn the so-called "good student", but also have strong innovation capabilities and the overall quality of the spirit of challenge, and social put forward higher requirements for the country's higher education. In the electronic information in educational reform, various competitions culture theories with practice and a good style of study, the spirits of perseverance, innovation and unity, it is the successful explore path to train good quality, high quality talents.

Keywords: electronic competition; innovation spirit; innovation ability

1 INTRODUCTION

The reforms of world's higher education are also in the direction of approaching to the cultivation of students' innovative spirit and practical ability.[1] The U.S. government's rebuilding education campaign is designed to implement the system of education reform, smoothly and efficiently and help students shift from school to job training, work or advanced study. Russia's "education, science, production" into one, India's "Million Software Talent Project", etc., are all in the focus on exercising talents' innovative spirit and practical ability.[2,3]

2 CHARACTERISTICS OF INNOVATION TALENT

The human creativity reflected in many ways, it can be divided into scientific creativity and artistic creativity activities. Electronic innovation belongs to the scope of scientific innovation activities, the subjects of electronic competition come from the actual demands, some of them have targeted and flexibility, which fully mobilize the students to develop their creative potential, and cultivate a sense of teamwork and dedication. Innovative talents not only have a solid foundation of knowledge, but also have a high sense of responsibility.[4,5]

Looking at the industry's innovative talents, they have the following characteristics:

1. Curious
   The people who are indifferent to the around things are impossible to innovate. Only a one who has passion for life, be true to his post, can it in order to be good at thinking, asking questions, solving problems. The electronic race is a project that theory and practice are closely tied together, only through constantly self-questioning, can it make the completion of the project more and more complete.
2. Thoroughly insight
   A talent with creativity, has a deep insight, he can see through the phenomenon to grasp the nature of the problem, master the essence rather than floating on the surface. The electronic races make the students find their own shortcomings in practice and work life, find a solution to the problems, clear their improvement directions.
3. Sensitive wit
   Creative talents have a strong ability to respond to the circumstances, but also have a strong ability of anti-failure, they accumulate self-confidence in small improvements, form a character of unflustered to changes and conundrums as time pasts, electronic competitions can make students clear their ideas, learn and use lively, comprehend by analogy.

4. Creative spirit

That the ability to produce extraordinary cogitations. The cogitations are rare, novelty and even whimsical on the surface. But these bizarre ideas often produce the discoveries of genius.[6] According to previous electronic competitions, as long as completed, it often is the level of good work, more unique the ideas and methods are, more impressed to the expert judges they will be, more tending to stand out.

3 IMPROVE CREATIVE TALENT AND AWARENESS WITH COMPETITION

Along with the National Undergraduate Electronic innovation experimental program, the National Undergraduate Mathematical Modeling, Freescale Semiconductor and so on such college competition projects being more and more cognitive to college students, these events have achieved consensus and attention by education administration departments at all levels and higher institutions at the same time.[7,8] To the Northeast Petroleum University as an example, in each year, more than 1000 students who come from non-electronic major electronic design basic elective courses enroll in this course, more than 300 trained students participate in the electronic contests, the rewards improve year by year. By training and constantly testing, that enable students better understand the hardships and joys of scientific research, lay a solid foundation for the students to engage in scientific research and in future employment. Facing with the problem, group members benefit by mutual discussions, assuming jointly. To train the students the spirit of unity and cooperation, they fully enjoy the competition process. In the course of competition, participating students mostly sophomore, junior students, they are actively collecting related information, constantly testing, for each race group that is a big challenge, most teams are able to follow the prescribed order under the such large pressure, eventually can basically complete the task. Although the plan may not be the best, they may not win, but they will feel big gains. Through these continuous competitions, they make the student gradually improve the ability of solving the questions, cultivate their innovation consciousness, enhance their self-confidence. So far, the exams for postgraduate schools increase the proportion of reexamination and problem solving ability assessment, being part of the competitions can raise the hit rate.[9]

In the case of teaching outlay, our school finance 0.5 million Yuan to set up a electronic design of comprehensive innovation lab, construct the electronic design foundation course into the teaching reform implementation plan. By such developing comprehensive experiments plan way, we enhance students' practical ability, improve the students' ability to analyze and solve problems. Electronic design contests promote the teaching reform, which achieve two two-prize and two three-prize in 2011. It has played a leading and exemplary role in the province's electronics and electronics course teaching reform and construction.

4 IMPROVE TEACHING METHODS, TARGETING FOR IMPROVING THE STUDENTS' ABILITY OF INNOVATION AND PRACTICE

Electronic race must be consciously carried out the spirit of quality-oriented education, so that students can not only learn many important electronic design concepts, methods and applications, but also can learn to infer other things from one fact through the questions, so as to really make them comprehend the methods of innovative thinking and the essence of spiritual. In order to make the electronic design become the students' handy weapon that will be beneficial for a lifetime.

In the usual electronic teaching, it should introduce basic electronic combined with practical application, rather than only clearing the basic theories. If only teaching electronic course in the traditional way, students will feel no use to learn, it will result in mental weariness. So, we take the application as the main line, according to the actual facing problems, lead them into our teaching contents, to improve students' interests in learning and enhance their spirit of exploration. Due to the rapid development of modern electronic technology, new devices emerge in an endless stream, new ideas and new technology ceaseless emerge in large numbers and other factors, the teaching method cannot follow the prescribed orders, be immutable and frozen, but it should make a change. To change continue education for innovative education, to excessive from the teaching simple of the teacher as the center, the classroom as the center, teaching impart knowledge as the center for the teaching method of the student as the center, practice as the center, cultivating students' ability of analyzing and solving problem as center.[10] This will help ease the teachers' insufficient of deficient electronic design and impart knowledge quantity, it will contribute to the promotion of teaching reform and quality education level, will help to comprehensive improve the students' innovation spirit and practice ability training.

Because of the Internet shortcut, convenience and sharing resource, it makes itself become one of the most efficient ways of spreading information.

Electronic design contains very rich contents which are comprehensive, strong and widely knowledge. It is the key to mastering electronic design that how to build an efficient, fast, rich knowledge base. At the same time the electronic design involves the new technology and the knowledge renews quickly. Modern electronic technology developments change rapidly, the new devices, new design means and methods emerge in an endless stream. For the completion of the same task, using the new design means and methods, the use of new integrated devices, can play a multiplier effect for yielding twice the result with half the effort. For example, at this time, the Electronic Design Automation (EDA) technology, programmable logic devices and high performance microcontroller development have made the traditional electronic design means and methods become obsolete, well the only way of traditional printing books to spread knowledge apparently has lagged behind. A real-time, fast and efficient dissemination of knowledge must be by way of imminent.

Accordingly, to expand the inter scholastic cooperation and exchanges, well also to let everyone have a stable place for discussing about the electronic design problems, we should establish the electronic design website. By advanced modern education technology, make the college further modernization, adapt to the needs of economic and social development, renew ideas and change ideas. Strengthen ability trains and improve the comprehensive qualities while imparting knowledge to students.

5 CONCLUSION

By various types of electronic competition, it can indeed improve the students' creative consciousness and ability, but also expose some problems, for example: some students' thinking is not quite clear when they were meeting the question, feel unable to start, very passive. Some students proposed schemes were relatively seldom, the treatments were not flexible enough, they were appearing relatively inflexible etc. The cause of these problems is the students themselves, while teachers should take the responsibility. Because some teachers influence by traditional education, still use the traditional idea to guide students, can't give priority to the students, while some teachers are self stick in the mud. These factors affect the students' innovation consciousness and the cultivation of the spirit of challenge. Therefore, we should continue to reform and exploration, through various kinds of electronic competitions and academic exchange and cooperation, to cultivate high-quality comprehensive talents with innovation for the country step by step.

ACKNOWLEDGEMENTS

Key project of heilongjiang province education scientific project (project number **GBB1212014** and **GBC1212017**); Special comprehensive education reform pilot project of heilongjiang province project (project number **JGZ201201044**); The educational reform project in heilongjiang province department of education (project number **JG2012010083**).

REFERENCES

[1] Sun Yan, Wang Xiaodi, Tian Wenzhi. Technology Association Activities' Effect in Cultivating Undergraduate Innovative Quality [J], Research and Exploration in Laboratory, 2010(10).
[2] Liu Xiaorong. Talk About the Cultivation of Innovation Ability from the Extracurricular Activities of Science and Technology [J], Science & Technology Information, 2011(22).
[3] Xi Jinhui, Xie Yingjie, Ji Zhe. The Cultivation of University Students' Innovative Thinking and Ability [J]. China Education Innovation Herald, 2008(19).
[4] Li Xing. Experiment Teaching and Undergraduate Innovative and Practical Competence [J]. Experiment Science & Technology, 2008(05).
[5] Chen Yadan, Sun Yu. Brief Discussion on the Cultivation of Modern Undergraduates' Innovation Ability [J]. Journal of Changchun University of Science and Technology (Social Sciences Edition), 2007(06).
[6] Li Yueying. On Training the Engineering Graduate Student's Ability of Practice and Innovation [J]. Technology and Innovation Management, 2007(06).
[7] Zhao Shan. Academic Atmosphere and the Cultivation of Postgraduates' Creative Ability [J]. Science & Technology Information, 2010(31).
[8] Zeng Hongyuan. Discussion on the Cultivating College Students' Innovation Ability [J]. Forum on Contemporary Education, 2007(3).
[9] Jie Xiangwu, Zhang Linli. Robot and the cultivation of innovation ability in college students [J]. Popular Science & Technology, 2012(02).
[10] Fu Jianxi, Ye Peiqingguang. Design of electromechanical integration practice teaching and cultivation of innovation ability of College Students [J]. China Education Innovation Herald, 2008(01).

Computer, Intelligent Computing and Education Technology – Liu, Sung & Yao (Eds)
© 2014 Taylor & Francis Group, London, ISBN 978-1-138-02469-4

The grain size analysis of Upper Ganchaigou group in Qaidam Basin

Rui Tang, You-Bin He & Jun Tang
School of Geoscience, Yangtze University, Wuhan, Hubei, China

Yu Zhang, Chun Liao & Jin-Lan Wei
Exploration and Development Research Institute of Qinghai Oilfield Company, Dunhuang, Gansu, China

ABSTRACT: The rocks of Upper Ganchaigou Formation of Qaidam Basin, China, predominantly include sandstones of medium to fine grain-size, with subordinate shale and hummocky cross-bedding. Textural parameter like mean, standard deviation, skewness and kurtosis are calculated using standard methods to understand the transportation and the depositional environment of the sediments in a part of Ganchaigou Formation. Granulometric analyses through Grapher software indicate the presence of fluvial environment interrupted with beach and tidal environments prevailed during the time of deposition of the sediments in this part of Qaidam Basin during the neogene period time.

Keywords: Qaidam Basin; panchet; textural parameters

1 INTRODUCTION

Textural parameters of clastic sediments are often used to understand the history of sedimentation (Inman, 1952; Folk and Ward, 1957; Passega, 1957, 1964; Visher, 1969; Awasthi, 1970; Folk, 1974; Chakrabarti, 1977; Sengupta, 1977; Friedman, 1979; Pettijohn et al., 1987; Tucker, 1988; Buckley and Cranston, 1991). Although, some authors questioned the viability of application of granulometric methods (Schlee et al., 1964; Solohub and Kolvan, 1970), Martins (2003) showed the applicability of these methods for understanding of the depositional setup of sediments by analyzing a data set comprising thousands of samples from known depositional environments. The present study through Grapher software throws light on the temporal changes of granulometric parameters (mean grain size, sorting coefficient, skewness and kurtosis) of Upper Ganchaigou Formation sediments. The results provide insight into the transportational and depositional of Upper Ganchaigou Formation as well as the validity of the earlier findings (Robinson, 1970; Ghosh et al., 1994; Bandyopadhyay et al., 2002).

2 RESEARCH AREA AND GEOLOGICAL BACKGROUND

The Qaidam Basin is an Inland Basin that from the collision between the Indosinian Plate and the Eurasian Plate during the Mesozoic and Cenozoic—Era. It has experienced three stages consist of a edge fault depression (period J, K), a depression period (E-N22) and a rising fold period (N22-Q). The Youshashan Oilfield oil is located in a down-warping region to the west of Qaidam Basin in Qinghai province, the Mangya Downwarping Region—the Lion Ditch-Youshashan secondary tectonic belt (Fig. 1).

The Youshashan Oilfield is mainly composed of the lower Youshashan formation (N21) and the upper Ganchaigou formation (N1), with a thickness of 500–900 m and a depth of, 20–1200 m.

On the Ganchaigou Formation (N1), the sediment are of lighter color, such as gray, brown, grayish green, grayish white, grayish yellow and so on. The types of rock are mainly composed of

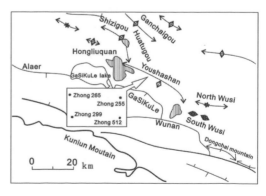

Figure 1. Tectornic Map of regions at Youshashan Oilfield in Qiadam Basin.

sandstone, siltstone and claystone, with a thickness of 650 m. With the use of lenses, horizontal bedding development, and wavy bedding, pyrite and authigenic minerals can be observed occasionally.

3 METHODOLOGY

The sediments were classified according to their sand silt clay ratio as described by Shepard (1954). Grain size parameters (mean size, standard deviation, skewness and kurtosis) were computed using the graphical method (Folk and Ward, 1957). Graphic median value of $\Phi50$ denoting half of the particles by weight are coarser to it and half is fine. Graphic mean (Mz) is a measure of central tendency, which is calculated by the formula ($\Phi 16 + \Phi 50 + \Phi 84)/3$. The inclusive graphic standard deviation (σI) is the measure of sorting or uniformity of particles size distribution and it is calculated by the formula ($\Phi84 - \Phi16)/4 + (\Phi95 - \Phi5)/6.6$. The graphic skewness (Ski) measures the symmetry of the distribution or predominance of coarse or fine-sediments. It is calculated by the formula $[(\Phi84 + \Phi16 - 2\Phi50)/(\Phi84 - \Phi16) + (\Phi95 + \Phi5 - 2\Phi50)/(\Phi95 - 2\Phi5)]$. The negative value denotes coarse-skewed material, whereas, the positive value represents more material in the fine-tail i.e., fine-skewed (Bapi, Dipsikha, 2011).

The Graphic Kurtosis (KG), is the peakedness of the distribution and measures the ratio between the sorting in the tails and central portion of the curve. If the tails are better sorted than the central portions, then it is termed as platykurtic, where as, leptokurtic, if the central portion is better sorted. If both are equally sorted then mesokurtic condition prevails. It is calculated by the formula $(\Phi95 - \Phi5)/2.44 (\Phi75 - \Phi25)$.

4 RESULTS

4.1 C-M plot of Passega and mode of transport

The relationships of 'C' or the coarser one percentile value in micron and 'M' which is median value in micron on logprobability scale are plotted to evaluate the hydrodynamic condition during sedimentation (Passega, 1957, 1964). The sediments of present study are mostly plotted in fields VI, VII and V which are suspension sediments which may contain rolled grains smaller than 1 mm (Fig. 2). All the sediment samples were collected from the cross-bedding foreset units representing bedload sediments. However, the fine-grained sediments may be attributed to the diagenetic effect for which a signature of suspension population is observed (Bapi, Dipsikha, 2011). These finer grains might have been transported for long

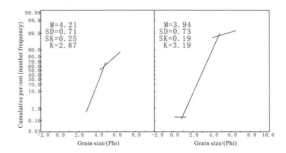

Figure 2. Plots of Upper Ganchaigou sandstones in the CM diagram. According to this plot sandstones of present study deposited mostly in the emerged bar facies followed by topset fill of a dead arm of a channel and submerged bank facies in a fluvial environment.

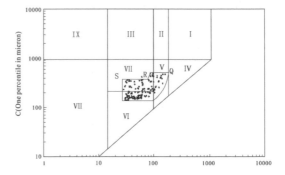

Figure 3. Cumulative frequency curve plotted at probability scale of sediments of Upper Ganchaigou Formation after Visher (1969).

distances in suspension before being rolled. Later on, Peiry (1988) has modified the Passega's diagram and identified different facies of a fluvial regime (Fig. 2). According to this plot sandstones of present study deposited mostly in the emerged bar facies followed by topset fill of a dead arm of a channel in the Delta-shallow lake deposition environment.

4.2 Log-probability curves and depositional environment

When The lognormal subpopulations in bedload and suspended load are identifiable (cf. Visher, 1969). The sediment transport was mainly carried out by saltation (Fig. 3). The suspension was sparse, as can be observed in Figure 3. Suspension and saltations domain of size-populations are shown by the present samples (Fig. 5). The traction between saltation and suspension is normally near 3Φ value. The rolling load commonly represents minor (£5%) quantity of poorly-sorted sediments while the suspension load may vary from about 20 to 40%.

The saltation load is comparatively better sorted than the suspension population and is occasionally divided under influence internal forces responsible for rolling and sliding, into two sub-populations, truncating around 1. 5Φ value (Visher, 1969). In the present study saltation population is dominant. Sediments of Upper Ganchaigou formation indicate fluvial, natural levee, tidal inlet, wave zone, and beach and dune environments of deposition.

5 CONCLUSIONS

The rocks of Upper Ganchaigou Formation of Qaidam Basin, China, predominantly include sandstones of medium to fine grain-size, with subordinate shale and hummocky cross-bedding. Fluvial regime of sedimentation with subordinate beach environment is also revealed from then log-probability plots. Sediments were in suspension and saltation before being deposited.

REFERENCES

Awasthi A K (1970). Skewness an environmental indicator in Solani River System. Sediment Geol, 4(1–2): 177–183.

Bapi Goswami, Dipsikha Ghosh (2011). Understanding the transportational and depositional setting of Panchet Formation, Purulia and Bankura districts of West Bengal, India—Evidence from grain size analysis. Front. Earth Sci., 147(1–2): 138–149.

Bandyopadhyay S, Roy Chowdhury T K, Sengupta D (2002). Taphonomy of some Gondwana vertebrate assemblages of India. Sediment Geol, 147(1–2): 219–245.

Buckley D E, Cranston R E (1991). The use of grain size information in marine geochemistry. In: Syvistki J P E, ed. Principles, Methods and Application of Particle Size Analysis. New York: Cambridge University Press, 283–292.

Folk R L, Ward W C (1957). Brazos River bar: A study in the significance of grain 27 size parameters. J Sediment Petrol, 27: 3–26.

Ghosh S C, Nandi A, Ahmed G (1994). Study of Permo-Triassic boundary in Gondwana Sequence of Raniganj basin, India. In: 9th International Gondwana Symp, Hyderabad, India, 179–193.

Ghosh S C (2002). The Raniganj Coal Basin: An example of an Indian Gondwana rift. Sediment Geol, 147(1–2): 155–176.

Martins L R (2003). Recent sediments and grain-size analysis. Gravel, 1: 90–105.

Passega R (1957). Texture as characteristics of clastic deposition. Am Assoc Pet Geol Bull, 41: 1952–1984.

Passega R (1964). Grainsize representation by CM patterns as a Geological Tool. J Sediment Petrol, 34: 830–847.

Robinson P L (1970). The Indian Gondwana formations— A review. First International Symposium on Gondwana Stratigraphy, I.U.G.S, South America, 201–268.

Tang Rui, He You Bin etc (2003). The storm deposits sedimentary formation in upper Ganchaigou group of Youshashan oilfield in Qaidam basin, Advanced Materials Research, v 779, p 1376–1378.

Computer, Intelligent Computing and Education Technology – Liu, Sung & Yao (Eds)
© 2014 Taylor & Francis Group, London, ISBN 978-1-138-02469-4

Practical teaching exploration on cultivating applied electromechanical engineering talents

C.H. Pan
Department of Chemistry, Cangzhou Normal University, Cangzhou, Hebei, China

H.Y. Wang
Department of Mechanical Engineering, Cangzhou Normal University, Cangzhou, Hebei, China

ABSTRACT: Practical teaching is the key to cultivating applied electromechanical talents and also the guarantee to the training quality of applied talents. The practical ability, comprehensive application ability and creative thinking ability of the students must be obtained through corresponding practice teaching. In order to realize the goal of training applied mechanic talents, the author puts forward new measures to construct improved practical teaching system and implement full range of practical activities, and comes up with new ideas for the training of the overall quality of applied talents.

Keywords: electomechanical engineering; applied talents; practical teaching

1 INTRODUCTION

Applied electromechanical engineering need to emphasize the combination of learning and using, pay attention to the cultivation of the engineering practical ability and cultivate applied engineering talents with innovative consciousness. They should have not only a solid basis of professional disciplines and strong practical and innovation abilities but also good physical and psychological quality and excellent professional accomplishment so that they can design, manufacture, manage and sell mechanical products in first line of industrial production. In recent year how to improve students' practical and comprehensive application ability is a hot topic in the teaching of engineering-oriented Universities.

According to the teaching idea of applied talents training, we Mechanical and Electrical Engineering Department Mechanical and Electrical Engineering Department Mechanical and Electrical Engineering Department make full use of the teaching resources in Mechanical and Electrical Engineering Department and the local area to reform the practical teaching of mechanical specialty and have obtained good teaching effect. The practical teaching reform can make the students get the basic knowledge, professional knowledge and practical ability related to their major, and enhance students' professional ability and innovation consciousness.

2 THE GOALS AND OBJECTIVES OF THE PRACTICE TEACHING SYSTEM REFORM IN ENGINERY SPECIALTY

Practice teaching system is defined as using the theory and method of systematic science to make overall design of the various elements in the practice teaching process according to the personnel training objectives and establishing a teaching system with rational structure and optimized function through the reasonable arrangement of the curriculum and the teaching practice optimization (including experiment, practice, course design, graduation design, innovation and entrepreneurship training programs), academic competition and social production practice.

To build and improve the practice teaching system must be in accordance with the talent demand of science and technology progress and social development, with the basic ability training as the basis, the comprehensive quality cultivation as the core, the innovation spirit as the main line. We must improve the students' humane accomplishment, moral cultivation and comprehensive quality, to develop good character contribute to personal development so as to foster students' ability. The overall goal is to cultivate the students' scientific experiment ability, engineering design ability, professional practice ability, scientific research ability and to forge their innovation consciousness, spirit and ability.

The construction of practice teaching system should be in accordance with such requirements as focusing on the foundation, strengthening training and integration and cultivating ability. The basic principles are as follow:

1. On the basis of students' practical ability, make systematic design and planning, thereby optimizing the practice teaching system, combining the teaching theory and practice and complete the organic unity of training objectives, teaching content, teaching method and teaching management system.
2. Focus on the students' practical ability and innovation ability. Establish teaching base and operation mode which combine teaching and learning both in and outside the campus, in class and extracurricular to promote the harmonious development of students' knowledge, ability and quality.
3. Reform the practice teaching links such as experiment method, practice, course design and graduation design, with modern economic and social development, technology development, industrial structure adjustment and modern education technology as the platform, to apply the contemporary high-tech, new technology and modern educational technology in the process of practice teaching.
4. Try to embody the professional ability. Establish and perfect the practice teaching system on the basis of the professional ability to determine the core link of practice teaching and determine the core curriculum and knowledge so as to cultivate students' basic ability required by their specialty.

3 THE BASIC CONTENTS AND STRATEGIES OF PRACTICE TEACHING SYSTEM REFORM IN ENGINERY SPECIALTY

As a complete practice teaching training scheme, practice teaching system focuses on the integration of proper course arrangement and practice so as to realize the cultivation of talents with practice teaching characteristics through the best management mode to meet the national talent goals and the demand of social personnel training. Therefore, we should combine the construction of teaching system with the high-quality applied talent training goal, follow the law of education and teaching, take all kinds of practice teaching links into consideration, make reasonable arrangement, and make continuous development and improvement to train top innovative talents for the society.[1]

3.1 Construct a reasonable practice teaching system

Through the analysis of the practice teaching development trend in enginery specialty, we find that in the practice teaching system the practical courses and projects should focus on its advanced nature, openness and innovation to form the complete multi-level and multi-form practical teaching system suitable for the practice teaching development. Therefore, we have established three levels of practice teaching system: basic experiment and basic skills training, curriculum design and manufacturing integration, and comprehensive graduation design and graduation practice so that every student can learn comprehensive technical skills.

3.2 Arrange teaching content reasonably

Arrange more design or comprehensive practice content and reduce verification content to fully mobilize the students' autonomy, independence and thinking ability and train their innovation consciousness.

Set the training content reasonably and make the training be of series and convergence to the students' comprehensive design skills and teamwork spirit as far as possible.

Strengthen the graduate design management to train students' integrity ability, project comprehensive ability and project development experience. Therefore, in the teaching platform arrangement, the practice teaching content should be able to meet the target of applied talents training and achieve the training objective.

3.3 Pay attention to the systematic, engineering, practicability and comprehension of the practice teaching content

Emphasize the link like curriculum design with strong practicability. With the comprehensive training program as the core, the utility as the goal, emphasize engineering and practice-oriented pursue the training environment close to practice in the setting of experiment and practice content and form. Training method should embody practicability and objective.

Break the constraints of the original single curriculum system. Combine the graduation design and research, the mechanical course design, machinery manufacturing technology and design and innovation training, and 3D computer aided design and dynamic simulation mechanism structure design. Offer comprehensive course design fusing many the knowledge and content in many courses to make the teaching content practicality, consistency and scalability.

Carry out technical training and certification actively. In order to meet the employment needs of students, combine the academic education and occupation qualification certificate training.

3.4 Adopt flexible and diversified teaching methods

The cultivation of applied talents needs to handle the relationship between theory education and practice teaching, the professional curriculum and the present demands of talents, and students' use of brains and hands. Try to avoid bucket- type education. We should have with the students learn initiatively and complete independently according to the requirement of contents so that they can be part of the practice process. In this way we can train the students' ability to solve problems independently and to innovate.[2]

3.5 Strengthen the construction of laboratory teachers: Adopt modern teaching methods such as multimedia and network to improve teaching effect and cultivate the students' comprehensive abilities

Comprehensive and innovative experiment projects need high-quality personnel to develop and use. Change the obsolete idea that experiment technical work is low level teaching. Strengthen the training of experiment personnel and improve their education level, professional title structure and comprehensive quality. Construct a good laboratory team to provide high-quality teacher guarantee for practice teaching.

In the practice teaching process, we can establish practice teaching management system, make convenient and suitable multimedia courseware and establish network experimental teaching platform to provide students with online learning of the verification experiment and traditional simulation experiments. In this way the test items, contents, equipment, methods, goals and test reports can be available on the Internet to facilitate students' learning and improve experimental teaching effect. Make full use of the modern teaching means and technology to expand the amount of knowledge and information of the students. Thus, they can not only acquire perceptual cognition on professional background and objects, but also can have more time to engage in comprehensive and designing experiments to improve their comprehensive experimental ability and creative consciousness.

3.6 Construct effective practice teaching evaluation system to improve teaching quality

A good evaluation system can not only stimulate the students' learning motivation effectively but also be beneficial to the evaluation of teaching effect. The traditional evaluation of student learning is teacher-oriented. The assessment is based on the subject or topic completion and defense situation. The evaluation is mostly decided by subjective judgment of teachers. The students themselves and the other students in the same group can not participate in the evaluation. In fact the evaluation on practical teaching teachers should also be made from much more perspectives to make the teaching model real where teachers evaluate learning; students evaluate teaching; teaching benefits teachers as well as students.[3]

3.7 Guide and develop students' extracurricular innovation activities

Application and innovation ability is contained in human consciousness and attribute and the individual potential which is formed through long-term training, experience and accumulation and can make people thinking and action enter a mastery, creative freedom.[4] In order to make the students have the property and quality, we must expand the cultivation time and space from class to extra-curricular and from within the school to the outside to form a full range of educational environment. We have set up a student research team and Invention Association in our department. We organize the students to participate in college mechanical innovation design competition and science and technology innovation activities and provide a platform for students to develop their engineering design thinking, engineering innovation, the spirit to innovate and the abilities to analyze and solve practical engineering problems.

4 CONCLUSION

Mechanical engineering is very practical and aimed at training applied talents. Practice has proved that practical teaching ideas and methods mentioned in this paper are conducive to cultivate the practice ability of the students and improve their overall quality, which is a successful applied talents practice teaching reform.

ACKNOWLEDGEMENTS

This work was financially supported by Higher Education Association of Hebei province (GJXH2013-28): Practical Teaching Exploration on Cultivating Applied Electromechanical Engineering Talents.

REFERENCES

[1] Yan Xuhui (2009) Discussion on the training mode of mechanical professional application talents [J]. Small and medium-sized enterprise management and technology. (11): 64–65.

[2] Zhong Liping, Shi Junxia, Zhang Wenfeng (2011) The Exploration of the "3 + 1" Applied Talents' Cultivation in Mechanical Major under the Background of Excellent Engineers Training [J]. Science and Technology Management Research. (16):158–165.

[3] Tang Rui, Wen Guang. A Practical Teaching Research on the Training of Application-oriented Students of Electromechanical Engineering [J]. Journal of Panzhihua University. 2007,(8):124–126.

[4] Zhao Yong Cheng, Liu Jun. The Reform and Practice of Practical Teaching System of Mechanical Design, Manufacturing and Automation Specialty [J]. Journal of Langfang Teachers College (Natural Science Edition). 2012,(2):122–124.

Computer, Intelligent Computing and Education Technology – Liu, Sung & Yao (Eds)
© *2014 Taylor & Francis Group, London, ISBN 978-1-138-02469-4*

The simulation and analysis of background noise effect on inter-satellite link

Juan Gao
School of Non-Commissioned Officer of Changping, Academy of Equipment, Beijing, China

Yao-Yu Zhang
Changchun Institute of Optics, Fine Mechanics and Physics, Chinese Academy of Science, Changchun, Jilin, China

Wei-Dong Liang
School of Non-Commissioned Officer of Changping, Academy of Equipment, Beijing, China

ABSTRACT: In this paper, the influence factors of inter-satellite communication, such as background noise, electronic noise, and jitter noise, are analyzed firstly. Then according to the relative position of satellites and background interference sources, a model of disturbance of background noise on satellite communication inter-satellite link, which is relevant to FOV (Field of View), is proposed and the conditions of inter-satellite disturbance is obtained. In order to verify the model, a Iridium constellation simulation is established with STK (Satellite Tool Kit). The simulation result proves that both the model and the analysis method are high-effective in determining the disturbance at any time, which is helpful to select routing of inter-satellite link.

Keywords: satellite communication; inter-satellite link; background noise; STK

1 BACKGROUND

How to take full advantage of the use of space and to build communications link between satellites have became a hot research topic, with the development of communication and aerospace technology. United States, Japan and Europe have carried out researches on the subject, and some have entered the practical stage, such as Iridium, Teledesic and Milstar systems. The research of inter-satellite link technology has been taken more attention to in China, and several space experiments have been carried out in order to enter the practical stage gradually.

2 CONCEPTION AND CHARACTERISTICS OF INTER-SATELLITE LINK

Inter-satellite link refers to the communication link between satellites. The beam of inter-satellite link does not point to the earth but to other satellites, which is different from traditional satellite communications. In a satellite communication system with inter-satellite link, information can be sent from the ground station to the satellite through the uplink, then it reaches the terminal satellite via inter-satellite link and finally it sent to the terminal

ground station through the downlink. At last, it reaches the end user (Fig. 1).

The functions and characteristics of inter-satellite link are:

1. It avoids transmitting the information back to the ground for processing and routing, and reduces the communication delay;
2. It can be taken as a backup of ground communication network, which improves the reliability of the overall communication network;
3. When the user and the station do not see a certain satellite simultaneously, the communication line can be established by using inter-satellite link;
4. It simplifies gateway ground station structure, reducing the number of gateway stations, such as Globalstar (without inter-satellite link) needs approximately 100 ground gateway stations

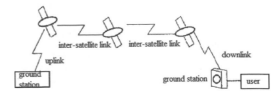

Figure 1. Communication process of inter-satellite link.

to provide global services, while Iridium (with inter-satellite link) needs only six.

3 THE FACTORS THAT AFFECT THE INTER-SATELLITE LINK COMMUNICATION

As the space environment and parameters of satellite are quite complex, inter-satellite link communication is inevitably affected by various factors, such as background noise, the system electronic noise and jitter noise. Among these noises, background noise refers to the background disturbance of noise interference sources in space (mainly refers to the sun, as to the laser inter-satellite link, the moon's reflection, starlight and scattered light from the surface and clouds also need to be considered). Strong interference may completely cover communication signals and causes communication interrupt, this interference can be fatal in some cases. Such as system with laser inter-satellite link, when the laser receiver head faces to the sun or the moon in working condition, physical damage of the photoelectric detector will occur. For a high frequency (such as Ka band) link, the inter-satellite link will be interrupted when the background interference is in high level of intensity.

4 BACKGROUND NOISE MODEL

Since interrupted operations caused by interruptions in inter-satellite need to be shunted by other link, the system's traffic management and routing problems are influenced. This interference is a dynamic process, and thus more difficult to analyze. However, whether there is still some regularity to follow to identify whether the inter-satellite link is disturbed by background noises. After in-depth analysis, we found the law, and proposed a method that made a judgment whether the link is blocked. Simulation based on STK and 66 satellite constellations of Iridium is carried out, and the simulation has not only obtained the number of blocked inter-satellite links at some point, but also easily determined which link is blocked, thereby provides the basis for routing and constellation design.

For interstellar communication, due to that the relative positional relationship between the satellites are constantly changing and there is still "jitter" when satellites are in orbit, the receive/send device of an inter-satellite link must have a certain Field of View (FOV). Precision laser inter-satellite link's FOV is typically 2 degree, while that of some simply rough alignment ones can reach 45 degrees. Thus inter-satellite link's FOV and the spatial relationship between satellite and interference source, as is shown in Figure 2, shall be paid serious attention to in the background noise disturbance analysis of inter-satellite link (In the following discussion, we suppose the sun as the source of interference).

As illustrated in Figure 2, set the earth's core as the observation point, the viewing angle of sun edge is about 0.5347 degrees. Because the satellite's altitude has several orders of magnitude difference compared with the average earth-sun distance, we can also assume that the viewing angle of a satellite as the observation point to observe the sun edge is 0.5347 degrees. As the satellite is in constant motion, when the sun falls into FOV of inter-satellite link communication, the strong sun light, electromagnetic interference interrupts the inter-satellite link, so that the work of two satellite nodes is affected. The analysis results of background noise can be indicated by the number of affected nodes or that of the blocked links. Because when the link between a satellite and another is disturbed, the link between the satellite and other satellites can still work, so we use the number of blocked links for analysis.

Figure 2 shows that, S2 must enter the FOV of S1 if when one want S1 to communicate with S2, assume that the upper edge of the FOV angle coincides with the lower edge of 0.5347 degrees angle, S1 and S2 are in the critical state, then the included angle between line of satellites S1 and S2 and line of the sun and S1 is θ (as is shown in Fig. 2), and

$$\theta = \frac{f + 0.5347}{2}.$$

If the FOV is moved upward, the inter-satellite between them would be disturbed, thus we conclude disturbing conditions of the link as:

$$\theta \leq \frac{f + 0.5347}{2} \qquad (1)$$

where, f is the FOV of inter-satellite link communication.

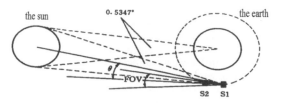

Figure 2. Disturbed condition model of the sun towards the inter-satellite link.

According to the above equation, we proposed a distinguishing method of interference among two satellites S1, S2 and the sun:

1. Select the satellites that furthest from the sun in S1 and S2.
   If

   $$|S - S_1| \geq |S - S_2|,$$

   we get

   $$\vec{A} = S_1 - S \quad \vec{B} = S_1 - S_2 \qquad (2)$$

   Else

   $$\vec{A} = S_2 - S \quad \vec{B} = S_2 - S_1 \qquad (3)$$

2. Calculate the disturbance viewing angle θ

   $$\theta = \arccos \frac{\vec{A} \cdot \vec{B}}{|\vec{A} \| \vec{B}|} \qquad (4)$$

3. Judgment, if inequality (1) is satisfied, the inter-satellite link between S1 and S2 is blocked by interference of the sun.

We shall know the coordinates of S1, S2 and the sun in a certain coordinate system respectively to determine whether the inter-satellite link is blocked using the method above. If the satellite constellation parameters are known, it is easy to calculate the θ. But we can not pre-determine which link between two satellites will be disturbed, so lots of calculations are required, and the workload is very large, therefore we need to find better analysis tools.

5 SIMULATION AND ANALYSIS

In order to further simplify the calculation and to discuss the impact of background interference on the entire satellite communication system, we took Iridium's 66 satellite constellations as a reference, and simulated the conditions of blocked inter-satellite links by using the STK satellite simulation toolkit.

Satellite simulation toolkit STK (Satellite Toll Kit), as an aerospace and satellite system analysis tool, is developed by Analytical Graphics Inc. in US. It analyses and displays complex algorithms in visual forms, and its powerful simulation function for satellite systems has greatly reduced the complexity of satellite system analysis.

The simulation process of "impact of background noise on inter-satellite link" using STK

is shown in Figure 3, but there are two points required to be explained:

1. Calculate θ. By substitution of FOV, according to the system requirements, in equation (1), θ is obtained.
2. Set Satellite constraints: In the STK software, there is a satellite bound term option, you can set the Solar Exclusion Angle: Depending on the object from the source object to the connection: the minimum included angle between line from the source to the target and that of the source to the sun.

Simulation model parameters: Satellite: 66; orbital plane: 6; orbital altitude: 780 km (485 miles); orbital plane inclination: 86.4 degrees; orbital period: 100 minutes and 28 seconds; number of inter-satellite links: 4, one forward link, one backward link, and the other two are cross-links.

The inter-satellite link model of constellations is shown in Figure 4. Where "o" refers to satellites; the line between satellites refers to the inter-satellite

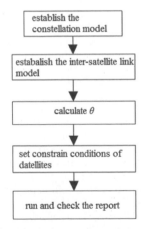

Figure 3. STK simulation flow diagram.

Figure 4. Constellation inter-satellite link model of Iridium.

1305

Table 1. Status reports of inter-satellite links of Satellite1301.

Time (UTCG)	Number of accesses	Access objects
1 Jun 2008 12:20:00.00	4	Satellite1302: Satellite1201: Satellite1311: Satellite1401
1 Jun 2008 12:21:00.00	4	Satellite1302: Satellite1201: Satellite1311: Satellite1401
1 Jun 2008 12:22:00.00	3	Satellite1201: Satellite1311: Satellite1401
1 Jun 2008 12:23:00.00	3	Satellite1201: Satellite1311: Satellite1401
1 Jun 2008 12:24:00.00	3	Satellite1201: Satellite1311: Satellite1401

link, for example, four links of Satellite1301 of are 1301–1311, 1301–1302, 1301–1201 and 1301–1401. Set the start time "1 June 2002" and the step length 60 s to simulate the disturbance conditions of inter-satellite links in one orbit period, the simulation has not only obtained the number of disturbed inter-satellite links at some point, but also easily determined which link is blocked, thereby provides the basis for routing and constellation design.

Table 1 shows the inter-satellite link report obtained by simulation (take Satellite1301 as an example). As can be seen from Table 1, Satellite1301 had 4 inter-satellite links at 12:20 on June 1, 2008, namely with Satellite1302, with Satellite1201, with Satellite1311 and with Satellite1401, and the link between Satellite1302 is blocked due to background interference. Analyses of other links are the same as the above.

6 CONCLUSION

We can obtain the following conclusions by theoretical analysis and simulation:

1. The disturbance of background noise to inter-satellite links can be analyzed by investigating the relative position between satellites and the interference sources.
2. The disturbance condition of links in a certain time can be determined rapidly and intuitively by establishing an inter-satellite link model based on STK and setting the constrain conditions.

REFERENCES

[1] Liang Yue-jie, "Carries on the Satellite Interspace Link Analysis Using STK", Journal of Henan Normal University (Natural Science), Vol. 37, pp47–49, 2009.
[2] Yang Ying and Wang Qi, STK in the Application of Computer Simulation, National Defence Industry Press, 2005.
[3] Ding Shu-quan, The Application of STK in Simulation and Analysis of Space Mission, National Defence Industry Press, 2011.
[4] Zhang Ya-sheng, Fan Peng-shan, Liu Hai-yang, Mastering Satellite Toll Kit (STK), National Defence Industry Press, 2011.
[5] Hu Cai-bo, Wang Hong-bing, and Hu Li-li, "Using STK to Analyze Access and Coverage of Navigation Satellite", GNSS World of China, pp40–43, 2007.
[6] Analytical Graphics INC (AGI), STK User's Manual Version8.1.1, 2002.
[7] Dai Ming-xin, Zhang Wen-ming, and Wang Xue-song, "Design and Simulation of SAR Satellite Orbit Prediction Based on STK", Mordern Defence Technology, Vol. 36, pp5–9, 2008.
[8] Zhang Sheng, Yuw Ting-gao, and Xu Jing, "Research on the Simulation of ECM to the Satellite Communication Links Based on STK", Electronic Warfare, Vol. 2, pp12–16, 2008.
[9] Zhang Zhan-yue, Xu Yan-li, and Zeng Guo-qiang, "Analysis on the STK-based Space Mission Simulation", Journal of the Academy of Equipment Command & Technology, Vol. 17, pp48–51, 2006.

Computer, Intelligent Computing and Education Technology – Liu, Sung & Yao (Eds)
© 2014 Taylor & Francis Group, London, ISBN 978-1-138-02469-4

Research on key technology of uplink arraying for deep space exploration

Yong-Qiang Li & Xiao-Ming Zhang
School of Non-Commissioned Officer of Changping, Academy of Equipment, Beijing, China

ABSTRACT: This paper is an overview of uplink arraying technology for deep space exploration. Under the background that uplink and downlink array technologies are applied in deep space exploration, the concept of antenna arraying is induced. Then arraying scheme, influence factors, and key techniques including phase adjusting method, adjusting target selection, and atmosphere influence are summarized. The research provides a reference for China's future engineering application.

Keywords: deep space exploration; antenna arraying; space TT&C

1 INTRODUCTION

With the continuous development of space technology, the world saw the rise of an upsurge of deep space exploration. It is another space technology development area that follows satellite applications and manned space flight.

The Opportunity and Spirit Martian probe of American have successfully landed on Mars. The Cassini probe, which reached Saturn, has successfully launched onto Titan. The Voyager 2 of NASA (National Aeronautics and Space Administration) used ground antenna arraying of deep space network to improve the amount of data returned in the late 1980s when it came close to Uranus and Neptune.

The lunar exploration project of China is proposed in the 90 s of last century. Change 1 satellite was successfully launched on October 24, 2007. The first-stage project has been successfully realized, the measurement and control system has accomplished the mission, which indicates that China has entered the era of deep space exploration, In addition, YH-1 as China's first Mars probe has also been included in the plan. Throughout the flight of a deep space probe, measurements and controls shall be done to ensure the accuracy of its flight track. However during the detection process, information needs to be send back, so communication system of deep space TT&C, as the only information line of space exploration, is crucial.

Aiming at the characteristics of deep space exploration such as long distance, large delay and high data bandwidth requirements, a variety of technical measures are applied to improve the communication quality of deep space exploration, and increasing the size of the antenna is one

among them, however the antenna aperture size at present has almost reached the limit. The development strategy of NASA's DSN (Deep Space Network deep Space Network) identifies two possible ways: one is turning to optical communication system, and improving the performance through higher operating frequency; the other is to achieve higher gain through a large group of small antenna arrays, namely antenna arraying technology.

2 DEFINITION AND ADVANTAGES OF ANTENNA UPLINK ARRAY

2.1 *Definition of antenna uplink arraying*

The so-called antenna arraying technology is using a large amount of antennas in different locations to form an antenna array, the antennas transmits or receives the same signal and the signals are synthesized at the receiving end to obtain the desired high SNR or Equivalent Isotropic Radiated Power (EIRP), in order to realize the measurement and control of a deep space probe. This concept combines practical applications of antenna uplink and downlink arraying. In the downlink applications, the ultimate purpose of arraying is to improve the SNR of the synthesized signal. According to Shannon's theorem,

$$C = B \log_2 \left(1 + \frac{S}{N} \right)$$

where C is the channel capacity, B is the channel bandwidth, S/N is the signal to noise ratio, it can be seen from the above equation that improving the signal to noise ratio leads to increasing of the channel capacity, which means the capability to receive data in a greater information rate. In the uplink applications, the fundamental objective of arraying is to improve the Equivalent Isotropic Radiated Power (EIRP), thereby increasing the data rate or emergency communications capabilities to enhance the ability such as searching for lost aircraft targets and sending more control information.

2.2 *Principle and advantages of uplink arraying*

The principle of antenna uplink arraying is similar to that of the general phased array launching system, that is to enhance the signal of the target by properly delaying the phase and time of signals transmitted from the antennas.

Far field EIRP value of the uplink antenna array synthesized by a number of same antennas aligned in high phase precision is

$$EIRP_A = N^2 GP$$

where N is the number of antennas, G is the gain of a single antenna, P is the transmit power of an antenna. Noting that EIRP value of the uplink arraying is proportional to the square of the number of antennas, therefore much higher EIRP values can be achieved in theory.

Increasing the uplink EIRP by using antennas array is very important for tasks under abnormal conditions, as well as routine tasks, the requirements are as follows:

1. Test and control requirements under normal conditions. One is to improve the uplink data transmission rate, which ensures more command information and data transmission, thereby meets design requirements of a more flexible system. The other is to extend the operation distance of a test and control station for further targets detecting.
2. Test and control requirements under abnormal conditions. One is make sure special mission data can be uploaded to the spacecraft under the condition when it is at risk and time-critical cases. Unforeseen events can make the direction of spacecraft's main antenna deviate from the earth, only a low gain or isotropic antenna can receive signals from the earth, therefore the power of signal transmitted from the ground station shall be increased.

In addition, the transmitting antenna array also has many advantages compared with a single large antenna, such as higher resource utilization, better system availability and maintenance flexibility, better anti-failure robustness and more convenient for system upgrade and so on.

In general, the future deep space test and control systems would have more powerful, flexible and effective communication capabilities if transmitting antenna array is achieved.

3 THE ARRAYING SCHEME

Uplink arraying system is composed of signal combination, signal allocation and transmission system. Signals generated by the signal processing center are modulated and allocated to the transmission array elements, and transmitted via the antenna after amplified. A reference subsystem with high precision and stable frequency is needed for a high-precision phase measurement array. Currently, maximum frequency reference of NASA is 100 MHz, the order of the stability of different antennas is few Hertz a day. Such high-precision reference frequency can reduce the frequency of the uplink calibration. Phase of the signal in the transmission process will be influenced by atmospheric transmission characteristics, weather conditions and other physical factors, thereby affecting the synthesis results. In order to achieve phase alignment, phase calibration for each array element shall be carried out, the calibration solution and calibration target selection are hot researches currently. At present, selectable calibration target includes calibration tower, quasars, radio star and so on. Calibration at present can be divided into two categories according to the difference of phase calibration position.

3.1 *Phase adjustment on the earth*

Ground phase alignment (Fig. 1) refers to achieve efficient synthesis of signal transmitted by antennas at the target location by adjusting the delay and

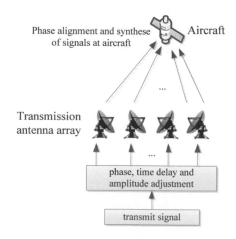

Figure 1. Phase adjustment on the earth.

phase of the transmitted signal via ground devices. The scheme has the following characteristics:

1. The system is a transmission array composed of many parabolic antennas, and the distance between each antenna reaches several thousands wavelengths or even longer.
2. Signal from each antenna shall have correct phase and time delay, so that each signal can be relevantly synthesized when reaching the target location, therefore signal energy is enhanced.

We can regard the phase control array system as an application of local transmission array. For such a phased array system, the distance between array elements is generally one half of the wavelength. For conventional phased arrays, the actual application requires that phase error between array elements is less than 20°. For X/Ka band, the distance between array elements approximate 1.5 and 0.5 cm. Even for such small element spacing, careful engineering to maintain the alignment of the phase and amplitude is still required, in order to ensure the combined beam of the entire transmission frequency range and the desired direction at the desired beam tends in the far field. In addition, the array elements of conventional compact array have a uniform temperature and mechanical property, and the change of statistical properties is similar.

For the case of off-site arraying, the spacing between the array elements reaches up to tens or even hundreds of kilometers, the temperature and mechanical properties between array elements vary greatly. In order to achieve the purpose of uplink signal phase coherent, a very stable system need to be established firstly, and then the phases and time delays of antennas shall be calculated by using the far-field target calibration system at an accurately known position, and finally the aligned signal that meet the requirements shall be transmitted.

3.2 Phase adjustment of the spacecraft

Phase adjustment of spacecraft (Fig. 2) refers to that the signal transmitted from antennas applies code/frequency division multiple access system, and the signals received by spacecraft are extracted, phase aligned and effectively combined. The scheme has the following characteristics:

1. The system is a transmission array composed of many parabolic antennas, and the distance between each antenna reaches several thousands wavelengths or even longer.
2. This technology is based on the satellite-borne multi-channel digital receiver, which has the ability to receive N signals transmitted from uplink antennas and to combine the signals effectively.

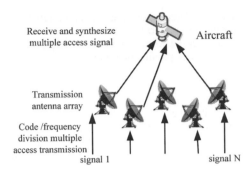

Figure 2. Phase adjustment of spacecraft.

Aiming at N ground stations versus a single spacecraft case, the ground stations transmit signal by using code division multiple access and frequency division multiple access technology, and the satellite borne receiver uses a single antenna, a single set of receiver chain, a single AD to complete uplink signal reception, down-conversion and sampling, and then the separation of multiple signals, delay/phase alignment and synthesis are completed in numeric field. Compared with phase adjustment on ground, this technology can preferably use adaptive processing techniques in order to overcome complicated calibration of the phase and delay issues caused by atmospheric scintillation, structural changes, and vibration of antennas on ground and group delay caused by uplink devices of antennas, as well as instability of real-time synthesis caused by poor calibration instantaneity. Therefore, you can get more stable and reliable arraying results. However, the key of this technology is the miniaturization of satellite borne signal processing device.

4 THE KEY TECHNOLOGIES

4.1 Phase calibration methods

In order to maximize the received power of the spacecraft during the working process of uplink, the system demands that all arriving signal carrier phase aligned. Take superposition of 2 constant amplitude pure carrier signal as an example, the synthesized signal is

$$E(t) = A\cos(2\pi ft + \theta_1) + A\cos(2\pi ft + \theta_2)$$

If

$$\theta_1 = \theta_2$$

We have

$$E(t) = 2A\cos(2\pi ft + \theta_1)$$

After coherent addition of two signals, the amplitude of spacecraft received signal is doubled, and the corresponding power of the original is four times power of the original signal; if

$$\theta_2 - \theta_1 + \pi$$

Thus we have

$$E(t) = 0$$

Signal received by the spacecraft drops to 0 due to cancellation. How to complete the calibration of the carrier phase, to achieve carrier signal alignment is a key technical problem of uplink antenna arraying.

There are two kinds of phase calibration methods namely open loop and closed loop. Because of the characteristics of deep space exploration missions, such as long delay and great attenuation, the closed loop calibration method can not be applied. Therefore the current researches focus on the selection and calibration strategy of open loop calibration method. Institute of Modern Communication of Peking University proposed a master-slave open loop synchronization adjustment strategy based on periodic downlink beacon signal. It adjusts phases of uplink signals transmitted by the antenna array by using the time difference information of downlink timing signal from the receiving aircraft.

Calibration targets can generally be divided into two categories namely active (including receivers) and passive (reflector). Active targets are restricted by scheduling and collaboration flying of the target aircraft. The main disadvantage of passive target is that if radar cross-section remains unchanged, the signal to noise ratio decreases with four square of distance, therefore the distance between passive target and the array shall be sufficiently short while radar cross-sectional area as large as possible. In general, passive targets are more suitable for the case that each antenna of array has a large EIRP value. For a small-diameter antenna, the calibration tower method can also be applied, but it also needs an in-orbit spacecraft, because we need to calibrate all directions in actual dynamic environment.

4.2 The effects of space transmission to phase calibration

The delay and phase differences of antenna signals introduced by space transmission channel are mainly due to tropospheric scintillation and ionospheric scintillation.

Tropospheric scintillation is caused by tropospheric temperature, humidity inverter or turbulent motion, which results in inhomogeneity of the refraction index of electromagnetic waves, and it makes the amplitude and phase of spacecraft received signal change in random fluctuation. Tropospheric scintillation is related to physical parameters (temperature, humidity, wind speed, etc.), latitude and season (including diurnal variation, seasonal variation). Moreover if antenna elevation angle goes lower, the path that waves go through the troposphere becomes longer, the scintillation becomes more significant.

Ionospheric scintillation is due to inhomogeneity and random time variation of the ionosphere, it results in wave scattering, so that the amplitude and phase received fluctuates. Ionospheric scintillation is related to operating frequency, location, geomagnetic activity and the local season, time and so on, while it is greatly related to the geomagnetic latitude and local time.

The effects of space transmission to off-site arraying, either upward or downward, shall be taken more attention to. Take uplink array as an example, according to NASA's relevant information, for the X-band uplink array (with the baseline approximate to 1.6 km), that is equipped in Goldstone, during 95% of the time, the expectation (not calibrated) of signal loss due to phase error caused by atmospheric changes is less than 0.7 dB, when the elevation angle is greater than 18°. Therefore, when the size of the X-band arraying is less than 1 km, it may not be necessary to carry out continuous monitoring of atmospheric changes, but if the size is more than 1 km, or when frequency band is higher, atmospheric correction becomes necessary.

Effects of space transmission can be compensated by two methods. One method is using the measurement value obtained by downlink processing to calculate the correction factor, and transmitting it to the uplink for phase, delay and amplitude correction. This method is suitable for cooperative target, but with a certain lag. The other one is transmitting radar signal to a near-earth orbit target, and determining the changes of troposphere and ionosphere. This method can be applied to non-cooperative targets. However, it requires radar signal processing device and a calibration target near the spacecraft in addition.

5 CONCLUSIONS

Deep space exploration related technical issues are always at the forefront of TT&C communication technology because of its long working distance. The universe is boundless, which promotes the generation of new conceptions, theories and methods. Research of antenna arraying, especially uplink arraying technology, is of great significance both in theory and application.

REFERENCES

[1] YU Xiao-li, Sun Jia-qi. Study on long baseline antenna arraying correlation processing technology[J]. Radio Engineering, 2012, 42(4), 41–42.

[2] He Guo-long, Li Guo-min. A parallel carrier phase calibration method for uplink antenna arrays[J]. Journal of Spacecraft TT&C Technology, 2012, 31(1).

[3] David H. Rogstad, Alexander Mileant, Timothy T. Pham. Antenna arraying techniques in the deep space network[M]. Wiley, 2005.

[4] Liu Hong, Ren Shu-bo, Wu Jian-jun, et al. Uplink arraying based on the periodic downlink standard time signal[J]. Chinese High Technology Letters, 2012, 33(8).

Computer, Intelligent Computing and Education Technology – Liu, Sung & Yao (Eds)
© 2014 Taylor & Francis Group, London, ISBN 978-1-138-02469-4

Graduates in the job causes and countermeasures

Bing Liu & Hua Chen
Department of Automotive, Zheng Zhou Technical College, Zhengzhou, China

ABSTRACT: The current employment situation of college students increasingly severe employment pressure increases, and the difficult employment has become a focus of attention of the community to focus problems. This paper analyzes the impact of student employment difficulty factors: socio-economic development, political system, cultural traditions, the students themselves, etc. These interrelated and mutually restraining factors related to the healthy development of higher education, implement the scientific concept of development, the implementation of this strategy and build a harmonious society and other major issues. Finally, appropriate policy is proposed according to the employment of university students during the main problems.

Keywords: college students; employment; reasons; countermeasures

1 INTRODUCTION

With the adjustment and reform of higher education deepening our college students' employment policies in recent years, employment continued to increase the difficulty of college students. The employment situation is increasingly grim. According to statistics of the Ministry of Education data, college employment rates were 70%, 68%, 68% in 2007, 2008, and 2009, respectively. Graduates Employment issues become the focus of attention of the problem. Employment is the people's livelihood, is the basic premise and ways to improve the lives of the people. It is not only related to the vital interests of the students themselves and their families realize the value, but also to the development of education in China, to achieve this strategy, building a harmonious society and other major issues. College students are valuable human resources of the country. Employment has grown from a difficult problem of family problems, school problems as a social problem. Successful employment graduates have a very important significance. Therefore, analysing of the main problems existing in the process of employment of university students and proposing appropriate policies are a major task for theorists and educators.

2 MAIN FACTORS AFFECTING STUDENTS' EMPLOYMENT DIFFICULTIES

The main factors affecting the employment of university students have a difficult socio-economic development, political system, cultural traditions, college students' own circumstances, etc. These factors are interlinked and mutually constraints. Only in-depth analysis of the causes of employment of university students, we can solve targeted this problem to promote the employment of them from a fundamental way.

2.1 *A sharp increase in the number of university graduates and slow job growth contradicts*

In recent years, along with college enrolment, gross enrolment rate increased year by year, by moving elite education to mass stage. The number of college graduates has gone beyond the demand of the market, due to the immaturity of market and socio-economic development of the job market but not a corresponding increase in real demand for talent, especially with the college to match job is limited, resulting in China's economic development out of touch with the real needs of subjective human talent needs. In addition, the overall employment situation from the point of view, the urban labour force employment, re-employment of laid-off workers and migrant workers "sambong overlay", cause huge employment pressure. "Graduates Employment" and college enrolment is not simply equate. But in fact, it is undeniable that too fast, or too large universities "enrolment" increased employment difficult.

2.2 *The education and the job market demand contradicts*

Overall, the total still existing between our talents and needs of nation-building has a larger gap.

However, due to their ability of graduates of higher education institutions and other causes and a variety of objective problems, make the total lack of talent and an oversupply of college graduates contradictions exist, graduates and academic structures and difficult training mode is also quite reasonable certain relationship. At present, although the quality of education in higher education has been full attention, but has not yet reached its desired effect. At present many schools can not scientifically be set according to the market demand for professional, there is a professional setting, discipline construction lagged response to the needs of society's ills, produced out of the university culture "product"— the graduates, their quality does not meet the needs of social and economic restructuring re-instil the theory and practice of light, knowledge, skills, training, resulting in structural contradictions and social needs of students' quality incompatible. That is out of the knowledge structure of higher education to train students, skill structure does not meet the market demand, and we can not meet the requirements of employers. On the one hand, graduates can not be recognized by society, hiring, on the other hand, society can not get the right talent available. This apparent rigid dislocation of higher education is a great waste of resources, a painful experience of education and the whole society. In addition, some schools were upgraded into a comprehensive university, and the establishment of a number of liberal arts majors while the community arts students graduated from these schools is not high recognition rate, which to some extent also caused a lot of good college job difficult.

2.3 Career guidance college students do not place

College Students is a comprehensive project in which career guidance is an important part of college, career guidance could help students learn to work as soon as possible to meet the job requirements, adapt relationships, thereby open up the situation, the development of self. But now, many colleges and universities for college students is not enough emphasis on career guidance, career guidance personnel quality needs to be improved, graduate employment guidance department did not fully play the role. From school career guidance department personnel constitute failure to adapt to the structural feature set requirements of market economy can not provide appropriate career guidance services for students, resulting in the presence of graduate employment difficulties.

2.4 The concept of college careers behind

Career Outlook is fundamental views and opinions of people on career aspirations, career motivation, career standards, is choosing the views of world, life and values focused on career issues reflect [2]. Professional orientation college careers college career oriented concept is the ultimate expression. Concept of occupation determines the employment of graduates in the attitude and behaviour.

Formation of students' employment outlook is influenced by many factors of social, political, economic and cultural, has obvious characteristics of the times. After continuous accumulation of various ethnic groups in different production life long practice, and gradually formed its own unique way of thinking and behaviour as well as a series of related thoughts, ideas, habits and psychological character [3]. These cultural accumulations through the socialization process from generation to generation, and it permeates every aspect of human social life, as a constraint to people's ideas and behaviour of the strong force. Under the influence of traditional culture in our society, everyone wants to "learn and become officials." For thousands of years this kind of thinking rooted in people's minds, almost every child has experienced it since childhood students education, is the teacher, the parents kept saying in the ears of students that they should become officials, scientists, and so on in the future when grown up. For a long time, the image has been ingrained favored college, college identity in the eyes of many people, but also directly and decent employment, higher incomes and a respectable social status equal to the same. This makes the hearts of Chinese people have a mind that the "cadres" are the values of promise. Employment cultural accumulation and employment impact of the cultural atmosphere at all times and restrict the employment of college students and career.

With the development of China's college enrollment and higher education, higher education in China has grown from "elite education" to "mass education" stage. But "elite consciousness" remain in the consciousness of college students, they have high expectations of employment, such as non-metropolitan do not go, do not enter non-big business, non-paying quit, which is "popular" in higher education and social needs of multi-level formation of dislocation, resulting in "unemployment", the impact of today's college orientation in the job search process has become difficult employment caused by the phenomenon of college subjective reasons [4]. In addition, the employment of graduates of the family also have an important impact on the family is a cohesive social and psychological groups, parents have too high hopes for their graduates' success, even graduates do in the future idealized employment outlook design, parents still remain in the elite education, the current employment situation lack the necessary understanding that the university is "carp leaping", has a "cadre" status, we must find a good job considered employment, the lag employment outlook parents have an important impact on the employment outlook of their graduates, has become an important factor affecting the employment of college students.

2.5 College students re-reward the contribution of light

Strongly influenced by the market economy seeks profit, competitive, contemporary college students in the choice of occupation inevitably manifested in certain practical, utilitarian tendencies. Currently, many students in the course of employment overemphasis on working conditions, the pursuit of an easy life and work, not comprehensive, objective and correct understanding of self, ignoring its own characteristics and long-term development and employer requirements, they tend to value the coastal economically developed areas lack of grassroots level, hard work, hard work spirit, unwilling to grassroots, to the west, where the country needs most to make contributions.

They pay more attention to themselves, the amount of substance, as a measure of the quality of the working environment professional values, standards of personal values. Even when in the pursuit of self-realization, but also reflects the need to "self" rather than "society" can not deal with personal and social right to obtain and dedication relationship.

3 COUNTERMEASURES

3.1 Establish and promote role models, an incentive function of ideological and political education

Vigorously publicize and report all walks of life to make a greater contribution to the emergence of the outstanding graduates deeds, to create a good atmosphere for public opinion, education, guide students to firmly establish the diligent and pragmatic, dedicated, hard work, proper employment outlook grassroots service, taught concept Confucius said: "The body is not to make the trip; their body is not correct, although that is not from the errors of their body: If Masato Ho" [5]. Successful employment figures by promoting advanced thinking, deeds, education students to improve their understanding, political consciousness and moral character is one of the main methods of ideological and political education. Inviting successful employment of graduates in particular, to carry out a successful alumni back to his alma mater, lectures, by telling their own life experience, self-perception,

college students can cause resonance, cleaning the soul, get rid of the haze on the road to employment, has strong persuasive easy student recognition and acceptance. Hu Jintao, general secretary of China of the efforts required to achieve it, "no matter where, no matter what position, should be mindful of the motherland, the heart of the nation, consciously put personal ambition to unify the whole nation with a common ideal, the personal financial struggle remitted to the rejuvenation of China's tide of history to achieve their maximum ... value of life in the service of the motherland and the people" [6].

3.2 Guide students to actively participate in social practice

Practical education is to improve the overall quality of college training and the promotion of an important part of student employment. By guiding college students understand the country and increase their abilities, contributing to society, enhance social responsibility, to prepare for future employment. College students are an active group, and they are full of vigor and vitality, the most receptive to new ideas, new things. Schools should explore new ways to open up new ways to take a variety of forms, establishing a social security system college practice, practice base through the creation of employment, vacation social practice, research, training and other activities, guide students out of school, to the grassroots, rural areas, where the country need most. Practical educational activities can motivate students to consciously strengthen professional ethics, and gradually cultivate the professionalism, spirit and indomitable will train hard work, and lay a solid foundation for future selection grassroots employment.

3.3 Updating the concept of employment to determine the appropriate employment expectations

Guiding positive change their concept of employment of college graduates is the current and future employment phase of an important part of college. With the continuous expansion of the scale of higher education, it has evolved from the old "elite education" to today's "public education". If college students still favor status itself, this concept has been departure from the reality of social development. Currently, some college students' employment standards and their own talent market conditions are not very clear. They don't know "what I can do" in the employment. Therefore, the students must adjust employment expectations, updating the concept of employment with the times, and establish employment outlook popular.

Make the right career aspirations and pragmatic employment orientation combine their own ideals and needs of the country and society unify their personal career choices combined with social reality, career development have realistic basis points before the realization of the ideal reliable platform. Do not just stare at the big cities, big institutions, big companies hold, college students should take precautions for their personality, interests, hobbies, temperament and ability to conduct an objective, comprehensive analysis, weaknesses, ahead of his own career planning, targeted knowledge of land reserves and social practice.

3.4 Colleges of education and teaching reform

Colleges and universities are to optimize professional settings, improve the teaching level, improve quality of personnel training, and enhance students' ability to adapt to the society and the market. Institutions of higher learning in the development of enrollment plan, should give full consideration to the quality of teachers, school size, market demand and other factors, a reasonable set of professional, to avoid a large number of popular professional duplication phenomenon. Reform education system, the introduction of teaching students scoring mechanism and competition mechanism in teaching arrangements, and promote teachers to improve teaching quality. Continue to strengthen and improve the employment guidance, to gradually put into an important indicator of college graduates assessment, highlighting the important role in the reform and development of graduates of colleges and universities, the majority of teachers teaching cultivate awareness, advocacy teachers consciously thinking political education combined with professional education, courses teaching should make full use of this channel, the ideological and political education into the first class professional education, the education of students in moisturizes things in silence, guide students, stable student professional thinking, strengthen students' career ideal.

3.5 Strengthen employment guidance

Colleges trained people, if not in employment, it can not become a reality, the role of productivity; it can not provide services for country and society. With the deepening of reform and change in the personnel system and our labor market system graduates, college functionally significant changes occurred. Neither the continuation of the traditional institutions of higher learning "Package distribution" role, can not be irresponsible to graduate to the market a push, it is not only a manager, but also a service provider, the final task is to promote the functions and student employment.

Strengthening employment guidance of college students is college student's full employment, stable employment and career needs of sustainable development. Strengthen employment guidance should be starting college start, a new life into the school, you have to let it understand the importance of employment, providing a full range of career guidance and counseling services, through the analysis of the employment situation, career talk, employment report, so that students understand career and develop career planning, career choices and enhance market awareness, legal awareness, sense of competition, established career aspirations and goals in life; enable students to master the necessary employment policies and employment skills, employment adjustment mentality, cultivate a healthy employment and entrepreneurship psychology, clarify their position in life, and establish efforts. College career concept formation is a continuous and gradual process that requires a longer time education, training and accumulation, and therefore should not be confined to college students' career guidance in the fourth grade graduation provisional stage; it should run through the whole process of the University. Strengthen employment guidance should focus on college students to guide and encourage students to the basic employment and self-employment. President Hu Jintao pointed out, "The majority of young people to consciously personal fate with the fate of the motherland and the nation closely linked to the pursuit of personal ideals with the great cause of building a moderately prosperous society closely linked, consciously serving the motherland, and selfless dedication to the community hard work, relentless progress, creating a fiery regrets youth in social practice, eternal youth" [7]. In addition, the employment of college graduates competent authorities should maintain the market on the basis of the original positive for graduates explore careers and provide a broader stage. Strengthen University "relationships units" contact and close cooperation is the only way schools can create their own brand, to be invincible in the fierce market competition.

4 CONCLUSION

Graduate Employment is a systematic project, which affected the political, economic, cultural and other factors, therefore, need to address this issue of participation of various social forces to work together to guide students to establish a scientific concept of employment, career outlook, healthy attitude to actively participate in the competition for jobs; seeing the students' employment situation is grim at the same time, you should see the implementation of the sustainable development of China's national economy, the western development strategy and the strategy of rejuvenating the country, providing employment for college students a broad platform; another, university's increasing emphasis on employment of college students, school construction and professional training model has also been some adjustments, career guidance universities are constantly improving, providing strong support for the employment of university students.

REFERENCES

[1] Xie Heping. Counterparts and adaptation: university personnel training and the labor market two relational models [J]. Xinhua Digest, 2005.8.

[2] Guo Sen. Update the concept of employment is the key to employment of university students [J], "personnel training", 2007.

[3] Hua Zhong. "Introduction to Political Science" [M], Renmin University of China Press, November 2000 No. l, pp. 6I.

[4] People's Education Channel: "alms talk Graduates Employment: Unemployed industry do not have respect and co-existence", March 19, 2008.

[5] Sun Jingtan. "The Analects • XIII" [M], 2002,2 edition of July, page 13.

[6] Hu Jintao to promote the great cause of the motherland in the new century fully prepared. Congratulatory speech at the Fourth National Congress of the Chinese Young Pioneers on.

[7] CPC Central Committee General Secretary and State President Hu Jintao July 25, 2004, delivered an important speech at the fifth most stressed Zhongnanhai Huairen Central with the new leadership group members and representatives of discussion groups.

Computer, Intelligent Computing and Education Technology – Liu, Sung & Yao (Eds)
© *2014 Taylor & Francis Group, London, ISBN 978-1-138-02469-4*

Study on teachers' practical knowledge ability of job-oriented education

Xiu-Lai Gu
Bengbu Automobile NCO Academy, Bengbu, China

ABSTRACT: At present, the model of some military academies has changed from academic education into job-oriented education, and the teachers enduring job-oriented education meet the new requirements which need the teachers to renew educational concepts, and have innovative ways of thinking and abundant practical knowledge. But the condition that teachers' teaching disconnects educational and teaching practice directly affects the update of teachers' professional level. The author thinks that practical knowledge is the community of experience and theory, a kind of comprehensive knowledge dominating the teachers' teaching activities. This paper focuses on how to improve the teacher's practical knowledge ability.

Keywords: job-oriented education; teacher; practical knowledge; ability

In recent years, some researchers appeal to strengthening teachers' practical knowledge in Chinese teacher group construction. Along with the disconnection of job-oriented education and academic education, the development of job-oriented academies rely on their teachers' professional development which can be realized by reflecting in practice, increasing teachers' practical knowledge, constructing study platform and accelerating teachers to update their theoretic and practical knowledge.

1 THE CHARACTERISTICS OF TEACHERS' PRACTICAL KNOWLEDGE

Practical knowledge is the knowledge that teacher can learn from individual experience with systematical reflection on personal practice. In the acquirement of the knowledge, the most important aspect is the combination of subject and object. During the teaching process, subject is the teacher's individual comprehension and experience which are experience knowledge corresponding to teaching learnt at some concrete teaching process and disciplinary knowledge structure comprehended when the teacher learnt some concerned disciplinary knowledge. Object points to the objective and universal theories and rules which can be expressed clearly with concepts and theories. The combination of subject and object include the experience with theoretical guidance and the theory with experience support. Therefore, practical knowledge is the integration of experience and theory, a kind of comprehensive knowledge dominating teachers' teaching activities.

1.1 *Expression feature*

1.1.1 *Scene feature*

It, without invariable mode, comes into being during the concrete teaching scene in job-oriented education, closely combines with concrete discipline and adapts to daedal concrete scenes.

1.1.2 *Taking theoretic knowledge as support*

Teachers can not form practical ability only relying on theoretic knowledge. Theoretic knowledge is significant for the construction of practical knowledge, which is the support to practical knowledge, yet absolutely not the whole. That is to say, having theory does not mean to have practical ability.

1.1.3 *Development*

Teachers' practical knowledge ability consistently develop during the construction process, including comparative fundamental practical knowledge and more advanced practical knowledge, which relate closely to teachers' unceasing accumulation of personal experience and incessant abundance of personal knowledge.

1.2 *Construction characteristics*

1.2.1 *The unceasing optimization process of teachers knowledge structure*

Teachers' practical knowledge is the integration of a lot of knowledge. However, it is not only the mixture of knowledge, but also a stationary entirety, like common concrete, via the interactivities among some materials. Therefore, the formation of practical knowledge is not the simple knowledge addition but the formation process of teachers' knowledge structure. Such knowledge structure is the basis that dominates teachers to choose and estimate in concrete teaching scenes of job-oriented education. All knowledge possessed by teachers can be obtained by directly and indirectly. However, by whatever means to be obtained, the knowledge must be brought into teachers' primary knowledge structure on the basis of their comprehension, and then be re-constructed according to the characteristics of job-oriented education.

1.2.2 *Comprehension and emphasis process of teachers' practical wisdom*

Teachers' practical knowledge ability needs the support of theoretic knowledge, yet the theoretic knowledge can be transformed into practical knowledge only by teachers' personal experience, which is not only something come through but also some comprehension or cognition during the experience or some deep impression. The formation and obtainment of practical knowledge differ entirely from teachers' other knowledge. The theoretic knowledge can be learnt only by teachers' teaching, but the practical knowledge must be learnt by experience during some concrete fulfillment according to concrete question scene. That is, learning from doing. During the process of doing, teachers will encounter creativity and all kinds of uncertainty. Only when teachers individually search and think in this uncertain, wondering and puzzling teaching career, teachers can get true teaching experience and form their own practical knowledge ability.

1.2.3 *The process of consistent reflection*

The formation of teachers' practical knowledge ability needs teachers' consistent reflection on the teaching of job-oriented education, and re-build teachers' self-value. When building personal cognition, comprehension of all things and views and individual teaching theory and method, teachers can comparatively treat their own teaching processes, discover problems, and then find out the methods and strategies of resolutions, supervise the effects of the resolutions and realize entirely objective evaluation on teaching. Teachers' reflection process is a kind of study and research based on experience. Only that experience is added to reflection can make experience be teachers' study resources. In the process of reflection inspection, personal experience can be consistently increased, modified and consummated as provide strong support to the new inspection of future new knowledge

and theory. Experience plus reflection is the path of teachers' study and the only way for teachers' professional development.

2 EFFECT OF TEACHERS' PRACTICAL KNOWLEDGE ABILITY IMPROVEMENT

2.1 *Contributions to teachers' professional development*

The practical knowledge ability dominates teachers' choice and judgment at teaching in job-oriented education, and influence on their choice, filtration, study and application to theoretic knowledge. Therefore, on certain degree, the accumulation situation of teachers' practical knowledge directly affects subsequently teachers' development and study. It is favorable for teachers' long term and even lifetime professional development to improve teachers' practical knowledge ability and attach importance to the integration of theoretic cognition and experience.

2.2 *Contributions to the improvement of teaching ability*

Teachers' practical knowledge ability contributes to the progress of teaching ability, because the formation process of practical knowledge is the process of experience. Only in the teaching experience process, teachers' language expression ability, organization and management ability, teaching ability in classroom, etc. can be effectively guided and practically trained, which provide stationary foundation. During the teaching experience and teachers' personal impression, teachers' teaching consciousness and correct self-cognition ability improved, and their own practical teaching ability has been formed and improved in direct teaching and education activities.

3 APPROACH TO IMPROVEMENT OF TEACHERS' PRACTICAL KNOWLEDGE ABILITY

3.1 *Strengthen specific train and improve teachers' whole quality*

Teachers' professional level and working ability is the core of the core in the job-oriented education in military academies, and the whole quality of their teachers is the future of the academy and the armed force, so that the comprehensive cultivation of teachers must be attached importance to. For example, new teachers who just enter the career need comprehensive and systematic training at teaching theory, knowledge structure and professional skills, etc. As for the teachers with certain teaching experience, they must pay attention to study overseas and domestic new thought, theories and the disciplinary frontiers knowledge of the corresponding to teaching and education and broaden their horizons.

3.2 Construct two-way communication system and increase teachers' practical experience

In job-oriented education, it is necessary for teachers to have abundant practical experience and certain appointed experience. The construction of rational two-way communication system can simulate the renewal of teachers' disciplinary knowledge and increase the quantity of high-tech knowledge, which is significant for the optimization of teacher group structure, improvement of teachers' practical knowledge ability and job-orient education quality maintenance. Multi-level and multi-form communication system is necessary. The deputy appointment of young teachers should be appointed to company level, so that they can know the equipment utilization, management, maintenance and fault diagnosis, etc. in armed force, and provide technical service for the units with their own disciplinary and fundamental knowledge, and even accumulate practical experience. Teachers with middle and high level title of a technical or professional post go to units with their research according to teaching requirement and consummate the integrative combination between armed force units and academies. At the same time, the academies can retain the leaders and experts with abundant experience and high theoretic level from units as teachers to introduce the conditions and requirements of the armed force units to increase the specific of the teaching in job-oriented education. The cadres in a specific technique field and the management cadres can be took as necessary supplement for the teacher group in job-oriented education academies. Therefore, the two-way communication system between academies and armed force units is a kind of effective method to improve teachers' practical knowledge ability.

3.3 Reflect at practice to improve teachers' practical knowledge ability

Reflection is an effective method to quicken disciplinary development from the angle of teachers themselves. In 1989, Posner, American psychologist, brought out an equation for teachers' improvement, Improvement = Experience + Reflection. That is to say, it is significant for teachers' improvement to reflect in teaching practice. Reflection is to be contextualized and individualized, which can not be formalized, and, with irreplaccability, can not be obtained by other persons' direct teaching. Without reflection in teaching process, teachers can not get any improvement. Teachers' reflection must be an active and unfeigned activity, because active reflection can maintain teachers' positivity, which makes any teaching practice better than the further and improves teachers' development, and make teachers get practical knowledge. By reflecting teaching practice, teachers can consistently adjust their own teaching theory and activities, construct themselves new disciplinary knowledge, and can be internalized as practical knowledge, to improve their teaching ability.

4 CONCLUSION

Cadets at the condition of job-oriented education have higher psychological development level and more social experience than cadets at academic education, and need more complex teaching activities. Practical knowledge ability makes teachers, facing complicated and variable teaching and education activities, grasp observantly the pulse and opportunity of the activities' development, solve creatively problems, organize teaching activities with high efficiency and better cultivate qualified talents for the construction of the Armed Force.

REFERENCES

[1] Lizhi Zhang, Haozheng Qin. The teacher education practice thinking knowledge. Modern university Education, 2009, (3).
[2] Xiangming Chen. Practical knowledge: the knowledge base of the professional development of teachers. Peking University education review, 2003, (1).
[3] Yigang Lin. Discussion "reflective practice" teacher education. Teacher Education Research, 2008, (6).
[4] Liujing Zhong, Yanhui Wang. Teachers professional development office on Military Academy. Research on university teachers Chinese, 2009, (4).

Computer, Intelligent Computing and Education Technology – Liu, Sung & Yao (Eds)
© 2014 Taylor & Francis Group, London, ISBN 978-1-138-02469-4

Some thoughts on improving the professional education teachers structure

En-Bing Fu
Bengbu Automobile NCO Academy, Bengbu, China

ABSTRACT: The paper firstly analyzes the current problems of military education teachers structure, and then from perfecting the teachers "army officers and colleges two-way communication" system to adapt to the development requirements of professional education, standardization and innovation management mode and teachers professional education teachers structure to put forward the measures to solve the problems of establishing the related laws and regulations etc.

Keywords: professional education; teacher; teachers structure

Currently, the military academic professional education is still in the transition phase, lacking of theoretical research and practical experience, there are many teachers' structural bottlenecks restricting the development of our military institutions serving education. Therefore, the successful experience of civil vocational schools, the introduction of advanced management concepts and methods to enhance their teaching structure management, building architecture education teacher tenure, serving educational institutions for the development of our military is necessary and significant.

1 BOTTLENECKS OF MILITARY ACADEMIC PROFESSIONAL EDUCATION TEACHER STRUCTURE

There currently are obvious problems in military academic professional education teacher structure, which restricts the development of professional education, mainly in the following three aspects.

1.1 *Professional education teacher lacks of force practices*

Military professional education is a specialized education around professional ability, which requires teacher not only have worked on the basis of profound knowledge, but also have a solid practical ability and job training objects serving the needs and development potential has profound understanding. The survey results show that the current requirements for teacher education experience working with the office of education is still a great gap. 80% of teachers did not have served, 75% of the faculty are not on behalf of the over

post. Through the survey, highlights a prominent issue is the existence of the current faculty shortage military occupational experience and accumulated experience of teachers, resulting in the actual teaching and research from the troops, pertinence. Some of the research participants as reflected in, and now some teachers understand teaching but do not understand the actual forces, the general principle can speak but can not lecture for individual needs, and even a lot of things teachers know, students also know; students do not know, teachers Do not know; some emerging professional or even a more serious student teachers with respect to the knowledge and experience of inversion phenomenon, students want to learn urgently, teachers did not. Teaching out of touch, teach non-use, it is clearly difficult to adapt to the objective needs of the education office.

1.2 *Training and management of professional education teacher lags*

To promote the development of professional education, we must firmly establish the "teacher training earlier" concept, using a higher starting point, more effectively strengthen teacher training and strive to build a high-quality teachers to adapt to serve the educational needs of the team. However, the current actual situation, training teaching staff, there are still many problems, teacher training support system is not perfect, very limited strength training, teaching and research mission of the institutions but also very heavy, although developed training system, but due to lack of maneuverability, often useless. Most teachers are side to observe the military academies, while practice, while exploration, relying on self-teaching thinking, and gradually formed its own teaching perspectives, principles, methods, processes, etc., experienced in the amount of formal education is not theoretical training much. After the transition to serving education, teacher education institutions serving more arduous task of training these teachers is necessary to fill the general education curriculum, but also learn office of education-related knowledge, but also learn practical skills, which requires multi-channel training methods. The survey shows that either the concept or the mechanism for serving education teacher training and management is still in a relatively closed state, multi-channel training methods are not fully operational, restricting the training of education instructors working team.

1.3 *Professional education teacher building rules and regulations are not sound enough*

Currently, our military professional education teacher working on team building rules and regulations, there is no one unified team of military academies serving education teacher training, use, manage, on behalf of the post exchange laws or regulations on teacher education office management system, exchange system, professional classification, an acting exercise and other content troops still lack a unified, comprehensive and detailed specifications. Meanwhile, the incumbent faculty selection, appointment, on behalf of the job, promotion, incentives and other mechanisms to be further improved. Flow problems, especially in the more prominent faculty, above the battalion officers, most of them have a stable family, troubled if job changes, family members will be employment, transfer of children, housing and other issues.

2 OPTIMIZATION MEASURES TO IMPROVE THE STRUCTURE OF MILITARY ACADEMIC PROFESSIONAL EDUCATION TEACHER STRUCTURE

Reasonably optimizing structure of teacher education in military academies, in essence, is a kind of control activities, the core of its contents, is that the structure of the problems for the teacher to take measures to adjust some structure to reduce the deviation between them and the target.

2.1 *Establish and improve the military officers and teachers colleges two-way communication system*

2.1.1 *Establish a multi-level, multi-form of communication system*
We must pay attention to the selection of outstanding senior army officers commanding military

forces to enrich teaching institutions, while also focusing on excellent teaching arrangement corresponding primary key to the troops serving officer position and a standardized system of teaching personnel selection and use. This term exchange system generally 2–3 years as a rotation period, after the expiration of any need to re-arrange the teaching according to the respective military positions. We should establish the system of military academic teacher to force to hold a post. Under the headquarters unified planning and arrangements, institutions according to its own mission, organization of trainers on a large scale, with the task, there is a particular focus on active duty on behalf of the unit object. This reduces the force reception devoted to the organization of work burden, while research institutions can directly support the forces, and to get real jobs now experienced teacher training, teaching in favor of rich content. At the same time, we should build forces to carry out project-oriented faculty research system. According to the teaching and research needs of the institutions Force needs, organizational instructor for frontline troops or carry out regular research institutions regularly invite military leaders to make the case for military construction and other special reports, but also to promote exchanges and force institutions to improve the overall quality of teaching staff and effective way to serve the quality of education.

2.1.2 *Establish inspection, supervision and evaluation of management mechanism*
Post Education institutions code faculty exchanges with military officers should be conducted under the unified leadership and organization of higher authorities in. To communicate at any time to track the situation of the investigation, and the establishment of relevant information databases, in order to grasp all aspects of task performance and the exchange of personnel situation. First, we should determine their office location, and further determined in accordance with their duties and professional situation is the same bit positions on the exchange or on the same professional exchanges. Second, identify research topics and mission objectives. They determined that the period for the exchange of research, it raised during his tenure insights based on research completed research tasks, and also can be used to guide the research of military construction, to explore the path of research into combat, thus improving exchange effect. Finally, the establishment of evaluation reporting system worked. Regular assessment work to strengthen the exchange of personnel, the development of different stages, different tasks and content of exchanges during the evaluation of the project; were also exchanges of personnel to report

regularly to the organization. During the exchange of outstanding performance, outstanding achievements talent to priority, the priority was promoted job title, and during the generation of job performance evaluation in general or those who fail, then in principle it can level the promotion of new technologies or administrative duties.

2.2 Adapt to the development requirements of professional education and innovate faculty management model

2.2.1 The implementation of rigid management and incentives combined with the best teachers inspire operational effectiveness

The basic system management institutions and regulations to protect the basic premise of building healthy and smooth development of institutions, it is absolutely not arbitrarily wavering, any slack and destruction, nor with the transfer of individual leaders will, free of interest and attention changed. Therefore, a rigid system of norms and regulations and other aspects of the management of the institutions must be resolutely implemented. However, for individual faculty actions standardized, rigorous of the rigid constraints of the regime alone is not enough. This requires us to focus on rigid management system and regulations, while the management of the teaching staff, with particular emphasis on exploration and building incentives. Generally speaking, is to "uphold the principle of hierarchical management, the establishment and implementation of each of their duties headquarters, divisions, colleges, departments, Department of interrelated and mutually reinforcing five management system"; adhere to norms management principles, to establish and improve the scientific system of teaching staff qualifications, professional and technical positions appointment system, job responsibility system, assessment evaluation system, reward system, elimination system, transferring the AC system, security system treatment system; adhere to the principle of non-equilibrium management establish a sound mechanism for scientific and rational system of competition, incentive and restraint mechanisms.

2.2.2 Adhere to process management and goal management, and maximize the mobilization of teaching self-management talent and creative spirit

Management of the teaching staff, teachers must work from the specific characteristics of the starting, the implementation of macro-control, micro-release, insists the main goal management, process management, supplemented and organically combine the two. Target management is the core faculty management. The primary task

of faculty managers lies in correctly determining the objectives and implementation of scientifically objective. Develop a series of strategic management and management programs in order to achieve the target number of faculty and effectiveness, structure optimization objectives, the overall quality of training objectives, targets treatment to protect the overall management on the subject of optimization. In goal-oriented management, the process should be an appropriate balance between management, namely the implementation of the objectives of the course or the main part of the key aspects of the implementation of rigid management and monitoring, as well as the time to find and correct the problem, ensure the completion of management objectives, and in other non-primary sectors or aspects should be the implementation of flexible management, giving more autonomy to the teaching staff, do not be too strict uniform requirements. In this way, you can reflect on the teaching staff of the current and future development work uniform requirements; there are strong incentives and guide.

2.3 Standardize the professional education teacher structure, and establish the relevant laws and regulations

2.3.1 Establish and improve relevant legal system

We should build into the overall teachers structure of the institutions serving the educational system take into consideration, the top-level laws and regulations designed to improve the overall planning, the establishment of a sound legal system of teacher education institutions serving management, in order to standardize the education faculty office organizational structure and management team the division of responsibilities, serving faculty professional classification, early, middle and senior eligibility requirements for institutions serving faculty of different ranks, military, and political work, logistics, equipment, various types of professional training on behalf of the job requirements, etc., in order to back the institutions, for example, to clear logistics Command, logistics management, rear professional service, logistics, teachers and other professional staff in all aspects of the specific regulatory requirements.

2.3.2 Improve research and demonstration, and effectively improve the quality of legislation

We should improve the operability and normative of laws and regulations, under active duty officer law and institutions educational regulations, in order to train highly qualified teaching staff, focusing on preparations for military struggle and military institutions serving the needs of education. Such as "military instructor pilot educational institutions serving system regulations," we should take the above-mentioned laws and regulations based on the "instructors" system gradually integrated into the army cadres' exchange of large systems to formatting the "green channel" of selection of instructor institutions. Specific provisions, an instructor must have a clear selection criteria and job position and life. Second, we must be clear vocational instructors, grading and evaluation, incentive regulations. Third, we need a clear and stable relation with the flow and exchange programs. Fourth, we need a clear channel and training in the form of training instructors. Five, Using specific safeguard mechanisms to solve the instructor's worries. Only a sound legal system, in order to standardize education teacher tenure structure, ensure the healthy development of tenure faculty ranks, thus ensuring the army worked in education levels steadily.

REFERENCES

[1] Duan Linlin. Computer multimedia courseware teaching optimization design[J]. China modern education equipment. 2006,(1), P15–19 (Ch).
[2] Hu Shuixing. Application of multimedia classroom teaching problems and Solutions[J]. Modern distance education and research. 2005,(1), P5–8 (Ch).
[3] Li Dongxiang, Wang Yang. Multimedia Courseware Effectiveness Influence of the Teachers Literacy[J]. Journal of Anhui University, 2011,45(4), P56–57 (Ch).
[4] Zhu Zhiting. Modern education technology into information technology eduction[M]. Beijing: Higher Education Press, 2011.89–99.

Computer, Intelligent Computing and Education Technology – Liu, Sung & Yao (Eds)
© *2014 Taylor & Francis Group, London, ISBN 978-1-138-02469-4*

Studying on strengthening technology of automotive safety technology and improving vehicle safety

En-Bing Fu

Bengbu Automobile NCO Academy, Bengbu, China

ABSTRACT: Auto parts of good and bad will directly affect the safety of the car, are directly related to the people's life safety and security in wealth. This article mainly from the car's active safety technology and passive safety technology two aspects elaborated the importance of car parts, and how to improve the safety of the car.

Keywords: automobile; active safety technology; passive safety technology

As traffic tools of the modernization and absolute number increase sharply, traffic accidents are also increasing. Car accident has become severe global social issues. Undoubtedly, advanced auto safety facilities are the driving safety indispensable safeguard. So, we should start, from technology to research and development of high performance, high safety car, also want to strengthen the regular inspection in cars, so timely maintenance investigation, make cars often in good technical status, so as to improve the safety performance of the car.

1 AUTOMOBILE ACTIVE SECURITY TECHNOLOGY

1.1 *The ASR drive torque control system*

ABS are used to prevent car braking process wheel lock, will wheel sliding rate control in ideal range, so as to shorten the braking distance, improve automobile braking direction stability and steering control, so as to improve the safety of the car. Along with the increase of vehicle performance requirements, not only in braking process required to prevent wheel lock, and asked the driver to prevent drive roller skating turn in the process, making cars in the direction stability, driving process steering control ability and acceleration performance, so are improved by the car drive torque steering system ASR (Accelerations Regulation) Slip. ASR is the perfect complement and ABS ASR, but most alone is set with ABS combined together, commonly used ABS/ASR says, called antiskid control system.

ASR is mainly used to prevent car in the beginning, accelerate the wheels, guarantee slip in the car accelerated rate and improve the stability in bad pavement drive attached conditions. It makes no difference speed in the car lock ice roads and muddy road started and to improve its capacity, also can prevent high in speed by turning cars gliding pavement and rear lateral spreads phenomenon.

Anyhow, prevent the wheel because ASR slip, can maximize the engine driving moment of cars had enough, ensure the longitudinal force, lateral force and manipulation of power, make cars in starting, steering and accelerate the process, in gliding and muddy road, in a mountain area downhill process can steadily driving, guarantees the safety, reducing tire wear and fuel consumption, and improves the car driving capability.

1.2 *CCS cars cruise control system*

Auto cruise Control System (Cruiser Control System, abbreviation for CCS) is can make automobile work in engine favorable speed range, reduce driver's driving manipulate labor intensity, improve the driving comfort the automatic driving device.

Car Cruising System (CCS) role is required by the driver: after a normally-closed switch, no speed on the accelerator pedal can automatically keep the speed, make the vehicle with the fixed speed. Using this device, when on the highway after a long time, the driver driving not have to control the accelerator pedal, reduce fatigue, while reducing unnecessary speed change, can reduce save fuel.

Auto cruise control system is the earliest development of the automotive electronic control system. This system USES another speed sensor, will speed signal input engine control microcomputer, by microcomputer control vacuum system work. This system can make use of the server, speed control switch lever and brake pedal on vacuum lift switches etc, its function and basic system the same.

In this system, electronic control device can accord change of driving resistance, automatic regulation engine throttle Angle, make the speed constant. Such not only reduce unnecessary speed change, which saves fuel, also reduced the driver's burden. The electronic cruise control system which is shown in Figure 2.

2 AUTOMOBILE PASSIVE SAFETY TECHNOLOGY

2.1 Seat belt

Car seat belt is a safety device, it can in car collision or sharp turn, make crew to keep its original position as possible without mobile and rotation, avoid collision with in-car hard parts caused damage. Seat belts and airbags, as modern cars are safety devices, but the long history of the former, popularize the scope.

The seemingly simple seat belt actually not "simple". Attention has been at the forefront of traffic safety, through the analysis of general motors after a car accident found: seat belt not only makes people protect the lives, can be in more than half of the accident to reduce or even eliminate drivers, motorists are the chance of injury. Car collision or unexpected emergency braking force generated great inertia, will allow the driver and passenger and car windscreen, steering wheel, seat, collision happened objects such as secondary to drive is caused extremely easily crew serious damage, even drive occupant seats or threw the apex, seat belts can will ride in the seat. Bondage personnel When has the accident, which can effectively prevent the collision, and its buffer role can absorbs a great deal of kinetic energy, reduce rides personnel extent of the injuries.

Fasten your seat belt airbags play our role is also an important condition. Because the airbag to maximize role for the ride in the impact of the physical location, sitting instant action have extremely strict and the requirements. Otherwise, the airbag started strong instantaneous wallops to head are fragile site, may cause serious damage, especially for children, this damage can be fatal. Even the most ordinary three belts, try a can timely in crash that lived rides the bundle, ensure the upper part of a ride in the airbag fully extended range, make the airbag most effectively play efficacy. Accordingly, must not because the car is equipped with airbags and feel carefree seat belt fastened, only to reduce or eliminate the traffic accident happen.

2.2 The airbag

When the front collision happened strong, because inertia, who rides the body forward fast moving, then seat belts and will try to "pull" rides on person

the body, absorb some of the impact energy, while the airbag with "the eyepiece trend" inflatable and completely open; Then the rides the upper body will sink to airbags, gas also began from the vent air uniform escaping, and absorbed most of the impact energy; Subsequently, the ride back seat and return to the body. Above the whole process is almost always happens in a flash, who rides the completely in passive situation, in this case, the passive rely on auxiliary occupant protection system is the only option. Airbags development design is based on the protection on seat belt Co., Ltd.; they cooperate with each other to ride the play the auxiliary protective effect.

Seat belt usage in under the condition of the crew, balloon help reduce chest, head and facial injuries in the seriousness of the collision. When car collision happened before, the first is the car to stop motion, car under the action of inertial force crews to go forward with the original speed still sport. Not wearing a seatbelt crews will and steering dish, front windscreen together, so it can be severely hurt; Wearing a seatbelt as car stop the crew can stop moving forward movement and gradually. If collision violent, crew forward movement of the seat belts, even faster in the complete stop before motion, still and in-car things together. If this fashion in steering the disk or within the popup balloon inflated dash, it can protect the occupant reduce the possibility of car together with things, more uniform dispersion head, chest, absorb the impact energy of movement, thus crew has added effect of seat belts.

In addition to seat belts and airbags outside car passive safety technology includes car bumper, automobile safety glass, security body, occupant head and neck protection system (WHIPS), etc. These vehicles to improve the safety performance has very important contribution.

3 AUTOMOBILE PASSIVE SAFETY NEW TECHNOLOGY

3.1 Adaptive Constraint Technology System (ARTS)

New Adaptive Constraint Technology System (ARTS) use a series of sensors to monitor the driver seat, seat belt use, in front of the occupant take quality and location and intensity of the collision of the collisions and collision force direction, then according to the specific information such as the collision of each front airbag characteristics of the crew on regulated. The system can further reduce due to improper airbag for crew on the damage, especially for smaller front row figure crew.

3.2 *Automobile energy-absorbing direction column*

Auto absorbing in automobile direction tubing through collisions of redistribution to steering wheel wallop, would wallop path to deliver shunt quickly, making the minimum of load on the steering wheel. The steering column by hollow tubes and steering bearings form. Traditional hollow tubes and the steering column steering bearings is integral, steering shaft top and steering connections, the connecting with direction below. And suck can direction string of characteristic is will the steering column in two, divided into unblock steering column and the steering column under two parts; Inside of the steering shaft also divided into two sections, with outgoing quarter agencies between them connected. Once a collision make direction, outgoing quarter mechanism has displacement bottom tailormade steering shaft will fold, under the steering column move on the steering column, to achieve "indented within" and thus expand space reduce damage.

4 AUTOMOBILE ACTIVE SAFETY NEW TECHNOLOGY

4.1 *Eye Car skills*

Eye Car technology can make each driver eyes in the same relative height, guarantee of pavement and the surrounding a six-lane unimpeded sight and best visibility. This technology can also offer a specific driving environment.

Eye Car through the use of first-class motor mobile automatic will different figure driver's eyes tuned to the same height to solve the problem, meanwhile, visibility of steering dish, brake and accelerate pedals and floor and the central adjustment to constitute console to their respective driving conditions. Meanwhile to the former pillar design, will it again from drivers sights removed. Because the bus driver received the most crucial information generally have 90% from outside, acquired

through the eyes observe. So, this improvement for vehicle safety is of great significance.

4.2 *Cam Car technology*

Cam Car technology aims to help improve the driver of perception. The technical features are:

1. Installed in the car to camera system on both sides before to make drivers can bypass the large vehicle behind a car or see ahead of pedestrians. In a typical driving situation in the crowded traffic, the pilot of the centre-left cornering could more easily view the opposite of vehicles.
2. Side after buy video camera provides broader visual profile of vision. The camera coverage than traditional rearview mirror wants wide, especially for the adjacent driveway.
3. Installed in a car, the four miniatures sectored form to decorate after a camera can obtain the car panoramic perspective. Image via electronic synthesis, has the zoom and 160° wide-angle ability.
4. "night eye" (Night Eye) camera can be in low illumination conditions, when the car is in reverse gear, even in a dark cases can also provide car close range after small images.

5 CONCLUSION

Anyhow, car active safety technology and passive safety technology for the safety of automobile driving is very important, and besides, such as environmental factor, artificial factor of the vehicle safety is also very important. Therefore, we must be prepared to all aspects of requirements and technology, to ensure the safety of vehicle driving.

REFERENCES

[1] Xiangbi, An. Car Performance And Testing. Beijing: Godden Shield Press, 2006.
[2] Xuanmeng, Cui. Automobile Fault Diagnosis Technology. Beijing: People's Traffic Press, 2005.

Computer, Intelligent Computing and Education Technology – Liu, Sung & Yao (Eds)
© 2014 Taylor & Francis Group, London, ISBN 978-1-138-02469-4

Discussion on environmental education of college students

Hai-Yun Qi, Yan-Xia Liu & Shi-Gang Geng
Environmental Management College of China (EMCC), Qinhuangdao, Hebei, China

ABSTRACT: With the rapid development of economy, the human society appears a lot of environmental problems, and the environment is worsening. Protect environment and improve the quality of it has become a pressing matter of the moment. College students as a group of high qualified, the improvement of their environmental quality will contribute to the whole people's awareness transformation. How to improve college students' environmental quality, is the focus of research of environmental educators. This paper analyses the current situation of Chinese environment quality of college students, and puts forward some countermeasures for strengthening the environmental education. As a case, it shows that how Environmental Management College of China (EMCC) to carry out environmental education.

Keywords: college students; environmental education; environmental awareness

1 GENERAL INTRODUCTION

At present, China and the world is facing environmental pollution and ecological destruction challenge. Protection of the environment needs everyone's interest and participation. Improving environmental consciousness of the whole people, is an essential strategic measures of the sustainable development of human society. College students as a group of high qualified, the improvement of their environmental quality will contribute to the whole people's awareness transformation. Popularizing environmental education to enhance the whole people's especially the young college students' environmental consciousness, is an important means to solve environmental problems.

2 PRESENT SITUATION OF ENVIRONMENT QUALITY EDUCATION FOR COLLEGE STUDENTS IN CHINA

At present, students environmental awareness are strengthing with the social attention to environmental problems, but a lot of teachers' and students' environmental awareness and knowledge level is still in the lower level, because their understand most from books or television publicity not systematic studies. Students are also lack of environment knowledge, that will directly affect the students' environmental quality improvement.

For the moment, many colleges did not pay enough attention to environmental education. In these colleges, environmental education course is not much for non environmental specialty students. That is because of the lack of correct understanding and full attention of environmental education. Professional teachers are also important factors. That has affected a wide range of environmental education.

Even if the environmental education courses has been offered as an elective course in some colleges, but they are also still belong to the "vulnerable groups" compared with the business management, law, computer and other popular courses in colleges and universities. The students who elective the environmental education courses are not many, and so, the environment education can not reach the expected effect.

3 COUNTERMEASURES FOR STRENGTHENING THE ENVIRONMENTAL EDUCATION IN COLLEGES

How to carry out the environmental education in colleges, and improve college students' environmental quality, can be considered from the following aspects.

3.1 *The leadership pay full attention to education*

The leadership of the colleges must pay full attention to environmental education. It is very important and necessary to improve the environmental quality of students. The colleges should improve the status of environmental education in the teaching activities, and develop the environmental education regulation on the college level, in order to promote the teaching departments to value the environmental education courses.

3.2 Scientific design and offer environmental education courses

The improvement of college Students' environmental awareness, must rely on the college education system. Colleges should offer specialized courses of environmental education, in order to create a good atmosphere of environment education, and carry out various methods of environmental education activities. Environmental education should be included in the talent training scheme, especially for the non environmental specialty.

Of course, it is the best to establish a compulsory course in environmental education courses. If not, as an elective course, strategies should be adopted to stimulate students' interest in the environmental education course, to ensure the teaching effect of the course. The strategies can include many aspects, such as class hour, content, teaching methods, assessment methods etc.

One thing to note is that, the class hour of environmental education course should not be too much, in case students appear negative emotions. At the same time, the teaching content and methods should be combined with the characteristics of different specialties.

3.3 Scientific selection of environmental education teachers

If you want develop the efficiently in colleges, selection of environmental education teachers is the most can not be ignored. The teachers should be professional teachers of environmental science. And in the teacher teams of environmental education courses, there should be have some professional teachers of the students' specialty, in order to make the courses design can combine with the students' specialty. That will be interesting and efficient for environmental education.

Certainly, the teachers of the courses should have the basic teaching ability such as others teachers. Because he is the director and screenwriter of the whole class, he must control of the classroom of the environmental education courses.

The teaching content and courseware should be updated timely. Especially the new occurring environmental events every year should be added to the teaching contents. Such as the Songhua River pollution incidents in 2006, the Environmental Protection Storm in 2007, the Frozen of Chinese South in 2008, the Human Climate Conference in 2009, the World Climate Disaster (fire, flood, drought) in 2010. There are many environmental events every year. We can choose the bigger public concerns to discuss with students in the classroom, and give the deep meaning of the events to the students, so as to improve the students' consciousness of environmental protection.

Also, we need to make full use of infiltrating environmental protection knowledge and consciousness in other courses. So, it is necessary to carry out environmental protection knowledge training to all teachers.

3.4 Carry out environmental education through various forms

In addition to the classroom teaching of compulsory courses, elective courses, and other course infiltration, college environmental education forms should diversify. We can mobilize the student association or student union to carry out varied environmental education activities. For example, environmental protection festival promotional activities, practice base, environmental treatment facilities and nature reserve visiting, investigation, interesting experiments, biodiversity survey, investigation etc, can make students more intuitive understanding of the environment, and fully arouse the initiative of students to protect the environment.

4 CASE ANALYSIS: ENVIRONMENTAL EDUCATION COURSE IN ENVIRONMENTAL MANAGEMENT COLLEGE OF CHINA

Environmental education course in Environmental Management College of China Opened earlier. It is a compulsory course for all students including non environmental majors in the College. The course offers on the first grade. The contents covers basic environmental protection knowledge and hot issues, what is shown as follows:

- Environment, environmental problems and environmental protection
- Policies, laws and regulations of environmental protection in China
- The world environmental protection actions
- The Sustainable development
- Be kind to nature
- The hot issues in the field of environmental protection at present

The characteristics of environmental education course in Environmental Management College of China are as follows.

4.1 Excellent teachers

Environmental Management College of China is approved by urban and rural construction and environmental protection department, recorded by The Ministry of education in 1981. It is a full-time college for cultivation of environmental protection personnel Primarily. It is one of the earliest to carry out environmental education in Colleges and universities in china.

The College has a great advantage for environmental education. There arc many influence professor in the field of environmental protection in the College, who have rich teaching experience and practice of environmental education, and pay attention to environmental protection objective. These professor's teaching effect in environmental education course were praised by the students. The teacher team is composed of six professors, and a teacher arranged by the college dean's office to assistant the course. All of that ensured the teaching effect of environmental education.

4.2 *Complete practical teaching facilities*

The College has complete practical teaching facilities, including a plurality of special environmental education laboratory, for example, "Sino Dutch water treatment demonstration research and training center" is the Asian aid project of Holland, and many campus training base, for example, "environmental monitoring and control technology training base" supported by the central financial.

In addition, there are a lot of natural teaching resources in the campus, what is made of precious trees and botany laboratory.

Environmental education course in Environmental Management College of China organizes students to visit these facilities and resources, to ensure students understanding of environmental pollution control while learning of theoretical knowledge.

4.3 *Different teaching content and methods according to different specialties*

Environmental education course as an interdisciplinary course in Environmental Management College of China, students of the course have different professional backgrounds. In this context, only a kind of teaching method is difficult to achieve the best results of environmental education. So, we adopted more flexible and effective teaching methods according to different specialty students.

– Develop moot court activities for law specialty
Law specialty students have gradually learned the course of law when study of environmental education course. Taking into account the students expertise and interest, the topic of "policies, laws and regulations of environmental protection in China" develop moot court activities

but not lecturing method. For example, there is a learning situation of noise pollution case. The students cosplay judge, plaintiff, defendant and other participants in the proceedings in the situation. For the legal defense, students should consult a lot of information relevant the "case". This process will develop students' consciousness of environmental protection, and increase students learning interest and enthusiasm to the follow-up courses.

– Give environmental protection homework for environmental art specialties
Students of environmental art specialties have the expertise of painting. The environmental education course for them can let the students creative environmental protection works, such as propaganda. The students create works from their own perspective on the environment, and there are so many amazing creative. On one hand, these works makes the students imagination, collecting material, deepen the understanding of environmental protection. On the other hand, these works are displayed in the campus, also provided material for college education on environmental protection propaganda.

– Encourage students to write essays through search learning information
The aim of the environmental education course is not to make students learn a large number of professional knowledge, but to understand the present situation of pollution of the environment, foster the consciousness of environmental protection. So, our teachers determine the scope of topics, and then, studcnts select one topic to write an essay according to their interests and hobbies. Through this form, each student broaden their horizons, and improve their sense of responsibility and mission of protect environment.

Students essays such as *my understanding and responsibility of the environment, environmental protection is the only way of human development* are all the fruit of environmental education.

4.4 *Students receive environmental education out of the classroom*

We believe, the environmental education for college students should not be confined to the classroom. With the help of the resources the Ministry of environmental protection and education center, and the atmosphere of environmental protection on campus, and the environmental volunteer activities, the college offer many forms environmental education.

– Invite outside expert lectures to expand teachers and students horizons
All teachers and students can be encouraged to listen to the lectures, to learn environment

protection knowledge, enjoy the great ingenuity of environmental protection, and expand their view of environmental protection.

– Improve the students' awareness of environmental protection combined with the student association activities

The college has Natural Home, Green Youth League and so on more than 30 green associations. The environmental education course encourages and assists students to participate the student association activities. Such as, bird watching activity on Animal Day.

5 SUMMARY

College Students' environmental awareness has important significance for environmental protection and sustainable development in China. College Students has very strong plasticity. Colleges and universities should further strengthen the environmental education for students, to improve the environmental awareness of them, to help them become friendly partners with the environment.

ACKNOWLEDGEMENT

Fund Support: this study is the scientific research fund project of Qinhuangdao Science and Technology Bureau named research on *Qinhuangdao present situation of College Students' environmental quality and the model of environmental education (No. 201302A312)*.

REFERENCES

[1] S.J. Ding & P. Xu & J.Z. Liu. Exploration and practice of the environmental consciousness education of non environmental specialty [J]. Education and Vocation, 2011(18): 166–167.

[2] S.G. Geng & H.Y. Qi. How to Train New kind of Environmental Personnel [J]. World Environment, 2012(1): 78–79.

[3] B.N. Ren & J. Geng. Problems and Suggestions of Environmental Education of Non-environmental Specialty of Chinese Universities [J]. Guangdong Chemical Industry, 2012, 39(3): 247–248.

[4] B.M. Liao. Discussion on Environmental Education [J]. Education and Vocation, 2009(23): 165–167.

Research on current situation and influence factors of college students' sports lifestyle

Zhong-Xin Zhang
Wushu Department, Hebei Institute of Physical Education, Shijiazhuang, China

Qiu-Sheng Yu & Jing-Yi Wu
Department of Physical Education, Hebei University of Technology, Tianjin, China

ABSTRACT: By the method of documentary and investigation, the importance, necessity and current situation of college students' sports lifestyle is analyzed deeply to point out that the sports lifestyle is the significant way to promote physical and mental health of college students, and the effective approach to join "school sports" to "lifetime sports".

Keywords: current situation; health; sports lifestyle; influence factors

1   INTRODUCTION

College students' physical and mental health is not optimistic. Unreasonable lifestyle is the main reason. Lack of physical activity and exercise is a typical characteristic feature. In July 1996, the U.S. governer in the White House has issued a government report "about the relationship between sports and health": physical activity of moderate intensity is enough to reach the purpose of promoting health. The 47th world health assembly in 1997, a joint meeting has been held by World Health Organization and International Olympic Committee, which a complete point of view of health promotion is expounded that worldwide sports promote positive life and worldwide sports serve for health.[1] The implementation of sports lifestyle can completely get rid of the bondage of purely utilitarian of college sports. The existence mode of sports transforms from "survival—development" to "survival—enjoyment—development". Cultivating college students' sports lifestyle is the need of their self development and the development of social sports. Sports lifestyle is the inevitable requirement of college sports development. Through the methods of literature, questionnaire, and logical analysis, present situation and influence factors of college students' sports lifestyle are discussed in further depth to provide theoretical basis and guarantee for the realization of the sports lifestyle in universities.

2   THE RESEARCH METHODS

2.1   *Documentary*

Through collecting relevant documents more than 30 articles related theories are grasped in detail about college students' health and present situation of the sports lifestyle.

2.2   *Survey method*

Through the questionnaire the internal factors and the external environmental factors of college students' sports lifestyle are mastered in-depth understanding; A survey is conducted on limiting factors of college students' sports lifestyle. Using four grade stratified sampling and systematic random sampling method, 720 students in hebei university of technology participate in the survey. The result of 180 students each grade give researchers the first-hand information. 698 questionnaires are recycled, and recovery rate is 96.9%. 664 questionnaires are effective. Effective rate is 92.2%.

2.3   *Mathematical statistics*

The SPSS11.0 statistical software is used for statistical analysis.

3   RESULTS AND ANALYSIS

3.1   *Research on the connotation and denotation of sports lifestyle of college students*

Life style is the sum of all behaviors and characteristics of the life. It is a pattern of behavior of a person forming in the long life. It is the result of joint action of economic, political, social, cultural and other aspects. Sports lifestyle means that physical activity behavior gets into individual daily life under the current objective social conditions when people's conception is guided by new values in order to get health, which can meet the needs of diffrent levels in order to form a kind of daily behavior of living expenses. Therefore, we call the stable form and behavior characteristics of the sports activities *sports lifestyle*. The realization of the university sports lifestyle resolve the problem how the college students engage in sports activities. Sports lifestyle is a healty and self-conscious life way of college students. And it is an effective method to improve people's quality of life to achieve reunification of the purpose and means of sports.

3.2 *Research on the importance and necessity of college students' sports lifestyle*

Sports lifestyle has become an effective way to improve the quality of body and improve the quality of life. Survey shows that physical exercise standard indexes are growing rapidly in grade one or two at college, but are descending in grade three or four because there is no physical education. In recent years, physical constitution test results show that college students' fitness and health situation have some severe problems, such as falling endurance quality indicators. A survey by Zeng tsinghua on 1750 college students' lifestyle shows that 80.4% of college students do not have the habit of daily exercise, including 67.1% boy proportion and 89% girls. The exercise rate of 63.1% college students can not reach twice a week and 30 minutes each time. The proportion of the sedentary college students for more than 4 hours every day reach 31.4%. Many factors affect college students' physical health, which include unhealthy lifestyle accounted it for 60%. Lack of exercise is salient feature, including the insuffiicient time and intensity of physical exercise. Another survey shows that 63.4% of the knowledge and skills needed for sports population come from the school teaching. 50.83% of the sports population still adhere to participate in the favorite sports at school, which fully shows that school physical education plays a basic and important role for social sports.

In view of the fall of students' fitness we can conclude that the physical exercise habit and the formation of the sports lifestyle is effective way to solve the health problem of the college students fundamentally. In 1994, the meeting the Health Promotion and Physical Activity of World Health Organization and the international association of sports medicine international conference urge governments to promote the development of mass sports and make it become a component of public Health and social policy, which can create social and sports environment to help citizens to form and maintain active physical lifestyle. In the meeting, seven central tasks are clearly put forward including "to make sports become the foundation

of healthy lifestyle" and so on.[2] According to the "Maslow hierarchy of need theory", sports belong to people's high-level needs to realize self value. Its two big social functions of physical activity are to improve the level of human body health and enrich people's leisure life in order to achieve people's spiritual happiness finally. This need is the root and essence of the implementation of sports life under the modern social situation.

3.3 *Research on the influence factors of college students' sports lifestyle*

The feasibility of the college students' sports life style is the basic problem, the main factors affecting the analysis from the following aspects.

3.3.1 *The subject of physical activity—internal factors of college students*
1. The college students' cognitive level on sports lifestyle
   Implementation of the sports lifestyle at college is influenced by many factors, but the subjective factors play a decisive role. Students' level of understanding of sports life style, which determine the values and the philosophy of life, affect the quality of his life. Survey results show that: 96% of the students can recognize the movement "is very important to the effect of health of body and mind", also can agree with the role of tireless energy, descending physical tension and anxiety, improving people's character, temperament and the will. From the cognitive, most students support the idea that the sports can be "a valid mean" of lifelong sports, and it is necessary or important to "master a method of lifelong sports", however, the view that "it is necessary to the formation of habits" accounts for only about 31%. The results show that the concept of "Life Sports" and "sports life style" is too ambiguous for college students to understand the Internal nature and external performance of sports lifestyle, although the view that life sports is beneficial for study and life is accepted. The connotation and extension of sports life style is not recognized by the public.
2. The situation of the habits of sports lifestyle
   Survey shows that there are several common forms of physical activity at college now, including physical education class, morning exercises, recess, and several types of extra-curricular activities, sports competition and training, and performance. P.E. Class is compulsory course in grade one or two in the university, and the participation rate is 100%. In grade three or four there are elective courses, and the participation rate is low and not more than 5%. The rest to

participate in sports clubs, associations, other sports skill learning is about 2%. The number of participating in the sports theory knowledge training, lectures, reading books, fitness exercise prescription and learning methods, is less and the frequency is low. The data of "sports involvement in life field" is only about 6.3%.

3.3.2 The objective condition of the physical activity—the external environmental factors of the college students

1. The P.E teachers' dominant role of the subjectivity of students

The guiding ideology of PE teaching in the university adheres to the principle of healthy sports, happy sports and lifelong sports; Physical education teachers in the class can teach more than one kind of physical exercise method to improve the students' cognitive level in sports and stimulate their interests in sports. But the disadvantage is that their professional knowledge needs to be further improved, for example, most physical education teachers don't teach students knowledge of sports health care or rehabilitation, and none of them guides students independently to formulate exercise prescription that no students can formulate reasonable exercise prescription for their own physical condition.

2. The management of the PE department school and school rules related to sports

Sports venues, facilities, and equipment is the carrier of students participating in sports, but per capita venues is not enough and indoor stadium penetration rate is very low, which is undervalued; There are faulty sports teachers in most of the universities. The investment needs of facilities management and maintenance shoule be strengthened. Most universities have introduced various policies and regulations, such as morning exercises system, sunshine sports project, but the efficiency is not high.

3.3.3 The form of phisical activities—various sports means

Physical activities establish a relationship between subject and object through a variety of sports means. It is the result of interaction between subject and object. Physical activity is varied and rich in its content, including all sports events. Sports in colleges is closely related with social sports, as many as 20 several. The unification of some colleges and society is realized.

Another survey on students shows that the limiting facrors of sports lifestyle involves: time, energy, and the understanding of sports, the awareness of health, economic condition, the influence of university physical education teachers, the influence

of the environment, etc. In short, limiting time and pressure restrict the process of sports lifestyle. In addition, there is no sports atmosphere for students, and physical education teachers can not play a role fully. But sports authorities should coordinate superior to create opportunities for students to provide physical training environment. If the rational use of space equipment and the role of PE teachers as a fitness instructor can be made fully to encourage students to use spare time to participate in sports, it is feasible for sports to be a way of life.

4 CONCLUSIONS AND COMMENDATIONS

College life-style sports should be closely connected with the social sports. Its location accords with the goal of college physical education in order to improve health, increase knowledge, develop students self health care consciousness and the habit of lifelong physical exercise. The guiding ideology of physical education aims to be "health first", "lifetime sports" and "quality-oriented education". Teachers in class teach students physical exercise knowledge and skills, and necessary fitness measures and health care knowledge to promote students to master the application in the family and social physical activities. College students can be the forerunner of sports lifestyle, which is the inevitable outcome of the development of the "mass sports" and "lifetime sports". That is the stable foundation to improvc hcalth conditions of whole people.

Educator comenius once proposed "education is life".[3] The American educator John Dewey proposed "education is the process of life",[4] the modern educational idea is that education and life is a same process. College students' sports lifestyle make physical education activities become a way of life. Education is not only for tomorrow, but also making the students enjoy the life and make a new life in the course of their physical educational activities. Sports lifestyle will be the last step of college physical education.

REFERENCES

[1] Press of World Health Organization;WHO Meeting Stresses Health benefits of "Active Living". 1997, 6 March.
[2] Bulletin of World Health Organization [Z]. 1995: 135–136.
[3] [Czech] Comenius. Great Didactic of Comenius [M], Beijing: People's Education Press, 1994:64.
[4] Zhao Xianglin, Wang Chengxu. Dewey education works [M], Beijing: People's Education Press, 1981-28.

Computer, Intelligent Computing and Education Technology – Liu, Sung & Yao (Eds)
© *2014 Taylor & Francis Group, London, ISBN 978-1-138-02469-4*

Construction of English-learning pattern for art-and-PE students

Xia Zhao

School of Foreign Languages, Si Chuan University of Science and Engineering, Zigong, Si Chuan, China

ABSTRACT: College English teaching is a long-term task, which is very complex and complicated. The most difficult part is the teaching for students who major in art and PE in this huge teaching system. Most of these students learn English with no passion and interest because of their low ability of mastering a language, which makes a great impact on college English teaching at many universities. It's extremely urgent for college English teachers to change the way of teaching and take some effective measures to deal with this big problem.

Keywords: English teaching; art and PE majors; English-learning pattern

1 INTRODUCTION

The effective application of class teaching as well as reasonable evaluation of class-teaching efficiency plays a vital role in the reform of college English teaching, and it even influences the overall process to some extent. The college students who major in art and PE lack of the basic knowledge of English, and they have no interest of learning it. How to make these students have enthusiasm for English and how to modify their learning pattern becomes the biggest challenge for the college English teachers now. As the saying goes, a small typo ruins the whole page, the college English teaching maybe greatly influenced if this difficult problem cannot be dealt with smoothly.

2 RENOVATION OF TEACHING MATERIALS

Recently, many colleges and universities take the book of New Horizon as the teaching material in Sichuan province. That series is the recommendation of college English teaching reform made by the Ministry of Education. The content is extensive and practical and with various patterns. However, it's a little bit complicated for Art-and-PE majors, to a certain extent, it's beyond their comprehension. The series of Innovation College English published by East China Normal University, instead, is more suitable for non-English majors, especially Art-and-PE students whose English is so poor. The teaching material consists of three parts, including Teacher's Book of Integrated Course, Student's Book of Integrated Course, and Self-Access Learning Book. Student's Book

of Integrated Course is used for class teaching directly, and it has eight units with one specific topic respectively. Each unit has five parts, including Listening Comprehension, Reading Comprehension, Intensive Reading, as well as Oral Practice and Writing (Grammar as the preliminary). The purpose of this series of teaching materials is to cultivate the college students' basic knowledge of English, and tries to pay more attention to enhance their competence of cultural understanding.

In the first two years of college life, teachers can adopt these teaching materials reasonably, from Book I to Book III, with increasing tasks step by step. Moreover, the college English teaching should not be ignored even when the students enter the senior year. The lower-class compulsory course can be changed into the higher-class elective course, so that most of the students can still come into contact with English frequently. In this stage, some special teaching materials like Music English, Art English and PE English can be chosen to help those students know more vocabularies about their majors and intensify their interest on English as well.

College English teaching for Art-and-PE students is a long-term controversial issue. How to make them love English becomes a troublesome problem for college English teachers. Many of those students have poor performance of English when they are in middle school, and they often skip classes. They show little interest in learning English when having classes, and many of them even have disgusting feeling for it.[1] This kind of students may have fear and anxiety in the process of English learning. Their pronunciation and intonation is incorrect, they may feel dizzy when answering questions, some of them even can not speak a word; they just keep silent all the time.[2] Therefore, the choice of the teaching materials and the arrangement of the teaching procedures seem more important than ever before. Innovation College English not only makes emphasis on self-access learning, but it's also flexible and accessible. So long as the teachers use this material reasonably and pay attention to the diversified teaching methods, Art-and-PE students greatly can improve their comprehensive capability of English without doubts.

3 INNOVATION OF TEACHING METHODS

The arrangement of the teaching methods can greatly influence the students' acceptance of English, and reasonable teaching tasks can make the students feel at ease and deal with them with confidence under the guidance and help of their teachers. On the contrary, it may bring stress, confusion and boredom to them and let them loss the passion of learning English. Therefore, college English teachers should make full consideration of the students' acceptance of the teaching methods and course contents, and attempt to have some adjustment and improvement according to the practical situation.

3.1 *Review of the basic knowledge*

The radical problem for Art-and-PE students to learn English well is that they lack of the basic knowledge of this language, many of those students are unaware of the lingual information which should be learnt from the very beginning of language learning. There are lots of grammatical matters that they didn't understand from middle school to college, the more trouble they have, the less interest to learn it, and finally they have no choice but to give up completely. College English teachers should supply some basic knowledge to the students when they're freshmen and make sure that they review them frequently. Taking Innovation College English as an example, in each unit's listening exercise of preliminary stage, some relevant information about phonetics should be given to the students according to their difficult requirement. Besides, in the grammatical exercise after Intensive Reading, some important lingual information should be expanded, for instance, Word Formation, Direct Speech and Indirect Speech, Subjunctive Mood, Attributive Clause and so on.

3.2 *Application of the simple learning task*

Acting as a special group in college English teaching, Art-and-PE students have their own specific characteristics, such as their quick minds and personality traits.[3] In the first semester of college English teaching, the teacher can help the students start to make the duty report, letting them speak English as much as possible. They can talk about anything they like, and the content ranges from the easy jobs to the complex ones. If the students encounter some unexpected difficulties in the beginning, the teacher may offer some help.

3.3 *Intensification of the cultural knowledge*

In the senior year of college English teaching, teachers should tell the differences of culture between Chinese and English to the students. Language is not only the representation of culture, but also the important part of it. Only do the learners realize the cultural differences between Chinese and English, they can use this language correctly. The teacher could add some more cultural background information to the students in the teaching process, such as western beliefs, arts, laws, customs, morals, religion and so on. We teachers should not only create an easy and comfortable English learning environment but also make learners understand the language in its cultural context; also we teachers should be sensitive to students' effective needs and make them feel that they are working on something together with the teacher. If the relationship between the teacher and the students and among the students themselves is friendly and cooperative, teaching will go on well and learning takes place.

4 TRANSFORMATION OF IDEAS BETWEEN TEACHERS AND STUDENTS

With the extensive development of the college English teaching reform, teachers must realize that it's urgent to change the teaching ideas. The reform of the teaching patterns, methods and contents demand that the teachers change and update their teaching philosophy. Meanwhile, we teachers have to enrich the professional qualification in order to improve the teaching capability, and can be capable of applying modern teaching technology such as network and multi-media method to adapt to the new teaching model as soon as possible.[4] English teachers are not the saints, so they may make mistakes in the teaching process. We teachers should listen to the students' comments frequently, and encourage them to give some suggestions for the teacher's teaching methods and contents at the end of the semester. The relationship between the teacher and the students can be inversed; sometimes the teacher can learn something valuable from the students. Therefore, in the series of teaching-and-learning process, a teacher can be a student to learn from them, and a student can be an expert to point out the problems made by the teacher. It should be mentioned that a teacher needs to improve his or her own efficiency because it may affect the learning interest and efficiency of the students.[5] The high efficient teacher can take the teaching activities more positively and make more challenging teaching strategies. It can be very precious for the Art-and-PE students whose English are not so good.

5 CONCLUSIONS

College English teaching is a large project, and needs continuous change and improvement. S.P. Corder once said, An effective language teaching should not violate the natural process but to adapt to it; an effective language teaching should not prevent the learning but to be helpful for it. We should not let the students to adapt to the teacher and the teaching materials but to let the teacher and the materials to meet their needs.[6] The college English teachers should make whole effort to cultivate the students' learning interest and make a reasonable leaning pattern for them. Updating the teaching contents, changing the teaching methods as well as the teaching conception is all what we should think about.

The last but not the least important thing the author would like to say is that although the improvement of the language competence is important, the promotion of the personal moral character and spiritual intelligence is even more valuable. It's hoped that the college English teachers from different places and areas work together to improve the Art-and-PE students' cross-cultural communicative ability so as to make them become inter-disciplinary talents for the society.

ACKNOWLEDGEMENT

It is a project supported by the Teaching Reform and Research Program of Si Chuan University of Science & Engineering (JG-1362).

REFERENCES

[1] Diao Huimin. The Research Analysis and Strategy of Psychological Obstacles for the College English Learning of Art-and-PE Students [J]. Science & Technology Information, 2008 (32): 194.

[2] Wang Yinquan, Wan Yushu. Foreign Language Learning Anxiety and the Influence on the Learning [J]. Foreign Language Teaching and Research, 2001 (2): 122–126.

[3] Luo Feng, Huang Haowen. The Analysis of English Learning Situation and Strategy of Art-and-PE Students—Taking Local Universities as an Example [J]. Journal of Hunan University of Science and Engineering, 2011 (8): 165–167.

[4] Li Shiqiang. On the Reform of College English Teaching and the New Role of the Teachers [J]. Journal of Yunnan Nationalities University (Social Sciences), 2004 (6): 153–156.

[5] Gao Sixia. A Research on Teacher Efficacy in Relation to College English Teaching Reform [J]. Foreign Language and Literature, 2011 (5): 128–133.

[6] Liu Xiaoyang. College English Teaching Situation and Deliberation on the Art-and-PE Students [J]. Science & Technology Information, 2009 (27): 17.

Computer, Intelligent Computing and Education Technology – Liu, Sung & Yao (Eds)
© 2014 Taylor & Francis Group, London, ISBN 978-1-138-02469-4

Students' emotion recognition from microblog

B. Sun, J.B. Chen & Y.N. Liu
College of Information Science and Technology, Beijing Normal University, Beijing, China

ABSTRACT: The college students' extreme emotional performance presented by suicide has become a world problem, it also contains other phenomenon, like poisoning, violence, confused, misanthropy, low self-esteem, etc. And because of the complex social environment and the increasing competition, it becomes more and more serious. According to statistics, 80% of the college students have their own blogs or microblogs which most of them use to express their emotions. Owing to the development of affective computing and natural language processing, it would be helpful for the automatic emotion recognition of college students in microblog. It can help teachers or psychological counseling agencies to detect and track the emotional states of college students, and take psychological counseling for the abnormal emotional students. In this paper, we constructed theme dictionary and emotion dictionary firstly; secondly, constructed the emotional semantic chunks by the core emotion words from the emotion dictionary; thirdly, designed an algorithm to compute the emotional state through emotional value and other microblog information. We also outlined the approach of Students Emotion Recognize System, and discussed the problem of this method and the future directions of this research.

Keywords: emotion recognition; emotion analysis in microblog; students' suicide; affecting computing

1 GENERAL INTRODUCTION

Cognition and emotion play important role in students' psychological development. The classification of educational goals—affective domain (D.R. Krathwohl; B.S. Bloom; B.B. Masia, 1964), they introduce emotion as a educational goal, and spread around the world. Previously, most of research and teaching focused on improve the cognitive level, emotional domain only study on academic emotion, involving interest in learning, learning attitude, learning research will, values and other aspects of learning. few concerned about student life emotions, including love, health, employment, family factors, and these factors have a strong impact on students' emotional states.

In this paper, we analyze students' daily life emotion in microblog, dynamic detecting and tracking students emotional information, feedback student information which has severe negative emotions to teachers or psychological counseling agencies, in order to adjust their emotion in time.

2 BACKGROUND & SIGNIFICANCE

Contemporary college students are confronted with more and more stress, such as the busy study, the intense competition and the enormous pressure on employment etc. College students are not only simple minded but are in the period of forming the view of life. Therefore, they are easily affected by negative thoughts. In recent years, self-murder rate of college students is on the rise. Accordingly, the reasons of suicide also become more and more complex. In addition, higher education has such a phenomenon: Despite it pays attention to the learning achievement but loses sight of cultivating of emotion.

Therefore, the early prediction of the college students' extreme events and the research of the influencing factors is to provide early warning for preventing and decreasing extreme events of young students. The research has attracted wide attention of academic. The study of this problem is also more widely and deeply. However, human emotion is a very complex psychological phenomenon that has the characteristics of dynamic and implicit. Moreover, It is difficult to use conventional methods to track the long-term of students emotional changes.

The text sentiment analysis began in the late 1990s, is to determine the speaker or author's attitude toward a particular topic. It is a interdisciplinary research involves mechanics, natural language processing and psychology, etc. In recent years, it becomes a research focus of NLP. The scholar around the world have more and more attention to identify the emotion by natural language processing technology. In March 2004, the research about "explore the emotion attitude" which is organized by the American association of artificial intelligence organization promoted the research of emotional text classification.

According to statistics, 80% of the students have their own micro-blog account, they express their feelings through micro-blog, We got 1000 characters of micro-blog information from about 800 undergraduates by Sina API, including 2000 emoticons that provided by Sina microblog. In this paper, we use this information as the training and test data to analyze the emotion that contains in the micro-blog contains.

3 CORE METHODS

Emotional analysis involves many aspects of natural language processing, such as Chinese words segmentation, named entity recognition, syntactic analysis, semantic analysis, and so on. For the emotion analysis from microblog text, emotional dictionary is the basic work, we established a emotional dictionary which includes new-created-words, pseudo-words, emoticon; On the other hand, construct semantic chunk based on HNC, Dependency grammars and Case grammars, which is upon the core emotional words, add the other adjective and adverb, compute the emotional value of the whole emotional semantic chunk.

3.1 *Structure of students' emotional dictionary*

There are domain features and user group features. Students emotion dictionary has some typical feature: new-created-words, pseudo-words, use lots of emoticon, ignore the grammar.

In this paper, my emotional dictionary based on two existing dictionary: One of that is HowNet (Chinese/English Vocabulary for Sentiment Analysis (VSA)) which includes 12000 emotional words, divided into two emotional polar (Positive and negative). The other is Emotional Ontology from DUT, which contains 27467 emotion related words, includes Noun, verb, adjective, adverb, divided into 7 emotional classes, 21 subclasses, 11 levels of emotional intensity emotional words, Application of these emotional intensity, assigned the value to emotional words in my dictionary.

Appling rule mixed statistic method to build students' emotional dictionary, divided emotional word into 2 polarities, and 3 intensities, specific method states as follows.

Step 1, based on Emotional Ontology, emotional words frequency statistics in students' emotional corpus, selected some typical emotion words as seed word.

Step 2, compute the co-occurrence rate between New-created-words, Pseudo-words, Emoticon (NPE, for short) and Seed Word (SW) in 10 million word Sina Microblog corpus, the seed word of highest co-occurrence rate as the NPE emotion value:

$$\text{PMI(NPE, SW)} = \log\left(\frac{P(\text{NPE \& SW})}{P(\text{NPE})P(\text{SW})} \right)$$

SO-PMI (NPE) = SO-PMI as the NPE emotion value, the emotion polar of NPE as the SO-PMI value. Where pword as the positive seed emotional word in the set of Pset, and nword as the negative.

Step 3, manual marked the emotional intensity of adverbs in HowNet.

By above steps, built a emotion dictionary, with emotional polar and intensity, as core emotion words, prepare for emotional chunk.

3.2 *Build emotional semantic chunk*

Emotional semantic chunks refers to the emotional word-centered, expressing complete semantic blocks. Usually, it is a group of adjectives and adverbs.

Firstly, find the core emotional word, because the microblog text limited to 140 words, it express emotion coherent, easy to find the core emotional word.

Secondly, Chinese Valence distance is generally not more than three words away, looking adverbs distance of 3 words from forward and backward.

Finally, compute the emotional intensity of whole emotional semantic chunk as the text emotion.

4 SYSTEMATIC DESIGN

The framework of emotion recognition for microblog information of college students as shown in Figure 1.

Firstly, using API to obtain their Sina microblog information that include text, emoticons and publish date etc.

After that, preprocessing the information that obtained in step 1, including tag the word segmentation and the part of speech of the words.

And then, importing the two emotion dictionary, emotion dictionary (for details see Section 3.1) and topic dictionary of the life of the students. In this paper, we use five types of emotional words for the latter one which is Chinese Semantic Dictionary (CSD) developed by Yu Shiwen who is a professor working in Peking University. They are the

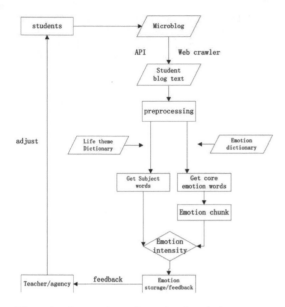

Figure 1. System chart of emotional analysis.

affection between loves, the emotion in process of learning and working, the affection suffering from disease, the emotion in interpersonal and family relationships, the emotion caused by economic pressure. After get the key words of micro-blog information, we can divide it into positive or negative according to expected of key words.

Finally, expected of key words is multiplied by the value of emotion calculated by cmotional semantic chunk, then we can get the emotional intensity of students.

5 EXPECTATION

The results of process accessed in students' emotional portfolio, teachers can inquire students' information at any time. And feedback students' information while students negative emotion more than warning, specific information as follows:

$$(\eta + m_n^t) - N$$

where M_n^t stands for student n emotion states at time t, m_n^t stands for current emotional value, η, emotional decay coefficient, $\eta = 1/T$ (T $\in$ 1,2,3); T stands for the time interval between the occurrence of the two emotions (by day, Calculated by 24 hours), $T = 1$ if occur in the same day, $T = 3$, if time interval more than 3 days. N is the threshold of warning, $N = 1/n \sum_1^n M_n^t$, stands for the average value of emotion in the same class at time t,

teachers could adjust the value of N, According to the characteristics of students.

Students which M_n^t value less than 0, sent his/her information to teachers. Teachers decide which approach to take, in order to avoid the occurrence of extreme events.

6 CONCLUSION & FUTURE WORK

According to the World Health Organization (WHO) 2013 data of October, there are 1 million people worldwide die by suicide each year. In China this number is 287 (2010 data) thousand which is still growing year by year, and it has become one of the main death among young people aged under 35, where the number of young people have suicidal thoughts is about 10 to 20 times of the suicide number.

Due to the popularity of microblog and other Web 2.0 technologies, access to personal emotional information from the text to be an effective mean, however, in the detail analysis procession there are some difficult problems: the writing style is different to each person; the way to express feelings vary greatly; also the extensive use of metaphor rhetoric in text, which cause a lot of troubles in the process of the analysis.

The differences in each person's emotional intensity, personality factors such as character, emotional threshold is the problem needed to be solved, we will do further research. With the rapid development of E-learning, like the growing influence of MOOCs and the expanding of enrollment, the phenomenon of teachers and students separating from each other become more apparent, and the attention to student' emotion has become more lower. Through this study can solve the issue of distance education lacking of emotion to some extent.

REFERENCES

[1] Zhu Z.L. & Huang C.H. & Li Y. Hong J.J. 2011. Study on the measure method of academic emotions. *China Educational Technology* 2011(6):55–60.
[2] Hao Y.J. & Wang J.G. & Zhao Q.B. 2013. Design and implementation of learning support system based on OCC. *Distance Education in China* 2013(2): 26–31.
[3] He B. 2011. Study on the design of affective computing model in e-Learning. *Journal of Distance Education* 2011(8):103–110.
[4] Wang Z.L. 2009. *Artificial Emotion*. Beijing: China Machine Press.
[5] Jie Y.G. 2007. The Research of Intelligent E-Learning System Based on Artificial Psychology. *University of Science and Technology Beijing.*
[6] Guo S.B. 2008. Research on Methods of Personalized Affective Modeling. *Taiyuan University of Technology.*

[7] Rodriguez P. & Ortigosa A. & Carro R.M. 2012. Extracting Emotions from Texts in E-learning Environments. *Sixth International Conference on Complex, Intelligent, and Software Intensive Systems*:887–892.

[8] Li J. & Ren, F. 2008. Emotion Recognition from Blog Articles. *IEEE International Conference on Natural Language Processing and Knowledge Engineering—NLP-KE:1-8.*

[9] Chang Q.Q. & Ren F.J. 2010. A blog emotion corpus for emotional expression analysis in Chinese. *Computer Speech and Language:*2010. (24): 726–749.

[10] Yang C. & Lin K.H.Y. & Chen H.H. 2007. Building Emotion Lexicon from Weblog Corpora. *Proceedings of the ACL 2007 Demo and Poster Sessions. Prague, 133–136 June 2007.*

[11] Whitelaw C. & Garg N. & Argamon H. *2005.* Using Appraisal Groups for Sentiment Analysis. *CIKM'05, Bremen, Germany, October 31–November 5.*

[12] Li Z.L. 2011. The E-Learning System Model Based on Affective Computing. *ICAIC 2011, Part III, CCIS 226, 495–500.*

[13] Li Z.L. 2011. What's in a Note? Sentiment Analysis in Online Educational Forums. *University of Toronto.*

Computer, Intelligent Computing and Education Technology – Liu, Sung & Yao (Eds)
© 2014 Taylor & Francis Group, London, ISBN 978-1-138-02469-4

WebQuest English teaching model

L.J. Diao
Department of English, Cangzhou Normal University, Cangzhou, Hebei, China

ABSTRACT: When computer enters the field of English teaching, changes would undoubtedly take place. This paper is trying to elaborate the issues concerning WebQuest English Teaching Model, which is a Computer- and Classroom-Based College English Teaching Model. The whole paper is therefore written around the following three questions: theoretical basis, learning patterns and design principles of WebQuest English teaching model and tries to offer a new perspective to integrate computer into English teaching.

Keywords: WebQuest; theoretical basis; pattern; principle

1 INTRODUCTION

Since the 1990s, information technology has been developing by leaps and bounds. To be adapted to this development, we need to do research in how to integrate computer well into the teaching, including its theoretical basis, learning patterns and design principles. Particularly in the present College English Teaching Reform, this research turns to be very urgent.

WebQuest is a kind of online inquiry activities. WebQuest English teaching model is a web-based inquiry teaching model which integrates computer into English teaching. As a specific form of inquiry learning activities, WebQuest is mainly dependent on the powerful Internet information resources to train students' inquiry ability. During WebQuest, learners can maximize the use of cyber resources to take the initiative to find out the unknown problems in the field of foreign languages, explore the solution, construct knowledge and therefore learn a foreign language.

2 THEORETICAL BASIS OF WEBQUEST ENGLISH TEACHING MODEL

WebQuest English teaching model is mainly based on the three theories, namely, Bruner's discovery learning theory, Dewey's "learning by doing" theory and Vygotsky's theory of social constructivism.

Bruner believes that discovery is not limited to man searching for unknown things, but should refer to all the methods by which people use their intelligence to obtain knowledge on their own.[1] In our teaching, if the teacher just guides them to take the initiative to learn, the students will learn through their own discovery, summarize the principles or rules, and also feel happy and satisfied because of a sense of achievement. As a result, they will have more power to learn. And the knowledge gained will be more profound, not easy to forget and can be widely applied in practice. It is no doubt that this method contributes to the development of intelligence. Therefore, the theory of Bruner is to encourage each student to become a "discoverer".

Dewey advocates that students should learn by doing.[2] He believes that it is unrealistic to require children to obtain knowledge not from activities but from lectures because children's interest lies mainly in activity during their growth. "Learning by doing" is children's natural desire, which is beneficial to their overall development and can enable children to acquire knowledge and train abilities.

Vygotsky believes that attention should be paid to cultural and social roles in the process of learning.[3] Culture is the main power of intellectual development, whose mechanism is social interaction. Language development is a way of cultural heritage, therefore must grow with culture synchronously. Interaction between learning and environmental culture is very important in the learning process because personal knowledge is constructed in the social cultural environment.

The three theories above explain the different methods of human learning from different perspectives, but their purposes are the same, that is, the process of constructing the learning knowledge actively is in accordance with the nature of human active exploration.

3 LEARNING PATTERNS OF WEBQUEST ENGLISH TEACHING MODEL

The objective of WebQuest learning is to have the learners make full use of time and information and help the learners analyze, synthesize and evaluate various information resources. Therefore, according to the inquiry learning time WebQuest learning can be divided into two types: short-term WebQuest learning model and long-term WebQuest learning model.

Short-term learning model emphasizes the acquisition and integration of knowledge. Learners obtain and understand a certain amount of useful information, and construct knowledge actively based on the information. Short-term model (about 1–3 hours) can be used for daily teaching.

Long-term learning model emphasizes the development and refinement of knowledge. Learners usually planned search for information of complete subject in a planned way and make further information analysis and more comprehensive knowledge reorganization. The long-term model may last a week or a month, most of which is used for group cooperative subject research.

4 DESIGN PRINCIPLES OF WEBQUEST ENGLISH TEACHING MODEL

In general, the design of WebQuest teaching model should follow five principles, FOCUS principles: F-Find great sites, O-Orchestrate your learners and resources, C-Challenge your learners to think, U-Use the medium, S-Scaffold high expectations.

4.1 Find great sites

In this model, it is very important for students to choose suitable learning sites because the right sites can provide appropriate learning materials to learners so that classroom learning can be fully extended. To find great sites, students must pay attention to three aspects.

4.1.1 Be skilled in using search engines, such as Google, Baidu etc
In the search for related learning information, search techniques and advanced rules of search engines should be mastered in order to find the needed information quickly and efficiently.

4.1.2 Further analyze web page information
According to the statistics the Internet the number of web pages are up to 550 billion.[4] Around 1 billion can be found through search engines, in which English websites or sites suitable for learning English are also countless. In addition many archives, database and museums which can be found through network may also become the selected objectives of English learners.

4.1.3 Be skilled in collecting the great websites found
Once found great sites or resources that can help the learners to learn English effectively, you should keep them up timely and track them constantly.

4.2 Coordinate and organize learners and learning resources

It is an important part of WebQuest learning to coordinate and organize learners and arrange for learning resources reasonably. These two aspects should be paid attention to in the design of WebQuest learning.

The first question is how to organize the learners. Successful WebQuest learning should be related with the harmonious group learning environment and harmonious group learning environment needs to coordinate and organize the learners well. The coordination and organization of the learners should include the following aspects: positive interaction, role coordination, labor division and cooperation. In WebQuest learning, learners will explore certain information according to their learning tasks, and make timely interaction and mutual promotion at the same time. In the process of interaction, the learners need to clear their respective roles and understand that the task is not easy to complete without partner support. Team members must have a clear role division so that each can be responsible for certain aspect of a task. On this basis, team members must know how to cooperate with each other and learning tasks can be successfully completed only by cooperation.

Next comes to the effective organization and reasonable arrangements for learning resources. The network learning resources are very rich, so in WebQuest learning we should pay attention to how to optimize and organize these learning resources. Optimization and organization of learning resources usually have two cases: the lack of hardware and software application.

If there are not enough computer equipments in teaching, teachers should take possible measures to make up. For example, teachers only use one computer to guide the class discussion to coordinate the learning rhythm. In hardware-limited conditions, learning centers can be set according to a certain proportion and students can take turns to use the equipment. In Internet-limited conditions, teachers should pay attention to stagger the periods of offline and online activities for students to maximize the function and advantage of the network. If students cannot surf the Internet, teachers can download the content of the related websites and provide it to the students to learn offline. In software application, teachers should understand various websites related to English learning and other online learning software as far as possible, so that we can use a variety of software flexibly to optimize and organize abundant learning resources.

4.3 *Stimulate learners to think*

Generally speaking, in WebQuest learning we can adopt the following methods to guide and motivate learners to think.

4.3.1 *Make tasks challenging*
The design and selection of tasks must consider the difficulty in its completion. The difficulty of the task is not only reflected in the students' understanding of the task, but more important is to reflect the students' abilities to solve problems, make innovative design and logical judgment.

4.3.2 *Make tasks authentic*
Task design should be close to the real life and the topic of the task should come from social practice. At the same time we should pay attention to the feasibility of the activities in the task so that students can learn language skills used in real life.

4.3.3 *Make tasks comprehensive*
Give an overall consideration to the task designing. The task should be of certain difficulty and can make the students learn to analyze problems from multi-perspectives through the task to improve their abilities to solve problems.

4.3.4 *Select media*
WebQuest English teaching is not limited to the use of cyber source, but can make full use of books, magazines and other media to achieve the learning objectives. Therefore, in the selection of the media we should pay attention to several aspects:

First of all, we should be aware that Internet is not only a kind of computer network, more importantly is man's network and expert resource network. In addition to select proper, interesting web pages for learning, learners can find a lot of expert intelligence resource.

Secondly, attention should be paid to communicate with others in the learning process. Learners can communicate with experts or other learners through BBS, E-mail and other platforms. Through interaction on the network, learners can learn from each other, inspire ideas and improve together.

Thirdly, pay attention to the reasonable selection of learning content. Network is a multimedia environment and can provide an unlimited amount of learning resources. Make reasonable selection,

you can improve your learning efficiency. Otherwise, the abuse of network audio and video multimedia content will distract the learners so that they cannot achieve the desired learning effect.

4.4 *Help learners to achieve a high level of learning expectations*

WebQuest learning allows students to learn in an normally unimaginable situation so as to achieve a learning effect which is difficult to obtain in traditional teaching, because in WebQuest teaching model, teachers can help students to build "scaffolds". For instance, if the teacher asks the students to analyze and classify soft drinks in the global market, he should provide supporting information such as sites related to beverages, various reviews, and production and sales of websites in the relevant countries or regions.

Generally, WebQuest English teaching can provide three kinds of scaffolds: acceptance scaffold, conversion scaffold and output scaffold. The role of acceptance scaffold is to teach learners how to use the given network learning resources to learn. In WebQuest learning, learners often face tremendous cyber information. Lack of guidance, learners may not know what course to take. Therefore, specific acceptance scaffold tend to be reflected in the examples of observation guidance, meeting skills, online dictionary. Conversion scaffold mainly refers to certain methods and techniques in WebQuest learning such as comparison, induction, summary, conclusion, discussion, reasoning and decision-making. In the learning process, learners can change the received information into a new form by processing and restructuring, which needs the help of conversion scaffold. Output scaffold mainly refers to learners presenting their own understanding and results through learning, which can use certain output scaffold such as template, writing guidance, multimedia and various components.

In a word, the role of scaffolds is to help learners surpass his previous language ability so as to internalize the learning content more effectively and complete the learning task independently.

5 THE DISADVANTAGE OF WEBQUEST MODE

The tasks in the WebQuest model are selected and determined by the teachers. The learning goal of the students is to complete the tasks assigned by the teacher. Therefore, the tasks may become passive learning. However, the self-regulated learning is corresponding with the passive learning. In the actual learning, there are less fully independent and non-independent learning, and most learning are between the two. So learning cannot be divided into independent and non-independent, only considering the autonomous degree of learning. Autonomous learning is to cultivate students' abilities to discover problems, learn autonomously, think independently, make subjective judgment and solve problems. For example, students can choose learning contents, learning methods, learning progress, which embodies student-oriented. In the task modules in WebQuest mode, in most cases the teachers ask questions, which cannot widely consider different student's individual interest, personal choice and the students' different knowledge, emotion and cognitive level. The students' learning motivation is not self driving and the learning content is not chosen by the students themselves. Through the above analysis, we can see that from the students' perspective autonomous learning in the WebQuest mode is not fully autonomous learning to a large degree.

6 CONCLUSION

As a new method to integrate computer technology into English teaching, WebQuest English Teaching Model has its own advantages as well as disadvantages, which needs to be improved constantly in College English Teaching Reform.

ACKNOWLEDGEMENT

This work is financially supported by Higher Education Association of Hebei Province (GJXH2013-32): Research on Cultivating Applied Translation Talents in Colleges.

REFERENCES

[1] Brunner, J.S. (1960) The Press of Education. Cambridge, MA: Harvard University Press.
[2] Dewey, J. (1970) Experience of Education. NY: Collier.
[3] Vygotsky, L. (1978) Mind in Society. Cambridge, MA: Harvard University Press.
[4] Chen Jianlin (2005) From the auxiliary to the dominant: a new development trend in computer foreign language teaching[J]. Computer-assisted Foreign Language Education. (6):18–19.

Computer, Intelligent Computing and Education Technology – Liu, Sung & Yao (Eds)
© *2014 Taylor & Francis Group, London, ISBN 978-1-138-02469-4*

On methods of cultivating applied translation talents

L.J. Diao

Department of English, Cangzhou Normal University, Cangzhou, Hebei, China

ABSTRACT: To cultivate lots of applied translation talents is one school-running aim for colleges. Therefore all the colleges should understand the connotations of the applied translation talents based on their own features. In order to cultivate excellent applied translation talents for the regional economy, colleges should take the skill-oriented and translation comprehension-oriented principles and abide by the following strategies: adjusting the curriculum in accordance to the translation market; reforming the teaching methods and optimizing the teaching resources; cultivating qualified teachers in order to develop the Ss' translation comprehension.

Keywords: applied translation talents; connotation; cultivating strategies

1 INTRODUCTION

Since 2006, more than 60 undergraduate universities approved by the Ministry of Education have set up translation major. Domestic translation scholars have conducted deep and comprehensive research on translation teaching and the results are quite abundant, but papers involved in the research on cultivating applied translation talents in colleges are rare.

2 CONNOTATION OF APPLIED TRANSLATION TALENTS

In the reform in recent years, many colleges and universities haven't grasp the connotation and extension of applied talents exactly and have not specific definition of translators' connotation such as knowledge, ability and quality and their construction relationship. Therefore, how to combine the concrete specialty to cultivate translators is even vague.

The standard of distinguishing talents should be based on the nature of the work function, not the specific work content.[1] Thus, the talents can be divided into research talents and applied talents. The former mainly explore the nature of things while the latter apply the scientific principles found to social practice. Most of the talents today can be classified as applied talents. According to the differences of work function, the applied talents can be divided specifically as follows:

1. The project-oriented. They converse the scientific principles and discipline knowledge into the design schemes and design drawings depending on the specialty basic theory, professional knowledge and basic skills.
2. The technology-oriented. They mainly engage in such activities as product development, production management and business decision and change the design or drawing into product.
3. The skill-oriented. They rely on skilled operating skills to complete the manufacture of products and turn decisions, designs and plans into reality and different types of products.

Because the universities must take on the responsibility of serving the local economy, the training objectives of translation major should be refined as training skill-oriented applied translation talents. Specifically, according to the demand of regional social development, college running conditions and the situation of students, we should cultivate a large number of skill-oriented applied translation talents in many areas such as business, news, science and technology, foreign affairs, tourism, media and so on. Its ability connotation should include translation ability, IT knowledge, learning ability, team spirit, CAT (machine aided translation) ability, knowledge and experience in related fields. In addition, applied talents can also be divided into business translators, foreign affairs translators, tourism translators based on different professional fields. The above skill-oriented above refers to both the translation skills necessary to translation talents and the training principle technology as core and ability as center.

3 CULTIVATING METHODS OF APPLIED TRANSLATION TALENTS BASED ON TECHNOLOGY AS CORE AND ABILITY AS CENTER

Cultivating applied translation talents in colleges must make great efforts to meet requirements of regional economic and social development, especially the need for translators. Local colleges should adhere to the principle with technology as the core, ability as the center.[2] The specific methods are as follows:

3.1 Explore the market and adjust the curriculum

Applied translation model and courses should follow the principles of Skopos Theory, namely social demand determines the process and mode of talent training.

3.1.1 Offer localization courses reasonably and promote the localized translation ability

With the development of economic globalization and political multi-polarization process, localization industries have formed and developed rapidly, which leads to a sharp rise in the localization of talents. Language translation is a main problem to be solved in localization. Therefore, local colleges and universities should be combined with the development of the localization industries to adjust the courses actively, offer scientific translation and commercial translation training courses reasonably, and set localization courses and business training aimed at improving the localization translation ability selectively.

3.1.2 Understand the regional foreign personnel status and cultivate abilities to handle foreign affairs

Applied translation talents mainly include business translators, foreign affairs translators, tourism translators, namely talents concerning foreign affairs. Only the combination with foreign-related courses and international trade courses can cultivate qualified talents effectively.

3.1.3 Discern the local publicity situation and cultivate publicity translation ability

Nowadays, whether national or regional, publicity is just politics, economy and business card. Translation of publicity materials is the main way for foreign propaganda. In the process of cultivating translation talents, the college aimed at serving the local economy should offer courses to serve the local publicity. When we offer knowledge reserve for students, we should cultivate their sense of teamwork, terminology management, machine aided translation and localization translation abilities

at the same time. Set up courses to improve sub-translation abilities, with the translation ability as the center. Translation ability is a comprehensive reflection of the translators' bilingual ability, translation thinking ability, bilingual cultural quality and skills required in the translation work. Translation teaching aims to cultivate students' ability of translation. According to the training objectives of translation talents in local institutions, this article comes up with some ideas from the three curriculum modules: language knowledge and ability, translation knowledge and skills, related knowledge and skills. Language knowledge and ability are also divided into English pronunciation, vocabulary, grammar, English reading and writing skills, Chinese knowledge and writing ability, language and thinking ability and language learning ability. Translation knowledge and skills are divided into four sub-skills: interpret skills, interpret theories, intercultural communicative competence and translators' comprehensive quality. Related knowledge and skills are divided into three general sub-skills: Chinese and foreign social culture, linguistic and literary knowledge, computer and network.

3.2 Optimize the teaching resources and reform the teaching method

Teaching is the specific process of training applied translation talents and plays a decisive role in the latter. At present, the domestic translation scholars often lament that the traditional teaching mode is lagging behind the social translation practice seriously. Therefore, it is imperative to optimize the teaching resources and reform the teaching method.

3.2.1 Adhere to the student-centered concept and the principle of translation ability as the core

Adhere to the student-centered concept consistent with constructivist theory, which emphasizes of students' active exploration and discovery of knowledge and the active construction of the meaning of the learned knowledge. It is different from the traditional teaching, where the knowledge is sent from the teachers' mind to the students' notebook. With the students as the center, the focus is learning, while with the teacher as the center, the focus is teaching. In terms of teaching form, teachers are required to ensure plenty of practice. As to the teaching contents, the selected translation cases are required to be modern, practical and the content should be involved in science and technology, economy and trade, tourism, law, politics, advertising and so on. The teachers can even invite students to participate in compiling teaching plan and choose teaching content.

3.2.2 Adopt the process approach to raises the students' good translation habits

Teachers should encourage the students to learn from each other and discuss cooperatively in the process of translation so as to cultivate students' teamwork skills and ability to use tools. Teachers can actively focus on the students' translation process, affirming their strength and giving more praise and encouragement in order to cultivate the students' translation strategy ability and process ability. At the same time, let the students understand the true meaning of the idea that the translation is just better not the best, aiming to encourage students to learn from each other and cultivate their good translation habits.

3.2.3 Strengthen the application of modern education technology in translation teaching

Encourage translation teachers in local colleges to change their ideas actively, be familiar with the use of various teaching resources, and develop the corresponding translation teaching courseware. If the condition is available, it is necessary to offer network education to realize the online Q & A and interaction. Or with the project application, course construction as an opportunity, colleges can increase funding and policy support, encourage teachers to design interactive, personalized teaching mode. Teachers and students can also cooperate to build translation corpus to cultivate students' autonomous learning, terminology management and CAT machine-aided translation ability.

3.3 Strengthen the construction of teacher team to improve the students' translation abilities

The core task of Higher education is to cultivate high-quality talent with innovative consciousness, thinking and abilities, which is dependent on the teachers. At the same time, training the applied translation talents relies on not only the excellent translation teaching mode, but also subject to the teachers' grasp directly. To meet the requirements, we can take several measures.

3.3.1 Form a high level translation teacher team with construction of quality project as an opportunity

By the means of educational reform, exquisite curriculum, teaching team building, form a translation teacher team with moderate scale, reasonable structure and standard management gradually. At the same time, the team members, especially the people responsible for translation teaching team should have a high academic level, rich translation experience in the field of translation, and abilities of coordination, management and leadership.

3.3.2 Encourage teachers to acquire translation theory and related theories such as linguistics, communication science and literature by self-learning

Translation theory is required for high quality translation teaching, because only the master of translation theory and translation of knowledge in teaching, teachers may answer freely, can let the Translation Classroom explain profound theories in simple language, do a job with skill and ease. In addition, teachers can also participate in the students a translation practice or corpus, so as to realize the translation skill a translation to the benign development of the energy.

3.3.3 In addition, we can ask the department to establish reasonable teacher training system

Establish a long-term cooperation mechanism system with the translation companies and enterprises to build translation training center so as to improve the teachers' translation teaching and research ability gradually. When the conditions are available, we also should establish stable cooperation relations with be several corresponding enterprises by means of the various ways such as industry associations, alumni, relevant government agencies in order to build a teaching team and academic team cooperatively and to achieve an all-win situation for enterprise, school and students.

4 OFFER APPROPRIATE COURSES TO DEVELOP STUDENTS' TRANSLATION SKILLS

To a translator, translation and interpretation ability is the most basic ability. Curriculum cultivating the ability should include the following.

The first category is the courses to cultivate the students' basic quality of literary translation and translation criticism. The courses have an irreplaceable role in the course of cultivating the students' translation ability and literacy. Literary translation quality and ability is the basis for various applied translation. But such courses should be few but good, in literary translation criticism and appreciation. The purpose is to let students understand and learn the excellent translation and translation strategies to arouse the students' interest in active learning and enthusiasm.

The second category is the courses such as liaison interpreting, consecutive interpreting, thematic interpretation which adapt to the market demand and are the core of students' translation skills training. The purpose is to help students master the professional translation in the fields of foreign affairs, trade, education, culture, science and technology and military.

The last category is translation variation courses. Translation variation refers to the non-complete translation in which translators should interpret related content of the original work by means of increasing, reducing, narrating and changing according to the demand of specific readers under the specific conditions. The instant information communication requirements in modern society and market put forward different demands for translation purposes. The traditional word for word and sentence for sentence translation form cannot meet the need of society for practical writing translation like science and technology English. Nowadays, information transfer oriented translation like English for science and technology should consider the different needs and priorities of different translation methods in order to guarantee the timeliness, accuracy and pertinence and to keep up with the pace of development of science and technology and society. Through the teaching practice of translation variation course, students can master more practical writing translation skills.

5 CONCLUSION

National medium and long-term educational reform and development plan (2010–2020) clearly puts forward the idea that colleges focus on expanding the scale of cultivating applied, compound and skill-oriented talents and colleges need to seek rational position, overcome the tendency of homogenization and form their own school running idea and style.[3] That is both an opportunity and a challenge to local colleges. Colleges and universities should train translators combined with the connotation and cultivating methods of applied translation talents cultivation to promote local economic development.

ACKNOWLEDGEMENT

This work is financially supported by Higher Education Association of Hebei Province (GJXH2013-32): Research on Cultivating Applied Translation Talents in Colleges.

REFERENCES

[1] Ji Chengjun. A Probe into the Classification and Cultivation of Applied Talents[J]. Chinese College Teaching. 2006, (6):57–59.
[2] Yan Xiaoying. Training Ways of Applied Translation Talents in Teaching-oriented Local Universities[J]. Journal of Chengdu Normal University. 2013, (5):91–93.
[3] National Medium and Long-term Educational Reform and Development Plan (2010–2020) [Z]. Beijing: People's Publishing House. (2010):30–31.

Computer, Intelligent Computing and Education Technology – Liu, Sung & Yao (Eds)
© 2014 Taylor & Francis Group, London, ISBN 978-1-138-02469-4

Structural mechanics teaching experience and discussions on improving the teaching methods

Y.E. Hao & B.L. Cui
College of Architecture and Engineering, Yan'an University, Yan'an, China

ABSTRACT: Structural mechanics is an important specialized fundamental course for civil engineering specialty, but in this course learning, students' universal reactions are that the contents are difficult to grasp and the learning outcome is not good. Based on years of front-line teaching practice and experience, both the teachers' "teaching" problems and students' "learning" problems existing in classroom teaching of structural mechanics are analyzed, for teachers some suggestions are presented to perfect their teaching methods and improve the learning effect. Meanwhile, it is aimed to exchange experiences with each other and explore the best teaching methods so as to improve the teaching quality.

Keywords: structural mechanics; teaching experience; teaching method; existing problems; suggestions

1 INTRODUCTION

Structural mechanics is an important specialized fundamental course for civil engineering specialty in colleges, serving as a bridge connecting basic courses with specialized courses and lying in the core position as a connecting link in the whole course system of civil engineering specialty. Based on higher mathematics, theoretical mechanics, material mechanics and other courses, structural mechanics provides necessary knowledge of mechanics and calculation methods for steel structure, reinforced concrete structure, soil mechanics and foundation engineering, structure seismic and other follow-up specialized courses, as well as their curriculum design and graduation design. At present, most universities regard structural mechanics as one of the necessary subjects in postgraduate entrance examination of majors relating to civil engineering. It is not hard to draw the conclusion that the teaching quality of structural mechanics not only directly influents the teaching effect of subsequent specialized courses, but also affects issues like the further study of students and the development of their working ability after they enter the society.

With the continuous enlargement of college enrollment, higher education is transforming from "elite" education to "popularization" education, leading to the decreasing quality of students. In addition, after the previous civil engineering major adjusts to "big civil" system, structural mechanics tends to be a wider coverage of the teaching contents and a tight arrangements of class hour. Students generally reflect that it is quite hard to master the

contents due to the above reasons. Considering the characteristics of structural mechanics and students' reception after the enlargement of college enrollment, how to help students master the specified contents in the structural mechanics outline and know the new techniques in the current field of engineering has become a tough task for teachers. Teachers need to constantly gain teaching experience, explore and practice methods of new forms and better effect so as to cultivate compound talents with both "thick foundation and wide caliber" and creative thinking ability. According to the years of front-line teaching practice and experience, the author summarizes and analyzes the commonly existing problems of both teachers and students, enlightens from those problems and then puts forward some suggestions for teachers to improve their teaching effects.

2 EXPERIENCE GAINED IN THE TEACHING OF STRUCTURAL MECHANICS

In the teaching process, students are a main body, and teachers play a leading role. There is an interactive relationship between teaching and learning. Students are the main body, which means the students are the object of teaching. The purpose of teaching is to help students acquire the knowledge, so students' acquirement of the knowledge and skills should be the ultimate goal and evaluation standard of teaching. Teachers play a leading role means that they should select appropriate teaching content according to the training objectives to guide and help students acquire the basic principles and skills of the curriculum, as well as develop their thinking way to analyze and solve problems and practical competence. Also, to be a good learning guide and advisor[1] for students, teachers should take the actual situation of the students into consideration when reforming the teaching methods, so as to arouse and cultivate students' interests. Thus, the teaching methods and the hard-work of students are the two key factors playing essential roles in improving the teaching quality of that course. Teachers must understand the actual situation of students in the learning process, constantly dig out their own teaching problems, and adjust their teaching methods in time so as to improve the teaching effects.

2.1 The existing problems of students in learning

In recent years, the author has been engaged in teaching structural mechanics, and analyzed the reasons of bad learning effects, poor grades and the proportion of students in Table 1 through summarizing and conducting statistics about the study situation of different level students in successive years (including school attendance, classroom discipline, homework completion, answering questions and test scores).

2.2 The existing problems of teachers in the teaching process

Through the discussion with peers of rich teaching experience and attending the courses taught by young teachers, and combining with his own teaching experience, the author finds out the following problems existing in the teaching of structural mechanics: (1) Teachers pay less attention to class management, only focusing on teaching. They do not stop the behaviors disturbing the class orders, so that the classroom is always in chaos. When teaching, the teachers do not check the number of students attending the class, and do not emphasize the connection between the attendance rate and usual-time grades, resulting in the incorrect study attitude of some students such as their frequent late-arriving, early-leaving and even truancy. Even though showing up on class, some students choose to play mobile phone and talk with others, rather than listen to the teachers. The languid and looser learning habit seriously impact on the teaching quality on class. (2) The teachers adopt the instilling teaching method, that is, teachers teach alone with students just as their listeners, making the whole class a "one-role play" of teachers without interactions with students. Besides, there are not class hours for students to ask questions, discuss and exchange opinions with each other. Above reasons lead to the lack of enthusiasm and initiative of students in learning, and even their weary mood. (3) When teaching, teachers do not pay attention to the mutual penetration and connection between the structural mechanics knowledge and the professional knowledge, always center on the teaching of single course, and only focus on theoretical derivation and analysis calculation, rather than develop students' ability to solve the practical engineering problems by using the knowledge learned on class. Even though a large amount of time and energy are spent on learning mechanics knowledge, students are still helpless in face of actual problems. This could even affect the understanding and learning of the subsequent curriculum, and make students more confused when they have to use mechanics knowledge and methods to handle practical problems. (4) The teaching mode

Table 1. Reasons of poor learning effect and the proportion of students.

Serial number	Reasons of poor learning effect	Ratio
1	Some students with solid foundation have poor self-control ability and incorrect attitude. They do not work hard, always skip class or talk on class and seldom focus on the course so that they cannot catch up with the class schedule, and always get unsatisfactory grades.	5%
2	Some students with weak foundation cannot learn the previous courses like mathematics, theoretical mechanics and material mechanics well, which make it pretty hard for them to continue studying.	8%
3	Some students think more class hours should be arranged because the contents are too much and teachers taught too fast on class. It is quite difficult for them to digest all the knowledge, understand the contents completely and keep up with teachers. They cannot integrate the knowledge of different parts well.	20%
4	Some students cannot finish the homework independently. They are lack of patience to do homework and always copy each other's homework in order to finish the task. They find it quite easy to understand the teachers on class but hard to work some problems, which leads to the poor learning outcome.	15%

is too simple and teaching method is relatively backward. Teachers usually speed up teaching in order to finish the teaching contents in the limited class hours due to a small amount of information that can be conveyed on each class, which makes it hard for students to fully grasp the contents. On class, the boring mechanics knowledge and the traditional chalk, blackboard and dictation teaching mode with teachers always lead to the easy distraction of students' attention, depressing class atmosphere and cannot effectively stimulate students' interest in learning.

3 SUGGESTIONS ABOUT IMPROVING THE TEACHING METHODS AND THE TEACHING EFFECT OF STRUCTURAL MECHANICS

3.1 *To be strict with the students, strengthen management and improve the teaching quality on class*

Besides focusing on the course, teachers should improve their class control ability. They should be strict with their students at ordinary times, establish a standardized system of checking on class attendance, insist on checking the student number on each class and connect the class attendance results with the usual-time grades of students. Also, they should ask students to devote themselves on class, finish their homework carefully and timely after class, and discuss the questions they do not understand with classmates and teachers promptly. A reasonable curriculum examination evaluation system should be set up, the former evaluation criteria which only concentrates on the final exam grades should be abolished and usual-time homework, class questioning and attendance should

be proportionally introduced into the curriculum evaluation system. The exam grades can be divided into the mid-term and final twice to check the periodical learning outcome of students and the teaching effect of teachers, which on the one hand, can help students find out the knowledge they do not acquire, and on the other hand, can help teachers find out the existing teaching problems through the mid-term exam grades of students to improve their teaching effect. Only by strengthening management, correcting students' study attitude and letting them ideologically attached to the course at ordinary times, can the learning enthusiasm be aroused, as well as the teaching quality on class be improved.

3.2 *To be familiar with training objectives of the major and determine reasonable teaching contents*

The main knowledge systems in the existing structural mechanics textbooks of all versions are shown in Table 2. These contents should be chosen reasonably and expanded appropriately according to specialized directions and training objectives because different specialized directions focus on different knowledge. When teaching, teachers should spend more time and energy teaching the important content needed to be master by the students and try best to make sure that students can fully understand the contents and use them flexibly. As for those contents only needed to be known by the students, teachers can just make a brief introduction of them. For example, for bridge engineering major, the internal force calculation method of two-hinged arch and fixed arch, the influence line of determinate structure and indeterminate structure are quite important contents,

Table 2. Main knowledge systems in structural mechanics textbooks.

Serial number	Main contents in structural mechanics	Task	Calculation method
1	Determinate structure (including statically determinate beam, statically determinate frame, three hinged arch, statically determinate truss and composite structure)	The calculation of internal force (M, V, N)	Equilibrium equation
		The calculation of displacement (Δ)	Unit-load method
2	Indeterminate structure (including statically indeterminate beams, statically indeterminate frame, frame, statically indeterminate arch, statically indeterminate truss and composite structure)	The calculation of internal force (M, V, N)	Precise method: force method, displacement method; Evolutionary method: moment distribution method, shear distribution method
		The calculation of displacement (Δ)	Unit-load method
3	Dynamic calculation of structure	The calculation of dynamic response {P(t), y(t) etc.}	Flexibility method, stiffness method

which are the basis for design and calculation of arch bridges in the bridge engineering. However, for constructional engineering, those contents are not so important and a brief introduction of them is enough for students. For the structural mechanics provided housing constructional engineering direction, envelope diagram of internal force, shear distribution method of continuous beam, hierarchical method and inflection point method, the concept of plastic hinge in the structural ultimate load have to be introduced in order to link with the subsequent courses like reinforced concrete and the structure of high-rise buildings. For constructional engineering major students, they are quite important, while for bridge engineering students, much attention need not be paid to them.

3.3 To strengthen the connection between the contents in structural mechanics and relating specialized courses in order to make a solid foundation for the subsequent specialized courses

Teachers should be quite familiar with the whole curriculum system and constantly emphasize which part of the contents in the subsequent courses closely link to the knowledge of structural mechanics being taught, letting students know the study purpose and helping them make a solid foundation for the subsequent specialized courses. For example, the internal force and displacement calculation of determinate structure and indeterminate structure are very important in structural mechanics. Some students do not understand the purpose of internal force and displacement calculation. As teachers, they should tell their students clearly that in reinforced concrete course, they can attribute rebar for concrete components or test the strength of the components according to internal force, and in steel structure course, they can test the strength and stability of components according to internal force. The displacement calculation is to meet the needs of normal use and ensure the maximum deflection of the components does not exceed the limit value, in order to eliminate the sense of unsafety caused by excessive deflection.

3.4 To adopt heuristic teaching method to cultivate students' self-study ability and stimulate their interests in learning

Heuristic and interactive teaching aims at letting students think independently and acquiring knowledge actively through the inspiration and guidance of teachers.[2] It is a good way to cultivate students' creativity. At the same time, teachers should elaborately select the contents to deliver and then teach them carefully on class, focusing on the qualitative analysis and method analysis. Teachers should cultivate the associative thinking ability, innovative thinking ability of students and leave some thinking space for them, letting them draw the conclusions through their own thinking. For example, when teaching the displacement calculation of indeterminate structure, teachers should first let students review the displacement calculation method of determinate structure, and then let them calculate the displacement of indeterminate structure by the displacement calculation method of determinate structure, and finally tell them how to transfer the displacement calculation of indeterminate structure to that of basic system (determinate structure) under the combined action of load and other unknown forces, that is the displacement calculation of determinate structure. This not only stimulates students' interest, but also develops their ability to analyze problems. Self-study is one of the promises to guarantee the teaching effect. Teachers should arrange some contents for self-study, and then ask students to summarize and conclude those contents on class, and finally answer the questions students encounter in their self-study. This not only livens up the class atmosphere, but also cultivates students' self-study ability. Those equipped with self-study ability can find answers to the practical engineering problems by themselves in their future work. In addition, for those students who have extra energy and time to study more, teachers should introduce some magazines relating to the contents on class to them, guiding them to do selective reading spontaneously in order to broad their horizon.

3.5 To change the single teaching mode, and use the teaching means that combines multimedia with traditional methods

Teaching means of traditional dictation, blackboard-writing has many disadvantages. A small amount of information can be conveyed on each class, a great many class hours are needed and the image processing function is quite weak. Compared with traditional teaching methods, multimedia teaching has incomparable advantages. For example, pictures, text, sound and video can be used by teachers, providing many kinds of stimulation to students' sense organs, which effectively help students understand and memorize the contents on class. A large amount of information can be conveyed on each class, teaching efficiency is enhanced and the limited class hours are saved, which greatly improve the teaching quality. Multimedia has been widely used in structural mechanics classes so far.

However, multimedia teaching has its own limitations. For example, the rough multimedia course-ware always bore students. The courseware is shown so fast that students cannot catch up with the contents taught by their teachers. Also, the thoughts of teachers may be controlled by the courseware, so that they cannot adjust the teaching speed and contents timely in accordance with their own ideas and the students' reaction, the lack of emotion communication between teachers and students is not conducive to impart knowledge. In the traditional teaching mode, by the blackboard-writing, teachers can lead students to write the process of formula derivation, theoretical analysis and calculation in detail, and remind them where to pay attention, drawing pictures on the blackboard while explaining them. They speak in measured tones and emphasize the key points, starting with the easy parts then deepening step by step, so that students can easily master the knowledge. This traditional teaching method can increase the communication and interaction between teachers and student. Teachers can know whether students have understood the contents or not, as well as their problems and cruxes through students' reaction on class, and then take countermeasures in time, which is conducive to the leading role played by teachers and can effectively improve the teaching effect.[3] In practical teaching, multimedia teaching and traditional blackboard-writing method should be combined together, making up each other's deficiencies and learning from each other, so that students can keep up with the contents taught by teachers, the key points and difficult parts can be stressed and good teaching effect can be achieved.

4 CONCLUSIONS

The teaching effect is closely linked with students' "learning" and teachers' "teaching". When teaching structural mechanics, the principle "students are a main body and teachers play a leading role" should be fully embodied, so that the internal motivation can be completely aroused and students can really know how to study. Teachers should also constantly gain and enrich their teaching experience, explore and improve their teaching methods in order to improve teaching effect and quality.

REFERENCES

[1] Ma Yun-ling, Xie Bing; Several Points on the Improvements of Structural Mechanics Classroom Teaching [J] Journal of LuoYang Institute of Technology (Social Science), 2002, 20(4):93–94.
[2] Gong Wei-ping, Geng Meng-qin, Suo Feng-ping; Discussion on Structural Mechanics Teaching Reform of Civil Engineering [J]. Shanxi Architecture, 2007, 33(31):206–207.
[3] Hua Xiao-ji; The Reflection of Teaching Practice and the Reform of Teaching Methods of Structural Mechanics [J]. Journal of East China Jiaotong University, 2007, 24:139–140.

Computer, Intelligent Computing and Education Technology – Liu, Sung & Yao (Eds)
© 2014 Taylor & Francis Group, London, ISBN 978-1-138-02469-4

The CET online permission ticket printing system of Zunyi medical university

Y. Sima & X. Zeng
Zunyi Medical University, Guizhou, Zunyi, China

ABSTRACT: First of all, this paper expounds the necessity of designing the system of online print of CET permission ticket, analyzes the problems existing in traditional in Zunyi medical university; Secondly, the system of online print of the CET permission ticket was carried on the concrete analysis and design; Finally, by comparing the traditional way of permission ticket system with the online mode, it is concluded that the online system can improve the work efficiency and has more advantages.

Keywords: permission ticket; B/S; design; CET

1 INTRODUCTION

With the popularity of computer network, how to work efficiently that based on network technology has become a importance problem for each unit. At present, the informatization construction of Zunyi medical university is being carried out in full swing. Among them, In order to strengthen the examination management work, and put an end to use fake id fraud, to ensure fairness and justice, improve the supervisor check examinee identity in venue management link work efficiency. The school to apply for the educational reform project design "College English Test Permission Ticket Online Printing System" in order to improve the efficient management of test affairs personnel to the examination link.

2 SYSTEM DESIGN

2.1 *Structure design*

In order to make the system designer can carry on the management and convenient for the system upgrade, the online submission system based on B/S structure of design patterns. B/S mode makes the client computer system structure by itself to install the browser can access the server resources, the access mode maximum limit reduces the load of the client computer resources, at the same time by the server load most of the transaction. The structure also has a dedicated database server.

2.2 *Function design*

The user of System including administrators and examinee. The administrator can manage test time,

test site, the level and examinee photos and print; Examinee can according to their own information into the interface to your admission ticket printing.

The administrator can manage the corresponding site acquisition examinee photos and; Support a variety of ways of examinee information input; Support external data import; Convenient data query; Manage the examinee examination room and seat.

Examinee will be able to use any computer's browser to enter their admission ticket print interface and for printing. Admission ticket printing times there is a certain limit, if more than the rated frequency should be print request to the administrator. The process is as shown in Figure 2.

2.3 *Data base design*

The main field are designed as shown in Table 1.

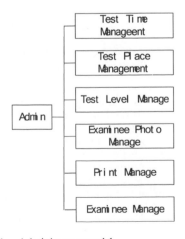

Figure 1. Administrator model.

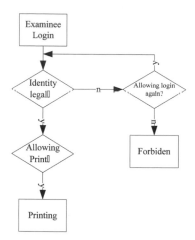

Figure 2. Examinee model.

Table 1. Main field.

Field name	Type	Bytes
Identity	nvarchar	20
dateTime	time	20
school	nvarchar	20
campus	nvarchar	12
department	nvarchar	40
professional	nvarchar	40
InSchoolYear	nvarchar	8
class	nvarchar	4
examineeNo	nvarchar	20
registrationNo	nvarchar	20
addressNo	nvarchar	20
seatNo	nvarchar	4
photo	nvarchar	2

2.4 Security design

In order to ensure the system data are not malicious modified or deleted, in the design process introduces.

Three mechanisms has been introduced in this online system for protect system data.

2.4.1 Permission set

Permissions is according to the characteristics of the user itself to the limitation of access control, the system used the permissions set mainly comes from three aspects: 1, the database level permissions; 2, view level of permissions; Level 3, roles, permissions Settings. All three of these permissions will automatically block certain data information, in order to protect the data.

2.4.2 Encryption algorithm

In order to ensure the user's password is not stolen, the system introduced cryptography MD5 one-way hash algorithm. The real data in the database is not the password itself, but by the 256 calculated MD5 hash data, even let the cat out of the hash data stored in the database, it is hard to find the corresponding user password.

2.4.3 Electronic signature

Electronic signature is a form of electronic signature, electronic signature operation can be converted to the technology of image processing and paper document stamped and operating the same visual effects, at the same time using the electronic signature technology to ensure the authenticity and integrity of electronic information and signature nonrepudiation.

3 SYSTEM IMPLEMENTATION

3.1 Development tool

The online submission system is designed on the platform of Visual Studio 2008 with the language of c #, and chose the SqlServer 2005 as database. In order to facilitate the use of all kinds of users, the system uses Web as development modal.

3.2 Core code

```
protected void Page_Load(object sender,
EventArgs e)
{
    if (Session["SId"].ToString().Trim() == "")
    {
        Response.Redirect("Default.aspx");
    }
    else
    {
        string StuId = Session["SId"].ToString().
Trim();
        string FilePath = Server.MapPath("/DB/
DB.xls");
OleDbConnection conn = new OleDbConnect
ion("Provider=Microsoft.Jet.OLEDB.4.0;Data
Source=" + FilePath + ";Extended Properties=Excel
8.0;");
        conn.Open();
        string strcmd = "select * from [DB$] where
Identity='" + StuId + "'";
        OleDbCommand cmd = new Ole
DbCommand (strcmd, conn);
        OleDbDataReader dr = cmd.Execute
Reader();
        if (!dr.Read())
        {
            dr.Close();
            conn.Close();
```

```
Response.Write("<script>alert('noexist');
location='Default.aspx'</script>");
        }
        else
        {
            LblCET.Text = dr["Level"].ToString().
Trim();
            LblTestNum.Text = dr["permission
No"].ToString().Trim();
            LblStuName.Text = dr["name"].To
String().Trim();
            LblStuNum.Text = dr["examineeNo"].
ToString().Trim();
            LblStuID.Text = dr["Identity "].ToString().
Trim();
            LblTime.Text = dr["dateTime"].To
String().Trim();
            Lblxueyuan.Text = dr["department"].
ToString().Trim() + " " + dr["professional"].
ToString().Trim() + " " + dr["class "].ToString().
Trim();
            Lblkaochang.Text = "Address:" + dr
["addressNo"].ToString().Trim();
            Lblzuowei.Text = "Seat" + dr["seatNo"].
ToString().Trim();
            Image1.ImageUrl = "/pic/" +
dr["Identity"].ToString().Trim() + ".jpg";
            dr.Close();
            conn.Close();
        }
    }
}
```

4 CONCLUSION

The printing effect of permission ticket as shown
in Figure 3.

The teaching reform project of "The CET
Online Permission Ticket Printing System" from
Zunyi medical university used for examine work,
and highlights the contrast the traditional management method is more advantage.

The CET online permission ticket printing system in Zunyi medical university works well. The
system can carry on the promotion in the national
computer rank examination and other important

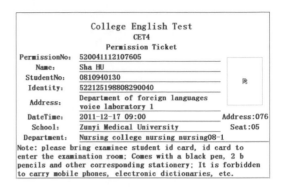

Figure 3.   Permission ticket.

examination after the commissioning period will
do perfect, all of this will effectively improve the
work efficiency and economic benefit.

ACKNOWLEDGEMENTS

Grateful Corresponding author X. ZENG who
put time and effort for the papers and information system, Also thinks to QIAN KE HE J ZI
LKZ[2011]22 and ZUNYI MEDICAL UNIVER-
SITY J-1-1 for their support and sponsorship.

REFERENCES

Chen J. 2005. Application of Dynamic Web Technique
    in Making Admission Cards for Examination. Journal
    of Hainan Normal University. 18:226~229.
Deng Y.Q., J. Gong, H. Shi. 2012. Concise Guide to
    Cryptography, China. Tsinghua University Press.
Hu X.D., Q.F. Wei, R. Hu. 2012. Applied Cryptography,
    China. Publishing House of Electronics Industry.
Liang Q. 2011. Design and Implementation of Admis-
    sion Ticket Printing System Based on C#, China.
    Computer Programming Skills and Maintenance.
    27:25~26.
Wan Y.X. 2001. Legal Issues Relating to Electronic Sig-
    natures, China. People's Court Press.
Zeng X. 2013. The Design of Strain Management Infor-
    mation System Based on B/S Scheme, China. Journal
    of Medical Informatics. 33:32~34.
Zhang L.M. 2010. ASP.NET development paradigm real
    book (using C#), China. Science Press.

Computer, Intelligent Computing and Education Technology – Liu, Sung & Yao (Eds)
© *2014 Taylor & Francis Group, London, ISBN 978-1-138-02469-4*

Design and development of orienteering teaching aided platform based on embedded system

R. Ni
Department of Information Science and Electrical Engineering, Shandong Jiao Tong University, Jinan, Shandong, China

ABSTRACT: This paper first analyzes the current situation and problems of orienteering and the impact of modern technology on the directional movement, puts forward the design thought to develop directional motion platform in intelligent mobile phone base on embedded system. In addition, the article gives a detailed analysis of the design and implementation process in the system structure, software function, database design, etc. With the platform, we can easy organization orienteering activities, especially to carry out teaching activities in the campus. It can optimize the active tool, maintain the fairness of the activities, improve the safety of participants, and develop the traditional directional movement organization.

Keywords: directional motion; embedded system; teaching aid software

1 GENERAL INTRODUCTION

Orienteering originated in Sweden and spread to China since 80's in last century. It is a green outdoor sports project, with an integration of mental, physical and entertainment. At present, with the coming of the leisure society, social function of sports has been completed from production to life, group to individual, tool to toy transformation, and in this process, the directional movement has been rapid development in our country. This is not only reflected in the professional team of the organization, but to the general public. In addition, in some universities of China, orienteering sport has been set to one of the sports curriculum with its unique charm. But as the physical education activities, orienteering also exist many problems.

First of all, the organizers will need to survey the terrain carefully, setting multiple check points, making the route line, registering the contestants. All these preparations must be completed quickly and accurately. It seems difficult to achieve.

Second, in the course of the game, fairness should as far as possible to ensure that activities. It includes how to confirm whether the participants reached the corresponding check point and whether there is damage to others sign and etc. Ordinary PE is unable to provide a referee team service.

Third, how to ensure the security of participants is another key issue. The orienteering is an outdoor sport, security participants become more complex. This includes the organizers should grasp the participant's position timely, current state of emergency, whether and how to send out a distress signal. This series of problems are hampering the sport into the rapid development stage. The development of embedded system based on intelligent mobile phone as a representative of the offers the opportunity to resolve these contradictions. We design an orienteering teaching auxiliary platform which is based on the embedded system provides a solution to the problem. The system includes course preparation, class participation, curriculum monitoring, data analysis, physical security, social function. This greatly improves the implementation of directional movement into the curriculum.

2 SYSTEM STRUCTURE ANALYSIS

2.1 *The analysis of system architecture*

Orienteering Teaching Aided Platform is mainly divided into mobile phone APP, communication server, database and communication protocol of four modules, the system structure is shown in Figure 1.

The system roles include organizers, the teachers, participants, etc. Through the system platform, the role of teacher can realize the map tag, develop route, monitoring, participation and testing point check, etc. Participants can realize activity participation, map query, testing point mark, alert for help, and other functions.

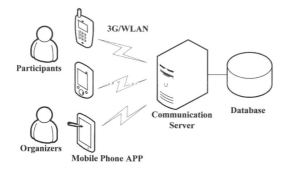

Figure 1.   System architecture.

2.2   Mobile phone APP

Mobile phone APP is equivalent to the client software of the whole system. It is installed on a smart phone or other embedded mobile devices on the directional movement of the software. On the one hand, it is a substitute for traditional directional movement tools. APP implementation maps generated automatically, tag maps checkpoints, distinguish the north-south direction, and other functions, by using the electronic map, GPS function of smart phones. On the other hand, the client software interacts with the server information in real time. According to different object login to complete the function of the organizers and participants. This includes the functions of real-time positioning, state police, send distress, social microblogging etc. which is needed by participants and the organization monitoring functions needed by organizers.

2.3   Communication server

The APP connects to the communication server in real time by wireless network such as 3G or WLAN. Server receives the data passed by participants. It's including online information, reaching information of fixed checkpoints, the final time used, alert information when they meet dangerous, etc. The server broadcast messages when emergency.

2.4   Database

Database store the current and historical information, activity information and participants. On the one hand, it can undertake activities result statistics; on the other hand the server can provide the data analysis and activity track.

2.5   Communication protocol

This system uses the communication protocol of asynchronous communication. The time interval of transmitting character is arbitrary. The advantage of the communication mode is simple, cheap, but the transmission efficiency is low. The system uses package of java.nio to achieve the interaction between the APP client and server, and overcomes the disadvantages of asynchronous communication. Because the interaction is more frequent, system selection long connection mode, combined with the heartbeat detection, the client APP once disconnects from the server, the server immediately by rewiring operation.

3   DEMAND ANALYSIS AND DESIGN OF SOFTWARE FUNCTION

3.1   Demand analysis of mobile APP

The design function of directional motion platform mobile phone client includes the following six aspects:

A. Registration

It plays two roles in the function, one can collect customer information, on the other hand, can assign a name to the user, to participate in the activities of the process, according to the number of participants to collect information.

B. Create a group

Users can choose to create activities or to participate in the activities according to their own needs. Once the teacher user created activities, student users within a certain range around can search to it through the directional motion client, and then participate in group activities. Teachers can specify a period of time to forbidden users to add before the start of the event.

The function of the activity diagram is shown in Figure 2.

C. Electronic map

The teacher user can set a range of activity in the electronic map downloaded by their APP and set a number of check points. A Toast statement will be created in the student users' APP when they reached the corresponding check point. It also will be send to the server at

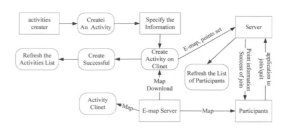

Figure 2.   Activity diagram of create a group.

the same time, so that the organizers can easily make the statistics of the users.

D. Real time communication

In the moving process, the user can interact with activities in the activity room by sending short message. Report the travel schedule, so that other users to understand. It can also ensure that the contestants security to a certain extent. The function diagram is shown in Figure 3.

E. Ask for help

The client APP placed a SOS button in the lower left corner. Once the user is in danger or need for help, press this button can send its current location and other information to other users and organizations. This greatly reduces the risk of.

F. Social microblogging

The user can be involved in the activities of the place, the time to send to QQ or Sina micro-blog.

3.2 Main relationship table design of database

On the system platform, the main design of the database table is composed of the following 8 tables, the logic relations as shown in Figure 4.

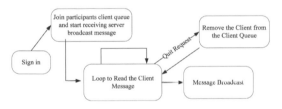

Figure 3. Activity diagram of real time communication.

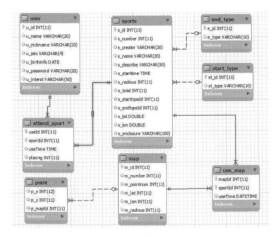

Figure 4. E-R diagram of database.

A. USER TABLE

This table contains the fields of ID, username, password, nickname, birthday, sex, etc. It stores personal information of users.

B. START_TYPE TABLE

This table contains the fields of ID, star type name. The using of this table is easy to make changes to the start type.

C. END_TYPE TABLE

The fields of ID, end type name are in this table. This table is also making easy to change the end type in sports table.

D. SPORTS TABLE

This table is an important table in this system. It includes the fields of ID, number, creator, name, describe, start time, radius, total point, start type, end type, Longitude, Latitude, etc.

Every activity created by creator will be record in this table. The record will be given a new ID by system. The fields of name, describe, start time, end time, radius, type will be fill by creator though the system tool window. The data of longitude and latitude will be filled by the e-map system.

E. MAP TABLE

This table includes ID, number, check point number, Longitude, Latitude, radius, etc. These data will help the system to create an e-map of every activity by using the API of Google MAP or Baidu Map. It's also helping the participants to make sign on the checkpoint in the e-map.

F. POINT TABLE

ID, X coordinate, Y coordinate, ID map is in this table. It's a subclass of the map table.

G. USE_MAP TABLE

This table is a relationship between the table of map and sports. This is a relationship of m to n.

H. ATTEND_SPORTS TABLE

Table sports and table user are linked together through the table of attend sports. Many people can participate in an activity; an activity can contain multiple users.

4 IMPLEMENTATION OF SYSTEM

Figures 5 and 6 is an operating screen of mobile phone terminal program.

First is the login window, the other is an e-map with checkpoints during the orienteering.

The system has been successfully tested in Shandong Jiaotong University's first bicycle riding activities, and introduces the teaching activities. The school teachers and students are very satisfied with the system, said the implementation has been largely improved the Orienteering into campus.

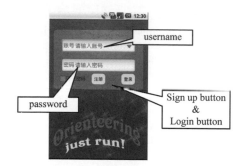

Figure 5

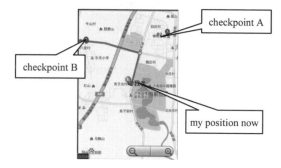

Figure 6

ACKNOWLEDGEMENTS

This work was financially supported by the scientific research foundation of Shandong Jiaotong University, Research on Shandong digital identification platform of traffic accidents and the data mining on the cause of accidents. Z201211.

REFERENCES

Benlei, Su. Campus directional simple cross-country teaching operation. *Journal of Chongqing University of Arts and Sciences (Natural Science Edition)*, 2012(31):98–101.

Deyin, Li & Songqiao, Chen. *Orienteering guidance.* Beijing: Surveying and Mapping Press.

Liangyin, Li. Analysis of WebCT Orienteering Teaching Terrace Study. *Journal of Jilin Institute of Physical Education*, 2012(28):115–117.

Qiuyue, Liu. Present situation and Countermeasures of the directional movement of the colleges and universities in Jiangsu. *Sport*, 2012(12):91–93.

Wei, Lun. Application of GIS technology in the field of sports. *Nei Jiang Ke Ji*, 2012(33):103–104.

Xianfeng, Song & Xiang, Wang. Development and Prospect of Orienteering in China. *Zhejiang Sport Science*, 2005(4):40–43.

Computer, Intelligent Computing and Education Technology – Liu, Sung & Yao (Eds)
© *2014 Taylor & Francis Group, London, ISBN 978-1-138-02469-4*

Research on anti-printing technology to scan in drawings

Yong-Hui He
Shandong Yingcai University, Shandong, China

ABSTRACT: Confrontation print scan through research in the field of digital watermarking situation and summarized, analyzed the print scan distortion effects on engineering drawings, and after comparing before and after printing and scanning, printing and scanning around looking for features anti-invariant values.

Keywords: drawing; digital watermark; characteristic constant value

1   INTRODUCTION

Digitized drawings, refers to the traditional paper maps or other materials (analog signal) converted by a certain method of computer input devices and recognizable drawing data (digital signal) process, the purpose is to facilitate further computer for storage and processing of data. Realization of drawing digitization key is accurate, quick and convenient for drawing data the old maps were digitized, standardization of data collection, on the basis of all the data for efficient editing, updating, storage. With CAD (Computer Aided Design) technology digitized drawings, is to complete engineering drawings into a computer store, a better way to edit and output maps tasks, its strong support management, decision support functions are also to be applied in practical work and play.

2   RESEARCH STATUS OF ANTI PRINT SCAN THE FIELD OF DIGITAL WATERMARKING

Real production practice involves the use of a printer for printing the drawing operation, in the case of this process, there occurs an unavoidable that some details of the local, and there will be the same as the original drawing is not the case, this is the print distortion; and this situation is somewhat similar, and sometimes when we do use a scanner to scan the drawing, when a similar situation occurs, is due to the nature of the scanner's features, drawing on a certain degree of distortion sometimes occur. Currently, the research concentrated on digital watermark difficulties watermark printing, and relatively little research literature in this direction.

Such as the approach and techniques, based on research of the characteristics of color drawings based on the use CIELab color space, the use of certain methods to achieve watermark embedding work, which uses the DCT coefficients drawings take on this factor ways and means of linear operation, he used several experimental validation repetitive work, concluded: using this algorithm embedded watermark, there is a practical feature is able to tell whether there is piracy from happening, if after a scan is shown to be genuine, and if two scans are detected that piracy has occurred. Haisheng and other presents a watermarking algorithm, in essence also Pictured in color printing works based on the use characteristics CIELab color space to add a watermark to do work on it. Zhang and other research work focused on selecting different areas watermark, they chose the space domain, you can add a watermark in it anti-print scanning, due to the presence of the spatial domain pixel value is unstable, there is a big change characteristics, so to watermark to go through a complicated process. Lin (Lin) conducted a study on the Fourier transform his main research is the Fourier transform of the crop, rotate, zoom and other features, fragile watermarking research in the field, earlier research they conducted, the results of their study is the use of log-polar map, or log-log map the spatial Fourier transform coefficients, where the watermark, this approach can be effective against printing and scanning attacks. Li Gang, etc. Based on the study of binary drawing printed on the drawings, targeted text area made full use of the space, and then watermarked operating on this basis, then make the text area is divided into several blocks, watermark a numerical value determined by the characteristic amount value, which is the area of the 0/1 ratio of the feature quantity. Tada Xi (Tadashi Mizumoto) like the case of print scans were studied before and after comparison of the changes they studied drawing RGB values, because of the large differences in distress, the RGB values to make the watermark detection process, the presence of greater difficulty, they found that the watermark printing scan interference effects in the transform domain is relatively small, we can use this property to embed a watermark in the DCT coefficients of frequency, this watermark is robust watermarking. In the literature, based on the analysis of cattle less variety of situations, such as Akira and causes an impact study of print scan parties face in the drawing, and finally select the related operations on the drawing to embed watermarks in DCT domain.

PhotoShop is the most common and popular software engineering drawings related to processing, the software contains a certain watermark function, which is to add a watermark embedded program, this feature Digimarc developed by the department in terms of resistance to printing and scanning capabilities, the said functions can be embedded in a program or a certain effect, the drawback is that there is a watermark which can carry the limitations in the face of the geometric transformation processing of high sensitivity, which is mainly used for security watermarks. Photo Check software system developed by the company from Alp Vision is a watermark security algorithm, which implements the basic watermark content, mainly used in the protection of the passport, is the first to embed watermarks in the passport photo, when the use of a passport the use of certain detection method can determine.

Currently, most of the major engineering drawings for the general study of anti print scan watermarking algorithm, such as used in resident safety, is concentrated in the authentication process single photos. And comparing ordinary drawing can be found, drawing ordinary drawing do not have many features, the first is the existence of a simple texture detail its features, and the uneven distribution of texture detail. Further, on the whole, there is also a considerable area clean background areas, these areas are generally all white or substantially all white, medium and high frequency components in the flat region of the less available for the lack of sufficient redundancy embedded watermark space. But in practice a lot and takes a long time to save important documents, such as business engineering drawings, confidential documents, papers and so on in printed form to achieve its dissemination and use of function, this drawing is the need to protect their integrity. Therefore, we should study the characteristics and properties of engineering drawings to proceed, from the anti-print scan digital watermarking aspects related to the theory and technology of digital watermarking applications which in reality has important value and significance.

3 PRINT SCAN DISTORTION EFFECTS ON ENGINEERING DRAWINGS

3.1 Print impact caused on the drawing

Examine the current use of printing equipment; laser printers commonly used type of system. In essence, the current commonly used laser printers are dot-matrix printer attributes, which is characterized by the thickness of the drawing when you print, which utilizes a matrix of black and white dots in shades technologies they use halftone (Halftone).[1-3] Halftone technology, understand its essence is not to use all the colors, but to use a small amount of color to complete the performance of continuous-tone drawings. These drawings include grayscale drawings, colored drawings, speaking from the digital domain is to use part of the gray-tone drawings quantization operation, making the value of engineering drawings and in some cases can be done with a small number of similar multi-color color color engineering drawings, quantized, from visual effects to inspect, we will find the original drawing in the visual and quantified after drawing almost the same, there is no difference. This is because the human eye has a low-pass filter resistance, which can lead people in the halftone drawings of observation, the human eye can not consciously take the initiative to exist in the original part of incoherence between the pixel do obfuscated, so since, in the human eye, halftone and continuous tone drawings drawing little difference.

Tones[4-6] on a laser printer technology is accomplished by dithering. Principle of law is the basis of jitter in the drawing with the texture characteristics. Each single small part of the investigation on the drawing, with the texture similarity, pixel gray values are similar, it is a group of pixels to represent a set of print dots, the overall effect of these gray pixels of interest are employing visual space and integrated low-pass characteristics given. Typically, drawings and original output jitter law[7,8] broadly consistent with, and distortion often appears on local details. In practice, a composite halftone dot changes shape due to many factors, and diffusion, and absorption characteristics of the paper smoothness of the composite halftone dot like a laser beam or the like may also cause the output lead drawing blurred.

3.2 Drawing affected scanning process

Scanner scan quality is affected by many factors, greatly related technologies used in its own impact on the scan quality, the most important is the capacity and performance of sampling sensors. Sampling capability by A/D converter receiving the voltage coming from the sensor to obtain the size of the capacity-constrained. The technical conditions are now on the scanner electronics reflects the input light is essentially a linear manner to reflect, but on the human visual analysis, the human eye feels light and reflective recorded directly on the picture feels light, its is essentially a logarithmic curve. Located in a dark or dark drawing detail reflected light curve with the steepest characteristic, as a basis, can be different from the human eye to distinguish between true under the same circumstances, the scanner after processing, the result is the opposite can not distinguish different points may be the same. CCD sensors are generally used electronics to a flatbed scanner, the device CCD sensor area on the perception of the imaging optical lens, the image is scanned from a drawing after the resulting optical lens optical processing, CCD's main task is to carry out photoelectric conversion. Since the test from the, CCD scanner treatment process is a necessary condition to be wired lighting, as also its cost-ray imaging.

The scanner is scanning process, the first photoelectric conversion function using CCD analog drawings come after the A/D converted digital drawings. In the performance of the sensor sensitivity of the light to some extent by the individual CCD sensor cells, electrical isolation between the environment and the effects of noise isolation in the process of generation of noise in the sense that it is difficult to avoid, these noise generated from the electronic circuit element itself insurmountable nature is instability. The scanner on the distribution of the sampling points per unit area is determined by the scan resolution DPI, for a particular print engineering drawings, scanned using a resolution should be maintained at a high level, which would render the drawing in low resolution to a certain extent some local loss of detail, they may appear so confused and pitting on the scan output drawings. If the watermark in the drawing board put undesirable scanner, a deflection phenomenon occurs when the scanned drawing no consistency with the original, but this can still be utilized drawings, they may be considered is drawing process after printing engineering drawings, this pathway is to identify and deal with known, is the geometric transformation pathways, including rotation, translation and other means, but these maps also contain noise distortion scan maps.

4 FEATURES ANTI-INVARIANT VALUES BEFORE AND AFTER PRINTING AND SCANNING

Survival can be seen from the aforementioned characteristics and the digital watermark, the digital work includes a built-in particular a digital watermark in the dissemination process works, the communication process is often encountered in the operation of a conventional or modified encountered non-bona fide attack and destroy, when these situations occur, digital watermarking functionality and performance will be affected, its detection and extraction of the good features of this case should have a role would not normally occur. In general, have a good performance in the testing procedures and the extraction process digital watermarking scheme, while its digital watermark should also have better robustness, watermark information is embedded digital features used in digital multimedia carrier, in its nature has some commonality, some of their characteristics is being modified or and after comparison is not changed before the attack.

In contrast, some of their focus is not watermarking algorithm watermarks stability, and to focus on the vulnerability, which is embedded watermark is robust enough to be concerned about some of the digital watermarking algorithm, the watermark information they are placed in the field not those around the same characteristics, but the watermark is placed on the rear that is easy to modify or change the number of attacks of characteristics. This algorithm can achieve a function in terms of safety, that is, if the drawing has not been modified, it can be accurately related information is extracted, to a lesser extent once the modification is that the algorithm can not detect the watermark presence information, and more difficult to make the embedded watermark information extraction process it. In short, the watermarking algorithm, whether it is high robustness, or vulnerability, from the point of view of their design principles, the situation can change in a certain way by their carrier after being attacked out of the analysis, the focus changes after the attack vector data, the performance characteristics of the digital change. Embedded watermark information, usually from the start to find a digital feature, based on the characteristics needed to go first and then embedded information.

In general, similar changes are not occurring before and after the attack signatures looking up more laborious. Various anti print scan digital watermarking algorithm, the watermark robustness of performance in the case is the focus of their attention. Due to the mathematical model correction method print scanning process under attack, there are many to implement practical difficulties and problems, should use different print scans before and after comparisons and to analyze. Its goal is to find ways and may exist in this process does not occur or almost digital signature does not change, which is good for the design of robust algorithms, it is a crucial task.

In selecting the embedded domain, the high demand for robust digital watermark, the watermark is usually embedded in general will do the work in the transform domain, do not work on almost spatial domain, the kind of pixel values directly on the changes as a means to ensure the watermark robustness of the approach is very undesirable. We fully analyze geometric attacks based on the actual situation related field of digital engineering drawings before DFF domain coefficients have to maintain good stability characteristics constant, in other words, when subjected to translation, rotation, scale changes such the handling and operation of the coefficient is constant, for the above reasons, for which the DFT domain characteristics related work, the relevant figure is fully utilized in the field of the relevant anti-scan digital watermark printing programs designed more, and more innovative ideas. In addition, some studies have tried to print digital watermarking algorithm resistant design of scanning performance in the DCT domain, DWT domain.

If better print invariant feature scans before and after the attack can be found, the process of printing and scanning correction using a mathematical model is not necessary, if we can design a digital watermark to have good performance in terms of capacity, that capacity, then to a certain extent on the impact of a breakthrough in the field generated, in practice there will be a good application prospect. So, although the amount of calculation can be achieved in the field of watermarking algorithm miniaturization while facing feature selection requirement is high, is required to select those characteristics can be maintained constant. Current research in the field, there is another solution. It is characterized by the first printing scan process characterization, means for using the mathematical model is, to reduce the impact of the object by using the inverse process, is to reduce the impact of printing scans, the watermark extraction work is achieved by an algorithm preset, the algorithm is typically a robust algorithm. The program also has some shortcomings and bad problems, mainly reflected in the process may have a new distortion occurs, the timing appears in inverse correlation processing procedure, so the watermark detection and extraction of essential function will be to a certain extent, the role of the positive aspects of this technique is not very clear. We are in the process of designing watermarking method, using mathematical methods of distortion print scanning process will inevitably arise should be avoided, the best method is characterized by the use of digital printing and scanning unchanged before and after the embedded information.

Looking for a scan after the originals are still changing print features a design of robust digital watermarking algorithm necessary and crucial prerequisite of its decision whether or not to complete the performance and life of digital watermarking.

Production and living practices, experiments and related theoretical analysis shows that the spatial domain print scan drawings there is a big impact; examine the embedding of work from the way we will find space can be embedded only the spatial domain, transform domain we mainly on drawing transform domain coefficients due to printing and scanning and impact.

5 CONCLUSIONS

When analyzing the visual effects from the drawing, we will find on the drawing there is always some specific areas, which are large and have a consistent distribution characteristic property, which is one of the characteristics of the drawing. Such an area is generally the performance of all white, sometimes expressed as approximate all white.

The actual study, we noticed that the drawing is closely related to the quality and the quality printers and scanners to print scanned by further improving the robustness and watermark capacity and fitness in a small engineering environment is the block our future research directions.

ACKNOWLEDGMENT

This work is supported by Shandong Yingcai University key issues (13YCZDZR01).

REFERENCES

[1] A.M. Alattar. Smart Image Using Digimarc's Watermarking Technology. IS&T/SPIE's 12th International Symposium on Electronic Imaging. San Jose, California, 2000,3971(25),23–28

[2] Hsu Chiou-Ting, Wu Ja-Ling. Hiding digital watermarks in image[C]. IEEE Trans. On Image Processing, 2004, 8(1): 58–68.

[3] Tirkel A, Rankin G., Schyndel R van, Ho W, Mee N and Osbome C. Electronic watermark[C]. Proceedings DICTA 2003, 12(2):666–672.

[4] Guo Yunbiao, Lin daimao, Nu xiamu, Hu Lan and Zhou linna, A Secure Steganographic Scheme in Binary Image, IIHMSP'05, Lecture notes in computer science. 2005,9.

[5] Wong P.W. A watermark for image integrity and ownership verification. Portland OR: Proc. Of IS& PIC Conf., 2005.

[6] Fridrich J, Goljan M and Baldoza A.C. New fragile authentication watermark for images. Proc. ICIP, Vancouver, Canada, Sep, 2007:446–449.

[7] Nopporn and Sangiamkun W. Digital watermarking technique for image authentication by neighboring block similarity measure. Proc. IEEE Region 10 International on Electrical and Electronic Technology: 734~747.

[8] Li D-T. Oblivious fragile watermarking scheme for image authentication. IEEE, 2010: 3445~3448.

Computer, Intelligent Computing and Education Technology – Liu, Sung & Yao (Eds)
© 2014 Taylor & Francis Group, London, ISBN 978-1-138-02469-4

Study on the promotion of information level of archives in higher occupation colleges

Feng-Li Zhang
Environmental Management College of China, Qinhuangdao, Hebei, China

ABSTRACT: At present, generally higher level of information archives of ordinary colleges and Universities. The higher occupation colleges owing to the great gap compared to various reasons and information level of college archives, the important significance of archival information in Colleges and universities is expounded, the main factors of higher occupation college archives information is analysis, the enhancing the level of information archives in higher occupation colleges from aspects of the consciousness of archives information, infrastructure construction, the construction of archival information resources, the file personnel team construction is proposed in this paper

Keywords: higher vocational college; archives; information

1 THE SIGNIFICANCE OF ARCHIVES INFORMATION IN THE UNIVERSITY

With the rapid development of science and technology, we have entered a new era of information and network. It is strong impact and far-reaching influence to the archival work with the development of information construction. The traditional manual mode of archives management has been unable to meet the need of archives in the new era, a large number of electronic documents has been in the digital campus, a lot of photos, videos, images are produced from the modern digital devices, and the new challenges has been brought on these new media files, filing, storage used to archive work. Only to adapt to the new era of development, to speed up the construction of archival information, to meet the needs of users, the maximum for the school and the society to provide services, the healthy development of archival undertaking is promoted.

2 THE PRESENT SITUATION OF HIGHER OCCUPATION COLLEGES ARCHIVES INFORMATION

In recent years, the rapid development of higher occupation education in our country, the rapid growth in the number of schools, the school continues to expand the scale and the way of running school. The higher occupation colleges occupy half of the country in the whole higher education in quantity, the number of students, and has become an important part of higher education in china. At present, the majority of college archives information level is higher, the archives information level is still a considerable gap between the higher vocational colleges and universities. Impact of Higher Vocational Colleges archives not only higher occupation education, controlled also by its own conditions. Generally existing in archives information consciousness is not strong, not enough attention on the phenomenon of archives information, not thinking comprehensively and in-depth research on the construction of archives information. Though the computer management of archives is implemented in many higher vocational colleges, the archives management software are stand-alone version of network. The utilization of archives or operation are by manual primarily and are supplemented by computer operation. Archives information in most vocational colleges are incomplete, resulting in the collection is not rich, the construction of archival information resources is not high. Higher vocational colleges in the developing stage, many aspects of investment of fundamental construction of the campus, teachers team construction of archives construction, less investment, lack of funds, lack of management personnel, professional level is low, is the prominent problems in the construction of archives information in most higher vocational colleges.

3 THE MAIN FACTORS WHICH RESTRICT THE HIGHER OCCUPATIONAL COLLEGE ARCHIVES INFORMATION

The majority of our higher occupation colleges are upgraded from secondary occupation college or adult college. So the school history is generally shorter and the scale is generally small, there are many constraints, resulting in archives information construction is facing many problems and directly affects the college archives information.

3.1 Have no a strong sense of archives information in higher vocational college

Looking from the present situation, the archives do not been paid enough attention to in the vocational colleges, by the effect of "heavy teaching, light archives" traditional ideas, it is been thought the archives department not essential, not to mention the information construction in archives, archives information is also a job needs a lot of money, but slow, keep from talking about general leadership. Leadership only attach importance to teaching, scientific research, enrollment in the school influential sector, which provides services to archives work is said seriously, do not pay attention to. On the one hand, the leadership level do not pay attention to archives information, archives information will not be put on the annual plan, the school limited funds not be put to the construction of archival information, and archives information necessary equipment is not been perfected, archives information talent is shortage, resulting in archives information can not be carried out smoothly. On the other hand, the relevant departments and staff do not understand the file and has no consciousness of archives, and they think it doesn't matter with archives, so they do not give the archives work vigorously support. Again, because of the level of information of archives is limited for the archives working personnel, and have no the support of leaders and relevant departments, the slack mood will be produced, archives information consciousness is not strong. These three factors influence each other, resulting in higher Vocational Colleges archives information level is not high.

3.2 Academies are lack of investment and the infrastructure on archives promotion of information is insufficient

A complete set of modernizing facility is required on archives promotion of information, it not only includes hardware such as computer, printer, servicer and so on, but incudes the corresponding software such as files management software, kinds of data base, website etc. Because of lacking funds, the infrastructure on files promotion of information is not sufficient in academies. Although some computers, files management software have been equipped, it's just stand-alone and only can realize catalogues referring, simple recording by hands and so on. Even if the web edition has been installed, the files still can't be transmitted, utilized and shared.

3.3 Staffs on files promotion of information are shortage in academies

When listing facts use either the style tag List signs or the style tag List numbers. At present staffs on archives promotion of information are not enough. Besides they don't have good education and have little professional knowledge, which blocks the files information construction. The professional files management staffs who have no good education and low post always do several jobs at the same time and many of them have no opportunities to attend the professional training after they join the work. They are short of necessary theory knowledge about files and have no information technology. The management is just based on their experience for them. Professional staffs on files information who have good understand on files management are extremely demanded, the deficiency of them has hindered the progress of the files promotion of information in academies.

4 THE ANALYSIS ON THE SOLUTION OF SOLVING ARCHIVES PROMOTION OF INFORMATION

4.1 Strengthen guidance and enhance the sense of files promotion of information

Archives information is a basic job in academies. It's an important indicator for the academy education level and influence the comprehensive development of academies. The most significant mission of the academy leader is changing their idea and aware of the importance. On the one hand, with the attention of leaders, the construction of the files promotion of information will be supported at the human resource, material resources, financial resources and it will be carried out thoroughly. On the other hand, in order to make relevant departments and personnel know the importance of archives information, enhance their files promotion of information sense and develop their habit of settling files, the files department should strengthen the publication and receive the support from the workers. Besides, realizing their duty, changing their traditional working habit, learning new knowledge and skills and being a qualified files worker should be every archives workers' duty.

4.2 Increase the investment and strengthen the construction of the infrastructure

The NO.27 order of the Ministry of Education and State Archives Administration provides that academies should set up the special funds which are used to purchase the equipment of the files information and modernization and guarantee the construction of the files promotion of information will be synchronized with the digitization of school. According to the document, the special funds should be set every year and ensure the construction. When the files departments buy new equipment, the demand and funds should be considered and it would be better to buy those with high cost performance. And the related management software, database and website should be introduced at the same time.

4.3 Strengthening the construction of archival information resources

Archive information resource construction is the core and foundation of archives information construction. The difference between higher vocational colleges and the ordinary universities is the major setup with industrial characteristics. Vocational colleges main to train application-oriented talents, hence, higher vocational colleges should focus on establishing professional focused majors and excellent courses to reflect the database files with characteristic of schools. Stepping up efforts to the collection of archives data, focusing on collecting archives data which reflect its school-running characteristics and major characteristics. Optimize the structure of library, enriched the contents of the collection; and besides digitizing the existing paper files which are precious, fragile and high vulnerability. On the basis of the establishment of library file directory, archives management facilitates the construction of full-text database, multimedia database and the special database step by step, do basic support for the construction of the archives information construction.

4.4 Speed up the construction of archives information talents

In The Information Era, archival datas need to use modern information equipment, technology and method to receive, store and provide use for it. Archives management mode changed dramatically. Archives management is no longer a simple sense of the archives management. Archives informatization is a highly technical work. The level of archivists of archives information construction has a close relationship with the success or failure. Higher vocational colleges should introduce archives management professional and computer professional talents to inject new forces to the archives management. At the same time support the archivists to universities and colleges of undergraduate course major of archives for further study, regularly organized archivists out for investigation research, actively participate in training courses to learn more things of archives information. Archivists optimize the knowledge structure through learning, communication, training methods, etc. File workers are becoming inter-disciplinary talents of new era, who are not only has file professional knowledge but also master the modern information technology.

4.5 Establish archives information website construction

As the network has become more and more popular, higher vocational colleges establish archives information web site by making full use of campus network. Archives information is an important window for archives and is based on archives website construction as a platform. We should take an active part in carry out archives information posted online. The services such as query the file information on the Internet, remote directory search on the net, etc, will be an important form for archives department to provide services. Archives website transmit, manage and use of the electronic documents on the internet, digitalize the archival information, automate the archives management and networking the service of archives.

In a word, archives information is in the developing stage in higher vocational colleges, is a long-term and arduous task. Due to the history of each school is different, no fixed pattern for reference, archive departments in higher vocational colleges can only continue to explore and sum up experience. Out of a file of information for their own road of development of the schools.

ACKNOWLEDGEMENT

Corresponding author: Yan-Xia LIU, Environmental Management College of China, E-mail: 109483131@qq.com.

REFERENCES

[1] Fengli Zhang. Some reflections on file information construction [J]. Magnificent Writing, 2013(3):305.
[2] Jie Liang. The Practice of Information Construction of Teachers' Professional Files in Vocational Colleges [J]. Luzhou Vocational and Technical College, 2010(2):53–56.

[3] Meiqiong Chen. The Status of Files Information of Colleges and Universities in Information Society and Its Countermeasures [J]. Journal of Fuqing Branch of Fujian Normal University, 2009(3):27–30.

[4] Jinguan Chen. Taent Cultivation Model for Archives Information Construction [J]. Zhejiang Archives, 2003.10.

[5] Suying Xu. Discussion on Enterprise Archives Work [J]. Science and Technology Information, 2010(29):613.

Computer, Intelligent Computing and Education Technology – Liu, Sung & Yao (Eds)
© 2014 Taylor & Francis Group, London, ISBN 978-1-138-02469-4

Teaching design of "discrete mathematics" for information security in police colleges

Jian-Ying Xiong
Department of Public Security Technology, Jiangxi Police College, Jiangxi, China

ABSTRACT: The paper is focus on exploring teaching methods for basic theory courses to application-oriented in public security school. Through a comprehensive analysis of discrete mathematics courses, we know its basic knowledge structure, and believed that it has an important status in information security professional teaching at public security university. A combination teaching model was proposed based on the features of the major and the characteristics of the curriculum structure. Under the context of public security, we introduce case teaching, experimental teaching, and importing learning to stimulate students' interest in learning. Teaching practice result shows that it has improved learning efficiency significantly and can expand their knowledge.

Keywords: discrete mathematics; public security school; information security; teaching mode

1 INTRODUCTION

With the development of information society, information security problems caused by people's attention, especially information security under computer network environment. In order to adapt to the needs of public security work under new situation, and the national Twelfth Five-Year Development Plan, information security professionals as a new major of public security school, is aim to train application-oriented and senior specialized technical personnel who related to network information security. They should need a solid basic computer-related expertise, information technology, network security, and computer crime [1].

Discrete mathematics is not only a basic curriculum of computer science in common college, but also an important theoretical course of computer-related profession in the public security institutions. The main contents of the course includes mathematical logic, sets and relations, algebraic systems, and graph theory. The study is characterized by discrete data objects, data representation, and the relationship between mathematics and other analytical content. The course has much concept, high abstract, closely logical connection between the chapters, and a special characteristics of reasoning, that induce a difficult for students to understand and master [2]. "Discrete Mathematics" as the basis of theory, has a relatively simple teaching methods, is difficult for student to learn, and a low efficiency to teach. Although information security professionals are computer-related professional, but compared with the pure computer science and

technical expertise, it is more targeted at police information quality education [3]. Discrete mathematics as the professional basic courses needs to highlight the usefulness through the teaching process. The teaching content and teaching methods must reflect the needs of professional features. It should combined with the characteristics of the knowledge module and professional specialty, and help students to fully develop self-confidence, stimulate interest in learning, improve ability to learn, expand the application level [4]. Aiming at the characteristics of the course, the paper analyzes the value of the course in professional knowledge system, combined teaching experience and student interest, summed up a set of suitable teaching methods of the courses in public security institutions. It fully integrated police-related cases in teaching, such as cases reasoning, encryption and decryption. By analyzing the characteristics of each part of the teaching content, we introduce case guiding to combine theoretical knowledge with professional application, which prove that the teaching effectiveness has improved significantly in practice.

2 COURSE ANALYSIS

2.1 *Application analysis*

Discrete mathematics is important to the study of computer science, which combines discrete mathematics questions about computer science. The course includes mathematical logic, sets and relations, algebraic systems and graph theory.

1. Mathematical logic: it is the key for computer logic design; mathematical logic can be used to symbolic calculus, formula derivation, game playing. And the problems such as event troubleshooting, and proving the correctness of the program is also inseparable from mathematical logic.
2. Sets and relations: it is important to programming, data structures, database, information retrieval, algorithm design, and computer theory. For example, characteristic function to describe a collection of elements is the basic of fuzzy theory; partial ordering relation can sort out the chain of evidence.
3. Algebraic system: it is constructed using the method of mathematical model algebra. It has a practical significance for computer program theory, data structures, data security, coding theory, and logic circuit design.
4. Graph theory: it can be used to transport network, set theory and matrix theory, etc. in the field of computer science, graph theory is important to organizational theory and logic design of the switch, artificial intelligence, computer graphics, operating systems, compiler writing and information Search.

2.2 *Professional value analysis*

Discrete Mathematics is specialist and different from mathematics and other basic mathematics. It has closely ties with the follow professional courses in the profession of network security. It is not only the preorder courses of data structures, operating systems, compiler theory and digital logic, but also play an important role to train students in computer science logical reasoning and abstract thinking ability. As the Figure 1, discrete mathematics courses which with a typical professional basic feature, supporting multi-professional courses. The degree of students master the curriculum has a direct impact on teaching effectiveness of other professional courses.

In addition, discrete mathematics is widely used mathematical methods. In short, it permeates

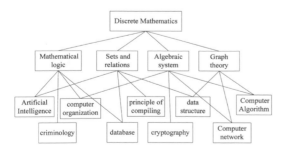

Figure 1.   The connection between the courses.

all aspects of network and computer-related technology. It occupies an important and prominent position in information security knowledge system in public security school. But it has much concept, involves more theoretical and stronger abstract, which made students learning hardly than higher mathematics, and never see the specific application in computer science. Students don't pay attention to the course, so how to improve the education efficiency has outstanding significance for the undergraduate teaching.

3   TEACHING METHODS

After the analyzing the professional status and knowledge systems of discrete mathematics, we should to emphasize the need to learn the course in the teaching process, and combined with the characteristics of each knowledge module. Some teaching methods are adopted in the class as follows.

3.1 *Case teaching*

Introduction of case teaching that not only can help students self-learning ability, but also contribute to the practical problems objective to form abstract mathematical model, and cultivate academic thinking habits to develop mathematical models. Throughout the body of knowledge, mathematical logic, relations, and graph theory have stronger practical application. So introduce some interest cases after students understand and master the basic concept will not only expand knowledge points, but also have a deepen understanding of the knowledge and methods [5].

Especially for police officers, the case reasoning also needs to use mathematical logical knowledge.

Use an Instructional Case Example: police officers heard a jewelry store theft of a diamond necklace, known reconnaissance results are as follows:

1. A or B salesperson stealing a diamond necklace.
2. If B is crime, then the crime time is not in Business hours.
3. If the testimony provided by A is correct, then the container is unlocked.
4. If the testimony of A is incorrect, then the crime occurred during business hours.
5. The container is locked.

Let p: A is crime, q: B is crime, r: committed crimes during business hours, s: testimony provided by A is correct, t: container is locked
Premise: $p \vee q$, $q \rightarrow \neg r$, $s \rightarrow \neg t$, $\neg s \rightarrow r$, t

1. $s \rightarrow \neg t$
2. t
3. $\neg s$ 1) and 2) refusing to take formula

4. ¬ s → r
5. r   3) and 4) Hypothetical reasoning
6. q → ¬ r
7. ¬ q   5) and 6) refused to take the formula
8. p ∨ q
9. p   7) and 8) disjunctive syllogism

3.2 *Knowledge extension method*

Importing method can help teachers paving the way to teach new knowledge. It is a method that teachers use a variety of teaching methods to stimulate students' curiosity, open students' thinking in order to introduce new teaching content according to the psychological characteristics of students and teaching objectives. The common way including: design problems, tell story and so on.

Use an Instructional Import Example: When teachers teach graph theory, use Hamilton map to solve problem.

If seven cases are arranged to trial within seven days, the case dealt with same judge can't be ranked in consecutive two days. How to prove that if there is no more than four cases dealt by same judge, the trial arrangement meets the above requirements is always possible.

Let G be a graph has seven nodes, and each node corresponds to one case. If any two nodes corresponding cases are served by a different judge, then there is an edge between two nodes. Because each judge is responsible for no more than four cases, the degree of each node is at least 3, and therefore the degree of any two nodes and at least six, so there is always a Hamilton G pathway, which corresponds to an appropriate arrangement in seven cases. Use the follow graph as an example, each node has at least 3 degree, if each node only has 3 degree, then 3 times 7 is 21, according to Handshake theorem, at least one node should greater than or equal to 4, as the node 3 has 4 degree, the Hamilton pathway is as the Dotted line marked.

3.3 *Knowledge expansion method*

Currently, many algorithms is related to discrete mathematics, such as rough set attribute reduction are on the basis of the indistinguishable relationship, which is an equivalence relation; the nature of the Caesar cipher is group theory; Euler's theorem is the mathcmatical basis of RSA cryptography; ant colony optimization algorithm which is a combination of algorithms used to solve problems in graph theory Hamilton circuit. In the teaching process teacher should be appropriate to extend knowledge, that can extend the students' knowledge structure, to understand the whole preface disciplines and computer networks, strengthen confidence in the professional learning.

3.4 *Frontier expansion method*

Problem in many frontier police also need to use theoretical knowledge of discrete mathematics, for example, Grujičić use graph theory to design an emergency program optimal resource supply for special forces of the Republic of Serbia [6]; Khalid has used network flow knowledge to control and improve traffic [7]; Meng has used graph theory approach to traffic patrol, and police services platform locating problem [8].

Use a Suspicious place searching route example as shown in Figure 3. Several locations are approximate geographical location connected marked by transit time. And we can use a graph to describe it as Figure 4.

Figure 3.   Actual time cost between each location.

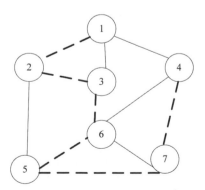

Figure 2.   Use Hamilton to model the example.

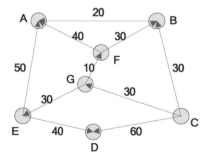

Figure 4.   Description of graph.

If the police want to search every place in a shortest time, it is a traveling salesman problem; if the police is at one place, and want to go to other place in a short time, it is a shortest path problem.

3.5 *Frontier expansion method*

Discrete Mathematics is a highly abstract, highly summarized, strong logical theory courses, students are often difficult to understand. If introduce the appropriate experimental exercise in the course of teaching, which can be specifically verify basic theory, but also lay the foundation and cultivate students' practical ability and innovation ability. Combined with information security professional training direction, different experiment content is designed according to the teaching content. Students can use the C language to exercise these experiments, and can be discussed by cooperation or by grouping completed.

4 TEACHING EVALUATION

Teaching effectiveness evaluation is carried out to determine its direct role in all aspects of teaching and learning activities, is an important part of the teaching work. Effective implementation of teaching evaluation is an important means to promote the continuous development of students,

Table 1. Experiment content.

Content of chapter	Experiment
Mathematical logic	A lie detector
Closure operation or connected graph	Warshall algorithm
Partial order relation	Job scheduling problem
Graph theory	Traffic flow calculation
Tree	Huffman coding

Table 2. Evaluation result.

Evaluation content	A	B
1. Whether course has practical value	32.5%	77.5%
2. It will help other professional course learning	37.5%	82.5%
3. The course is helpful to exercise your mind	37.5%	75%
4. The course is difficult	85%	52.5
5. Course learning efficiency is improved	–	75%

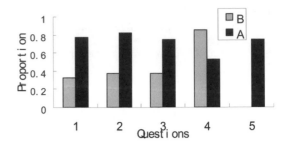

Figure 5. Compared result.

more progressive and continuous improvement of teachers' teaching practice. In order to evaluate the impact on student learning bring by teaching methods, a question questionnaire is designed as Table 2 according to the curriculum for students to understand. Teaching process is divided into two segments A and B. A segment is a status using ordinary teaching methods, B segment is a status use improving teaching methods, the survey results show that the improved teaching methods of teaching to bring significant results as the compared in Figure 5.

5 CONCLUSIONS

Discrete mathematics of Information security professionals must highlight the basic features as a public security profession. It should focus on the application of mathematical knowledge and appropriate weakening proof of the fundamental principles and theorem. Teaching should combined with professional features to arrange teaching content; complemented by experimental and a variety of interactive teaching model to effectively improve students' ability; so that it will improve logical thinking and analytical skills to solve practical problems. In this paper, we adopt various methods including case introduction method, knowledge extension method, expanding the frontiers of knowledge to improve student learning method proactive, to develop students' awareness of innovation. And combined with professional features to design experiments to highlighting the practical aspects, improve application awareness.

ACKNOWLEDGEMENTS

The research is supported by Jiangxi education planning project "student's police information ability training of the public security school under police informationization environment."

REFERENCES

[1] Hui Wang, Binjun Wang. reform of discrete mathematics curriculum teaching for major of Network security and law enforcement, Journal of Chinese People's Public Security University (Science and Technology), 2012. no. 2

[2] Xu Zhoubo, Gu Tianlong, Discussion on Case Teaching of Discrete Mathematics Bascd on OBDD, Computer Education, 2010. no. 2

[3] Epp, Susanna S. Discrete mathematics with applications. CengageBrain. com, 2010.

[4] Holmquist, Mikael, and Thomas Lingefjard. "Mathematical modelling in teacher education." Mathematical Modelling in Education and Culture ICTMA10 (2003): 197–208.

[5] Xue Zhan-ao, Qi Ge, Du Hao-cui, Li Xia, Research on the Classroom-import Method of the Discrete Mathematics, Computer Education, 2010. no, 8.

[6] Grujičić, Igor, and Zorica Stanimirović. "Variable neighborhood search method for optimizing the emergency service network of police special forces units." Electronic Notes in Discrete Mathematics 39 (2012): 185–192.

[7] Khalid, Mohd Sazali, Tan Lai Wai, and Tutut Herawan. "Road Traffic Engineering Application in Mathematics Information Technology." Proccdia-Social and Behavioral Sciences 59 (2012): 204–211.

[8] Meng, Ji Xian, and Xin Zhong Lu. "The Application of Graph Theory Method in the Problem of Traffic Patrol Police Service Platform's Site Selection." Applied Mechanics and Materials 246 (2013): 723–727.

Computer, Intelligent Computing and Education Technology – Liu, Sung & Yao (Eds)
© 2014 Taylor & Francis Group, London, ISBN 978-1-138-02469-4

How can beginners grasp the tennis forehand and backhand batting techniques more quickly

X.W. Sun

Shandong Transport Vocational College, Weifang, China

ABSTRACT: Forehand and backhand technology is the basic skills of tennis, for tennis beginners, can quickly and accurately grasp the forehand and backhand batting technique is very important, it can rapidly enhance confidence for beginners. Method and essentials of this paper introduces the tennis forehand and backhand batting, and puts forward some reference suggestions, provide a theoretical reference for beginners training.

Keywords: forehand and backhand technology; tennis beginners; enhance confidence

Tennis is not only very popular and fun but also an elegant sport. Playing tennis tennis symbolizes civilization, elegance and grace. Being a kind of enjoyment, batting a nice ball each time will make people excited, happy and clinking. It is not only a kind of entertainment and a kind of way to promote health, but also a kind of artistic pursuit and enjoyment, of course an exciting sport. The tennis movement benefits someone directly, for example: tennis is suitable for different age and aerobic exercise; tennis being a net movement, without body contact, does not injure people; in addition to the above benefits, playing tennis minimizes the distance between lovers and friends. In modern society, people's work and life pressure is relatively large, and tennis is precisely physical exercise, mental and physical pleasure to release the pressure and to make friends.

Playing tennis has many benefits, but is not like beginners of the sports of badminton and table tennis, relatively slow and easy to use. If beginners play them a little, they can rapidly improve skills and self-confidence. Tennis ball being quickly, it is not easy to use, which makes many beginners give up learning tennis. I think we should first understand the technology and beginners learning methods and steps of tennis, step by step to determine their confidence in learning. Forehand and backhand technology is the basic skills of tennis, and it is first important for beginners to master the technology. Here are the two movement technique and way to practice in my own ideas.

1 FOREHAND

1.1 *The preparatory position*

Preparatory position (with the right hander as an example, the same below): face the net, legs open, slightly wider than shoulders, keep your feet a little fretting, and pay attention that the feet cannot jump at the same time, upper body slightly forward, the focus on the front foot. The right hand with the continental (inside of the racket face perpendicular to the ground plane on the left edge) light grip handle, the left hand to hold the racket throat, arms bent a shot in the chest, racket head higher than racket handle. Looking at the practice direction, it is important to relax the body, shoulder and grip, hard into the swing smoothly.

1.2 *Grip and pace*

The eyes focus on the ball to judge the trajectory and rotation mode of the ball in advance. When judged as the forehand to ball and placement, the left hand adjust to board surface, at the same time the feet start, moving the ball back.

1.2.1 *Forehand grip*

There are four main ways to grip the racket: Continental style, Eastern style, Western style, Ultra-Western style. It is recommended for beginners to hit the ball with Western grip. Supposed that the racket face assumed by perpendicular to the ground plane on the left edge of 1 edge is a continental grip, then east mouth on 2 edges, western style on the 3 edges. Tennis forehand is topspin. Topspin translation is not simple in the air movement, but rotates forward. It is easy to control topspin, and the ball over the net after the fall of it. The ground bounce angle of the ball is small and has a big forward momentum, so the ball is not easy to get out the line. Beginners may hit the ball to net at the beginning because of the body coordination.

1.2.2 Footpaces and judgment

It is best to swing relatively fixed arm action in forehand and backhand for beginners. That is to say when the ball and the ball distance is relatively fixed, the beginners adjust the distance between the ball and racket in pace and pace. It is also crucial to judge the ball rotation, which determines the pace moving direction and distance. If it is the backspin ball after landing, a sharp deceleration, the beginners move to a landing place. If it is the topspin ball after landing, moving forward to the fall behind.

1.3 Paces and racket

After judging the ball rotation rapidly, move in place to the judgment and adopt the semi open stance straight racket.

1.3.1 Semi open

When batting, move the body center of gravity from left to right. When all the focus moving to the right leg, left leg move to the front angle of 45 ° mobile and stabilize the body from the foot on the ground, simultaneously turn the body to the right rear axle on the right shoulder to hip, shoulder rotation of 90 degrees, hip rotation of 45 degrees, two shoulders lined vertically with the net, left hand pointing to the direction of the ball, then the left knee bending right knee ratio, lowering the center of gravity to the lowest point.

1.3.2 Racket

Direct racket can have more control, in shorter time, to generate higher racket head speed around the racket. Although the surround racket can increase the head speed, the racket head control and time will be affected. It is recommended for beginners to straight racket. When the pace in place, with the mobile semi open stance of center of gravity, and the right hand to right rear straight racket, racket handle pointing to the direction of the ball, racket head slightly higher than that of the handle, the wrist moving back, the arm took the handle, elbow bending 150 degrees.

1.4 Stroke and follow through

Beginners should hit the ball bounce after falling, adjusting with the ball distance well, acting from the right leg, gravity transiting from right leg to left leg, hip, shoulder and arm swinging the ball after batting direction, follow through to the top of the left shoulder, then the center of gravity to the left leg, the body pointing towards the net.

1.4.1 Arm

In the arms swing to hit the ball, maintain the elbow to the racket as far as possible when the angle, the ball after the elbow close shot and left shoulder.

1.4.2 Wrist

Hit a ball in the back of the wrist to keep constant to reduce wrist force. That is to say the swing force is transferred to the arm up, not the wrist, which will also help control the racket. The wrist shot rotates according to the position of the ball turns in the cross section to produce friction between the racket and the ball. But beginners should also pay attention to the forward of the racket before batting power, guaranteeing the force of batting.

1.4.3 Batting point

In order to control the ball better, the batting point must be controlled a relatively fixed distance to the body. The batting point is in front of the body, left toe parallel to the line.

2 BACKHAND

2.1 Ready position

The preparatory position agrees with the forehand. Beginners are recommended to use two handed backhand.

2.2 Grip and pace

The eyes focus on the ball to judge the ball trajectory and the ball rotation mode in advance. When judged as the backhand ball and ball placement, move feet to the rear of the ball.

2.2.1 Backhand grip

Beginners adopt Continental Style. When judging the ball flying towards your backhand direct, grip left hand quickly to help your right hand into the backhand grip. If acting from the ready position without adjustment, grip the handle on the right above the left hand.

2.2.2 Footpace and judgment

paces agree with the forehand. When the distance of the ball and the body is relatively fixed, beginners need to assure the ball rotation and ball distance.

2.3 Pace and racket

Judge the rotation of the ball rapidly then move in place and straight racket in the closed stance.

2.3.1 Closed pace
On the left axis, turn to the left rear shoulder to hip, left foot to 90 degrees to the left and bottom line parallel, weight decrease, song left knee, and the right leg to leg transition, while the right foot left front, left, center left, right in front of the net.

2.3.2 Racket
Rotate left rear turning the shoulder and hip to drive the right hand to the left rear racket, sucking in stomachs, at the same time left hand holding the right hand above the handle, wrist taut, back, shoulders and clamping, the upper right hand thumb near the left leg, the handle pointing to the direction of the ball, swing the elbow naturally bending about 150 degrees. Backhand backswing movements should be better than the forehand swing.

2.4 Stroke and follow through

Beginners should grip the racket from the racket to forward waving hands, wrist fixed, from the left, center of gravity transiting from left leg to right leg, turn the shoulders, torso and hip simultaneously, and swing forward. After batting the follow through transiting to the right shoulder above, the focus falls on the right leg, the body faces to the net, the whole process of center of gravity and swing trajectory turns up to the highest point.

2.4.1 Arms
Before swinging to hit the ball, maintain the angle of the elbow to the racket as far as possible and hit the ball after the elbow close shot and right shoulder. Based on the left arm force in the whole process of batting, right arm controls the direction and stability.

2.4.2 Wrist
Wrist remains unchanged up down and left arm pushes force forward, which can reduce the wrist force and help to control the racket. The wrist shot rotates in the cross section according to the rotation and position of the ball. It is recommended for beginners here to backhand face to open (perpendicular to the ground) in the flat.

2.4.3 Batting point
Due to the sending of hands to bat the ball, forwarding distance is shorter than the forehand a little, so backhand batting point slightly backword and closer to the body than forehand batting point, but the distance of batting point of and the body is relatively fixed. The batting point stands in front of the body and the right foot toe parallels to the line.

3 THE BACKHAND BATTING PRACTICE METHODS AND STEPS

It is vitally important for beginners to pick out practice methods and steps. Beginners exercising pace by pace can help the movement pattern. Only in this way can beginners grasp the batting skills better.

3.1 Pace training methods and steps

As is already mentioned above, pace is one of the basic skills of tennis. The batting point and body distance are maintained invariant, so pace is the foundation to master and use batting technology.

3.1.1 Ability training
Beginners practice pace ability through the high leg lift, running small pace, folding legs run, cross pace, running small pace crossing line.

3.1.2 Footpace
Beginners can make the coordination and grasp the rhythm of footpaces through around mobile and swinging practice.

3.2 Batting practice and procedure in place

Batting in place is vital to fixed swing.

3.2.1 Batting the ball in advance
First beginners racket ball well, tossing the ball at the batting point and letting the ball fall free. Practitioners see the ball ball bounce and fall and then bat the ball.

3.2.2 Preparatory batting posture in advance
After acquainted with preparatory batting posture, beginners can wait for batting the ball from preparatory position in place.

3.3 Tossing ball practice before batting

After the patterning of batting in place and racketing quickly, beginners can practice batting ball through tossing in the side of the front three meters, ball straight and forward, making them feel meeting the ball.

3.3.1 Bracketing the ball stably at batting point
Tossers try to throw the ball accurately, so that practitioners can racket or pace from the preparatory position directly or adjusting lightly.

3.3.2 Racketing the ball from tossing point un-fixedly

Tossers gradually adjust the falling placement of the ball, letting the practitioners pace and racket lead shot, return rapidly after batting the ball.

3.3.3 Distance adjustment of tossing ball

The distance between the practicer and tosser should be adjusted to increase the tossing speed gradually, so that practitioners gradually increase the speed of judgment and the paces to the ball.

3.4 Net ball feeding practices and procedures

Net ball feeding practices are in a practice swing set and mastering the basic pace and the racket.

3.4.1 Feeding ball directed spin

Tossers feed the ball in the net with the racket batting bottom rubbing, letting the ball slightly downward, so that the ball forward at slow speed after landing, paying attention that the ball should be paid to in place.

3.4.2 Suspension feeding ball un-fixedly

After the master 3.4.1, beginners can master the forehand and backhand batting technique through the usage of feeding ball with the change of speed and depth. They can improve the practice efficiency and change with the help of the tossers.

3.5 Forehand and backhand batting practice to the wall

Batting practice to the wall is a good method for beginners only, which is adopted after the patterning set of pace.

3.5.1 Practice to the wall initially

It is very effective for beginners to practice to the wall, but as the ball trajectory and preparatory time is short, so it is difficult to control the ball. The beginners practicing to the wall can let the racket face open, continuous practice forehand or backhand, and away from the wall of 4 meters or not too far away, try not to force, swing amplitude should not be too much, so beginners can face the wall half turn, let the racket time fuller.

3.5.2 Skilled and control

After mastering 3.5.1, beginners can increase and the distance of the wall and the force of batting the ball and control the height of hitting wall using rotation of the ball. Beginners can also transform your backhand and forehand alternately based on their own idea. This is the way to practice topspin better.

4 CONCLUSION

In a word, for beginners, to establish confidence in yourself is the first step. Only the correct grasp of the forehand and backhand batting technique, in order to constantly improve their own self-confidence, In the good sense of self, the premise, you can enjoy the play, play their style.

REFERENCES

[1] JF Wang. Analysis of tennis forehand stroke technique difficulties[J]. Journal of Xi'an Aviation Technology College. 2010 (1).
[2] 《Tennis》 magazine. Tennis technology solutions[M]. Beijing: People's Sports Press. 2004.
[3] XK Wei. Ethnic Colleges and universities public sports course. BeiJing. Beijing Sport University press. 2005(8).
[4] Zhw Jiang. Research on increasing the flat serve success rate[J]. Sports Science. 2000(7).

The relationship between Facebook use and psychological well-being: An example of Taiwan college students

Wei-Hsin Hsu
National Chengchi University, China

Sen-Chi Yu
National Taichung University of Education, China

Min-Ning Yu
National Chengchi University, China

Wen-Ping Lan
National Taichung University of Education, China

Lung-Ching Shie
Taichung Municipal Chongde Junior High School, China

ABSTRACT: The main purpose of this study was to investigate the correlations between Psychological Well-Being (PWB) and three measures of Facebook usages (Facebook usage time, FUT; number of Facebook friends, NFF; and Facebook Psychological Involvement Scale, FPIS). The sample comprised 1135 college students (463 male, 672 female) from 17 universities in Taiwan. The analytical results showed that the structural equation coefficient of FPIS-PWB were much significantly stronger than those of FUT-PWB and NFF-PWB. These finding all indicated that using Facebook may associate with some positive psychological outcomes. FPIS is a better indicator of Facebook usage since FPIS combined both qualitative and quantitative elements of Facebook usage such as psychologically salience of Facebook, emotional support and recreation of Facebook.

Keywords: Facebook; psychological well-being; structural equation modeling

1 INTRODUCTION

Social Network Sites (SNS), equipped with various functions such as email, blog and instant messaging, are essential for internet users. The most popular SNS in recent years is Facebook. 89% of social network site users had a Facebook account (Yu, Hsu, Yu, & Hsu, 2012).

Some research had shown that Facebook usage had some positive psychological consequences, such as subjective well-being and social capital (Ellison, Steinfield, & Lampe, 2007). However, the correlation between Facebook usage and Psychological Well-Being (PWB) was rarely investigated. Besides, most studies have adopted usage time and number of Facebook friends as variables to measure Facebook usage (Ross, et al., 2009). However, Facebook usage time is difficult to measure accurately since it can easily be confounded with total time spent online. Additionally, number of Facebook friend is subject to memory bias. To measure Facebook usage more accurately, Yu et al. (2012)

developed and validated the Facebook Psychological Involvement Scale (FPIS) which combined both qualitative and quantitative elements of Facebook usage. The main purpose of this study was to investigate the correlations between PWB and three measures of Facebook usages (usage time, number of Facebook friends, and FPIS).

The hypotheses of this study are as follows:

H1. The regression coefficient between FPIS and PWB is higher than the coefficient between Facebook Usage Time (FUT) and PWB.

H2. The regression coefficient between FPIS and PWB is higher than the coefficient between Number of Facebook Friends (NFF) and PWB.

2 METHODS

2.1 *Measures*

2.1.1 *Psychological Well-Being Scale (PWBS)*
This study used the Psychological Well-Being Scale (PWBS) developed by Yu, Hsieh, Lin, Chen, and

Tseng (2011). The theoretical foundation of PWBS was based on Ryff's (1989) psychological well-being theory. The PWBS is 18-item, five-pointed, and comprised six factors: self-acceptance, positive relations with others, autonomy, environmental mastery, purpose in life, and personal growth.

Concerning the psychometric properties of the PWBS in this study, the Cronbach's α was 0.890, indicating good reliability. The analytical results of Confirmatory Factor Analysis (CFA) showed good data-model fit (chi-square = 1343.260, df = 128, p = 0.000, CFI = 0.942, RMSEA = 0.0915, 90% CI [0.0871, 0.0960], SRMR = 0.0791), indicating good validity.

2.1.2 Facebook Psychological Involvement Scale (FPIS)

This study used the the Facebook Psychological Involvement Scale (FPIS) developed by Yu et al. (2012). The FPIS is 27-item, four-pointed, and comprised three factors: salience, involvement in emotional support of Facebook, and involvement in Facebook recreation.

Concerning the psychometric properties of the PWBS in this study, the Cronbach's alpha was 0.899, indicating good reliability. The analytical results of Confirmatory Factor Analysis (CFA) showed good data-model fit (χ^2 = 2497.909, df = 316, p = 0.000, CFI = 0.940, RMSEA = 0.078, 90% CI [0.0752, 0.0809], SRMR = 0.0756), indicating good validity.

2.1.3 Facebook usage behaviour scale

This scale was used to measure length of time spent on the internet and Facebook per day, and number of Facebook friends.

2.2 Sample

The sample comprised 1135 college students (463 male, 672 female) from 17 universities in Taiwan.

3 RESULTS AND DISCUSSIONS

This study applied Structural Equation Modeling (SEM) by LISREL 8.80 software to analyze the data. Conventional linear regression approaches can be accurately applied to only variables without measurement error. If the variables are latent, namely with measurement error, Structural Equation Modeling (SEM) is a better solution than regression (Yu, Lin, & Hsu, 2013). In SEM, the structural equation coefficient with standardized solution is similar to standardized regression coefficients but more accurate. The analytical results of SEM were shown in Figure 1 and Figure 2.

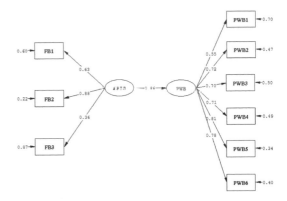

Figure 1.   Structural equation coefficient of FPIS-PWB.

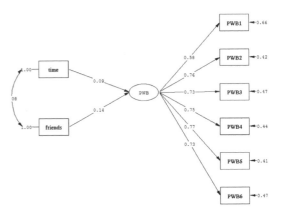

Figure 2.   Structural equation coefficients of FUT-PWB and NFF-PWB.

As shown in these Tables, the structural equation coefficient between FPIS and PWB, FUT and PWB, and NFF and PWB were 0.86, 0.09, and 0.014, respectively. The analytical results showed that the structural equation coefficient of FPIS-PWB were much significantly stronger than those of FUT-PWB and NFF-PWB. Therefore, the hypothesis H1 and H2 were verified.

The analytical results showed that FPIS positively correlated with PWB, this result was similar to Ross et al. (2009) and Hew (2011). Ross et al. found Facebook usage correlate with subject well-being. These finding all indicated that using Facebook may associate with some positive psychological outcomes.

The analytical results also found the correlations of FUT-PWB and NFF-PWB were positive but weak. We argued that some Facebook friends were acquaintances or nod friends, seldom provided social or emotional support. Therefore, correlation of NFF-PWB was only 0.14, a weak association.

As for the correlation of FUT-PWB is also weak with a value of 0.09, we argued that Facebook usage time is difficult to measure accurately since it can easily be confounded with total time spent online. On the contrary, FPIS is a better indicator of Facebook usage since FPIS combined both qualitative and quantitative elements of Facebook usage such as psychologically salience of Facebook, emotional support and recreation of Facebook.

ACKNOWLEDGMENT

The authors would like to thank the National Science Council of Taiwan (R.O.C) financially supporting this research under Contract No. NSC 101-2511-S-142-009-MY2 and NSC-99-2511-S-142-009-MY3.

REFERENCES

Ellison, N.B., Steinfield, C., & Lampe, C. (2007). The benefits of Facebook "friends:" Social capital and college students' use of online social network sites. *Journal of Computer-Mediated Communication, 12*(4), 1143–1168. doi: 10.1111/j.1083-6101.2007.00367.x.

Hew, F.K. (2011). Students' and teachers' use of Facebook. *Computers in Human Behavior, 27*(2), 662–676. doi: 10.1016/j.chb.2010.11.020.

Ross, C., Orr, E.S., Sisic, M., Arseneault, J.M., Simmering, M.G., & Orr, R.R. (2009). Personality and motivations associated with Facebook use. *Computers in Human Behavior, 25*(2), 578–586. doi: 10.1016/j.chb.2008.12.024.

Ryff, C.D. (1989). Happiness is everything, or is it? Explorations on the meaning of psychological well-being. *Journal of Personality and Social Psychology, 57*(6), 1069–1081. doi: 10.1037/0022-3514.57.6.1069.

Yu, M.M., Hsieh, J.C., Lin, S.Y., Chen, P.L., & Tseng, H.C. (2011). Confirmatory study of model of teachers' subjective well being. *Journal of Testing, 58*, 55–85.

Yu, S.C., Hsu, W.H., Yu, M.M., & Hsu, H.Y. (2012). Is the use of social networking sites correlated with internet addiction? Facebook use among Taiwanese college students. Poster session presented at International Conference on Information and Computer Applications (ICICA 2012), Aug 22–23, 2012, Paris, France.

Yu, S.C., Lin, Y.H., & Hsu, W.H. (2013). Applying structural equation modeling to report psychometric properties of Chinese version 10-item CES-D depression scale. *Quality & Quantity, 47*(3), 1511–1518. doi: 10.1007/s11135-011-9604-0.

Computer, Intelligent Computing and Education Technology – Liu, Sung & Yao (Eds)
© *2014 Taylor & Francis Group, London, ISBN 978-1-138-02469-4*

Study on independent learning model foreign language based on multimedia network

Yu-Chun Chen
Teacher's College, Beihua University, Jilin, China

ABSTRACT: In this paper, the theory of constructivism and humanism were discussed and the foreign language teaching effective which used of modern information technology and autonomous learning mode of teaching practice related was issued. The practice teaching mode was affirmed the effectiveness of this independent learning model in the Teaching of Foreign Languages. Also the worth thinking and learning were raised in issues.

Keywords: foreign language teaching; multimedia; networking; self-learning mode

1 INTRODUCTION

With the rapid development of China's economy, the community's demand for increasing is applications of talent to make an unprecedented development of higher education. October 2000, the State Department of Higher Education issued a "foreign language teaching basic education requirements." "Basic requirements" clearly stated that in order to be practical, to apply for the purpose of "teaching ideas and teaching foreign language curriculum objectives are to develop students' language proficiency. The educational features and fully reflects the new direction of reform of college English teaching philosophy, has been fully affirmed the administrations of education and of teachers and students. "Basic requirements" also pointed out that "teaching methods and the use of computers actively introducing multimedia, networking and other modern technology to improve foreign language teaching conditions in schools. Organize a variety of foreign language students to participate in extracurricular activities, to create a good atmosphere for learning foreign language, to inspire students learning a foreign language consciousness and enthusiasm."

Since education has its own peculiarities, and institutions in recent years, the quality of students is not high, making our foreign language teaching faced with various difficulties. After our foreign language learning situation for students is survey found: Students learn self-awareness and foreign language learning habits are generally poor. So, how to make full use of existing resources, how to change the concept of the teacher as soon as possible, to promote change the way students learn, so that foreign language teaching as much as possible

to achieve the "basic requirements" and curriculum requirements, to meet the needs of the community as much as possible for talent, is currently the majority of teachers in the teaching practice is an urgent need to solve the problem. Therefore, constructivist learning theory-based learning theory and the modern theory of modern education structure as the theoretical basis, in the current educational model class system in seeking a practical foreign language training model self-learning ability, cultivating students' innovative spirit, to enhance the quality of foreign language education is the requirements of the new curriculum reform, but also higher education needs of their own development.

2 THEORETICAL BASIS

2.1 *Constructivist theory*

Constructivism (constructivism), also known as structuralism, the Swiss psychologist Jean Piaget (J. Piajet) first proposed. Constructivist theory holds that knowledge is not taught by teachers get, but learners in certain situations that social and cultural background, with the help of others (including teachers and learning partners) to help with the necessary learning materials, through the construction of meaning obtained.

Constructivism advocated under the guidance of teachers, learner-centered learning, that is, both emphasized the role of the learner's cognitive subject, without neglecting the teacher's guidance, the teacher is to help the construction of meaning, facilitator, rather than imparting knowledge and instilling those. Students are the subject of information processing is active construction of meaning, rather than passive recipients of external stimuli and infused objects. Only full play the main role of students, allow students to actively participate in the whole process of teaching students to have better creative spirit and innovative ability to adapt to the requirements of the new century talents.

2.2 *Humanistic theory*

Humanistic Psychology fifties and sixties of the 20th century in the United States the rise of a school of psychology, which is the main representative of Maslow (A Maslow) and Rogers (CRRogers). The humanistic theory, in any case, a person's actions depend on how he is from his own perspective to the perception of the world. Therefore, it is not only the cognitive processes of learning of knowledge, experience, and also the need to meet their emotional process.

Human teaching theory emphasizes learner-centered teaching methods; emphasizes the duality of teaching objectives, namely, emotional and cognitive development goals development goals. In practice, emphasizing learners to be responsible for their own learning. Teachers are no longer independent study disseminators of knowledge, but the learner guidance and consultancy. Change this concept, teaching from the past to "teach" as the standard, into "learning" as the standard. Learning process both process knowledge, skills, methods to obtain, but also process emotions, attitudes, values, culture.

2.3 *Discovery learning theory*

Famous psychologist Bruner (Brunner) emphasizes discovery learning theory; students should take the initiative to find a student, rather than passively accepting the process of knowledge. In the teaching process, students who are actively exploring learning, the teacher's role is to create a problem scenario, lead to students' interest in knowledge itself, resulting in cognitive demand, stimulate the

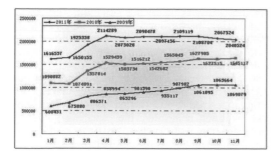

Figure 1. Humanistic theory development trend.

motivation of self-exploration, rather than imparting knowledge readily available.

Vygotsky's "zone of proximal development theory" that the development of students, there are two levels: one is the existing level of the students, the other is the student's level of development possible. Gap between the two is the most recent development area. Teaching should focus on the student's zone of proximal development, to provide students with the contents of the difficulty of mobilizing the enthusiasm of the students to play to their potential, beyond its zone of proximal development and development to achieve the level of difficulty, and then on the basis of the next development area.

"Only for the most recent teaching development zones, in order to promote the development of students, and stay in the present teaching development zone, only hinder the development of students. Process of development of the zone of proximal development is the continuous process of converting existing development zones, namely the unknown into the known, the conversion will not be put into the process of energy can not be." Indeed, to do so, it must, as Ausubel says, to understand students' cognitive structure, before teaching the teachers must first understand what the student has mastered, to the students of knowledge, "bottom", so, on this basis in order to allow students to recent developments in the area. These self-learning theory and practice have some inspiration and guidance for the promotion of educational practice independent learning.

3 FOREIGN LANGUAGE COURSES TEACHING PRACTICE

Foreign Language Teaching Hospital bold attempt to make full use of modern information technology and multimedia technology, build self-study foreign language teaching, conduct small-scale experimental study in teacher Education, Department of Chemical Engineering and four classes in civil and commercial department. Dean of students in accordance with the arrangements of course, every other week for two hours at room multimedia self-learning, extra-curricular also free on the machine learning.

The general idea of our school foreign language courses teaching model used is: the dominant position of outstanding students to participate in the main teaching objectives embodied consciousness and self-development, cultivate independent learning and innovation. Before class, the teacher according to the actual situation of the student study guide program design, layout learning tasks, give students a clear learning objectives

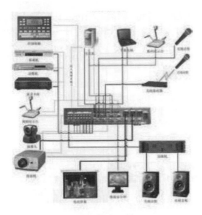

Figure 2. Multimedia network topology.

for each unit, so that students set their own learning goals according to their own circumstances, to realize what they need to learn, learning to be to what standard, and how to meet these standards. The study guide program should be specific, clear, should help students to recall and apply have some knowledge of student learning and to follow the order of thinking, should help students master the learning strategy that allows students to continue to guide the guidance outline in learning to read, really play a supporting role.

In the independent learning process, teachers how to test whether students completed the learning objectives? What there is not complete? This requires teachers to students' learning progress and to monitor the quality of learning. This stage, teachers and students can be two-way communication, teachers ask students to difficult problems, teachers to students to ask questions to check learning. Met the students themselves can not solve the task of learning, teachers guide students to discuss also be resolved through the exchange of students between cooperation and promote common improved. If, after independent learning and cooperative learning among students through individual, as well as unresolved issues, then you need to focus on parts of these teachers detailed explanation. Because they have been exploring cooperative learning and students' self-learning among students, so the teacher to explain different from the general to explain everything, but a real problem for the students encountered in targeted and focused on combing explain the relationship between the structure and logic of knowledge. Also note that while teachers grasp the actual situation of poor students, and provide timely help and counseling.

This stage student sub-group activities in the classroom or in the classroom courseware multimedia classroom presentation, to ensure that each member of the team has a chance. When finished, the students of different groups from the content of the statement or performance, class performance, oral use and timing and scoring four aspects give their assessment, selected the best teams and individuals; supplement teachers' comments, pointing out the strengths and weaknesses of the exhibition summary. Finally, teachers and students to learn to summarize the activities of the unit presented the next learning task.

4 TEACHING EVALUATION

The self-learning mode using modern multimedia technology to create authentic language environment for students to improve students' foreign language self-learning ability, to a certain extent, also reflects the advantages of personalized education, has been welcomed by the students. For 300 students conducted a questionnaire survey for students to feedback and evaluation on many aspects

Table 1. Interest in learning English, comparative analysis of attitudes.

Motivation and attitude	Before experiment	After experiment
I am very interested in learning English	3.08	3.45
I have confidence in learning English	3.25	3.48
I think I have completed the task of practical value when motivation is enough	3.68	3.74

Table 2. Learning habits survey analysis.

Study habits	Before experiment	After experiment
I take the initiative to preview	2.98	4.21
I often review their notes after class	2.62	3.34
I often go to the library to find information	2.60	3.97
I use the Internet to get information on a wider expansion of the knowledge of English	1.90	3.12
I often read English stories and other reading materials in English	2.08	3.22
I used to watch English movies	2.52	3.05

of foreign language self-study teaching model, and a statistical analysis of the data.

From the statistical results, through the implementation of the autonomy of classroom teaching, students' interest in foreign language learning class is significantly enhanced, to learn foreign language more confident than before. Thus, the teaching focus on the active participation of students, students 'self-learning ability, guiding students to learn how to learn, is in line with students' psychological needs.

Comparison showed that most students can now effectively use resources, such as libraries and the Internet for learning, teachers can take the initiative to complete the pre-assignment arrangement, because they do not feel you can not participate in class discussions prep, but can not detect the completion of the classroom, not Find extensive information on group activities can not be carried out smoothly. This shows that the new teaching model can encourage students to take the initiative to develop a preview before class, after-school self-review, and an extensive collection of good practice information.

In the new teaching model to implement the process, experiments focus on training teachers on student learning strategies for students to consciously try and use foreign language learning strategies. From the comparison we can see that the students have a better understanding of the important role played in foreign language learning strategies learning and learning strategies through specialized training, most students have mastered some common learning strategies, and know how to these strategies used in their foreign language learning.

5 CONCLUSION

Independent learning model is the traditional lecture-style teaching mode opposition, but a combination of traditional classroom teaching and independent learning. Traditional teaching system will help students master the knowledge and self-learning mode is focusing interest in learning, learning strategies, develop students' independent innovation ability, their advantages and disadvantages, we should promote complementary integration of a variety of teaching modes.

Independent learning model is not "lazy teaching mode" in the experimental implementation of the independent learning model, we found that, independent learning model than we envisaged before the experiment demands on teachers and students to be much higher, but also the more specific.

There are some issues we need further consideration, such as: the new teaching model how to take advantage of modern educational technology; How to improve the balance of the students involved in the cooperation; autonomy, cooperation and explore ways of learning that focuses on both contact with each other but also how to arrange your time to achieve optimization of classroom teaching, which needs further research and discussion in the future, and thus the research into this subject in depth.

Table 3. Comparative analysis of communicative competence.

Communicative competence	Before experiment	After experiment
I often communicate with teachers and classmates learning experience	2.35	3.58
I make good use of every opportunity to use English in real communication	1.90	2.35
I actively answer questions posed by the teacher in the classroom, not afraid of mistakes, afraid of ridicule	2.98	3.25
I often collaborate with other students companions or group to complete a task	3.50	4.20
In the communication, I often help of gestures, facial expressions, etc. to express	2.32	2.80

Table 4. Planned results.

Plan	Before experiment	After experiment
I have developed learning programs each semester	2.30	4.06
I was able to develop a weekly or daily schedule their learning	2.42	3.41
In addition to the completion of the learning task teacher, I also developed extracurricular English learning program	2.20	3.13

REFERENCES

Chen Feng-juan, 2004. Lab report on improving students' foreign language self-learning ability.
High Geely, 2005. Analysis summarized the domestic situation of foreign language self-study and research.

Meng M, 2006. Based teaching model autonomous learning.

Pang Weiguo, 2003. Independent study: Principles and Strategies of learning and teaching.

Peixin Ning, 2005. Instructional design-oriented learners.

State Department of Higher Education, 2000. Foreign language teaching basic education requirements.

Wang Sheng, 2003. Subjects participatory Teaching.

Wen Weili, 2009. Train foreign language self-learning ability of students segmented pedagogy.

WU Li Gang, 2003. Principle mode and teaching activities.

WU Li Gang, 2003. Principle mode and teaching activities.

Computer, Intelligent Computing and Education Technology – Liu, Sung & Yao (Eds)
© 2014 Taylor & Francis Group, London, ISBN 978-1-138-02469-4

Research the Internet platform for the new way of psychology education

Dian-Zhe Xu
School of Economic Management, Beihua University, Jilin City, China

ABSTRACT: Internet has been used widely as a new way in psychological research. In this paper, the brief history of web-based psychological research was introduced firstly, and then its methodological advantages and disadvantages were discussed. The advantages which include high validity, multiple subjects, more convenient, lower cost, etc. but this new way is also accompanied with some limits, such as experiment control is loose, all of the research can not be done in the Internet, etc. In spite of these disadvantages, more attention should be paid to Internet in psychological research.

Keywords: psychology; Internet platform; new way

1 INTRODUCTION

Internet impact on humans is revolutionary, involving all areas of human life and academic. For psychology, the Internet is not only a need to study new objects, but also a new research tool can be widely used. As a whole, the current research on network and psychology can be divided into two parts: the main part of the impact of the Internet on human psychology and behavior, the so-called network psychology, such as on-line offensive, online dating, network into addiction research, anonymity, websites and other man-machine interface. Also part of the main study is how to use the Internet and its impact on psychological research methods, such as in psychological research. This paper discusses the topic.

2 LIMITATIONS OF TRADITIONAL RESEARCH METHODS OF PSYCHOLOGY

Study psychology, is inseparable from the subjects and the main trial. Commonly used in psychology research methods includes experiments, observation, testing method and the simulation method. The psychological research is inseparable from a research tool, currently used research tools including a pen and paper, computer, instrument designed for special purposes (eg eye tracker, fMRI, Skinner boxes) and so on. Different research tools on the main test subjects, research methods and findings are influential. About this impact psychologists put forward a variety of arguments. The argument to the sixties and seventies in the 20th century reached its peak.

Firstly, psychology is the study of homogeneity test is a serious problem. Some even scoffed, "is based on the study of psychology freshmen, rats and patients." Homogeneity of the subjects of psychological research makes a low external validity, pervasive poor conclusions. Secondly, the number of test is relatively small, statistical validity of research findings (Statistic Power) is low. In addition, it is difficult to recruit some special subjects, such as the mother of triplets, drug addicts, homosexuals, brain injury patients, many studies are not conducted. In addition, critics also include: difficult to eliminate the main trial expected effect (Experimenter bias) and volunteer bias (Volunteer bias), etc.; difficult to be motivated to participate in the experimental test has a relatively clear understanding, especially those who can not see the recruitment of study subjects of advertising, but did not participate in the possible motives of the study subjects, personal characteristics and proportion. Finally, in the laboratory of

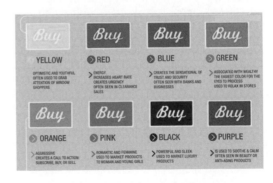

Figure 1. Color psychology describe the Internet.

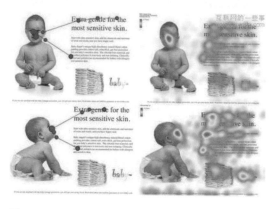

Figure 2.   Internet advertising stimulus mode.

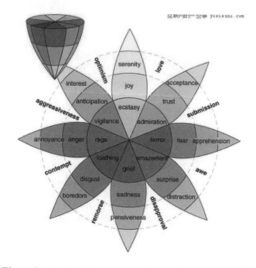

Figure 3.   Internet interconnection and product design.

psychology research lab requires a certain space and equipment, research assistants need to pay salaries, need to follow a certain order arrange subjects participated in the experiment, and can only work in a certain time, please try to be the laboratory do research, etc., these shortcomings have limited the study of psychology, making the rise in the cost of the study. However, the advent of the Internet, with its global ("everywhere"), weather ("the ever-present") and other characteristics, profoundly affected the study of psychology.

3   A BRIEF HISTORY OF THE INTERNET-BASED PSYCHOLOGICAL RESEARCH

3.1   *A brief history of the Internet*

History of the Internet is at least 30 years. The predecessor of today's Internet can be traced back to 1969, the U.S. Defense Department to build the ARPANET. E-mail (E-mail), electronic bulletin board (BBS), newsgroups (Newsgroup), IRC and other chat tools are developed in the seventies and eighties. But generally speaking, before the 1990s, the network application largely confined to academic circles, research and service in the military, users seldom. 1989 Tim Berners-Lee invented the World Wide Web, the Internet from the explosive into the lives of the general public, it becomes a powerful tool for social interaction, entertainment and commerce. As of the time of this writing, the author visited the site and found that there are more than 107 have been included in this study psychology increasingly long list. In the end who made the original historic attempt because of different criteria, different controversy. And to May 1999, this number had increased to 65, involving almost all areas of psychology. Which is social psychology, cognitive psychology research studies 13 studies, eight

sensation and perception, and five health psychology, developmental psychology research 43 clinical psychology studies, 3 individual cell research and industrial organizational psychology, the two physiological psychology, two emotional aspects of the research, a general psychology research?

3.2   *A brief history of the Internet-based psychological research*

Since 1995, some of the innovative spirit of the psychologists began to explore the use of the Internet to recruit subjects, and their research laboratories moved from narrow the vast Internet. June 17, 1998, at the APS (American Psychological Association) by John Krantz is responsible for maintaining the website lists 35 Internet based on psychology research. And to May 1999, this number had increased to 65, involving almost all areas of psychology. Which social psychology, cognitive psychology research studies 13 studies, eight sensation and perception, and five health psychology, developmental psychology research 43 clinical psychology studies, 3 individual cell research and industrial organizational psychology, the two physiological psychology, two emotional aspects of the research, a general psychology research. As of the time of this writing, the author visited the site and found that there are more than 107 have been included in this study psychology increasingly long list. In the end who made the original historic attempt because of different criteria, different controversy. Adopt more stringent criteria to divide, research John H. Krantz and his colleagues made "on female attractiveness decisive factor" can be considered a true history of online psychological

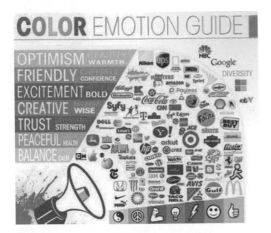

Figure 4.   Color psychology of the Internet.

experiment because it published in "Science" magazine, and the use of the experimental group design. The history of the first inter-group design using online psychology experiments "Cognitive Consistency of causal mechanisms," they use CGI, Java and JavaScript technologies and languages of the subjects were randomized.

The world's first online psychology laboratory is the first half of 1997 at Purdue University to establish the site is http://www.psych.purdue.edu/ ~ coglab, mainly engaged in the research and teaching of cognitive psychology. Currently, Italy and other European countries also have corresponding online psychology laboratory. Psychological research of China's first Internet-based master's thesis is Zhao Xiangyang "personality online information consultation consultants, web anonymity and job performance," at http://psyche.pku. Edu.cn/students. htm.

Overall, the current Internet-based multi-psychological research using online surveys, case studies and related research methods, and the number of online psychological experiment is still relatively small. However, more and more online psychological experiment more stringent goal to become a psychologist, because, after all, is a psychologist experimentally proven, relatively strong research methods.

3.3   Internet-based psychological research techniques

Based on experimental psychology from the mid-single computer is the beginning of the 1970s. Implemented in most of the current experimental psychology lab requires the use of C language, C++ language, Visual Basic or Delphi and other programming. But psychology experiments conducted on the Internet, you can use the front desk HTML, Java or JavaScript language to achieve, you can also use Macromedia Authorware software, the software is easy to use, and can Macromedia's Web site (http://www.macromedia.com) for free download. But backstage database, and server-side connection data storage and data transfer requires some programming skills. In short, from a technology point of view, doing psychological research on the Internet will not require more than the traditional psychology laboratory higher. Detailed description of the various main purpose of this article is not technical issues. In the "psychological experiments on the Internet," the third part of Michael H. Birnbaum editor of a more detailed comparison of the advantages and disadvantages of various techniques.

3.4   A brief history of the Internet-based psychological research

Since 1995, some of the innovative spirit of the psychologists began to explore the use of the Internet to recruit subjects, and their research laboratories moved from narrow the vast Internet. June 17, 1998, at the APS (American Psychological Association) by John Krantz is responsible for maintaining the website lists 35 Internet based on psychology Research. And to May 1999, this number had increased to 65, involving almost all areas of psychology. Which has 24 social psychology, cognitive psychology research studies 13 studies, eight sensation and perception, and five health psychology, developmental psychology research 43 clinical psychology studies, 3 individual cell research and industrial organizational psychology, the study of two physiological psychology, two emotional aspects of the research, a general psychology research. As of the time of this writing, the author visited the site and found that there are more than 107 have been included in this study psychology increasingly long list. In the end who made the original historic attempt because of different criteria, different controversy. Adopt more stringent criteria to divide, research John H. Krantz and his colleagues made "on female attractiveness decisive factor" can be considered a true history of online psychological experiment because it published in "Science" magazine, and the use of the experimental group design. The history of the first inter-group design using online psychology experiments "Cognitive Consistency of causal mechanisms," they use CGI, Java and JavaScript technologies and languages of the subjects were randomized.

3.5   Advantages of Internet-based psychological research

A new study whether the method is feasible, we must first examine its validity. There are two methods that can be used to prove based on.

Figure 5.　Color psychology Internet platform interface.

Validity of psychological was researched the Internet. The first method is the use of psychological research has been conducted over traditional research methods compared with that comparison between consistency and validity. The second is to be compared with the theoretical expectation that construction of the new method described validity.

Krantz, who has done a summarized, analyzed more than 20 studies on the Internet before May 1999, some of these studies using questionnaires, some use scales, and some experimental design. Variable studies involving very broad, from personality variables such as self-monitoring (Self-Monitoring) to cognitive variables such as decision-making. Summary description, based on a high degree of consistency between the validity of psychological research and psychological studies of Internet use traditional means, and compare with the theoretical expectations, the new method also has high construct validity.

In fact, regardless of construct validity, consistency or validity, internal validity of the new method is emphasized. In addition to the internal validity and external validity is also a very important issue. Summary Krantz et al., also analyzed based on psychological research in the case of Internet subjects such as sex, race, country or region, and language. Study shows that because of the large number and diversity of subjects, based on the external validity of psychological research over the Internet using traditional methods of psychological research to be high, and that this is one of the biggest advantages of the new method. However, in general, psychological research on the Internet is still relatively small; the study of the validity of the problem is just beginning, but also the need for more in-depth research.

4　THE LIMITATIONS OF PSYCHOLOGICAL RESEARCH BASED ON THE INTERNET

First, not all psychological research can be carried out by the network. Based on the fact that all networks are closely dependent on the computer, only when the person next to the computer in order to proceed. With cognitive neuroscience experiments require means PET, fMRI, ERP and other scientific studies, the need for injection of drugs, or feeding experiments, experiments need to measure physiological indices, some of the accuracy requirements of a very high reaction experiments, currently on not on the Internet, or may never be on the Internet.

Secondly, the control problems in research (includes control of test and environmental factors). The traditional strengths of controlled laboratory studies are more stringent, and psychology-based research network will not be able to do so sophisticated control. This can be seen as a flaw in Internet-based psychological research. But some people think that psychology is a basic principle: When not strictly controlled, can be balanced by randomization. Psychology-based research network can recruit diverse subjects (such as different age, race, region and country, educational level, economic status, etc.), are facing a variety of experimental test of environmental factors (such as different monitors, different resolutions, different browsers, etc.) through a random distribution of the experimental conditions, can also ensure the internal validity of the study, but at the same time improving the external validity and conclusions of universality.

5　CONCLUSION

1970s, the computer enters the psychology laboratory, making psychological research can be more rigorous and precise control. The last years of the 20th century, the Internet has entered a psychology research, making it more diverse in the recruitment of subjects, a huge amount of psychological research. Computer and Internet use have increased the validity of psychological research. Of course, the use of the Internet to do psychological research also has some limitations, however, as a new research tool, psychologists should get more attention.

REFERENCES

Granic I, Lamey AV. 2000. The self-organization of the Internet and changing modes of thought. http://www.elsevier.com/ locate/newideapsych. New Ideas in Psychology, 2000.
http://psych.hanover.edu/aps/exponnet.html.
http://www.psych.purdue.edu/~coglab. Netlabs of Cognitive Psychology in Purdue University.
Michael H. Birnbaum et al., 2000. Psychology Experiments on the Internet.
Wallace P. 1999. The Psychology of the Internet.

Computer, Intelligent Computing and Education Technology – Liu, Sung & Yao (Eds)
© 2014 Taylor & Francis Group, London, ISBN 978-1-138-02469-4

Research on teaching methods of Modern dance to college students based on digital multimedia technology

Yuan-Ying Gao
Teacher's College Beihua University, Jilin, China

ABSTRACT: The research presents a new configuration building based on internet integration to reform digital multimedia technology of digital multimedia technology. It is based on internet that is the digitizing region. This assumption is supported by the wire & wireless networks systems that for a digital station. Digital multimedia technology model shows that teaching & learning are possible operating, which helps the reform path of court system during the digitization process.

Keywords: teaching methods; Modern dance; college students; digital multimedia technology

1 INTRODUCTION

In the 17th Congress of the Chinese Communist Party, Comrade Hu Jintao pointed out: "vigorously promote theoretical innovation and give Modern dance of contemporary China distinct characters of practice, national characteristics, and characteristics of the times the theoretical system of socialism with Chinese characteristics outreach activities to promote. Contemporary Chinese Modern dance." Promote the popularization of Modern dance, there are various paths, but now with the development and popularization of Chinese network technology, how to use modern Internet technology to promote the popularization of Modern dance is a new and difficult subject, this article will do the following aspects of the preliminary exploration.

2 MEANING OF MODERN DANCE POPULARITY OF ONLINE EDUCATION

In order to better understand the meaning of Modern dance popularization of online education, let us understand the meaning of the popularization of Modern dance; it has broad and narrow sense. Popularization of Modern dance, including broad popularity and the popularity of contemporary Chinese Modern dance basic principles of Modern dance, Modern dance popularity narrowly mainly refers to the popular Contemporary Chinese Modern dance is now mainly in terms of academics to study and narrow explore the popularization of Modern dance, namely the theoretical system of socialism with Chinese characteristics.

Development of network technology in the ascendant, along with online education is also becoming increasingly popular and popular, online education is the use of modern network technology and computer technology, and modern teaching philosophy as a guide, to provide learners with an across time and space constraints maximize the use of computer resources and educational resources to facilitate autonomous learning, creative learning new educational model. However, if Modern dance does not occupy this position, then a variety of non-Marxist or anti-Marxist bound to occupy. Therefore, we should make full use of modern network technology, to further promote the popularization of Modern dance. Meaning of Modern dance popularization of online education is an excellent resource for the shared use of online education, individualized instruction, and other interactive features to promote the basic principles of Modern dance and Modern dance of contemporary China, to make these ideas and theories popularity, popularization, specific, action guide masses become conscious identity, the people transform nature into a material force of society and transformation, to play its due role in the great practice of socialism.

3 CHARACTERISTICS OF MODERN DANCE POPULARIZATION OF ONLINE EDUCATION

3.1 *The rapid integration of resources*

Since the party's congress report of contemporary Chinese Modern dance since the research on this new topic after another, how will the outcome of the Marxist theory of the rapid popularization of research focused integration is a critical issue, network media become a powerful tool that goal, the network media have unlimited capacity, high-speed concentration, it can be a variety of research results popularization of Modern dance, literature materials to electronic journals, e-books and other forms of highly concentrated form special education sites, achieve the rapid integration of resources, such as Figure 1.

3.2 *Popular theory of propaganda*

As Mao Zedong said, "Any ideas, and if not linked to the objective reality of things, if there is no need for an objective reality, if not the master of the people, even the best of things, even Modern dance-Leninism, it is not play a role." With the development of computer network information technology, China's computer users has surpassed the U.S. as the most in the world, online media has entered every household, online education is widely publicize the popularization of Modern dance provides a platform guarantee, whether government officials, businessmen hawkers, professors and scholars, students, or the general public more access to the Internet and enjoy the speed and convenience it brings, popular with Modern dance during network popularization process is illuminated can say for sure: online education to promote theoretical propaganda become popular.

3.3 *Interactive forms of learning*

In the online education environment, the Macross and multimedia nature of the network, learning is no longer adhere to the traditional one-way form of communication, but in the context of equal dialogue and exchange of information dissemination, which gives Marxist theory learner brings

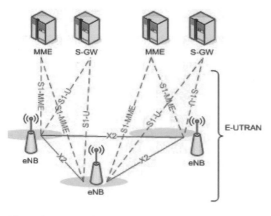

Figure 1.   Network structure.

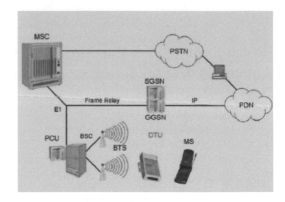

Figure 2.   Network topology.

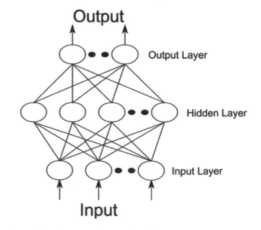

Figure 3.   Data exchange flowchart.

unprecedented convenience and positive factors, both theoretical researchers, or ordinary people, can take advantage of online education in the form of Modern dance popularization of this proposition for interactive discussion and research, and then crash out more ideological spark that theory tends to improve and mature.

3.4 *Lifelong learning theory*

With the advent of the era of knowledge explosion, stunning speed of updating knowledge, the concept of lifelong learning as more and more people have accepted, while the Marxist Popular Education is a complex system engineering, which requires us to constantly explore learning, broaden horizons Marxist theory to explore its theoretical meaning, so that the times. Learning as a lifestyle trend of social development, online education is an effective way to achieve lifelong learning theory, the stage, China is gradually building an open network education system, compared with traditional education, for those who desire it people to continue their education and an open window.

4 POPULARIZATION OF MODERN DANCE ROUTE NETWORK IN EDUCATION

4.1 Government-led push to build a solid bastion of Modern dance popularization of online education

Implementation of Modern dance popularization of online education requires not only give full play to the leading role of the government, but also with schools and other aspects of the power of the masses, and thus build a "push-led government, school education as the main mass participation-based" Trinity Online education system, to avoid the potential risk of Modern dance popularity of online education is very important.

First, invest the necessary funds to support the development of key technologies network, building a firm strategic positions. For the popularization of Modern dance education platform—a network carrier to maintain stable and efficient operation, the development of a specific network communication technology, network information using sophisticated operation to control the direction of public opinion and the emotional responses of Internet users, the government must invest the necessary funds to research and development in line with the characteristics of the information age science communication technologies, such as Focus research users, emotional excitation of information technology, information resources showing fine control order, the network analysis and interactive response to comments technologies, etc., in order to build a strong strategic position as a solid education theoretical system of socialism with Chinese characteristics.

Second, the development of relevant laws and regulations or normative documents is clearly defined goals and tasks Modern dance popularization of online education. Popularization of Modern dance in the direction of online education is determined by its objectives and tasks, the most important issue which is the popularization of Modern dance propaganda. Approach to this issue, I believe that the government needs to be clearly defined through the development of relevant laws and regulations or programmatic document, that the provisions of the objectives and tasks of Modern dance popularization of online education is: theoretical system of socialism with Chinese characteristics as a guide, using scientific concept of development in line with the existing social system, culture and social norms of qualified

citizens. "its essence is to develop four", "five love" good citizenship.

Third, the unified planning of the contents are Modern dance popularization of online education. As we all know, the content is to further refine the goals and tasks, in order to ensure the realization of the target, the central government must be on the content planning Modern dance popularization of online education efforts, that the central government should implement a highly centralized management of its educational content, in particular requests and comments on the core content, the local government or educational institutions in the context of the implementation of strict compliance, combined with their own reality, the flexibility to carry out online education popularization of Modern dance.

Fourth, integration of propaganda is forces and work together to promote the popularization of Modern dance. In emphasizing the use of online media propaganda of Modern dance popularization of education, the Government should integrate various propaganda forces, such as newspapers, television and other media, co-operative education popularization of Modern dance.

4.2 School education as the main form of online education popularization of Modern dance forefront

First, online education plays an increasingly important role in school education. School education is a part of education, from early childhood to higher education, school education on the formation of a person's outlook on life and values have a crucial role in school education including traditional education and modern education (mainly online education), but the quality and quantity of traditional education is largely restricted conditions for running schools, and online education is different, its learning time, learning sites, students and school-based conditions are not limited, and can be combined in different school teacher teaching; teaching content can be video, audio, graphics and other multimedia forms show, and enhance students' interest in learning, greatly improving the efficiency of teaching school.

Second, the mass is an essential attribute of Modern dance and fundamental requirements; the school's "Red Site" is the forefront of their propaganda. The school is the hub of intellectuals, reform and opening up 30 years ago, the popular theory of Modern dance gradually maturing, and formed a theoretical system of socialism with Chinese characteristics, in which the important role of intellectuals in terms of publicity and ideological construction of the system is self-it being understood, however, why the popularity of Marxist theory, the main character is based on the practice of Modern dance, which concentrated expression in Marx's theses on Feuerbach.

Third, online education in schools helps the spread of Marxist theory mass timeliness and coherence, to better serve the masses. Has a strong network across time and space, a new theoretical research tenacious vitality or not, where you can get a better test, because the network brought together many experts and scholars at home and abroad, they are infinitely extended schools with limited resources, by network media, the whole world can share resources, make rational use of resources is maximized, which is the rapid development of Marxist theory has an important role in promoting. Today, more and more people are accepting different forms of online education schools and online education schools have become the latest to impart knowledge, theoretical discussion of important platform for online education popularization of Marxist theory of the urgent need for rapid development and timely updates, therefore, responsible online education schools Modern dance theory can quickly and effectively influence the important mission of the masses.

4.3 With mass participation, based on network education popularization of Modern dance fundamental requirement

First, the broad participation of the masses is a prerequisite Modern dance popularization of online education.

The rapid development of the information society, the popularity of computer application technology, making online education is being accepted by more and more people, however, due to the occult network, how to get the masses to actively participate in the Marxist theory of learning which is currently more difficult to question, because Marxist theory is logical thinking, theoretical inference, practical summary of the product, with strong theoretical nature, only a small portion of people understand easily accepted by the masses rather than theorists, they accepted scientific theories and understood mainly from real life, so must the people straightaway, loved, easy to accept the language and methods of Marxist propaganda. The so-called popular is by no means vulgar Marxist propaganda in simple language, but you can not reduce its scientific nature and the theoretical value, in the final analysis is to work hard so easily accepted by the masses, guided only by a reasonable and orderly manner, in order to attract the masses to participate to the theoretical study and discussion of Modern dance in the past.

Second, the core of Modern dance popularization of online education system is the masses fully grasp the theoretical system of socialism with Chinese characteristics and is used to guide practice.

Dialectical materialism theory is from practice, which in turn acts on the practice. The people is the creators of history, are the practice of the subject, is to recognize and transform the world's major power, but in order to make Modern dance has practical significance, it is only to be understood by the masses, to master in order to play in practice should some effect. As Marx "<Critique of Hegel's Philosophy> Introduction" and said: "Theory, once grasped by the masses, will become a material force" Thus, the use of online media for promotion of Marxist theory, the must take the popular masses values positioned on practice. Because there can be a lack of practical thinking and the power of the popular impulse, and left the popular, practical, lost the most solid popular base and body strength. So fundamental Modern dance popularization of online education requirement is that the scientific theory of revolutionary practice of the conscious action of the masses to go, and used to guide the masses of the various practices to conform to the characteristics of contemporary Chinese society essentialism requirements.

5 SUMMARY

While the popularity of online education Modern dance has a lot of advantages, but there are also some potential risks.

The first alert to penetrate is a variety of non-Marxist ideology, and always adheres to the dominance of Modern dance. China is still in the primary stage of socialism, is the transition from a socialist planned economy to a socialist market economy, which also caused profound changes in people's ideas, the price-oriented. The openness characteristics of the network, so that you can take advantage of Western bourgeois information on China's penetration decadent bourgeois ideology, in addition to our current thinking there are still some remnants of feudalism, so we have to make Modern dance occupy network positions. "In the construction of the network position, to make the system of theories of socialism with Chinese characteristics into the economy, politics, education, science, culture, art and commerce sites, play a variety of ideological construction site guidance, intellectual support, the role of spiritual power."

Second, strengthen the benign guidance of the hotspot, to avoid distortion and misunderstanding of the facts. Direct expression of the network is open, everyone is free to express their views, opinions of the masses in favor of the one hand, and to reflect public opinion, on the other hand due to the impact of various factors, some of users published some extreme remarks, and these will be using some people with ulterior motives, distorted facts, repeated "water" hype, aroused even foreign media attention, then we have to use Modern dance and other mainstream consciousness to resolve these events, so that users receive a baptism of Modern dance Meanwhile, to clarify the truth of the incident, the emotional stability of Internet users, network public opinion always grasp the initiative.

REFERENCES

Guo Furong, 2004. Enjoy the value of modern ideological and political education of China.

Han Z.T, 2002. The essential characteristics of cyber building and its Irregular jurisdiction.

Kuo-Sheng Chang, 2010. The ideological and political education of University students into a kind of enjoyment.

Li Jinyuan, 2011. Analysis of online class room building challenge the existing modern dance teaching and Irregular legislation to improve.

Lu Yao, 2010. The meaning of online class room and cyberbuilding information perspective Study.

Ting W.Z. 2010. Cyber building cases continued to increase attention should be paid.

Research on fatigue failure mechanism and fatigue life model of the Self-Piercing Riveting

Rui-Jun Liu, Xing Wang & Xiang-Wen Dang

Automotive and Architectural Engineering College, Beihua University, Jilin City, China

ABSTRACT: Self-Piercing Riveting (SPR) connect strength which to extend the fatigue life have been researched for a long time, but the effect is not obvious. The SPR fatigue failure mechanism and reasons was research and the fatigue life calculation in the different stages was summarized, then the distinction among the different models of SPR fatigue life was analyzed especially. Finally a fracture mechanics of the SPR connect applications was introduced to improve the fatigue life of SPR.

Keywords: SPR; extend; fatigue failure mechanism; fatigue life model

1 INTRODUCTION

Self-piercing riveting process can punching, riveting, once completed, can be effective for coatings and coating steel, alloy plate, polymer materials and composites new technology connection. In order to achieve self-pierce riveting technology in the field of dynamic load applications are solved self-pierce riveting fatigue design and fatigue life assessment connection. Items to be based on the actual car running, riveting study of factors affecting the strength of the mechanism of fatigue failure and fatigue life assessment. Fatigue test method using orthogonal design riveting point multi-component analysis of the structure under various failure modes riveting, multi-component fatigue failure mechanisms; riveting point of fretting statics and dynamics analysis, by simplifying the stress and strain fields, based on a combination of fatigue failure mechanism established riveting process parameters, material properties, environmental factors riveting point dynamic load off brittle fracture and ductile failure probability equivalent model; based on fatigue cumulative damage theory, plasticity, fracture mechanics and reliability theory to determine the plastic deformation, breaking strength factor equivalent function to establish the mechanism of fatigue damage and destruction of riveted steel bridge riveted structures certainty and probabilistic fatigue life assessment model. Fracture mechanics of plates and shells using finite element theory regression riveted structure experimental data, failure analysis and fatigue life assessment model modified model riveting member.

2 STUDY OF STATUS SPR FATIGUE LIFE ASSESSMENT

Self-piercing riveting connected by the advent of advanced technology has attracted the interest of many scholars. Since 1990, foreign scholars have started on the self-pierce riveting technology research. The main representative of the United Kingdom, Germany and the United States Salzman, Fatemi, William Gryc, GS Booth, KW Young, A. Chrysanthou, etc research focused on the following areas: 1. To determine the principles and laws of self-pierce riveting process parameters; 2. Since punch riveting and welding, bonding strength compared to traditional riveting; 3. Self-pierce riveting finite element simulation of the static strength of the connection; 4. Self-pierce riveting equipment development and so on. Overall, the study of foreign scholars in the self-pierce riveting process static connectivity has been quite extensive, mature, research results have been applied in the field of white goods, the framework structure. Currently, less fatigue strength of the punch rivet connection and fatigue life prediction from the research and application areas, especially on the fatigue life assessments have not been reported. Project applicant is one of the earliest domestic self-pierce riveting technology research staff, mainly for early self-piercing riveting process and the influence of process parameters riveting intensity of other aspects of the research. In addition, the domestic to Huang Chao East China Jiaotong University, Tsinghua University, aged wave, LIN Zhong-qin Tianjin University and Shanghai Jiaotong University other scholars of self-pierce riveting studied different aspects of

East China Jiaotong University, which in 2006 declared "self-piercing riveting theory and key technology research" was funded by the national Science Foundation. For self-pierce riveting domestic scholars study is divided into the following areas: 1. Self-pierce riveting technology applications and prospects; 2. From punch riveting process parameters; 3. Self-piercing riveting process parameters affect the connection to the connection strength; 4. Self-pierce riveting connection failure modes and failure analysis and so on. No information on self-pierce riveting fatigue failure mechanisms and life assessment of research reports.

The project intends to connect based on self-pierce riveting fatigue failure mode, Self-pierce riveting process parameters affect the mechanism of material properties, riveted structure, use of the environment, load and riveting defects and their impact on the fatigue failure correlation. According to self-pierce riveting fatigue failure mechanisms, fatigue cumulative damage theory, fracture mechanics and reliability theory, the fatigue life assessment model connection points

provide a theoretical basis for the effectiveness of self-pierce riveting assessment and repair. In order to ensure the validity and relevance of the research project for lightweight body parts covered by self-piercing riveting point of connection for the study, the content of research projects in the automotive actual working conditions.

3 RESEARCH PROJECTS, RESEARCH OBJECTIVES

3.1 Research

1. Research riveting pressure, BHF, the structure of the die, the material properties and structural rivets, rivet heat treatment, surface treatment rivets, riveting structure, riveting material properties, stacking order riveting material, surface treatment riveting material and other effects on the fatigue strength of the connection process parameters;
2. According to self-pierce riveting impact of fatigue failure in form of connection, self-piercing riveting analysis of process parameters, the connection to participate in the body (rivets, connecting plate) surface treatment and differences in thermal expansion coefficient, electrochemical reactions, metal corrosion, load and other factors on fatigue failure;
3. Based on cumulative damage theory of fatigue, fracture mechanics and reliability theory, research, etc., under variable amplitude loading fatigue life of self-pierce riveting assessment of the connection.

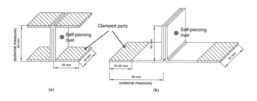

Figure 1. Geometry of the specimens.

Table 1. Definition of the specimens.

	ID specimen		Thickness		Material			
Configuration	U-shaped	Peeling	Plate 1 (mm)	Plate 2 (mm)	Plate 1	Plate 2	Rivet[a]	Die[a]
c1	s1	p1	2	2	AA6060 T4	AA6060 T4	C 5×6	DZ 090 2025
c2	s2	p2	2	2	AA6060 T6	AA6060 T6	C 5×6	FM 100 2018
c3	s3	p3	2	2	AA6060 T4	AA6060 T6	C 5×6	DZ 090 2025
c4	s4	p4	2	2	AA6060 T6	AA6060 T4	C 5×6.5	DZ 090 2025
c5	s5	p5	2	3	AA6060 T4	AA6060 T4	C 5×6.5	FM 110 2017
c6	s6	p6	2	3	AA6060 T6	AA6060 T6	C 5×6.5	FM 110 2017
c7	s7	p7	2	3	AA6060 T4	AA6060 T6	C 5×6.5	FM 110 2017
c8	s8	p8	2	3	AA6060 T6	AA6060 T4	C 5×6.5	FM 110 2017
c9	s9	p9	3	2	AA6060 T4	AA6060 T4	C 5×6.5	FM 110 2017
c10	s10	p10	3	2	AA6060 T6	AA6060 T6	C 5×6.5	FM 110 2017
c11	s11	p11	3	2	AA6060 T4	AA6060 T6	C 5×6.5	DZ 090 2025
c12	s12	p12	3	2	AA6060 T6	AA6060 T4	K 5×7	FM 110 2017
c13	s13	p13	3	3	AA6060 T4	AA6060 T4	K 5×8	FM 120 2019
c14	s14	p14	3	3	AA6060 T6	AA6060 T6	K 5×8	FM 120 2019
c15	s15	p15	3	3	AA6060 T4	AA6060 T6	K 5×8	FM 120 2019
c16	s16	p16	3	3	AA6060 T6	AA6060 T4	K 5×8	FM 120 2019

Table 2. Experimental results.

| Specimen ID | Loading angle | U-shaped and peeling specimens | | | | | |
| | | F_{zmax} (kN) | | d_{Fmax} (mm) | | Failure modes | |
		Tests	Simulations	Tests	Simulations	Tests	Simulations
s9	0	6.17	5.79	6.57	4.13	Fs3	*Fs1*
s9	45	2.93	3.86	2.99	1.43	Fs1 + Fs4	Fs1 + Fs4
s9	90	1.97	1.47	3.16	1.24	Fs4	Fs4
p9		1.04	0.64	12.31	2.19	Fp1	Fp1
s10	0	7.55	7.96	4.11	3.60	Fs1	Fs1 + Fs4
s10	45	3.71	4.44	1.66	0.91	Fs1 + Fs4	Fs1
s10	90	2.91	1.92	2.93	0.69	Fs4	Fs4
p10		1.68	0.79	8.86	1.80	Fp1	Fp1
s11	0	5.95	7.01	3.21	3.86	Fs1	Fs1
s11	45	3.90	4.95	2.61	2.19	Fs1 + Fs4	Fs1 + Fs4
s11	90	2.78	2.99	3.72	2.91	Fs4	Fs4
p11		1.58	1.44	11.57	7.39	Fp1	Fp1
s12	0	8.07	10.36	6.24	5.31	Fs3	*Fs1*
s12	45	3.77	6.01	3.16	3.88	Fs1 + Fs4	Fs1 + Fs4
s12	90	2.62	1.55	3.93	1.79	Fs4	Fs4
p12		1.17	0.79	11.61	4.97	Fp1	Fp1
s13	0	7.87	7.77	3.07	4.83	Fs1	Fs1
s13	45	5.31	5.61	4.57	3.63	Fs1 + Fs4	Fs1 + Fs4
s13	90	4.54	3.81	6.09	4.01	Fs4	Fs4
p13		2.35	1.97	18.65	11.56	Fp1	Fp1
s14	0	9.84	11.43	3.13	5.66	Fs1	Fs1
s14	45	6.92	8.04	3.23	2.82	Fs1 + Fs4	Fs1 + Fs4
s14	90	5.85	6.46	5.11	2.88	Fs4	Fs4
p14		3.22	3.28	18.48	10.47	Fp1	Fp1
s15	0	8.49	8.27	3.38	4.78	Fs1	Fs1
s15	45	5.78	5.51	4.51	4.09	Fs1 + Fs5	Fs2 + Fs5
s15	90	5.30	6.05	6.11	5.58	Fs5	*Fs4*
p15		2.77	3.36	15.86	18.75	Fp2	Fp2
s16	0	9.20	11.05	3.72	5.96	Fs1	Fs1
s16	45	5.85	7.08	3.55	4.01	Fs1 + Fs4	Fs1 + Fs4
s16	90	4.80	3.81	5.12	3.62	Fs4	Fs4
p16		2.63	1.97	13.55	7.36	Fp1	Fp1

3.2 *Research objectives*

1. To determine the effects of self-pierce riveting intensity factors and the influence of the right to re-connect.
2. To determine the self-pierce riveting fatigue failure mechanism.
3. The establishment of the environment based on the use of self-pierce riveting connection fatigue life assessment model.

3.3 *Intends to solve key scientific issues*

1. Self-pierce riveting nonlinear regression function to connect the fatigue strength factors into linear equality constraints and linear inequality constraints.

Figure 2. Failure in the form and amount of displacement.

2. Self-piercing riveting connection matrix A0 fatigue life assessment model uncertainty and sensitivity matrix OK.
3. Morbid question fatigue life assessment model linear process.

4. Analyses to be undertaken research programs and feasibility. (Including a description of research methods is technical routes, experimental method, the key technologies, etc.).

3.4 *Finite element model and meshing*

UG NX is powerful modeling functionality behind many output formats for data exchange. Built a good model parasolid ANSYS output file format can be accepted, so that we can apply the powerful modeling capabilities UG NX modeling, using ANSYS finite element analysis of the powerful features of the C-frame be checked statics.

UG NX modeling application should be noted that the simplified model, the C-frame we need to be finite element mesh, which requires not have a very sharp angle and bosses, and should be appropriate to simplify the model (such as the C-frame several holes are omitted when the threaded hole during meshing will not affect the outcome of the die and fixed, so that will be beneficial to divide the finite element mesh and the final calculation.

After generating the solid model, you can model the finite element mesh. ANSYS Meshing provides four methods: extension division, image division, dividing freedom and adaptive division.

Four meshing method does not exist merits of good or bad to say, the general method can be selected according to the specific shape of the division as well as the difficulty of meshing solid model. In comparison, the freedom of the division of solid model shape requirements are lower, it is relatively easy to implement, so this method uses a free-division.

Before meshing even better definition of material properties for C-frame, pre-defined materials as HT300 features are: elastic modulus E = 1.2e5Mpa, Poisson's ratio $\mu = 0.25$.

Before meshing should first select the type of unit, depending on the shape, material and analysis requirements C-frame, the choice of cell type is SOLID45, this cell type is mainly used for 3-D physical structure. Combination unit 10 from the node, and with an intermediate node element, thus improving the precision of analysis; each node has three degrees of freedom x, y, z direction of displacement. Unit has plasticity, creep, swelling, stress stiffening, large deformation and large strain characteristics.

When loading a specific finite element model of the force, the actual direction of the force should be loaded in the force plane. While the front has been divided finite element mesh, but you can still force loading force on the specific area of the solid model. Solving, ANSYS software will automatically convert these forces to the finite element model. Of course, you can also use the command

of ANSYS SFTRAN, the force on the solid model to the finite element model, the results of this and the system will automatically convert the same. When performing finite element analysis, analysis of the model to correct the constraints and loads, analysis of the C-riveted frame, too, and whether or not loaded properly bound and also determines the final results of the analysis is correct.

In determining the mesh method, the cell type selected, but also to determine the accuracy of meshing. 3-D solid models, setting accuracy of methods are: SMRTSIZE and ESIZE. Which are set directly ESIZE unit size, and is set SMRTSIZE division level of accuracy, this level does not directly reflect the size of the unit, this method depends on the complexity of the division of shape, that the more complex shapes zoning more thinner, but the other divided regions may be quite rough? Here the use of ESIZE command to set the precision setting accuracy: ESIZE, 0.009, 0.009 said baseline length unit is 9 mm. And if necessary, it can be the appropriate local area mesh refinement.

3.5 *Research methods*

1. Theoretical analysis of factors affecting the fatigue strength of self-pierce riveting connections and build self-pierce riveting model according to the punch, blank holder, rivets, die and mechanical properties to be riveted sheet metal, motion characteristics and material properties.
2. Rivet connection model to simulate the impact of different parameters on the fatigue strength of riveted by self-piercing.
3. According to the fatigue strength of riveted factors obtained by simulation, developed on the basis of self-pierce riveting factors connected orthogonal fatigue strength testing program,

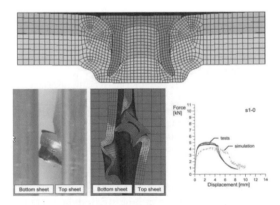

Figure 3. Failure in the form and amount of displacement simulation.

according to the test program made riveting sample.

4. To the load connection point of the actual vehicle running as the input waveform universal testing machine, the fatigue strength of the test specimen. The simulation result was verified by experimental data, by means of self-correction data regression punch riveting connection model.

5. Expert advice, theoretical analysis, multivariate statistical study of the impact test method combines the connection weights of each factor fatigue strength weight.

6. Fatigue strength of theoretical analysis from punch riveting connection mechanism, designed for anti-fatigue mechanism based on the impact. Using self-piercing riveting connection model and test combination, designed to verify the effect of fatigue, in order to verify the accuracy of the impact mechanism and relevance.

7. According to the theory of fatigue damage accumulation, fracture mechanics, fatigue life and reliability theory to establish the impact assessment model based on the mechanism riveting intensity.

4 RESEARCH PROGRAMS

According riveting process, from preliminary analysis of the factors that may affect the strength of the punch rivet connection; design is based on the car running and the connection strength factors affecting self-pierce riveting static pull test fatigue orthogonal connections; determine the impact strength of the connection based on orthogonal test results the weighting factors and their impact; finite element model based on the factors affecting self-pierce riveting constraint connection strength.

According to the results of orthogonal experiment and simulation results from the punch riveting connection strength finite element model to analyze the reasons for self-pierce riveting and mechanism of fatigue failure; using orthogonal experiment method based on self-pierce riveting fatigue failure mechanism of fatigue design connection orthogonal test, validate fatigue design effect; designed according to self-pierce riveting failure fatigue, further improve the self-pierce riveting connection strength finite element model.

Self-piercing riveting establish fatigue life assessment model tests and finite element simulation method combines life assessment models using modified until a fatigue life assessment model to meet project requirements.

5 KEY TECHNOLOGIES

1. Under cyclic loading, self-piercing kinetic and static analysis fretting rivets connection point.

2. Self-piercing riveting to establish a connection point equivalent models, stress, strain field analysis and simplification.

3. During the simulation, and connection failure in the form of a physical quantity equivalent determined.

4. Assessment model to determine the lifetime fracture stress intensity factor and fracture functions.

5. Linear regression irregular data processing.

6 CONCLUSION

1. From other scholars just punch riveting strength of connection under normal, and the project is proposed based on self-pierce riveting connection strength automotive research environment, closer to the actual conclusion of the study. Research results of the project can be self-pierce riveting technology for manufacturing lightweight vehicles provide theoretical support.

2. Other studies on the effects of self-pierce riveting just the connection strength of individual factors were analyzed, the project is not only a comprehensive analysis of all the factors that influence the riveting intensity, but also the existence of the relationship between the factors were analyzed, and determine the effects of different factors weight.

3. Self-piercing riveting first proposed connection point of fatigue life assessment of research.

4. First proposed adding riveting process parameters influencing factors in fatigue life assessment model fracture function.

ACKNOWLEDGEMENTS

Jilin Province Department of Education "twelfth-five" scientific and technological research projects [2013-166].

REFERENCES

Hana L. & A. Chrysanthou. 2006. Mechanical behaviour of self-piercing riveted multi-layer joints under different specimen configurations.

Li B. & A. Fatemi. 2005. An experimental investigation of deformation and fatigue behavior of coach peel riveted joints.

Porcaroa R. & A.G. Hanssen. 2005. The behaviour of a self-piercing riveted connection under quasi-static loading conditions.

Porcaroa R. & M. Langsethb. 2007. Crashworthiness of self-piercing riveted connections.

Computer, Intelligent Computing and Education Technology – Liu, Sung & Yao (Eds)
© *2014 Taylor & Francis Group, London, ISBN 978-1-138-02469-4*

The government's public information management and service based internet ages

Ying Luo

School of Economic Management, Beihua University, Jilin City, China

ABSTRACT: The public information is the important strategic resources for people to carry on the public life, raising the public living quantity. The new development opportunities were provided for the public management of governments with the information society developmentally. Public information is a public good, public information management is the basis for the work of the government's public administration and important content. Public information management requirements government fully taking advantage of information technology, in terms of institutions and ideas, also has to be improved.

Keywords: public information; public management; government's public administration; service

1 INTRODUCTION

Public administration is public information generation, transmission and processing process, citizens living in the sovereign and the principal position in the public administration, citizens should be aware that public information and supervise the government. Public information refers to information in the public domain, is the sum of public life and public administration information about. Specifically, the main public information, including public administration, public affairs, public life, public interest information. Public areas are a human system; public information includes common environment information, the common system information, a common structure information, public information and public process information element. Public information is the subject of citizens should be aware of all the information, including the three aspects: 1) the government's information. Overall information including the government composed of government information, information behavior and the effect of the government, the government in the past, present and future information. Specifically, there are: Status government institutions, such as the government's functions, powers, composition, responsibilities and institutional settings; cases of government activity sites, such as the more significant work items, time, place and procedures for work, the government enacted legislation, decrees, policies and institutions, etc.; relationship information within the government, such as the contents of the internal division of labor, power relations and functions relations; 2) information about citizens. Including the overall composition of the citizens, the interests and rights of distribution, survival and living conditions, the relationship between citizens and government, etc.; 3) all other aspects of social and economic information relating to the rights and interests of citizens.

2 PUBLIC INFORMATION ON THE SIGNIFICANCE OF GOVERNMENT

2.1 *Public information is the basis of government performance*

Efficient government is a public issue can be handled promptly government, which requires the government to social problems are comprehensive, accurate and rapid understanding and the ability to timely and effective response. Not difficult to imagine, "blind" government and "deaf" the government will inevitably bring the absence of public power. Sound and efficient government requires not only the body, but also requires a keen eye and quick reactions. Government public policy makers must vision, there is no adequate information it is impossible to develop a scientific decision-making. Good premise services must be accurate grasp of customer needs and respond quickly, and without adequate public information resources, "Customer Center" and "citizen orientation" can only be empty talk. If the government does not know what their clients requirements, as doctors do not know what disease the patient is suffering and can not remedy, the salesman does not understand customer needs not recommend commodities. Such doctors are quacks, so the salesman should be laid off. Similarly, you can not achieve effective management of public information the government should step down.

Figure 1. Internet era government information pathways.

2.2 *Public information is a prerequisite for the establishment of a democratic type of government*

People are the source of public power, the government is to serve the people, and citizens have the right to know public information, monitoring the government, constrained government, the obligation to provide public information to citizens. Citizens to find, receive and impart information is, of course, the meaning of modern democracy, government is obliged to ensure that citizens can be convenient and low-cost access to public information. Only citizens to public information as a precondition before they can effectively supervise and restrain government. Government Information in the natural dominance of information, studies have shown that government control of information resources, if there is no transparent information disclosure mechanism, under conditions of asymmetric information, it is difficult to citizens as principals and as agents of the government equality of the game, the client's interests are likely to be violated. The Democratic government requires citizens to freedom of expression and freedom of speech. Hegel said that truth is freedom of the mind, too, political freedom and freedom of expression must be true citizens of public information as a precondition.

3 THE SIGNIFICANCE OF PUBLIC INFORMATION FOR CITIZENS

3.1 *Good public information management and service is an inherent requirement of citizens the right to information*

The right to information is the basis for citizens of other rights; this will be confirmed in the vast majority of sovereign states and international organizations in the form of legislation. The United Nations General Assembly adopted a resolution for the first time confirmed the freedom of information is a fundamental right, it declared: "Freedom of information is a fundamental human right, the other cornerstone of freedom to pursue the UN Declaration of Human Rights Article stipulates that the United Nations." Everyone has the right to freedom of opinion and expression, this right includes uninterrupted by any means to have perspective and to seek, receive and disseminate information and ideas of freedom. The United Nations views and freedom of expression established by the UN Human Rights Commission in the Office of the Special Reporter on the report's contents as a basic human right to information has been clarified, and urged countries should amend their laws or enact new laws to ensure public right to information obtained by many countries in domestic law also made corresponding provisions.

3.2 *To achieve the interests of citizens as a precondition to public information*

Is essentially a process of public administration to achieve the interests of citizens, including a series of iterative links, that expression of interest, the interests of comprehensive, policy development and communication, policy implementation, policy feedback, and its essence is to generate public information, the transmission and reception of process, is the process of transfer and sharing of public information. Realization of citizens' interests are citizens of the multi-game process, the inherent requirements of the game this game parties have sufficient information to carry out the game under symmetric information conditions. Realization of citizens' interests in the real level of performance for the government to provide public services, if citizens do not understand government

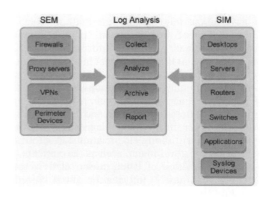

Figure 2. Common information model.

information on what services the government can not know how to obtain these services. Overall, the handling of public administration through public information to complete the implementation process and the public interest in public affairs, public information is of great significance for public administration, this importance with the advent of the Internet age is more prominent.

4 INTERNET ERA GOVERNMENT PUBLIC INFORMATION AS A STRATEGIC RESOURCE MANAGEMENT

Public administration body can quickly, accurately and fully grasp and handle public information not only determines the efficiency of management, and is a measure of whether the Government has an important reference standard of responsiveness. Traditional government bureaucracy organization management is based on closed-end management, which emphasizes the implementation of the political administration, ignoring the government should change with a corresponding adjustment to the social environment, so it has obvious flaws. From the perspective of information theory point of view, is actually a process of public administration public information input, conversion, output and feedback. Not difficult to see, in the closed state government, the governing body for receiving outside information is indirect. Government only concerned with the implementation of political decisions, the result is to reduce the sensitivity to environmental change management system, while the external changes unresponsive government is necessarily inefficient. So, faced with the complex challenges of the Internet age environment, the establishment is an open responsive government to become the inevitable choice of society.

The importance of public information in the public administration more and more obvious, with the corresponding public information power has become an important part of a country's overall competitiveness, and its prominent position in the growing power of public information is public information refers to a country's production and supply capabilities. It mainly consists of a national innovation and application of information technology capabilities, governments, businesses and citizens access to public information, productivity and development of space processing, conversion, transmission, supply and protect its security capabilities, information economy, public information production and institutional arrangements and other aspects of the supply. With the global information society is undoubtedly a public information resource network

and global public information resource sharing features, however, as the other side of the coin, public information between the various national competitions becoming increasingly fierce force. Therefore, to enhance the power of public information is the information society to become the government's strategic objectives and important part of public administration.

To realize the power of public information to enhance strategic objectives, the government should play a major role in promoting the process of national social information, public information infrastructure provided by the government, to become a pioneer in the application of information technology, developed countries have led to government information society of the plan, in which the construction of e-government for promoting social information critical power. Government, through the formulation of public policy and the implementation of public administration, guidance, and promote innovation and application of information technology, the development of the information economy, and promote economic productivity and improve information to provide a broader space for development.

As the production and supply of public information resources management as the primary function of government in the system of government functions in a more important position in the government will likely re-integration and distribution of its internal and external resources to achieve the goal of optimizing the management of public information, these resources include organizational resources, capital and human resources. For example, the establishment of specialized is government information leading institutions, the establishment of public information management institutions to invest more funds to purchase equipment information, training civil servants to use information technology to public management, information skills training for citizens, develop and implement narrowing the "digital divide" programs.

5 GOVERNMENT SHOULD ADDRESS THE IMBALANCE OF INFORMATION SUBJECT TO KNOWN

5.1 *The public's right to know information*

For a long time, the government is the largest owner and controller information. Government-level management and limited range to communicate with the public relevant information, causing the government to make decisions in the absence of a public situation, the lack of positive interaction between government agencies and the public, create a divide between the information and blind to each other either because the people are unaware of, "so that by it", or the public has lost confidence in the government. Under the conditions of modern democracy, the people only understood the government to supervise the government. If a country's political life is not enough transparency, communication channels blocked, information is untrue, etc., will result in administrative affairs and social management of abnormal inefficient, or even out of control. Establish an information disclosure system to ensure the public's right to know information, is both a symbol of social civilization and progress, but also the basis of harmonious social integrity ethics.

5.2 The openness of information channels

To break the information monopoly, truly transparent information disclosure, the Government must first change our concepts, establish and improve information channels open accountability. Long-standing one-way dissemination of information, resulting in many people does not enjoy the right to know should enjoy. Isolation of public policy and the public formed a privileged part of the administrative bureaucracy in the possession of public information and interpretation aspects. Therefore, the information channels open building is one of service to the policy. Make public disclosure of information at all levels to deal directly with the public to meet the information needs of direct real-life experience in the information exchange platform to wait. To see the new information and communication order increasingly demand, especially to break new technological invention, new inventions will be the real birth of new information and communication tools, and constantly explore new ways of information dissemination, make full use of network technology and communication technology transfer public information and the management of public affairs, to increase government transparency and responsiveness, enhance trust between the public and the government to improve the government's ability to collect and process information.

6 CONCLUSION

Service-oriented government administration, citizen focus is to establish government based on the will of the citizens and civic action to the government accountability system. Government action path should be from the outside, that is determined by the citizens' expectations of government

policy blueprint designed to determine the needs of the citizens by the government supply of public goods and services connotation, citizen satisfaction by the decision of the Government of the effectiveness of policy implementation by evaluation of the citizens decide on government policies change direction. Only focus on institution building in these areas, it captures the service-oriented government building not fundamental. Simple open government, public notices and hearings approach, did not rise to the legal regulations can not meet the administrative, scientific and democratic administrative law administrative requirements. If there is no specific, clear validation rules, called the government on major issues to be publicized, important decisions to conduct hearings and experts will, maybe it will become a mere formality, or only in obedience citizen status. If public policy can not form the state of interaction and trust between government and citizens, citizens are not up to the subject of the state administrative center, policies and services, is unlikely to explain such a government is a service-oriented government. Therefore, the government should truly reflect on the service specific service procedures, and methods of service delivery. Of course, in the process of reform, can not herd, nor weaken the authority of the government, but to the typical model, driven in general, a sound system and fully open.

REFERENCES

Chenzheng Gang, Yu Zhengliang, 2009. Century rheological power.
Floor 培敏, 2010. Government reshape the Internet age.
Huo Guoqing, 2012. Three levels of information resources management.
Liguan Chang, Chung Chang-standard, 2012. On the security and confidentiality of e-government.
PR China editor, foreign government information disclosure system compares 2003.
Summer Book chapter, 2006. Administrative management.
Wang Zhongtuo, 2000. Informatization and manage change.
Xie Yang Qun, 2010. U.S. federal government information resources management.
Xiong Chengyu, 2002. Information society.
Zhang Chengfu, 2010. e-government: development and prospects.
Zhou Hongren, 2011. e-government: the government structure of the information age.
Zhou Xiaoying, Wang Yingwei, 2004. Government information management.

Computer, Intelligent Computing and Education Technology – Liu, Sung & Yao (Eds)
© 2014 Taylor & Francis Group, London, ISBN 978-1-138-02469-4

Design Internet-based distance learning platform for ideological & political education about kindergarten teachers

Yu-Ji Gao

Teacher's College, Beihua University, Jilin, China

ABSTRACT: Internet is a rapid spread Digital technology for Information transfer. It is used heavily in Information dissemination due to the growing use of unofficial exchange such as express feelings and Information dissemination. Internet-based distance learning platform relating to multimedia is reviewed in this paper. The mechanics of multimedia and the types of application forms that may occur are introduced. The design & development of distance learning platform such as s interaction and communication are discussed. The prediction of multimedia in wireless networks when Internet is configuration to create education platform of the ideological and political are also introduced. The objective of this paper is to introduce recent achievement in learning platform construction of ideological and political education and to provide a basis for further research.

Keywords: design & development; internet; distance learning platform; kindergarten teachers

1 INTRODUCTION

E-learning is not just the teaching material available online, and more between students and teachers, adequate communication and exchanges between students and students, due to the separation in the space between the remote teaching teachers and students, this communication and exchange is particularly important, in addition to the traditional teaching process to ensure the quality of teaching in some of the key aspects of such assignments, examinations, library, notes, records, etc., should be able to get good support on the Internet. Supports all communication and exchange as well as key aspects of teaching, we need some special tools to support the existing Internet technology does not provide these tools, hence the need for tool development. Also online interactive programming, is generally non-computer professional teachers are difficult to do, there is an urgent need to support a set of online teaching platform that provides comprehensive tools for teachers to support the implementation of online teaching, program design complexity shield, so that teachers can concentrate on teaching, but also makes online teaching from simple teaching to become a full interactive information dissemination and exchange of virtual learning communities.

A complete network teaching platform should be composed of four systems: online teaching support system, online educational management system, development tools, online courses and online teaching resources management system four subsystem architecture.

Teaching Support Network is built on a common platform for Internet/Intranet basis, and specifically for distance learning based on two-way multimedia communication networks and software systems to provide comprehensive services in the rich resources on the basis of discipline, subject teachers in accordance with the teaching requirements and teaching plans, and according to their own teaching characteristics, the development of network courseware, teaching some of the aid network support tools, to carry out two-way distance learning, teaching management system can guarantee this kind of teaching more efficient, and more standardized.

2 ONLINE TEACHING

Network teaching system is a set of services to provide remote teaching system software, it is the core of the network courseware in support of teaching management system, the rational and effective use of pedagogical resources for the implementation of a full range of modern distance education services, and it network courseware and distance learning schools organic integration services. Network teaching system is not only reflected the advanced computer science and technology, but it is important to comply with the general rules of modern education, to provide a truly effective means of modern education, distance education.

2.1 *Streaming lectures*

On the Internet, video and audio data to be transferred large amounts of data must be used streaming technology, the traditional document is downloaded first and then view, this is not suitable for multimedia information. Because the amount of data is the user may need to wait to see before too long. The streaming technology is such a technique, a part of the customer to download the file, unzip the part and start playing the contents of the section before the rest of the file soon. Playback will create a data buffer. While the front of the downloaded file clip is played, the subsequent parts will be downloaded multimedia files. Teachers can allow users on-demand streaming media delivery systems based video courseware to teach, you can also see in the online real live teachers, has a great prospect in distance education.

Courseware on-demand system is actually a suitable teaching VOD (Video On Demand) video-on-demand system, which differs from the ordinary VOD is: courseware on demand not only play the voice and video, but also need to synchronize playback of teachers to teach writing on the blackboard, mostly PowerPoint or HTML based script. The main function of a brief list is as follows.

Digitized live lectures: Lectures video information prior digitized and converted to a format compatible streaming media stored on the server. While the teacher lectures using PowerPoint or HTML server-side script is also stored.

Synchronized video playback and teaching notes: When a user on the client-demand appropriate curriculum, teachers will be teaching video and synchronized PowerPoint or HTML script playback. Users can pause to a particular script or HTML viewing PowerPoint lecture was live, you can also pause live to teach a certain period to see the corresponding PowerPoint or HTML script.

Electronic pointer: In the process of playing video and speech, there can be various types of electronic pointer, pointer movement control by the time playing video, synchronized with the video to indicate teaching focus.

Unlike on-demand, streaming radio synchronization instruction is not stored in advance and then play the video, it will not be stored directly after the digital video broadcast to a group of client player. Thus, it is real-time and synchronous.

Support for multiple classrooms simultaneously broadcast video: multiple video streams simultaneously broadcast to different classrooms. Users can switch between the classroom, watching the different classes live. Support the broadcast data backup server: streaming media server streaming video can be digitized data back to the memory for future demand services.

2.2 *Adaptive hypermedia learning*

As the students participate in distance learning from all walks of life, they do not have a uniform starting point, the ability uneven; therefore, distance learning systems must be able for students with different abilities, different forms of teaching. Adaptive hypermedia teaching refers to the individual characteristics of the student's ability to dynamically presents the most relevant content and teaching learners currently based hypermedia learning ability. It has two meanings, first select learning content, the system according to study history and the ability to estimate, select students have not mastered or not studied teaching content, these learning content is closest to the current student ability. Learning content selection and organization of cognitive unit as the smallest unit, a unit that is a cognitive knowledge teaching objectives set forth in the response to this point a little knowledge to start teaching content is called a cognitive unit. Each learning stage, you can choose one or several cognitive units. Secondly, in the organization of learning content, the system will be based on the student's ability to estimate and students' cognitive style, choose the most suitable way of presenting the content of learners.

2.3 *Evaluation system*

Evaluation system includes test database, test paper generation tools, test process control systems and test results analysis tools, job layout and marking tools. The main function is to test database resources a course questions are organized according to certain educational measurement theory, provide material for the arrangement of the test questions papers generate jobs and provide support for the evaluation of the disciplinary structure of students' test scores. Test papers generation tool based on the purpose of the test is to be automatically withdrawn from Test Questions, composed of teachers meet the intent of the examination papers, depending on the purpose of the exam, you can have intelligent test paper, relative evaluation test paper, absolute evaluation test paper, etc. three roll mode, in addition, can also be requested at the same, generate a different a, B roll, to prevent cheating. Testing process control system mainly to complete the online testing process control, such as remote real-time monitoring, locking system when needed, do not allow students to view and test-independent control test time, when the automatic assignment and so on. Test results analysis tools are generally based on the answer to each question in the case of students knowledge and, for some measure of education for Statistics and Analysis, based on the significance of these metrics are specific instructions, adjust the teaching process and activities, and specific students are given the diagnosis, recommendations for the next study. Also in accordance with the statistics exam tests the quality of the theoretical analysis of the use of educational assessment topics, such as discrimination and difficulty. Job layout and marking tools can be the basis of the test database systems, automatic forming operations, and posted on the Internet, collecting and marking.

2.4 Automatic answering system

Auto Q & A knowledge base is an adaptive system that automatically answering and manual answering of two parts. In the instructional design phase, teachers will be the subject of the most common difficult problems by a certain organization, stored in the knowledge base in the field, when describing the students when they encounter difficult problems, submit questions through the network remotely, the system will be submitted to the student's Description of the problem, knowledge base in the field of intelligent search (mainly used in auto technology Chinese word segmentation, full-text search, semantic matching network, keyword indexing, etc.), according to retrieve content related to the degree level, will answer this question presented to students. When knowledge is not retrieved answer this question, the system will notify the student and take two approaches for subsequent processing: 1) automatically issues sent to preside this course subject teachers by e-mail, when after the teacher to answer this question, the system will automatically answer e-mail sent to students; 2) will be answering questions posted on the bulletin board, seek answers, it was after their answers, the system will notify the student by e-mail. After that, the system will answer questions grouped into the domain knowledge base so that other students encountered similar problems, automatic answer can be given. Completeness and intelligence systems will continue to expand along with the knowledge base, and continue to expand. Auto Q & A also provides online Q & A feature, students log on to the Chat Room, you can send the issue to the public whiteboard answering chamber, presided over the teacher or other students for students to make an appropriate answer, and answer sent to the public whiteboard.

2.5 Teachers and interactive tools

Exchanges between teachers and teaching activities are a very important aspect. Through the exchange, students can get answers to your questions, teachers can understand students' current learning situation. Establish an effective communication environment in distance learning activities so that students and teachers can be easily distributed in different places of exchange, which can effectively improve the quality of distance learning activities.

In order to effectively support among teachers and students located in remote communication, remote communication tools should include synchronous/asynchronous discussion boards, e-mail programs, collaboration tools and other text-based communication tools, should also desktop video conferencing system to provide include graphics, voice, video, whiteboard and other multimedia support.

2.6 Learning management system

No matter how high the system has the intelligence, the computer can not replace human teachers, the computer can liberate humanity from simple repetitive intellectual labor, but the process of teaching the advanced diagnostics, management, reasoning must be done by a human teacher, We can say that the lack of teacher participation in human learning systems, learning is not a perfect system, Internet-based teaching system, the human teacher's participation is still very important, it can make up for lack of intelligent computer systems. Learning Management should have the function are: targeted counseling, troubleshooting, collaborative monitoring, implementation of intelligent, personalized distance learning environment, performance management, learning progress management, student work area, laptop classroom management.

3 NETWORK ACADEMIC MANAGEMENT SYSTEM

Teaching management living a crucial role in distance education, it plays the deployment of teaching resources, organization of teaching activities, summarized the important role of education data. Teaching management system enables the smooth implementation of the teaching, but also realizes the whole process of teaching management modernization and standardization of the management, while also timely and accurately reflects the teaching situation, analyze effectiveness of teaching. Teaching management can be divided into three separate modules: Course management, educational administration and system management, which provides comprehensive services for students, teachers, and administrators. Students can save through their own personal profile management system, timely access to the latest information released by educational institutions, such as teachers get help and counseling; teachers can set curriculum and teaching programs through the management system to see the files of students, provide targeted help; administrators can manage the files of teachers, student records, publishing the latest information on distance learning system management and maintenance.

3.1 Academic management system

Registered certification Student records management, teachers file management, data statistics and analysis, information, administrative document management, teacher evaluation management, student learning assessment management. Professional and curriculum management: including professional setup, management, set up professional courses, management, training development and adjustment programs. Course management: including the establishment of courses specified courses related personnel (such as developers, teaching staff, teaching assistants and students) permissions and passwords, assign established curriculum-related facilities, such as mail, discussion boards, website and so on.

Course content publishing: teachers develop course content will be uploaded onto the corresponding distance learning system, online publishing, implementation of online teaching.

Teaching plans to release: release a course teaching plan, provide query, modify, and delete functions.

Course Management: Students can have the online course, choose to learn some courses, course selection system automatically configures the resources for students to learn and record the course learning process.

3.2 System management

System settings, maintenance functions: it is responsible for the daily maintenance of the system, parameter setting, data backup and recovery. System integrity and data security are mainly by the consistency of the module to be guaranteed.

Network accounting management: Provides billing source data acquisition functions.

Access Control: the system users into different roles, different roles assign different functions, different permissions. For different users, only he can access the function interface; control the display of irrelevant information.

Data backup: regular backup of critical data on the system, and the backup file detailed records should an accident occur, the system can be restored based on the recorded data backup and backup data.

4 SUMMARY

Internet-based remote network education is beneficial complement the variety of teaching modes; it may be one of the next major teachings. In the field of computer, communications and education in the field of joint efforts, distance education network will give people work and life have a profound impact. Meanwhile, research on online teaching and Internet collaborative teaching will also be applied to other areas of the Internet to provide some methods and ideas.

REFERENCES

Gang F.M. 2004. Enjoy the value of modern ideological and political education of China.
Guo Furong, 2004. Enjoy the value of modern ideological and political education of China.
Kuo-Sheng Chang, 2010. The ideological and political education of University students into a kind of enjoyment.
Kuo-Sheng Chang, 2010. The ideological and political education of kindergarten teachers into a kind of enjoyment.
Liang, K.N. 2010. Microblog under the rise of ideological and political work.
Li Jinyuan, 2011. Analysis of online community building challenge the existing criminal law and criminal legislation to improve.
Lu Yao, 2010. The meaning of online community and cyberbuilding information perspective Study.
Ting W.Z. 2010. Cyber building cases continued to increase attention should be paid.
Tong, M.F. 2010. Electronic literature "Forward" has become a spam loudspeakers.

Computer, Intelligent Computing and Education Technology – Liu, Sung & Yao (Eds)
© 2014 Taylor & Francis Group, London, ISBN 978-1-138-02469-4

Research on the virtual economy prediction of stability and security based on information processing

Xue-Zhen Ma
Jilin Railway Vocational and Technology College, Jilin, China

ABSTRACT: In the contemporary economy, economic stability, systemic risk and economic security has been a hot research topic among economists. Based on the real economy and virtual economy system, a comparative analysis of the system based on the virtual economy demonstrates the basic operating rules and characteristics, proposed and demonstrated a "virtual economic stability of contemporary economic stability and security of the core areas of the national economy" theory proposition. The stability is the virtual economy, in fact, the study of risk for the system to provide economic support in theory, so as to guarantee national security surveillance.

Keywords: virtual economy stability; systematic risk; economy safety; prediction

1 INTRODUCTION

Traditionally, economic stability, the core meaning is the real economy price stability. Because, price instability leads to inflation or deflation will disrupt macroeconomic order, thus affecting the allocation of resources, affecting the welfare of society as a whole to grow. However, since the 1980s the situation changed rapidly with the economic liberalization and financial deepening, deepening economic virtualization, before and after the 1990s, in the case of price stability, as the real estate bubble, stock market crash, financial derivatives caused by the collapse of speculation, international hedge funds caused the speculative tide in the financial conditions of globalization, the rapid spread by infecting mechanism as "cosmopolitan" or "international" economic turmoil have been common; between money supply and prices that kind of almost fixed relationship would cease to exist, not only by controlling the money supply is no longer able to effectively control the price level, and even the control of the money supply itself has become a problem. Statistical accounting of those who have been excluded repeated transactions, which is seen as unrelated to GDP creation of speculative activity on the one hand to create a "large number" of the rich, and for a number of emerging industry, the emerging markets brings a huge amount of money; on the other hand often catastrophic "financial crisis" and "currency crisis" transported to various parts of the world. To the late 1990s, the market economy, the monetary authorities have adjusted the country's own policies, began to "asset prices" into the policy to monitor the basic

category. Obviously, the virtual economy turmoil has become the focus of attention. It makes people almost forget that the virtual economy has enormous benefits for them.

Virtual rapid economic development of the basic reason is that the nature of the market economy itself, the essential attribute of the market economy the natural development (or liberalization). The market economy is the essential attribute value, rather than material. Despite the economic substance properties and benefits for the people's consumption is fundamental, but of the market economy of the "rules of the game" is, it's not fundamental. The market economy is the most basic rules of the game "value added" or "money", and this fundamental "value relationship" must pass money to the performance, development and evolution of the form of value and value-added in the form of evolution will inevitably continue to increase. "Virtual economy" activities and making it the market economy is increasingly becoming "important." The economy is reclassified as: virtual economy and real economy an important objective is to distinguish between their different operation modes: real economy is the technology and production cost price support system, the virtual economy is the heart of the price support system. The former showed a price with the downward trend in technological progress, thus diminishing marginal returns become a universal law; latter is the heart of the price support system, heart and other factors led to its herd there is a positive feedback and the universal law of increasing marginal revenue. In this way, the virtual economy to the volatility inherent (or instability) will increase as it increases the proportion of the economy began to affect the operation of the entire economy, making the 1990s, the economic stability of the origin is from the real economy prices stabilize gradually shift the virtual economy system stability.

2 THE CONCEPT OF VIRTUAL ECONOMY AND REAL ECONOMY

Cheng Siwei definition of virtual economy: the virtual economy is the economic activity and the virtual capital to the financial system as the main support of the relevant circular motion, simply put, is to direct the activities of money begets money. In financial markets, the first through the exchange, the exchange of IOU money, stocks, bonds, and at the appropriate time, and through the exchange of the promissory notes, stocks, bonds, and then changed back to money, money begets money directly. Its essence is the virtual capital to the value of independent operation for the purpose of an equity transaction. Fictitious capital is highly developed market economy and monetary capitalization products, both the performance of the capital value of the securities represented by the uncertainty, but also the performance of the uncertainty of the ownership attribution.

The real economy is the material goods and spiritual production, sale and provision of related services, economic activity. Specific form of the entity's economic performance exists for the process of social reproduction of money capital, production and other capital and capital goods, which are the real capital, namely the implementation of the different capital functions. Compared is the virtual economy and real economy, with a high degree of mobility, instability, high-risk and high speculative characteristics.

U.S. financial crisis is also largely ineffective supervision. In order to stabilize the relationship between virtual economy and real economy, the financial regulatory system should be through the entire operation of the virtual economy regulation and constraints. China currently has the CSRC, CIRC and the CBRC, and the internal organization is constantly being improved, according to relevant laws and regulations are promulgated in accordance with the practice needs to continue to make the changes. Construction supervision through the financial system, strengthen the supervision of listed companies, the development of the capital market under the strict supervision of the banking system and to establish and improve asset management and credit risk assessment system. From the financial regulatory system construction, we should gradually rich supervisory experience, in order to facilitate full play to the functions of

the regulatory body that runs in virtual economic health supervision.

3 RELATIONS VIRTUAL ECONOMY AND REAL ECONOMY

3.1 *Entity economic decisions virtual economy*

The real economy is the foundation of the virtual economy. Commodity exchange in particular appears to generate money into the real economy, marked a new stage. Under the commodity currencies economic conditions, resulting in a need for monetary funds transfers on uneven objective monetary wealth distribution. Determines the existence of private ownership of the currency swap can take the remaining places lending practices. In such lending practices, the lender in order to ensure their claims are often required to master a written certificate of debts that such certificates or IOU became the earliest form of fictitious capital. Get credit lending activities accordingly interest income has subsequently evolved into the first virtual economic activity. An economic activity in the virtual economy is only human to a certain stage of economic development entities to adapt to the needs of the real economy generated; the real economy is always the foundation of human existence and development of society.

3.2 *Physical state of the economy is the basis for the healthy operation of the virtual economy*

Virtual economy is the real economy system, but also dependent on the real economy system. When the real economy running in good condition, the virtual economy will thrive; And when the macroeconomic downturn, for various reasons resulting in the real economy is a problem, would ultimately affect the conduction and the virtual economy. As well as the macroeconomic situation of sluggish decline in the quality of listed companies will weaken the stock price stability. Because of this, the real economy has always maintained a good momentum of development is the key to ensure the healthy operation of the virtual economy.

3.3 *Virtual economy with relative independence*

Virtual economy is based on the real economy, and thus the development of the virtual economy needs to be adapted to the real economy, the real economy to adapt to the development stage. But the virtual economy and real economy is not synchronous development, but has its own operating rules, thereby forming a relatively independent economic area of activity. Virtual economy is way interested bills and trading activities in the area of special economic interest form, mainly refers to the relative independence of the financial sector in the real economy, stocks and other financial instruments, but also by a variety of derivative securities stock options, futures contracts, etc. form, they have no direct contact with the real economy, and thus making the virtual economy of scale often produce large deviations from economies of scale entities.

4 IMPLICATIONS OF THE U.S. FINANCIAL CRISIS ON CHINA'S ECONOMIC DEVELOPMENT VIRTUAL

4.1 Maintaining coordination between the virtual economy and the real economy

Modern market economy is the real economy and the virtual economic interdependence, the dialectical unity of the interaction. Entity economic decisions virtual economy, virtual economy and have an adverse effect on the real economy with relative independence. To correctly understand and handle well the relationship between the real economy and the virtual economy, in order to better play the role in promoting the virtual economy to the real economy. Coordination of virtual economy and real economy, is to make the virtual economy can be separated from the real economy this basis, the two are off to see whether the state of the virtual economy remained stable, while the measure of the virtual economy is stable or not, the key is to look at it can not create a good market conditions for the real economy, can play a catalytic role in its real economy. Causes of the financial crisis, even though the United States is multifaceted, but the deeper reason is that over-expansion of the virtual economy, which led to a serious imbalance in the virtual economy and real economy, which caused the asset bubble burst, leading to the outbreak of the crisis.

4.2 Construction supervision of financial system, strengthen financial supervision

U.S. financial crisis is largely ineffective supervision. In order to stabilize the relationship between virtual economy and real economy, the financial regulatory system should be through the entire operation of the virtual economy regulation and constraints. China currently has the CSRC, CIRC and the CBRC, and the internal organization is constantly being improved, according to relevant laws and regulations are promulgated in accordance with the practice needs to continue to make the changes. Construction supervision through the financial system, strengthen the supervision of

listed companies, the development of the capital market under the strict supervision of the banking system and to establish and improve asset management and credit risk assessment system. From the financial regulatory system construction, we should gradually rich supervisory experience, in order to facilitate full play to the functions of the regulatory body that runs in virtual economic health supervision.

4.3 Adjust the structure of the real economy, virtual solid foundation for economic development

Structure of the real economy and the U.S. financial crisis has also long been the U.S. high consumption and low savings unreasonable formed a great relationship. The real economy is the foundation of the virtual economy, so the only rational economic structure of the entity, established on the basis of the virtual economy was healthy development. To promote the healthy development of the virtual economy, we need to constantly adjust the industrial structure. The real economy is escalating industrial process. If the existing industrial and product saturation, industry can not successfully upgrade will be a lot of money into the stock market and real estate market, the virtual economy could evolve into a bubble economy, and ultimately led to the outbreak of the crisis. For China, the most important development of the virtual economy is to build high-tech industries as the basis, to promote the development of new technology industries, and these industries led industrial development system.

In recent years, due to the impact of the Double Surplus and other factors, China has also emerged excess liquidity, too much money concentrated in real estate, stocks and resource-based products and other market areas. Although the government's macro-control measures to curb the further development of adverse effects, but to guide the coordination of virtual economy and real economic development, prevent and mitigate the excessive expansion of the virtual economy which could lead to a bubble economy, China is still current and future macro-control can not be ignored the issue is important to ensure stable economic development.

4.4 Active role in the virtual economy to the real economy

1. Promote optimal allocation of social resources
2. Provide financial support for the real economy
3. Helps to spread business risk
4. Beneficial ownership reorganization deepen enterprise reform.

4.5 *The negative impact of the virtual economy to the real economy*

1. Virtual economic expansion over the possibility of increased economic turmoil entity
2. Virtual economy led to excessive expansion of the formation of the bubble economy
3. Expansion will cover up over the virtual economy overheating economy.

5 MODEL AND EMPIRICAL

We are through the PPI, SP and HS three variables seeking to get their time-varying variance of its fluctuations characteristic graph, GARCHPPI, GARCHSP, GARCHHS denote the time-varying variance of the four variables. As can be seen in Figure 1, SP volatility of stock price indices largest real estate price volatility clustering feature is most obvious, which fully shows that real estate prices more volatile PPI indicates the real economy more vulnerable to the purchaser's psychological factors. Products from the supply in terms of the real economy, with product launches, development, maturity and decline to a price fall, and the other from the demand is concerned, obey the principle

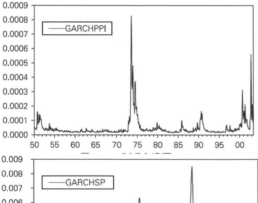

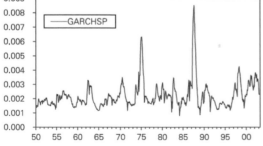

Figure 1. PPI schematic fluctuations.

of diminishing marginal utility, so the price of the real economy showed a return to characteristics.

6 CONCLUSION

Virtual economy system risk is the economic system in a virtual bubble economy caused by excessive volatility in the possibility of bubble economy crisis significance lies in the bubble caused by the economic recession or economic stagnation. From a system point of view, when a subsystem of the system to react, and the reaction and the role of the entire system, then on the existence of endogenous systemic risk. Endogenous uncertainty is the result of each are interrelated exogenous uncertainty notable feature is every time the results are unrelated. When the investor's strategy will be imitated, then it will have to consider other investors, and if the impact will also affect the behavior of other market participants, the system will amplify the original shock impact. When the market is in a stable state, as the uncertainty is exogenous and not much harm, however, is not the case in times of crisis. Risk management system goal is to cope with the crisis, rather than in the steady state what role. Therefore, the uncertainty of exogenous shocks caused by the impact of the economic system can be divided into two phases, the first is the exogenous shocks own energy level, and the second is amplified by the economic system in the endogenous level of energy. Experience has shown that only the latter is often fatal harm to the system. If the risk is magnified, the system will be fed back into the real economy, causing the value of the relationship between the real economy system disorders, endanger national security.

REFERENCES

Guo Furong, 2004. Enjoy the value of modern ideological and political education of China.
Kuo-Sheng Chang, 2010. The ideological and political education of University students into a kind of enjoyment.
Li Jinyuan, 2011. Analysis of online community building challenge the existing criminal law and criminal legislation to improve.
Lu Yao, 2010. The meaning of online community and cyberbuilding information perspective Study.
Ting W.Z. 2010. Cyber building cases continued to increase attention should be paid.
Tong, M.F. 2010. Electronic literature "Forward" has become a spam loudspeakers.

Computer, Intelligent Computing and Education Technology – Liu, Sung & Yao (Eds)
© *2014 Taylor & Francis Group, London, ISBN 978-1-138-02469-4*

Research on the change trend of civil and commercial law in socio-economic management

Lian-Peng Wang
Law College Beihua University, China

ABSTRACT: Civil and commercial law play more important role in the maintenance of public order and promoting social economic development. However, with economic development and social life of change, Civil and commercial law have increasingly come under the impact of other systems. In such circumstances, civil and commercial law have also had to adjust its systems to adapt to the changing social and economic life. In this paper, the Changes and developments of civil and commercial law are investigated in accordance with both basic principles and basic system based on reconstruction of the value system of civil and commercial law.

Keywords: civil and commercial law; impact; reconstruction

1 INTRODUCTION

With the rapid economic development of the times, the civil and commercial law of agency is arrival of the letter on behalf of the foot inch. Will become increasingly prominent position. Coupled with the development of the national legislature in order to meet the needs of the times and a lot of civil and commercial legislation and improve the work. For example, the "Contract Law", "Property Law" and "tort law" to represent the part of the civil and commercial legislation has been introduced and has been implemented. However, with the development and changes of the times, civil and commercial law of what happened, how the times are changing impact on civil law deserves to be discussed. As in all areas of human society ever penetration technology, which is changing the patterns of development and economic and social development process, they also made it to the traditional factors of production from the beginning of the era of the information-based, technology and science and technology as the representative of the era. Information Age to showcase a broad prospect for significantly improved the quality of life of the new era. Bring economic development to a new situation, but also to people's daily lives, and made more comprehensive civil and commercial requirements and challenges. Civil and Commercial Law only adapted to the requirements of the information age with an open mind and spirit of seeking truth from facts deal with complex issues, in order to avoid falling into a stretched embarrassment. From this perspective, the analysis of civil law has positive significance for improving the efficiency of civil and commercial law in the change and development of the information age, type font, size and spacing.

2 SOCIAL AND ECONOMIC DEVELOPMENT IMPACT ON THE VALUE SYSTEM OF CIVIL LAW

2.1 *Impact on the socio-economic development of civil and commercial value*

With the continuous development of social economy, safety and efficiency became the basis for the value of the pursuit of civil and commercial law. Among the traditional civil law, security has always been subordinate to a derivative position. For example, in a traditional transaction, transaction security, as defined mainly refers to information, delivery and credit secure three areas. In reality the trading process in which the impact of information security on the entire transaction is generally small, third-party access to transaction information does not constitute a significant threat to the security of transactions. Meanwhile, the traditional transaction was crunching the trading transaction security issues often do not exist.

With the advent of the information age, information technology subject to civil and commercial freedom provides a more convenient and vast space. In the information age, the Internet broke the boundaries and geographical constraints. Body can act according to their own will to a network tool for anyone with any information elsewhere called you engage in civil and commercial activities. In this case, the market is an organic whole, its openness makes it possible to obtain any information they want from them. You can also publish their information to any person. This is the main achievement of freedom to provide a solid foundation.

2.2 New era on the civil law system of values required to reconstruct

Value system of the new era is the main civil and commercial law, including freedom, equality, equity, security and efficiency. Among these, the value of freedom is still the foundation of the whole system. Other fundamental values embodied; equality, compared with the traditional meaning of civil law has a different connotation, has instrumental value and targeted values: fairness, is the most essential value of the pursuit of civil and commercial law; safe, although it is the new era basic and instrumental value civil and commercial law, but because of the special nature of the information age, security should be an important goal of the information age as the pursuit of civil and commercial law; efficiency, which is one of the fundamental value of civil and commercial law, and has important value position. However, the safety and effectiveness of a pair of conflicting values, civil and commercial legislation in the process of how to be a reasonable balance between the two should be an important goal of the legislation.

3 CHANGES IN CIVIL AND COMMERCIAL LAW RELATED TO THE OCCURRENCE OF NEW ERA

3.1 Changes in the basic principles of civil law aspects of the new era

New era commercial law neutrality refers to equality in the information age. The relevant conditions for participation to all the main civil and commercial transactions among people engaged in commercial activities and needs, including related technical, trading platforms should remain neutral, can not appear, such as preferences and maintenance. E-commerce law, for example, equal neutrality should do these points: First, the technical aspects of equality law on e-commerce and various key encryption method should be treated equally so, there can be no discrimination; secondly, equal medium of exchange, then the principle of equality mainly in communications, wireless, cable and broadcast communications and so should be treated equally; Third, the implementation of equality, civil law should not only implement e-commerce law, but also should not be neglected other relevant law, and for national and international e-commerce activities should be treated equally: Fourth, equal

protection, e-commerce law should not only be protected against businesses and domestic clients, but also to give equal protection to consumers and foreign consumers.

Safety is defined in the information age have a more extensive and profound meaning, the so-called safety principles refers to all civil and commercial activities should be safe as the basis and prerequisite for the corresponding legislation should reflect and reflect on the safety requirements. To protect the safety of e-commerce, for example, the implementation of the electronic commerce act, this is both an important purpose. E-commerce is also a fundamental principle formulated. An important feature of the information age is sufficient efficient and fast, efficient and fast and this should be on the basis of safety, especially as virtualization, security, network information is particularly important. Here there is a certain connotation of safety changes, including so few: First, the physical network is more a lack of environmental issues, making the storage amount of information leakage or loss, etc.: Second, due to human impact. Such as hacking and illegal interception, storage and dissemination is information on modifications and so on. Therefore, the current legislation is largely set by the network and physical security brawl digital certification, signature and payment terms to achieve security objectives. Civil law has been changes by the security policy also reflects a change in civil law in order to adapt to the information age and carried out.

Fair, just and effective legal profession has been plagued an important problem. Said on behalf of the law as an impartial, fair and its birth is to appear. At the same time, the law or the establishment is an economic foundation. In the legislative process, it should be understood that these two basic meaning, the only way to be completely defined the basic principles of law. The basic principles of the law enacted at various times embodied is different this time because the law needs to reflect the interests of the ruling class demands of various periods. In today's information age, the benefits of the principle of civil law that requires civil and commercial legislation and related activities and so should be in line with improving economic efficiency and promoting efficiency goals construction, reflecting the information age, Internet freedom and civil law's overall effectiveness and value.

3.2 Changes in the scope of the new era of basic and fundamental civil law system

A mature and complete civil and commercial legal system is reflected in the current period of civil and commercial law as well as the main content of the facts of life to have the basic conditions. From this perspective, this mature and improve generally have a certain narrowness, that has staged some extent. With the continuous development of social economy, the traditional range of civil and commercial rights system has been out of wet expansion, which is mainly reflected in the following aspects: First, the exclusive right to use the repository. An important feature of the information age is that all the information has become an important civil and commercial life, the provision and development of information has become the cause of civil and commercial activities in most of the key issues and key success factors. Therefore, in the course of civil and commercial legislation should not have the originality of this band, but people on the development and investment information base necessary to make some contribution to civil and commercial rights to be protected by their fruits of labor, to avoid dampen their enthusiasm for work? Currently, civil and commercial law for the exclusive right to use such information in the database is still not perfect, but with the economic and social development, the scope of the rights of civil and commercial matters such changes have taken place, to a certain connotation Nob and expansion; secondly, exclusive right to use the domain name. Currently, there is not a precise and civil law for the exclusive right to define the domain of the evening. Domain name refers to the juice of a computer connected to the virtual address on the Internet. By domain name can make the information on your computer to access the network, communications liaison, while also being able to access your other computers to facilitate the storage of information resources. With networking and commercial information, the use and extent of use of the various sectors of the domain name deepening domain name has gradually become a symbol marking commercial network economy, almost traditional knowledge economy era of corporate trademarks and other intellectual property rights, and has the same effect. At this time, the domain name has been become a set of commercial value and use one of the important functions in business competition chips. Once the transaction is in the body double was the key to the right to use the domain name, then he got the exclusive right to use the domain name. Civil law should recognize this phenomenon and features of the rational planning and integration. Third, copyright information networks have the right to control its spread in the two works and the network information for its production. Due to the need to consider the network to work with the information, which includes audio, video, etc., they have a variety of transmission routes and modes of transmission. Network information is combined with the use of interactive forms of communication, not the traditional one-way communication. Thus, in the legislative process this information should be copyright protected areas Anjou to them, so that the information on its copyright owners can make work, sound recording and video products spread on the network spread in the network become a new civil and commercial rights.

3.3 Social and economic development to expand the civil law of the object

An important feature of the Internet is that they have open, which makes the source of its information, and more open channels and rich. Its open nature of the exchange of information also provides a wider space. And improve the value of the Internet has spread its complete transformation occurred in information delivery and performance, etc., while the value of the information itself has become a subject can not ignore the practical significance. This is because the information has an associated property interests with economic interests, but also as a person of interest privacy. Taking into account the important status and role of information in the Internet age in civil and commercial activities should be emphasis on civil and commercial information, which needs to be reflected in the legislative process, but also should be asked all the main civil and commercial matters built up contact such as the repository of the exclusive right of the copyright control mentioned above which are all incorporated into the adjustment range of civil and commercial law. In addition, taking into account the interests of other principles and rights should be incorporated into civil law corresponding to them.

At the same time, the law or the establishment is an economic foundation. In the legislative process, it should be understood that these two basic meaning, the only way to be completely defined the basic principles of law. The basic principles of the law enacted at various times embodied is different this time because the law needs to reflect the interests of the ruling class demands of various periods. In today's information age, the benefits of the principle of civil law that requires civil and commercial legislation and related activities and so should be in line with improving economic efficiency and promoting efficiency goals construction, reflecting the information age, Internet freedom and civil law's overall effectiveness and value.

3.4 Civil and commercial development will achieve global unity

Civil and Commercial Law as an adjustment to all the rights and obligations of civil and commercial activities among a general term, which should be based on object relations legislation in civil and commercial activities of the network as part of its role. When the economy is a single economic market countries independent existence and the market corresponding to the legal system is relatively independent. However, with the continuous development of economic times, the network will all civil and commercial activities of the various countries around the world have linked up to promote the integration of the global economy. Due to the integration of the global Internet trends and the gradual integration of features, making the global network of civil and commercial activity has more commonality and universality. At this time, the concept of law worldwide, values and performance standards will gradually become so unified, and the development of a unified civil law tends to become an inevitable trend, also spoke.

To protect the safety of e-commerce, for example, the implementation of the electronic commerce act, this is both an important purpose. E-commerce is also a fundamental principle formulated. An important feature of the information age is sufficient efficient and fast, efficient and fast and this should be on the basis of safety, especially as virtualization, security, network information is particularly important. Here there is a certain connotation of safety changes, including so few: First, the physical network is more a lack of environmental issues, making the storage amount of information leakage or loss, etc.: Second, due to human impact. Such as hacking and illegal interception, storage and dissemination is information on modifications and so on. Therefore, the current legislation is largely set by the network and physical security brawl digital certification, signature and payment terms to achieve security objectives. Civil law has been changes by the security policy also reflects a change in civil law in order to adapt to the information age and carried out.

With networking and commercial information, the use and extent of use of the various sectors of the domain name deepening domain name has gradually become a symbol marking commercial network economy, almost traditional knowledge economy era of corporate trademarks and other intellectual property rights, and has the same effect. At this time, the domain name has been become a set of commercial value and use one of the important functions in business competition chips. Once the transaction is in the body double was the key to the right to use the domain name, then he got the exclusive right to use the domain name. Civil law should recognize this phenomenon and features of the rational planning and integration. Third, copyright information networks have the right to control its spread in the two works and the network information for its production. Due to the need to consider the network to work with the information,

which includes audio, video, etc., they have a variety of transmission routes and modes of transmission. Network information is combined with the use of interactive forms of communication, not the traditional one-way communication. Thus, in the legislative process this information should be copyright protected areas Anjou to them, so that the information on its copyright owners can make work, sound recording and video products spread on the network spread in the network become a new civil and commercial rights.

4 CONCLUSIONS

From the form of performance in terms of civil law and civil law embodied in the Department of Anglo-American law is different. French and German civil law which is represented primarily by civil law code in the form of legislation and the corresponding performance out: The common law is mainly in the large number of legal cases on the basis of the judgment come. American scholar Ezra Pound once said: Once the common law judges to implement the law, directly or indirectly, they always used to be in the past judicial experience applicable to the case in front of, rather than an abstract system will be placed in the case, the exact logical framework of.

Under the framework of civil law based on civil law and is by no means any product, but each country set up according to their own social habits, customs or practices, etc., especially the rules of economic development in the commodity form and practices. For example, the German Civil Code that originated in the Germanic law, and Germanic law in different regions and countries there are many unwritten customary law. These civil habits, particularly on commodity trading habits and so on foot in order to adapt and meet the needs of economic development of a country. At the same time, these rules are still the precise legal language by reasoning and deductive logic. This also reflects an aspect of the civil law and common law to some extent, as well as the integration point in common.

REFERENCES

Chen Yunxiong, 2006. Improve our commercial agent theoretical foundation and its related rules.
Nguyen Chan Lin, 2000. On the perfection of commercial agent system.
Xiao Na, 2006. Comparison and selection of commercial agency legislation.
Xiao Navy, 2006. Comparison and selection of commercial agency legislation.
Zhang Lanlan, 2001. Discussion on construction of commercial agent system.

Computer, Intelligent Computing and Education Technology – Liu, Sung & Yao (Eds)
© *2014 Taylor & Francis Group, London, ISBN 978-1-138-02469-4*

Network-based distance management platform based on QQ group for ideological and political education

Li-Xin Zhang
Beihua University Teacher's College, Jilin, China

ABSTRACT: Network is a rapid spread Digital technology for Information transfer. It is used heavily in Information dissemination due to the growing use of express feelings and Information dissemination. Network-based distance management platform relating to ideological and political education is reviewed in this paper. The mechanics of QQ group and the types of application forms that may occur are introduced. The design & development of distance management platform such as s interaction and communication are discussed. The prediction of QQ group in wireless networks when Network is configuration to create education platform of the ideological and political are also introduced. The objective of this paper is to introduce recent achievement in management platform construction of ideological and political education and to provide a basis for further research.

Keywords: QQ group; design & development; ideological & political; distance management platform

1   INTRODUCTION

QQ group referred, often network user's nickname "collar", is based on user relationship information sharing, dissemination and acquisition platform. The emergence of QQ group epoch-making significance, it marks the era of the personal Network. QQ group can get in the colors of the Network age college students of all ages and favorable, this must be from the "QQ group" powerful and college students to seek their own development needs two to illustrate. From the technical characteristics of the micro-blog, it gives college students love new things provides powerful features, such as a significant reduction in the threshold of user access to technology, to the QQ group easy-to-use and more convenient. QQ group Bowen upper limit of 140 words turns civilians and Shakespeare pulled the same horizontal line, resulting in a lot of original content produced explosive. The QQ group release students capture the interest and enthusiasm of the analysis of the problem, each valuable insights in a short space actively interpretation and dissemination. In addition, the QQ group network community more powerful such as QQ group, just click on "follows", you can receive immediate access to "follow" any information released. On the surface, QQ group is the miniaturization of the original blog, but in fact, the advantages of micro-Bo lies not only in its short, depends on its comprehensive and cross-platform property. The QQ group comprehensive blog, forums, chat and other network functions, and can achieve linkage with SMS,

MMS, Network chat, e-mail, instant stronger. Therefore, from the technical characteristics of the micro-Bo, it provides powerful networking features to meet the wide range of needs of students.

2   STUDENTS SEEK THEIR OWN ENVELOPMENTS NEEDS

QQ group is able to meet the needs of college student's personality development. Along with the growth of college students, the pursuit and the desire to show their personalities is increasingly strong. Modern society, the personality symbol of self-confidence, breakthrough force and innovation, personalized so that students revert to their "own", and "own" based on the breakthrough and development, rather than on others "unified". In the meantime, the behavior of individuals has enough opportunities and rights conditions contributed personalized indispensable. QQ group new media It is in this sense that meet the individual needs of the contemporary college students, which implements the abandoning of interpersonal and mass media, non-quantifiable information and a variety of functions to provide participants with numerous optional opportunity to, giving each participant a "knowledge" and that the rights and freedoms and making it the main body of the expression of opinion. QQ group meet the needs of the development of College Students' Interpersonal. Good interpersonal development of students has a pivotal role. In modern society, learning, living, fast-paced and strong pressure, the students need to participate in social interaction in cyberspace to expand their social circle, to ease the social pressures and stresses of everyday life. In QQ group, students can cover all topics of real-time network, public events, current events, hot spots; personal feelings commence immediate rapid exchange of this kind of open, equal exchange for college students to create a new interpersonal environment and interpersonal development.

However, the emergence of QQ group will allow the dissemination of information emerging from the authority of the government, schools, ideological and political educators and parent's control. QQ group "read to share the" right to speak "to the center, so that students have found a possibility to become" new opinions class, originally belonged to the community "junior" college students in society also have a certain impact on the possibilities. In the context of micro-Bo, their "voice" is no longer small-scale entertain themselves, the propagation characteristics of the micro-Bo lead to a wide audience, which also stimulated young personality from another dimension elite consciousness, as well as traditional colleges and universities ideological and political education mode educators unilateral control voice dissatisfaction and resistance to erosion of the traditional authority of the ideological and political education of college students.

QQ group is relative real user identity, to tell their kind of realism and a sense of security, and do not have to worry about no reason to incur the kind of cynical anonymous forum, thus helping students to express their rich experience and ease its psychological tension, lubricate their interpersonal relationship. The QQ group meets the needs of college student's emotional development. With today society rapidly changing situation, the values of the college students is in a diversified portfolio of unprecedented and even the phenomenon of coexistence of pluralistic values. Pluralistic values a direct result of the diversity of the students on the emotional needs absolute authority of worship, absolute single emotional needs be gone, replaced by a multi-scene emotional needs, and the formation of the complex emotional needs structure, both low-level substance-related emotional and physiological needs, and the high level of emotion associated with the psychological, spiritual needs. QQ group exchanges of the world because there is no face-to-face embarrassment, and independent of time, space, the limit of the carrier, which fully express their emotions technology platform for college students to help meet college students a healthy and joyful emotional needs of social interaction and enjoy novel high culture entertainment emotional needs, enhance self-learning knowledge of emotional needs, vested groups, love and respect, understanding the emotional needs, and so on.

3 RATIONAL RESPONSE OF THE IDEOLOGICAL AND POLITICAL EDUCATION

Traditional kindergarten teachers ideological and political education through classroom education, establish typical propaganda guidance and other methods, an important feature of these methods is authoritative, clear information directional mapping efforts. Ideological and Political workers by taking control of the right to speak, that is a conscious choice of suitable materials to the object of education, high strength spread contains specific information in order to facilitate the thinking and behavior of the object of education shift. However, the emergence of micro blog will allow the dissemination of information emerging from the authority of the government, schools, ideological and political educators and parent's control. Micro blog "read to share the" right to speak "to the center, so that students have found a possibility to become" new opinions class", originally belonged to the community "junior" kindergarten teachers in society also have a certain impact on the possibilities. In the context of micro-Bo, their "voice" is no longer small-scale entertain themselves, the propagation characteristics of the micro-Bo lead to a wide audience, which also stimulated young personality from another dimension elite consciousness, as well as traditional colleges and universities ideological and political education mode educators unilateral control voice dissatisfaction and resistance to erosion of the traditional authority of the ideological and political education of kindergarten teachers. The original A/B two sets of comparative data table, as shown in Table 1.

Two groups before and after training difference:

A: −0.90, −0.11, −0.15, −0.45, −0.62
B: −0.02, −0.06, −0.05, −0.03, −0.67

Indicators increase the value of the sensitivity test of the "T" word. As shown in Table 2.

QQ group "read to share the" right to speak to the center, so that students have found a

Table 1. A/B two sets of comparative data.

$(\rightarrow)$			$(\rightleftharpoons)$		
8.9	9.21	8.29	9.21	8.40	8.9
11.4	10.19	10.07	10.19	11.47	11.4
8.37	10.21	10.04	10.21	8.41	8.37
9.38	8.69	8.34	8.69	9.42	9.38
9.51	9.15	8.54	9.15	10.08	9.51

Table 2. Indicators increase the value.

	$\bar{x}$	S	t	p
A	0.434	0.3326	2.331	$(0.053) > 0.05$
B	0.040	0.0245		

possibility to become "new opinions class", originally belonged to the community "junior" college students in society also have a certain impact on the possibilities. In the context of micro-Bo, their "voice" is no longer small-scale entertain themselves, the propagation characteristics of the micro-Bo lead to a wide audience, which also stimulated young personality from another dimension elite consciousness, as well as traditional colleges and universities ideological and political education mode educators unilateral control voice dissatisfaction and resistance to erosion of the traditional authority of the ideological and political education of college students.

From the "portal", "blog" to "micro blog", information dissemination confined space gradually open, legal or illegal, healthy or unhealthy information to quickly enter the field of vision of university students, the university is no longer able to effective supervision, Ideological and Political workers no longer be able to carefully and consciously avoid the potential negative impact of certain adverse information on kindergarten teachers, it is difficult to play good information pollution, junk information "gatekeeper" role and reduce destruction university students ideological and political the various confounders steady-state within the educational system. Since the vast amounts of information can be obtained from the micro-blog in a very short time, kindergarten teachers are often difficult to spam messages from the brain "filter", a lot of information is hard to determine the authenticity of good and bad, popular fragmentation false. Insiders pointed out that since the micro blog contributed large-scale Network-based "crowd", then all kinds of rumors and even slander can spread the fastest in all directions to meet the public's psychological adventures. 'Micro blog' forward 'has become a spam megaphone', "micro blog is a good spam manufacturing plant flat display of all information and to spam enough exposure opportunities."

4 RATIONAL RESPONSE OF THE IDEOLOGICAL AND POLITICAL EDUCATION

Traditional college students ideological and political education through classroom education,

establish typical propaganda guidance and other methods, an important feature of these methods is authoritative, clear information directional mapping efforts. Ideological and Political workers by taking control of the right to speak, that is a conscious choice of suitable materials to the object of education, high strength spread contains specific information in order to facilitate the thinking and behavior of the object of education shift. However, the emergence of QQ group will allow the dissemination of information emerging from the authority of the government, schools, ideological and political educators and parent's control. QQ group "read to share the" right to speak "to the center, so that students have found a possibility to become" new opinions class, originally belonged to the community "junior" college students in society also have a certain impact on the possibilities. In the context of micro-Bo, their "voice" is no longer small-scale entertain themselves, the propagation characteristics of the micro-Bo lead to a wide audience, which also stimulated young personality from another dimension elite consciousness, as well as traditional colleges and universities ideological and political education mode educators unilateral control voice dissatisfaction and resistance to erosion of the traditional authority of the ideological and political education of college students.

From the "portal", "blog" to "QQ group", information dissemination confined space gradually open, legal or illegal, healthy or unhealthy information to quickly enter the field of vision of university students, the university is no longer able to effective supervision, Ideological and Political workers no longer be able to carefully and consciously avoid the potential negative impact of certain adverse information on college students, it is difficult to play good information pollution, junk information "gatekeeper" role and reduce destruction university students ideological and political the various confounders steady-state within the educational system. Since the vast amounts of information can be obtained from the micro-blog in a very short time, college students are often difficult to spam messages from the brain "filter", a lot of information is hard to determine the authenticity of good and bad, popular fragmentation false.

However, the emergence of QQ group will allow the dissemination of information emerging from the authority of the government, schools, ideological and political educators and parent's control. QQ group "read to share the" right to speak "to the center, so that students have found a possibility to become" new opinions class, originally belonged to the community "junior" college students in society also have a certain impact on the possibilities. In the context of micro-Bo, their "voice" is no longer small-scale entertain themselves, the propagation characteristics of the micro-Bo lead to a wide audience, which also stimulated young personality from another dimension elite consciousness, as well as traditional colleges and universities ideological and political education mode educators unilateral control voice dissatisfaction and resistance to erosion of the traditional authority of the ideological and political education of college students.

From the "portal", "blog" to "QQ group", information dissemination confined space gradually open, legal or illegal, healthy or unhealthy information to quickly enter the field of vision of university students, the university is no longer able to effective supervision, Ideological and Political workers no longer be able to carefully and consciously avoid the potential negative impact of certain adverse information on college students, it is difficult to play good information pollution, junk information "gatekeeper" role and reduce destruction university students ideological and political the various confounders steady-state within the educational system. Since the vast amounts of information can be obtained from the micro-blog in a very short time, college students are often difficult to spam messages from the brain "filter", a lot of information is hard to determine the authenticity of good and bad, popular fragmentation false.

Insiders pointed out that since the QQ group contributed large-scale Network-based "crowd", then all kinds of rumors and even slander can spread the fastest in all directions to meet the public's psychological adventures. 'QQ group' forward 'has become a spam megaphone', "QQ group is a good spam manufacturing plant flat display of all information and to spam enough exposure opportunities."

5 CONCLUSION

Through the QQ group grasp the college students' ideological context. QQ group as a "face" is behind the innovative interactive way to help colleges and universities ideological and political workers to keep abreast of changes in students' ideological grasp the idea of "context" of the students, and then be targeted for ideological and political education. In order to effectively grasp the students' ideological dynamic, universities should strive to build the QQ group platform system, smooth information transfer channels. First, colleges and universities can rely on campus Moral website, create a micro-blog publishing platform to promote online interaction between schools and students, students and students, to grasp the students' ideological trends, strengthen ideological education and guidance. Second, colleges and universities rely on student cell phone user base, the establishment of mobile QQ group publishing platform to promote the interaction of teachers and students, life and point-to-point information for the majority of students, in particular, do not have a computer, Network inconvenience students to open up quick and easy information delivery channels. Third, college students QQ group as the basis to establish QQ group mass mailing platform to promote multi-level schools, colleges, classes, students, flat, equal exchange. Fourth, colleges and universities to the reality of student groups as the basis to establish the QQ group classification platform, to further enhance the relevance and effectiveness of ideological and political education.

REFERENCES

Gang F.M. 2004. Enjoy the value of modern ideological and political education of China.

Guo Furong, 2004. Enjoy the value of modern ideological and political education of China.

Kuo-Sheng Chang, 2010. The ideological and political education of University students into a kind of enjoyment.

Kuo-Sheng Chang, 2010. The ideological and political education of kindergarten teachers into a kind of enjoyment.

Liang, K.N. 2010. Microblog under the rise of ideological and political work.

Li Jinyuan, 2011. Analysis of online community building challenge the existing criminal law and criminal legislation to improve.

Lu Yao, 2010. The meaning of online community and cyberbuilding information perspective study.

Ting W.Z. 2010. Cyber building cases continued to increase attention should be paid.

Tong, M.F. 2010. Electronic literature "Forward" has become a spam loudspeakers.

Computer, Intelligent Computing and Education Technology – Liu, Sung & Yao (Eds)
© 2014 Taylor & Francis Group, London, ISBN 978-1-138-02469-4

Virtual trading assessment techniques based on China's foreign exchange reserves data

Ya-Ning Cheng

School of Economic Management, Beihua University, Jilin City, China

ABSTRACT: This paper introduces a practical configuration trading game based on China's foreign exchange reserves data. It is based on real data and trading rule, which is issued 2011. This assumption is supported by the different trading patterns that for different trading purposes. The trading platform is constructed on by the fully understandings of whole transaction process. Assembly language technology region shows that configuration is a possible operating, which makes virtual trading game of the Forex trading into reality.

Keywords: virtual trading; assessment techniques; assembly language; forex

1 INTRODUCTION

China's foreign exchange reserves rapid growth after 2000, China's foreign exchange reserves exceeded $ 100 billion for the first time in November 1996; five years later, this figure was doubled to $ 200 billion. In the end of February 2006, the first time China surpassed Japan, ranking first in the world; October of the same year, China's foreign exchange reserves exceeded $ 1 trillion mark for the first time. In June 2009, the foreign exchange reserves exceeded $ 2 trillion since then less than a year, foreign exchange reserves increased to $ 3,000,000,000,000, a growth rate as high as 50%, at the end of 2010, the foreign exchange reserves of U.S. $ 28,437 million, an increase of 18.7%; the end of 2011, the country's foreign exchange reserves of U.S. $ 31,811 million (see Fig. 1), foreign exchange reserves are still among the first in the world. Such a huge foreign exchange reserves means that China has plenty of international payments.

It enhances China's foreign affordability and the ability to adjust the balance of payments, improve the country's international credit strength and resilience of the international financial risk, and provide a solid guarantee for the country's progressive reform. However, the foreign exchange reserves is a double-edged sword, foreign exchange reserves are not better, the rapid expansion of the scale of foreign exchange reserves led to the intensification of the domestic base money, promote the excessive growth of monetary credit, causing investment expansion, inflationary pressures increase and asset bubbles appear, endangering the financial security of our country.

2 THE STATUS QUO OF CHINA'S FOREIGN EXCHANGE RESERVES AND THE EASONS FOR THE CONTINUED GROWTH

Before 1978, China's internal implementation of a highly centralized planned economy, less involved in international economic exchanges. Relatively limited scale is China's foreign exchange reserves. Since the reform and opening up, China's rapid economic development, openness continues to increase. In the context of economic and financial globalization, the international balance of payments situation has undergone great change in our country. With the influx of foreign trade volume increased and foreign capital, makes a huge balance of payments surplus faster pace of accumulation of foreign exchange reserves. 1980, China's foreign exchange reserves of only $ 2.26 billion, to 1981, foreign exchange reserves amounted to 118.9, the growth rate reached 429%. Subsequent annual foreign exchange reserves also increased steadily. The twenty-first century, China's foreign exchange reserves appear unusual growth. In 2001, foreign

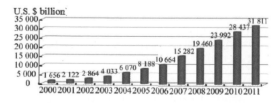

Figure 1. 2011 year–2000 year, China's foreign currency reserves.

exchange reserves amounted to 212.17 billion U.S. dollars, an increase of $ 46.6 billion over the previous year, an increase of 28.15%; to the 2002 foreign exchange reserves amounted to 286.41 billion U.S. dollars, an increase of $ 74.24 billion the previous year, a growth rate of 34.99%; to the end of 2004, foreign exchange reserves amounted to 609.93 billion U.S. dollars, an increase of 206.68 billion U.S. dollars, an increase of 51.25%: the end of 2006, China's foreign exchange reserves have reached $ 1.0663 trillion, as the world's largest foreign exchange reserves.

3 FOREIGN EXCHANGE RESERVES GROWTH MOTIVATION

The trade surplus is the main source of China's foreign exchange reserves from 1994 to 2011; China has maintained a trade surplus for 18 consecutive years. In 1994 and 1998, China's trade surplus overall showing a trend of increasing year by year: in 1994, only $ 5.4 billion, to $ 16.7 billion in 1995, increased to $ 43.47 billion in 1998, an average annual growth rate reaching a high of 65% or more. 1999 2004 trade surplus with slight fluctuations stage, the full year 2004 trade surplus of 32.09 billion U.S. dollars, an increase of approximately 29.4% as compared to 2003. Into 2005, China's trade surplus momentum suddenly increases the year of 2005, up to $ 102 billion trade surplus surge of 217.9 percent compared to 2004. Into 2007, the momentum of rapid growth of the trade surplus has not yet deceleration, the annual trade surplus amounted to U.S. $ 2,618.3 million; 2010 full-year trade surplus of U.S. $ 1,831 million, down 6.4%; 2011 annual cumulative trade surplus of U.S. $ 1,551.4 million, a year-on-year decrease of 14.5% (see Fig. 2). Huge trade surplus from 1994 to 2011 for 18 consecutive years, resulting in the rapid growth of China's foreign currency reserves, but also led to more and more international trade friction, China's monthly trade figures and even has thus become the world's attention "sensitive signal." Determine whether the balance of trade surplus in the international indicators, differences

compared with the total import and export trade Soon (inverse), less than 10% of the basic normal, "10%" can also be referred to as trade imbalances "alert line."

With China's accession to the WTO, greatly accelerated the development of foreign trade, foreign exchange reserves sufficient to meet the demand for imports of advanced technology and equipment; three is able to meet the greater needs of residents in the normal use of foreign exchange.

Foreign direct investment in China is also an important source of foreign exchange reserve growth. True leap of FDI in China began in 1992 and thereafter, showing the increase in geometric progression, the actual use of FDI in 1991 was only $ 4.366 billion in 1992 rose to $ 11.007 billion, a growth rate of up to 152.11 percent; 1993 FDI for 27.515 billion U.S. dollars, the growth rate of 149.98 percent; 1995, foreign direct investment reached 37.521 billion U.S. dollars of foreign direct investment in 1998 reached $ 454.63. FDI exceeded $ 50 billion in 2002 to $ 52.743 billion; exceeded $ 60 billion in FDI in 2004, reaching $ 60.63 billion; FDI declined slightly in 2005, to $ 60.325 billion in 2008; 2006, FDI rising trend of high-speed, with an average growth rate of 15.45% (see Fig. 4). In 2009, affected by the financial crisis, international capital flows decreased significantly in 2009, the actual use of FDI amount of $ 90,033,000,000, a year-on-year growth rate for the year to 2.6% full year 2010 non-financial areas newly approved the establishment of foreign invested enterprises 27,406, an increase of 16.9%; actual use of FDI in the amount of $ 105.74 billion, a year-on-year growth of 17.4%, for the first time exceeded 100 billion U.S. dollars, the highest level. In 2011, the number of newly established foreign-invested enterprises to 27,712, an increase of 1.1%; actual use of FDI in the amount of 1,160.11 billion U.S. dollars, an increase of 9.7%. The annual eastern part of the actual use of FDI in 2011% of $ 604 million, a year-on-year growth of 7.5%, accounting for 83.3% of the national total; central region of the actual use of FDI was $ 7.836 billion, a year-on-year growth of 14.3%, accounting for 6.8% of the national total; western the actual use of FDI in the region of $ 11.571 billion, accounting for 9.97% of the national total.

4 THE POSITIVE EFFECT OF FOREIGN EXCHANGE RESERVES CONTINUED GROWTH

Some of China's foreign exchange reserves are an important means of economic regulation, to achieve internal and external balance. In general, an increase in foreign exchange reserves can not

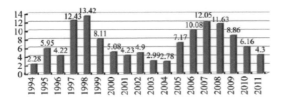

Figure 2. Trade surplus accounted for the proportion of total trade in 2011, 1994.

only enhance the ability of macro-control, but also conducive to the maintenance of national and corporate reputation in the international arena to help expand international trade, attract foreign investment, domestic enterprises to reduce financing costs, prevent and resolve international financial risks.

1. An adequate international reserve is significantly enhancing our ability to pay, improve China's comprehensive national strength. Foreign exchange reserves are an important indicator of a country reflects the comprehensive national strength. As China's open economy continues to develop, the rapid expansion of the scale of China's foreign trade, foreign trade dependence continues to increase. Therefore, to maintain adequate foreign exchange reserves, China's comprehensive national strength not only improved, but also for our ability to maintain international payment in international trade, balance of payments adjustment to provide effective protection.

2. So that China's foreign exchange reserves adequate solvency enhancements to improve the country's international reputation. International financial institutions and banks in foreign loans are often borrowing countries to advance the investigative capacity to repay debt. Status of a country's foreign exchange reserves was held by the credit investigation, one of the important indicators of country risk assessment. For our country to foreign governments, international financial institutions to borrow foreign debt, investment income due to the different projects and recovery period, it must have sufficient reserves to protect against debt and credit crisis.

3. Adequate foreign exchange reserves so that our country can effectively intervene in currency markets to maintain the currency exchange rate stability. How much of a country's foreign exchange reserves have demonstrated its ability to intervene in foreign exchange markets and maintains the currency exchange rate. When the appreciation of the RMB suffered great pressure in the short term, when the central bank will buy foreign exchange, selling Renminbi, on the contrary, when the Yuan faces depreciation pressure, the central bank's foreign exchange reserves will be thrown out, the purchase of Yuan to maintain exchange rate basically stable. China is currently implementing a market-based managed floating exchange rate system, ample foreign exchange reserves for the effective prevention of financial crisis, to maintain investor confidence in its currency stable and has an important role.

4. Adequate reserves effectively promoted the development of the domestic economy. First, to improve the country's foreign exchange reserves adequate external financing capacity, reduce domestic institutions to enter the international market, financing costs, to encourage domestic enterprises to "go out" to seek better investment environment and greater profit margins; Second, adequate foreign exchange reserves in the deepening economic reform, industrial restructuring and improve production technology and other aspects can play an important role. With China's accession to the WTO, greatly accelerated the development of foreign trade, foreign exchange reserves sufficient to meet the demand for imports of advanced technology and equipment; three is able to meet the greater needs of residents in the normal use of foreign exchange.

5 THE NEGATIVE IMPACT OF FOREIGN EXCHANGE RESERVES CONTINUED GROWTH

Reserves as a sign of national economic and financial strength, which make up the national balance of payments deficit, weather the financial storm, stabilize their exchange rates and maintain the material basis of its international reputation. For developing countries, tend to be higher than the normal level of foreign exchange reserves held. However, foreign exchange reserves are not better, in recent years; the rapid expansion of the scale of China's foreign exchange reserves to the economic development generated a lot of negative effects.

1. High foreign exchange reserves were caused by the high cost of ownership, resulting in idle resources and funds. In China's foreign exchange reserves, a large proportion of the loan borrowed, the interest cost is relatively high. Because foreign exchange reserves are a symbol of real resources, it is the opportunity cost of holding. Opportunity cost of holding reserves equal to the productivity of domestic capital reserves held by subtracting the yield. If the country holds huge foreign exchange reserves and borrowed a lot of debt, equal to domestic funds are cheap to foreigners abroad to use the same time have high borrowing money from abroad, the potential loss is obvious. At the same time, hold temporarily abandon the use of foreign exchange reserves, said a certain amount of real resources and, thus, improve the loss caused by these resources into economic growth and income levels. Therefore, when the ratio of reserves are borrow too high, too much

to hold reserves uneconomical, will also affect domestic economic growth.

2. High foreign exchange reserves led to excess liquidity in China at this stage the main reason and to some extent exacerbated inflationary pressures. Excess liquidity refers to the money supply exceeds the demand for money in the real economy, which is growing faster than the real GDP growth rate. In China's money supply, foreign exchange has accounted for about 70%. Affected compulsory settlement system, the central bank to buy foreign currency non-willingness, so that the corresponding base money, by the action of the multiplier effect of the money supply will be greatly increased, thus forming the current excess liquidity and inflationary pressures.

3. The rapid growth of foreign exchange reserves increased pressure on RMB appreciation, thereby affecting the competitiveness of China's exports. In theory, a country's foreign exchange reserves increase, the country will make the currency exchange rate to rise. From China's actual situation, the RMB exchange rate with the increase in foreign exchange reserves gradually increased, from $ 1 in 1994 against 8.7 Yuan, up to the current U.S. dollar to 6.67 Yuan, up 23.33 percent appreciation. In China's exports among enterprises with low price advantage to occupy the international market, and continued to rise in the RMB exchange rate situation, our export commodity quotations will be improved, many small and medium foreign enterprises due to the loss of the price advantage and have bankruptcy. Therefore, an increase of RMB exchange rate on China's export growth is clearly unfavorable.

4. High foreign exchange reserves, increasing the difficulty and risk management is reserve assets. In the financial globalization, the rapid massive international capital flows, interest rate and exchange rate fluctuations in the financial market is very intense. As the country's foreign exchange reserves of wealth, it's too large will cause the country's wealth is a huge risk among high foreign exchange reserves management to increase the value of reserve assets brought difficulty. In China's foreign exchange reserves of $ 2.4 trillion, accounting for about 70% of U.S. dollar assets, the yen is about 10%, about 20% of the euro and the British pound. Treasury revised data on February 26 this year, released by the U.S. dollar assets held in our country has $ 894.8 billion invested in U.S. Treasury bonds, and to now have $ 900 billion of U.S. Treasury bonds, in which the long-term U.S. Treasury $ 825.1 billion, accounting for China's holdings of U.S. Treasury bonds 92%. It can be seen that China's foreign exchange reserves mainly invest in U.S. Treasury bonds, so bring along two related questions: First, U.S. trends in recent years, showing a weak exchange rate fell, the dollar continued to depreciate, so China's foreign exchange reserves of U.S. dollar assets will follow "shrink", resulting in huge losses. Second, more than half of China's foreign exchange reserves to buy U.S.

6 CONCLUSION

First foreign exchange management reform settlement and sales, the gradual transition from a mandatory foreign exchange settlement for the wishes of foreign exchange settlement and sales, improve banking exchange position management. China banks mandatory settlement and sales system, phasing out a voluntary settlement and sales system, replaced by the proportion of the settlement and sales in foreign-funded enterprises can reduce operating costs. Second, improve the foreign exchange write-off policy. Under the existing conditions, to improve the central bank's sterilization policy has become a priority. Continue to develop new financial instruments; formation of the short-term lending market, short-term paper market and the discount market, and to provide a basis for the central bank to use monetary policy tools to regulate financial markets. Third, the intensity is open market operations. Currently, in open market operations, China's corporate bonds and government bonds is relatively high and stable income, but are generally a five-year period or more long-term bonds, which affect the enthusiasm of the commercial banks to participate in open market operations, and therefore need to continuously optimize the term structure of China's bond, in order to more effectively reduce the cost of the changes in China's foreign exchange reserves.

REFERENCES

Cheng Peng-fei, Yan Hao-wen, Han Zhen-hui, 2008. An Algorithm for Computing the Minimum Area Bounding Rectangle of an Arbitrary Polygon.

Gabrielidesa N.C., A.I. Ginnisa, P.D. Kaklisa. 2007. Smooth branching surface construction from cross sections.

Guo Furong, 2004. Enjoy the value of modern ideological and political education of China.

Yi-Jun Yang, Jun-Hai Yong, Hui Zhang, 2006. A rational extension of Piegl's method for flling n-sided holes.

Yong Jun, 2005. A piecewise hole filling algorithm in reverse engineering.

Computer, Intelligent Computing and Education Technology – Liu, Sung & Yao (Eds)
© *2014 Taylor & Francis Group, London, ISBN 978-1-138-02469-4*

Network communication for volunteer position management of sports events

Shi-You Liu

Institute of Physical Education, Beihua University, Jilin, China

ABSTRACT: This paper presents a new method of network communication configuration design. It is based on t wireless sensor networks that the overlap region does not blur under interference. This assumption is supported by the observation that for an overlap of up to 50 cm, the large deviation occurs only at the ends of the overlap. It is more useful for volunteer position management, where fixed position and Real-time communication's method involves difficult mathematics. This method may also be easily extended to deal with non-linearity in the position management.

Keywords: networks; major sports events; wireless sensor; volunteer position management

1 INTRODUCTION

With modern large sports games developments, its scale more and larger, and with volunteers with degree level in deepening, the expansion of fields, the management of volunteers to more and more become the modern large-scale sports events to the success of the key factors. Because of the nature of the volunteers is different from the ordinary full-time personnel, for the management of volunteers can't fit right general human resources management theory. Therefore, how to large sports games volunteers management has been sports theory and practice workers of discussion. The success of the Olympic Games held in Beijing, thanks to the success of the volunteer management. Therefore, to discuss the success of Beijing Olympic Games volunteer management experience, in the days of the large sports games held to have the important meaning.

2 RESEARCH STATUS AND MANAGEMENT OF SPORTS VOLUNTEER INCENTIVE

In many studies related to sports volunteers and volunteers in the Olympic Games, mostly concentrated on the study of the Olympic sports volunteer or volunteer connotation, value and management, specializing on sports volunteer incentives in the country is now almost still a blank. Studies in Western countries incentives to sports volunteers, volunteer sports appear as early as when he had begun. The earliest studies focused on the study of sports volunteer motivation, understanding

the different motivations of sports volunteers and adhere to sports participation or service launched in the middle of motivation. Multi achieved using questionnaires or interviews. The results showed that: interest in sports is the primary factor in most of the sports volunteer participation. And: motivation of male participation than women. Secondly, they themselves can have more opportunities to show their service to the community and also to the majority of people are also involved in motivation sports services. In all the motivation, the most important is "a chance to travel or to pass the time."

2002 Twynam hoe, who continue their studies, the Canadian women's curling tournament volunteers motivated a large study found that the main motivation for volunteers factor levels in four areas, four levels of the most important factors motivation is "I can make the game a success," "to create a better society," "want a meaningful thing", "is my life's opportunities," the purpose of motivating factors are level, the most important is "because my friends to participate in curling tournament", "People expect me to become a volunteer," "I want to continue the family tradition of volunteer" and "I do not have other things to do, etc." traditional factors are external dimension. Visible, the main motivation motivates them to participate in volunteer service entertainment and self-improvement as well as social services, mostly for intrinsic motivation. The results also show that the motive of these is major sports events has many volunteers are seen as a form of entertainment and leisure experiences, motivate them to participate in the main motivation is to serve the community and to improve the self.

3 THE MAIN FEATURES OF THE CURRENT STUDY

3.1 Studies focused on the motivation of volunteers in sport

Some of the existing research on sports volunteers motivated and more focused on the motivation of the volunteer study, using questionnaires and interviews to understand the motivation and willingness of sports volunteers, which made some of the measures and methods of management, or specialized research on sports volunteers motivated. Studies such as domestic Zhang Zhen (1994) to women's participation in sports volunteering, motivation factors are: Zizhuzhuren, contribute to the community, family and self-realization, emotional satisfaction, social contacts, learn something new and to strike a future reward of seven, Paul Cheng study (1997) for the region to participate in middle school PE teacher they drink Stadium volunteering motivation, the study found, with emphasis sort are: the development of self and interpersonal factors, factors of social services, social recognition and achievement factors and Mu Zhongfu (1998) volunteers for the study of the potential market area and its stadium considerations, the study will be divided into considerations: the organization of work, intrinsic motivation and extrinsic incentives three horizontal surfaces within the findings of the most important factor in the motivation for the consideration of its intrinsic motivations include: increasing knowledge and skills to help others, enrich their lives, make friends, get social experience, good turn deserves another, for future work (career) help, volunteer groups, whether there are important figures appear. Other studies are generally motivated volunteer organization.

3.2 The main object of study is a university student volunteers and some young volunteers

Previous studies on sports volunteers, the main object of study is to select some individuals directly involved in the sport of volunteer service, these individuals are mostly college students and young volunteers, especially some major sporting events, requires a lot of volunteers when the dominant student volunteers, for example, the Olympic volunteers. So did some research specifically for college students volunteer motivation and willingness to carry out research, such as General, Department of Taiwan scholars made "motivation and willingness to study the movement of college students volunteer to participate", the domestic research on student volunteers there Gong Hua River "student volunteers participation motivation factor structure", established seven factor structure model: self-actualization, self-improvement, social responsibility, environmental impact, communication needs, and a total of seven factors egoistic altruism, by T-test found: on volunteer activities, student volunteers and community volunteers in self-realization, there are differences on social responsibility, environmental impact and altruism four factors: gender differences in student volunteers are also needed on the factors interaction: student volunteers did not significantly in age, education, professional differences, and the study also developed a "university student volunteers motivation Questionnaire." And Fang's "Shanghai Student Volunteer Service", on condition of Shanghai college students from the rise and development of volunteering, participating subjects, content services, organization and patterns, functional analysis, the main problems and corresponding solutions in five aspects of a more comprehensive and systematic research. The volunteer studies on other populations are relatively small.

3.3 Survey research methods are mainly

And research, like other volunteers, current research on sports volunteers mostly in the questionnaire-based. The questionnaire included selected "Volunteer Activities Survey", "incentive Scale", "college students to participate in sports volunteer willingness questionnaire" and so on, in 1998 Farrell, J, M; J0h11Ston, M, E and 1'wyll hoe, GD (1998) amended the "special events volunteer motivation Scale" (special Event Volunteer Motivation scale, SEvMs), since then, many scholars use SEvMS questionnaire study of sports volunteers.

3.4 Research results and findings

Previous studies have indicated that the outcome of the sports volunteers: the same motivation to participate in volunteer service is self-sacrifice, altruism and also includes instrumental motivation is to say volunteers can be helpful to others, so that the volunteers in volunteer service get strong interest and satisfaction, learning experiences and opportunities for growth may also contribute to the community. Overall, studies on volunteers have focused on the study of the motivation of volunteers. The findings will also motivate volunteers and satisfaction linked.

In this study, questionnaires implemented questionnaire was used Farrell, J, M,; Johllston, M, E and 1'wyIl, GB (1998) Correction of "special events Volunteer Motivation Scale" (SpecialEvemvolunteer Motivation Scale, SEVMS).

Use the findings described SPSS11.5 statistical analysis, reliability analysis, factor analysis, regression analysis.

This study used Likert attitude scale commonly used in reliability testing methods "Cmnbach c"

Table 1. A/B two sets of comparative data.

x^2	df	x^2/df	RMSEA	SRMR	GFI	IFI	CFI	NNFI
999.67	340	2.92	0.081	0.072	0.90	0.90	0.90	0.88

factor and "split-half reliability (split-hmfreliabil not)." After analysis, the resulting 28 entries in the first part of the questionnaire, the overall more pha = 0.8270, shown to have good reliability.

4 STUDY DESIGN

4.1 Research ideas and research framework

The starting point of this study is the relationship between motivation for major sports events volunteers between demand and incentive management, if managers incentives to meet the needs of the motivation of volunteers, the volunteers will play the role of incentives in order to effectively serve major sports events; If managers can not meet the needs of incentives motivated volunteers, volunteer work enthusiasm will drop even halfway launch. How to stimulate the motivation of volunteers? How to maintain and strengthen the motivation of volunteers? This will depend on our manager's effective incentives and methods. This study provides S SE VI questionnaires and interviews, China's sports volunteers understand the current voluntary service, adhere to service and different motivations to quit, and the relationship between sport and management needs of volunteers, made by sports organizations and management studies those for large-scale events in the sport volunteers should take effective incentive model and method, and thus effectively manage large-scale sporting events volunteers.

Volunteers participate in major sporting events inspire volunteerism is the status quo: the proportion of college student's volunteer more, low levels of social participation.

4.2 Research objectives

The selected subjects in this study is 2005 National Games in Nanjing, sports volunteers, given the current situation of sports volunteers and research purposes of this paper, the sports volunteer is defined as: the process of organizing major sporting events in the preparation and, and does not expect any material of return, dedicated their time, energy, skill, effort to complete the tasks assigned to the organizing committee person. Its inner meaning has two aspects: first, certain activities by organizations such as the Young Volunteers Association, does not contain personal spontaneous behavior: Second, their behavior includes

Table 2. Sort volunteers motivation factors.

M	SD
4.323	0.82
3.808	0.517
4.075	0.240
3.403	0.568
3.13	0.650

Table 3. Motivation five-factor model.

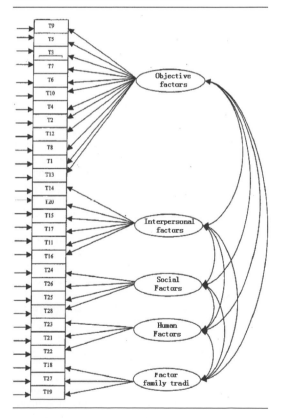

both voluntary act without any mandatory governmental organizations also includes participation behavior. Object of this study is limited to the volunteer service organization in the framework of the organizing committee, does not include any spontaneous behavior of individuals.

4.3 Research methods

Access to a large number of relevant literature data management (organizational behavior, human resource management, sports management), psychology, sociology and other related books at home and abroad in the field of sports and volunteer motivation and management: through a variety of journals, newspapers, CD-ROM internet search, access to a large number of documents relating to volunteers, volunteers and Olympic sports volunteers: Collect all of the various government departments and volunteer documents related laws, regulations, etc.: collect the relevant documents of various volunteer organizations. The above literature provides a theoretical basis for the study.

Interview techniques use large sporting events sports volunteers and managers were interviewed, combined with the results of a literature review to determine the motive of sports volunteers to participate in sports activities and reasons for volunteering or adhere dropouts.

5 RESEARCH TOOLS

The questionnaire used in this study is (Fa Ding ell, J, M,; Jollllscon, M, E and. 1w). Ila plus, GD (1998) Correction of "large-scale sporting events Volunteer Motivation Scale" (special Evem v01 umeer Motivalion scale, SEVMS). Questionnaire is divided into two parts, the first part of a five-point Likert scale, the subjects according to their real feelings or motives willingness to answer, from strongly agree, agree, neutral, disagree, and strongly disagree, 5 were given, 4,3,2,1 score, the higher the score the subjects in a theme, which means that the higher the level of agreement for the project, otherwise lower. The second part is the personal background information, including the subject of schools, read professional, Science, education, whether to participate in other volunteer service, whether voluntary service leadership certificate and whether interested in volunteering for sports seven.

6 STATISTICAL ANALYSIS

Use SPSSll. 5 pairs of test sample background data for frequency distribution, percentage, mean and standard deviation, to describe characteristics of each sample allocation scenario variables; 28 for the first part of the questionnaire using Likert attitude scale entry commonly used in reliability testing methods "Cronbach a" factor and the "split-half reliability (split-11 alfrcliability)", in order to test the reliability of the test tool to explore the internal consistency of the questionnaire for each subject; using structural equation model of the questionnaire data, confirmatory factor analysis, the use of LIS XI} L8.30 statistical software was tested on 332 formal test data obtained confirmatory factor analysis to examine the five-factor model fit indices; Finally, using regression analysis, the study sample various background variables affect the degree of motivational factors, understand the background to the motivation of the factors affecting the level of participation.

7 CONCLUSION

1. Motivated volunteers volunteering major sports events can be divided into five factors: the purpose of factors, interpersonal factors, social factors, personal factors, family tradition factor. Which the highest purpose of motivating factors, followed by social factors, interpersonal factors, personal factors, and motivation to participate in the family tradition factor to a minimum. Average number of subjects involved in motivation of 3.95, indicating the extent of the volunteers at all levels has a high motivation factor.

2. In this study, seven different background variables and motivation factors were compared; results showed that in addition to the school and no significant gender differences, other background variables in the target level of motivational factors, personal factors and social factors dimension levels were significantly difference, 94.5% of volunteers interested in sports volunteering.

3. Volunteers participate in major sporting events inspire volunteerism is the status quo: the proportion of college student's volunteer more, low levels of social participation: main government incentives and management, lack of specialized organizations and incentive theory: lack of a stable professional volunteer's team of volunteer's inadequate resources: internal incentive excessive: volunteer more internal conflicts and external conflicts.

REFERENCES

Hong W.H, 2007. During the Su-mei. Impact of different masses to participate in the Sports Tour.

Ming K.H, 2011. Policy and Regulation Department of the China National Tourism Administration.

Peng Qin, 2008. Sports Tourism Management Measures in the Next 5–10 Years.

Tian Pu, 2009. Efforts to Achieve by the Sports Powers Sports Power Forward.

Wan Xia, Shao Kai, Xiao-chen, 2010. The Dilemma of Sports Tourism Industry in China.

Study on ideological and political education of college students based on Internet

Lan Wu
School of Marxism, Beihua University, Jilin, China

ABSTRACT: With the increasing Internet applications popularly, ideological and political education of college students is face new challenges. How to improve the effectiveness of ideological and political education in network background is the most important works. The two methods were proposed to actively promote ideological and political education ranks. Firstly, ideological and political education network position was used against intrusion of harmful information by setting barrier "blocking". Secondly, the students' socialist core value system was strengthen by a "spare" approach education.

Keywords: network; students; ideological & political education; socialism; education

1 INTRODUCTION

With the rapid development of the Internet, the network has become a university student learning, living an important and indispensable component. Mutual economic and cultural exchanges in the world via the Internet spread to college students thinking, attitudes, values, and so had a profound impact, but also to the ideological and political education presents many new challenges. Network is a double-edged sword, both positive role, but also has a negative impact, we can not because the network exists and drawbacks depending on the network as a "scourge", take a negative attitude or even escape. Should strive to achieve positive development, full use, strengthen management, while avoiding disadvantages, as I used to. Therefore, we must strengthen the leadership of the university network construction and management; strengthen ideological and political education team building, to "block", "sparse" combined with the ideological position of Marxist theory and network positions occupied universities. So as to withstand the negative effects of economic globalization, the completion of the party and state colleges and universities develop the socialist cause given qualified builders and reliable successor's sacred mission.

Improve the effectiveness of ideological and political education in network background to strengthen the leadership of the campus network construction and management, and actively promote ideological and political education ranks, with the ideological and political education network position occupied by "blocking" the way to set a barrier to prevent invasion of harmful information. Use of "sparse" approach to strengthen the students' socialist core value system of education.

2 PROMOTE IDEOLOGICAL AND POLITICAL EDUCATION RANKS

2.1 *Campus network security management functions under the jurisdiction of the party committee*

University party committee should fully understand the importance of the campus network construction and management, strengthen the construction of the campus network of unified leadership and management, give full play to the campus network in the "cohesive people, the image outside" in the role, so that the campus network becomes promote the theme, an important means of carrying out ideological and political education. First, we should work into the ideological and political education school party agenda, clearly defined campus network security by the party primarily responsible for the management functions. To be established by the party responsible for the comrades in charge of ideological and political work for the leader, in charge of the network construction work of school leaders and school advocacy work, student work, network technology and other departments responsible comrades of the ideological and political education work leading group under the unified leadership of party committees. Improve the overall level of campus construction sites, to ensure truly become college campus site to learn knowledge, broaden their horizons, strive positions. Secondly, we must ensure the safe operation of the basic network infrastructure investment and maintenance, in particular, to focus on strengthening information security infrastructure work, increased information security system key technologies, equipment investment, and included in network and information security in the annual budget special funds. To introduce advanced equipment, good layout of the campus network, connect to the network and to ensure the smooth running quickly, should be directly connected to the campus network ports each student dormitories, each classroom for ideological and political education into the dormitory, classroom do basic work. Again, in order to ensure safe operation of the campus network must be trained computer and network knowledge of relevant personnel. For ordinary teachers, to train them to master the basic knowledge of computers and networks, enabling them to do more skilled and teaching networks combined. Also training network professionals as the campus network administrators, to equip them with a more comprehensive knowledge of computers and networks, can be related to the campus network construction and maintenance.

2.2 *Strengthen ideological and political education ranks*

Currently, the ideological and political education team mainly consists caucus cadres, political counselor, ideological and political theory courses for teachers and related network technicians, all of whom have their own expertise, but less obvious. Understand the theory of ideological and political education of teachers is not familiar with the characteristics and laws of network information dissemination, network technology staff knows their ideological and political level and there is a big gap. These two parts of people, whether former network technology, network transmission characteristics of learning and applying the law, or the latter theory of ideological and political education to understand and master, we need a long time to do it. Therefore, we must strengthen the cultivation of the two parts of people, making it as soon as both the ideological and political theory with higher literacy and information management capabilities with network compound talents.

3 STRENGTHEN THE NETWORK OF STRICT MANAGEMENT

3.1 *Set the filter on the campus network*

With the popularity of online media in the university campus, its importance is increasingly irreplaceable, but the difficulty of controlling the economic

and cultural information from different countries is growing, its disadvantages are also obvious, must go through an effective means to prevent the harmful information intrusion. "Blocking" is essential to the use of technical means filtering and shielding bad information, the use of coercion network regulations, norms of network behavior, in order to achieve the purpose of purifying cyberspace.

Due to the characteristics of age for college students determine their new, extraordinary and special things curious and interested. Therefore, in order to prevent the occurrence of curiosity which led to bad network behavior, but also in Western countries in order to better prevent "Network cultural hegemony" and "Internet culture erosion", "blocking" is essential barrier. In recent years, China has made some progress in this area, such as the development of the "Guardian of the East", "Internet police 110" and other filtering software. This software can filter pornography, crime, cults and other undesirable information, by limiting access to the site, limited access time, leaving the user logging offending behavior and alert the administrator via the screen or sound. Universities can use the software to set the "Filter" on the campus network. At the same time, to establish a campus network security system for school characteristics, and actively explore the development for the campus network, hardware and software to filter out harmful information and spam, to strengthen the entrance channel of Internet regulation and supervision, strict campus network information the quality.

3.2 *Establish and improve network monitoring and management mechanisms*

Accelerate the process of facing the network, you must filter harmful information while building on the college network behavior monitoring mechanism and improve the management system, strengthening the network monitoring and management. First, the university should be based on relevant national laws and regulations, combined with the actual school, develop practical campus network and information security management system. Such as: the campus network system hardware management system, campus network administrator responsibilities at all levels of the campus network management team building and training system, the campus network information dissemination and management systems, network behavior management system and students, teachers and self-management system to build portals. Only by establishing sound scientific, comprehensive network security management system in order to ensure the normal operation of the campus network, the better for school teachers and students in all aspects of work and service. The second is to establish and improve network and information security monitoring mechanisms. The school authorities should fulfill their duties, strengthen cooperation and improve coordination mechanisms, online monitoring mechanism, reported receiving mechanism for people to participate supervision mechanism, timely communication, the formation of joint management of the overall force. As established by the ideological and political education of workers and technical personnel of the network "Internet police" force, as coordinator of the campus network a variety of network behavior, supervision, inspection, online decadent bourgeois ideology, pornographic and other harmful information from the source to eliminate foundation upon which spread to eliminate reactionary, obscene living space porn sites.

4 STRENGTHEN THE POSITIVE EDUCATION OF COLLEGE STUDENTS

4.1 Training students to establish a correct outlook on life and values

College students ideological and political education alone simple administrative means to prevent the invasion of harmful information is not the most effective way to be in the "blocking" at the same time in the form of education and persuasion, and make the best use of harmful information to guide students to identify, correct motivation Internet effectively self-discipline and self-management in a network environment, improve the ability to distinguish right from wrong and the ability to resist erosion decadent ideas.

First, Use the Marxist ideological position occupied positions in universities and networks to prevent and diverse opposition guiding ideology, strengthen college students identify and resist all kinds of erroneous ideas of capacity. In close connection with the new changes in the international situation and the domestic reform and opening up new, ideological and political education closer to real life, richer flavor of the times, and easier for the students to accept. Secondly, we must vigorously carry out world, life and values education. Culture around "four" is new fundamental goal, to promote the overall situation, and selfless dedication. Undergraduates have a firm belief in the noble sentiments and scientific healthy and civilized lifestyle to prevent the adverse effects of money worship, hedonism, extreme individualism and other decadent ideas generated by the growth of college students. Again, students are

training to establish a common ideal of socialism with Chinese characteristics. At this stage, the construction of socialism with Chinese characteristics and achieve the great rejuvenation of the Chinese nation is the common ideal of our peoples. College students are building socialism with Chinese characteristics force, represents the future direction of China and hopes to undertake the historical mission of the great rejuvenation of the nation. Strengthening of economic globalization and networking background ideal education, National Socialism with Chinese characteristics common education is essential for college students. Colleges and universities to strengthen through the campus network and the various forms of college global, national education, so that students not only to see the opportunities and challenges facing the cause of socialism with Chinese characteristics, but also to see the cause of socialism with Chinese characteristics has the vitality. Promptly corrected exists in college vague or even wrong understanding, so that they consciously to their ideals into building socialism with Chinese characteristics to go, to recognize their historic mission, and the value of their own into the goal, work hard.

4.2 Cultivate the sense of mission and responsibility

Patriotism is new era of the Chinese nation, not only to undertake the history of the fine tradition of patriotism, but also to absorb the fresh spirit of the times richer connotation. At this stage, carrying forward the national spirit and the spirit of the age is to promote patriotism. Carry forward the national spirit; we should educate college students dedicated to the cause of building and defending the socialist modernization, dedicated to promoting the reunification of the motherland. It is every citizen's Republic of China, including university students must adhere to the position and attitude. Spirit of the age, to educate college students emancipate the mind, seek truth from facts, advance with the times, innovation, despite the difficulties, indomitable, hard work, pragmatic, fame and fortune, dedication, strive to cultivate the spirit of reform and innovation of college students, ability to innovate, innovative personality and other aspects of quality. To take full advantage of the network to carry out ideological and political education to cultivate not only books, not only on, good to break the routine, independent thinking, independent judgment analysis capabilities. College Students' self-reliance, independence, innovative and enterprising spirit, enhance social responsibility and historic mission of university students.

5 WAYS TO ENHANCE THE USE OF NETWORK IDEOLOGICAL AND POLITICAL EDUCATION INDOCTRINATION EFFECTIVENESS

5.1 *Marxist establishment of various websites and improve the ideological and political education should be the amount of information*

Has now established a lot of publicity Marxism website, such as Tsinghai University's "Red website," CSU "sublimation Network" website, "Shanghai Red," "innovation and development of Marxism," "Marxism-Leninism-Mao Zedong Thought library" websites. These sites update faster, using its Marxist propaganda, greatly improving the dissemination of information. In the website you can around some major social issues, political issues comment or conduct online surveys online dialogue. With these comments, findings and dialogue, to find out the ideological trend of students, support proper perspective, critics wrong speech, indirect guidance for students and indoctrination.

5.2 *Construction of a high-quality, highly-skilled team of ideological and political education indoctrination*

Under the Internet age, educators must accept new ideas, master and flexible use of the new media network, closer to college students, college students into the network of life, instilling the skills and methods of research networks, active in the Network indoctrination work. At the same time, study hard, study the trend of the development of Marxism, Marxist grasp the latest content development, improve their literacy, improve their knowledge structure, expand their amount of information, with the correct ideological and political education, a reasonable answer in reality college various problems encountered in eliminating A hard boot to use the Marxist stand, viewpoint and method to understand the problem, research questions, solve problems, in practice, the object of the Marxist indoctrination for their thoughts and actions.

5.3 *Focus on the timeliness of network characteristics. Enhanced online indoctrination efforts*

Now, the network has gone deep into the political, economic, cultural and other fields, which greatly affects the college's spiritual world, it has an open, interactive, inclusive, convenience and anonymity,

both difficult to manage and control, but also a variety of political forces want to compete for new positions and new areas. Therefore, we need to build fusion of ideology, knowledge, interest and service in one of the main campus educational sites, expanding educational space; also adept at using modern media means, to carry out ideological education lively, enhanced online indoctrination efforts, form a network of ideological and political education system and work together online and offline, to enhance the attractiveness and appeal of the ideological and political education.

5.4 *Use interactive features of the network, the establishment of two new bi-mode equal to instill*

Network has some interactivity. Network instill ideological and political education should make full use of the advantages of the network, educators must overcome traditional indoctrination exists subject to the object of one-way traffic education, should establish a new model of equality between the two two-way communication, the new concepts, restore the true colors of indoctrination station. In parallel with the ideological and political education indoctrination through online communication, voice mail, on-line discussions, etc., on an equal dialogue with users especially students, to keep abreast of their ideological trends, thereby enhance the ideological and political education targeted propaganda. Conversely, if the subject of university students not given due attention, then knowledge, feelings, Italy, the line will be subject to different degrees of inhibition, the effect of the impact theory of indoctrination of college students. Therefore, in the indoctrination process, from the traditional to instill body-centered, "I hear you talk, I hit you pass," the one-way traffic pattern was changed to two-way interactive network as the carrier mode.

REFERENCES

Hu, M.S, 2003. Clinical and experimental research center Shenshao treatment of depression angina.
Ma F.M, 2009. Personality characteristics of patients with depression correlation with the severity.
Sen W.Y, Wu W. Zh. 2000. Social support, psychological research relationships Control and Psychological Health.
Sun Wei, 2001. Inpatients Health Education Nursing.
Yang F.G, 2007. Ming, patients with depression and other psychological characteristics and nursing intervention.

Computer, Intelligent Computing and Education Technology – Liu, Sung & Yao (Eds)
© 2014 Taylor & Francis Group, London, ISBN 978-1-138-02469-4

Teaching reform of fundament of mechanical design for material forming & control engineering specialty

L. Wang, K. Zhang & X.R. Lv
School of Mechanical Engineering, Shenyang University of Technology, Shenyang, China

ABSTRACT: This paper studies the teaching method of the Fundament of Mechanical Design for the Material Forming & control specialty, considering both of the specialty characteristics and the course content, in view of the present difficulties in teaching the course. The paper suggests that the teaching process should tell students the course objective and cultivate students' interest. It is also suggested that the course content, experiment teaching and curriculum design should be improved to enhance effectiveness of the course teaching.

Keywords: material forming and control engineering specialty; fundament of mechanical design; teaching reform

1 INTRODUCTION

Fundament of Mechanical Design is a compulsory main technological basic course for machinery specialties, machinery-based specialties or some others. It serves as a connecting link in the whole undergraduate teaching program and plays an essential role for students to study the following professional courses and start their post-graduate professional careers. In the course theory and practice are closely related. On the one hand, it greatly depends on the higher mathematics, engineering drawing, theoretical mechanics, material mechanics and material science. On the other hand, it is closely linked with the engineering practice [1,2]. Hence, students, lacking of either of those knowledge or experiences, will face some difficulties when learning this course which always makes the teacher hit out at random. Therefore, the paper studies the teaching method of the Fundament of Mechanical Design for the Material Forming & control specialty, considering both of the specialty characteristics and the course content, in view of the present difficulties in teaching the course [3]. The paper will also discuss the course objective and how to cultivate students' interest.

2 HOW TO IMPROVE TEACHING QUALITY

2.1 *Defining the teaching objective of the course in material forming and control specialty*

The professional knowledge of material forming and control specialty includes the basic theory of material science and engineering, materials processing and controlling engineering, mold design and manufacture and so on. The student of the specialty are expected to be engaged in researching, designing, development and management in machinery, mould, material processing. Obviously, the specialty is closed related with the machinery engineering. For example, the mould design and manufacture and the computer aided designing are both based on the machinery designing. Higher precision, lower margin and more glabrous surface are now expected for foundry products and these requires advanced casting facility and more machinery automation. As engineering and technical personnel, it is necessary to grasp the structure and operational principle of the related instruments and equipments. Therefore, the students of material forming and control specialty should realize that the basic knowledge of machinery engineering is needed and this course needs to be studied well [4].

2.2 *Cultivating students' interest in the course*

The participatory teaching method should be applied to cultivate students' interest in studying the course. Due to the teaching content of the course involves plenty of formula, tables and charts, students often lack interest in learning. In the teaching practice, teachers should takes into consideration the characteristics of material forming and control specialty and introduce a series of mechanical structures and parts that are not only involved with the course, but also related closely to the material forming and control specialty. Students should be encouraged to participate to analyze and discuss the mechanical principles in those structures and parts. The teacher can interpret knowledge points of the course through solving the problems involved in the analysis and discussion. The method can not only cultivate students' interests but also show the close relationship between the course and their specialty which are necessary for them to learn the course well.

The teacher should find out the regulations in the course and take them as the main clue of the teaching process. The course takes the common mechanical structures and parts as study objects and includes many chapters or sections. These looks like higgledy-piggledy which can keep students from digesting the course conception and idea of the course. Virtually, the course content includes a series of regular things which can show the high logicality of the machinery subject. If a teacher can grasp the regulations and focus on them in the classroom, students can not only easily obtain the knowledge of the course but also improve their engineering designing ability.

2.3 Improving course content of the fundament of mechanical design

To bring up students the ability to analyze and solve the practical problem and build the new course system, we break the traditional boundary of mechanical principle and mechanical design courses and combine them with the instruments and equipments in their specialty together. The course content should focused on the course objective, i.e., to grasp the basic knowledge, designing principles and skills involved in their specialty. The course content should also emphasis on bringing up the practicability, ability and creativity of the students.

Theoretical content, therefore, should not overly emphasis on the theoretical analysis and too much knowledge introduction which can make the students lack of the system relationships. The theoretical course should be always coupled with the practical course and take the application as its objective. The theoretical knowledge can work, be grasped easily, and be created and developed only when it is applied into the practice. We should not only take the particular feature of the course but also notice its relationship with other courses which can bring up the internal logicality.

In the process of teaching, the appropriate use of multimedia and object demonstrations can show students the machine composition and movement and the parts and their assemblage visually and intuitively. With these multimedia and object demonstrations, the notable problem in structure designing should be emphasized which can make intense impression to the students to grasp these designing content and the assemblage relationship among the parts.

2.4 Strengthening the experimental teaching

The course is of great practicability and involves with the actual production and living and thus should emphasis on the experimental teaching elements. It is not only the platform where the theory is coupled with practice, but also the way through which students can exert their creativity and actual ability. In the experiments, students can be encouraged to exert their subjective initiative and design with their respective term. With the lab resource, students can try the practical application of the theory they had learned in the classroom and validate it at the same time. That is irreplaceable for the theoretical teaching. The experiment teaching can not only induce students to think independently, train their ability to practice and operate and startup their experiment research career, but also train their interests in the course.

To fully make use of the experiment teaching, it should be breakthrough that the experiment teaching just takes the role of verification and presentation for class teaching as what they did in the past. A new experiment teaching system needs to be built up, which focuses on the student cultivation and develops the open laboratory teaching pattern and the modular and hierarchical experimental project. On the experiment content, we need to develop more comprehensive experiments when keeping some necessary traditional simple experiments. The experiments, especially the new developed ones, should make every effort to close to the instruments and equipments of Material Forming & control specialty. The experimental teaching method should transform from the traditional validation and demo experiment to the designing experiment. The latter always encourages students to independently think design experiment plan and trains students' engineering consciousness and creative design ability.

2.5 Valuing the curriculum design

Curriculum design is one of the best methods of applying theory knowledge to practice and an chance to develop the innovative ability of students. We should encourage students to create their own design of their respective interested equipment based on the characteristics of material forming and control engineering.

In the curriculum design, more freedom and less related materials are provided to students which can give them more space to think independently so that they learn to analyze the teaching material of sample data, figure, and propose innovation.

We need to encourage them for the innovative design and timely find out their problems and point out the reason. The total purpose is to improve the design level of students.

In the conclusion and oral defense of the curriculum design, students will be required to review and conclude their designing process systematically and comprehensively. The conclusion and oral defense will push better thinking about the remained problems in their respective curriculum design and more rigorous working style in the future machine designing.

3 TRAINING ENGINEERING CONSCIOUSNESS OF STUDENTS

The learning of this course can not only lay a solid theoretical foundation for the students, but also can cultivate the students' engineering ideas, let students learn to use the engineering practical ideas to think about and deal with the problem.

This article would address the connotation of the engineering consciousness, teaching contents, teaching methods, practice teaching, etc., make students pay attention to this, especially the cultivation of engineering consciousness, and improve the learning interest of students and the teaching quality of teachers obviously.

3.1 *Connotation of the engineering consciousness*

Engineering consciousness refers to the dynamic response of human brain to artificial material, natural environment, and economic environment. On the basis of full grasp of the natural law, it means the mind able to respect nature, protect nature, reasonably develop and utilize natural conditions to complete a project, and create new material wealth.

The connotation of engineering consciousness is extremely rich, including the innovation consciousness, practice consciousness, times consciousness, economic and social consciousness, management consciousness and moral consciousness and so on. In modern society, it is widely believed that the engineering technicians who only have a kind of consciousness and are lack of other consciousnesses don't possess broad vision, understand problem with one-sided view, and are difficult in bearing the social burden.

Accordingly, in the teaching process the engineering consciousness should be penetrated constantly, so that the students could unconsciously generate the concept of engineering consciousness and improve the innovative design ability in infection and edify [5].

Mechanical design refers to the plan and design of the machinery with expected function, or the promotion of the original performance. The birth of a machine derives from the sense of need, the initiation of design idea, the confirmation of design requirements, and then goes through the design, manufacturing, authentication, until the product approval. It is a complicated and meticulous process. As a result, the fundament of mechanical design is the best course for college students to cultivate the engineering quality. In the process of the explanation of chapters, the teachers should focus on this guiding ideology, and highlight the training of "quality consciousness", "efficiency consciousness" and "economy consciousness", so that the students can really understand and realize the essence of engineering consciousness of this course. Ascertaining the concept of engineering consciousness can avoid the case that the students thinking problems tend to idealization, beautification, and excessive pursuit of quality, and are divorced from the engineering practice.

3.2 *Adjusting the teaching content to cultivate students' engineering consciousness*

The prominent characteristics of the mechanical design basis are practical, and closely linked to real life and production. When students learn this course, they have finished some practical teaching links, such as metalworking practice, cognition practice, and professional practice. However, they lack engineering consciousness, and their classroom learning tends to remain at the theoretical level. Consequently, it is difficult to in-depth study of professional knowledge, resulting in the difficulty in studying this course.

Therefore, the arrangement of the teaching content should take the cultivation of the students' ability of part design as principal line, and the enlightenment of the engineering consciousness as the purpose. Introducing one or two typical machines, such as internal combustion engines, throughout the course of teaching content, the theory should be closely associated with the practice, and the teaching should focus on the systematicness and relevance of the course content.

The content arrangement of every chapter should strengthen the "quality consciousness" and "safety consciousness". Namely, the designed parts should possess perfect service ability and reliability and sufficient strength and stiffness, in case the parts encounter failure due to the impact and vibration. Accordingly, the students should recognize the importance of failure modes, stress analysis, strength design and checking of the parts, and improve the enthusiasm in learning course.

At the same time, the students should enhance the economy consciousness and innovation consciousness. Furthermore, the teachers can let good students take part in the scientific research, so as to cultivate the students' engineering awareness.

3.3 Adjusting teaching methods to cultivate students' engineering consciousness

In order to improve the teaching effect, the traditional teaching mode can be combined with heuristic and interactive teaching method. Heuristic teaching is an advanced and scientific teaching method. During the teaching, teachers ask questions from different angles and ways, and then enlighten the students gradually, which can cause the students to think independently, and arouse their curiosity.

The interactive teaching is an important factor to improve the teaching effect. Teaching is a two-way behavior. While teachers play a leading role, the more emphasis should be laid on the main body status of students in the teaching process. The enthusiasm, initiative and participation of students' study should be fully aroused. In class, teachers should always pay attention to student's emotion, and apply the questioning and discussion modes to perform interactive teaching [6]. Finally, the teachers carry out the summary and conclusion, and make the students accept knowledge in a relaxed, pleasant atmosphere. After class the teachers understand the learning effect of students by talking with students and answering questions, so they can adjust the teaching progress and improve the teaching method.

3.4 Cultivating students' engineering consciousness in the teaching practice

Experiment teaching and course design can fully develop the students' observation, attention, imagination, thinking ability and innovation ability.

The curriculum design can apply theory knowledge to practice, and is a good chance to develop the innovative ability of students. In curriculum design, when the students receive commitments, the teachers should fully arouse the enthusiasm of students in observing the entity in lab. As little as possible to give information and scope to students, the teachers should give students more space to think, make students learn to analyze the data and figure in teaching material, and cultivate their innovative consciousness. After the bold innovation and design, the students can produce several sets of solution. Then, the most reasonable plan can be confirmed through the discussion and demonstration, thus cultivating the overall concept of students.

When the teachers fulfill the summary and reply to mechanical design basic course, they can ask students to carry out the systematic and comprehensive review and summary to their design, which can

prompt students to think about the problems they don't understand or have not considered, and cultivate the rigorous work style of students. Through the practical exploration in emphasizing the cultivation of engineering consciousness during the "Fundament of Mechanical Design" course, we recognize that only grasping the prominent characteristics of engineering and practice, the boring professional theoretical knowledge can be taught incisively and vividly. Otherwise, the simple lecture is difficult to obtain ideal classroom effect.

The cultivation of engineering consciousness and the promotion of engineering quality can conduce to the future study and work of students.

4 CONCLUSIONS

The course, fundament of mechanical design, was very important for students of the Material Forming & control specialty. The paper suggested that defining the teaching objective, cultivating the interest in studying, reforming curriculum content, strengthening the experimental teaching and valuing the curriculum design could improve the course teaching effect.

ACKNOWLEDGMENT

This research is supported by the General Program of Education and Science of Liaoning Province during the 12th Five-Year Plan Period, No. JG11DB207.

REFERENCES

[1] Yang Kezhen, Cheng Guangyun. Mechanical design foundation. Beijing: higher education press, 1999.
[2] Tian Fang, Zhang Xiuhong. Improve the students' practical training comprehensive ability. Journal of mechanical design teaching seminars, 2007.
[3] Tian Fang. Mechanical design. Journal of high-quality goods curriculum construction and practice of national mechanical design teaching conference, 2009.
[4] Shi Congji, Sun Lipeng. Mechanical design course design teaching reform practice. Journal of the national mechanical design teaching conference, 2009.
[5] Wang Guihe, Lv Jianguo. Connotation and cultivation way of engineering consciousness of engineering college students. Chinese geological education, 2006, 4: 62–64.
[6] Chang Zhibin, Gui Dingyi, Ren Bailin, Zhang Chenyang. Cultivation of students' engineering consciousness and innovation ability combined with the engineering practice. Higher education research of mechanical industry, 2001, 2: 61–63.

Newly-founded undergraduate college academic journals' scientific orientation and way of reform

Yan-Xia Liu

Editorial Department, Environmental Management College of China, Qinhuangdao, Hebei, China

ABSTRACT: With the luxuriantly rise up of newly-founded colleges in China, some problems about organizational system, editorial staff development, internal and external manuscript disposal arose in editorial departments of academic journals, so it is necessary to scientifically orientate the academic journals in combination with the colleges' status and the social environment, and to carry out reform on defining editorial departments' organizational system, strengthening editorial staff construction, being strict with the internal manuscripts and attracting excellent external manuscripts, in order to fulfill academic journals' scientific development.

Keywords: newly-founded undergraduate colleges and universities; scientific orientation; reform; editorial departments' organizational system; editorial staff; manuscripts submitted for publication

1 NEWLY-FOUNDED UNDERGRADUATE COLLEGES AND UNIVERSITIES' FLOURISH IN CHINA

From 1978 up to now, newly-founded undergraduate colleges and universities have bloomed in China. Only in 1998, 77 higher institutions incorporated into 31 undergraduate colleges or universities, 161 colleges implemented system transfer, 14 colleges and universities implemented co-construction, 39 colleges carried out the cooperation in school running. Also the government dismissed 108 adult colleges whose teaching conditions were seriously unqualified.[2] In the past 15 years, in accordance with the approval process "west one year, middle east one year, private colleges one year", China promoted the setting of newly-founded undergraduate universities and colleges in a planned way and step by step. By May 2013, the newly-founded undergraduate colleges and universities were totally 346.[3]

In the world, usually based on the gross enrollment ratio, higher education is divided into three stages: gross enrollment ratio below 15% is elite education stage; 15%~50% is the popularization stage of higher education; More than 50% is universalization stage. In 2010, China's higher education gross enrollment ratio was 26.5%, and 26.9% in 2011. The 2013 Government Work Report pointed out, to comprehensively improve education quality and level, the higher education gross enrollment ratio was planned to reach 30%. It's thus clear that China has entered the populariza-tion stage of higher education. In some developed cities such as Beijing, Shanghai, Tianjin, Nanjing, etc., since 2003 the gross enrollment ratio of higher education was above 50%. It can be said that newly founding undergraduate colleges and universities on such a large scale and at such fast speed, is unique in the world.

2 THE CURRENT SITUATION OF THE JOURNALS OF NEWLY FOUNDED UNDERGRADUATE COLLEGES AND UNIVERSITIES

2.1 *Journal editorial department's organizational system mismatches with undergraduate colleges and universities*

Somebody compared the journals of vocational colleges to "chicken ribs": tasteless but wasteful to discard. The metaphor appears to be humorous, but the real description of vocational college journals' position. At present most editorial department of social science in vocational colleges are independent division-level management units, but the majority of physical science journal, is only the section-level units, and affiliated to the scientific research office, educational administration office, library, etc. The organizational system of journal editorial department are in chaos. Because journal editorial department did not receive enough attention from the college, editing personnel is not enough, the funding is lack. And this situation still continues when the higher vocational colleges has transformed into undergraduate colleges or universities.

2.2 *Editing staff is unstable and inadequate*

The longtime neglect of journal editorial department led to its organizational system level is low, which in turn led to the expansion of editor team were trapped into a dilemma: on the one hand, school leaders don't agree the editorial department to import talents from outside, on the other hand, the school teachers don't want to work in editorial department with such low level organizational system. More seriously, many journal editors considering their own benefits and the future development space, always have the idea of "going out". As a result, journal editorial department is facing the situation unable to bring in new talents and unable to retain experienced editors. In addition, the journal editorial department's post setting and the actual work needs were in conflict, editorial department cannot bring work division of labor refinement to editing affairs, editing and proofreading, editors always take on all the roles, this undoubtedly distracted the editors' attention, affected the redaction level of the journal.

3 NEWLY-FOUNDED UNDERGRADUATE COLLEGE AND UNIVERSITY JOURNAL'S SCIENTIFIC ORIENTATION

The famous economist and Xiamen University's former President Professor Yanan Wang once pointed out that judging a university was mainly from three aspects: teaching, library, and journal. Beijing Normal University Professor Jingwen Zhong said: "Journal is the face of a university." And another famous Chinese ancient building and ancient garden expert, Professor Congzhou Chen emphasized, "if you want to do a good job in a university, you have to do a good job in the journal." Between journal and university, and to some extent, there is a mutual support relationship, the journal has irreplaceable functions on promoting the progress of the whole school development, so it is necessary for the journal to make scientific orientation of newly-founded undergraduate universities and colleges.

The scientific orientation of newly founded undergraduate college and university journals, is to take the school and the journal's scientific development as guidance, from the reality of the school and its own, to reasonably, accurately and scientifically determine the type and characteristic of running the journal and the goal, to realize the comprehensive and coordinated development of the school and the journal. The scientific orienta-

tion of newly-founded undergraduate university and college journal should be based on the practice, strive to achieve three coordinated development: the coordinated development of the school and the journal, the journal's own coordinated development, the coordinated development of the society the journal.

3.1 *Combined with the school's status*

The newly-founded undergraduate universities and colleges have their own features: (1) The hardware and software facilities are unsound, the management is still in transition stage; (2) At the beginning of transformation, the school put more focus on teaching but not for others; (3) the school's overall scientific research atmosphere, teachers' scientific research ability is weak, teachers do research and publish academic thesis only under the pressure of professional title appraisal. Therefore, as the journal hosted by colleges and universities, ought to make orientation according to the school's status. As a direct reflection on the school's teaching and scientific research, as the window of colleges and universities, reflecting comprehensive and diversified characteristics is also the journal's inevitable choice.

3.2 *Combined with the social environment*

College and university running must face the society and run the school open. Against this background the journal running also face the society. Combined with the social environment, the scientific orientation of newly-founded undergraduate university and college journal should pay attention to three aspects: the school's service industry, service area, and special advantages compared with other colleges and universities. The journal editorial department should hold the editorial committee, solicit opinions from the editorial advisory board members, locate afresh to itself on the basis of objectively analyzing and evaluating on the school discipline, the scientific research level and academic advantages and characteristics, neither being over-ambitious, nor being forward-looking. At the same time, the journal editorial department should avoid the tendency of one-sided pursuit of all kinds.

4 NEWLY-FOUNDED UNDERGRADUATE COLLEGE AND UNIVERSITY JOURNAL'S REFORM DIRECTION

From the booming of newly-founded undergraduate universities and colleges and the present situation of the journals, it is not hard to see there is certain resistance in journal reform and the reform is imperative. Based on many years experience and observation, the author thinks the reform on the newly-founded undergraduate college and university journals can start from the following aspects.

4.1 Definite editorial department's organizational system

How a journal runs is closely related to the journal editorial department's organizational system. According to File No.4 released by the Propaganda Department of the Central Committee of the CPC in 1984, the *Management of Sci-tech Periodicals* promulgated by the State Science and Technology Commission and the State Press and Publication Administration on June 5, 1991, and *The Measures for the Administration of College Journal* promulgated by the General Office of the Ministry of Education in 1998, public published college and university journal editorial department should be included in scientific research units, and be treated as division-level management unit directly led by the president of the college or university.

First of all, the journal is the school's periodical, it should be directly led by the school (college) head, but considering the history and the present situation of most colleges or universities, some transitional measures can be taken. Secondly, the journal editing work should be part of the teaching and scientific research work, is a different division of teacher team. Since the journal editorial department belong to academic institutions, it should not belong to administrative units, and therefore the editors should not work in their office and hold office hours as those in administrative units. In view of this, the journal editorial department may apply the "three half"and "a unified" system: deputy division-level management unit, elastic work hours and unified leadership under the president.

4.2 Strengthen the construction of editor team

The *Management of Sci-tech Periodicals* promulgated in 1991 clearly defined: "The organizational structure of full-time editors in sci-tech periodical editorial department should be allocated according to the task, usually not less than three people for quarterly (or half yearly), not less than five for bimonthly, not less than seven people for monthly, and allocate a certain number of full-time editor assistant." However, the newly-founded undergraduate college and university journal editorial department did not arouse enough attention from the leaders, there is a large gap between its post setting and the

Management of Sci-tech Periodicals. The editors usually have multiple roles such as editors, editor assistants and proofreaders. Only strengthening journal editing team construction can make the journal editorial department has a detailed division and improve the editing level.

In addition, the school should also increase funding support for the journal editorial department, which can guarantee the editors have enough economic ability to go out for academic exchanges and strengthen the external exchange and cooperation.

5 CONCLUSION

Newly founding undergraduate colleges and universities is not just to construct new campus, it needs the transformation in supporting mechanism as well as in system and educational ideas. The journal also needs to act on the organizational system and management system, to construct the editorial department that meets the needs of undergraduate college and university, to realize the coordinated development of the school, the journal and the society. Undoubtedly, the scientific development of the journal needs the support and attention from the school and the school leaders. The reform on the newly-founded undergraduate college and university journals requires the scholars and editors to do more further research, and to explore from the aspects of subject content, the characteristic columns constantly.

ACKNOWLEDGEMENT

Fund Support: This project is the scientific research fund project of Environmental Management College of China "Research on Newly-founded Undergraduate College Academic Journals' Scientific Orientation and Development" (No. 2014014).

REFERENCES

[1] Ping Li. Thirty Years' Retrospect of China's System Reform for Higher Education and Management[J]. Journal of Technology College Education, 2008, 27 (3): 31–33.
[2] Yufeng Wang. Cause Exploration on the Booming of Newly Built Undergraduate Colleges and Universities in Our Country[J]. Higher Education Exploration, 2010(6): 31–35.
[3] Yufeng Wang. Retrospect and Prospect on Newly Built Undergraduate Colleges and Universities in Our Country for 15 Years[J]. Higher Education Research, 2013(5): 15–21.

[4] Jianjun Dong. Function Analysis on Newly Built Undergraduate College and University Journal[J]. Journal of Changchun University of Technology (Social Sciences Edition), 2009, 21(3): 118–120.

[5] Xiurong Li, Yuling Xia, Congming Li. A SWOT Analysis of Journals of Newly-established Local Undergraduate Universities[J]. Journal of Tangshan College, 2008, 21(6): 86–88.

[6] Jilin Wang, Yang Huang. Core Competitiveness of New College Depends on the Characteristics of Strategic[J]. Journal of Jinling Institute of Technology (Social Science Edition), 2008, 22(1): 93–96.

Computer, Intelligent Computing and Education Technology – Liu, Sung & Yao (Eds)
© 2014 Taylor & Francis Group, London, ISBN 978-1-138-02469-4

Strengthening journal construction of higher institution to improve Qinhuangdao City's soft cultural power

Yan-Xia Liu & Hai-Yun Qi
Environmental Management College of China, Qinhuangdao, Hebei, China

ABSTRACT: Journal of Handan College, Journal of Hengshui University and Journal of Huizhou University's outstanding contribution to improving local soft cultural power, provided indisputable evidences for improving local soft cultural power by strengthening journal construction of higher institution, also proved the feasibility and scientificity to improve Qinhuangdao City's soft cultural power by strengthening journal construction of higher institution. Thus Qinhuangdao City should give full play to journals' oriented and promotion functions of higher institutions, exploit Qinhuangdao City's cultural resources, establish feature columns, improve residents' overall qualities, popularize environmental protection ideas, so as to make contribution to Qinhuangdao City's garden and ecological type modern seaboard city and state environmental protection model city construction.

Keywords: Qinhuangdao City; journals of higher institutions; soft cultural power; practical evidences; oriented function; promotion function; feature columns

1 THE RESEARCH BACKGROUND

Former U.S. defense assistant minister, the famous scholar Joseph Nye, is one of the founders of the new liberalism school of international relations theory, who focuses on the interdependence, international system and the traditional balance of power theory in international relations. In 1990, Joseph Nye published the article *Soft Power* in *Foreign Policy* magazine, in the same year published the book *Bound to Lead: The Changing Nature of American Power* which made the term "soft power" popular and became a special term frequently used after the cold war.[1]

Joseph Nye argues that a country's comprehensive national strength includes "hard power" presented by economy, technology, military, territory, population, and natural resources et al, as well as the abstract and nonmaterial "soft power" presented by culture, ideological appeal and moral values et al.[1] Cultural power just belongs to the "soft power" in the comprehensive national strength.

The report of the 17th national congress pointed out: "Adhere to the direction of socialist advanced culture, rise the upsurge of socialist cultural construction, stimulate the creativity of the whole nation culture, enhance the national cultural soft power."[2] As China's further open coastal port city approved by the State Council and the famous tourist city, in the urbanization process Qinhuangdao must pay attention to soft power's quick and steady improvement, shape the city brand, develop special tourism resources, set up the enterprise brand, improve the whole quality of the residents, and increase the influence power. Journal as the higher institutions' window to the outside, not only shows the college teachers' academic studies and scientific research level, but also has significant role in promoting the influence of the college and the city, and improving the overall quality of the residents.

At present, the overseas research on soft power concentrated in the national level, such as world politics, foreign policy and the comprehensive national strength, the research of regional cultural soft power was not much. Domestic study of improving regional cultural soft power most focused on the regional culture, government management and service, human resources and living environment, etc. Scholar proposed the ways to promote the realization of Qinhuangdao soft power mainly including human resources security, public administration and management, building a city business card,[3] the development of urban culture connotation, development of special tourism resources, setting up enterprise brand, attaching great importance to the conference and festival, improving the overall quality, improving the influence of colleges and universities, etc.,[4] but lack of theoretical and empirical research on improving the cultural soft power of Qinhuangdao city by university journals.

The author analyzed the role and influence of university journals on the regional cultural soft power ascension, explored the new ways to promote Qinhuangdao cultural soft power by strengthening the construction of college and university journals through consulting relevant literatures.

2 THE FUNCTION ORIENTATION OF UNIVERSITY JOURNALS AND ITS EFFECTS ON ENHANCING REGIONAL CULTURAL SOFT POWER AND INFLUENCE

2.1 *The position and functions in higher learning institutions*

The famous economist and Xiamen University former president professor Ya-nan Wang once pointed out that judging a university mainly from three aspects: teaching, library and journal. Beijing Normal University professor Jing-wen Zhong said: "Journal is the face of higher learning institutions." It's obvious that the relationship between journals of colleges and universities and schools is mutual support and influential to a certain extent, journals of colleges and universities plays an irreplaceable role in flourishing the school's academic career, cultivating innovative talents, promoting the teaching quality and the progress and development of the whole school. As an important part of higher institutions' teaching and research units, journal is an important garden and window reflecting the school's teaching, scientific research, and the development of domestic and international academic exchange. The position and role of journals in the colleges and universities performance in: showing academic achievements, promoting the transformation of achievements, spreading advanced culture, expanding school influence, building academic platform, promoting academic exchanges, leading the academic trend, promoting discipline construction, fostering academic rookies, integrating the academic resources, and promoting the development of the school.[5]

2.2 *The role in promoting local cultural soft power*

Guiding role: Political guiding ideology, cultural propaganda and noble taste is the general nature of periodicals. Journal is the special periodical for academic report, reflecting some phenomenon and problems in social, natural, philosophy and other fields and carrying out systematic research and discussion. As a result, journals of higher educational institutions also has the general nature of the periodicals, and this nature determines that the journal has the function of spreading the values, guiding the development of civilization, and plays a guiding role of benchmarking to readers.

Journals' political nature determines the they should carry out the party's guidelines and provide the correct political perspective for readers, journals' cultural nature determines they have the functions of leading the culture to develop in the direction of scientific, quality, and industrialization. The noble nature of journals shows that the readers can benefit from getting sense of beauty and artistic beauty as well as purifying hearts, and improving self-cultivation.

Promoting role: College and university journals are the important power to promote the local cultural soft power construction. After the 3rd plenary session of the party's 11th congress, the ideological and cultural construction in China has made great development, but compared with the high-speed development of the socialist market economy, ideological and cultural construction can't satisfy people's growing spiritual and cultural needs both in depth and breadth. College and university journals as the carrier of ideological theory and academic achievements, has the characteristics of knowledge intensive, theoretical and forward-looking and predictability, at the same time can provide theoretical basis for the local government's macro decision-making, provides the basis for cultural theory of innovation platform and impulsion. As the important carrier of theoretical innovation and culture innovation, college and university journals have the characteristics that the subjects are complete, the knowledge is concentrated, the theory is rich. The journals are prospective and predictive, can provide theoretical basis for the local government's macroscopical decision and provide platform and motive power for the innovation in cultural theory. As the carrier of theoretical and cultural innovation, college and university journal also shoulder the arduous historical mission providing ideological weapon, spiritual motivation, intellectual support, theoretical service and public opinion environment for the local economic and cultural development. College and university journals' strategic, fundamental, macroscopic and historical characteristics play an indispensable role in the development of local economic and cultural soft power construction.

3 THE FEASIBILITY AND SCIENTIFICITY OF IMPROVING QINHUANGDAO CULTURAL SOFT POWER THROUGH STRENGTHENING UNIVERSITY JOURNALS' CONSTRUCTION

3.1 *The case study*

If the above function orientation of university journals and their effect analysis on enhancing regional cultural soft power, provided theory basis for enhancing regional cultural soft power through strengthening the construction of university journals, then *Handan College Journal*, *Journal of Hengshui College*, and *Journal of Huizhou University*'s outstanding contribution to the local cultural soft power promotion provided indisputable reality basis for improving local cultural soft power through strengthening the college and university journals' construction.

3.2 The feasibility and scientificity of improving Qinhuangdao cultural soft power through strengthening university journals' construction

Qinhuangdao, was named because in 215 BC the First Emperor of Qin east toured here and sent for the immortal into the sea, is the only city named by the name of an emperor in Chinese history. The historical origin together with its blue sea, sands, forest and other unique natural landscape, and Shanhaiguan, Beidaihe, Nandaihe renowned Chinese and foreign cultural landscape make Qinhangdao the famous "Summer Capital" of China.

Currently, Qinhuangdao has a reasonable layout and categories of education system, including Yanshan University, Northeast University at Qinhuangdao, Hebei Normal University of Science and Technology, Environmental Management College of China, Hebei Vocational and Technical College of Building Materials, Qinhuangdao Institute of Technology, Hebei Institute of Foreign Languages and so on more than 10 universities, among which Yanshan University, Hebei Normal University of Science and Technology, and Environmental Management College of China have journals. These university journals have both social science and natural science edition, the columns involve a wide range, the published papers have relatively high academic level. For example, Environmental Management College of China has a number of teachers listed in the expert database of Qinhuangdao city. They proposed a lot of advices and recommendations for Qinhuangdao city development planning and environmental protection planning, did related researches on Qinhuangdao city development planning and environmental protection planning. Their scientific research achievements were published in the Journal of Environmental Management College of China and achieved good social benefits. From the above analysis it can be seen that improving Qinhuangdao cultural soft power through strengthening the construction of university journals has certain feasibility and scientificity.

4 THE NEW APPROACHES TO IMPROVING QINHUANGDAO CULTURAL SOFT POWER THROUGH STRENGTHENING THE CONSTRUCTION OF UNIVERSITY JOURNALS

4.1 Mining the cultural resources of Qinhuangdao, setting up special columns

Qinhuangdao city has deep historical and cultural deposits, there are a lot of exploring space. Journals of humanities and social sciences in Qinhuangdao area should give full play to its function of serving local economic and cultural construction, set up special columns such as "Qin culture research", "Qinshihuang research", "Qinhuangdao history culture research" and "Qinhuangdao historical celebrities research", "Great Wall culture", widely collect anecdotes of famous people, appreciating painting and calligraphy and poetry, build historical celebrity archives et al. In addition, the journal editorial department still can give full play to their social influence, hold some high level academic research activities on a regular basis.

4.2 Improving residents' comprehensive qualities, publicizing environmental protection concepts

Qinhuangdao city melts three types of tourism resources: the nature, the humanities, the society. Among natural resources the mountains and sea are most prominent, among humanistic resources the Pass and the Great Wall are most famous, among social resources Beidaihe celebrity villas are most attractive. These tourism resources protection and rational development, on the one hand, need the municipal government and relevant departments make scientific and reasonable protection and utilization planning, on the other hand also need the general public to cherish these precious resources.

ACKNOWLEDGEMENT

Corresponding Author: Hai-Yun QI, Environmental Management College of China, E-mail:qihaiyun322@foxmail.com.

REFERENCES

[1] Xiang-rong Zeng, Min Qiu. Expect China to write the legend in the next 30 years [N]. Guangzhou Daily, 2008-12-02 (A9).
[2] Ai-wen Chen, Ai-hua Zheng. The significance and paths of improving cultural soft power [J]. Journal of Chongqing University of Science and Technology (Social Sciences Edition), 2008 (12):138,142.

[3] Ya-jun Zhang, Chun-wei Yu, Xiang-jiang Yang. Reflections on Striving to build Qinhuangdao "soft power" [J]. Market Modernization, 2007(33):236.

[4] Yi-jian Liu, Yu-Jing Chu, Na Li, etc. Countermeasures study on improving Qinhuangdao soft cultural power [J]. Commodity and Quality:Academic Observation, 2011(10):240.

[5] Ling-zhi Liu. Rethinking the Role of College Journals in the Development of Institutions of Higher Learning [J]. Journal of Taizhou Polytechnic College, 2009, 9(4):104–107.

Author index

Matsuda, Y. 1021
Mei, H. 707
Mei, L. 1089
Meng, W. 1147
Meng, Y.F. 999
Miao, Z.Y. 1115
Mou, Z.-J. 771
Mu, H.-W. 1291

Nan, S.-J. 599
Ni, R. 1365
Nie, F.-Y. 191, 915

Olefirenko, N.V. 965
Ou, J. 563
Ou, W.-S. 901

Pan, C.H. 1299
Pan, Q. 755
Park, B.K. 661
Peng, J. 69
Peng, J. 1163
Peng, L. 215
Peng, L. 969
Peng, X.-Q. 231
Peng, Y. 209
Peng, Y. 681

Qi, C.-W. 107
Qi, H.-Y. 587, 1077,
    1331, 1453
Qi, J. 893
Qian, K.G. 1151
Qian, Y.X. 59
Qin, J.-L. 695
Qin, M. 509, 1277
Qiu, F.X. 489
Qiu, Y. 457
Qiu, Y.P. 839
Qu, H.-Q. 385, 1065

Ren, F.R. 897
Ren, P. 1139
Ren, S. 1291
Ren, W.-Z. 299
Ren, Y.-F. 107
Ren, Z.P. 1003
Ruan, B.S. 681

Shang, F.-J. 695
Shen, G.Q. 1015
Shen, Y. 147, 881
Shi, D.L. 13
Shi, T.Y. 165
Shi, Y. 273
Shi, Y. 711

Shi, Y.Q. 1003
Shie, L.-C. 1387
Shu, M. 749, 755
Shu, S. 23
Shu, X.-L. 1053
Sima, Y. 595, 1361
Solomon, O. 873
Song, Z.W. 1029
Stolbov, D.V. 965
Sui, X. 625
Sun, B. 417, 1343
Sun, C.-S. 635
Sun, F.X. 263
Sun, J.M. 699
Sun, L. 205, 927, 931
Sun, L. 255
Sun, L.H. 1143
Sun, L.L. 951
Sun, L.M. 183, 809
Sun, S. 493
Sun, W.J. 1115
Sun, X.W. 1383
Sun, Y. 381
Sun, Y. 717
Sun, Z.Q. 653

Ta, L. 587
Tak, H. 661
Tan, L. 983, 987
Tan, S.-C. 1287
Tan, X. 175
Tang, C.F. 745
Tang, J. 1295
Tang, R. 1295
Tang, S.-Q. 437
Tao, B. 527, 531, 535,
    539, 543
Tao, G.-B. 1291
Tian, C.Y. 707
Tian, Y. 55
Tian, Y. 941
Tu, J.-B. 385, 1069, 1073
Tu, Y.-H. 1007
Tuo, M.-F. 451

Wan, Z. 9, 749, 755
Wang, B.P. 1147
Wang, C. 605
Wang, C.B. 851
Wang, C.T. 1143
Wang, C.X. 1227
Wang, D.-M. 835
Wang, F. 413
Wang, G.S. 1133
Wang, G.X. 361
Wang, G.-Y. 563

Wang, H. 155
Wang, H. 277, 765
Wang, H.B. 957
Wang, H.-J. 447
Wang, H.J. 991
Wang, H.-X. 317
Wang, H.Y. 1299
Wang, J. 131
Wang, J. 995, 1215
Wang, J. 1025
Wang, J.-B. 317
Wang, J.-C. 1247
Wang, J.-H. 225
Wang, J.-J. 1111
Wang, J.-S. 635
Wang, J.W. 267
Wang, J.-Y. 1291
Wang, J.Y. 621
Wang, K. 143, 1255
Wang, K. 263
Wang, L. 523
Wang, L. 703, 1445
Wang, L.H. 1123
Wang, L.-P. 1425
Wang, M.M. 493
Wang, P. 1127
Wang, Q.-L. 289
Wang, Q.P. 1123
Wang, R.G. 329
Wang, S.Y. 357, 923
Wang, T.C. 151
Wang, T.-F. 975, 979
Wang, W. 505
Wang, X. 13
Wang, X. 87, 95
Wang, X. 221
Wang, X. 669, 1407
Wang, X. 803
Wang, X.L. 333
Wang, X.Q. 1015
Wang, Y. 13
Wang, Y. 505
Wang, Y. 699
Wang, Y. 1015
Wang, Y. 1181
Wang, Y.D. 469
Wang, Y.L. 59
Wang, Y.-L. 631
Wang, Y.Q. 961
Wang, Y.-X. 305
Wang, Y.Y. 605
Wang, Y.-Y. 815
Wang, Y.Z. 605
Wang, Z.-H. 175
Wang, Z.H. 237
Wei, C.-X. 131